W9-ADN-718

An Introduction
to Probability Theory
and Its Applications

An Introduction to Probability Theory and Its Applications

WILLIAM FELLER
Eugene Higgins Professor of Mathematics
Princeton University

VOLUME II

John Wiley & Sons, Inc.
New York • London • Sydney

COPYRIGHT © 1966
BY
JOHN WILEY & SONS, INC.

All Rights Reserved

This book or any part thereof must not be reproduced in any form without the written permission of the publisher.

SECOND CORRECTED PRINTING, NOVEMBER, 1966

LIBRARY OF CONGRESS CATALOG CARD NUMBER: 50-8529

PRINTED IN THE UNITED STATES OF AMERICA

To

O. E. Neugebauer

o et praesidium et dulce decus meum

Preface

At the time the first volume of this book was written (between 1941 and 1948) the interest in probability was not yet widespread. Teaching was on a very limited scale and topics such as Markov chains, which are now extensively used in several disciplines, were highly specialized chapters of pure mathematics. The first volume may therefore be likened to an all-purpose travel guide to a strange country. To describe the nature of probability it had to stress the mathematical content of the theory as well as the surprising variety of potential applications. It was predicted that the ensuing fluctuations in the level of difficulty would limit the usefulness of the book. In reality it is widely used even today, when its novelty has worn off and its attitude and material are available in newer books written for special purposes. The book seems even to acquire new friends. The fact that laymen are not deterred by passages which proved difficult to students of mathematics shows that the level of difficulty cannot be measured objectively; it depends on the type of information one seeks and the details one is prepared to skip. The traveler often has the choice between climbing a peak or using a cable car.

In view of this success the second volume is written in the same style. It involves harder mathematics, but most of the text can be read on different levels. The handling of measure theory may illustrate this point. Chapter IV contains an informal introduction to the basic ideas of measure theory and the conceptual foundations of probability. The same chapter lists the few facts of measure theory used in the subsequent chapters to formulate analytical theorems in their simplest form and to avoid futile discussions of regularity conditions. The main function of measure theory in this connection is to justify formal operations and passages to the limit that would never be questioned by a non-mathematician. Readers interested primarily in practical results will therefore not feel any need for measure theory.

To facilitate access to the individual topics the chapters are rendered as self-contained as possible, and sometimes special cases are treated separately ahead of the general theory. Various topics (such as stable distributions and renewal theory) are discussed at several places from different angles. To avoid repetitions, the definitions and illustrative examples are collected in chapter VI, which may be described as a collection of introductions to the subsequent chapters. The skeleton of the book consists of chapters V, VIII, and XV. The reader will decide for himself how much of the preparatory chapters to read and which excursions to take.

Experts will find new results and proofs, but more important is the attempt to consolidate and unify the general methodology. Indeed, certain parts of probability suffer from a lack of coherence because the usual grouping and treatment of problems depend largely on accidents of the historical development. In the resulting confusion closely related problems are not recognized as such and simple things are obscured by complicated methods. Considerable simplifications were obtained by a systematic exploitation and development of the best available techniques. This is true in particular for the proverbially messy field of limit theorems (chapters XVI–XVII). At other places simplifications were achieved by treating problems in their natural context. For example, an elementary consideration of a particular random walk led to a generalization of an asymptotic estimate which had been derived by hard and laborious methods in risk theory (and under more restrictive conditions independently in queuing).

I have tried to achieve mathematical rigor without pedantry in style. For example, the statement that $1/(1 + \xi^2)$ is the characteristic function of $\frac{1}{2}e^{-|x|}$ seems to me a desirable and legitimate abbreviation for the logically correct version that the function which at the point ξ assumes the value $1/(1 + \xi^2)$ is the characteristic function of the function which at the point x assumes the value $\frac{1}{2}e^{-|x|}$.

I fear that the brief historical remarks and citations do not render justice to the many authors who contributed to probability, but I have tried to give credit wherever possible. The original work is now in many cases superseded by newer research, and as a rule full references are given only to papers to which the reader may want to turn for additional information. For example, no reference is given to my own work on limit theorems, whereas a paper describing observations or theories underlying an example is cited even if it contains no mathematics.[1] Under these circumstances the index of authors gives no indication of their importance for probability theory. Another difficulty is to do justice to the pioneer work to which we owe new directions of research, new approaches, and new methods. Some theorems which were considered strikingly original

[1] This system was used also in the first volume but was misunderstood by some subsequent writers; they now attribute the methods used in the book to earlier scientists who could not have known them.

and deep now appear with simple proofs among more refined results. It is difficult to view such a theorem in its historical perspective and to realize that here as elsewhere it is the first step that counts.

ACKNOWLEDGMENTS

Thanks to the support by the U.S. Army Research Office of work in probability at Princeton University I enjoyed the help of J. Goldman, L. Pitt, M. Silverstein, and, in particular, of M. M. Rao. They eliminated many inaccuracies and obscurities. All chapters were rewritten many times and preliminary versions of the early chapters were circulated among friends. In this way I benefited from comments by J. Elliott, R. S. Pinkham, and L. J. Savage. My special thanks are due to J. L. Doob and J. Wolfowitz for advice and criticism. The graph of the Cauchy random walk was supplied by H. Trotter. The printing was supervised by Mrs. H. McDougal, and the appearance of the book owes much to her.

October 1965 WILLIAM FELLER

Abbreviations and Conventions

Iff is an abbreviation for *if and only if.*

Epoch. This term is used for points on the time axis, while time is reserved for intervals and durations. (In discussions of stochastic processes the word "times" carries too heavy a burden. The systematic use of "epoch," introduced by J. Riordan, seems preferable to varying substitutes such as moment, instant, or point.)

Intervals are denoted by bars: $\overline{a, b}$ is an open, $\overline{|a, b|}$ a closed interval; half-open intervals are denoted by $\overline{a, b|}$ and $\overline{|a, b}$. *This notation is used also in higher dimensions.* The pertinent conventions for vector notations and order relations are found in V,1 (and also in IV,2). The symbol (a, b) is reserved for pairs and for points.

$\mathfrak{R}^1, \mathfrak{R}^2, \mathfrak{R}^r$ stand for the line, the plane, and the r-dimensional Cartesian space.

1 refers to volume one, Roman numerals to chapters. Thus **1**; XI,(3.6) refers to section 3 of chapter XI of volume **1**.

▶ indicates the end of a proof or of a collection of examples.

$\mathfrak{n}$ *and* $\mathfrak{N}$ denote, respectively, the normal density and distribution function with zero expectation and unit variance.

O, o, and $\sim$. Let u and v depend on a parameter x which tends, say, to a. Assuming that v is positive we write

$$\left.\begin{array}{l} u = O(v) \\ u = o(v) \\ u \sim v \end{array}\right\} \qquad \text{if } \frac{u}{v} \qquad \begin{cases} \text{remains bounded} \\ \to 0 \\ \to 1. \end{cases}$$

$f(x)\, U\{dx\}$. For this abbreviation see V,3.

Regarding Borel sets and Baire functions, see the introduction to chapter V.

Contents

An Introduction to Probability Theory and Its Applications

CHAPTER I

The Exponential and the Uniform Densities

1. INTRODUCTION

In the course of volume **1** we had repeatedly to deal with probabilities defined by sums of many small terms, and we used approximations of the form

$$\mathbf{P}\{a < \mathbf{X} < b\} \approx \int_a^b f(x)\,dx. \tag{1.1}$$

The prime example is the normal approximation to the binomial distribution.[1] An approximation of this kind is usually formulated in the form of a limit theorem involving a succession of more and more refined discrete probability models. In many cases this passage to the limit leads conceptually to a new sample space, and the latter may be intuitively simpler than the original discrete model.

Examples. (*a*) *Exponential waiting times.* To describe waiting times by a discrete model we had to quantize the time and pretend that changes can occur only at epochs $\delta, 2\delta, \ldots$. The simplest waiting time $\mathbf{T}$ is the waiting time for the first success in a sequence of Bernoulli trials with probability p_δ for success. Then $\mathbf{P}\{\mathbf{T} > n\delta\} = (1-p_\delta)^n$ and the expected waiting time is $\mathbf{E}(\mathbf{T}) = \delta/p_\delta$. Refinements of this model are obtained by letting δ grow smaller in such a way that the expectation $\delta/p_\delta = \alpha$ remains fixed. For small δ and fixed t we have

$$\mathbf{P}\{\mathbf{T} > t\} = \left(1 - \frac{\delta}{\alpha}\right)^{t/\delta} \approx e^{-t/\alpha} \tag{1.2}$$

[1] *Further examples:* The arc sine distribution, chapter III, section 5; the distributions for the number of returns to the origin and first passage times in III,6 and III,8; the limit theorems for random walks in XIV; the uniform distribution in problem 20 of XI,7.

approximately, as can be seen by taking logarithms. This model considers the waiting time as a geometrically distributed discrete random variable, and (1.2) states that "in the limit" one gets an exponential distribution. From the point of view of intuition it would seem more natural to start from the sample space whose points are real numbers and to introduce the exponential distribution directly.

(*b*) *Random choices*. To "choose a point at random" in the interval[2] $\overline{0, 1}$ is a conceptual experiment with an obvious intuitive meaning. It can be described by discrete approximations, but it is easier to use the whole interval as sample space and to assign to each interval its length as probability. The conceptual experiment of making two independent random choices of points in $\overline{0, 1}$ results in a pair of real numbers, and so the natural sample space is a unit square. In this sample space one equates, almost instinctively, "probability" with "area." This is quite satisfactory for some elementary purposes, but sooner or later the question arises as to what the word "area" really means. ►

As these examples show, a continuous sample space may be conceptually simpler than a discrete model, but the definition of probabilities in it depends on tools such as integration and measure theory. In denumerable sample spaces it was possible to assign probabilities to *all* imaginable events, whereas in general spaces this naïve procedure leads to logical contradictions, and our intuition has to adjust itself to the exigencies of formal logic. We shall soon see that the naïve approach can lead to trouble even in relatively simple problems, but it is only fair to say that many probabilistically significant problems do not require a clean definition of probabilities. Sometimes they are of an analytic character and the probabilistic background serves primarily as a support for our intuition. In such situations the use of probabilistic terms is as innocuous as the familiar reference to masses and centers of gravity in abstract spaces. More to the point is the fact that complex stochastic processes with intricate sample spaces may lead to significant and comprehensible problems which do not depend on the delicate tools used in the analysis of the whole process. A typical reasoning may run as follows: if the process can be described at all, the random variable **Z** must have such and such properties, and its distribution must therefore satisfy such and such an integral equation. Although probabilistic arguments can greatly influence the analytical treatment of the equation in question, the latter is in principle independent of the axioms of probability. Specialists in various fields are sometimes so familiar with problems of this type that

[2] Intervals are denoted by bars to preserve the symbol (a, b) for the coordinate notation of points in the plane. See the list of abbreviations at the front of the book.

they deny the need for measure theory because they are unacquainted with problems of other types and with situations where vague reasoning did lead to wrong results.[3]

This situation will become clearer in the course of this chapter, which serves as an informal introduction to the whole theory. It describes some analytic properties of two important distributions which will be used throughout this book. Special topics are covered partly because of significant applications, partly to illustrate the new problems confronting us and the need for appropriate tools. It is not necessary to study them systematically or in the order in which they appear.

Throughout this chapter probabilities are *defined* by elementary integrals, and the limitations of this definition are accepted. The use of a probabilistic jargon, and of terms such as random variable or expectation, may be justified in two ways. It may be interpreted as a technical aid to intuition based on the formal analogy with similar situations in volume **1**. Alternatively, everything in this chapter may be interpreted in a logically impeccable manner by a passage to the limit from the discrete model described in example (2.*a*). Although neither necessary nor desirable in principle, the latter procedure has the merit of a good exercise for beginners.

2. DENSITIES. CONVOLUTIONS

A *probability density on the line* (or $\mathcal{R}^1$) is a function f such that

$$f(x) \geq 0, \qquad \int_{-\infty}^{+\infty} f(x)\, dx = 1. \tag{2.1}$$

For the present we consider only piecewise continuous densities (see V,3 for the general notion). To each density f we let correspond its *distribution function*[4] F defined by

$$F(x) = \int_{-\infty}^{x} f(y)\, dy. \tag{2.2}$$

[3] The roles of rigor and intuition are subject to misconceptions. As was pointed out in volume **1**, natural intuition and natural thinking are a poor affair, but they gain strength with the development of mathematical theory. Today's intuition and applications depend on the most sophisticated theories of yesterday. Furthermore, strict theory represents economy of thought rather than luxury. Indeed, experience shows that in applications most people rely on lengthy calculations rather than simple arguments because these appear risky. [The nearest illustration is in example (5.*a*).]

[4] We recall that by "distribution function" is meant a right continuous non-decreasing function with limits 0 and 1 at $\pm\infty$. Volume **1** was concerned mainly with distributions whose growth is due entirely to jumps. Now we focus our attention to distribution functions defined as integrals. General distribution functions will be studied in chapter V.

It is a monotone continuous function increasing from 0 to 1. We say that f and F are *concentrated on the interval* $a \leq x \leq b$ if f vanishes outside this interval. The density f will be considered as an assignment of probabilities to the intervals of the line, the interval[5] $\overline{a, b} = \{a < x < b\}$ having probability

$$(2.3) \qquad F(b) - F(a) = \int_a^b f(x)\, dx.$$

Sometimes this probability will be denoted by $\mathbf{P}\{\overline{a, b}\}$. Under this assignment an individual point carries probability zero, and the closed interval $\overline{a, b}$ has the same probability as $\overline{a, b}$.

In the simplest situation the real line serves as "*sample space*," that is, the outcome of a conceptual experiment is represented by a number. (Just as in volume **1**, this is only the first step in the construction of sample spaces representing sequences of experiments.) *Random variables* are functions defined on the sample space. For simplicity we shall for the time being accept as random variable only a function $\mathbf{U}$ such that for each t the event $\{\mathbf{U} \leq t\}$ consists of finitely many intervals. Then

$$(2.4) \qquad G(t) = \mathbf{P}\{\mathbf{U} \leq t\}$$

is well defined as the integral of f over these intervals. The function G defined by (2.4) is called the *distribution function* of $\mathbf{U}$. If G is the integral of a function g, then g is called the *density of* the distribution G or (interchangeably) the density of the variable $\mathbf{U}$.

The basic random variable is, of course, the coordinate variable[6] $\mathbf{X}$ as such, and all other random variables are functions of $\mathbf{X}$. The distribution function of $\mathbf{X}$ is identical with the distribution F by which probabilities are defined. Needless to say, any random variable $\mathbf{Y} = g(\mathbf{X})$ can be taken as coordinate variable on a new line.

As stated above, these terms may be justified by mere analogy with the situation in volume **1**, but the following example shows that our model may be obtained by a passage to the limit from discrete models.

Examples. (*a*) *Grouping of data.* Let F be a given distribution function. Choose a fixed $\delta > 0$ and consider the discrete random variable $\mathbf{X}_\delta$ which for $(n-1)\delta < x < n\delta$ assumes the constant value $n\delta$. Here $n = 0, \pm 1, \pm 2, \ldots$. In volume **1** we would have used the multiples of

---

[5] For the notation see the list of abbreviations at the front of the book.

[6] As far as possible we shall denote random variables (that is, functions on the sample space) by capital boldface letters, reserving small letters for numbers or location parameters. This holds in particular for the coordinate variable $\mathbf{X}$, namely the function defined by $\mathbf{X}(x) = x$.

δ as sample space, and described the probability distribution of $\mathbf{X}_\delta$ by saying that

$$\mathbf{P}\{\mathbf{X}_\delta = n\delta\} = F(n\delta) - F((n-1)\delta). \tag{2.5}$$

Now $\mathbf{X}_\delta$ becomes a random variable in an enlarged sample space, and its distribution function is the function that for $(n-1)\delta < x \leq n\delta$ equals $F(n\delta)$. In the continuous model $\mathbf{X}_\delta$ serves as an approximation to $\mathbf{X}$ obtained by identifying our intervals with their endpoints (a procedure known to statisticians as grouping of data). In the spirit of volume **1** we should treat $\mathbf{X}_\delta$ as the basic random variable and δ as a free parameter. Letting $\delta \to 0$ we would obtain limit theorems stating, for example, that F is the limit distribution of $\mathbf{X}_\delta$.

(*b*) For $x > 0$ the event $\{\mathbf{X}^2 \leq x\}$ is the same as $\{-\sqrt{x} \leq \mathbf{X} \leq \sqrt{x}\}$; the random variable $\mathbf{X}^2$ has a distribution concentrated on $\overline{0, \infty}$ and given there by $F(\sqrt{x}) - F(-\sqrt{x})$. By differentiation it is seen that *the density* g of $\mathbf{X}^2$ is given by $g(x) = \frac{1}{2}[f(\sqrt{x}) + f(-\sqrt{x})]/\sqrt{x}$ for $x > 0$ and $g(x) = 0$ for $x < 0$. Similarly, the distribution function of $\mathbf{X}^3$ is given by $F(\sqrt[3]{x})$ and has density $\frac{1}{3}f(\sqrt[3]{x})/\sqrt[3]{x^2}$. ▶

The *expectation of* $\mathbf{X}$ is defined by

$$\mathbf{E}(\mathbf{X}) = \int_{-\infty}^{+\infty} x\, f(x)\, dx \tag{2.6}$$

provided the integral converges absolutely. The expectations of the approximating discrete variables $\mathbf{X}_\delta$ of example (*a*) coincide with Riemann sums for this integral, and so $\mathbf{E}(\mathbf{X}_\delta) \to \mathbf{E}(\mathbf{X})$. If u is a bounded continuous function the same argument applies to the randon variable $u(\mathbf{X})$, and the relation $\mathbf{E}(u(\mathbf{X}_\delta)) \to \mathbf{E}(u(\mathbf{X}))$ implies

$$\mathbf{E}(u(\mathbf{X})) = \int_{-\infty}^{+\infty} u(x)\, f(x)\, dx; \tag{2.7}$$

the point here is that the expectation can be calculated without explicit use of the distribution of $u(\mathbf{X})$ (see **1**; IX,2). The same argument applies to unbounded variables such as $\mathbf{X}^2$.

The *second moment* of $\mathbf{X}$ is defined by

$$\mathbf{E}(\mathbf{X}^2) = \int_{-\infty}^{+\infty} x^2 f(x)\, dx, \tag{2.8}$$

provided the integral converges. Putting $\mu = \mathbf{E}(\mathbf{X})$ *the variance of* $\mathbf{X}$ is again defined by

$$\operatorname{Var}(\mathbf{X}) = \mathbf{E}((\mathbf{X}-\mu)^2) = \mathbf{E}(\mathbf{X}^2) - \mu^2. \tag{2.9}$$

Note. If the variable **X** is *positive* (that is, if the density f is concentrated on $\overline{0, \infty})$ and if the integral in (2.6) diverges it is harmless and convenient to say that **X** *has an infinite expectation* and write $\mathbf{E}(\mathbf{X}) = \infty$. By the same token one says that **X** has an infinite variance when the integral in (2.8) diverges. For variables assuming positive and negative values the expectation remains undefined when the integral (2.6) diverges. A typical example is provided by the density $\pi^{-1}(1 + x^2)^{-1}$.

The notion of density carries over to higher dimensions, but the general discussion is postponed to chapter III. Until then we shall consider only the analogue to the product probabilities introduced in definition 2 of **1**; V,4 to describe combinations of independent experiments. In other words, in this chapter we shall be concerned only with product densities of the form $f(x)\,g(y)$, $f(x)\,g(y)\,h(z)$, etc., where $f, g, \ldots$ are densities on the line. Giving a density of the form $f(x)\,g(y)$ in the plane $\mathcal{R}^2$ means identifying "probabilities" with integrals:

$$\mathbf{P}\{A\} = \iint_A f(x)\,g(y)\,dx\,dy. \tag{2.10}$$

Speaking of "*two independent random variables* **X** *and* **Y** *with densities* f *and* g" is an abbreviation for saying that probabilities in the (**X**, **Y**)-plane are assigned in accordance with (2.10). This implies the multiplication rule for intervals, for example $\mathbf{P}\{\mathbf{X} > a, \mathbf{Y} > b\} = \mathbf{P}\{\mathbf{X} > a\}\,\mathbf{P}\{\mathbf{Y} > b\}$. The analogy with the discrete case is so obvious that no further explanations are required.

Many new random variables may be defined as functions of **X** and **Y**, but the most important role is played by the sum $\mathbf{S} = \mathbf{X} + \mathbf{Y}$. The event $A = \{\mathbf{S} \leq s\}$ is represented by the half-plane of points (x, y) such that $x + y \leq s$. Denote the distribution function of **Y** by G so that one has $g(y) = G'(y)$. To obtain the *distribution function of* $\mathbf{X} + \mathbf{Y}$ we integrate in (2.10) over $y \leq s - x$ with the result

$$\mathbf{P}\{\mathbf{X}+\mathbf{Y} \leq s\} = \int_{-\infty}^{+\infty} G(s-x)\,f(x)\,dx. \tag{2.11}$$

For reasons of symmetry the roles of F and G can be interchanged without affecting the result. By differentiation it is then seen that *the density of* $\mathbf{X} + \mathbf{Y}$ *is given by either of the two integrals*

$$\int_{-\infty}^{+\infty} f(s-y)\,g(y)\,dy = \int_{-\infty}^{+\infty} f(y)\,g(s-y)\,dy. \tag{2.12}$$

The operation defined in (2.12) is a special case of the convolutions to be introduced in V,4. For the time being we use the term convolution only for densities: *The convolution of two densities f and g is the function defined by* (2.12). *It will be denoted by $f * g$.*

Throughout volume **1** we dealt with convolutions of discrete distributions, and the rules are the same. According to (2.12) we have $f * g = g * f$. Given a third density h we can form $(f * g) * h$ and this is the density of a sum $\mathbf{X} + \mathbf{Y} + \mathbf{Z}$ of three independent variables with densities f, g, h. The fact that summation is commutative and associative implies the same properties for convolutions, and so $f * g * h$ is independent of the order of the operations.

Positive random variables play an important role, and it is therefore useful to note that *if f and g are concentrated on $\overline{0, \infty}$ the convolution $f * g$ is defined by*

$$(2.13) \qquad f * g(s) = \int_0^s f(s-y)\, g(y)\, dy = \int_0^s f(x)\, g(s-x)\, dx.$$

Note *on the notion of random variable.* The use of the line or the Cartesian spaces $\mathfrak{R}^n$ as sample spaces sometimes blurs the distinction between random variables and "ordinary" functions of one or more variables. In volume **1** a random variable $\mathbf{X}$ could assume only denumerably many values and it was then obvious whether we were talking about a function (such as the square or the exponential) defined on the line, or the random variable $\mathbf{X}^2$ or $e^{\mathbf{X}}$ defined in the sample space. Even the outer appearance of these functions was entirely different inasmuch as the "ordinary" exponential assumes all positive values whereas $e^{\mathbf{X}}$ had a denumerable range. To see the change in this situation, consider now "two independent random variables $\mathbf{X}$ and $\mathbf{Y}$ with a common density f." In other words, the plane $\mathfrak{R}^2$ serves as sample space, and probabilities are defined as integrals of $f(x)f(y)$. Now every function of two variables *can* be defined *in* the sample space, and then it becomes a random variable, but it must be borne in mind that a function of two variables can be defined also without reference to our sample space. For example, certain statistical problems compel one to introduce the random variable $f(\mathbf{X})f(\mathbf{Y})$ [see example VI, (11.*d*)]. On the other hand, in introducing our sample space $\mathfrak{R}^2$ we have evidently referred to the "ordinary" function f defined independently of the sample space. This "ordinary" function induces many random variables, namely $f(\mathbf{X})$, $f(\mathbf{Y})$, $f(\mathbf{X} \pm \mathbf{Y})$, etc. Thus the same f may serve either as a random variable or as an ordinary function.

As a rule (and in each individual case) it will be clear whether or not we are concerned with a random variable. Nevertheless, in the general theory there arise situations in which functions (such as conditional probabilities and expectations) can be considered either as free functions or as random variables, and this is somewhat confusing if the freedom of choice is not properly understood.

Note *on terminology and notations.* To avoid overburdening of sentences it is customary to call **E**(**X**), interchangeably, expectation of the variable **X**, or of the density f, or of the distribution F. Similar liberties will be taken for other terms. For example, convolution really signifies an operation, but the term is applied also to the result of the operation and the function $f \star g$ is referred to as "the convolution."

In the older literature the terms distribution and frequency function were applied to what we call densities; our distribution functions were described as "cumulative," and the abbreviation c.d.f. is still in usage.

3. THE EXPONENTIAL DENSITY

For arbitrary, but fixed, $\alpha > 0$ put

$$(3.1) \qquad f(x) = \alpha e^{-\alpha x}, \qquad F(x) = 1 - e^{-\alpha x}, \quad \text{for} \quad x \geq 0$$

and $F(x) = f(x) = 0$ for $x < 0$. Then f is an exponential density, F its distribution function. A trite calculation shows that *the expectation equals* α^{-1}, *the variance* α^{-2}.

In example (1.*a*) the exponential distribution was derived as the limit of geometric distributions, and the method of example (2.*a*) leads to the same result. We recall that in stochastic processes the geometric distribution frequently governs waiting times or lifetimes, and that this is due to its "lack of memory," described in **1**; XIII,9: *whatever the present age, the residual lifetime is unaffected by the past and has the same distribution as the lifetime itself.* It will now be shown that this property carries over to the exponential limit and to no other distribution.

Let **T** be an arbitrary positive variable to be interpreted as life- or waiting time. It is convenient to replace the distribution function of **T** by its *tails*

$$(3.2) \qquad U(t) = \mathbf{P}\{\mathbf{T} > t\}.$$

Intuitively, $U(t)$ is the "probability at birth of a lifetime exceeding t." Given an age s, the event that the residual lifetime exceeds t is the same as $\{\mathbf{T} > s+t\}$ and the conditional probability of this event (given age s) equals the ratio $U(s+t)/U(s)$. This is the residual lifetime distribution, and it coincides with the total lifetime distribution iff

$$(3.3) \qquad U(s+t) = U(s)\, U(t), \qquad s, t > 0.$$

It was shown in **1**; XVII,6 that a positive solution of this equation is necessarily of the form $U(t) = e^{at}$, and hence *the lack of aging described above in italics holds true iff the lifetime distribution is exponential.*

We shall refer to this lack of memory as the *Markov property* of the exponential distribution. Analytically it reduces to the statement that only for the exponential distribution F do the tails $U = 1 - F$ satisfy (3.3), but this explains the constant occurrence of the exponential distribution in Markov processes. (A stronger version of the Markov property will be described in section 6.) Our description referred to temporal processes, but the argument is general and the Markov property remains meaningful when time is replaced by some other parameter.

Examples. (*a*) *Tensile strength.* To obtain a continuous analogue to the proverbial finite chain whose strength is that of its weakest link denote by $U(t)$ the probability that a thread of *length* t (of a given material) can sustain a certain fixed load. A thread of length $s+t$ does not snap iff the two segments individually sustain the given load. Assuming that there is no interaction, the two events must be considered independent and U must satisfy (3.3). Here the length of the thread takes over the role of the time parameter, and the length at which the thread will break is an exponentially distributed random variable.

(*b*) *A free-path problem.* By a star is meant a ball of fixed radius $\rho > 0$. Consider an ensemble of stars in space and choose for the origin a point not contained in any star. Taking the x-axis as representative of an arbitrary direction we are interested in the *longest interval* $\overline{0, x}$ *not intersecting any star.* It represents the *visibility in the x-direction.* The same description applies in two dimensions to *visibility in a forest* when the trees are taken as circular cylinders.

The visibility depends on the structure of the star field, and many models are conceivable. We describe the ensemble by Poisson distributions which serve as a model of "perfect randomness" in astronomy, physics, and statistics; more will be said about this in the next section. At this stage the notion of perfect randomness is undefined and we are free to introduce it by arbitrary *postulates*; the question then arises as to the existence of actual models obeying our postulates (in other words, whether or not the postulates are self-contradictory). Speaking intuitively, the first property that perfect randomness should have is the lack of interaction between different regions: from what occurs within region A it should be impossible to draw conclusions about stars in region B. *If* the ensemble of stars enjoys this property we can repeat the argument of the last example: The probability that a segment of length $s+t$ intersects no star must be the product of the corresponding probabilities for the two segments of length s and t. Under these conditions *the visibility in a given direction must be an exponentially distributed random variable.* [See example (4.*b*).]

The big *if* on which the argument depends is by no means trivial since it compels us to admit that stars overlap (for otherwise mutual distances of centers would exceed 2ρ and this would represent a form of interaction). This is of no practical consequence if the radius ρ is small in comparison with the average distance between nearest neighbors, and astronomers accept the model as a reasonable approximation. ▶

The next theorem will be used repeatedly.

Theorem. *If* $\mathbf{X}_1, \ldots, \mathbf{X}_n$ *are mutually independent random variables with the exponential distribution* (3.1), *then the sum* $\mathbf{X}_1 + \cdots + \mathbf{X}_n$ *has a density* g_n *and distribution function* G_n *given by*

$$g_n(x) = \alpha \frac{(\alpha x)^{n-1}}{(n-1)!} e^{-\alpha x} \qquad x > 0 \tag{3.4}$$

$$G_n(x) = 1 - e^{-\alpha x}\left(1 + \frac{\alpha x}{1!} + \cdots + \frac{(\alpha x)^{n-1}}{(n-1)!}\right) \qquad x > 0. \tag{3.5}$$

Proof. For $n = 0$ the assertion reduces to the definition (3.1). The density g_{n+1} is defined by the convolution

$$g_{n+1}(t) = \int_0^t g_n(t-x)\, g_0(x)\, dx, \tag{3.6}$$

and assuming the validity of (3.4) this reduces to

$$g_{n+1}(t) = \frac{\alpha^{n+1}}{(n-1)!} e^{-\alpha t} \int_0^t x^n\, dx = \alpha \frac{(\alpha t)^{n+1}}{(n+1)!} e^{-\alpha t}. \tag{3.7}$$

Thus (3.4) holds by induction for all n. The validity of (3.5) is seen by differentiation. ▶

The densities g_n are among the *gamma densities* to be introduced in II,2. They represent the continuous analogue of the negative binomial distribution found in **1**; VI,8 for the sum of n variables with a common geometric distribution. (See problem 7.)

4. WAITING TIME PARADOXES. THE POISSON PROCESS

Denote by $\mathbf{X}_1, \mathbf{X}_2, \ldots$ mutually independent random variables with the common exponential distribution (3.1), and put $\mathbf{S}_0 = 0$,

$$\mathbf{S}_n = \mathbf{X}_1 + \cdots + \mathbf{X}_n, \qquad n = 1, 2, \ldots. \tag{4.1}$$

We introduce a family of new random variables $\mathbf{N}(t)$ as follows: $\mathbf{N}(t)$ *is the number of indices* $k \geq 1$ *such that* $\mathbf{S}_k \leq t$. The event $\{\mathbf{N}(t) = n\}$ occurs iff $\mathbf{S}_n \leq t$ but $\mathbf{S}_{n+1} > t$. As $\mathbf{S}_n$ has the distribution G_n the probability of this event equals $G_n(t) - G_{n+1}(t)$ or

$$\mathbf{P}\{\mathbf{N}(t) = n\} = e^{-\alpha t}\frac{(\alpha t)^n}{n!}. \tag{4.2}$$

In words, *the random variable* $\mathbf{N}(t)$ *has a Poisson distribution with expectation* αt.

This argument looks like a new derivation of the Poisson distribution but in reality it merely rephrases the original derivation of **1**; VI,6 in terms of random variables. For an intuitive description consider chance occurrences (such as cosmic ray bursts or telephone calls), which we call "arrivals." Suppose that there is no aftereffect in the sense that the past history permits no conclusions as to the future. As we have seen, this condition requires that the waiting time $\mathbf{X}_1$ to the first arrival be exponentially distributed. But at each arrival the process starts from scratch as a probabilistic replica of the whole process: The successive waiting times $\mathbf{X}_k$ between arrivals must be independent and must have the same distribution. The sum $\mathbf{S}_n$ represents the epoch of the nth arrival and $\mathbf{N}(t)$ *the number of arrivals* within the interval $\overline{0, t}$. In this form the argument differs from the original derivation of the Poisson distribution only by the use of better technical terms.

(In the terminology of stochastic processes the sequence $\{\mathbf{S}_n\}$ constitutes a *renewal process* with exponential *interarrival times* $\mathbf{X}_k$; for the general notion see VI,6.)

Even this simple situation leads to apparent contradictions which illustrate the need for a sophisticated approach. We begin by a naïve formulation.

Example. *Waiting time paradox.* Buses arrive in accordance with a Poisson process, the expected time between consecutive buses being α^{-1}. I arrive at an epoch t. What is the expectation $\mathbf{E}(\mathbf{W}_t)$ of my waiting time $\mathbf{W}_t$ for the next bus? (It is understood that the epoch t of my arrival is independent of the buses, say noontime sharp.) Two contradictory answers stand to reason:

(*a*) The lack of memory of the Poisson process implies that $\mathbf{E}(\mathbf{W}_t)$ should be independent of t, that is, $\mathbf{E}(\mathbf{W}_t) = \mathbf{E}(\mathbf{W}_0) = \alpha^{-1}$.

(*b*) The epoch of my arrival is "chosen at random" in the interval between two consecutive buses, and for reasons of symmetry $\mathbf{E}(\mathbf{W}_t) = \frac{1}{2}\alpha^{-1}$.

Both arguments appear reasonable and both have been used in practice. What to do about the contradiction? The easiest way out is that of the formalist, who refuses to see a problem if it is not formulated in an impeccable manner. But problems are not solved by ignoring them.

We now show that *both* arguments are substantially, if not formally, *correct*. The fallacy lies at an unexpected place. It is connected with a phenomenon known from general renewal theory, where it caused serious trouble before it was properly understood. ►

We are dealing with a sequence of interarrival times

$$\mathbf{X}_1 = \mathbf{S}_1, \qquad \mathbf{X}_2 = \mathbf{S}_2 - \mathbf{S}_1, \ldots .$$

By assumption the $\mathbf{X}_k$ have a common exponential distribution with expectation α^{-1}. Picking out "any" particular $\mathbf{X}_k$ yields a random variable, and one has the intuitive feeling that its expectation should be α^{-1} provided the choice is done without knowledge of the sample sequence $\mathbf{X}_1, \mathbf{X}_2, \ldots$. But this is not true. In the example we chose that element $\mathbf{X}_k$ for which $\mathbf{S}_{k-1} < t \leq \mathbf{S}_k$, where t is fixed. This choice is made without regard of the actual process, but it turns out that the $\mathbf{X}_k$ so chosen has the *double* expectation $2\alpha^{-1}$. Given this fact, the argument (*b*) of the example postulates an expected waiting time α^{-1} and the contradiction disappears.

This solution of the paradox came as a shock to experienced workers, but it becomes intuitively clear once our mode of thinking is properly adjusted. Roughly speaking, a long interval has a better chance to cover the point t than a short one. This vague feeling is supported by the following

Proposition. *Let* $\mathbf{X}_1, \mathbf{X}_2, \ldots$ *be mutually independent with a common exponential distribution with expectation* α^{-1}. *Let* $t > 0$ *be fixed, but arbitrary. The element* $\mathbf{X}_k$ *satisfying the condition* $\mathbf{S}_{k-1} < t \leq \mathbf{S}_k$ *has the density*

$$v_t(x) = \begin{cases} \alpha^2 x e^{-\alpha x} & \text{for } 0 < x \leq t \\ \alpha(1+\alpha t)e^{-\alpha x} & \text{for } x > t. \end{cases} \tag{4.3}$$

The point is that the density (4.3) *is not the common density of the* $\mathbf{X}_k$. Its explicit form is of minor interest.

Proof. Let k be the index such that $\mathbf{S}_{k-1} < t \leq \mathbf{S}_k$ and put $\mathbf{L}_t$ equal to $\mathbf{S}_k - \mathbf{S}_{k-1}$. We have to prove that $\mathbf{L}_t$ has density (4.3). Suppose first $x < t$. The event $\{\mathbf{L}_t \leq x\}$ occurs iff $\mathbf{S}_n = y$ and $t - y < \mathbf{X}_{n+1} \leq x$ for some combination n, y. This necessitates $t - x \leq y \leq t$. Summing over all possible n and y we obtain

$$\mathbf{P}\{\mathbf{L}_t \leq x\} = \sum_{n=0}^{\infty} \int_{t-x}^{t} g_n(y) \cdot [e^{-\alpha(t-y)} - e^{-\alpha x}]\, dy. \tag{4.4}$$

But $g_0(y) + g_1(y) + \cdots = \alpha$ identically, and so

$$\mathbf{P}\{\mathbf{L}_t \leq x\} = 1 - e^{-\alpha x} - \alpha x e^{-\alpha x}. \tag{4.5}$$

By differentiation we get (4.3) for $x < t$. For $x > t$ a similar argument applies except that y ranges from 0 to t and we must add to the right side in (4.4) the probability $e^{-\alpha t} - e^{-\alpha x}$ that $0 < t < \mathbf{S}_1 < x$. This completes the proof. ►

The break in the formula (4.3) at $x = t$ is due to the special role of the origin as the starting epoch of the process. Obviously

$$\lim_{t\to\infty} v_t(x) = \alpha^2 x e^{-\alpha x}, \tag{4.6}$$

which shows that the special role of the origin wears out, and for an "old" process the distribution of $\mathbf{L}_t$ is nearly independent of t. One expresses this conveniently by saying that the "*steady state*" *density* of $\mathbf{L}_t$ is given by the right side in (4.6).

With the notations of the proof the waiting time $\mathbf{W}_t$ considered in the example is the random variable $\mathbf{W}_t = \mathbf{S}_k - t$. The argument of the proof shows also that

$$\begin{aligned} \mathbf{P}\{\mathbf{W}_t \leq x\} &= e^{-\alpha t} - e^{-\alpha(x+t)} + \sum_{n=0}^{\infty} \int_0^t g_n(y)[e^{-\alpha(t-y)} - e^{-\alpha(x+t-y)}]\, dy \\ &= 1 - e^{-\alpha x} \end{aligned} \tag{4.7}$$

Thus $\mathbf{W}_t$ *has the same exponential distribution as the* $\mathbf{X}_k$ in accordance with the reasoning (*a*). (See problem 8.)

Finally, a word about the *Poisson process.* The Poisson variables $\mathbf{N}(t)$ were introduced as functions on the sample space of the infinite sequence of random variables $\mathbf{X}_1, \mathbf{X}_2, \ldots$. This procedure is satisfactory for many purposes, but a different sample space is more natural. The conceptual experiment "observing the number of incoming calls up to epoch t" yields for each positive t an integer, and the result is therefore a step function with unit jumps. The appropriate sample space has these step functions as sample points; the sample space is a function space—the space of all conceivable "paths." In this space $\mathbf{N}(t)$ is defined as the value of the ordinate at epoch t and $\mathbf{S}_n$ as the coordinate of the nth jump, etc. Events can now be considered that are not expressible in terms of the original variables $\mathbf{X}_n$. A typical example of practical interest (see the ruin problem in VI,5) is the event that $\mathbf{N}(t) > a + bt$ for some t. The individual path (just as the individual infinite sequence of ± 1 in binomial trials) represents the natural and unavoidable object of probabilistic inquiry. Once one gets used to the new phraseology, the space of paths becomes most intuitive.

Unfortunately the introduction of probabilities in spaces of sample paths is far from simple. By comparison, the step from discrete sample spaces to the line, plane, etc., and even to infinite sequences of random variables, is neither conceptually nor technically difficult. Problems of a new type arise in connection with function spaces, and the reader is warned that we shall not deal with them in this volume. We shall be satisfied with an honest treatment of sample spaces of sequences (denumerably many coordinate variables). Reference to stochastic processes in general, and to the Poisson process in particular, will be made freely, but only to provide an intuitive background or to enhance interest in our problems.

Poisson Ensembles of Points

As shown in **1**; VI,6, the Poisson law governs not only "points distributed randomly along the time axis," but also ensembles of points (such as flaws in materials or raisins in a cake) distributed randomly in plane or space, provided t is interpreted as area or volume. The basic assumption is that the probability of finding k points in a specified domain depends only on the area or volume of the domain, but not on its shape, and that occurrences in non-overlapping domains are independent. Easy formal calculations may lead to interesting results concerning such random ensembles of points, but the remarks about the Poisson process apply equally to Poisson ensembles; a complete probabilistic description is complex and beyond the scope of the present volume.

Examples. (*a*) *Nearest neighbors.* The interarrival times in a Poisson process may be described as distances between nearest neighbors. This notion carries over to the plane. Saying that the nearest neighbor to 0 has a distance $\leq r$ amounts to saying that a disk of radius r contains at least one point of the ensemble. For a true Poisson ensemble the probability of finding no point within any domain of area v equals $e^{-\alpha v}$, and it is thus seen that the *distribution of nearest neighbors in a Poisson ensemble in* $\mathfrak{R}^2$ *is given by* $1 - e^{-\alpha\pi r^2}$; in $\mathfrak{R}^3$ we get $1 - e^{-\beta r^3}$ where $\beta = \frac{4}{3}\pi\alpha$.

(*b*) *Free paths.* We return to the free path or visibility example (3.*b*). In the present terminology it is assumed that the *centers* of the stars represent a sample from a Poisson ensemble, and that each star is a ball of radius ρ. (This implies the possibility of overlaps.) It is assumed that the origin is not contained in any star, and we are interested in the distance **L** of the *nearest neighbor in the x-direction* (that is, the longest segment $\overline{0, a}$ on the x-axis not intersecting any star).

We have already seen on a priori grounds that **L** should have an exponential distribution. This result will now be derived computationally from the *assumed* properties of the stellar system. The event $\{\mathbf{L} > x\}$ means that no star *center* is contained within any sphere of radius ρ with center at a point of $\overline{0, x}$, and it is known in advance that the sphere about the origin contains no center. The union of the remaining spheres is a domain Ω bounded by a circular cylinder and two hemispheres with centers at 0 and x, respectively. The volume of Ω is evidently $\pi\rho^2 x$, and hence $\mathbf{P}\{\mathbf{L} > x\} = e^{-\alpha\pi\rho^2 x}$. It follows not only that the distribution is exponential, but also that we have found the relation between its parameter and the ensemble of stars. (In $\mathfrak{R}^2$ the area of Ω is obviously $2\rho x$ and hence one has $\mathbf{P}\{\mathbf{L} > x\} = e^{-2\alpha\rho x}$.) ►

5. THE PERSISTENCE OF BAD LUCK

As everyone knows, he who joins a waiting line is sure to wait for an abnormally long time, and similar bad luck follows us on all occasions. How much can probability theory contribute towards an explanation? For an answer we consider three examples typical for a variety of situations. They illustrate unexpected general features of chance fluctuations.

Examples. (*a*) *Record values.* Denote by $\mathbf{X}_0$ my waiting time (or financial loss) at some chance event. Suppose that friends of mine expose themselves to the same type of experience, and denote the results by $\mathbf{X}_1, \mathbf{X}_2, \ldots$. To exclude bias we assume that $\mathbf{X}_0, \mathbf{X}_1, \ldots$ are mutually independent random variables with a common distribution. The nature of the latter really does not matter but, since the exponential distribution serves as a model for randomness, we assume the $\mathbf{X}_j$ exponentially distributed in accordance with (3.1). For simplicity of description we treat the sequence $\{\mathbf{X}_j\}$ as infinite.

To find a measure for my ill luck I ask how long it will take before a friend experiences worse luck (we neglect the event of probability zero that $\mathbf{X}_k = \mathbf{X}_0$). More formally, we introduce the waiting time $\mathbf{N}$ *as the value of the first subscript n such that* $\mathbf{X}_n > \mathbf{X}_0$. The event $\{\mathbf{N} > n-1\}$ occurs iff the maximal term of the n-tuple $\mathbf{X}_0, \mathbf{X}_1, \ldots, \mathbf{X}_{n-1}$ appears at the initial place; for reasons of symmetry the probability of this event is n^{-1}. The event $\{\mathbf{N} = n\}$ is the same as $\{\mathbf{N} > n-1\} - \{\mathbf{N} > n\}$, and hence for $n = 1, 2, \ldots$,

$$\mathbf{P}\{\mathbf{N} = n\} = \frac{1}{n} - \frac{1}{n+1} = \frac{1}{n(n+1)}. \tag{5.1}$$

This result fully confirms that I have indeed very bad luck: *The random variable* $\mathbf{N}$ *has infinite expectation*! It would be bad enough if it took on the average 1000 trials to beat the record of my ill luck, but the actual waiting time has infinite expectation.

It will be noted that the argument does not depend on the condition that the $\mathbf{X}_k$ are exponentially distributed. It follows that whenever the variables $\mathbf{X}_j$ are independent and have a common continuous distribution function F the first record value has the distribution (5.1). The fact that this distribution is independent of F is used by statisticians for tests of independence. (See also problems 10 and 11.)

The striking and general nature of the result (5.1) combined with the simplicity of the proof are apt to arouse suspicion. The argument is really impeccable (except for the informal presentation), but those who prefer to rely on brute calculation can easily verify the truth of (5.1) from the direct definition of the probability in question as the $(n+1)$-tuple integral of $\alpha^{n+1}e^{-\alpha(x_0+\cdots+x_n)}$ over the region defined by the inequalities $0 < x_0 < x_n$ and $0 < x_j < x_0$ for $j = 1, \ldots, n-1$.

An *alternative derivation* of (5.1) is an instructive exercise in conditional probabilities; it is less simple, but leads to additional results (problem 9). Given that $\mathbf{X}_0 = x$, the probability of a greater value at later trials is $p = e^{-\alpha x}$, and we are concerned with the waiting time for the first "success" in Bernoulli trials with probability p. The conditional probability that $\mathbf{N} = n$ given $\mathbf{X}_0 = x$ is therefore $p(1-p)^{n-1}$. To obtain $\mathbf{P}\{\mathbf{N} = n\}$ we have to multiply by the density $\alpha e^{-\alpha x}$ of the hypothesis $\mathbf{X}_0 = x$ and integrate with respect to x. The substitution $1 - e^{-\alpha x} = t$ reduces the integrand to $t^{n-1}(1-t)$, the integral of which equals $n^{-1} - (n+1)^{-1}$ in agreement with (5.1).

(*b*) *Ratios.* If $\mathbf{X}$ and $\mathbf{Y}$ are two independent variables with a common exponential distribution, the ratio $\mathbf{Y}/\mathbf{X}$ is a new random variable. Its distribution function is obtained by integrating $\alpha^2 e^{-\alpha(x+y)}$ over $0 < y < tx$, $0 < x < \infty$. Integration with respect to y leads to

$$\mathbf{P}\left\{\frac{\mathbf{Y}}{\mathbf{X}} \leq t\right\} = \int_0^\infty \alpha e^{-\alpha x}(1 - e^{-\alpha t x})\, dx = \frac{t}{1+t}. \tag{5.2}$$

The corresponding *density* is given by $(1+t)^{-2}$. It is noteworthy that *the variable* $\mathbf{Y}/\mathbf{X}$ *has infinite expectation.*

We find here a new confirmation for the persistence of bad luck. Assuredly Peter has reason for complaint if he has to wait three times as long as Paul, but the distribution (5.2) attributes to this event probability $\frac{1}{4}$. It follows that, on the average, in one out of two cases either Paul or Peter has reason for complaint. The observed frequency increases in practice because very short waiting times naturally pass unnoticed.

(*c*) *Parallel waiting lines.* I arrive in my car at the car inspection station (or at a tunnel entrance, car ferry, etc.). There are two waiting lines to choose from, but once I have joined a line I have to stay in it. Mr. Smith, who drove behind me, occupies the place that I might have chosen and I keep watching whether he is ahead of or behind me. Most of the time we stand still, but occasionally one line or the other moves one carlength forward. To maximize the influence of pure chance we assume the two lines stochastically independent; also, the time intervals between successive moves are independent variables with a common exponential distribution. Under these circumstances the successive moves constitute Bernoulli trials in which "success" means that I move ahead, "failure" that Mr. Smith moves. The probability of success being $\frac{1}{2}$ we are, in substance, dealing with a symmetric random walk, and the curious properties of fluctuations in random walks find a striking interpretation. (For simplicity of description we disregard the fact that only finitely many cars are present.) Am I ever going to be ahead of Mr. Smith? In the random walk interpretation the question is whether a first passage through $+1$ will ever take place. As we know, this event has probability one, but the expected waiting time for it is infinite. Such waiting gives ample opportunity to bemoan my bad luck, and this only grows more irritating by the fact that Mr. Smith argues in the same way. ►

6. WAITING TIMES AND ORDER STATISTICS

Given an ordered n-tuple $(x_1, \ldots, x_n)$ of real numbers, we may reorder it in increasing order of magnitude to obtain the new n-tuple

$$(x_{(1)}, x_{(2)}, \ldots, x_{(n)}) \quad \text{where} \quad x_{(1)} \leq x_{(2)} \leq \cdots \leq x_{(n)}.$$

This operation applied to all points of the space $\mathcal{R}^n$ induces n well-defined functions, which will be denoted by $\mathbf{X}_{(1)}, \ldots, \mathbf{X}_{(n)}$. If probabilities are defined in $\mathcal{R}^n$ these functions become random variables. We say that $(\mathbf{X}_{(1)}, \ldots, \mathbf{X}_{(n)})$ is obtained by reordering $(\mathbf{X}_1, \ldots, \mathbf{X}_n)$ according to increasing magnitude. The variable $\mathbf{X}_{(k)}$ is called kth-*order statistic*[7] of the given sample $\mathbf{X}_1, \ldots, \mathbf{X}_n$. In particular, $\mathbf{X}_{(1)}$ and $\mathbf{X}_{(n)}$ are the *sample extremes*; when $n = 2\nu + 1$ is odd, $\mathbf{X}_{(\nu+1)}$ is the *sample median.*

We apply this notion to the particular case of independent random variables $\mathbf{X}_1, \ldots, \mathbf{X}_n$ with the common exponential density $\alpha e^{-\alpha x}$.

Examples. (*a*) *Parallel waiting lines.* Interpret $\mathbf{X}_1, \ldots, \mathbf{X}_n$ as the lengths of n service times commencing at epoch 0 at a post office with n counters. The order statistics represent the successive epochs of terminations or, as one might say, the *epochs of the successive discharges* (the "output process"). In particular, $\mathbf{X}_{(1)}$ is the waiting time for the first discharge. Now if the assumed lack of aftereffect is meaningful, the waiting time $\mathbf{X}_{(1)}$ must have the Markov property, that is, $\mathbf{X}_{(1)}$ must be exponentially distributed. As a matter of fact, the event $\{\mathbf{X}_{(1)} > t\}$ is the simultaneous realization of the n events $\{\mathbf{X}_k > t\}$, each of which has probability $e^{-\alpha t}$; because of the assumed independence the probabilities multiply and we have indeed

$$\mathbf{P}\{\mathbf{X}_{(1)} > t\} = e^{-n\alpha t}. \tag{6.1}$$

[7] Strictly speaking the term "sample statistic" is synonymous with "function of the sample variables," that is, with random variable. It is used to emphasize linguistically the different role played *in a given context* by the primary variable (the sample) and some derived variables. For example, the "sample mean" $(\mathbf{X}_1 + \cdots + \mathbf{X}_n)/n$ is called a statistic. Order statistics occur frequently in the statistical literature. We conform to the standard terminology except that the extremes are usually called extreme "*values.*"

We can now proceed a step further and consider the situation at epoch $\mathbf{X}_{(1)}$. The assumed lack of memory seems to imply that the original situation is restored except that now only $n - 1$ counters are in operation; the continuation of the process should be *independent of* $\mathbf{X}_{(1)}$ and a replica of the whole process. In particular, the waiting time for the next discharge, namely $\mathbf{X}_{(2)} - \mathbf{X}_{(1)}$, should have the distribution

$$\mathbf{P}\{\mathbf{X}_{(2)} - \mathbf{X}_{(1)} > t\} = e^{-(n-1)\alpha t} \tag{6.2}$$

analogous to (6.1). This reasoning leads to the following general proposition concerning the order statistics for independent variables with a common exponential distribution.

Proposition.[8] *The n variables* $\mathbf{X}_{(1)}, \mathbf{X}_{(2)} - \mathbf{X}_{(1)}, \ldots, \mathbf{X}_{(n)} - \mathbf{X}_{(n-1)}$ *are independent and the density of* $\mathbf{X}_{(k+1)} - \mathbf{X}_{(k)}$ *is given by* $(n-k)\alpha e^{-(n-k)\alpha t}$.

Before verifying this proposition formally let us consider its implications. When $n = 2$ the difference $\mathbf{X}_{(2)} - \mathbf{X}_{(1)}$ is the *residual waiting time* after the expiration of the shorter of two waiting times. The proposition asserts that this residual waiting time has the same exponential distribution as the original waiting time and is independent of $\mathbf{X}_{(1)}$. This is an extension of the Markov property enunciated for *fixed epochs* t to the chance-dependent stopping time $\mathbf{X}_{(1)}$. It is called the *strong Markov property*. (As we are dealing with only finitely many variables we are in a position to *derive* the strong Markov property from the weak one, but in more complicated stochastic processes the distinction is essential.)

The *proof of the proposition* serves as an example for formal manipulations with integrals. For typographical simplicity we let $n = 3$. We start from the remark[9] that

$$\begin{aligned} \mathbf{P}\{\mathbf{X}_{(1)} > t_1, \mathbf{X}_{(2)} - \mathbf{X}_{(1)} > t_2, \mathbf{X}_{(3)} - \mathbf{X}_{(2)} > t_3\} &= \\ = 3!\,\mathbf{P}\{\mathbf{X}_1 > t_1,\ \mathbf{X}_2 - \mathbf{X}_1 > t_2,\ \mathbf{X}_3 - \mathbf{X}_2 > t_3\}&, \end{aligned} \tag{6.3}$$

which follows from the fact that the $3!$ permutations of $\mathbf{X}_1, \mathbf{X}_2, \mathbf{X}_3$ have the same probability distribution. (Purely analytically, the space $\mathcal{R}^3$ is partitioned into six parts congruent to the region defined by $x_1 < x_2 < x_3$, each contributing the same amount to the integral. The boundaries where two or more coordinates are equal have probability zero and play no role.) To obtain the probability (6.3) we have to integrate $\alpha^3 e^{-\alpha(x_1+x_2+x_3)}$ over the region defined by the inequalities

$$x_1 > t_1, \qquad x_2 - x_1 > t_2, \qquad x_3 - x_2 > t_3.$$

[8] This proposition has been discovered repeatedly for purposes of statistical estimation but its nature remains obscure without appeal to the Markov property. See also problem 14.

[9] Most calculations of similar probabilities start from the same principle.

A simple integration with respect to x_3 leads to

$$(6.4)\qquad \begin{aligned} 3!e^{-\alpha t_3}\int_{t_1}^{\infty}\alpha e^{-\alpha x_1}\,dx_1\int_{x_1+t_2}^{\infty}\alpha e^{-2\alpha x_2}\,dx_2 &= \\ = 3e^{-\alpha t_3-2\alpha t_2}\int_{t_1}^{\infty}\alpha e^{-3\alpha x_1}\,dx_1 &= e^{-\alpha t_3-2\alpha t_2-3\alpha t_1}. \end{aligned}$$

Thus the joint distribution of the three variables $\mathbf{X}_{(1)}$, $\mathbf{X}_{(2)}-\mathbf{X}_{(1)}$, $\mathbf{X}_{(3)}-\mathbf{X}_{(2)}$ is a product of three exponential distributions, and this proves the proposition.

It follows in particular that $\mathbf{E}(\mathbf{X}_{(k+1)}-\mathbf{X}_{(k)}) = 1/(n-k)\alpha$. Summing over $k = 0, 1, \ldots, \nu-1$ we obtain

$$(6.5)\qquad \mathbf{E}(\mathbf{X}_{(\nu)}) = \frac{1}{\alpha}\left(\frac{1}{n} + \frac{1}{n-1} + \cdots + \frac{1}{n-\nu+1}\right).$$

Note that this expectation was calculated without knowledge of the distribution of $\mathbf{X}_{(\nu)}$ and we have here another example of the advantage to be derived from the representation of a random variable as a sum of other variables. (See **1**; IX,3.)

(*b*) *Use of the strong Markov property.* For picturesque language suppose that at epoch 0 three persons *A*, *B*, and *C* arrive at a post office and find two counters free. The three service times are independent random variables **X**, **Y**, **Z** with the same exponential distribution. The service times of *A* and *B* commence immediately, but that of *C* starts at the epoch $\mathbf{X}_{(1)}$ when either *A* or *B* is discharged. We show that the Markov property leads to simple answers to various questions.

(i) What is the probability that *C* will not be the last to leave the post office? The answer is $\frac{1}{2}$, because epoch $\mathbf{X}_{(1)}$ of the first departure establishes symmetry between *C* and the other person being served.

(ii) What is the distribution of the time **T** spent by *C* at the post office? Clearly $\mathbf{T} = \mathbf{X}_{(1)} + \mathbf{Z}$ is the sum of two independent variables whose distributions are exponential with parameters 2α and α. The convolution of any two exponential distributions is easily found (problem 6), and it is seen that **T** has density $u(t) = 2\alpha(e^{-\alpha t} - e^{-2\alpha t})$ and $\mathbf{E}(\mathbf{T}) = 3/(2\alpha)$.

(iii) What is the distribution of the epoch of the *last* departure? Denote the epochs of the successive departures by $\mathbf{X}_{(1)}$, $\mathbf{X}_{(2)}$, $\mathbf{X}_{(3)}$. The difference $\mathbf{X}_{(3)} - \mathbf{X}_{(1)}$ is the longer of two exponential service times, and so

$$\mathbf{P}\{\mathbf{X}_{(3)} - \mathbf{X}_{(1)} \leq t\} = (1 - e^{-\alpha t})^2.$$

This distribution again has u as density. Now $\mathbf{X}_{(1)}$ is independent of $\mathbf{X}_{(3)} - \mathbf{X}_{(1)}$ and has density $2\alpha e^{-2\alpha t}$. The convolution formula used in

(ii) shows therefore that $\mathbf{X}_{(3)}$ has density $4\alpha[e^{-\alpha t} - e^{-2\alpha t} - \alpha t e^{-2\alpha t}]$ and $\mathbf{E}(\mathbf{X}_{(3)}) = 2/\alpha$.

The advantage of this method becomes clear on comparison with direct calculations, but the latter apply to arbitrary service time distributions (problem 18).

(*c*) *Distribution of order statistics.* As a final exercise we derive the distribution of $\mathbf{X}_{(k)}$. The event $\{\mathbf{X}_{(k)} \leq t\}$ signifies that at least k among the n variables $\mathbf{X}_j$ are $\leq t$. This represents at least k "successes" in n independent trials, and hence

$$\mathbf{P}\{\mathbf{X}_{(k)} \leq t\} = \sum_{j=k}^{n} \binom{n}{j} (1 - e^{-\alpha t})^j e^{-(n-j)\alpha t}. \tag{6.6}$$

By differentiation it is seen that the *density of* $\mathbf{X}_{(k)}$ is given by

$$n\binom{n-1}{k-1}(1 - e^{-\alpha t})^{k-1} e^{-(n-k)\alpha t} \cdot \alpha e^{-\alpha t}. \tag{6.7}$$

This result may be obtained directly by the following loose argument. We require (up to terms negligible in the limit as $h \to 0$) the probability of the joint event that one among the variables $\mathbf{X}_j$ lies between t and $t + h$ and that $k - 1$ among the remaining $n - 1$ variables are $\leq t$, while the other $n - k$ variables are $> t + h$. Multiplying the number of choices and the corresponding probabilities leads to (6.7). Beginners are advised to formalize this argument, and also to derive (6.7) from the discrete model. ▶

7. THE UNIFORM DISTRIBUTION

The random variable $\mathbf{X}$ *is distributed uniformly in the interval* $\overline{a, b}$ if its density is constant $= (b-a)^{-1}$ for $a < x < b$ and vanishes outside this interval. In this case the variable $(\mathbf{X}-a)(b-a)^{-1}$ is distributed uniformly in $\overline{0, 1}$, and we shall usually use this interval as standard. Because of the appearance of their graphs the densities of the uniform distribution function are called "*rectangular*."

With the uniform distribution the interval $\overline{0, 1}$ becomes a sample space in which probabilities of intervals are identical with their lengths. The sample space corresponding to two independent variables $\mathbf{X}$ and $\mathbf{Y}$ that are uniformly distributed over $\overline{0, 1}$ is the unit square in $\mathcal{R}^2$, and probabilities in it are defined by their area. The same idea applies to triples and n-tuples.

A uniformly distributed random variable is often called a "*point* $\mathbf{X}$ *chosen at random*." The result of the conceptual experiment "n independent random choices of a point in $\overline{0, 1}$" requires an n-dimensional hypercube for its probabilistic description, but the experiment as such yields n points $\mathbf{X}_1, \ldots, \mathbf{X}_n$ *in the same interval.* With unit probability no two of them are equal, and hence they partition $\overline{0, 1}$ into $n + 1$ subintervals. Reordering the n points $\mathbf{X}_1, \ldots, \mathbf{X}_n$ in their natural order from left to right we get n new random variables which will be denoted by $\mathbf{X}_{(1)}, \ldots, \mathbf{X}_{(n)}$. These are the *order statistics* defined in the last section. The subintervals of the partition are now $\overline{0, \mathbf{X}_{(1)}}$, then $\overline{\mathbf{X}_{(1)}, \mathbf{X}_{(2)}}$, etc.

The notion of a *point chosen at random on a circle* is self-explanatory. To visualize the result of n independent choices on the circle we imagine the *circle oriented* anticlockwise, so that intervals have left and right endpoints and may be represented in the form $\overline{a, b}$. Two points $\mathbf{X}_1$ and $\mathbf{X}_2$ chosen independently and at random divide the circle into the two intervals $\overline{\mathbf{X}_1, \mathbf{X}_2}$ and $\overline{\mathbf{X}_2, \mathbf{X}_1}$. (We disregard again the zero-probability event that $\mathbf{X}_1 = \mathbf{X}_2$.)

Examples. (*a*) *Empirical interpretations.* The *roulette wheel* is generally thought of as a means to effect a "random choice" on the circle. In numerical calculations to six decimals the *rounding error* is usually treated as a random variable distributed uniformly over an interval of length 10^{-6}. (For the error committed by dropping the last two decimals the discrete model with 100 possible values is more appropriate, though less practical.) The waiting time of a passenger arriving at the *bus station* without regard to the schedule may be regarded as uniformly distributed over the interval between successive departures. Of wider theoretical interest are the applications to *random splittings* discussed in section 8. In many problems of mathematical statistics (such as non-parametric tests) the uniform distribution enters in an indirect way: given an arbitrary random variable $\mathbf{X}$ with a continuous distribution F the random variable $F(\mathbf{X})$ *is distributed uniformly over* $\overline{0, 1}$. (See section 12.)

(*b*) *The induced partition.* We prove the following proposition: *n independently and randomly chosen points $\mathbf{X}_1, \ldots, \mathbf{X}_n$ partition $\overline{0, 1}$ into $n + 1$ intervals whose lengths have the common distribution given by*

$$\mathbf{P}\{\mathbf{L} > t\} = (1-t)^n, \qquad 0 < t < 1. \tag{7.1}$$

Note that (7.1) refers to the *tail* of the distribution.

Intuitively one might expect that at least the two end intervals should have different distributions. That all $n + 1$ intervals should have the same distribution becomes clear on considering the equivalent situation on the (oriented) circle of unit length. Here $n + 1$ points $\mathbf{X}_1, \ldots, \mathbf{X}_{n+1}$ chosen independently and at random partition the circle into $n + 1$

intervals, and for reasons of symmetry these intervals must have the same distribution. Imagine now the circle cut at the point $\mathbf{X}_{n+1}$ to obtain an interval in which $\mathbf{X}_1, \ldots, \mathbf{X}_n$ are chosen independently and at random. The lengths of the $n+1$ intervals of the induced partition are the same, and they have a common distribution. That this distribution is given by (7.1) may be seen by considering the leftmost interval $\overline{0, \mathbf{X}_{(1)}}$. Its length exceeds t iff all n points $\mathbf{X}_1, \ldots, \mathbf{X}_n$ are in $\overline{t, 1}$, and the probability of this event is $(1-t)^n$.

It is a good exercise to verify the proposition in the special case $n = 2$ by inspection of the three events in the unit square representing the sample space. [For a computational verification note that the probability of the event $\{\mathbf{X}_{(k+1)} - \mathbf{X}_{(k)} > t\}$ equals the integral of the constant function 1 over the union of the $n!$ congruent regions defined either by the string of inequalities $x_1 < \cdots < x_k < x_k + t < x_{k+1} < \cdots < x_n$ or by similar strings obtained by permuting the subscripts. A more streamlined calculation leading to a stronger result is contained in example III, (3.*c*).]

(*c*) *A paradox.*[10] Let two points $\mathbf{X}_1$ and $\mathbf{X}_2$ be chosen independently and at random on the circle of unit length. Then *the lengths of the two intervals* $\overline{\mathbf{X}_1, \mathbf{X}_2}$ *and* $\overline{\mathbf{X}_2, \mathbf{X}_1}$ *are uniformly distributed, but the length* $\boldsymbol{\lambda}$ *of the one containing the arbitrary point P has a different distribution* (*with density* $2x$).

In particular, each of the two intervals has expected length $\frac{1}{2}$, but the one containing P has expected length $\frac{2}{3}$. The point P being fixed, but arbitrary, one has the feeling that the interval covering P is chosen "without advance knowledge of its properties" (to borrow a phrase from the philosophers of probability). Certainly naïve intuition is not prepared for the great difference between covering or not covering an arbitrary point, but after due reflection this difference becomes "intuitively obvious." In fact, however, rather experienced writers have fallen into the trap.

For a proof imagine the circle cut at P leaving us with two points chosen independently and at random in $\overline{0, 1}$. Using the same notation as before the event $\{\boldsymbol{\lambda} < t\}$ occurs iff $\mathbf{X}_{(2)} - \mathbf{X}_{(1)} > 1 - t$ and by (7.1) the probability for this equals t^2. The variable $\boldsymbol{\lambda}$ has therefore density $2t$, as asserted. (Beginners are advised to try a *direct* computational verification.)

(*d*) *Distribution of order statistics.* If $\mathbf{X}_1, \ldots, \mathbf{X}_n$ are independent and distributed uniformly in $\overline{0, 1}$, the number of variables satisfying the inequality $0 < \mathbf{X}_j \leq t < 1$ has a binomial distribution with probability of

[10] Closely related to the waiting time paradox of section 4.

"success" equal to t. Now the event $\{\mathbf{X}_{(k)} \leq t\}$ occurs iff at least k among the variables are $\leq t$ and hence

$$\mathbf{P}\{\mathbf{X}_{(k)} \leq t\} = \sum_{j=k}^{n} \binom{n}{j} t^j (1-t)^{n-j}. \tag{7.2}$$

This gives us the distribution function of the kth order statistics. By differentiation it is found that *the density of* $\mathbf{X}_{(k)}$ *is given by*

$$n\binom{n-1}{k-1} t^{k-1}(1-t)^{n-k}. \tag{7.3}$$

This may be seen directly as follows: The probability that one among the $\mathbf{X}_j$ lies between t and $t+h$, and that $k-1$ among the remaining ones are less than t while $n-k$ are greater than $t+h$, equals

$$n\binom{n-1}{k-1} t^{k-1}(1-t-h)^{n-k}h.$$

Divide by h and let $h \to 0$ to obtain (7.3).

(*e*) *Limit theorems.* To see the nature of the distribution of $\mathbf{X}_{(1)}$ when n is large it is best to introduce $\mathbf{E}(\mathbf{X}_{(1)}) = (n+1)^{-1}$ as a new unit of measurement. As $n \to \infty$ we get then for the tail of the distribution function

$$\mathbf{P}\{n\mathbf{X}_{(1)} > t\} = \left(1 - \frac{t}{n}\right)^n \to e^{-t}. \tag{7.4}$$

It is customary to describe this relation by saying that *in the limit* $\mathbf{X}_{(1)}$ *is exponentially distributed with expectation* n^{-1}. Similarly

$$\mathbf{P}\{n\mathbf{X}_{(2)} > t\} = \left(1 - \frac{t}{n}\right)^n + \binom{n}{1}\frac{t}{n}\left(1 - \frac{t}{n}\right)^{n-1} \to e^{-t} + te^{-t}, \tag{7.5}$$

and on the right one recognizes the tail of the gamma distribution G_2 of (3.5). In like manner it is easily verified that for every fixed k as $n \to \infty$ *the distribution of* $n\mathbf{X}_{(k)}$ *tends to the gamma distribution* G_k (see problem 31).

Now G_k is the distribution of the sum of k independent exponentially distributed variables while $\mathbf{X}_{(k)}$ is the sum of the first k intervals considered in example (*b*). We can therefore say that the lengths of the successive intervals of our partition behave in the limit as if they were mutually independent exponentially distributed variables.

[In view of the obvious relation of (7.2) with the binomial distribution the central limit theorem may be used to obtain approximations to the distribution of $\mathbf{X}_{(k)}$ when both n and k are large.]

(*f*) *Ratios.* Let $\mathbf{X}$ be chosen at random in $\overline{0, 1}$ and denote by $\mathbf{U}$ the length of the *shorter* of the intervals $\overline{0, \mathbf{X}}$ and $\overline{\mathbf{X}, 1}$ and by $\mathbf{V} = 1 - \mathbf{U}$ the length of the longer. The random variable $\mathbf{U}$ is uniformly distributed between 0 and $\frac{1}{2}$ because the event $\{\mathbf{U} < t < \frac{1}{2}\}$ occurs iff either $\mathbf{X} < t$ or

$1 - \mathbf{X} < t$ and therefore has probability $2t$. For reasons of symmetry $\mathbf{V}$ is uniformly distributed between $\frac{1}{2}$ and 1, and so $\mathbf{E}(\mathbf{U}) = \frac{1}{4}$, $\mathbf{E}(\mathbf{V}) = \frac{3}{4}$. What can we say about the ratio $\mathbf{V}/\mathbf{U}$? It necessarily exceeds 1 and it lies between 1 and $t > 1$ iff either

$$\frac{1}{1+t} \leq \mathbf{X} \leq \tfrac{1}{2} \qquad \text{or} \qquad \tfrac{1}{2} \leq \mathbf{X} \leq \frac{t}{1+t}.$$

For $t > 1$ it follows that

$$\mathbf{P}\left\{\frac{\mathbf{V}}{\mathbf{U}} \leq t\right\} = \frac{t-1}{t+1}, \tag{7.6}$$

and the density of this distribution is given by $2(t+1)^{-2}$. It is seen that $\mathbf{V}/\mathbf{U}$ *has infinite expectation.* This example shows how little information is contained in the observation that $\mathbf{E}(\mathbf{V})/\mathbf{E}(\mathbf{U}) = 3$. ▶

8. RANDOM SPLITTINGS

The problem of this section concludes the preceding parade of examples and is separated from them partly because of its importance in physics, and partly because it will serve as a prototype for general Markov chains.

Formally we are concerned with products of the form $\mathbf{Z}_n = \mathbf{X}_1\mathbf{X}_2 \cdots \mathbf{X}_n$ where $\mathbf{X}_1, \ldots, \mathbf{X}_n$ are mutually independent variables distributed uniformly in $\overline{0, 1}$.

Examples *for applications.* In certain collision processes a physical *particle* is split into two and its mass m divided between them. Different laws of partition may fit different processes, but it is frequently assumed that the fraction of parental mass received by each descendant particle is distributed uniformly in $\overline{0, 1}$. If one of the two particles is chosen at random and subject to a new collision then (assuming that there is no interaction so that the collisions are independent) the masses of the two second-generation particles are given by products $m\mathbf{X}_1\mathbf{X}_2$, and so on. (See problem 20.) With trite verbal changes this model applies also to splittings of mineral grains or pebbles, etc. Instead of masses one considers also *energy losses* under collisions, and the description simplifies somewhat if one is concerned with changes of energy of the *same* particle in successive collisions. As a last example consider the changes in the *intensity of light* when passing through matter. Example (10.*a*) shows that when a light ray passes through a sphere of radius R "in a random direction" the distance traveled through the sphere is distributed uniformly between 0 and $2R$. In the presence of uniform absorption such a passage would reduce the intensity of the incident ray by a factor that is uniformly distributed in an interval $\overline{0, a}$ (where $a < 1$ depends on the strength of absorption). The scale factor does not seriously affect our model and it is seen that n independent passages would reduce the intensity of the light by a factor of the form $\mathbf{Z}_n$. ▶

To find the distribution of $\mathbf{Z}_n$ we can proceed in two ways.

(i) *Reduction to exponential distributions.* Since sums are generally preferable to products we pass to logarithms putting $\mathbf{Y}_k = -\log \mathbf{X}_k$. The $\mathbf{Y}_k$ are mutually independent, and for $t > 0$

$$\mathbf{P}\{\mathbf{Y}_k \geq t\} = \mathbf{P}\{\mathbf{X}_k \leq e^{-t}\} = e^{-t}. \tag{8.1}$$

Now the distribution function G_n of the sum $\mathbf{S}_n = \mathbf{Y}_1 + \cdots + \mathbf{Y}_n$ of n independent exponentially distributed variables was calculated in (3.5), and the distribution function of $\mathbf{Z}_n = e^{-\mathbf{S}_n}$ is given by $1 - G_n(\log t^{-1})$ where $0 < t < 1$. The density of this distribution function is $t^{-1} g_n(\log t^{-1})$ or

$$f_n(t) = \frac{1}{n!}\left(\log \frac{1}{t}\right)^n, \qquad 0 < t < 1. \tag{8.2}$$

The substitution $t = e^{-x}$ shows that f_n is indeed a density with *expectation* 2^{-n}.

Our problem is solved explicitly. This method reveals the advantages to be derived from an appropriate transformation, but the success depends on the accidental equivalence of our problem with one previously solved.

(ii) *A recursive procedure* has the advantage that it lends itself to related problems in general. Let $F_n(t) = \mathbf{P}\{\mathbf{Z}_n \leq t\}$ and $0 < t < 1$. By definition $F_1(t) = t$. Suppose F_{n-1} known and consider that $\mathbf{Z}_n = \mathbf{Z}_{n-1}\mathbf{X}_n$ is the product of two independent variables. Given $\mathbf{X}_n = x$ the event $\{\mathbf{Z}_n \leq t\}$ occurs iff $\mathbf{Z}_{n-1} \leq t/x$ and has probability $F_{n-1}(t/x)$. Summing over all possible x we obtain

$$F_n(t) = \int_0^1 F_{n-1}\left(\frac{t}{x}\right) dx. \tag{8.3}$$

This formula permits us in principle to calculate successively $F_2, F_3, \ldots$. In practice it is preferable to operate with the corresponding densities f_n. By assumption f_1 exists. Assume by induction the existence of f_{n-1}. Recalling that $f_{n-1}(s) = 0$ for $s > 1$ we get by differentiation from (8.3)

$$f_n(t) = \int_t^1 f_{n-1}\left(\frac{t}{x}\right)\frac{dx}{x}, \qquad 0 < t < 1, \tag{8.4}$$

and trite calculations show that f_n is indeed given by (8.2).

9. CONVOLUTIONS AND COVERING THEOREMS

The results of this section have a mild amusement value in themselves and some obvious applications. Furthermore, they turn up rather unexpectedly in connection with seemingly unrelated topics, such as significance tests in harmonic analysis [example III, (3.*f*)], Poisson processes [XIV,(2.*a*)], and random flights [example (10.*e*)]. It is therefore not surprising that all formulas, as well as variants of them, have been derived repeatedly by different methods. The method used in the sequel is distinguished by its simplicity and applicability to related problems.

Let $a > 0$ be fixed, and denote by $\mathbf{X}_1, \mathbf{X}_2, \ldots$ mutually independent random variables distributed uniformly over $\overline{0, a}$. Let $\mathbf{S}_n = \mathbf{X}_1 + \cdots + \mathbf{X}_n$. Our first problem consists in finding the distribution U_n of $\mathbf{S}_n$ and its density $u_n = U_n'$.

By definition $u_1(x) = a^{-1}$ for $0 < x < a$ and $u_1(x) = 0$ elsewhere (rectangular density). The higher u_n are defined by the convolution formula (2.13) which in the present situation reads

$$(9.1)\qquad u_{n+1}(x) = \frac{1}{a}\int_0^a u_n(x-y)\,dy = \frac{1}{a}\,[U_n(x) - U_n(x-a)].$$

It is easily seen that

$$(9.2)\qquad u_2(x) = \begin{cases} xa^{-2} & 0 \le x \le a \\ (2a-x)a^{-2} & a \le x \le 2a, \end{cases}$$

and, of course, $u_2(x) = 0$ for all other x. The graph of u_2 appears as a triangle and u_2 is called *triangular density*. Similarly, u_3 pieces together three quadratic polynomials defined, respectively, in $\overline{0, a}$, $\overline{a, 2a}$, and $\overline{2a, 3a}$. Continuing in this fashion the general rule for expressing u_n soon becomes apparent, but to put it in symbols we introduce the following

Notation. *We write*

$$(9.3)\qquad x_+ = \frac{x + |x|}{2}$$

for the positive part of x. For typographical convenience we write $f_+(x)$ [instead of $f(x)_+$] for the positive part of $f(x)$ and, in particular, $x_+^{\,n}$ for the positive part of x^n.

In other words, f_+ is a function such that $f_+(x) = 0$ wherever $f(x) \le 0$. (An equivalent standard notation is $f_+ = f \cap 0$.) Note that $(x-a)_+$ is zero for $x < a$ and a linear function when $x > a$. With this notation the uniform distribution may be written in the form

$$(9.4)\qquad U_1(x) = (x_+ - (x-a)_+)a^{-1}.$$

Theorem 1. *Let* $U_n(x) = \mathbf{P}\{\mathbf{S}_n \leq x\}$ *and denote by* $u_n = U_n'$ *the density of this distribution. Then for* $n = 1, 2, \ldots$ *and all* x

$$U_n(x) = \frac{1}{a^n n!} \sum_{\nu=0}^{n} (-1)^\nu \binom{n}{\nu} (x-\nu a)_+^n. \tag{9.5}$$

For[11] $n = 1, 2, 3, \ldots,$

$$u_n(x) = \frac{1}{a^n (n-1)!} \sum_{\nu=0}^{n} (-1)^\nu \binom{n}{\nu} (x-\nu a)_+^{n-1}. \tag{9.6}$$

Note that for a point x between $(k-1)a$ and ka only k terms of the series are different from 0. For $x < 0$ both sums are empty and therefore their value is 0. That $u_n(x)$ equals 0 for $x > na$ is not obvious from (9.6) but true.

Proof. For $n = 1$ the truth of (9.6) is obvious, and (9.5) reduces to (9.4). Assume (9.5). Formula (9.1) represents u_{n+1} as the difference of two known sums. Replacing the summation index ν in the first sum by $\nu - 1$ and recalling the identity

$$\binom{n}{\nu} + \binom{n}{\nu-1} = \binom{n+1}{\nu}$$

we get for $u_{n+1}(x)$ the right side of (9.6) with n replaced by $n + 1$. An integration shows the validity of (9.5) for $n + 1$, and this completes the proof.

(An *alternative proof* using the passage to the limit from the discrete model is contained in **1**; XI,7, problem 20.) ▶

Theorem 1 applies also to variables that are distributed uniformly in $\overline{-b, b}$ rather than $\overline{0, a}$. In fact, if $a = 2b$ the variables $\mathbf{X}_k - b$ are of this type, and to get the distribution of $\Sigma_1^n (\mathbf{X}_k - b)$ we have merely to replace x by $x + nb$ in (9.5) and (9.6). Thus *the density of n independent variables distributed uniformly in* $\overline{-b, b}$ *is given by*

$$u_n(x + nb) = \frac{1}{(2b)^n (n-1)!} \sum_{\nu=0}^{n} (-1)^\nu \binom{n}{\nu} (x + (n-2\nu)b)_+^{n-1}. \tag{9.7}$$

By unexpected luck an apparently unconnected problem finds its answer in (9.6). We prove this computationally, but a subsequent combinatorial argument will better explain the connection between the two problems.

---

[11] (9.6) remains true for $n = 1$ provided x_+^0 is defined to equal 0 for $x < 0$ and 1 for $x > 0$. Of course, U_1 has only one-sided derivatives at 0 and a.

Theorem 2.[12] *On a circle of length t there are given $n \geq 2$ arcs of length a whose centers are chosen independently and at random. The probability $\varphi_n(t)$ that these n arcs cover the whole circle is*

$$\varphi_n(t) = a^n(n-1)!u_n(t)\frac{1}{t^{n-1}}, \tag{9.8}$$

which is the same as

$$\varphi_n(t) = \sum_{\nu=0}^{n} (-1)^\nu \binom{n}{\nu}\left(1 - \nu\frac{a}{t}\right)_+^{n-1}. \tag{9.9}$$

Before proving it, we reformulate the theorem in a form to be used later. Choose one of the n centers as origin and open the circle into an interval of length t. The remaining $n - 1$ centers are randomly distributed in $\overline{0, t}$ and theorem 2 obviously expresses the same thing as theorem 3.

Theorem 3. *Let the interval $\overline{0, t}$ be partitioned into n subintervals by choosing independently at random $n - 1$ points $\mathbf{X}_1, \ldots, \mathbf{X}_{n-1}$ of division. The probability $\varphi_n(t)$ that none of these subintervals exceeds a equals* (9.9).

Note that $\varphi_n(t)$, considered for fixed t as a function of a, represents *the distribution function of the maximal length among the n intervals* into which $\overline{0, t}$ is partitioned. For related questions see problems 21–24.

Proof. It suffices to prove theorem 3. We prove the recursion formula

$$\varphi_n(t) = (n-1)\int_0^a \varphi_{n-1}(t-x)\left(\frac{t - x}{t}\right)^{n-2}\frac{dx}{t}. \tag{9.10}$$

Its truth follows directly from the definition of φ_n as an $(n-1)$-tuple integral, but it is preferable to read (9.10) probabilistically as follows. The smallest among $\mathbf{X}_1, \ldots, \mathbf{X}_{n-1}$ must be less than a, and there are $n - 1$ choices for it. Given that $\mathbf{X}_1 = x$, the probability that $\mathbf{X}_1$ is leftmost equals $[(t-x)/t]^{n-2}$; then $\mathbf{X}_2, \ldots, \mathbf{X}_{n-1}$ are distributed uniformly over the interval $\overline{x, t}$, and the (conditional) probability that they satisfy the conditions of the theorem is $\varphi_{n-1}(t-x)$. Summing over all possibilities we get (9.10). (Unconvinced readers should repeat the argument replacing the assumption $\mathbf{X}_1 = x$ by $x - h < \mathbf{X}_1 < x$.)

To simplify (9.10) we introduce new functions defined by

$$\varphi_n(t) = (n-1)!a^n w_n(t)\frac{1}{t^{n-1}}. \tag{9.11}$$

[12] For an elegant geometric proof see W. L. Stevens, *Solution to a geometrical problem in probability*, Ann. Eugenics, vol. 2 (1939) pp. 315–320. Stevens derives also the probability that there are exactly k gaps of length $\geq x$. With the convention of the last footnote, (9.9) is valid also for $n = 1$.

It is easily verified that $w_2 = u_2$ and

$$w_n(t) = \frac{1}{a}\int_0^a w_{n-1}(t-x)\,dx. \tag{9.12}$$

This is exactly the recursion formula (9.1) from which we started, and so $w_n = u_n$ for all n. ▶

Although this proves the theorem, it hardly explains the mysterious connection between the two probabilities occurring in (9.8). For a better understanding we now consider *the discrete analogue* to (9.8). This model is intuitively clear, and an *alternative proof* of the two theorems may be derived by an easy passage to the limit.

In order to preserve the notations let a and t be positive integers, and denote by $\mathbf{X}_1, \mathbf{X}_2, \ldots$ independent variables assuming the values $1, 2, \ldots, a$ each with probability a^{-1}. Denote by N_n the number of representations $t = y_1 + y_2 + \cdots + y_n$ of t as a sum of integers $y_j \leq a$. By the very definition $N_n = a^n\,\mathbf{P}\{\mathbf{S}_n = t\}$. On the other hand, let $\varphi_n(t)$ be the probability that $n - 1$ integers chosen independently and at random between 1 and t partition $\overline{0, t}$ into n subintervals of lengths $\leq a$. The number of choices being $\binom{t}{n-1}$, we have $N_n = \binom{t}{n-1}\varphi_n(t)$, and hence

$$\binom{t}{n-1}\varphi_n(t) = a^n\,\mathbf{P}\{\mathbf{S}_n = t\}. \tag{9.13}$$

This is the discrete analogue to (9.8). As $t \to \infty$ the binomial coefficient is $\sim t^{n-1}/(n-1)!$ and (9.13) takes on the form of (9.8). [To obtain (9.8) by a formal passage to the limit let the $\mathbf{X}_j$ assume values $h, 2h, \ldots, \alpha h$ and consider an interval of length τh; let $h \to 0$ and $\alpha h \to a$, $\tau h \to t$.]

10. RANDOM DIRECTIONS

Choosing a random direction in the plane $\mathfrak{R}^2$ is the same as choosing at random a point on the circle. If one wishes to specify the direction by its angle with the right x-axis, the circle should be referred to its arc length θ with $0 \leq \theta < 2\pi$. For random directions in the space $\mathfrak{R}^3$ the unit sphere serves as sample space; each domain has a probability equal to its area divided by 4π. Choosing a random direction in $\mathfrak{R}^3$ is equivalent to choosing at random a point on this unit sphere. As this involves a pair of random variables (the longitude and latitude) consistency would require postponing the discussion to chapter III, but it appears more naturally in the present context.

Propositions. (i) *Denote by* **L** *the length of the projection of a unit vector with random direction in* $\mathfrak{R}^3$ *on a fixed line, say the* x*-axis. Then* **L** *is uniformly distributed over* $\overline{0, 1}$, *and* $\mathbf{E}(\mathbf{L}) = \frac{1}{2}$.

(ii) *Let* **U** *be the length of the projection of the same vector on a fixed plane, say the* x, y*-plane. Then* **U** *has density* $t/\sqrt{1 - t^2}$ *for* $0 < t < 1$, *and* $\mathbf{E}(\mathbf{U}) = \frac{1}{4}\pi$.

The important point is that the two projections have different distributions. That the first is uniform is not an attribute of randomness, but depends on the number of dimensions. The counterpart to (i) in $\mathfrak{R}^2$ is contained in

Proposition. (iii) *Let* **L** *be the length of the projection of a random unit vector in* $\mathfrak{R}^2$ *on the* x*-axis. Then* **L** *has density* $2/(\pi\sqrt{1 - x^2})$, *and* $\mathbf{E}(\mathbf{L}) = 2/\pi$.

Proofs. (iii) If θ is the angle between our random direction and the y-axis, then $\mathbf{L} = |\sin \theta|$ and hence for $0 < x < 1$

$$\mathbf{P}\{\mathbf{L} \leq x\} = \frac{2}{\pi} \text{ arc sin } x. \tag{10.1}$$

The assertion now follows by differentiation.

(i), (ii). Recall the elementary theorem that the area of a spherical zone between two parallel planes is proportional to the height of the zone. For $0 < t < 1$ the event $\{\mathbf{L} \leq t\}$ is represented by the zone $|x_1| \leq t$ of height $2t$, whereas $\{\mathbf{U} \leq t\}$ corresponds to the zones $|x_3| \geq \sqrt{1 - t^2}$ of total height $2 - 2\sqrt{1 - t^2}$. This determines the two distribution functions up to numerical factors, and these follow easily from the condition that both distributions equal 1 at $t = 1$. ►

Examples. (*a*) *Passage through spheres.* Let Σ be a sphere of radius r and N a point on it. A line drawn through N in a random direction intersects Σ in P. Then: *The length of the segment NP is a random variable distributed uniformly between* 0 *and* $2r$.

To see this consider the axis NS of the sphere and the triangle NPS which has a right angle at P and an angle Θ at N. The length of NP is then $2r \cos \Theta$. But $\cos \Theta$ is also the projection of a unit vector in the line NP into the diameter NS, and therefore $\cos \Theta$ is uniformly distributed in $\overline{0, 1}$.

In physics this model is used to describe the passage of light through "randomly distributed spheres." The resulting *absorption of light* was used as one example for the random-splitting process in the last section. (See problem 26.)

(*b*) *Circular objects under the microscope.* Through a microscope one observes the projection of a cell on the x_1, x_2-plane rather than its actual shape. In certain biological experiments the cells are lens-shaped and may be treated as circular disks. Only the horizontal diameter of the disk projects in its natural length, and the whole disk projects into an ellipse whose minor axis is the projection of the steepest radius. Now it is generally assumed that the orientation of the disk is random, meaning that the direction of its normal is chosen at random. In this case the projection of the unit normal on the x_3-axis is distributed uniformly in $\overline{0, 1}$. But the angle between this normal and the x_3-axis equals the angle between the steepest radius and the x_1, x_2-plane and hence the ratio of the minor to the major axis is distributed uniformly in $\overline{0, 1}$. Occasionally the evaluation of experiments was based on the erroneous belief that the angle between the steepest radius and the x_1, x_2-plane should be distributed uniformly.

(*c*) *Why are two violins twice as loud as one*? (The question is serious because the loudness is proportional to the *square* of the amplitude of the vibration.) The incoming waves may be represented by random *unit* vectors, and the superposition effect of two violins corresponds to the addition of two independent random vectors. By the law of the cosines the square of the length of the resulting vector is $2 + 2 \cos \Theta$. Here Θ is the angle between the two random vectors, and hence $\cos \Theta$ is uniformly distributed in $\overline{-1, 1}$ and has zero expectation. The expectation of the square of the resultant length is therefore indeed 2. ►

By a *random vector in* $\mathcal{R}^3$ is meant a vector drawn in a random direction with a length $\mathbf{L}$ which is a random variable independent of its direction. The probabilistic properties of a random vector are completely determined by those of its projection on the x-axis, and using the latter it is frequently possible to avoid analysis in three dimensions. For this purpose it is important to know the relationship between the distribution function V of the true length $\mathbf{L}$ and the distribution F of the length $\mathbf{L}_x$ of the projection on the x-axis. Now $\mathbf{L}_x = \mathbf{XL}$, where $\mathbf{X}$ is the length of the projection of a *unit* vector in the given direction. Accordingly, $\mathbf{X}$ is distributed uniformly over $\overline{0, 1}$ and is independent of $\mathbf{L}$. Given $\mathbf{X} = x$, the event $\{\mathbf{L}_x \leq t\}$ occurs iff $\mathbf{L} \leq t/x$, and so[13]

$$(10.2) \qquad F(t) = \int_0^1 V\left(\frac{t}{x}\right) dx \qquad t > 0.$$

For the corresponding *densities* we get by differentiation

$$(10.3) \qquad f(t) = \int_0^1 v\left(\frac{t}{x}\right) \frac{dx}{x} = \int_t^\infty v(y) \frac{dy}{y},$$

[13] This argument repeats the proof of (8.3).

and repeated differentiation leads to

$$v(t) = -tf'(t), \qquad t > 0. \tag{10.4}$$

We have thus found *the analytic relationship between the density v of the length of a random vector in $\mathfrak{R}^3$ and the density f of the length of its projection on a fixed direction.* The relation (10.3) is used to find f when v is known, and (10.4) in the opposite direction. (The asymmetry between the two formulas is due to the fact that the direction is *not* independent of the length of the projection.)

Examples. (*d*) *Maxwell distribution for velocities.* Consider random vectors in space whose projections on the x-axis have the normal density with zero expectation and unit variance. The length of the projection is its absolute value and so

$$f(t) = \sqrt{\frac{2}{\pi}}\, e^{-\frac{1}{2}t^2}, \qquad t > 0. \tag{10.5}$$

From (10.4) then

$$v(t) = \sqrt{\frac{2}{\pi}}\, t^2 e^{-\frac{1}{2}t^2}, \qquad t > 0. \tag{10.6}$$

This is the Maxwell density for velocities in statistical mechanics. The usual derivation combines the preceding argument with a proof that f must be of the form (10.5). (For an alternative derivation see III,4.)

(*e*) *Lord Rayleigh's random flights in $\mathfrak{R}^3$.* Consider n *unit* vectors whose directions are chosen independently and at random. We seek the distribution of *the length* $\mathbf{L}_n$ of their resultant (or vector sum). Instead of studying this resultant directly we consider its projection on the x-axis. This projection is obviously the sum of n independent random variables distributed uniformly in $\overline{0, 1}$. The distribution function of this projection is given by (9.7) with $b = 1$. The *length* of this projection equals its absolute value, and using (10.4) we get after a simple differentiation

$$v_n(x) = \frac{-x}{2^{n-1}(n-2)!} \sum_{\nu=0}^{n} (-1)^\nu \binom{n}{\nu} (x+n-2\nu)_+^{n-2} \tag{10.7}$$

for $x > 0$, and $v_n(x) = 0$ for $x < 0$. This, then, is the density[14] of the length $\mathbf{L}_n$.

This problem occurs in physics and chemistry (the vectors representing, for example, plane waves or molecular links). The reduction to one dimension seems to render this famous problem trivial.

[14] The standard reference is to a paper by S. Chandrasekhar who calculated v_3, v_4, v_6 and the Fourier transform of v_n. Because he used polar coordinates, his $W_n(x)$ must be multiplied by $4\pi x^2$ to obtain our v_n. A direct derivation of (10.7) (by other methods) is due to Quenouille. Chandrasekhar's paper is reprinted in Wax (1954).

The same method applies to random vectors with arbitrary length and thus (10.4) enables us to *reduce random-walk problems in* $\mathfrak{R}^3$ *to simpler problems in* $\mathfrak{R}^1$. Even when explicit solutions are hard to get, the central limit theorem provides valuable information [see example VIII, (4.*b*)]. ►

Random vectors in $\mathfrak{R}^2$ are defined in like manner, but the relation corresponding to (10.4) is not as simple. The analogue to (10.2) is

$$F(x) = \frac{2}{\pi}\int_0^{\pi/2} V\left(\frac{x}{\sin\theta}\right)d\theta, \tag{10.8}$$

but to express V in terms of F we must depend on the relatively deep theory of Abel's integral equation.[15] We state without proof that if F has a continuous density f, then

$$1 - V(x) = x\int_0^{\pi/2} f\left(\frac{x}{\sin\theta}\right)\frac{d\theta}{\sin^2\theta}\,. \tag{10.9}$$

(See problems 27–28.)

Example. (*f*) *Binary orbits.* In observing a spectroscopic binary orbit astronomers can measure only the projections of vectors onto a plane perpendicular to the line of sight. An ellipse in space projects into an ellipse in this plane. The major axis of the true ellipse lies in the plane determined by the line of sight and its projection, and it is therefore reasonable to assume that the angle between the major axis and its projection is uniformly distributed. Measurements determine (in principle) the distribution of the projection. The distribution of the true major axis is then given by the solution (10.9) of Abel's integral equation. ►

11. THE USE OF LEBESGUE MEASURE

If a set A in $\overline{0,1}$ is the union of finitely many non-overlapping intervals $I_1, I_2, \ldots$ of lengths $\lambda_1, \lambda_2, \ldots$, the uniform distribution attributes to it probability

$$\mathbf{P}\{A\} = \lambda_1 + \lambda_2 + \cdots. \tag{11.1}$$

The following examples will show that some simple, but significant, problems lead to unions of infinitely many non-overlapping intervals. The definition (11.1) is still applicable and identifies $\mathbf{P}\{A\}$ with the Lebesgue measure of A. It is consistent with our program to identify probabilities with the integral of the density $f(x) = 1$, except that we use the Lebesgue integral rather than the Riemann integral (which need not exist). Of the

---

[15] The transformation to Abel's integral equation is by means of the change of variables

$$F_1(x) = F\left(\frac{1}{\sqrt{x}}\right), \qquad V_1(x) = V\left(\frac{1}{\sqrt{x}}\right), \qquad \text{and} \quad x\sin^2\theta = y.$$

Then (10.8) takes on the form

$$F_1(t) = \frac{1}{\pi}\int_0^t \frac{V_1(y)}{\sqrt{y(t-y)}}\,dy.$$

Lebesgue theory we require only the fact that if A is the union of possibly overlapping intervals $I_1, I_2, \ldots$ a measure $\mathbf{P}\{A\}$ exists and does not exceed the sum $\lambda_1 + \lambda_2 + \cdots$ of the lengths. For non-overlapping intervals the equality (11.1) holds. The use of Lebesgue measure conforms to uninhibited intuition and simplifies matters inasmuch as all formal passages to the limit are justified. A set N is called a *null set* if it is contained in sets of arbitrarily small measure, that is, to each ϵ there exists a set $A \supset N$ such that $\mathbf{P}\{A\} < \epsilon$. In this case $\mathbf{P}\{N\} = 0$.

In the following $\mathbf{X}$ stands for a random variable distributed uniformly in $\overline{0, 1}$.

Examples. (*a*) *What is the probability of* $\mathbf{X}$ *being rational*? The sequence $\frac{1}{2}, \frac{1}{3}, \frac{2}{3}, \frac{1}{4}, \frac{3}{4}, \frac{1}{5}, \ldots$ contains *all* the rationals in $\overline{0, 1}$ (ordered according to increasing denominators). Choose $\epsilon < \frac{1}{2}$ and denote by J_k an interval of length ϵ^{k+1} centered at the kth point of the sequence. The sum of the lengths of the J_k is $\epsilon^2 + \epsilon^3 + \cdots < \epsilon$, and their union covers the rationals. Therefore by our definition *the set of all rationals has probability zero*, and so $\mathbf{X}$ is irrational with probability one.

It is pertinent to ask why such sets should be considered in probability theory. One answer is that nothing can be gained by excluding them and that the use of Lebesgue theory actually simplifies matters without requiring new techniques. A second answer may be more convincing to beginners and non-mathematicians; the following variants lead to problems of undoubted probabilistic nature.

(*b*) *With what probability does the digit 7 occur in the decimal expansion of* $\mathbf{X}$? In the decimal expansion of each x in the open interval between 0.7 and 0.8 the digit 7 appears at the first place. For each n there are 9^{n-1} intervals of length 10^{-n} containing only numbers such that the digit 7 appears at the nth place but not before. (For $n = 2$ their endpoints are 0.07 and 0.08, next 0.17 and 0.18, etc.) These intervals are non-overlapping, and their total length is $\frac{1}{10}(1 + \frac{9}{10} + (\frac{9}{10})^2 + \cdots) = 1$. Thus our event has *probability* 1.

Notice that certain numbers have two expansions, for example $0.7 = 0.6999\ldots$. To make our question unequivocal we should therefore specify whether the digit 7 must or may occur in the expansion, but our argument is independent of the difference. The reason is that only rationals can have two expansions, and the set of all rationals has probability zero.

(*c*) *Coin tossing and random choice.* Let us now see how a "random choice of a point $\mathbf{X}$ between 0 and 1" can be described in terms of discrete random variables. Denote by $\mathbf{X}_k(x)$ the kth decimal of x. (To avoid ambiguities use terminating expansions when possible.) The random variable $\mathbf{X}_k$ assumes the values 0, 1, . . . , 9, each with probability $\frac{1}{10}$, and the $\mathbf{X}_k$ are mutually independent. Furthermore, we have the identity

$$\mathbf{X} = \sum_{k=1}^{\infty} \frac{1}{10^k} \mathbf{X}_k. \tag{11.2}$$

This formula reduces the random choice of a point $\mathbf{X}$ to successive choices of its decimals.

For further discussion we switch from decimal to *dyadic* expansions, that is, we replace the basis 10 by 2. Instead of (11.2) we have now

$$\mathbf{X} = \sum_{k=1}^{\infty} \frac{1}{2^k} \mathbf{X}_k \tag{11.3}$$

where the $\mathbf{X}_k$ are mutually independent random variables assuming the values 0 and 1 with probability $\frac{1}{2}$. These variables are defined on the interval $\overline{0, 1}$ on which probability is equated with Lebesgue measure (length). This formulation brings to mind the coin-tossing game of volume **1**, in which the sample space consists of infinite sequences of heads and tails, or zeros and ones. A new interpretation of (11.3) is now possible in this sample space. In it the $\mathbf{X}_k$ are coordinate variables, and $\mathbf{X}$ is a random variable defined by them; its distribution function is, of course, uniform. Note that the second formulation contains two distinct sample points 0111111 and 1000000 even though the corresponding dyadic expansions represent the same point $\frac{1}{2}$. Nevertheless, the notion of zero probability enables us to *identify the two sample spaces.* Stated in more intuitive terms, neglecting an event of probability zero the random choice of a point $\mathbf{X}$ between 0 and 1 can be effected by a sequence of coin tossings and, conversely, the result of an infinite coin-tossing game may be represented by a point x of $\overline{0, 1}$. Every random variable of the coin-tossing game may be represented by a function on $\overline{0, 1}$, etc. This convenient and intuitive device has been used since the beginning of probability theory, but it depends on neglecting events of zero probability.

(*d*) *Cantor-type distributions.* A distribution with unexpected properties is found by considering in (11.3) the contribution of the even-numbered terms or, what amounts to the same, by considering the random variable

$$\mathbf{Y} = 3\sum_{\nu=1}^{\infty} \frac{1}{4^\nu} \mathbf{X}_\nu. \tag{11.4}$$

(The factor 3 is introduced to simplify the discussion. The contribution of the odd-numbered terms has the same distribution as $\frac{2}{3}\mathbf{Y}$.) The distribution function $F(x) = \mathbf{P}\{\mathbf{Y} \leq x\}$ will serve as example for so-called singular distributions.

In the calculation we refer to $\mathbf{Y}$ as the gain of a gambler who receives the amount $3 \cdot 4^{-k}$ if the kth toss of a fair coin results in tails. This gain lies between 0 and $3(4^{-1} + 4^{-2} + \cdots) = 1$. If the first trial results in 1 the gain is $\geq \frac{3}{4}$, while in the contrary case $\mathbf{Y} \leq 3(4^{-2} + 4^{-3} + \cdots) = 4^{-1}$. Thus the inequality $\frac{1}{4} < \mathbf{Y} < \frac{3}{4}$ cannot be realized under any circumstances, and so $F(x) = \frac{1}{2}$ in this interval of length $\frac{1}{2}$. It follows that F can have no jump exceeding $\frac{1}{2}$.

Next notice that up to a factor $\frac{1}{4}$ the contribution of the trials number 2, 3, . . . constitute a replica of the whole sequence, and so the graph of F in the interval $\overline{0, \frac{1}{4}}$ differs from the whole graph only by a similarity transformation

$$F(x) = \tfrac{1}{2}F(4x), \qquad 0 < x < \tfrac{1}{4}. \tag{11.5}$$

It follows that $F(x) = \frac{1}{4}$ throughout an interval of length $\frac{1}{8}$ centered at $x = \frac{1}{8}$. For reasons of symmetry, $F(x) = \frac{3}{4}$ throughout an interval of length $\frac{1}{8}$ centered at $x = \frac{7}{8}$. We have now found three intervals of total length $\frac{1}{2} + \frac{2}{8} = \frac{3}{4}$ in each of which F assumes a constant value, namely $\frac{1}{4}, \frac{1}{2}$, or $\frac{3}{4}$. Consequently, F can have no jump exceeding $\frac{1}{4}$. There remain four intervals of length $\frac{1}{16}$ each, and in each of them the graph of F differs from the whole graph only by a similarity transformation. Each of the four intervals therefore contains a subinterval of half its length in which F assumes a constant value (namely $\frac{1}{8}, \frac{3}{8}, \frac{5}{8}, \frac{7}{8}$, respectively). Continuing in like manner we find in n steps $1 + 2 + 2^2 + \cdots + 2^{n-1}$ intervals of total length $2^{-1} + 2^{-2} + 2^{-3} + \cdots + 2^{-n} = 1 - 2^{-n}$ in each of which F assumes a constant value.

Thus *F is a continuous function increasing from $F(0) = 0$ to $F(1) = 1$ in such a way that the intervals of constancy add up to length* 1. Roughly speaking, the whole increase of F takes place on a set of measure 0. We have here a continuous distribution function F without density f. ▶

12. EMPIRICAL DISTRIBUTIONS

The "*empirical distribution function*" F_n of n points $a_1, \ldots, a_n$ on the line is the step function with jumps $1/n$ at $a_1, \ldots, a_n$. In other words, $n\,F_n(x)$ equals the number of points a_k in $\overline{-\infty, x}|$, and F_n is a distribution function. Given n random variables $\mathbf{X}_1, \ldots, \mathbf{X}_n$, their values at a particular point of the sample space form an n-tuple of numbers and its empirical distribution function is called the empirical sample distribution. For each x, the value $\mathbf{F}_n(x)$ of the empirical sample distribution defines a new random variable, and *the empirical distribution of* $(\mathbf{X}_1, \ldots, \mathbf{X}_n)$ represents a whole family of random variables depending on the parameter

x. (In technical language we are concerned with a stochastic process with x as time parameters.) No attempt will be made here to develop the theory of empirical distributions, but the notion may be used to illustrate the occurrence of complicated random variables in simple applications. Furthermore, the uniform distribution will appear in a new light.

Let $\mathbf{X}_1, \ldots, \mathbf{X}_n$ stand for mutually independent random variables with a common continuous distribution F. The probability that any two variables assume the same value is zero, and we can therefore restrict our attention to samples of n distinct values. For fixed x the number of variables $\mathbf{X}_k$ such that $\mathbf{X}_k \leq x$ has a binomial distribution with probability of "success" $p = F(x)$, and so *the random variable* $\mathbf{F}_n(x)$ *has a binomial distribution* with possible values $0, 1/n, \ldots, 1$. For large n and x fixed, $\mathbf{F}_n(x)$ is therefore likely to be close to $F(x)$ and the central limit theorem tells us more about the probable deviations. More interesting is the (chance-dependent) graph of $\mathbf{F}_n$ as a whole and how close it is to F. A measure for this closeness is the *maximum discrepancy*, that is,

$$\mathbf{D}_n = \sup_{-\infty<x<\infty} |\mathbf{F}_n(x) - F(x)| . \tag{12.1}$$

This is a new random variable of great interest to statisticians because of the following property. The *probability distribution of the random variable* $\mathbf{D}_n$ *is independent of* F (provided, of course, that F is continuous).

For the proof it suffices to verify that the distribution of $\mathbf{D}_n$ remains unchanged when F is replaced by a uniform distribution. We begin by showing that *the variables* $\mathbf{Y}_k = F(\mathbf{X}_k)$ *are distributed uniformly in* $\overline{0, 1}$. For that purpose we restrict t to the interval $\overline{0, 1}$, and in this interval we define v as the inverse function of F. The event $\{F(\mathbf{X}_k) \leq t\}$ is then identical with the event $\{\mathbf{X}_k \leq v(t)\}$ which has probability $F(v(t)) = t$. Thus $\mathbf{P}\{\mathbf{Y}_k \leq t\} = t$ as asserted.

The variables $\mathbf{Y}_1, \ldots, \mathbf{Y}_n$ are mutually independent, and we denote their empirical distribution by $\mathbf{G}_n$. The argument just used shows also that for fixed t the random variable $\mathbf{G}_n(t)$ is identical with $\mathbf{F}_n(v(t))$. Since $t = F(v(t))$ this implies that at every point of the sample space $\mathcal{R}^n$

$$\sup |\mathbf{G}_n(t) - t| = \sup |\mathbf{F}_n(v(t)) - F(v(t))| = \mathbf{D}_n.$$

This proves the proposition.

The fact that the distribution of $\mathbf{D}_n$ is independent of the underlying distribution F enables statisticians to devise tests and estimation procedures applicable in situations when the underlying distribution is unknown. In this connection other variables related to $\mathbf{D}_n$ are of even greater practical use.

Let $\mathbf{X}_1, \ldots, \mathbf{X}_n, \mathbf{X}_1^{\#}, \ldots, \mathbf{X}_n^{\#}$ be $2n$ mutually independent random variables with the common continuous distribution F, and denote the empirical distributions of $(\mathbf{X}_1, \ldots, \mathbf{X}_n)$ and $(\mathbf{X}_1^{\#}, \ldots, \mathbf{X}_n^{\#})$ by $\mathbf{F}_n$ and $\mathbf{F}_n^{\#}$, respectively. Put

$$\mathbf{D}_{n,n} = \sup_x |\mathbf{F}_n(x) - \mathbf{F}_n^{\#}(x)| . \tag{12.2}$$

This is the *maximum discrepancy between the two empirical distributions.* It shares with $\mathbf{D}_n$ the property that it does not depend on the distribution F. For this reason it serves in statistical tests of "the hypothesis that $(\mathbf{X}_1, \ldots, \mathbf{X}_n)$ and $(\mathbf{X}_1^{\#}, \ldots, \mathbf{X}_n^{\#})$ are random samples from the same population."

The distribution of $\mathbf{D}_{n,n}$ was the object of cumbersome calculations and investigations but in 1951 Gnedenko and Koroljuk showed that the whole question reduces to a random-walk problem with a well-known solution. Their argument is pleasing by its elegance and we use it as illustration of the power of simple combinatorial methods.

Theorem. $\mathbf{P}\{\mathbf{D}_{n,n} \le r/n\}$ *equals the probability in a symmetric random walk that a path of length $2n$ starting and terminating at the origin is contained in the closed interval* $\overline{-r, r}$.

Proof. It suffices to consider integral r. Order the $2n$ variables $\mathbf{X}_1, \ldots, \mathbf{X}_n^{\#}$ in increasing order of magnitude and put $\epsilon_k = 1$ or $\epsilon_k = -1$, according to whether the kth place is occupied by an $\mathbf{X}_j$ or an $\mathbf{X}_j^{\#}$. The resulting arrangement contains n plus ones and n minus ones, and all $\binom{2n}{n}$ orderings are equally likely. The resulting $2n$-tuples $(\epsilon_1, \ldots, \epsilon_{2n})$ are therefore in a one-to-one correspondence with the paths of length $2n$ starting and terminating at the origin. Now if $\epsilon_1 + \cdots + \epsilon_j = k$ the first j places contain $(j+k)/2$ unsuperscripted and $(j-k)/2$ superscripted variables, and so there exists a point x such that $\mathbf{F}_n(x) = (j+k)/2n$ and $\mathbf{F}_n^{\#}(x) = (j-k)/2n$. But then $|\mathbf{F}_n(x) - \mathbf{F}_n^{\#}(x)| = |k|/n$. The same argument in reverse completes the proof. ►

An *explicit expression* for the probability in question is contained in **1**, XIV,(9.1). In fact

$$\binom{2n}{n}\mathbf{P}\left\{\mathbf{D}_{n,n} \le \frac{r}{n}\right\} = w_{r,n}$$

is the probability that a particle starting at the origin returns at epoch $2n$ to the origin without having left the interval $\overline{-r, r}$. The last condition can be realized by putting absorbing barriers at $\pm r$, and so $w_{r,n}$ is the probability of a return to the origin at epoch $2n$ when $\pm r$ are absorbing barriers. [In **1**; XIV,(9.1) the interval is $\overline{0, a}$ rather than $\overline{-r, r}$. Our $w_{r,n}$ is identical with $u_{r,2n}(r)$.]

It was shown in **1**; XIV that a limiting procedure leads from random walks to diffusion processes, and in this way it is not difficult to see that the distribution of $\sqrt{n}\mathbf{D}_{n,n}$ tends to a limit. Actually this limit was discovered by Smirnov as early as 1939 and the similar limit for $\sqrt{n}\mathbf{D}_n$ by Kolmogorov in 1933. Their calculations are very intricate and do not explain the connection with diffusion processes, which is inherent in the Gnedenko-Koroljuk approach. On the other hand, they have given impetus to fruitful work on the convergence of stochastic processes (Billingsley, Donsker, Prohorov, Skorohod, and others).

It may be mentioned that the Smirnov theorems apply equally to discrepancies $\mathbf{D}_{m,n}$ of the empirical distributions of samples of different sizes m and n. The random-walk approach carries over, but loses much of its elegance and simplicity (Gnedenko, Rvačeva). A great many variants of $\mathbf{D}_{m,n}$ have been investigated by statisticians. (See problem 32.)

13. PROBLEMS FOR SOLUTION

In all problems it is understood that the given variables are *mutually independent.*

1. Let $\mathbf{X}$ and $\mathbf{Y}$ have densities $\alpha e^{-\alpha x}$ concentrated on $\overline{0, \infty}$. Find the densities of

(i) $\mathbf{X}^3$ (ii) $3 + 2\mathbf{X}$
(iii) $\mathbf{X} - \mathbf{Y}$ (iv) $|\mathbf{X} - \mathbf{Y}|$
(v) The smaller of $\mathbf{X}$ and $\mathbf{Y}^3$ (vi) The larger of $\mathbf{X}$ and $\mathbf{Y}^3$.

2. Do the same problem if the densities of $\mathbf{X}$ and $\mathbf{Y}$ equal $\frac{1}{2}$ in $\overline{-1, 1}$ and 0 elsewhere.

3. Find the densities for $\mathbf{X} + \mathbf{Y}$ and $\mathbf{X} - \mathbf{Y}$ if $\mathbf{X}$ has density $\alpha e^{-\alpha x}$ $(x > 0)$ and the density of $\mathbf{Y}$ equals h^{-1} for $0 < x < h$.

4. Find the probability that $\lambda^2 - 2a\lambda + b$ has complex roots if the coefficients a and b are random variables whose common density is

(i) uniform, that is, h^{-1} for $0 < x < h$
(ii) exponential, that is, $\alpha e^{-\alpha x}$ for $x > 0$.

5. Find the distribution functions of $\dfrac{\mathbf{X}+\mathbf{Y}}{\mathbf{X}}$ and $\dfrac{\mathbf{X}+\mathbf{Y}}{\mathbf{Z}}$ if the variables $\mathbf{X}$, $\mathbf{Y}$, and $\mathbf{Z}$ have a common exponential distribution.

6. If $\mathbf{X}$ and $\mathbf{Y}$ have the exponential densities $\alpha e^{-\alpha x}$ and $\beta e^{-\beta x}$ where $\alpha \neq \beta$, then $\mathbf{X} + \mathbf{Y}$ has density

$$\alpha\beta\,\frac{e^{-\alpha x} - e^{-\beta x}}{\beta - \alpha} \qquad x > 0.$$

7. Derive the convolution formula (3.6) for the exponential distribution by a direct passage to the limit from the convolution formula for the "negative binomial" distribution of **1**; VI,(8.1).

8. In the Poisson process of section 4, denote by $\mathbf{Z}$ the time between epoch t and the last preceding arrival or 0 (the "age" of the current interarrival time). Find the distribution of $\mathbf{Z}$ and show that it tends to the exponential distribution as $t \to \infty$.

9. In example (5.*a*) show that the probability of the first record value occurring at the nth place and being $\leq x$ equals

$$\frac{1}{n(n+1)}\,(1 - e^{-\alpha x})^{n+1}.$$

Conclude that the probability distribution of the first record value is $1-(1+\alpha x)e^{-\alpha x}$.

[More generally, if the $\mathbf{X}_j$ are positive and subject to an arbitrary continuous distribution F, the first probability equals $[n(n+1)]^{-1}F^{n+1}(x)$ and the distribution is $F-(1-F)\log(1-F)^{-1}$.]

10. *Platoon formation in traffic.*[16] Cars start successively at the origin and travel along the right x-axis *without passing*. Each car keeps a constant speed, but we consider the speeds $v_1, v_2, \ldots$ as a sample from a sequence of independent random variables with a common continuous distribution function F. When a car reaches a slower car it is compelled to trail it at the same speed. In this way platoons will form.

Show that *the probability of a given car being trailed by exactly n cars tends to* $[n(n+1)]^{-1}$ independently of the distribution F and the times of departure. The expected number of cars in the platoon is infinite.

11. *Generalization*[17] *of the record value example* (5.*a*). Instead of taking the single preliminary observation $\mathbf{X}_0$ we start from a sample $(\mathbf{X}_1, \ldots, \mathbf{X}_m)$ with order statistics $(\mathbf{X}_{(1)}, \ldots, \mathbf{X}_{(m)})$. (The common distribution F plays no role as long as it is continuous.)

(*a*) If $\mathbf{N}$ is the first index n such that $\mathbf{X}_{m+n} \geq \mathbf{X}_{(m)}$ show that $\mathbf{P}\{\mathbf{N} > n\} = m/(m+n)$. [In example (5.*a*) we had $m = 1$.]

(*b*) If $\mathbf{N}$ is the first index n such that $\mathbf{X}_{m+n} \geq \mathbf{X}_{(m-r+1)}$ show that

$$\mathbf{P}\{\mathbf{N} > n\} = \frac{\binom{m}{r}}{\binom{m+n}{r}}.$$

For $r \geq 2$ we have $\mathbf{E}(\mathbf{N}) = m/(r-1)$ and

$$\mathbf{P}\{\mathbf{N} \leq mx\} \to 1 - \frac{1}{(1+x)^r}, \qquad m \to \infty.$$

(*c*) If $\mathbf{N}$ is the first index such that $\mathbf{X}_{m+n}$ falls outside the interval between $\mathbf{X}_{(1)}$ and $\mathbf{X}_{(m)}$ then

$$\mathbf{P}\{\mathbf{N} > n\} = \frac{m(m-1)}{(m+n)(m+n-1)}, \quad \text{and} \quad \mathbf{E}(\mathbf{N}) < \infty.$$

12. For $j = 0, \ldots, n$ let $\mathbf{X}_j$ have density $\lambda_j e^{-\lambda_j x}$ for $x > 0$ where $\lambda_j \neq \lambda_k$ unless $j = k$. Put

$$\frac{1}{\psi_{k,n}} = (\lambda_0 - \lambda_k)\cdots(\lambda_{k-1}-\lambda_k)(\lambda_{k+1}-\lambda_k)\cdots(\lambda_n-\lambda_k).$$

Show that $\mathbf{X}_0 + \cdots + \mathbf{X}_n$ has density $\lambda_0 \cdots \lambda_n[\psi_{0,n}e^{-\lambda_0 x} + \cdots + \psi_{n,n}e^{-\lambda_n x}]$. *Hint:* Use induction, a symmetry argument, and problem 6. No calculations are necessary.

---

[16] G. F. Newell, Opns. Res. vol. 7 (1959) pp. 589–598.

[17] S. S. Wilks, J. Australian Math. Soc., vol. 1 (1959) pp. 106–112.

Special case:

$$f_n(x) = n\sum_{k=1}^{n}(-1)^{k-1}\binom{n-1}{k-1}e^{-kx}, \qquad x > 0,$$

represents the convolution of f_{n-1} with the density ne^{-nx}. Conclude that f_{n-1} is the density of the spread $\mathbf{X}_{(n)} - \mathbf{X}_{(1)}$ of a sample $\mathbf{X}_1, \ldots, \mathbf{X}_n$ if the $\mathbf{X}_j$ have the common density e^{-x}.

13. *Pure birth processes.* In the pure birth process of **1**; XVII,3 the system passes through a sequence of states $E_0 \to E_1 \to \cdots$ staying at E_k for a sojourn time $\mathbf{X}_k$ with density $\lambda_k e^{-\lambda_k x}$. Thus $\mathbf{S}_n = \mathbf{X}_0 + \cdots + \mathbf{X}_n$ is the epoch of the transition $E_n \to E_{n+1}$. Denote by $P_n(t)$ the probability of E_n at epoch t. Show that $P_n(t) = \mathbf{P}\{\mathbf{S}_n > t\} - \mathbf{P}\{\mathbf{S}_{n-1} > t\}$ and hence (using the last problem)

$$P_n(t) = \lambda_0 \cdots \lambda_{n-1}[\psi_{0,n}e^{-\lambda_0 t} + \cdots + \psi_{n,n}e^{-\lambda_n t}]. \tag{1}$$

The differential equations $P_0'(t) = -\lambda_0 P_0(t)$,

$$P_n'(t) = -\lambda_n P_n(t) + \lambda_{n-1}P_{n-1}(t), \qquad n \geq 1, \tag{2}$$

should be derived (*a*) from (1), and (*b*) from the properties of the sums $\mathbf{S}_n$.

Hint: Using inductively a symmetry argument it suffices to consider the factor of $e^{-\lambda_0 t}$.

Note. The differential equations (2) coincide with **1**; XVII,(3.2) and (1) represents the *general solution* with $P_0(0) = 1$.

14. In example (6.*a*) for parallel waiting lines we say that the system is in state k if k counters are free. Show that the birth process model of the last example applies with $\lambda_k = n - k$. Conclude that

$$P_k(t) = \binom{n}{k}(1 - e^{-\alpha t})^k e^{-(n-k)\alpha t}.$$

From this derive the distribution of $\mathbf{X}_{(k)}$.

15. Consider two independent queues of m and $n > m$ persons respectively, assuming the same exponential distribution for the service times. Show that the probability of the longer queue finishing first equals the probability of obtaining n heads before m tails in a fair coin-tossing game. Find the same probability also by considering the ratio $\mathbf{X}/\mathbf{Y}$ of two variables with gamma distributions G_m and G_n given in (3.5).

16. *Example of statistical estimation.* It is assumed that the lifetimes of electric bulbs have an exponential distribution with an unknown expectation α^{-1}. To estimate α a sample of n bulbs is taken and one observes the lifetimes

$$\mathbf{X}_{(1)} < \mathbf{X}_{(2)} < \cdots < \mathbf{X}_{(r)}$$

of the first r bulbs to fail. The "best unbiased estimator" of α^{-1} is a linear combination $\mathbf{U} = \lambda_1\mathbf{X}_{(1)} + \cdots + \lambda_r\mathbf{X}_{(r)}$ such that $E(\mathbf{U}) = \alpha^{-1}$ and $\mathrm{Var}(\mathbf{U})$ is smallest possible. Show that

$$\mathbf{U} = (\mathbf{X}_{(1)} + \cdots + \mathbf{X}_{(r)})\frac{1}{r} + \mathbf{X}_{(r)}(n-r)\frac{1}{r}, \quad \text{and then} \quad \mathrm{Var}(\mathbf{U}) = \frac{1}{r}\alpha^{-2}.$$

Hint: Do the calculations in terms of the *independent* variables $\mathbf{X}_{(k)} - \mathbf{X}_{(k-1)}$.

17. If the variables $\mathbf{X}_1, \ldots, \mathbf{X}_n$ are distributed uniformly in $\overline{0, 1}$ show that the

spread $\mathbf{X}_{(n)} - \mathbf{X}_{(1)}$ has density $n(n-1)x^{n-2}(1-x)$ and expectation $(n-1)/(n+1)$. What is the probability that all n points lie within an interval of length t?

18. Answer the questions of example (6.*b*) when the three service times are distributed uniformly in $\overline{0, 1}$.

19. Four points are chosen independently and at random on a circle. Find the probability that the chords $\mathbf{X}_1\mathbf{X}_2$ and $\mathbf{X}_3\mathbf{X}_4$ intersect: (*a*) without calculation using a symmetry argument; (*b*) from the definition by an integral.

20. In the random-splitting process of section 8 denote by $\mathbf{X}_{11}, \mathbf{X}_{12}, \mathbf{X}_{21}, \mathbf{X}_{22}$ the masses of the four fragments of the second generation, the subscript 1 referring to the smaller and 2 to the larger part. Find the densities and expectations of these variables.

21. Let $\mathbf{X}_1, \ldots, \mathbf{X}_n$ be distributed at random in $\overline{0, t}$ and denote by $p_n(t)$ the probability that all $n + 1$ subintervals of the partition are longer than h. Prove that

$$p_n(t) = \frac{n}{t^n} \int_0^{t-h} x^{n-1} p_{n-1}(x)\, dx$$

whence $p_n(t) = t^{-n}(t - (n+1)h)_+^{\,n}$.

[The distribution function of the *shortest subinterval* is given by $1 - p_n(t)$ with t fixed and $h > 0$ as independent variable.]

Hint:[18] Consider the event $\{\mathbf{X}_{(n)} = x\}$.

22. *Continuation.* Find the analogous relations for the probability $q_n(t)$ that all mutual distances of $\mathbf{X}_k$ exceed h (with no conditions concerning the endpoints).

23. *Continuation.* Without using the solution of the preceding problems show a priori that $p_n(t) = (t-2h)^n\, t^{-n} q_n(t-2h)$.

24. Formulate the analogue to problem 22 for a circle and show that problem 21 furnishes its solution.

25. An isosceles triangle is formed by a unit vector in the x-direction and another in a random direction. Find the distribution of the length of the third side (i) in $\mathcal{R}^2$ and (ii) in $\mathcal{R}^3$.

26. A unit circle (sphere) about 0 has the north pole on the positive x-axis. A ray enters at the north pole and its angle with the x-axis is distributed uniformly over $\overline{-\frac{1}{2}\pi, \frac{1}{2}\pi}$. Find the distribution of the length of the chord within the circle (sphere).

---

[18] [*Added in proof*] The same simple argument yields directly the following elegant general proposition derived recently by B. de Finetti from geometrical considerations. Denote the lengths of the successive subintervals of our partition by $\mathbf{L}_1, \ldots, \mathbf{L}_{n+1}$. Then *for arbitrary* $x_1 \geq 0, \ldots, x_{n+1} \geq 0$

$$(*) \qquad \mathbf{P}\{\mathbf{L}_1 > x_1, \ldots, \mathbf{L}_{n+1} > x_{n+1}\} = (t - x_1 - \cdots - x_{n+1})_+^{\,n}.$$

Problem 21 corresponds to the special case where all x_j equal h, whereas in example (7.*b*) only one among the x_j is positive. The covering theorem 9.3 may be derived from (*) using formula **1**; IV,(1.5) for the realization of at least one among N events.

[De Finetti's article appeared in the Giornale Istituto Italiano degli Attuari, vol. 27 (1964) pp. 151–173, in Italian.]

Note. In $\mathcal{R}^2$ the ray has a random direction and we are concerned with the analogue to example (10*a*). In $\mathcal{R}^3$ the problem is new.

27. The ratio of the *expected lengths* of a random vector and of its projection on the x-axis equals 2 in $\mathcal{R}^3$ and $\pi/2$ in $\mathcal{R}^2$.

Hint: Use (10.4) and (10.9).

28. The length of a random vector is distributed uniformly over $\overline{0, 1}$. Find the density of the length of its projection on the x-axis (*a*) in $\mathcal{R}^3$, and (*b*) in $\mathcal{R}^2$.

Hint: Use (10.4) and (10.9).

29. Find the distribution function of the angle between the x-axis and a randomly chosen direction in $\mathcal{R}^4$.

30. Find the analogue in $\mathcal{R}^4$ to the relation (10.2) between the distributions of the lengths of a random vector and that of its projection on the x-axis. Specialize to a unit vector to verify the result of problem 29.

31. *A limit theorem for order statistics.* (*a*) Let $\mathbf{X}_1, \ldots, \mathbf{X}_n$ be distributed uniformly in $\overline{0, 1}$. Prove that for k fixed as $n \to \infty$

$$\mathbf{P}\left\{\mathbf{X}_{(k)} \le \frac{x}{n}\right\} \to G_{k+1}(x), \qquad x > 0,$$

where G_k is the gamma distribution (3.5) [see example (7.*e*)].

(*b*) If the $\mathbf{X}_k$ have an arbitrary continuous distribution function F, the same limit exists for $\mathbf{P}\{\mathbf{X}_{(k)} \le \Phi(x/n)\}$ where Φ is the inverse function of F. (Smirnov.)

32. Prove the following variant of the Gnedenko-Koroljuk theorem in section 12:

$$\mathbf{P}\left\{\sup_x[\mathbf{F}_n(x) - \mathbf{F}_n\#(x)] \ge \frac{r}{n}\right\} = \frac{\binom{2n}{n-r}}{\binom{2n}{n}},$$

where $r = 1, 2, \ldots, n$. (In contrast to the original formulation the absolute values on the left are omitted and so only one absorbing barrier at r occurs in the associated random walk.)

33. *Downward runs.* The random variable $\mathbf{N}$ is defined as the unique index such that $\mathbf{X}_1 \ge \mathbf{X}_2 \ge \cdots \ge \mathbf{X}_{\mathbf{N}-1} < \mathbf{X}_{\mathbf{N}}$. If the $\mathbf{X}_j$ have a common continuous distribution F prove that $\mathbf{P}\{\mathbf{N} = n\} = (n-1)/n!$ and $\mathbf{E}(\mathbf{N}) = e$.

34. *Generation of exponentially distributed random variables from uniform ones.*[19] (*a*) In the preceding problem let F be the uniform distribution in $\overline{0, 1}$. Prove that

$$\mathbf{P}\{\mathbf{X}_1 \le x, \mathbf{N} = n\} = \frac{x^{n-1}}{(n-1)!} - \frac{x^n}{n!},$$

whence $\mathbf{P}\{\mathbf{X}_1 \le x, \mathbf{N} \text{ even}\} = 1 - e^{-x}$.

(*b*) Define $\mathbf{Y}$ as follows: A "trial" is a sequence $\mathbf{X}_1, \ldots, \mathbf{X}_\mathbf{N}$; it is a "failure" if $\mathbf{N}$ is odd. We repeat independent trials as long as necessary to produce a "success." Let $\mathbf{Y}$ equal the number of failures plus the first variable in the successful trial. Prove that $\mathbf{P}\{\mathbf{Y} < x\} = 1 - e^{-x}$.

[19] J. von Neumann, National Bureau of Standards, Appl. Math. Series, No. 12 (1951) pp. 36–38.

CHAPTER II

Special Densities. Randomization

The main purpose of this chapter is to list for reference the densities that will occur most frequently in the following chapters. The randomization procedure described in the second part is of general use. Its scope is illustrated by deriving certain distributions connected with Bessel functions which occur in various applications. It turns out that this simple probabilistic approach replaces involved calculations and hard analysis.

1. NOTATIONS AND CONVENTIONS

We say that a density f and its distribution F are *concentrated*[1] *on an interval* $I = \overline{a, b}$ if $f(x) = 0$ for all x outside I. Then $F(x) = 0$ for $x < a$ and $F(x) = 1$ for $x > b$. Two distributions F and G, and also their densities f and g, are said to be of the *same type* or to differ only by *location parameters* if they stand in the relationship

$$G(x) = F(ax + b), \qquad g(x) = af(ax + b), \tag{1.1}$$

where $a > 0$. We shall frequently refer to b as a *centering* parameter, to a as a *scale* parameter. These terms are readily understood from the fact that when F serves as distribution function of a random variable $\mathbf{X}$ then G is the distribution function of

$$\mathbf{Y} = \frac{\mathbf{X} - b}{a}. \tag{1.2}$$

Only the type of a distribution really matters, and, as a rule, we shall

[1] According to common usage the smallest closed interval I with this property is called the *support* of f. A new term is introduced because it will be used in the more general sense that a distribution may be concentrated on the set of integers or rationals.

exhibit only one specimen for each type. Appropriate location parameters reduce any finite interval to $\overline{0, 1}$ and we shall consider only densities concentrated on the whole line, the right half-line, or $\overline{0, 1}$. *Specifying* $0 < x < 1$ or $x > 0$ *will imply* $f(x) = 0$ *for all other* x.

The *expectation* m and *variance* σ^2 of f (or of F) are defined by

(1.3)
$$m = \int_{-\infty}^{+\infty} x\, f(x)\, dx, \qquad \sigma^2 = \int_{-\infty}^{+\infty} (x-m)^2 f(x)\, dx = \int_{-\infty}^{+\infty} x^2 f(x) - m^2,$$

provided the integrals converge absolutely. It is clear from (1.2) that in this case g has expectation $(m - b)/a$ and variance σ^2/a^2. It follows that for each type there exists at most one density with zero expectation and unit variance.

We recall from I,(2.12) that the *convolution* $f = f_1 * f_2$ of two densities f_1 and f_2 is the probability density defined by

$$f(x) = \int_{-\infty}^{+\infty} f_1(x-y)\, f_2(y)\, dy. \tag{1.4}$$

When f_1 and f_2 are concentrated on $\overline{0, \infty}$ this formula reduces to

$$f(x) = \int_0^x f_1(x-y)\, f_2(y)\, dy, \qquad x > 0. \tag{1.5}$$

This represents the density of the sum of two independent random variables with densities f_1 and f_2. Note that for $g_i(x) = f_i(x+b_i)$ the convolution $g = g_1 * g_2$ is given by $g(x) = f(x+b_1+b_2)$ as is obvious from (1.2).

We conclude by introducing the notation[2]

$$\mathfrak{n}(x) = \frac{1}{\sqrt{2\pi}}\, e^{-\frac{1}{2}x^2}, \qquad \mathfrak{N}(x) = \frac{1}{\sqrt{2\pi}} \int_{-\infty}^{x} e^{-\frac{1}{2}y^2}\, dy. \tag{1.6}$$

Our old acquaintance, the *normal density with expectation m and variance* σ^2, is defined by

$$\frac{1}{\sigma}\,\mathfrak{n}\left(\frac{x-m}{\sigma}\right) \qquad \sigma > 0.$$

Implicit in the central limit theorem is the basic fact that the *family of normal densities is closed under convolutions*; in other words, the convolution of two normal densities with expectations m_1, m_2 and variances σ_1^2, σ_2^2 is the normal density with expectation $m_1 + m_2$ and variance

[2] In volume **1** the normal density $\mathfrak{n}$ was denoted by φ, the distribution function $\mathfrak{N}$ by Φ.

$\sigma_1^2 + \sigma_2^2$. In view of what has been said it suffices to prove it for $m_1 = m_2 = 0$. It is asserted that

$$(1.7)\quad \frac{1}{\sqrt{2\pi}\,\sigma} \exp\left[-\frac{x^2}{2\sigma^2}\right] = \frac{1}{2\pi\sigma_1\sigma_2}\int_{-\infty}^{+\infty} \exp\left[-\frac{(x-y)^2}{2\sigma_1^2} - \frac{y^2}{2\sigma_2^2}\right] dy$$

and the truth of this assertion becomes obvious by the change of variables $z = y\dfrac{\sigma}{\sigma_1\sigma_2} - x\dfrac{\sigma_2}{\sigma\sigma_1}$ where x is fixed. (See problem 1.)

2. GAMMA DISTRIBUTIONS

The *gamma function* Γ is defined by

$$(2.1)\qquad \Gamma(t) = \int_0^\infty x^{t-1}e^{-x}\,dx, \qquad t > 0.$$

[See **1**; II,(12.23).] It interpolates the factorials in the sense that

$$\Gamma(n+1) = n! \qquad \text{for} \quad n = 0, 1, \ldots .$$

Integration by parts shows that $\Gamma(t) = (t-1)\,\Gamma(t-1)$ for all $t > 0$. (Problem 2.)

The *gamma densities* concentrated on $\overline{0, \infty}$ are defined by

$$(2.2)\qquad f_{\alpha,\nu}(x) = \frac{1}{\Gamma(\nu)}\,\alpha^\nu x^{\nu-1}e^{-\alpha x}, \qquad x > 0.$$

Here $\alpha > 0$ is the trivial scale parameter, but $\nu > 0$ is essential. The special case $f_{\alpha,1}$ represents the *exponential* density, and the densities g_n of I,(3.4) coincide with $f_{\alpha,n}$ $(n = 1, 2, \ldots)$. A trite calculation shows that *the expectation of* $f_{\alpha,\nu}$ *equals* ν/α, *the variance* ν/α^2.

The family of gamma densities is closed under convolutions:

$$(2.3)\qquad f_{\alpha,\mu} * f_{\alpha,\nu} = f_{\alpha,\mu+\nu} \qquad \mu > 0, \quad \nu > 0.$$

This important property generalizes the theorem of I,3 and will be in constant use; the *proof* is exceedingly simple. By (1.5) the left side equals

$$(2.4)\qquad \frac{\alpha^{\mu+\nu}}{\Gamma(\mu)\,\Gamma(\nu)}\,e^{-\alpha x}\int_0^x (x-y)^{\mu-1}y^{\nu-1}\,dy.$$

After the substitution $y = xt$ this expression differs from $f_{\alpha,\mu+\nu}$ by a numerical factor only, and this equals unity since both $f_{\alpha,\mu+\nu}$ and (2.4) are probability densities.

The value of the last integral for $x = 1$ is the so-called *beta integral* $B(\mu, \nu)$, and as a by-product of the proof we have found that

$$(2.5)\qquad B(\mu, \nu) = \int_0^1 (1-y)^{\mu-1}y^{\nu-1}\,dy = \frac{\Gamma(\mu)\,\Gamma(\nu)}{\Gamma(\mu+\nu)}$$

for all $\mu > 0$, $\nu > 0$. [For integral μ and ν this formula is used in **1**; VI,(10.8) and (10.9). See also problem 3 of this chapter.]

As to the *graph of* $f_{1,\nu}$, it is clearly monotone if $\nu \leq 1$, and unbounded near the origin when $\nu < 1$. For $\nu > 1$ the graph of $f_{1,\nu}$ is bell-shaped, attaining at $x = \nu - 1$ its maximum $(\nu - 1)^{\nu-1} e^{-(\nu-1)}/\Gamma(\nu)$ which is close to $[2\pi(\nu - 1)]^{-\frac{1}{2}}$ (Stirling's formula **1**; II, problem 12.22). It follows from the central limit theorem that $\sqrt{\nu/\alpha}\, f_{\alpha,\nu}(x\sqrt{\nu/\alpha}) \to \mathfrak{n}(x)$ as $\nu \to \infty$.

*3. RELATED DISTRIBUTIONS OF STATISTICS

The gamma densities play a crucial, though sometimes disguised, role in mathematical statistics. To begin with, in the classical (now somewhat outdated) system of densities introduced by K. Pearson (1894) the gamma densities appear as "type III." A more frequent appearance is due to the fact that for a random variable $\mathbf{X}$ with normal density $\mathfrak{n}$ the square $\mathbf{X}^2$ has density $x^{-\frac{1}{2}}\mathfrak{n}(x^{\frac{1}{2}}) = f_{\frac{1}{2},\frac{1}{2}}(x)$. In view of the convolution property (2.3) it follows that:

If $\mathbf{X}_1, \ldots, \mathbf{X}_n$ *are mutually independent normal variables with expectation* 0 *and variance* σ^2, *then* $\mathbf{X}_1^2 + \cdots + \mathbf{X}_n^2$ *has density* $f_{\frac{1}{2\sigma^2},\frac{n}{2}}$.

To statisticians $\chi^2 = \mathbf{X}_1^2 + \cdots + \mathbf{X}_n^2$ is the "sample variance from a normal population" and its distribution is in constant use. For reasons of tradition (going back to K. Pearson) in this connection $f_{\frac{1}{2},\frac{1}{2}n}$ is called *chi-square density with n degrees of freedom.*

In statistical mechanics $\mathbf{X}_1^2 + \mathbf{X}^2_2 + \mathbf{X}_3^2$ appears as the square of the velocity of particles. The velocity itself therefore has the density

$$v(x) = 2x\, f_{\frac{1}{2},\frac{3}{2}}(x^2).$$

This is the *Maxwell density* found by other methods in I,(10.6). (See also the example in III,4.)

In queuing theory the gamma distribution is sometimes called "Erlangian."

Several random variables (or "statistics") of importance to statisticians are of the form $\mathbf{T} = \mathbf{X}/\mathbf{Y}$, where $\mathbf{X}$ and $\mathbf{Y}$ are independent random variables, $\mathbf{Y} > 0$. Denote their distributions by F and G, respectively, and their densities by f and g. As $\mathbf{Y}$ is supposed positive, g is concentrated on $\overline{0, \infty}$ and so

$$\mathbf{P}\{\mathbf{T} \leq t\} = \mathbf{P}\{\mathbf{X} \leq t\mathbf{Y}\} = \int_0^\infty F(ty)\, g(y)\, dy. \tag{3.1}$$

* This section treats special topics and is not used in the sequel.

By differentiation it is found that *the ratio* $\mathbf{T} = \mathbf{X}/\mathbf{Y}$ *has density*

$$w(t) = \int_0^\infty f(ty)y\, g(y)\, dy. \tag{3.2}$$

Examples. (*a*) *If* $\mathbf{X}$ *and* $\mathbf{Y}$ *have densities* $f_{\frac{1}{2},\frac{1}{2}m}$ *and* $f_{\frac{1}{2},\frac{1}{2}n}$, *then* $\mathbf{X}/\mathbf{Y}$ *has density*

$$w(t) = \frac{\Gamma(\frac{1}{2}(m+n))}{\Gamma(\frac{1}{2}m)\,\Gamma(\frac{1}{2}n)} \frac{t^{\frac{1}{2}m-1}}{(1+t)^{\frac{1}{2}(m+n)}}, \qquad t > 0. \tag{3.3}$$

In fact, the integral in (3.2) equals

$$\frac{t^{\frac{1}{2}m-1}}{2^{\frac{1}{2}(m+n)}\,\Gamma(\frac{1}{2}m)\,\Gamma(\frac{1}{2}n)} \int_0^\infty y^{\frac{1}{2}(m+n)-1} e^{-\frac{1}{2}(1+t)y}\, dy \tag{3.4}$$

and the substitution $\frac{1}{2}(1+t)y = s$ reduces it to (3.3).

In the analysis of variance one considers the special case $\mathbf{X} = \mathbf{X}_1^2 + \cdots + \mathbf{X}_m^2$ and $\mathbf{Y} = \mathbf{Y}_1 + \cdots + \mathbf{Y}_n$ where $\mathbf{X}_1, \ldots, \mathbf{X}_m, \mathbf{Y}_1, \ldots, \mathbf{Y}_n$ are mutually independent variables with the common normal density $\mathfrak{n}$. The random variable $\mathbf{F} = \dfrac{n}{m}\dfrac{\mathbf{X}}{\mathbf{Y}}$ is called Snedecor's statistic and its density $\dfrac{m}{n}\, w\!\left(\dfrac{m}{n}x\right)$ is *Snedecor's density*, or the *F*-density. The variable $\mathbf{Z} = \log \frac{1}{2}\mathbf{F}$ is Fisher's *Z*-statistic, and its density *Fisher's Z-density*. The two statistics are, of course, merely notational variants of each other.

(*b*) *If* $\mathbf{X}$ *has density* $\mathfrak{n}$ *and* $\mathbf{Y}^2$ *density* $f_{\frac{1}{2},\frac{1}{2}n}$, *then* $\mathbf{X}/\mathbf{Y}$ *has density*

$$w(t) = \frac{C_n}{(1+t^2)^{\frac{1}{2}(n+1)}}, \quad \text{where} \quad C_n = \frac{1}{\sqrt{\pi}} \frac{\Gamma(\frac{1}{2}(n+1))}{\Gamma(\frac{1}{2}n)}. \tag{3.5}$$

In fact, $\mathbf{Y}$ has density $2x f_{\frac{1}{2},\frac{1}{2}n}(x^2)$ and (3.2) takes on the form

$$\frac{1}{\sqrt{2\pi}\, 2^{\frac{1}{2}n}\Gamma(\frac{1}{2}n)} \int_0^\infty e^{-\frac{1}{2}(1+t^2)y^2} y^n\, dy. \tag{3.6}$$

The substitution $s = \frac{1}{2}(1+t^2)y^2$ reduces (3.6) to (3.5).

In statistics (3.5) is called *Student's t density*. It is the density of the variable $\mathbf{X}/\sqrt{\mathbf{Y}_1^2 + \cdots + \mathbf{Y}_n^2}$ where $\mathbf{X}, \mathbf{Y}_1, \ldots, \mathbf{Y}_n$ are independent with a common normal density with zero expectation. (The variance plays no role for reasons of homogeneity.) ►

4. SOME COMMON DENSITIES

(*a*) *The bilateral exponential* is defined by $\frac{1}{2}\alpha e^{-\alpha|x|}$ where α is a scale parameter. It has zero expectation and variance $2\alpha^{-2}$. This density is *the convolution of the exponential density* $\alpha e^{-\alpha x}$ $(x > 0)$ *with the mirrored density* $\alpha e^{\alpha x}$ $(x < 0)$. In other words, the bilateral exponential is the density of $\mathbf{X}_1 - \mathbf{X}_2$ when $\mathbf{X}_1$ and $\mathbf{X}_2$ are independent and have the common exponential density $\alpha e^{-\alpha x}$ $(x > 0)$. In the French literature it is usually referred to as the "second law of Laplace," the first being the normal distribution.

(*b*) The *uniform* (or *rectangular*) density ρ_a and the *triangular* density τ_a concentrated on $\overline{-a, a}$ are defined by

$$\rho_a(x) = \frac{1}{2a}, \qquad \tau_a(x) = \frac{1}{a}\left(1 - \frac{|x|}{a}\right), \qquad |x| < a. \tag{4.1}$$

It is easily seen that $\rho_a \star \rho_a = \tau_{2a}$. In words: the sum of two uniformly distributed variables in $\overline{-a, a}$ has a triangular density in $\overline{-2a, 2a}$. [The repeated convolutions $\rho_a \star \cdots \star \rho_a$ are described in I,(9.7).]

(*c*) *Beta densities* in $\overline{0, 1}$ are defined by

$$\beta_{\mu,\nu}(x) = \frac{\Gamma(\mu+\nu)}{\Gamma(\mu)\,\Gamma(\nu)}(1 - x)^{\mu-1}\, x^{\nu-1}, \qquad 0 < x < 1, \tag{4.2}$$

where $\mu > 0$ and $\nu > 0$ are free parameters. That (4.2) indeed defines a probability density follows from (2.5). By the same formula it is seen that $\beta_{\mu,\nu}$ has expectation $\nu/(\mu+\nu)$, and variance $\mu\nu/[(\mu+\nu)^2(\mu+\nu+1)]$. If $\mu < 1$, $\nu < 1$, the graph of $\beta_{\mu,\nu}$ is U-shaped, tending to ∞ at the limits. For $\mu > 1$, $\nu > 1$ the graph is bell-shaped.

A simple variant of the beta density is defined by

$$\frac{1}{(1+t)^2}\,\beta_{\mu,\nu}\left(\frac{1}{1+t}\right) = \frac{\Gamma(\mu+\nu)}{\Gamma(\mu)\,\Gamma(\nu)} \cdot \frac{t^{\mu-1}}{(1+t)^{\mu+\nu}}, \qquad 0 < t < \infty. \tag{4.3}$$

If the variable $\mathbf{X}$ has density (4.2) then $\mathbf{Y} = \mathbf{X}^{-1} - 1$ has density (4.3).

In the Pearson system the densities (4.2) and (4.3) appear as types I and VI. The Snedecor density (3.3) is a special case of (4.3). The densities (4.3) are sometimes called after the economist *Pareto*. It was thought (rather naïvely from a modern statistical standpoint) that income distributions should have a tail with a density $\sim Ax^{-\alpha}$ as $x \to \infty$, and (4.3) fulfills this requirement.

(*d*) *The so-called arc sine density*

$$\frac{1}{\pi\sqrt{x(1-x)}}, \qquad 0 < x < 1 \tag{4.4}$$

is actually the same as the beta density $\beta_{\frac12,\frac12}$, but deserves special mention because of its repeated occurrence in fluctuation theory. (It was introduced in **1**; III,5 in connection with the unexpected behavior of sojourn times.)

The misleading name is unfortunately in general use; actually the distribution function is given by $2\pi^{-1} \arc \sin \sqrt{x}$. (The beta densities with $\mu + \nu = 1$ are sometimes referred to as "generalized arc sine densities.")

(*e*) *The Cauchy density* centered at the origin is defined by

$$\gamma_t(x) = \frac{1}{\pi} \cdot \frac{t}{t^2 + x^2}, \qquad -\infty < x < \infty, \tag{4.5}$$

where $t > 0$ is a scale parameter. The corresponding distribution function is $\pi^{-1} \arctan (x/t)$. The graph of γ_t resembles that of the normal density but approaches the axis so slowly that an *expectation does not exist.*

The importance of the Cauchy densities is due to the convolution formula

$$\gamma_s \star \gamma_t = \gamma_{s+t}. \tag{4.6}$$

It states that *the family of Cauchy densities* (4.5) *is closed under convolutions.* Formula (4.6) can be proved in an elementary (but tedious) fashion by a routine decomposition of the integrand into partial fractions. A simpler proof depends on Fourier analysis.

The convolution formula (4.6) has the amazing consequence that for independent variables $\mathbf{X}_1, \ldots, \mathbf{X}_n$ with the common density (4.5) *the average* $(\mathbf{X}_1 + \cdots + \mathbf{X}_n)/n$ *has the same density as the* $\mathbf{X}_j$.

Example. Consider a laboratory experiment in which a vertical mirror projects a horizontal light ray on a wall. The mirror is free to rotate about a vertical axis through A. We assume that the direction of the reflected ray is chosen "at random," that is, the angle $\boldsymbol{\varphi}$ between it and the perpendicular AO to the wall is distributed uniformly between $-\frac{1}{2}\pi$ and $\frac{1}{2}\pi$. The light ray intersects the wall at a point at a distance

$$\mathbf{X} = t \cdot \tan \boldsymbol{\varphi}$$

from O (where t is the distance AO of the center A from the wall). It is now obvious that the random variable $\mathbf{X}$ has density (4.5).[3] If the experiment is repeated n times the average $(\mathbf{X}_1 + \cdots + \mathbf{X}_n)/n$ has the same density and so the averages do not cluster around 0 as one should expect by analogy with the law of large numbers. ▶

[3] A simple reformulation of this experiment leads to physical interpretation of the convolution formula (4.6). Our argument shows that if a unit light source is situated at the origin then γ_t represents the distribution of the intensity of light along the line $y = t$ of the x, y-plane. Then (4.6) expresses *Huygens' principle*, according to which the intensity of light along $y = s + t$ is the same as if the source were distributed along the line $y = t$ following the density γ_t. (I owe this remark to J. W. Walsh.)

The Cauchy density has the curious property that if $\mathbf{X}$ has density γ_t then $2\mathbf{X}$ has density $\gamma_{2t} = \gamma_t \star \gamma_t$. Thus $2\mathbf{X} = \mathbf{X} + \mathbf{X}$ *is the sum of two dependent variables, but its density is given by the convolution formula.* More generally, if $\mathbf{U}$ and $\mathbf{V}$ are two independent variables with common density γ_t and $\mathbf{X} = a\mathbf{U} + b\mathbf{V}$, $\mathbf{Y} = c\mathbf{U} + d\mathbf{V}$, then $\mathbf{X} + \mathbf{Y}$ has density $\gamma_{(a+b+c+d)t}$ which is the convolution of the densities $\gamma_{(a+b)t}$ of $\mathbf{X}$ and $\gamma_{(c+d)t}$ of $\mathbf{Y}$; nevertheless, $\mathbf{X}$ and $\mathbf{Y}$ are not independent. (For a related example see problem 1 in III,9.)

[The Cauchy density corresponds to the special case $n = 1$ of the family (3.5) of Student's t densities. In other words, if $\mathbf{X}$ and $\mathbf{Y}$ are independent random variables with the normal density $\mathfrak{n}$, then $\mathbf{X}/|\mathbf{Y}|$ has the Cauchy density (4.5) with $t = 1$. For some related densities see problems 5–6.]

The convolution property (2.3) of the gamma densities looks exactly like (4.6) but there is an important difference in that the parameter α of the gamma densities is essential whereas (4.6) contains only a scale parameter. With the Cauchy density the *type* is stable. This stability under convolutions is shared by the normal and the Cauchy densities; the difference is that the scale parameters compose according to the rules $\sigma^2 = \sigma_1^2 + \sigma_2^2$ and $\alpha = \alpha_1 + \alpha_2$, respectively. There exist other *stable densities* with similar properties, and with a systematic terminology we should call the normal and Cauchy densities "symmetric, stable of index 2 and 1." (See VI,1.)

(*f*) *One-sided stable distribution of index* $\frac{1}{2}$. If $\mathfrak{N}$ is the normal distribution of (1.6), then

$$F_\alpha(x) = 2\left[1 - \mathfrak{N}\left(\frac{\alpha}{\sqrt{x}}\right)\right], \qquad x > 0, \tag{4.7}$$

defines a distribution function with density

$$f_\alpha(x) = \frac{\alpha}{\sqrt{2\pi}} \cdot \frac{1}{\sqrt{x^3}}\, e^{-\frac{1}{2}\alpha^2/x}, \qquad x > 0. \tag{4.8}$$

Obviously no expectation exists. This distribution was found in **1**; III,(8.*c*) and again in **1**; X,1 as limit of the distribution of recurrence times, and this derivation implies the *composition rule*

$$f_\alpha \star f_\beta = f_\gamma \qquad \textit{where} \qquad \sqrt{\gamma} = \sqrt{\alpha} + \sqrt{\beta}. \tag{4.9}$$

(A verification by elementary, but rather cumbersome, integrations is possible. The Fourier analytic proof is simpler.) If $\mathbf{X}_1, \ldots, \mathbf{X}_n$ are independent random variables with the distribution (4.7), then (4.9) implies that $(\mathbf{X}_1 + \cdots + \mathbf{X}_n)n^{-2}$ has the same distribution, and so the averages

$|\mathbf{X}_1 + \cdots + \mathbf{X}_n|n^{-1}$ are likely to be of the order of magnitude of n; instead of converging they increase over all bounds. (See problems 7 and 8.)

(*g*) Distributions of the form $e^{-x^{-\alpha}}$ ($x > 0$, $\alpha > 0$) appear in connection with order statistics (see problem 8). Together with the variant $1 - e^{-x^{\alpha}}$ they appear (rather mysteriously) under the name of *Weibull* distributions in statistical reliability theory.

(*h*) The *logistic distribution* function

$$F(t) = \frac{1}{1 + e^{-\alpha t - \beta}}, \qquad \alpha > 0 \tag{4.10}$$

may serve as a warning. An unbelievably huge literature tried to establish a transcendental "law of logistic growth"; measured in appropriate units, practically all growth processes were supposed to be represented by a function of the form (4.10) with t representing time. Lengthy tables, complete with chi-square tests, supported this thesis for human populations, for bacterial colonies, development of railroads, etc. Both height *and* weight of plants and animals were found to follow the logistic law even though it is theoretically clear that these two variables cannot be subject to the same distribution. Laboratory experiments on bacteria showed that not even systematic disturbances can produce other results. Population theory relied on logistic extrapolations (even though they were demonstrably unreliable). The only trouble with the theory is that not only the logistic distribution but also the normal, the Cauchy, and other distributions can be fitted to the *same material with the same or better goodness of fit*.[4] In this competition the logistic distribution plays no distinguished role whatever; most contradictory theoretical models can be supported by the same observational material.

Theories of this nature are short-lived because they open no new ways, and new confirmations of the same old thing soon grow boring. But the naïve reasoning as such has not been superseded by common sense, and so it may be useful to have an explicit demonstration of how misleading a mere goodness of fit can be.

5. RANDOMIZATION AND MIXTURES

Let F be a distribution function depending on a parameter θ, and u a probability density. Then

$$W(x) = \int_{-\infty}^{+\infty} F(x, \theta)\, u(\theta)\, d\theta \tag{5.1}$$

is a monotone function of x increasing from 0 to 1 and hence a distribution function. If F has a continuous density f, then W has a density w given by

$$w(x) = \int_{-\infty}^{+\infty} f(x, \theta)\, u(\theta)\, d\theta. \tag{5.2}$$

Instead of integrating with respect to a density u we can sum with respect

[4] W. Feller, *On the logistic law of growth and its empirical verifications in biology*, Acta Biotheoretica, vol. 5 (1940) pp. 51–66.

to a discrete probability distribution: if $\theta_1, \theta_2, \ldots$ are chosen arbitrarily and if $p_k \geq 0$, $\Sigma p_k = 1$, then

$$w(x) = \sum_k f(x, \theta_k)\, p_k \tag{5.3}$$

defines a new probability density. The process may be described probabilistically as *randomization*; the parameter θ is treated as random variable and a new probability distribution is defined in the x, θ-plane, which serves as sample space. Densities of the form (5.3) are called *mixtures*, and the term is now used generally for distributions obtained by randomization (even when the integration is with respect to a general distribution for θ).

We do not propose at this juncture to develop a general theory. Our aim is rather to illustrate by a few examples the scope of the method and its probabilistic contents. The examples serve also as preparation for the notion of conditional probabilities. The next section is devoted to examples of discrete distributions obtained by randomization of a continuous parameter. Finally, section 7 illustrates the construction of continuous processes out of random walks; as a by-product we shall obtain distributions occurring in many applications and otherwise requiring hard calculations.

Examples. (*a*) *Ratios.* If $\mathbf{X}$ is a random variable with density f, then for fixed $y > 0$ the variable $\mathbf{X}/y$ has density $f(xy)y$. Treating the parameter y as random variable with density g we get the new density

$$w(x) = \int_{-\infty}^{+\infty} f(xy)y\, g(y)\, dy. \tag{5.4}$$

[This is the same as formula (3.2) on which the discussion in section 3 was based. If $f = f_{1,\mu}$ and $g = f_{1,\nu}$, the resulting density w is given by (4.3).]

In probabilistic language randomizing the denominator y in $\mathbf{X}/y$ means considering the random variable $\mathbf{X}/\mathbf{Y}$, and we have merely rephrased the derivation of the density (3.2) of $\mathbf{X}/\mathbf{Y}$. In this particular case the terminology is a matter of taste.

(*b*) *Random sums.* Let $\mathbf{X}_1, \mathbf{X}_2, \ldots$ be mutually independent random variables with a common density f. The sum $\mathbf{S}_n = \mathbf{X}_1 + \cdots + \mathbf{X}_n$ has the density f^{n*}, namely the n-fold convolution of f with itself. [See I,2.] The number n of terms is a parameter which we now randomize by a probability distribution $\mathbf{P}\{\mathbf{N} = n\} = p_n$. The density of the resulting sum $\mathbf{S}_\mathbf{N}$ with the random number $\mathbf{N}$ of terms is

$$w = \sum_1^\infty p_n f^{n*}. \tag{5.5}$$

As an example take for $\{p_n\}$ the geometric distribution $p_n = qp^{n-1}$, and for f an exponential density. Then $f^{n*} = g_n$ is given by (2.2) and

$$(5.6)\qquad w(t) = q\alpha e^{-\alpha x}\sum_{n=1}^{\infty} p^{n-1}\frac{(\alpha x)^{n-1}}{(n-1)!} = q\alpha e^{-\alpha q x}$$

Thus w is again an exponential density.

(*c*) *Application to queuing.* Consider a single server with exponential servicing time distribution (density $f(t) = \mu e^{-\mu t}$) and assume the incoming traffic to be Poisson, that is, the inter-arrival times are independent with density $\lambda e^{-\lambda t}$, $\lambda < \mu$. The model is described in **1**; XVII,(7.*b*): Arriving customers join a (possibly empty) "waiting line" and are served in order of arrival without interruption. It was shown that the system tends to a steady state in which the probability of n customers in the line (waiting or being served) tends to qp^n where $p = \lambda/\mu$ [see **1**; XVII,(7.10) with $a = 1$]. Here $n = 0, 1, \ldots$. Consider now a customer arriving at epoch t. The total time $\mathbf{T}$ that he spends at the server is the sum of his own servicing time plus the servicing times of the n customers in the waiting line ahead of him; the density of $\mathbf{T}$ is therefore $f^{(n+1)*} = f_{\mu,n+1}$. Assuming the steady state distribution for the waiting line, the last example shows that *the total time spent by a customer at the server has density* $(\mu-\lambda)e^{-(\mu-\lambda)t}$ and expectation $1/(\mu-\lambda)$. (See problem 10.)

(*d*) *Waiting lines for buses.* A bus is supposed to appear every hour on the hour, but is subject to delays. We treat the successive delays $\mathbf{X}_k$ as independent random variables with a common distribution F and density f. For simplicity we assume $0 \leq \mathbf{X}_k \leq 1$. Denote by $\mathbf{T}_x$ the waiting time of a person arriving at epoch $x < 1$ after noon. The probability that the bus scheduled for noon has already departed is $F(x)$, and it is easily seen that

$$(5.7)\qquad \mathbf{P}\{\mathbf{T}_x \leq t\} = \begin{cases} F(t+x) - F(x) & \textit{for} \quad 0 < t < 1-x \\ 1 - F(x) + F(x)\,F(t+x-1) & \textit{for} \quad 1-x < t < 2-x \end{cases}$$

and, of course, $\mathbf{P}\{\mathbf{T}_x \leq t\} = 1$ for all greater t. The corresponding density is

$$(5.8)\qquad \begin{cases} f(t+x) & \textit{for} \quad 0 < t < 1-x \\ F(x)\,f(t+x-1) & \textit{for} \quad 1-x < t < 2-x. \end{cases}$$

Here the epoch x of arrival is a free parameter and it is natural to randomize it. For example, for a person arriving "at random" the epoch of arrival is a random variable distributed uniformly in $\overline{0, 1}$. The expected waiting time in this case equals $\frac{1}{2} + \sigma^2$ where σ^2 is the variance of the delay.

In other words, *the expected waiting time is smallest if the buses are punctual* and increases with the variance of the delay. (See problems 11–12.) ►

6. DISCRETE DISTRIBUTIONS

This section is devoted to a quick glance at some results of randomizing binomial and Poisson distributions.

The number $\mathbf{S}_n$ of successes in Bernoulli trials has a distribution depending on the probability p of success. Treating p as a random variable with density u leads to the new distribution

$$\mathbf{P}\{\mathbf{S}_n = k\} = \binom{n}{k} \int_0^1 p^k(1-p)^{n-k}\, u(p)\, dp \qquad k = 0, \ldots, n. \tag{6.1}$$

Example. (*a*) When $u(p) = 1$ an integration by parts shows (6.1) to be independent of k, and (6.1) reduces to the discrete *uniform distribution* $\mathbf{P}\{\mathbf{S}_n = k\} = (n+1)^{-1}$. More illuminating is an argument due to Bayes. Consider $n+1$ independent variables $\mathbf{X}_0, \ldots, \mathbf{X}_n$ distributed uniformly between 0 and 1. The integral in (6.1) (with $u = 1$) equals the probability that exactly k among the variables $\mathbf{X}_1, \ldots, \mathbf{X}_n$ will be $< \mathbf{X}_0$ or, in other words, that in an enumeration of the points $\mathbf{X}_0, \ldots, \mathbf{X}_n$ in order of magnitude $\mathbf{X}_0$ appears at the $(k+1)$st place. But for reasons of symmetry all positions are equally likely, and so the integral equals $(n+1)^{-1}$. ►

In gambling language (6.1) corresponds to the situation when a skew coin is picked by a chance mechanism and then trials are performed with this coin of unknown structure. To a gambler the trials do not look independent; indeed, if a long sequence of heads is observed it becomes likely that for our coin p is close to 1 and so it is safe to bet on further occurrences of heads. Two formal examples may illustrate estimation and prediction problems of this type.

Examples. (*b*) Given that n trials resulted in k successes (= hypothesis H), what is the probability of the event that $p < \alpha$? By the definition of conditional probabilities

$$\mathbf{P}\{A \mid H\} = \frac{\mathbf{P}\{AH\}}{\mathbf{P}\{H\}} = \frac{\displaystyle\int_0^\alpha p^k(1-p)^{n-k}\, u(p)\, dp}{\displaystyle\int_0^1 p^k(1-p)^{n-k}\, u(p)\, dp}. \tag{6.2}$$

This type of estimation was used by Bayes [with $u(p) = 1$]. Within the framework of our model (that is, if we are really concerned with a mixed population of coins *with known* density u) there can be no objection to the procedure. The trouble is that it used to be applied indiscriminately to judge "probabilities of causes" when there was no randomization in sight; this point was fully discussed in example (2.*e*) of **1**; V in connection with a so-called probability that the sun will rise tomorrow.

(*c*) A variant may be formulated as follows. Given that n trials resulted in k successes, what is the probability that the next m trials will result in j successes? The same argument leads to the answer

$$\frac{\binom{m}{j}\int_0^1 p^{j+k}(1-p)^{m+n-j-k}\,u(p)\,dp}{\int_0^1 p^k(1-p)^{n-k}\,u(p)\,dp}. \tag{6.3}$$ ►

Turning to the *Poisson* distribution let us interpret it as regulating the number of "arrivals" during a time interval of duration t. The expected number of arrivals is αt. We illustrate two conceptually different randomization procedures.

Examples. (*d*) *Randomized time.* If the duration of the time interval is a random variable with density u, the probability p_k of exactly k arrivals becomes

$$p_k = \int_0^\infty e^{-\alpha t}\frac{(\alpha t)^k}{k!}\,u(t)\,dt. \tag{6.4}$$

For example, if the time interval is exponentially distributed, the probability of $k = 0, 1, \ldots$ new arrivals equals

$$p_k = \int_0^\infty e^{-(\alpha+\beta)t}\frac{(\alpha t)^k}{k!}\,\beta\,dt = \frac{\beta}{\alpha+\beta}\cdot\left(\frac{\alpha}{\alpha+\beta}\right)^k \tag{6.5}$$

which is a geometric distribution.

(*e*) *Stratification.* Suppose there are several independent sources for random arrivals, each source having a Poisson output, but with different parameters. For example, *accidents* in a plant during a fixed exposure time t may be assumed to represent Poisson variables, but the parameter will vary from plant to plant. Similarly, *telephone calls* originating at an individual unit may be Poissonian with the expected number of calls varying from unit to unit. In such processes the parameter α appears as random variable with a density u, and the probability of exactly n arrivals during time t is given by

$$P_n(t) = \int_0^\infty e^{-\alpha t}\frac{(\alpha t)^n}{n!}\,u(\alpha)\,d\alpha. \tag{6.6}$$

For the special case of a gamma density $u = f_{\beta,\nu+1}$ we get

$$P_n(t) = \binom{n+\nu}{n}\left(\frac{\beta}{\beta+t}\right)^{\nu+1}\left(\frac{t}{\beta+t}\right)^n, \tag{6.7}$$

which is the limiting form of the *Polya distribution* as given in **1**; V,(8.3) and **1**; XVII,(11.2) (setting $\beta = a^{-1}$, $\nu = a^{-1} - 1$). ►

Note on spurious contagion. A curious and instructive history attaches to the distribution (6.7) and its dual nature.

The Polya urn model and the Polya process which lead to (6.7) are models for true contagion where every accident effectively increases the probability of future accidents. This model enjoyed great popularity, and (6.7) was fitted empirically to a variety of phenomena, a good fit being taken as an *indication of true contagion.*

By coincidence, the same distribution (6.7) had been derived previously (in 1920) by M. Greenwood and G. U. Yule with the intent that a good fit should *disprove presence of contagion.* Their derivation is roughly equivalent to our stratification model, which starts from the assumption underlying the Poisson process, namely, that there is no aftereffect whatever. We have thus the curious fact that a good fit of the same distribution may be interpreted in two ways diametrically opposite in their nature as well as in their practical implications. This should serve as a warning against too hasty interpretations of statistical data.

The explanation lies in the phenomenon of *spurious* contagion, described in **1**; V,(2.*d*) and above in connection with (6.1). In the present situation, having observed m accidents during a time interval of length s one may estimate the probability of n accidents during a future exposure of duration t by a formula analogous to (6.3). The result will depend on m, but this dependence is due to the method of sampling rather than to nature itself; the information concerning the past enables us to make better predictions concerning the future behavior of our sample, and this should not be confused with the future of the whole population.

7. BESSEL FUNCTIONS AND RANDOM WALKS

Surprisingly many explicit solutions in diffusion theory, queuing theory, and other applications involve Bessel functions. It is usually far from obvious that the solutions represent probability distributions, and the analytic theory required to derive their Laplace transforms and other relations is rather complex. Fortunately, the distributions in question (and many more) may be obtained by simple randomization procedures. In this way many relations lose their accidental character, and much hard analysis can be avoided.

By *Bessel function of order* $\rho \geq -1$ we shall understand the function I_ρ defined for all real x by[5]

$$(7.1)\qquad I_\rho(x) = \sum_{k=0}^{\infty} \frac{1}{k!\,\Gamma(k+\rho+1)} \left(\frac{x}{2}\right)^{2k+\rho}.$$

We proceed to describe three procedures leading to three different types of distributions involving Bessel functions.

[5] According to standard usage I_ρ is the "modified" Bessel function or Bessel function "with imaginary argument." The "ordinary" Bessel function, always denoted by J_ρ, is defined by inserting $(-1)^k$ on the right in (7.1). Our use of the term Bessel function should be understood as abbreviation rather than innovation.

(a) Randomized Gamma Densities

For fixed $\rho > -1$ consider the gamma density $f_{1,\rho+k+1}$ of (2.2). Taking the parameter k as an integral-valued random variable subject to a Poisson distribution we get [in accordance with (5.3)] the new density

$$(7.2)\qquad \begin{aligned} w_\rho(x) &= e^{-t}\sum_{k=0}^{\infty}\frac{t^k}{k!}f_{1,\rho+k+1}(x) \\ &= e^{-t-x}\sum_{k=0}^{\infty}\frac{t^k x^{\rho+k}}{k!\,\Gamma(\rho+k+1)}. \end{aligned}$$

Comparing terms in (7.1) and (7.2) one sees that

$$(7.3)\qquad w_\rho(x) = e^{-t-x}\sqrt{\left(\frac{x}{t}\right)^\rho}\, I_\rho(2\sqrt{tx}), \qquad x > 0.$$

If $\rho > -1$ then w_ρ *is a probability density* concentrated on $\overline{0, \infty}$. (For $\rho = -1$ the right side is not integrable with respect to x.) Note that t is not a scale parameter, so that these densities are of different types.

Incidentally, from this construction and the convolution formula (2.3) for the gamma densities it is clear that

$$(7.4)\qquad w_\rho \star f_{1,\nu} = w_{\rho+\nu}.$$

(b) Randomized Random Walks

In discussing random walks one pretends usually that the successive jumps occur at epochs $1, 2, \ldots$. It should be clear, however, that this convention merely lends color to the description and that the model is entirely independent of time. An honest continuous-time stochastic process is obtained from the ordinary random walk by postulating that the *time intervals between successive jumps correspond to independent random variables with the common density* e^{-t}. In other words, the epochs of the jumps are regulated by a Poisson process, but the jumps themselves are random variables assuming the values $+1$ and -1 with probabilities p and q independent of each other and of the Poisson process.

To each distribution connected with the random walk there corresponds a distribution for the continuous-time process, which is obtained formally by randomization of the number of jumps. To see the procedure in detail consider the position at a given epoch t. In the basic random walk the nth step leads to the position $r \geq 0$ iff among the first n jumps $\frac{1}{2}(n+r)$ are positive and $\frac{1}{2}(n-r)$ negative. This is impossible unless $n - r = 2\nu$ is even. In this case the probability of the position r just after the nth jump is

$$(7.5)\qquad \binom{n}{\frac{1}{2}(n+r)} p^{\frac{1}{2}(n+r)} q^{\frac{1}{2}(n-r)} = \binom{r+2\nu}{r+\nu} p^{r+\nu} q^{\nu}.$$

In our Poisson process the probability that up to epoch t exactly n jumps occur is $e^{-t}t^n/n!$ and so in our time-dependent process the probability of the position $r \geq 0$ at epoch t equals

$$(7.6)\qquad e^{-t}\sum_{\nu=0}^{\infty}\frac{t^{r+2\nu}}{(r+2\nu)!}\binom{r+2\nu}{r+\nu}p^{r+\nu}q^{\nu} = \sqrt{\left(\frac{p}{q}\right)^r}e^{-t}I_r(2\sqrt{pq}\,t)$$

and we reach two conclusions.

(i) If we define $I_{-r} = I_r$ for $r = 1, 2, 3, \ldots$ then *for fixed* $t > 0, p, q,$

$$(7.7)\qquad a_r(t) = \sqrt{\left(\frac{p}{q}\right)^r}\,e^{-t}\,I_r(2\sqrt{pq}\,t), \qquad r = 0, \pm1, \pm2, \ldots,$$

represents a probability distribution (that is, $a_r \geq 0$, $\Sigma\, a_r = 1$).

(ii) In our time-dependent random walk $a_r(t)$ *equals the probability of the position* r *at epoch* t.

Two famous formulas for Bessel functions are immediate corollaries of this result. First, with the change of notations $2\sqrt{pq}\,t = x$ and $p/q = u^2$, the identity $\Sigma\, a_r(t) = 1$ becomes

$$(7.8)\qquad e^{\frac{1}{2}x(u+u^{-1})} = \sum_{-\infty}^{+\infty}u^r\,I_r(x).$$

This is the so-called generating function for Bessel functions or *Schlömilch's formula* (which sometimes serves as definition for I_r).

Second, it is clear from the nature of our process that the probabilities $a_r(t)$ must satisfy the Chapman-Kolmogorov equation

$$(7.9)\qquad a_r(t+\tau) = \sum_{k=-\infty}^{\infty} a_k(t)\,a_{r-k}(\tau),$$

which expresses the fact that at epoch t the particle must be at some position k and that a transition from k to r is equivalent to a transition from 0 to $r - k$. We shall return to this relation in XVII,3. [It is easily verified directly from the representation (7.6) and the analogous formula for the probabilities in the random walk.] The Chapman-Kolmogorov relation (7.9) is equivalent to

$$(7.10)\qquad I_r(t+\tau) = \sum_{k=-\infty}^{\infty} I_k(t)\,I_{r-k}(\tau)$$

which is known as *K. Neumann's identity*.

(c) First Passages

For simplicity let us restrict our attention to symmetric random walks, $p = q = \frac{1}{2}$. According to **1**; III,(4.11), the probability that the *first passage* through the point $r > 0$ occurs at the jump number $2n - r$ is

$$(7.11)\qquad \frac{r}{2n-r}\binom{2n-r}{n}2^{-2n+r} \qquad n \geq r.$$

The random walk being recurrent, such a first passage occurs with probability one, that is, for fixed r the quantities (7.11) add up to unity. In our time-dependent process the epoch of the kth jump has the gamma density $f_{1,k}$ of (2.2). It follows that the epoch of the first passage through $r > 0$ has density

$$\sum_n \frac{r}{2n-r}\binom{2n-r}{n} 2^{-2n+r} f_{1,2n-r}(t) = \tag{7.12}$$
$$= e^{-t} \sum \frac{t^{2n-r-1}}{(2n-r-1)!}\left(\frac{r}{2n-r}\right) \cdot \frac{(2n-r)!}{n!(n-r)!} 2^{-2n+r} = e^{-t}\frac{r}{t} I_r(t).$$

Thus: (i) *for fixed* $r = 1, 2, \ldots$

$$v_r(t) = e^{-t}\frac{r}{t} I_r(t) \tag{7.13}$$

defines a probability density concentrated on $\overline{0, \infty}$.

(ii) *The epoch of the first passage through* $r > 0$ *has density* v_r. (See problem 14.)

This derivation permits another interesting conclusion. A first passage through $r + \rho$ at epoch t presupposes a previous first passage through r at some epoch $s < t$. Because of the independence of the jumps in the time intervals $\overline{0, s}$ and $\overline{s, t}$ and the lack of memory of the exponential waiting times we must have

$$v_r \star v_\rho = v_{r+\rho}. \tag{7.14}$$

[A computational verification of this relation from (7.12) is easy if one uses the corresponding convolution property for the probabilities (7.11).]

Actually the proposition (i) and the relation (7.14) are true for all positive values of the parameters r and ρ.[6]

8. DISTRIBUTIONS ON A CIRCLE

The half-open interval $\overline{0, 1}$ may be taken as representing the points of a circle of unit length, but it is preferable to wrap the whole line around the circle. The circle then receives an orientation, and the arc length runs from $-\infty$ to ∞ but $x, x \pm 1, x \pm 2, \ldots$ are interpreted as the same point. Addition is modulo 1 just as addition of angles is modulo 2π. *A probability density on the circle is a periodic function* $\varphi \geq 0$ *such that*

$$\int_0^1 \varphi(x)\, dx = 1. \tag{8.1}$$

[6] W Feller, Infinitely divisible distributions and Bessel functions associated with random walks. To appear in J. Soc. Indust. Appl. Math. (1966).

Examples. (*a*) *Buffon's needle problem* (1777). The traditional formulation is as follows. A plane is partitioned into parallel strips of unit width. A needle of unit length is thrown at random. What is the probability that it lies athwart two strips? To state the problem formally consider first the *center* of the needle. Its position is determined by two coordinates, but y is disregarded and x is reduced modulo 1. In this way "the center of the needle" becomes a random variable $\mathbf{X}$ on the circle with a uniform distribution. The *direction* of the needle may be described by the angle (measured clockwise) between the needle and the y-axis. A turn through π restores the position of the needle. Since we are dealing with a circle of unit length we denote the angle by $\mathbf{Z}\pi$. In Buffon's needle problem it is implied that $\mathbf{X}$ and $\mathbf{Z}$ are independent and uniformly distributed variables[7] on the circle with unit length.

If we choose to represent $\mathbf{X}$ by values between 0 and 1 and $\mathbf{Z}$ by values between $-\frac{1}{2}$ and $\frac{1}{2}$ the needle crosses a boundary iff $\cos \mathbf{Z}\pi > \mathbf{X}$ or $\cos \mathbf{Z}\pi > 1 - \mathbf{X}$. For reasons of symmetry the two events have equal probabilities and so the required probability is

$$(8.2) \qquad 2\int_{-\frac{1}{2}}^{\frac{1}{2}} \cos z\pi \cdot dz = \frac{2}{\pi}. \qquad ►$$

A random variable $\mathbf{X}$ on the line may be reduced modulo 1 to obtain a variable $\mathbf{X}^0$ on the circle. *Rounding errors* in numerical calculations are random variables of this kind. If $\mathbf{X}$ has density f the density of $\mathbf{X}^0$ is given by[8]

$$(8.3) \qquad \varphi(x) = \sum_{-\infty}^{+\infty} f(x+n).$$

Every density on the line thus induces a density on the circle. [It will be seen in XIX,5 that the same φ admits of an entirely different representation in terms of Fourier series. For the special case of normal densities see example XIX,(5.*e*).]

Examples. (*b*) *Poincaré's roulette problem.* Consider the number of rotations of a roulette wheel as a random variable $\mathbf{X}$ with a density f concentrated on the positive half-axis. The observed net result, namely the point $\mathbf{X}^0$ at which the wheel comes to rest, is the variable $\mathbf{X}$ reduced modulo 1. Its density is given by (8.3).

---

[7] The sample space of the pair $(\mathbf{X}, \mathbf{Z})$ is a torus.

[8] Readers worried about convergence should consider only densities f concentrated on a finite interval. The uniform convergence is obvious if f is monotone for x and $-x$ sufficiently large. Without any conditions on f the series may diverge at some points, but φ always represents a density because the partial sums in (8.3) represent a *monotone* sequence of functions whose integrals tend to 1. (See IV,2.)

One feels instinctively that "under ordinary circumstances" the density of $\mathbf{X}^0$ should be nearly uniform. In 1912 Poincaré put this vague feeling on the solid basis of a limit theorem. We shall not repeat his analysis because a similar result follows easily from (8.3). The tacit assumption is, of course, that the given density f is spread out effectively over a long interval so that its *maximum m is small.* Assume for simplicity that f increases up to a point a where it assumes its maximum $m = f(a)$, and that f decreases for $x > a$. Although $f(s) = 0$ for $s < 0$ we write

$$(8.4) \qquad \varphi(x) - 1 = \sum_n f(x+n) - \int_{-\infty}^{+\infty} f(s)\, ds.$$

For fixed x denote by x_k the unique point of the form $x+n$ such that $a+k \leq x_k < a+k+1$. Then (8.4) may be rewritten in the form

$$(8.5) \qquad \varphi(x) - 1 = \sum_{k=-\infty}^{+\infty} \int_{a+k}^{a+k+1} [f(x_k) - f(s)]\, ds.$$

For $k < 0$ the integrand is ≤ 0, and so

$$\varphi(x) - 1 \leq \sum_{k=0}^{\infty} [f(a+k) - f(a+k+1)] = f(a) = m.$$

A similar argument shows that $\varphi(x) - 1 \geq -m$. Thus $|\varphi(x) - 1| < m$ and so φ is indeed nearly constant.

The monotonicity conditions were imposed only for the sake of exposition and can be weakened in many ways. [Neat sufficient conditions can be obtained using Poisson's summation formula, XIX,(5.2).]

(*c*) *Distribution of first significant digits.* A distinguished applied mathematician was extremely successful in bets that a number chosen at random in the *Farmer's Almanac*, or the *Census Report* or a similar compendium, would have the first significant digit less than 5. One expects naïvely that all 9 digits are equally likely, in which case the probability of a digit ≤ 4 would be $\frac{4}{9}$. In practice[9] it is close to 0.7.

Consider the discrete probability distribution attributing to the digit k probability $p_k = \text{Log}\,(k+1) - \text{Log}\,k$ (where Log denotes the logarithm to the basis 10 and $k = 1, \ldots, 9$). Since $p_1 \approx 0.3$ this distribution differs markedly from the uniform distribution with weights $\frac{1}{9} = 0.111\cdots$. We now show [following R. S. Pinkham] that $\{p_k\}$ is plausible for the empirical distribution of the first significant digit for numbers taken at random from a large body of physical or observational data. Indeed, such a number may be considered as a random variable $\mathbf{Y} > 0$ with some unknown distribution. The first significant digit of $\mathbf{Y}$ equals 1 iff

[9] For empirical material see F. Benford, *The law of anomalous numbers*, Proc. Amer. Philos. Soci., vol. 78 (1938) pp. 551–572.

$10^k \leq \mathbf{Y} < 2 \cdot 10^k$, that is, if $k \leq \operatorname{Log} \mathbf{Y} < \operatorname{Log} 2+k$. Denote then by $\mathbf{X}^0$ the variable $\mathbf{X} = \operatorname{Log} \mathbf{Y}$ reduced modulo 1. If the spread of $\mathbf{Y}$ is very large, the distribution of $\mathbf{X}^0$ is likely to be close to the uniform distribution. But 1 is the first significant digit of $\mathbf{Y}$ iff $\mathbf{X}^0$ lies between 0 and Log 2, and the probability of this event is then close to Log 2. The same argument applies to the other digits. ▶

The convolution formula (1.5) and the argument leading to it remain valid when addition is taken modulo 1. Accordingly, *the convolution of two densities on the circle of length* 1 *is the density defined by*

$$w(x) = \int_0^1 f_1(x-y)\, f_2(y)\, dy. \tag{8.6}$$

If $\mathbf{X}_1$ and $\mathbf{X}_2$ are independent variables with densities f_1 and f_2 then $\mathbf{X}_1 + \mathbf{X}_2$ has the density w. Since these densities are periodic, *the convolution of the uniform density with any other density is uniform.* (See problem 15.)

9. PROBLEMS FOR SOLUTION

1. Show that the normal approximation to the binomial distribution established in **1**; VII implies the convolution formula (1.7) for the normal densities.

2. Using the substitution $x = \frac{1}{2}y^2$ prove that $\Gamma(\frac{1}{2}) = \pi^{\frac{1}{2}}$.

3. *Legendre's duplication formula.* From (2.5) for $\mu = \nu$ conclude that

$$\Gamma(2\nu) = \frac{1}{\sqrt{\pi}}\, 2^{2\nu-1}\, \Gamma(\nu)\, \Gamma(\nu+\tfrac{1}{2}).$$

Hint: Use the substitution $4(y - y^2) = s$ in $0 < y < \frac{1}{2}$.

4. If $g(x) = \frac{1}{2}e^{-|x|}$ find the convolutions $g * g$ and $g * g * g$.

5. Let $\mathbf{X}$ and $\mathbf{Y}$ be independent with the common Cauchy density $\gamma_1(x)$ of (4.5). Prove that the product $\mathbf{XY}$ has density $2\pi^{-2} \cdot \dfrac{\log |x|}{x^2 - 1}$.

Hint: No calculations are required beyond the observation that

$$\frac{a-1}{(1+s)(a+s)} = \frac{1}{1+s} - \frac{1}{a+s}.$$

6. Prove that if

$$f(x) = \frac{2}{\pi}\frac{1}{e^x + e^{-x}} \qquad \text{then} \qquad f*f(x) = \frac{4}{\pi^2}\frac{x}{e^x - e^{-x}}$$

(*a*) by considering the variables log $\mathbf{X}$ and log $\mathbf{Y}$ of the preceding problem; (*b*) directly by the substitution $e^{2y} = t$ and a partial fraction decomposition. (See problem 7 of XV,9.)

7. If $\mathbf{X}$ has the normal density $\mathfrak{n}$ then obviously $\mathbf{X}^{-2}$ has the stable density (4.8). From this conclude that if $\mathbf{X}$ and $\mathbf{Y}$ are independent and normal with zero expectations and variances σ_1^2 and σ_2^2, then $\mathbf{Z} = \mathbf{XY}/\sqrt{\mathbf{X}^2 + \mathbf{Y}^2}$ *is normal with variance* σ_3^2 such that $\dfrac{1}{\sigma_3^2} = \dfrac{1}{\sigma_1^2} + \dfrac{1}{\sigma_2^2}$. (L. Shepp.)

8. Let $\mathbf{X}_1, \ldots, \mathbf{X}_n$ be independent and $\mathbf{X}_{(n)}$ the largest among them. Show that if the $\mathbf{X}_j$ have:
(*a*) the Cauchy density (4.5), then

$$\mathbf{P}\{n^{-1}\mathbf{X}_{(n)} \le x\} \to e^{-t/(\pi x)}, \qquad x > 0$$

(*b*) the stable density (4.8), then

$$\mathbf{P}\{n^{-2}\mathbf{X}_{(n)} \le x\} \to e^{-\alpha\sqrt{2/(\pi x)}}, \qquad x > 0.$$

9. Let $\mathbf{X}$ and $\mathbf{Y}$ be independent with densities f and g concentrated on $\overline{0, \infty}$. If $\mathbf{E}(\mathbf{X}) < \infty$ the ratio $\mathbf{X}/\mathbf{Y}$ has a finite expectation iff

$$\int_0^1 \frac{1}{y} g(y)\, dy < \infty.$$

10. In example (5.*c*) let t be arbitrary and denote by $t+\mathbf{T}$ the epoch of the *first* discharge after t. Find the density of the waiting time $\mathbf{T}$. (Note the possibility of no customers present at epoch t.)

11. In example (5.*d*) show that

$$\mathbf{E}(\mathbf{T}_x) = F(x)(\mu+1-x) + \int_0^{1-x} t f(t+x)\, dt,$$

where μ is the expectation of F. From this verify the assertion concerning $\mathbf{E}(\mathbf{T})$ when x is uniformly distributed.

12. In example (5.*d*) find the waiting time distribution when $f(t) = 1$ for $0 < t < 1$.

13. Let $\mathbf{X}$ and $\mathbf{Y}$ be independent with the common Poisson distribution $\mathbf{P}\{\mathbf{X}=n\} = e^{-t}\, t^n/n!$ Show that

$$\mathbf{P}\{\mathbf{X}-\mathbf{Y}=r\} = e^{-2t} I_{|r|}(2t), \qquad r = 0, \pm 1, \pm 2, \ldots.$$

14. The results of section 7.*c* remain valid for unsymmetric random walks provided the probability of a first passage through $r > 0$ equals one, that is, provided $p \ge q$. Show that the only change in (7.11) is that 2^{-2n+r} is replaced by $p^n q^{n-r}$, and the conclusion is that for $p \ge q$ and $r = 1, 2, \ldots,$

$$\sqrt{\left(\frac{p}{q}\right)^r} e^{-t} \frac{r}{t} I_r(2\sqrt{pq}\, t)$$

defines a probability density concentrated on $t > 0$.

15. Let $\mathbf{X}$ and $\mathbf{Y}$ be independent variables and $\mathbf{X}^0$ and $\mathbf{Y}^0$ be the same variables reduced modulo 1. Show that $\mathbf{X}^0+\mathbf{Y}^0$ is obtained by reducing $\mathbf{X}+\mathbf{Y}$ modulo 1. Verify the corresponding formula for convolutions by direct calculation.

CHAPTER III

Densities in Higher Dimensions. Normal Densities and Processes

For obvious reasons multivariate distributions occur less frequently than one-dimensional distributions, and the material of this chapter will play almost no role in the following chapters. On the other hand, it covers important material, for example, a famous characterization of the normal distribution and tools used in the theory of stochastic processes. Their true nature is best understood when divorced from the sophisticated problems with which they are sometimes connected.

1. DENSITIES

For typographical convenience we refer explicitly to the Cartesian plane $\mathfrak{R}^2$, but it will be evident that the number of dimensions is immaterial. We refer the plane to a fixed coordinate system with coordinate variables $\mathbf{X}_1, \mathbf{X}_2$. (A more convenient single-letter notation will be introduced in section 5.)

A non-negative integrable function f defined in $\mathfrak{R}^2$ and such that its integral equals one is called a *probability density*, or density for short. (All the densities occurring in the chapter are piecewise continuous, and so the concept of integration requires no comment.) The density f attributes to the region Ω the probability

$$\mathbf{P}\{\Omega\} = \iint_{\Omega} f(x_1, x_2)\, dx_1\, dx_2 \tag{1.1}$$

provided, of course, that Ω is sufficiently regular for the integral to exist. All such probabilities are uniquely determined by the probabilities of rectangles parallel to the axes, that is, by the knowledge of

$$\mathbf{P}\{a_1 < \mathbf{X}_1 \leq b_1,\, a_2 < \mathbf{X}_2 \leq b_2\} = \int_{a_1}^{b_1}\int_{a_2}^{b_2} f(x_1, x_2)\, dx_1\, dx_2 \tag{1.2}$$

for all combinations $a_i < b_i$. Letting $a_1 = a_2 = -\infty$ we get the *distribution function* F of f, namely

$$(1.3) \qquad F(x_1, x_2) = \mathbf{P}\{\mathbf{X}_1 \leq x_1, \mathbf{X}_2 \leq x_2\}.$$

Obviously $F(b_1, x_2) - F(a_1, x_2)$ is the probability of a semi-finite strip of width $b_1 - a_1$ and, the rectangle appearing in (1.2) being the difference of two such strips, the probability (1.2) equals

$$F(b_1, b_2) - F(a_1, b_2) - F(b_1, a_2) + F(a_1, a_2)$$

(the so-called mixed difference). It follows that the knowledge of the distribution function F uniquely determines all probabilities (1.1). Despite the formal analogy with the situation on the line, the concept of distribution function F is much less useful in the plane and it is best to concentrate on the assignment of probabilities (1.1) in terms of the density itself. This assignment differs from the joint probability distribution of two discrete random variables (**1**; IX,1) in two respects. First, integration replaces summation and, second, probabilities are now assigned only to "sufficiently regular regions" whereas in discrete sample spaces all sets had probabilities. As the present chapter treats only simple examples in which the difference is hardly noticeable, the notions and terms of the discrete theory carry over in a self-explanatory manner. Just as in the preceding chapters we employ therefore a probabilistic language without any attempt at a general theory (which will be supplied in chapter V).

It is apparent from (1.3) that[1]

$$(1.4) \qquad \mathbf{P}\{\mathbf{X}_1 \leq x_1\} = F(x_1, \infty).$$

Thus $F_1(x) = F(x, \infty)$ defines the distribution function of $\mathbf{X}_1$, and its *density* f_1 is given by

$$(1.5) \qquad f_1(x) = \int_{-\infty}^{+\infty} f(x, y)\, dy.$$

When it is desirable to emphasize the connection between $\mathbf{X}_1$ and the pair $(\mathbf{X}_1, \mathbf{X}_2)$ we again speak of F_1 as *marginal* distribution[2] and of f_1 as marginal density.

The *expectation* μ_1 and *variance* σ_1^2 of $\mathbf{X}_1$—if they exist—are given by

$$(1.6) \qquad \mu_1 = \mathbf{E}(\mathbf{X}_1) = \int_{-\infty}^{+\infty}\int_{-\infty}^{+\infty} x_1 f(x_1, x_2)\, dx_1\, dx_2$$

[1] Here and in the following $U(\infty) = \lim U(x)$ as $x \to \infty$ and the use of the symbol $U(\infty)$ implies the existence of the limit.

[2] *Projection* on the axes is another accepted term.

and

$$\sigma_1^2 = \text{Var}(\mathbf{X}_1) = \int_{-\infty}^{+\infty}\int_{-\infty}^{+\infty} (x_1-\mu_1)^2 f(x_1, x_2)\, dx_1\, dx_2. \tag{1.7}$$

By symmetry these definitions apply also to $\mathbf{X}_2$. Finally, the *covariance* of $\mathbf{X}_1$ and $\mathbf{X}_2$ is

$$\text{Cov}(\mathbf{X}_1, \mathbf{X}_2) = \int_{-\infty}^{+\infty}\int_{-\infty}^{+\infty} (x_1-\mu_1)(x_2-\mu_2) f(x_1, x_2)\, dx_1\, dx_2. \tag{1.8}$$

The normalized variables $\mathbf{X}_i\sigma_i^{-1}$ are dimensionless and their covariance, namely $\rho = \text{Cov}(\mathbf{X}_1, \mathbf{X}_2)\sigma_1^{-1}\sigma_2^{-1}$, is the *correlation coefficient* of $\mathbf{X}_1$ and $\mathbf{X}_2$ (see **1**; IX,8).

A *random variable* $\mathbf{U}$ is a function of the coordinate variables $\mathbf{X}_1$ and $\mathbf{X}_2$; again we consider for the present only functions such that the probabilities $\mathbf{P}\{\mathbf{U} \leq t\}$ can be evaluated by integrals of the form (1.1). Thus each random variable will have a unique distribution function, each pair will have a joint distribution, etc.

In many situations it is expedient to *change the coordinate variables*, that is, to let two variables $\mathbf{Y}_1, \mathbf{Y}_2$ play the role previously assigned to $\mathbf{X}_1, \mathbf{X}_2$. In the simplest case the $\mathbf{Y}_j$ are defined by a linear transformation

$$\mathbf{X}_1 = a_{11}\mathbf{Y}_1 + a_{12}\mathbf{Y}_2, \qquad \mathbf{X}_2 = a_{21}\mathbf{Y}_1 + a_{22}\mathbf{Y}_2, \tag{1.9}$$

with determinant $\Delta = a_{11}a_{22} - a_{12}a_{21} > 0$. Generally a transformation of the form (1.9) may be described either as a mapping from one plane to another or as a change of coordinates in the same plane. Introducing the change of variables (1.9) into the integral (1.1) we get

$$\mathbf{P}\{\Omega\} = \iint_{\Omega_*} f(a_{11}y_1 + a_{12}y_2,\, a_{21}y_1 + a_{22}y_2) \cdot \Delta\, dy_1\, dy_2 \tag{1.10}$$

the region Ω_* containing all points (y_1, y_2) whose image (x_1, x_2) is in Ω. Since the events $(\mathbf{X}_1, \mathbf{X}_2) \in \Omega$ and $(\mathbf{Y}_1, \mathbf{Y}_2) \in \Omega_*$ are identical it is seen that *the joint density of* $(\mathbf{Y}_1, \mathbf{Y}_2)$ *is given by*

$$g(y_1, y_2) = f(a_{11}y_1 + a_{12}y_2,\, a_{21}y_1 + a_{22}y_2) \cdot \Delta. \tag{1.11}$$

All this applies equally to higher dimensions.

A similar argument applies to more general transformations, except that the determinant Δ is replaced by the Jacobian. We shall use explicitly only the *change to polar coordinates*

$$\mathbf{X}_1 = \mathbf{R}\cos\mathbf{\Theta}, \qquad \mathbf{X}_2 = \mathbf{R}\sin\mathbf{\Theta} \tag{1.12}$$

with $(\mathbf{R}, \mathbf{\Theta})$ restricted to $\mathbf{R} \geq 0$, $-\pi < \mathbf{\Theta} \leq \pi$. Here the density of $(\mathbf{R}, \mathbf{\Theta})$ is given by

$$g(r, \theta) = f(r\cos\theta, r\sin\theta)r. \tag{1.13}$$

In three dimensions one uses the geographic longitude φ and latitude θ (with $-\pi < \varphi \leq \pi$ and $-\frac{1}{2}\pi \leq \theta \leq \frac{1}{2}\pi$). The coordinate variables in the polar system are then defined by

$$(1.14)\quad \mathbf{X}_1 = \mathbf{R}\cos\mathbf{\Phi}\cos\mathbf{\Theta}, \qquad \mathbf{X}_2 = \mathbf{R}\sin\mathbf{\Phi}\cos\mathbf{\Theta}, \qquad \mathbf{X}_3 = \mathbf{R}\sin\mathbf{\Theta}.$$

For their joint density one gets

$$(1.15)\qquad g(r, \varphi, \theta) = f(r\cos\varphi\cos\theta,\, r\sin\varphi\cos\theta,\, r\sin\theta)r^2\cos\theta.$$

[In the transformation (1.14) the "planes" $\mathbf{\Theta} = -\frac{1}{2}\pi$ and $\mathbf{\Theta} = \frac{1}{2}\pi$ correspond to the half axes in the x_3-direction, but this singularity plays no role since these half axes have zero probability. A similar remark applies to the origin for polar coordinates in the plane.]

Examples. (*a*) *Independent variables.* In the last chapters we considered *independent* variables $\mathbf{X}_1$ and $\mathbf{X}_2$ with densities f_1 and f_2. This amounts to defining a bivariate density by $f(x_1, x_2) = f_1(x_1)f_2(x_2)$, and the f_i represent the marginal densities.

(*b*) "*Random choice.*" Let Γ be a bounded region; for simplicity we assume Γ convex. Denote the area of Γ by γ and put f equal to γ^{-1} within Γ and equal to 0 outside Γ. Then f is a density, and the probability of any region $\Omega \subset \Gamma$ equals the ratio of the areas of Ω and Γ. By obvious analogy with the one-dimensional situation we say that the pair $(\mathbf{X}_1, \mathbf{X}_2)$ is *distributed uniformly over* Γ. The marginal density of $\mathbf{X}_1$ at the abscissa x_1 equals the width of Γ at x_1 in the obvious sense of the word. (See problem 1.)

(*c*) *Uniform distribution on a sphere.* The unit sphere Σ in three dimensions may be represented in terms of the geographic longitude φ and latitude θ by the equations

$$(1.16)\qquad x_1 = \cos\varphi\cos\theta, \qquad x_2 = \sin\varphi\cos\theta, \qquad x_3 = \sin\theta.$$

To each pair (φ, θ) such that $-\pi < \varphi \leq \pi$, $-\frac{1}{2}\pi < \theta < \frac{1}{2}\pi$ there corresponds exactly one point on the sphere and, except for the two poles, each point of Σ is obtained in this way. The exceptional role of the poles need not concern us since they will have probability 0. A region Ω on the sphere is defined by its image in the φ, θ-plane, and the area of Ω equals the integral of $\cos\theta\, d\varphi\, d\theta$ over this image [see (1.15)]. For the conceptual experiment "random choice of a point on Σ" we should put $4\pi\mathbf{P}\{\Omega\} =$ area of Ω. This is equivalent to defining in the φ, θ-plane a density

$$(1.17)\qquad g(\varphi, \theta) = \begin{cases} \dfrac{1}{4\pi}\cos\theta & \textit{for}\quad -\pi < \varphi \leq \pi,\quad |\theta| < \frac{1}{2}\pi \\ 0 & \textit{elsewhere.} \end{cases}$$

With this definition the coordinate variables are independent, the longitude being distributed uniformly over $\overline{-\pi, \pi}$.

The device of referring the sphere Σ to the φ, θ-plane is familiar from geographic maps and useful for probability theory. Note, however, that the coordinate variables are largely arbitrary and their expectations and variances meaningless for the original conceptual experiment.

(*d*) *The bivariate normal density.* Normal densities in higher dimensions will be introduced systematically in section 6. The excuse for anticipating the bivariate case is to provide an easy access to it. An obvious analogue to the normal density $\mathfrak{n}$ of II,(2.1) is provided by densities of the form $c \cdot e^{-q(x_1,x_2)}$ where $q(x_1, x_2) = a_1x_1^2 + 2bx_1x_2 + a_2x_2^2$. It is easily seen that e^{-q} will be integrable iff $a_1a_2 - b^2 > 0$, and in this case the variances and the covariance are easily calculated. For purposes of probability theory it is preferable to express the coefficients a_i and b in terms of these variances and to *define the bivariate normal density centered at the origin by*

(1.18)
$$\varphi(x_1, x_2) = \frac{1}{2\pi\sigma_1\sigma_2\sqrt{1-\rho^2}} \exp\left[-\frac{1}{2(1-\rho^2)}\left(\frac{x_1^2}{\sigma_1^2} - 2\rho\frac{x_1x_2}{\sigma_1\sigma_2} + \frac{x_2^2}{\sigma_2^2}\right)\right]$$

where $\sigma_1 > 0$, $\sigma_2 > 0$, and $-1 < \rho < 1$. The integration with respect to x_2 is easily performed by the substitution $t = x_2/\sigma_2 - \rho\, x_1/\sigma_1$ (completing squares), and it is seen that φ indeed represents a density in $\mathcal{R}^2$. Furthermore, it becomes obvious that the *marginal* distributions for $\mathbf{X}_1$ and $\mathbf{X}_2$ are again normal[3] and that $\mathbf{E}(\mathbf{X}_i) = 0$, $\operatorname{Var}(\mathbf{X}_i) = \sigma_i^2$, $\operatorname{Cov}(\mathbf{X}_1, \mathbf{X}_2) = \rho\sigma_1\sigma_2$. In other words, ρ is the *correlation* coefficient of $\mathbf{X}_1$ and $\mathbf{X}_2$. Replacing x_i by $x_i - c_i$ in (1.18) leads to a normal density centered at the point (c_1, c_2).

It is important that *linear transformations* (1.9) *change a normal distribution into another normal distribution.* This is obvious from the definition and (1.11). [Continued in example (2.*a*).]

(*e*) *The symmetric Cauchy distribution in* $\mathcal{R}^2$. Put

$$u(x_1, x_2) = \frac{1}{2\pi} \cdot \frac{1}{\sqrt{(1 + x_1^2 + x_2^2)^3}}. \tag{1.19}$$

To see that this is a density note[4] that

$$\int_{-\infty}^{+\infty} u(x_1, y)\, dy = \frac{1}{2\pi} \cdot \frac{1}{1+x_1^2} \cdot \frac{y}{\sqrt{1 + x_1^2 + y^2}}\Bigg|_{-\infty}^{+\infty} = \frac{1}{\pi} \cdot \frac{1}{1 + x_1^2}. \tag{1.20}$$

[3] Contrary to a widespread belief *there exist non-normal bivariate* densities with normal marginal densities (two types are described in problems 2, 3; two more in problems 4 and 6 of V,11). In the desire to deal with normal densities, statisticians sometimes introduce a pair of new coordinate variables $\mathbf{Y}_1 = g_1(\mathbf{X}_1)$, $\mathbf{Y}_2 = g_2(\mathbf{X}_2)$ which are normally distributed. Alas, this does *not* make the joint distribution of $(\mathbf{Y}_1, \mathbf{Y}_2)$ normal.

[4] The substitution $y = \sqrt{1 + x_1^2}\tan t$ makes the calculation easy.

It follows that u is a density and that the marginal density of $\mathbf{X}_1$ is the *Cauchy density* γ_1 of II,(4.5). Obviously $\mathbf{X}_1$ has no expectation.

Switching to polar coordinates [as in (1.12)] $\mathbf{R}$ gets a density independent of θ and so the variables $\mathbf{R}$ and $\mathbf{\Theta}$ are stochastically independent. In the terminology of I,10 we can therefore say that with the symmetric Cauchy distribution $(\mathbf{X}_1, \mathbf{X}_2)$ *represents a vector in a randomly chosen direction with a length* $\mathbf{R}$ *whose density is given by* $r\sqrt{(1+r^2)^{-3}}$, whence $\mathbf{P}\{\mathbf{R} \leq r\} = 1 - \sqrt{(1+r^2)^{-1}}$. [Continued in example (2.*b*).]

(*f*) *The symmetric Cauchy distribution in* $\mathcal{R}^3$. Put

$$v(x_1, x_2, x_3) = \frac{1}{\pi^2} \cdot \frac{1}{(1 + x_1^2 + x_2^2 + x_3^2)^2}. \tag{1.21}$$

It is easily seen[5] that the marginal density of $(\mathbf{X}_1, \mathbf{X}_2)$ is the symmetric Cauchy density u of (1.19). The marginal density of $\mathbf{X}_1$ is therefore the Cauchy density γ_1. (Continued in problem 5.)

Although it will not play an explicit role in the sequel it should be mentioned that we can define *convolutions* just as in one dimension. Consider two pairs $(\mathbf{X}_1, \mathbf{X}_2)$ and $(\mathbf{Y}_1, \mathbf{Y}_2)$ with joint densities f and g, respectively. Saying that *the two pairs are independent* means that we take the four-dimensional space with coordinate variables $\mathbf{X}_1, \mathbf{X}_2, \mathbf{Y}_1, \mathbf{Y}_2$ as sample space and define in it a density given by the product $f(x_1, x_2)$ $g(y_1, y_2)$. Just as in $\mathcal{R}^1$ it is then easily seen that the joint density v of the sum $(\mathbf{X}_1+\mathbf{Y}_1, \mathbf{X}_2+\mathbf{Y}_2)$ is given by the convolution formula

$$v(z_1, z_2) = \int_{-\infty}^{+\infty}\int_{-\infty}^{+\infty} f(z_1-x_1, z_2-x_2)\, g(x_1, x_2)\, dx_1\, dx_2 \tag{1.22}$$

which is the obvious analogue to I,(2.12). (See problems 14–16.)

2. CONDITIONAL DISTRIBUTIONS

Suppose that the pair $(\mathbf{X}_1, \mathbf{X}_2)$ has a continuous density f and that the marginal density f_1 of $\mathbf{X}_1$ is strictly positive. Consider the conditional probability of the event $\mathbf{X}_2 \leq \eta$ given that $\xi < \mathbf{X}_1 \leq \xi + h$, namely

$$\mathbf{P}\{\mathbf{X}_2 \leq \eta \mid \xi < \mathbf{X}_1 \leq \xi + h\} = \frac{\int_\xi^{\xi+h} dx \int_{-\infty}^{\eta} f(x, y)\, dy}{\int_\xi^{\xi+h} f_1(x)\, dx}. \tag{2.1}$$

Dividing numerator and denominator by h, one sees that as $h \to 0$ the right side tends to

$$U_\xi(\eta) = \frac{1}{f_1(\xi)} \int_{-\infty}^{\eta} f(\xi, y)\, dy. \tag{2.2}$$

[5] Use the substitution $z = \sqrt{1 + x_1^2 + x_2^2}\tan t$.

For fixed ξ this is a distribution function in η with density

$$u_\xi(\eta) = \frac{1}{f_1(\xi)} f(\xi, \eta). \tag{2.3}$$

We call u_ξ the *conditional density of* $\mathbf{X}_2$ *given that* $\mathbf{X}_1 = \xi$. *The conditional expectation of* $\mathbf{X}_2$ *given that* $\mathbf{X}_1 = \xi$ *is defined by*

$$\mathbf{E}(\mathbf{X}_2 \mid \mathbf{X}_1 = \xi) = \frac{1}{f_1(\xi)} \int_{-\infty}^{+\infty} y f(\xi, y)\, dy \tag{2.4}$$

provided that the integral converges absolutely. With ξ considered as a variable the right side becomes a function of it. In particular, we may identify ξ with the coordinate variable $\mathbf{X}_1$ to obtain a random variable called *the regression of* $\mathbf{X}_2$ *on* $\mathbf{X}_1$ and denoted by $\mathbf{E}(\mathbf{X}_2 \mid \mathbf{X}_1)$. The appearance of $\mathbf{X}_2$ should not obscure the fact that this random variable is a function of the single variable $\mathbf{X}_1$ [its values being given by (2.4)].

So far we have assumed that $f_1(\xi) > 0$ for all ξ. The expression (2.4) is meaningless at any place where $f_1(\xi) = 0$, but the set of such points has probability zero and we agree to interpret (2.4) as zero at all points where f_1 vanishes. Then $\mathbf{E}(\mathbf{X}_2 \mid \mathbf{X}_1)$ is defined whenever the density is continuous. (In V,9–10 conditional probabilities will be introduced for arbitrary distributions.)

Needless to say, the regression $\mathbf{E}(\mathbf{X}_1 \mid \mathbf{X}_2)$ of $\mathbf{X}_1$ on $\mathbf{X}_2$ is defined in like manner. Furthermore, a *conditional variance* $\mathrm{Var}(\mathbf{X}_2 \mid \mathbf{X}_1)$ is defined by obvious analogy with (2.4).

These definitions carry over to higher dimensions, except that a density in $\mathfrak{R}^3$ gives rise to three bivariate and three univariate conditional densities [see example (*c*)].

Examples. (*a*) *The normal density.* For the density (1.18) obviously

$$u_\xi(y) = \frac{1}{\sqrt{2\pi(1-\rho^2)\sigma_2^{\,2}}} \exp\left[-\frac{\left(y-\rho\dfrac{\sigma_2}{\sigma_1}\xi\right)^2}{2(1-\rho^2)\sigma_2^{\,2}}\right] \tag{2.5}$$

which is a normal density with expectation $\rho \dfrac{\sigma_2}{\sigma_1} \xi$ and variance $(1-\rho^2)\sigma_2^{\,2}$. Thus

$$\mathbf{E}(\mathbf{X}_2 \mid \mathbf{X}_1) = \rho \frac{\sigma_2}{\sigma_1} \mathbf{X}_1, \qquad \mathrm{Var}(\mathbf{X}_2 \mid \mathbf{X}_1) = (1-\rho^2)\sigma_2^{\,2}. \tag{2.6}$$

It is one of the pleasing properties of the normal distribution that the regressions are *linear* functions.

Perhaps the earliest application of these relations is due to Galton, and one of his examples may illustrate their *empirical meaning*. Imagine that

$\mathbf{X}_1$ and $\mathbf{X}_2$ represent the heights (measured in inches from their respective expectations) of fathers and sons in a human population. The height of a randomly chosen son is then a normal variable with expectation 0 and variance σ_2^2. However, in the subpopulation of sons whose fathers have a fixed height ξ, the height of the sons is a normal variable with expectation $\rho \frac{\sigma_2}{\sigma_1} \xi$ and variance $\sigma_2^2(1-\rho^2) < \sigma_2^2$. Thus the regression of $\mathbf{X}_2$ on $\mathbf{X}_1$ indicates how much statistical information about $\mathbf{X}_2$ is contained in observation of $\mathbf{X}_1$.

(*b*) *Cauchy distribution in* $\mathcal{R}^2$. For the bivariate density (1.19) the marginal density for $\mathbf{X}_1$ is given in (1.20), and so the conditional density of $\mathbf{X}_2$ for given $\mathbf{X}_1$ is

$$u_\xi(y) = \frac{1}{2} \cdot \frac{1+\xi^2}{\sqrt{(1+\xi^2+y^2)^3}}. \tag{2.7}$$

Note that u_ξ differs only by the scale factor $\sqrt{1+\xi^2}$ from the density $u_1(y)$ and so all the densities u_ξ are of the same type. Conditional expectations do not exist in this example.

(*c*) *Cauchy distribution in* $\mathcal{R}^3$. It is easily seen that in example (1.*f*) the conditional density of $\mathbf{X}_3$ for given $\mathbf{X}_1$, $\mathbf{X}_2$ is

$$v_{\xi_1,\xi_2}(z) = \frac{2}{\pi} \cdot \frac{\sqrt{(1+\xi_1^2+\xi_2^2)^3}}{(1+\xi_1^2+\xi_2^2+z^2)^2}, \tag{2.8}$$

and the bivariate conditional density of $\mathbf{X}_2$, $\mathbf{X}_3$ for given $\mathbf{X}_1 = \xi$

$$v_\xi(y, z) = \frac{1}{\pi} \cdot \frac{1+\xi^2}{(1+\xi^2+y^2+z^2)^2}. \tag{2.9}$$

In terms of the conditional densities (2.3) the distribution function of $\mathbf{X}_2$ takes on the form

$$\mathbf{P}\{\mathbf{X}_2 < y\} = \int_{-\infty}^{y} \int_{-\infty}^{+\infty} u_\xi(\eta) \cdot f_1(\xi)\, d\xi\, d\eta. \tag{2.10}$$

In other words, the distribution of $\mathbf{X}_2$ is obtained by *randomization* of the parameter ξ in the conditional densities u_ξ, and so *every*[6] *distribution may be represented as mixture.* Despite this theoretical universality there is a great difference in emphasis. In some situations [such as example (*a*)] one *starts* from a bivariate distribution for ($\mathbf{X}_1$, $\mathbf{X}_2$) and derives conditional distributions, whereas in true randomization the conditional probabilities u_x are the primary notion and the density $f(x, y)$ is actually *defined* by $u_x(y) f_1(x)$. (This procedure of defining probabilities in terms of conditional probabilities was explained in an elementary way in **1**; V,2.) ►

[6] We have so far considered only continuous densities, but the general case will be covered in V,9. The notion of randomization was discussed in II,5.

3. RETURN TO THE EXPONENTIAL AND THE UNIFORM DISTRIBUTIONS

The object of this section is to provide illustrative examples to the preceding sections and at the same time to supplement the theory of the first chapter.

Examples. (*a*) *A characteristic property of the exponential distribution.* Let $\mathbf{X}_1$ and $\mathbf{X}_2$ be two *independent* random variables with densities f_1 and f_2, and denote the density of their sum $\mathbf{S} = \mathbf{X}_1+\mathbf{X}_2$ by g. The pairs $(\mathbf{X}_1, \mathbf{S})$ and $(\mathbf{X}_1, \mathbf{X}_2)$ are related by the linear transformation $\mathbf{X}_1 = \mathbf{X}_1$, $\mathbf{X}_2 = \mathbf{S} - \mathbf{X}_1$ with determinant 1 and by (1.11) the *joint density* of the pair $(\mathbf{X}_1, \mathbf{S})$ is given by $f_1(x)\,f_2(s-x)$. Integrating over all x we obtain the marginal density g of $\mathbf{S}$. *The conditional density u_s of $\mathbf{X}_1$ given that $\mathbf{S} = s$* satisfies

$$(3.1) \qquad u_s(x) = \frac{f_1(x)\,f_2(s-x)}{g(s)}.$$

In the special case of exponential densities $f_1(x) = f_2(x) = \alpha e^{-\alpha x}$ (where $x > 0$) we get $u_s(x) = s^{-1}$ for $0 < x < s$. In other words, *given that* $\mathbf{X}_1 + \mathbf{X}_2 = s$, *the variable* $\mathbf{X}_1$ *is uniformly distributed* over the interval $\overline{0, s}$. Intuitively speaking, the knowledge that $\mathbf{S} = s$ gives us no clue as to the possible position of the random point $\mathbf{X}_1$ within the interval $\overline{0, s}$. This result conforms with the notion of complete randomness inherent in the exponential distribution. (A stronger version is contained in example (*c*). See also problem 11.)

(*b*) *Random partitions of an interval.* Let $\mathbf{X}_1, \ldots, \mathbf{X}_n$ be n points chosen independently and at random in the (one-dimensional) interval $\overline{0, 1}$. As before we denote by $\mathbf{X}_{(1)}, \mathbf{X}_{(2)}, \ldots, \mathbf{X}_{(n)}$ the random points $\mathbf{X}_1, \ldots, \mathbf{X}_n$ rearranged in increasing order. These points divide the interval $\overline{0, 1}$ into $n + 1$ subintervals which we denote by $I_1, I_2, \ldots, I_{n+1}$ numbering them from left to right so that $\mathbf{X}_{(j)}$ is the right endpoint of I_j. Our first aim is to calculate the joint density of $(\mathbf{X}_{(1)}, \ldots, \mathbf{X}_{(n)})$.

The sample space corresponding to $(\mathbf{X}_1, \ldots, \mathbf{X}_n)$ is the n-dimensional hypercube Γ defined by $0 < x_k < 1$, and probabilities equal the (n-dimensional) volume. The natural sample space with the $\mathbf{X}_{(k)}$ as coordinate variables is the subset Ω of Γ containing all points such that $0 < x_1 \le \cdots \le x_n < 1$. The volume of Ω is $1/n!$ Evidently the hypercube Γ contains $n!$ congruent replicas of the set Ω and in each the ordered n-tuple $(\mathbf{X}_{(1)}, \ldots, \mathbf{X}_{(n)})$ coincides with a fixed permutation of $\mathbf{X}_1, \ldots, \mathbf{X}_n$. (Within Γ, in particular, $\mathbf{X}_{(k)} = \mathbf{X}_k$.) The probability that $\mathbf{X}_j = \mathbf{X}_k$ for some pair $j \neq k$ equals zero, and only this event causes overlaps among the various replicas. It follows that for any subset $A \subset \Omega$ the probability that $(\mathbf{X}_{(1)}, \ldots, \mathbf{X}_{(n)})$ lies in A equals the probability that $(\mathbf{X}_1, \ldots, \mathbf{X}_n)$ lies in one of the $n!$ replicas of A, and this probability in turn equals $n!$ times the volume of A. Thus $\mathbf{P}\{(\mathbf{X}_{(1)}, \ldots, \mathbf{X}_{(n)}) \in A\}$ equals the ratio of the volumes of A and of Ω, which means that *the n-tuple* $(\mathbf{X}_{(1)}, \ldots, \mathbf{X}_{(n)})$ *is distributed uniformly over the set* Ω of points such that

$$0 < x_1 \leq x_2 \leq \cdots < 1.$$

The joint density of our n-tuple equals $1/n!$ within Ω and 0 outside.

From the joint density of $(\mathbf{X}_{(1)}, \ldots, \mathbf{X}_{(n)})$ the density of $\mathbf{X}_{(k)}$ may be calculated by keeping x_k fixed and integrating over the remaining variables. The result is easily seen to agree with the density calculated by other methods in I,(7.2).

This example was treated in detail as an exercise in handling and computing multivariate densities.

(*c*) *The distribution of the lengths.* In the random partition of the preceding example denote the length of the kth interval I_k by $\mathbf{U}_k$. Then

$$(3.2) \qquad \mathbf{U}_1 = \mathbf{X}_{(1)}, \qquad \mathbf{U}_k = \mathbf{X}_{(k)} - \mathbf{X}_{(k-1)} \qquad \textit{for} \quad k = 2, 3, \ldots, n.$$

This is a linear transformation of the form (1.9) with determinant 1. The set Ω of points $0 < x_1 \leq \cdots \leq x_n < 1$ is mapped into the set $\Omega^\star$ of points such that $u_j \geq 0$, $u_1 + \cdots + u_n < 1$, and hence $(\mathbf{U}_1, \ldots, \mathbf{U}_n)$ *is distributed uniformly over this region.* This result is stronger than the previously established fact that the $\mathbf{U}_k$ have a common distribution function [example I,(7.*b*)].

(*d*) *Once more the randomness of the exponential distribution.* Let $\mathbf{X}_1, \ldots, \mathbf{X}_{n+1}$ be independent with the common density $\alpha e^{-\alpha x}$ for $x > 0$. Put $\mathbf{S}_j = \mathbf{X}_1 + \cdots + \mathbf{X}_j$. Then $(\mathbf{S}_1, \mathbf{S}_2, \ldots, \mathbf{S}_{n+1})$ is obtained from $(\mathbf{X}_1, \ldots, \mathbf{X}_{n+1})$ by a linear transformation of the form (1.9) with determinant 1. Denote by Ω the "octant" of points $x_j > 0$ $(j = 1, \ldots, n+1)$. The density of $(\mathbf{X}_1, \ldots, \mathbf{X}_{n+1})$ is concentrated on Ω and is given by

$$\alpha^{n+1} e^{-\alpha(x_1 + \cdots + x_{n+1})}$$

if $x_j > 0$. The variables $\mathbf{S}_1, \ldots, \mathbf{S}_{n+1}$ map Ω onto the region $\Omega^\star$ defined by $0 < s_1 \leq s_2 \leq \cdots \leq s_{n+1} < \infty$, and [see (1.11)] within $\Omega^\star$ the density of $(\mathbf{S}_1, \ldots, \mathbf{S}_{n+1})$ is given by $\alpha^{n+1} e^{-\alpha s_{n+1}}$. The marginal density of $\mathbf{S}_{n+1}$ is known to be the gamma density $\alpha^{n+1} s^n e^{-\alpha s}/n!$ and hence the *conditional density of the n-tuple* $(\mathbf{S}_1, \ldots, \mathbf{S}_n)$ *given that* $\mathbf{S}_{n+1} = s$ *equals* $n! s^{-n}$ *for* $0 < s_1 < \cdots < s_n < s$ (and zero elsewhere). In other words, given that $\mathbf{S}_{n+1} = s$ the variables $(\mathbf{S}_1, \ldots, \mathbf{S}_n)$ are uniformly distributed over their possible range. Comparing this with example (*b*) we may say that *given*

$\mathbf{S}_{n+1} = s$, *the variables* $(\mathbf{S}_1, \ldots, \mathbf{S}_n)$ *represent n points chosen independently and at random in the interval* $\overline{0, s}$ numbered in their natural order from left to right.

(*e*) *Another distribution connected with the exponential.* With a view to a surprising application we give a further example of a transformation. Let again $\mathbf{X}_1, \ldots, \mathbf{X}_n$ be independent variables with a common exponential distribution and $\mathbf{S}_n = \mathbf{X}_1 + \cdots + \mathbf{X}_n$. Consider the variables $\mathbf{U}_1, \ldots, \mathbf{U}_n$ defined by

$$\mathbf{U}_k = \frac{\mathbf{X}_k}{\mathbf{S}_n} \quad \textit{for} \quad k = 1, \ldots, n-1, \qquad \mathbf{U}_n = \mathbf{S}_n, \tag{3.3}$$

or, what amounts to the same,

$$\begin{aligned} \mathbf{X}_k &= \mathbf{U}_k\mathbf{U}_n \quad \textit{for} \quad k = 1, \ldots, n-1, \\ \mathbf{X}_n &= \mathbf{U}_n(1-\mathbf{U}_1 - \cdots - \mathbf{U}_{n-1}). \end{aligned} \tag{3.4}$$

The Jacobian of (3.4) equals $\mathbf{U}_n^{n-1}$. The joint density of $(\mathbf{X}_1, \ldots, \mathbf{X}_n)$ is concentrated on the region Ω defined by $x_k > 0$, and in it this density is given by $\alpha^n e^{-\alpha(x_1+\cdots+x_n)}$. It follows that the joint density of $(\mathbf{U}_1, \ldots, \mathbf{U}_n)$ is given by $\alpha^n u_n^{n-1} e^{-\alpha u_n}$ in the region $\Omega^\star$ defined by

$$u_1 + \cdots + u_{n-1} < 1, \qquad u_k > 0 \qquad k = 1, \ldots, n$$

and that it vanishes outside $\Omega^\star$. An integration with respect to u_n shows that the joint density for $(\mathbf{U}_1, \ldots, \mathbf{U}_{n-1})$ equals $(n-1)!$ in $\Omega^\star$ and 0 elsewhere. Comparing with example (*c*) we see that $(\mathbf{U}_1, \ldots, \mathbf{U}_{n-1})$ *has the same distribution as if* $\mathbf{U}_k$ *were the length of the* kth *interval in a random partition of* $\overline{0, 1}$ *by* $n - 1$ *points.*

(*f*) *A significance test in periodogram analysis and the covering theorem.* In practice, any continuous function of time t can be approximated by a trigonometric polynomial. If the function is a sample function of a stochastic process the coefficients become random variables, and the approximating polynomial may be written in the form

$$\sum_{\nu=1}^{n}(\mathbf{X}_\nu \cos \omega_\nu t + \mathbf{Y}_\nu \sin \omega_\nu t) \equiv \sum_{\nu=1}^{n} \mathbf{R}_\nu \cos(\omega_\nu t - \boldsymbol{\Phi}_\nu) \tag{3.5}$$

where $\mathbf{R}_\nu^2 = \mathbf{X}_\nu^2 + \mathbf{Y}_\nu^2$ and $\tan \boldsymbol{\Phi}_\nu = \mathbf{Y}_\nu/\mathbf{X}_\nu$. Conversely, reasonable assumptions on the random variables $\mathbf{X}_\nu$, $\mathbf{Y}_\nu$ lead to a stochastic process with sample functions given by (3.5). For a time it was fashionable to introduce models of this form and to detect "hidden periodicities" for sunspots, wheat prices, poetic creativity, etc. Such hidden periodicities used to be discovered as easily as witches in medieval times, but even strong faith must be fortified by a statistical test. The method is roughly as follows. A trigonometric polynomial of the form (3.5) with well-chosen frequencies $\omega_1, \ldots, \omega_n$ is fitted to some observational data, and a particularly large amplitude $\mathbf{R}_\nu$ is observed. One wishes to prove that this cannot be due to chance and hence that ω_ν is a true period. To test this conjecture one asks whether the large observed value of $\mathbf{R}_\nu$ is plausibly compatible with the hypothesis that all the n components play the same role. One assumes, accordingly, that the coefficients $\mathbf{X}_1, \ldots, \mathbf{Y}_n$ are mutually independent with a common normal distribution with zero expectation and variance σ^2. In this case (see II,3) the $\mathbf{R}_\nu^2$ are mutually independent and have a common exponential distribution with expectation $2\sigma^2$. If an observed value $\mathbf{R}_\nu^2$ deviated "significantly" from this predicted expectation one jumped to the conclusion that the hypothesis of equal weights was untenable, and $\mathbf{R}_\nu$ represented a "hidden periodicity."

The fallacy of this reasoning was exposed by R. A. Fisher (1929) who pointed out that the maximum among n independent observations does not obey the same probability distribution as each variable taken separately. The error of treating the worst case statistically as if it had been chosen at random is still common in medical statistics, but the reason for discussing the matter here is the surprising and amusing connection of Fisher's test of significance with covering theorems.

As only the ratios of the several components are significant we normalize the coefficients by letting

$$\mathbf{V}_j = \frac{\mathbf{R}_j^2}{\mathbf{R}_1^2 + \cdots + \mathbf{R}_n^2} \qquad j = 1, \ldots, n. \tag{3.6}$$

Since the $\mathbf{R}_j^2$ have a common exponential distribution we can use the preceding example with $\mathbf{X}_j = \mathbf{R}_j^2$. Then $\mathbf{V}_1 = \mathbf{U}_1, \ldots, \mathbf{V}_{n-1} = \mathbf{U}_{n-1}$, but $\mathbf{V}_n = 1 - \mathbf{U}_1 - \cdots - \mathbf{U}_{n-1}$. Accordingly, the n-tuple $(\mathbf{V}_1, \ldots, \mathbf{V}_n)$ *is distributed as the length of the n intervals into which* $\overline{0, 1}$ *is partitioned by a random distribution of* $n - 1$ *points. The probability that all* $\mathbf{V}_j$ *be less than a is therefore given by formula* I,(9.9) *of the covering theorem.* This result illustrates the occurrence of unexpected relations between apparently unconnected problems.[7] ►

[7] Fisher derived the distribution of the maximal term among the $\mathbf{V}_j$ in 1929 without knowledge of the covering theorem, and explained in 1940 the equivalence with the covering theorem after Stevens had proved the latter. [See papers No. 16 and 37 in Fisher's *Contributions to Mathematical Statistics*, John Wiley, New York (1950).] For an alternative derivation using Fourier analysis see U. Grenander and M. Rosenblatt (1957).

*4. A CHARACTERIZATION OF THE NORMAL DISTRIBUTION

Consider a non-degenerate linear transformation of coordinate variables

$$(4.1) \qquad \mathbf{Y}_1 = a_{11}\mathbf{X}_1 + a_{12}\mathbf{X}_2, \qquad \mathbf{Y}_2 = a_{21}\mathbf{X}_1 + a_{22}\mathbf{X}_2,$$

and suppose (without loss of generality) that the determinant $\Delta = 1$. If $\mathbf{X}_1$ and $\mathbf{X}_2$ are independent normal variables with variances σ_1^2 and σ_2^2 the distribution of the pair $(\mathbf{Y}_1, \mathbf{Y}_2)$ is normal with covariance $a_{11}a_{21}\sigma_1^2 + a_{12}a_{22}\sigma_2^2$ [see example (1.*d*)]. In this case there exist non-trivial choices of the coefficients a_{jk} such that $\mathbf{Y}_1$ and $\mathbf{Y}_2$ are independent. The following theorem shows that this property of the univariate normal distribution *is not shared by any other distribution.* We shall here prove it only for distributions with continuous densities, in which case it reduces to a lemma concerning the functional equation (4.3). By the use of characteristic functions the most general case is reduced to the *same* equation, and so our proof will really yield the theorem in its greatest generality (see XV,8). The elementary treatment of densities reveals better the basis of the theorem.

Theorem. *Suppose that* $\mathbf{X}_1$ *and* $\mathbf{X}_2$ *are independent, and that also the variables* $\mathbf{Y}_1$ *and* $\mathbf{Y}_2$ *of* (4.1) *are independent of each other. Then all four variables are normal, except if the transformation is trivial in the sense that either* $(\mathbf{Y}_1, \mathbf{Y}_2) = (a\mathbf{X}_1, b\mathbf{X}_2)$ *or* $(\mathbf{Y}_1, \mathbf{Y}_2) = (a\mathbf{X}_2, b\mathbf{X}_1)$.

The most interesting special case of (4.1) is presented by *rotations,* namely transformations of the form

$$(4.2) \qquad \begin{aligned} \mathbf{Y}_1 &= \mathbf{X}_1 \cos \omega + \mathbf{X}_2 \sin \omega \\ \mathbf{Y}_2 &= -\mathbf{X}_1 \sin \omega + \mathbf{X}_2 \cos \omega \end{aligned}$$

where ω is not a multiple of $\frac{1}{2}\pi$. Applying the theorem to such rotations we get

Corollary. *If* $\mathbf{X}_1$ *and* $\mathbf{X}_2$ *are independent and there exists one rotation* (4.2) *such that* $\mathbf{Y}_1$ *and* $\mathbf{Y}_2$ *are also independent, then* $\mathbf{X}_1$ *and* $\mathbf{X}_2$ *have normal distributions with the same variance. In this case* $\mathbf{Y}_1$ *and* $\mathbf{Y}_2$ *are independent for every* ω.

Example. *Maxwell distribution of velocities.* In his study of the velocity distributions of molecules in $\mathfrak{R}^3$ Maxwell assumed that in *every* Cartesian coordinate system the three components of the velocity are mutually

---

* This section treats a special topic and is not used in the sequel.

independent random variables with zero expectation. Applied to rotations leaving one axis fixed our corollary shows immediately that the three components are normally distributed with the same variance. As we saw in II,3 this implies the Maxwell distribution for velocities. ▶

The theorem has a long history going back to Maxwell's investigations. Purely probabilistic studies were initiated by M. Kac (1940) and S. Bernstein (1941), who proved our corollary assuming finite variances. An impressive number of authors contributed improvements and variants, sometimes by rather deep methods. The development culminates in a result proved by V. P. Skitovič.[8]

Now to the proof in the case of continuous densities. Denote the densities of $\mathbf{X}_j$ by w_j, those of $\mathbf{Y}_j$ by f_j. Under the assumption of the theorem we have [see (1.11)]

$$f_1(a_{11}x_1 + a_{12}x_2)f_2(a_{21}x_1 + a_{22}x_2) = w_1(x_1)\, w_2(x_2). \tag{4.3}$$

From this we shall deduce that

$$f_1(x) = \pm e^{\varphi_1(x)} \tag{4.4}$$

where φ_1 is a polynomial of degree 2 or lower. This implies the theorem since only normal densities are of this form.

For distributions with continuous densities the theorem is therefore contained in the following

Lemma. *Let f_1 and f_2 be continuous and not reducing to constants. Suppose that a functional equation of the form* (4.3) *holds with*

$$\Delta = a_{11}a_{22} - a_{12}a_{21} \neq 0.$$

If no coefficient a_{ij} vanishes, then (4.4) *holds with φ_1 a quadratic polynomial.*

If $a_{11}a_{12} \neq 0$ but $a_{21}a_{22} = 0$, then (4.4) *holds with φ_1 a linear function.*

(Needless to say, the same conclusions apply to f_2.)

A plausibility argument. Suppose that the functions in (4.3) are strictly positive and twice differentiable. Writing for abbreviation

$$\varphi_k = \log f_k, \qquad y_k = a_{k1}x_1 + a_{k2}x_2 \tag{4.5}$$

we get in this case

$$\varphi_1(y_1) + \varphi_2(y_2) = \log w_1(x_1) + \log w_2(x_2), \tag{4.6}$$

and from this by successive differentiations with respect to x_1 and x_2

$$a_{11}a_{12}\, \varphi_1''(y_1) + a_{21}a_{22}\, \varphi_2''(y_2) = 0. \tag{4.7}$$

[8] Izvestia Acad. Nauk SSSR, vol. 18 (1954) pp. 185–200. The theorem: Let $\mathbf{X}_1, \ldots, \mathbf{X}_n$ be mutually independent, $\mathbf{Y}_1 = \Sigma a_i\mathbf{X}_i$, and $\mathbf{Y}_2 = \Sigma b_i\mathbf{X}_i$ where no coefficient is 0. If $\mathbf{Y}_1$ and $\mathbf{Y}_2$ are independent the $\mathbf{X}_i$ are normally distributed.

Letting x_1 and x_2 vary so as to keep y_2 constant we see that $\varphi_1''(y_1) = \text{const}$ and so φ_1 is indeed a polynomial of first or second degree. The following proof is based on this argument except that derivatives are replaced by differences.

Proof *of the lemma.* Assume first that *no coefficient a_{jk} vanishes.* We begin by showing that the functions f_k *have no zeros.* Assume the contrary. There exists then an open domain Ω in which the two members of (4.3) have no zeros and on whose boundary they vanish. But the right side of (4.3) vanishes at (x_1, x_2) iff either $w_1(x_1) = 0$ or $w_2(x_2) = 0$ and so the boundary consists of segments of lines parallel to the axes. The same argument applied to the left side shows that the boundary consists of segments of lines on which either $y_1 = \text{const}$ or $y_2 = \text{const}$. This contradiction shows that no boundary exists.

We are now free to assume the f_k strictly positive and to start from (4.6). Define the difference operator Δ (depending on two arbitrary constants) by

$$\begin{aligned}\Delta u(x_1, x_2) = u(x_1+h_1, x_2+h_2) - u(x_1+h_1, x_2-h_2) - \\ - u(x_1-h_1, x_2+h_2) + u(x_1-h_1, x_2-h_2).\end{aligned} \tag{4.8}$$

When u depends only on one variable x_j we have $\Delta u = 0$, and from (4.6) we get therefore $\Delta\varphi_1 + \Delta\varphi_2 = 0$ [replacing (4.7)]. Now it is easily verified that $\Delta\varphi_k$ is a function of y_k alone, and hence the relation $\Delta\varphi_1 + \Delta y_2 = 0$ implies that $\Delta\varphi_1$ is a constant depending, of course, on h_1 and h_2. For an appropriate choice of h_1 and h_2 we conclude that with t arbitrary

$$\varphi_1(y_1+t) + \varphi_1(y_1-t) - 2\varphi_1(y_1) = \lambda_1(t) \tag{4.9}$$

does not depend on y_1.

This equation replaces the conclusion $\varphi_1''(y_1) = \text{const}$ of the plausibility argument and we show that *every continuous solution of* (4.9) *reduces to a quadratic polynomial.*

The function Φ defined by

$$\Phi(x) = \varphi_1(x) + \alpha + \beta x + \gamma x^2 \tag{4.10}$$

satisfies the identity

$$\Phi(x+t) + \Phi(x-t) - 2\Phi(x) = \lambda(t) \tag{4.11}$$

with $\lambda(t) = \lambda_1(t) + 2\gamma t^2$. We choose α, β, γ such that

$$\Phi(0) = \Phi(-1) = \Phi(1) = 0$$

and prove that every continuous function Φ satisfying these conditions vanishes identically. Assuming that Φ has a positive maximum we conclude from (4.11) that $\lambda(t) \leq 0$ in a neighborhood of the origin and $\lambda(t) < 0$ for some t. It follows then that Φ can have no minimum value, and as Φ vanishes at the three points $-1, 0, 1$ it must vanish identically in $\overline{-1, 1}$. It is then clear from (4.11) that $\Phi(x) = 0$ for all x and hence $\varphi_1(x) = -\alpha - \beta x - \gamma x^2$. This completes the proof when no coefficient a_{jk} vanishes.

The case when a coefficient vanishes is trivial. Assume, for example, that $a_{21} = 0$ but $a_{11} \neq 0$ and $a_{12} \neq 0$. Then $f_1(a_{11}x_1 + a_{12}x_2)$ is the product of a function of x_1 and a function of x_2, and so $f_1(s+t) = f_1(s)f_1(t)$. This functional equation occurred repeatedly, and we know that it implies $f_1(s) = e^{\lambda s}$. ►

5. MATRIX NOTATION. THE COVARIANCE MATRIX

The notation employed in section 1 is messy and becomes more so in higher dimensions. Elegance and economy of thought may be achieved by the use of matrix notation.

For ease of reference we summarize the few facts of matrix theory and the notations used in the sequel. The basic rule is: first rows, then columns. Thus an α by β matrix A has α rows and β columns; its elements are denoted by a_{jk}, the first index indicating the row. If B is a β by γ matrix with elements b_{jk} the product AB is the α by γ matrix with elements $a_{j1}b_{1k} + a_{j2}b_{2k} + \cdots + a_{j\beta}b_{\beta k}$. No product is defined if the number of columns of A does not agree with the number of rows of B. The associative law $(AB)C = A(BC)$ holds, whereas in general $AB \neq BA$. The *transpose* A^T is the β by α matrix with elements $a^T_{jk} = a_{kj}$. Obviously $(AB)^T = B^TA^T$.

A one by α matrix with a single row is called a *row vector*; a matrix with a single column, a *column vector*.[9] A row vector $r = (r_1, \ldots, r_\alpha)$ is easily printed, but a column vector is better indicated by its transpose $c^T = (c_1, \ldots, c_\alpha)$. Note that *cr is an α by α matrix* (of the "multiplication table" type) *whereas rc is a one by one matrix*, or scalar. In the case $\alpha = 2$

$$cr = \begin{pmatrix} c_1r_1 & c_1r_2 \\ c_2r_1 & c_2r_2 \end{pmatrix}, \qquad rc = (r_1c_1 + r_2c_2).$$

The *zero vector* has all components equal to 0.

By *identity matrix* is meant a square matrix with ones in the main diagonal and zeros at all other places. If I is the identity matrix with r rows and columns and A an r by r matrix, obviously $IA = AI = A$. By *inverse* of A is meant a matrix A^{-1} such that $AA^{-1} = A^{-1}A = I$. [Only square matrices can have inverses. The inverse is unique, for if B is any inverse of A we have $AB = I$ and by the associative law $A^{-1} = (A^{-1}A)B = B$.] A square matrix without inverse is called *singular*. The following elementary criterion holds. A matrix A is singular iff there exists a non-zero row vector x such that $xA = 0$. If A is singular so is its transpose A^T.

---

[9] This is really an abuse of language. In a concrete case x_1 may represent pounds and x_2 cows; then (x_1, x_2) is no "vector" in the strict sense.

A square matrix A is *symmetric* if $a_{jk} = a_{kj}$, that is, if $A^T = A$. The *quadratic form associated with a symmetric r by r matrix A* is defined by

$$xAx^T = \sum_{j,k=1}^{r} a_{jk}x_jx_k$$

where $x_1, \ldots, x_r$ are indeterminates. The matrix is *positive definite* if $xAx^T > 0$ for all non-zero vectors x. It follows from the last criterion that a positive definite matrix is non-singular. (For orthogonal matrices or rotations see section 6*a*.)

From now on we denote a point of the r-dimensional space $\mathfrak{R}^r$ by a single letter to be interpreted as a *row vector*. Thus $x = (x_1, \ldots, x_r)$ and $f(x) = f(x_1, \ldots, x_r)$, etc. Inequalities are to be interpreted coordinatewise: $x < y$ iff $x_k < y_k$ for $k = 1, \ldots, r$ and similarly for other inequalities. In the plane $\mathfrak{R}^2$ the relation $x < y$ may be read as "x lies southwest of y." A novel feature of this notation is that two points need not stand in either of the relations $x \leq y$ or $y < x$, that is, in higher dimensions the inequality $<$ introduces only a partial ordering.

We write $\mathbf{X} = (\mathbf{X}_1, \ldots, \mathbf{X}_r)$ for the row vector of the coordinate variables and use this notation for random variables in general (mainly for normally distributed variables).

If the variables $\mathbf{X}_1, \ldots, \mathbf{X}_r$ have expectations $\mathbf{E}(\mathbf{X}_j)$ we write $\mathbf{E}(\mathbf{X})$ *for the row vector with components* $\mathbf{E}(\mathbf{X}_j)$. The vector $\mathbf{X} - \mathbf{E}(\mathbf{X})$ has zero expectation. More generally, if $\mathbf{M}$ is a matrix whose elements $\mathbf{M}_{jk}$ are random variables we write $\mathbf{E}(\mathbf{M})$ for the matrix of elements $\mathbf{E}(\mathbf{M}_{jk})$ assuming that it exists.

Definition. *If* $\mathbf{E}(\mathbf{X}) = 0$ *the covariance matrix* $\text{Var}(\mathbf{X})$ *of* $\mathbf{X}$ *is the symmetric r by r matrix with elements* $\mathbf{E}(\mathbf{X}_j\mathbf{X}_k)$ *(provided they all exist). In other words*

$$\text{Var}(\mathbf{X}) = \mathbf{E}(\mathbf{X}^T\mathbf{X}). \tag{5.1}$$

For arbitrary $\mathbf{X}$ *we define* $\text{Var}(\mathbf{X})$ *to be the same as* $\text{Var}(\mathbf{X}-\mathbf{E}(\mathbf{X}))$.

The use of row vectors necessitates writing a *linear transformation from* $\mathfrak{R}^r$ *to* $\mathfrak{R}^m$ in the form

$$\mathbf{Y} = \mathbf{X}A, \tag{5.2}$$

that is,

$$y_k = \sum_{j=1}^{r} a_{jk}x_j \qquad k = 1, \ldots, m \tag{5.3}$$

where A is an r by m matrix. Obviously $\mathbf{E}(\mathbf{Y}) = \mathbf{E}(\mathbf{X})A$ whenever $\mathbf{E}(\mathbf{X})$ exists. To find the variances we assume without loss of generality $\mathbf{E}(\mathbf{X}) = 0$. Then $\mathbf{E}(\mathbf{Y}) = 0$ and

$$\mathbf{E}(\mathbf{Y}^T\mathbf{Y}) = \mathbf{E}(A^T\mathbf{X}^T\mathbf{X}A) = A^T\mathbf{E}(\mathbf{X}^T\mathbf{X})A. \tag{5.4}$$

We thus have the important result that

$$\text{Var}(\mathbf{Y}) = A^T \text{Var}(\mathbf{X})A. \tag{5.5}$$

Of particular interest is the special case $m = 1$ when

$$\mathbf{Y} = a_1\mathbf{X}_1 + \cdots + a_r\mathbf{X}_r \tag{5.6}$$

is an ordinary random variable. Here Var(**Y**) is the (scalar) quadratic form

$$\text{Var}(\mathbf{Y}) = \sum_{j,k=1}^{r} \mathbf{E}(\mathbf{X}_j\mathbf{X}_k)a_j a_k. \tag{5.7}$$

The linear form (5.6) vanishes with probability one if $\text{Var}(\mathbf{Y}) = 0$ and in this case every region outside the hyperplane $\Sigma a_k x_k = 0$ carries zero probability. The probability distribution is then concentrated on an $(r-1)$-dimensional manifold and is *degenerate* when considered in r dimensions. We have now proved that *the covariance matrix of any non-degenerate probability distribution is positive definite.* Conversely, every such matrix may serve as covariance matrix of a normal density (see theorem 3 of the next section).

6. NORMAL DENSITIES AND DISTRIBUTIONS

Throughout this section Q stands for a symmetric r by r matrix, and $q(x)$ for the associated quadratic form

$$q(x) = \sum_{j,k=1}^{r} q_{jk}x_j x_k = xQx^T \tag{6.1}$$

where $x = (x_1, \ldots, x_r)$ is a *row* vector. Densities in $\mathcal{R}^r$ defined by an exponential with a quadratic form in the exponent are a natural counterpart of the normal density on the line, and we start therefore from the following

Definition. *A density φ in r dimensions is called normal*[10] *and centered at the origin if it is of the form*

$$\varphi(x) = \gamma^{-1} \cdot e^{-\frac{1}{2}q(x)} \tag{6.2}$$

where γ is a constant. A normal density centered at $a = (a_1, a_2, \ldots, a_r)$ is given by $\varphi(x-a)$.

The special case of two dimensions was discussed in examples (1.*d*) and (2.*a*).

---

10 "*Degenerate*" normal distributions will be introduced at the end of this section.

To see the result of a non-singular linear transformation from $\mathbf{X} = (\mathbf{X}_1, \ldots, \mathbf{X}_r)$ to $\mathbf{Y} = (\mathbf{Y}_1, \ldots, \mathbf{Y}_r)$ we write it in the form $\mathbf{Y} = \mathbf{X}A$ where A is an r by r matrix with inverse $B = A^{-1}$. As was shown in section 1, the density of $\mathbf{Y}$ is obtained from (6.2) by the substitution $x = yB$ and multiplication by the determinant of B. Now

$$q(x) = xQx^T = yBQB^Ty^T. \tag{6.3}$$

It follows that the density of $\mathbf{Y}$ is again of the form (6.2) and we have thus the important

Lemma. *If* $\mathbf{X}$ *has density* (6.2) *and* A *is non-singular, then* $\mathbf{Y} = \mathbf{X}A$ *has a normal density induced by the matrix* $BQB^T = A^{-1}Q(A^{-1})^T$.

Consider now in particular the substitution defined by

$$y_1 = x_1, \ldots, y_{r-1} = x_{r-1}, \qquad y_r = q_{1r}x_1 + \cdots + q_{rr}x_r. \tag{6.4}$$

To show that it is non-singular we must verify that $q_{rr} \neq 0$. But if we had $q_{rr} = 0$, then for fixed values of $x_1, \ldots, x_{r-1}$ the density (6.2) would take on the form $\gamma^{-1}e^{-ax_r+b}$ and the integral with respect to x_r would diverge. Thus $q_{rr} \neq 0$, and the standard completion to squares shows that $q(x)$ reduces to the sum of y_r^2/q_{rr} and a quadratic form q' in the remaining $r - 1$ variables:

$$q(x) = \frac{1}{q_{rr}}\, y_r^2 + q'(y). \tag{6.5}$$

This induces a corresponding factoring of the density for $\mathbf{Y}$, and one sees that the marginal densities for $\mathbf{Y}_r$ and $(\mathbf{Y}_1, \ldots, \mathbf{Y}_{r-1}) = (\mathbf{X}_1, \ldots, \mathbf{X}_{r-1})$ are again normal. Proceeding by induction we get

Theorem 1. *All marginal densities of a normal density are again normal.*

The linear transformation leading to (6.5) results in a normal vector $(\mathbf{X}_1, \ldots, \mathbf{X}_{r-1}, \mathbf{Y}_r)$ such that $\mathbf{Y}_r$ is independent of $(\mathbf{X}_1, \ldots, \mathbf{X}_{r-1})$. Applying the same reduction to $(\mathbf{X}_1, \ldots, \mathbf{X}_{r-1})$ we get a vector

$$(\mathbf{X}_1, \ldots, \mathbf{X}_{r-2}, \mathbf{Z}_{r-1}, \mathbf{Y}_r)$$

such that $\mathbf{Y}_r$ and $\mathbf{Z}_{r-1}$ are independent of each other and of $(\mathbf{X}_1, \ldots, \mathbf{X}_{r-2})$. Proceeding in like manner and remembering that a superposition of linear transformations is equivalent to a single linear transformation we conclude that there exists a non-singular linear transformation $\mathbf{X} = \mathbf{Y}A^{-1}$ such that $\mathbf{Y} = (\mathbf{Y}_1, \ldots, \mathbf{Y}_r)$ has mutually independent normal components $\mathbf{Y}_k$. For reasons of symmetry $\mathbf{E}(\mathbf{Y}_k) = 0$. Putting $\mathrm{Var}(\mathbf{Y}_k) = \sigma_k^2$ we see that $\mathbf{Y} = (\mathbf{Y}_1, \ldots, \mathbf{Y}_r)$ has a normal density of the form (6.2) induced by the *diagonal matrix* D with elements σ_k^{-2}. [The norming constant γ is given by $\gamma^2 = (2\pi)^r \det D^{-1}$.] From the lemma it is seen that $Q = ADA^T$.

On the other hand, it follows from (5.5) that the covariance matrix $\mathrm{Var}(\mathbf{X}) = \mathbf{E}(\mathbf{X}\mathbf{X}^T)$ exists and that $D^{-1} = A^T\,\mathrm{Var}(\mathbf{X})A$. Thus $\mathrm{Var}(\mathbf{X}) = Q^{-1}$ and since determinants multiply we have

Theorem 2. *If* $\mathbf{X} = (\mathbf{X}_1, \ldots, \mathbf{X}_r)$ *has the normal density* (6.2) *then* $Q^{-1} = \mathrm{Var}(\mathbf{X})$ *and*

$$\gamma^2 = (2\pi)^r \cdot \det Q^{-1}. \tag{6.6}$$

Corollary. *If* $(\mathbf{X}_1, \mathbf{X}_2)$ *is normally distributed then* $\mathbf{X}_1$ *and* $\mathbf{X}_2$ *are independent iff* $\mathrm{Cov}(\mathbf{X}_1, \mathbf{X}_2) = 0$, *that is, iff* $\mathbf{X}_1$ *and* $\mathbf{X}_2$ *are uncorrelated.*

More generally, if $(\mathbf{X}_1, \ldots, \mathbf{X}_r)$ has a normal density then $(\mathbf{X}_1, \ldots, \mathbf{X}_n)$ and $(\mathbf{X}_{n+1}, \ldots, \mathbf{X}_r)$ are independent iff $\mathrm{Cov}(\mathbf{X}_j, \mathbf{X}_k) = 0$ for $j \leq n$, $k > n$.

Warning. The corollary depends on the joint density of $(\mathbf{X}_1, \mathbf{X}_2)$ being normal and *does not apply if it is only known that the marginal densities of* $\mathbf{X}_1$ *and* $\mathbf{X}_2$ *are normal.* In the latter case the density of $(\mathbf{X}_1, \mathbf{X}_2)$ need not be normal and, in fact, need not exist. This fact is frequently misunderstood (see problems 2–3).

Theorem 3. *A matrix M is the covariance matrix of a normal density iff it is positive definite.*

Since the density is induced by the matrix $Q = M^{-1}$ an equivalent formulation is: *A matrix Q induces a normal density* (6.2) *iff it is positive definite.*

Proof. We saw at the end of section 5 that every covariance matrix of a density is positive definite. The converse is trivial when $r = 1$ and we proceed by induction. Assume Q positive definite. For $x_1 = 0, \ldots, x_{r-1} = 0$ we get $q(x) = q_{rr}x_r^2$ and hence $q_{rr} > 0$. Under this hypothesis we saw that q may be reduced to the form (6.5). Choosing x_r such that $y_r = 0$ we see that the positive definiteness of Q implies $q'(x) > 0$ for all choices of $x_1, \ldots, x_{r-1}$. By the induction hypothesis therefore q' corresponds to a normal density in $r - 1$ dimensions. From (6.5) it is now obvious that q corresponds to a normal density in r dimensions, and this completes the proof. ▶

Example. *Sample mean and variance.* In statistics the random variables

$$\hat{\mathbf{X}} = \frac{1}{r}(\mathbf{X}_1 + \cdots + \mathbf{X}_r), \qquad \hat{\boldsymbol{\sigma}}^2 = \frac{1}{r}\sum_{k=1}^{r}(\mathbf{X}_k - \hat{\mathbf{X}})^2 \tag{6.7}$$

are called the sample mean and sample variance of $\mathbf{X} = (\mathbf{X}_1, \ldots, \mathbf{X}_r)$. It is a curious fact that *if* $\mathbf{X}_1, \ldots, \mathbf{X}_r$ *are independent normal variables with* $\mathbf{E}(\mathbf{X}_k) = 0$, $\mathbf{E}(\mathbf{X}_k^2) = \sigma^2$, *the random variables* $\hat{\mathbf{X}}$ *and* $\hat{\boldsymbol{\sigma}}^2$ *are independent.*[11] The proof illustrates the applicability of the preceding results. We put $\mathbf{Y}_k = \mathbf{X}_k - \hat{\mathbf{X}}$ for $k = 1, \ldots, r-1$ but $\mathbf{Y}_r = \hat{\mathbf{X}}$. The transformation from $\mathbf{X}$ to $\mathbf{Y} = (\mathbf{Y}_1, \ldots, \mathbf{Y}_n)$ being linear and non-singular, $\mathbf{Y}$ has a normal density. Now $\mathbf{E}(\mathbf{Y}_k\mathbf{Y}_r) = 0$ for $k = 1, \ldots, r-1$ and so $\mathbf{Y}_r$ is independent of $(\mathbf{Y}_1, \ldots, \mathbf{Y}_{r-1})$. But

$$(6.8) \qquad r\hat{\boldsymbol{\sigma}}^2 = \mathbf{Y}_1^2 + \cdots + \mathbf{Y}_{r-1}^2 + (\mathbf{Y}_1 + \cdots + \mathbf{Y}_{r-1})^2$$

depends only on $\mathbf{Y}_1, \ldots, \mathbf{Y}_{r-1}$, and thus $\hat{\boldsymbol{\sigma}}^2$ is indeed independent of $\mathbf{Y}_r = \hat{\mathbf{X}}$. ►

We conclude this general theory by an interpretation of (6.5) in terms of *conditional densities* which leads to a general formulation of the regression theory explained for the two-dimensional case in example (2.*a*).

To obtain the conditional density of $\mathbf{X}_r$ for given $\mathbf{X}_1 = x_1, \ldots, \mathbf{X}_{r-1} = x_{r-1}$ we must divide the density of $(\mathbf{X}_1, \ldots, \mathbf{X}_r)$ by the marginal density for $(\mathbf{X}_1, \ldots, \mathbf{X}_{r-1})$. In view of (6.5) the result is the one-dimensional normal density with expectation

$$(6.9) \qquad -(q_{1r}x_1 + \cdots + q_{r-1,r}x_{r-1})/q_{rr} = a_1x_1 + \cdots + a_{r-1}x_{r-1}$$

and variance q_{rr}^{-1}. (Here we put for abbreviation $a_k = -q_{kr}/q_{rr}$.) Accordingly

$$(6.10) \qquad \mathbf{E}(\mathbf{X}_r \mid \mathbf{X}_1, \ldots, \mathbf{X}_{r-1}) = a_1\mathbf{X}_1 + \cdots + a_{r-1}\mathbf{X}_{r-1}.$$

We saw also that

$$(6.11) \qquad \mathbf{T} = \mathbf{X}_r - a_1\mathbf{X}_1 - \cdots - a_{r-1}\mathbf{X}_{r-1}$$

is independent of $(\mathbf{X}_1, \ldots, \mathbf{X}_{r-1})$, and this property uniquely characterizes the coefficients $a_k = -q_{kr}/q_{rr}$. We have thus

Theorem 4. *If* $(\mathbf{X}_1, \ldots, \mathbf{X}_r)$ *has a normal density, the conditional density of* $\mathbf{X}_r$ *for given* $\mathbf{X}_1, \ldots, \mathbf{X}_{r-1}$ *is again normal. Furthermore, the conditional expectation* (6.10) *is the unique linear function of* $\mathbf{X}_1, \ldots, \mathbf{X}_{r-1}$ *making* $\mathbf{T}$ *independent of* $(\mathbf{X}_1, \ldots, \mathbf{X}_{r-1})$. *The conditional variance equals* $\text{Var}(\mathbf{T}) = q_{rr}^{-1}$.

General Normal Distributions

It follows from the lemma that if $\mathbf{X} = (\mathbf{X}_1, \ldots, \mathbf{X}_r)$ has a normal density, every non-zero linear combination $\mathbf{Y}_1 = a_1\mathbf{X}_1 + \cdots + a_r\mathbf{X}_r$ also has a normal density. The same is true of every pair $(\mathbf{Y}_1, \mathbf{Y}_2)$ provided that no linear relationship $c_1\mathbf{Y}_1 + c_2\mathbf{Y}_2 = 0$ holds. In this exceptional case the probability distribution of $(\mathbf{Y}_1, \mathbf{Y}_2)$ is concentrated on the line

[11] That this fact characterizes the normal distribution in $\mathfrak{R}^1$ was shown by Geary and by Lukacs.

with the equation $c_1y_1 + c_2y_2 = 0$ and hence it is singular *if viewed as a two-dimensional distribution.* For many purposes it is desirable to preserve the term normal distribution also for degenerate distributions concentrated on a lower-dimensional manifold, say on a particular axis. The simplest general definition is as follows: *The distribution of* $\mathbf{Y} = (\mathbf{Y}_1, \ldots, \mathbf{Y}_\rho)$ *is normal if there exists a vector* $\mathbf{X} = (\mathbf{X}_1, \ldots, \mathbf{X}_r)$ *with normal r-dimensional density such that* $\mathbf{Y} = a + \mathbf{X}A$ where A is a (constant) r by ρ matrix and $a = (a_1, \ldots, a_\rho)$. If $\rho > r$ the distribution of $\mathbf{Y}$ is degenerate in ρ dimensions. For $\rho \leq r$ it is non-degenerate iff the ρ forms defining $\mathbf{Y}_k$ are linearly independent.

6a. Appendix: Rotations

The construction in the proofs of theorems 1 and 2 shows that *there exists an r by r matrix A such that* $\mathbf{Y} = \mathbf{X}A$ *has mutually independent components* $\mathbf{Y}_k$, *and* $\mathbf{Y}_k$ *depends only on* $\mathbf{X}_1, \ldots, \mathbf{X}_k$. (The matrix A has only zeros above the diagonal.) It must be realized that such linear transformations are sometimes probabilistically meaningless. Thus, if $\mathbf{X}_1$ stands for a population size and $\mathbf{X}_2$ for temperature there exists essentially only one natural system of coordinate variables. On the other hand, if the sample space is really the Euclidean plane (rather than the combinatorial product of two axes) the coordinate system may be chosen in many equivalent ways. In such situations it is desirable to choose the coordinate system so as to obtain the simplest form for a given normal density. In this connection we are no longer concerned with general linear transformations but only with *rotations of coordinate axes.*

The following theorem is a direct consequence of the well-known reduction of quadratic forms (or symmetric matrices) to a normal form. It will not be used in this book and is stated for reference only. The proof is easier than would appear in general matrix theory (where more is proved at the same time). The relevant definitions and individual steps are listed here in the hope that some readers may find it interesting to complete the proof. This should be a good exercise in matrix calculus. The notations and centering are those of section 6. In particular $M = (m_{jk})$ is the covariance matrix in the given coordinate system.

Theorem. *Given a normal density in* $\mathfrak{R}^r$ *the coordinate axes can be rotated in such a way that the new coordinate variables are mutually independent normal variables.*

The underlying definitions are as follows. A row vector x is a unit vector if $xx^T = \Sigma x_k^2 = 1$. The angle ω between two unit vectors x and $\bar{x}$ is defined by $\cos \omega = x\bar{x}^T = \Sigma x_k\bar{x}_k$. An r by r matrix A is *orthogonal* if the transformation $y = xA$ sends unit vectors into unit vectors. Its determinant equals ± 1. *Rotations* are transformations induced by orthogonal matrices with determinant 1.

Three facts concerning rotations are required.

(1) A matrix A is orthogonal iff $AA^T = A^TA = I$.

(2) A rotation preserves angles between unit vectors.

(3) There exists an orthogonal matrix A whose last row is an arbitrarily prescribed unit vector.

For a *proof* of the theorem one has to verify successively the following facts.

(1) There exists a unit vector ξ such that $\Sigma m_{jk}\xi_j\xi_k \geq \Sigma m_{jk}x_jx_k$ for all unit vectors x.

(2) If $\xi = (0, 0, \ldots, 0, 1)$ is such a maximizing vector, then $m_{rk} = 0$ for $k = 1, \ldots, r-1$.

(3) There exists a rotation changing a maximizing vector ξ into $(0, \ldots, 0, 1)$. In the rotated coordinate system the last coordinate variable is independent of the first $r - 1$ coordinate variables. This reduces the problem from r to $r - 1$ dimensions, and one proceeds in like manner using rotations leaving the last axis fixed. The fact that $\mathbf{Y} = \mathbf{X}A$ has independent components means that A^TMA is diagonal.

*7. STATIONARY NORMAL PROCESSES

The purpose of this section is partly to supply examples of normal distributions, partly to derive some relations of considerable use in the theory of discrete stochastic processes and time series. They are of an analytic character and easily separated from the deeper stochastic analysis. In fact, we shall be concerned only with finite-dimensional normal densities or, what amounts to the same, their covariance matrices. The reference to random variables is essential for probabilistic intuition and as a preparation for applications, but at the present stage we are concerned only with their joint distributions; the random variables themselves are used merely as a convenient way of describing all marginal densities by indicating the corresponding collections $(\mathbf{X}_{\alpha_1}, \ldots, \mathbf{X}_{\alpha_k})$. By the same token a reference to an infinite sequence $\{\mathbf{X}_k\}$ implies merely that the number of terms in $(\mathbf{X}_1, \ldots, \mathbf{X}_n)$ may be taken arbitrarily large.

We shall, in fact, consider a doubly infinite sequence $\{\ldots, \mathbf{X}_{-2}, \mathbf{X}_{-1}, \ldots\}$. By this we mean simply that corresponding to each finite collection $(\mathbf{X}_{n_1}, \ldots, \mathbf{X}_{n_r})$ we are given a *normal* density with the obvious consistency rules. The sequence is *stationary* if these distributions are invariant under time shifts, that is, if all r-tuples of the form $(\mathbf{X}_{n_1+\nu}, \ldots, \mathbf{X}_{n_r+\nu})$ with

* Not used in the sequel. In particular, section 8 can be read independently. (See also XIX,8.)

fixed $n_1, \ldots, n_r$ have a common distribution independent of ν. For $r = 1$ this implies that the expectations and variances are constant, and hence there is no loss in generality in assuming that $\mathbf{E}(\mathbf{X}_n) = 0$. The joint distributions are completely determined by the covariances $\rho_{jk} = \mathbf{E}(\mathbf{X}_j\mathbf{X}_k)$ and the stationarity requires that ρ_{jk} depends only on the difference $|k - j|$. Accordingly we put $\rho_{j,j+n} = r_n$. Thus

$$r_n = \mathbf{E}(\mathbf{X}_k\mathbf{X}_{k+n}) = \mathbf{E}(\mathbf{X}_{k-n}\mathbf{X}_k), \tag{7.1}$$

whence $r_n = r_{-n}$. In effect we are dealing only with sequences of numbers r_n that can serve as covariances for a stationary process.

Throughout this section $\{\mathbf{Z}_n\}$ stands for a doubly infinite sequence of *mutually independent normal variables* normed by

$$\mathbf{E}(\mathbf{Z}_n) = 0, \qquad \mathbf{E}(\mathbf{Z}_n^2) = 1. \tag{7.2}$$

Three methods of constructing stationary sequences in terms of a given sequence $\{\mathbf{Z}_n\}$ will be described. They are in constant use in time series analysis and may serve as an exercise in routine manipulations.

Examples. (*a*) *Generalized moving average processes.* With arbitrary constants $b_0, b_1, \ldots, b_N$ put

$$\mathbf{X}_n = b_0\mathbf{Z}_n + b_1\mathbf{Z}_{n-1} + \cdots + b_N\mathbf{Z}_{n-N}. \tag{7.3}$$

In the special case of equal coefficients $b_k = 1/(N+1)$ the variable $\mathbf{X}_n$ is an arithmetic average of the type used in time series analysis to "smooth data" (that is, to eliminate local irregularities). In the general case (7.3) represents a linear operator taking the stationary sequence $\{\mathbf{Z}_n\}$ into a new stationary sequence $\{\mathbf{X}_n\}$. The fashionable term for such operations is "filters." The sequence $\{\mathbf{X}_n\}$ has covariances

$$r_k = r_{-k} = \mathbf{E}(\mathbf{X}_n\mathbf{X}_{n+k}) = \sum_\nu b_\nu b_{\nu+k} \qquad (k \geq 0) \tag{7.4}$$

the series having finitely many terms only.

Since $2\,|b_\nu b_{\nu+k}| \leq b_\nu^2 + b_{\nu+k}^2$ the expression (7.4) makes sense also for infinite sequences such that $\Sigma b_\nu^2 < \infty$. It is easily seen that the limit of a sequence of covariance matrices is again a covariance matrix and, letting $N \to \infty$, we conclude that *for any sequence* $b_0, b_1, b_2, \ldots$ *such that* $\Sigma b_n^2 < \infty$ *the numbers* r_k *of* (7.4) *may serve as covariances of a stationary process* $\{\mathbf{X}_n\}$. Formally we get for the new process

$$\mathbf{X}_n = \sum_{k=0}^{\infty} b_k\mathbf{Z}_{n-k}. \tag{7.5}$$

It can be shown without difficulty that every stationary process with covariances (7.4) is of this form, but the relation (7.5) involves infinitely many coordinates and we cannot justify it at present. (See XIX,8.)

(*b*) *The auto-regression process.* Since the inception of time series analysis various theoretical models have been proposed to explain empirical phenomena such as economic time series, sunspots, and observed (or imagined) periodicities. The most popular model assumes that the variables $\mathbf{X}_n$ of the process are related to our sequence $\mathbf{Z}_n$ of independent normal variables by an *auto-regression equation* of the form

$$a_0\mathbf{X}_n + a_1\mathbf{X}_{n-1} + \cdots + a_N\mathbf{X}_{n-N} = \mathbf{Z}_n. \tag{7.6}$$

This model is based on the empirical assumption that the value of the variable $\mathbf{X}_n$ at epoch n (price, supply, or intensity) depends on its past development superimposed on a "random disturbance" $\mathbf{Z}_n$ which is not related to the past. As is frequently the case, the assumption of *linear* dependence serves to simplify (or make possible) a theoretical analysis. More general models may be obtained by letting $N \to \infty$ or by letting the $\mathbf{Z}_n$ be the variables of another stationary process.

If $a_0 \neq 0$ one may choose $(\mathbf{X}_0, \ldots, \mathbf{X}_{N-1})$ in an arbitrary way and then calculate $\mathbf{X}_N, \mathbf{X}_{N+1}, \ldots$ and $\mathbf{X}_{-1}, \mathbf{X}_{-2}, \ldots$ recursively. In this sense (7.6) determines a process, but we ask whether there exists a *stationary* solution.

To answer this question we rewrite (7.6) in a form not involving the immediate predecessors of $\mathbf{X}_n$. Consider (7.6) with n replaced successively by $n-1, n-2, \ldots, n-\nu$. Multiply these equations by $b_1, b_2, \ldots, b_\nu$, respectively, and add to (7.6). The variables $\mathbf{X}_{n-1}, \ldots, \mathbf{X}_{n-\nu}$ will not appear in the new equation iff the b_j are such that

$$a_0b_1 + a_1b_0 = 0, \ldots, \quad a_0b_\nu + a_1b_{\nu-1} + \cdots + a_\nu b_0 = 0 \tag{7.7}$$

with $b_0 = 1$. The resulting identity is then of the form

$$a_0\mathbf{X}_n = b_0\mathbf{Z}_n + b_1\mathbf{Z}_{n-1} + \cdots + b_\nu\mathbf{Z}_{n-\nu} + \mathbf{Y}_{n,\nu} \tag{7.8}$$

where $\mathbf{Y}_{n,\nu}$ is a linear combination of $\mathbf{X}_{n-\nu-1}, \ldots, \mathbf{X}_{n-N-\nu-1}$ (with coefficients that are of no interest). In (7.8) we have expressed the variable $\mathbf{X}_n$ as a resultant of the chance contributions at epochs $n, n-1, \ldots, n-\nu$ and a variable $\mathbf{Y}_{n,\nu}$ representing the influence of the time before epoch $n-\nu$. As $\nu \to \infty$ this time becomes the "infinitely remote past" and in most situations it will have no influence. In passing to the limit we shall (at least temporarily) assume this to be the case, that is, we are looking for a process satisfying a limiting relation of the form

$$a_0\mathbf{X}_n = \sum_{k=0}^{\infty} b_k\mathbf{Z}_{n-k}. \tag{7.9}$$

(Roughly speaking we assume that the residual variables $\mathbf{Y}_{n,\nu}$ tend to zero. Other possible limits will be studied in the next example.)

Processes of the form (7.9) are the object of example (*a*) and we saw that a stationary solution exists whenever $\Sigma b_k^2 < \infty$. (If the series diverges, not even the expressions for the covariances make sense.) To solve the equations (7.7) for b_k we use the formal generating functions

$$A(s) = \Sigma a_k s^k, \qquad B(s) = \Sigma b_k s^k. \tag{7.10}$$

The equations (7.7) hold iff $A(s)\, B(s) = a_0 b_0$ and, A being a polynomial, B is rational. We can therefore use the theory of partial fractions developed in **1**; XI,4. If the polynomial $A(s)$ has distinct roots $s_1, \ldots, s_N$ we get

$$B(s) = \frac{A_1}{s_1 - s} + \cdots + \frac{A_N}{s_N - s} \tag{7.11}$$

and hence

$$b_n = A_1 s_1^{-n-1} + \cdots + A_N s_N^{-n-1}. \tag{7.12}$$

Obviously $\Sigma b_n^2 < \infty$ *iff all roots satisfy* $|s_j| > 1$, and it is easily verified that this remains true also in the presence of multiple roots. We have thus shown that a *stationary solution of the auto regression model* (7.6) *exists whenever all roots of the polynomial* $A(s)$ *lie outside the unit disk.* The covariances of our process are given by (7.4) and in the process the "infinitely remote past" plays no role. (For other solutions see the following example.)

(*c*) *Degenerate processes.* We turn to stationary sequences $\{\mathbf{Y}_n\}$ satisfying a "*stochastic difference equation*"

$$a_0 \mathbf{Y}_n + a_1 \mathbf{Y}_{n-1} + \cdots + a_N \mathbf{Y}_{n-N} = 0. \tag{7.13}$$

Typical special cases are

$$\mathbf{Y}_n = \lambda(\mathbf{Z}_1 \cos n\omega + \mathbf{Z}_{-1} \sin n\omega) \tag{7.14}$$

$$\mathbf{Y}_n = \alpha_1 \mathbf{Z}_1 + (-1)^n \alpha_2 \mathbf{Z}_{-1} \tag{7.15}$$

where the coefficients and ω are constants, and $\mathbf{Z}_1$ and $\mathbf{Z}_{-1}$ independent normal variables normed by (7.2). These processes satisfy (7.13), the first with $a_0 = a_2 = 1$ and $a_1 = -2 \cos \omega$, the second with $a_0 = -a_2 = 1$ and $a_1 = 0$. They are degenerate in the sense that the whole process is completely determined by two observations, say $\mathbf{Y}_{k-1}$ and $\mathbf{Y}_k$. These two observations can be taken as far back in the past as we please, and in this sense the process is completely determined by its "infinitely remote past." The same remark applies to any process satisfying a difference equation of the form (7.13), and hence these processes form the counterpart to example (*b*) where the infinitely remote past had no influence at all. ►

The theory of the difference equation (7.13) leads also to the *most general solution of the problem in example* (*b*). In fact, we have found *one* solution of (7.6), and the difference of two solutions satisfies (7.13). It follows that we can add to the solution of example (*b*) an arbitrary stationary sequence satisfying (7.13), and the latter will represent the contribution of the infinitely remote past.

A remark concerning the nature of the difference equation (7.13) is in order. If $\{\mathbf{Y}_k\}$ satisfies this equation there exists a linear relationship between the $N + 1$ variables $\mathbf{Y}_0, \mathbf{Y}_1, \ldots, \mathbf{Y}_N$ and hence their distribution must be degenerate (that is, it cannot have a density in $N + 1$ dimensions). Without loss of generality we may assume that the distribution of $(\mathbf{Y}_0, \ldots, \mathbf{Y}_{N-1})$ is not degenerate, for otherwise a linear combination of these variables would vanish, and because of the assumed stationarity this would imply that the process $\{\mathbf{Y}_k\}$ satisfies a difference equation of order $N - 1$ or lower. In other words, (7.13) is assumed to represent the difference equation of *lowest order* satisfied by $\{\mathbf{Y}_n\}$. The N-tuple $(\mathbf{Y}_1, \ldots, \mathbf{Y}_N)$ has then a density.

It will now be shown that the theory of stationary solutions of the difference equation (7.13) is intimately related to the "characteristic equation"

$$\xi^N + a_1\xi^{N-1} + \cdots + a_N = 0. \tag{7.16}$$

To each quadratic factor of the polynomial on the left there corresponds a second-order stochastic difference equation, and through it a process of the form (7.14) or (7.15). Corresponding to the factorization of the characteristic polynomial we shall thus represent the general solution of (7.13) as a sum of components of the form (7.14) and (7.15).

As before we assume the centering $\mathbf{E}(\mathbf{Y}_n) = 0$. The whole theory depends on the following lemma.

Lemma 1. *A stationary sequence with* $\mathbf{E}(\mathbf{Y}_n\mathbf{Y}_{n+k}) = r_k$ *satisfies the stochastic difference equation* (7.13) *iff*

$$r_n + a_1 r_{n-1} + \cdots + a_N r_{n-N} = 0. \tag{7.17}$$

Proof. Multiplying (7.13) by $\mathbf{Y}_0$ and taking expectations leads to (7.17). Squaring the left side in (7.13) and taking expectations yields $\Sigma\, a_j(\Sigma\, a_k r_{k-j})$, and so (7.17) implies that the left side in (7.13) has zero variance. This proves the lemma. ►

We proceed to derive the canonical form (7.22) for r_n. It is, of course, real, but it involves the roots of the characteristic equation (7.16), and we must therefore resort to a temporary use of complex numbers.

Lemma 2. *If* $\{\mathbf{Y}_n\}$ *satisfies* (7.13), *but no difference equation of lower order, then the characteristic equation* (7.16) *possesses* N *distinct roots* $\xi_1, \ldots, \xi_N$ *of unit modulus. In this case*

$$r_n = c_1\xi_1{}^n + \cdots + c_N\xi_N{}^n \tag{7.18}$$

with $c_j > 0$ *for* $j = 1, \ldots, N$.

Proof. Suppose first that the characteristic equation (7.16) has N *distinct* roots $\xi_1, \ldots, \xi_N$. Define r_n by (7.18) with arbitrary constants $c_1, \ldots, c_N$. It is obvious that these r_n satisfy the difference equation (7.17), and that the free parameters $c_1, \ldots, c_N$ may be adjusted so as to lead to prescribed values for $r_1, \ldots, r_N$. It follows that (in the case of distinct roots) *every* solution $\{r_n\}$ of the difference equation (7.17) is of the form (7.18). Now the covariances r_n of a stationary sequence remain bounded as $n \to \infty$ and $n \to -\infty$, and this is impossible unless either $|\xi_j| = 1$ or $c_j = 0$. The same argument applies when $\xi_1 = \xi_2$ is a double root, except that the first term on the right in (7.18) is replaced by $c_1 n\xi_1{}^n$. The boundedness of r_n again necessitates that $c_1 = 0$. We see thus that even in the presence of multiple roots r_n must be of the form

$$r_n = c_1\xi_1{}^n + \cdots + c_\rho\xi_\rho{}^n \tag{7.19}$$

where $\rho \leq N$ and $\xi_1, \ldots, \xi_\rho$ are distinct roots of the characteristic equation (7.16), all of unit modulus. It remains to prove that the number of terms appearing effectively in (7.19) cannot be less than N. For this purpose we note that $\xi_1, \ldots, \xi_\rho$ satisfy an equation of degree ρ with (possibly complex) coefficients α_k. It follows that the r_n satisfy a difference equation

$$r_n + \alpha_1 r_{n-1} + \cdots + \alpha_\rho r_{n-\rho} = 0 \tag{7.20}$$

analogous to (7.17). Now the covariances r_n are real numbers, and hence they also satisfy the difference equation obtained by taking the real part of (7.20). But by assumption the r_n satisfy no real difference equation of order $<N$, and so we must have $\rho = N$ and $c_j \neq 0$ for $j = 1, \ldots, N$. This completes the proof. ▶

For definiteness we formulate the final result for an *odd* integer.

Theorem. *Suppose that the stationary sequence* $\{\mathbf{Y}_n\}$ *satisfies the difference equation* (7.13) *with* $N = 2\nu + 1$, *but no difference equation of lower order. The characteristic equation* (7.16) *possesses* ν *pairs of complex roots* $\xi_j = \cos\omega_j \pm i\sin\omega_j$ (*with* ω_j *real*), *and one real root* $\omega_0 = \pm 1$. *The sequence* $\{\mathbf{Y}_n\}$ *is of the form*

$$\mathbf{Y}_n = \lambda_0\mathbf{Z}_0 \cdot \omega_0{}^n + \sum_{j=1}^{\nu} \lambda_j[\mathbf{Z}_j \cos n\omega_j + \mathbf{Z}_{-j}\sin n\omega_j], \tag{7.21}$$

where the $\mathbf{Z}_j$ are mutually independent normal variables normed by (7.2), *and the λ_j are constants. For this sequence*

$$r_n = \lambda_0^2\omega_0^n + \sum_{j=1}^{\nu} \lambda_j^2 \cos n\omega_j. \tag{7.22}$$

Conversely, choose real $\lambda_\nu \neq 0$ arbitrary and $\omega_0 = \pm 1$, and let $\omega_1, \ldots, \omega_j$ be distinct real numbers with $0 < \omega_j < \pi$. Then (7.21) *defines a stationary process with covariances* (7.22) *and satisfying a difference equation of order* $2\nu + 1$ *but no difference equation of a lower order.*

Proof. Since the r_n are real, lemma 2 implies that r_n is necessarily of the form (7.22). A trite calculation shows that the covariances of the sequence $\{\mathbf{Y}_n\}$ defined by (7.21) satisfy (7.22), and hence (7.17). By lemma 1 therefore $\{\mathbf{Y}_n\}$ satisfies the prescribed difference equation (7.13). From the construction of r_n it follows that no difference equation of order less than $N = 2\nu + 1$ is satisfied by our r_n, and hence $\{\mathbf{Y}_n\}$ cannot satisfy a difference equation of order less than N. Thus $\{\mathbf{Y}_n\}$ satisfies the stated conditions, but we have still to show that *every* sequence $\{\mathbf{Y}_n\}$ satisfying the given difference equation is of the form. For this purpose consider (7.21) for $n = 0, \ldots, 2\nu$ as a linear transformation from $(\mathbf{Z}_{-\nu}, \ldots, \mathbf{Z}_\nu)$ to $\mathbf{Y}_0, \mathbf{Y}_1, \ldots, \mathbf{Y}_{2\nu}$. It is easily seen that this transformation is non-singular, and so the covariance matrices of $(\mathbf{Z}_{-\nu}, \ldots, \mathbf{Z}_\nu)$ and $(\mathbf{Y}_0, \ldots, \mathbf{Y}_{2\nu})$ determine each other uniquely. We have assumed that the covariances of the $\mathbf{Z}_j$ are given by the identity matrix, and proved that the covariances of $\mathbf{Y}_n$ are given by (7.22). Because of the non-singular nature of the transformation it is equally true that the covariances (7.22) for $(\mathbf{Y}_n\}$ imply the covariances (7.2) for $\{\mathbf{Z}_n\}$.

This proves the direct part of the theorem. The converse part is reduced to it by considering the characteristic equation with the $2\nu + 1$ roots ω_0 and $\cos \omega_j \pm i \sin \omega_j$. ►

8. MARKOVIAN NORMAL DENSITIES

We turn to a discussion of the particular class of normal densities occurring in Markov processes. Without loss of generality *we consider only densities centered at the origin.* Then $\mathbf{E}(\mathbf{X}_k) = 0$ and we use the usual abbreviations

$$\mathbf{E}(\mathbf{X}_k^2) = \sigma_k^2, \qquad \mathbf{E}(\mathbf{X}_j\mathbf{X}_k) = \sigma_j\sigma_k\rho_{jk}. \tag{8.1}$$

The ρ_{jk} are the *correlation coefficients* and $\rho_{kk} = 1$.

Definition. *The r-dimensional normal density of* $(\mathbf{X}_1, \ldots, \mathbf{X}_r)$ *is Markovian if for* $k \leq r$ *the conditional density of* $\mathbf{X}_k$ *for given* $\mathbf{X}_1, \ldots, \mathbf{X}_{k-1}$ *is identical with the conditional density of* $\mathbf{X}_k$ *for given* $\mathbf{X}_{k-1}$.

Roughly speaking, if we know $\mathbf{X}_{k-1}$ (the "present") then the additional knowledge of the "past" $\mathbf{X}_1, \ldots, \mathbf{X}_{k-2}$ does not contribute any relevant information about the "future," that is, about any $\mathbf{X}_j$ with $j \geq k$.

Theorem 1. *For* $(\mathbf{X}_1, \ldots, \mathbf{X}_r)$ *to be Markovian*[12] *each of the following two conditions is necessary and sufficient:*

(i) *For* $k \leq r$

$$\mathbf{E}(\mathbf{X}_k \mid \mathbf{X}_1, \ldots, \mathbf{X}_{k-1}) = \mathbf{E}(\mathbf{X}_k \mid \mathbf{X}_{k-1}). \tag{8.2}$$

(ii) *For* $j \leq \nu < k \leq r$

$$\rho_{jk} = \rho_{j\nu}\rho_{\nu k}. \tag{8.3}$$

Proof. Since identity of densities implies equality of expectations, (8.2) is trivially necessary. Put

$$\mathbf{T} = \mathbf{X}_k - \frac{\sigma_k}{\sigma_{k-1}} \rho_{k-1,k}\mathbf{X}_{k-1}. \tag{8.4}$$

Then $\mathbf{E}(\mathbf{T}\mathbf{X}_{k-1}) = 0$ and $\mathbf{T}$ is the only variable of the form $\mathbf{X}_k - \lambda\mathbf{X}_{k-1}$ uncorrelated to $\mathbf{X}_{k-1}$. By theorem 6.4 we have $\mathbf{T} = \mathbf{X}_k - \mathbf{E}(\mathbf{X}_k \mid \mathbf{X}_{k-1})$, and hence (8.2) holds iff $\mathbf{T}$ is uncorrelated to $\mathbf{X}_1, \ldots, \mathbf{X}_{k-1}$, that is, iff

$$\rho_{jk} = \rho_{j,k-1}\rho_{k-1,k}, \qquad j \leq k. \tag{8.5}$$

In this case not only (8.2) holds, but also

$$\mathrm{Var}(\mathbf{X}_k \mid \mathbf{X}_1, \ldots, \mathbf{X}_{k-1}) = \mathrm{Var}(\mathbf{X}_k \mid \mathbf{X}_{k-1}) = \mathrm{Var}(\mathbf{T}), \tag{8.6}$$

and hence the corresponding conditional densities are the same. Thus (8.2) holds for all $k \leq r$ iff (8.5) is true, and in this case $(\mathbf{X}_1, \ldots, \mathbf{X}_r)$ is Markovian. As (8.5) is a special case of (8.3) the latter condition is sufficient. It is also necessary, for repeated application of (8.5) shows that for $j < \nu < k \leq r$

$$\frac{\rho_{jk}}{\rho_{\nu k}} = \frac{\rho_{j,k-1}}{\rho_{\nu,k-1}} = \frac{\rho_{j,k-2}}{\rho_{\nu,k-2}} = \frac{\rho_{j\nu}}{\rho_{\nu\nu}} = \rho_{j\nu} \tag{8.7}$$

and so (8.5) implies (8.3). ▶

Corollary. *If* $(\mathbf{X}_1, \ldots, \mathbf{X}_r)$ *is Markovian, so is every subset* $(\mathbf{X}_{\alpha_1}, \ldots, \mathbf{X}_{\alpha_\nu})$ *with* $\alpha_1 < \alpha_2 < \cdots < \alpha_\nu \leq r$.

This is obvious since (8.3) automatically extends to all subsets. ▶

[12] As usual in similar situations, we apply the term Markovian interchangeably to $(\mathbf{X}_1, \ldots, \mathbf{X}_r)$ and its density.

Examples. (*a*) *Independent increments.* A (finite or infinite) sequence $\{\mathbf{X}_k\}$ of normal random variables with $\mathbf{E}(\mathbf{X}_k) = 0$ is said to be a process with independent increments if for $j < k$ the increment $\mathbf{X}_k - \mathbf{X}_j$ is independent of $(\mathbf{X}_1, \ldots, \mathbf{X}_j)$. This implies, in particular, $\mathbf{E}(\mathbf{X}_j(\mathbf{X}_k - \mathbf{X}_j)) = 0$ or

$$\rho_{jk} = \frac{\sigma_j}{\sigma_k} \qquad j < k. \tag{8.8}$$

Comparing this with (8.3) one sees that a normal process with independent increments is automatically Markovian. Its structure is rather trite: $\mathbf{X}_k$ is the sum of the k mutually independent normal variables

$$\mathbf{X}_1, \mathbf{X}_2 - \mathbf{X}_1, \ldots, \mathbf{X}_k - \mathbf{X}_{k-1}.$$

(*b*) *Autoregressive models.* Consider a normal Markovian sequence $\mathbf{X}_1, \mathbf{X}_2, \ldots$ with $\mathbf{E}(\mathbf{X}_k) = 0$. There exists a unique constant a_k making $\mathbf{X}_k - a_k\mathbf{X}_{k-1}$ independent of $\mathbf{X}_{k-1}$, and hence of $\mathbf{X}_1, \ldots, \mathbf{X}_{k-1}$. Put

$$\lambda_k^2 = \operatorname{Var}(\mathbf{X}_k - a_k\mathbf{X}_{k-1})$$

and, recursively,

$$\begin{aligned} \mathbf{X}_1 &= \lambda_1\mathbf{Z}_1 \\ \mathbf{X}_k &= a_k\mathbf{X}_{k-1} + \lambda_k\mathbf{Z}_k \qquad k = 2, 3, \ldots \end{aligned} \tag{8.9}$$

The variables $\mathbf{Z}_k$ thus defined are easily seen to be independent and

$$\mathbf{E}(\mathbf{Z}_k) = 0, \qquad \mathbf{E}(\mathbf{Z}_k^2) = 1. \tag{8.10}$$

Now the converse is also true. If the $\mathbf{Z}_k$ are normal and satisfy (8.10), then (8.9) defines a sequence $\{\mathbf{X}_n\}$ and the very structure of (8.9) shows that $\{\mathbf{X}_n\}$ is Markovian. As an exercise we verify it computationally. Multiply (8.9) by $\mathbf{X}_j$ and take expectations. As $\mathbf{Z}_k$ is independent of $\mathbf{X}_1, \ldots, \mathbf{X}_{k-1}$ we get for $j < k$

$$a_k = \frac{\sigma_k}{\sigma_{k-1}} \frac{\rho_{jk}}{\rho_{j,k-1}}. \tag{8.11}$$

Now (8.5) is a simple consequence of this, and we know that it implies the Markovian character of the $\mathbf{X}_k$. Thus $(\mathbf{X}_1, \ldots, \mathbf{X}_r)$ *is Markovian iff relations of the form* (8.9) *hold* with normal variables $\mathbf{Z}_j$ satisfying (8.10). [This is a special case of example (7.*b*).] ►

So far we have considered only finite sequences $(\mathbf{X}_1, \ldots, \mathbf{X}_r)$, but the number r plays no role and we may as well speak of infinite sequences $\{\mathbf{X}_n\}$. This does *not* involve infinite sequence spaces or any new theory, but is merely an indication that a distribution for $(\mathbf{X}_1, \ldots, \mathbf{X}_r)$ is defined for all r. Similarly, we speak of a *Markovian family* $\{\mathbf{X}(t)\}$ when any *finite* collection $\mathbf{X}_1 = \mathbf{X}(t_1), \ldots, \mathbf{X}_r = \mathbf{X}(t_r)$ is Markovian. The description depends on the functions

$$\text{(8.12)} \qquad \mathbf{E}(\mathbf{X}^2(t)) = \sigma^2(t), \qquad \mathbf{E}(\mathbf{X}(s)\,\mathbf{X}(t)) = \sigma(s)\,\sigma(t)\,\rho(s,t).$$

In view of the criterion (8.3) it is obvious that *the family is Markovian iff for* $s < t < \tau$

$$\text{(8.13)} \qquad \rho(s,t)\,\rho(t,\tau) = \rho(s,\tau).$$

Despite the fancy language we are really dealing only with families of finite-dimensional normal distributions with covariances satisfying (8.13).

As explained in greater detail at the beginning of section 7, the sequence $\{\mathbf{X}_n\}$ is *stationary* if for each fixed n-tuple $(\alpha_1, \ldots, \alpha_n)$ the distribution of $(\mathbf{X}_{\alpha_1+\nu}, \ldots, \mathbf{X}_{\alpha_n+\nu})$ is independent of ν. A finite section of such a sequence may be extended to both sides, and hence it is natural to consider only doubly infinite sequences $\{\ldots, \mathbf{X}_{-2}, \mathbf{X}_{-1}, \mathbf{X}_0, \mathbf{X}_1, \ldots\}$. These notions carry over trivially to families $\{\mathbf{X}(t)\}$.

For a stationary sequence $\{\mathbf{X}_n\}$ the variance $\sigma_n{}^2$ is independent of n and in the Markovian case (8.3) implies that $\rho_{jk} = \rho_{12}^{|k-j|}$. Thus *for a stationary Markovian sequence*

$$\text{(8.14)} \qquad \mathbf{E}(\mathbf{X}_j\mathbf{X}_k) = \sigma^2\rho^{|k-j|}$$

where σ^2 and ρ are constants, $|\rho| < 1$. Conversely, a sequence with normal distributions satisfying (8.14) is Markovian and stationary.

In the case of a stationary family $\{\mathbf{X}(t)\}$ the correlation $\rho(s, t)$ depends only on the difference $|t - s|$ and (8.13) takes on the form

$$\rho(t)\,\rho(\tau) = \rho(t+\tau) \qquad \text{for} \quad t, \tau > 0.$$

Obviously $\rho(\tau) = 0$ would imply $\rho(t) = 0$ for all $t > \tau$ and also $\rho(\tfrac{1}{2}\tau) = 0$, and so ρ can have no zeros except if $\rho(t) = 0$ for all $t > 0$. Hence $\rho(t) = e^{-\lambda t}$ by the repeatedly used result of **1**; XVII, 6. Accordingly, *for a stationary Markovian family*

$$\text{(8.15)} \qquad \mathbf{E}(\mathbf{X}(s)\,\mathbf{X}(s+t)) = \sigma^2 e^{-\lambda t}, \qquad t > 0,$$

except if $\mathbf{X}(s)$ and $\mathbf{X}(t)$ are uncorrelated for all $s \neq t$.

Example. (*c*) *Stationary sequences* may be constructed by the scheme of the last example. Because of (8.11) we must have

$$\text{(8.16)} \qquad \mathbf{X}_k = \rho\mathbf{X}_{k-1} + \sigma\sqrt{1-\rho^2}\,\mathbf{Z}_k.$$

For each k it is possible to express $\mathbf{X}_k$ as a linear combination of $\mathbf{Z}_k$, $\mathbf{Z}_{k-1}, \ldots, \mathbf{Z}_{k-\nu}$, and $\mathbf{X}_{k-\nu}$. A formal passage to the limit would lead to the representation

$$\text{(8.17)} \qquad \mathbf{X}_k = \sigma(1-\rho^2)\sum_{j=0}^{\infty}\rho^j\mathbf{Z}_{k-j}$$

of $\{\mathbf{X}_k\}$ in terms of a doubly infinite sequence of independent normal variables $\mathbf{Z}_j$ normed by (8.10). Since $|\rho| < 1$ the convergence of the series is plausible, but the formula as such involves an infinite sequence space. [See the remarks concerning (7.5) of which (8.17) is a special case.] ►

It may be useful to discuss the relation of theorem 1 to the direct description of Markovian sequences in terms of densities. Denote by g_i the density of $\mathbf{X}_i$ and by $g_{ik}(x, y)$ the value at y of the conditional density of $\mathbf{X}_k$ given that $\mathbf{X}_i = x$. (In stochastic processes g_{ik} is called a transition density from $\mathbf{X}_i$ to $\mathbf{X}_k$.) For normal Markovian sequences we know that g_i is the normal density with zero expectation and variance σ_i^2, while

$$g_{ik}(x, y) = \frac{1}{\sigma_k\sqrt{1-\rho_{ik}^2}}\, n\left(\frac{y - \sigma_i^{-1}\rho_{ik}\sigma_k x}{\sigma_k\sqrt{1 - \rho_{ik}^2}}\right) \tag{8.18}$$

represents, for fixed x, a normal density with expectation $\sigma_i^{-1}\,\rho_{ik}\sigma_k x$ and variance $\sigma_k^2(1 - \rho_{ik}^2)$. Anyhow, let us proceed from scratch without use of theorem 1.

By the very definition the joint density of $(\mathbf{X}_i, \mathbf{X}_j)$ is given by $g_i(x)\, g_{ij}(x, y)$. The joint density for $(\mathbf{X}_i, \mathbf{X}_j, \mathbf{X}_k)$ is the product of this with the conditional density for $\mathbf{X}_k$ for given $\mathbf{X}_j$ *and* $\mathbf{X}_i$, but in view of the Markovian character the index i drops out if $i < j < k$ and the density of $(\mathbf{X}_i, \mathbf{X}_j, \mathbf{X}_k)$ is given by

$$g_i(x)\, g_{ij}(x, y)\, g_{jk}(y, z). \tag{8.19}$$

In the Markovian case the density of every n-tuple $(\mathbf{X}_{\alpha_1}, \ldots, \mathbf{X}_{\alpha_n})$ is given by a product of the form (8.19), but the densities g_{jk} cannot be chosen arbitrarily. Indeed, integration of (8.19) with respect to y yields the marginal density for $(\mathbf{X}_i, \mathbf{X}_k)$ and so we have the consistency condition

$$g_{ik}(x, z) = \int_{-\infty}^{+\infty} g_{ij}(x, y)\, g_{jk}(y, z)\, dy \tag{8.20}$$

for all $i < j < k$. This is a special case of the *Chapman-Kolmogorov identity* for Markov processes.[13] Very roughly, it expresses that a transition from x at epoch i to z at epoch k takes place via an arbitrary intermediate position y, the transition from y to z being independent of the past. It is obvious that with any system of transition probabilities g_{ik} satisfying the Chapman-Kolmogorov identity the multiplication scheme (8.19) leads to a consistent system of densities for $(\mathbf{X}_1, \mathbf{X}_2, \ldots, \mathbf{X}_r)$ and the sequence is Markovian. We have thus the following analytic counterpart to theorem 1.

---

[13] Other special cases were encountered in **1**; XV,(10.3) and XVII,(9.1). Note that the system (8.19) is the analogue to the definition **1**; XV,(1.1) of probabilities for Markov chains, except that there summation replaces the integration and that only stationary transition probabilities were considered.

Theorem 2. *A family* $\{g_{ik}\}$ *can serve for transition densities in a normal Markovian process iff it satisfies the Chapman-Kolmogorov identity and* $g_{ik}(x, y)$ *represents for each fixed* x *a normal density in* y.

Both theorems contain necessary and sufficient conditions and they are therefore, in a sense, equivalent. They are, nevertheless, of different natures. The second is really not restricted to normal processes; applied to families $\{\mathbf{X}(t)\}$ it leads to differential and integral equations for the transition probabilities and in this way it serves to introduce new classes of Markovian processes. On the other hand, from theorem 2 one would not guess that the g_{ik} are necessarily of the form (8.18), a result implicit in the more special theorem 1.

For reference and later comparisons we list here the two most important Markovian families $\{\mathbf{X}(t)\}$.

Example. (*d*) *Brownian motion* or *Wiener-Bachelier process.* It is defined by the condition that $\mathbf{X}(0) = 0$, and that for $t > s$ the variable $\mathbf{X}(t) - \mathbf{X}(s)$ be independent of $\mathbf{X}(s)$ with a variance depending only on $t - s$. In other words, the process has independent increments [example (*a*)] and stationary transition probabilities [but it is not stationary since $\mathbf{X}(0) = 0$]. Obviously $\mathbf{E}(\mathbf{X}^2(t)) = \sigma^2 t$ and $\mathbf{E}(\mathbf{X}(s)\mathbf{X}(t)) = \sigma^2 s$ for $s < t$. For $\tau > t$ the transition densities from (t, x) to (τ, y) are normal with expectation x and variance $\sigma^2(\tau - t)$. They depend only on $(y - x)/(\tau - t)$, and the Chapman-Kolmogorov identity reduces to a convolution.

(*e*) *Ornstein-Uhlenbeck process.* By this is meant the most general normal *stationary Markovian process* with zero expectations. Its covariances are given by (8.15). In other words, for $\tau > t$ the transition density from (t, x) to (τ, y) is normal with expectation $e^{-\lambda(\tau-t)}x$ and variance $\sigma^2(1 - e^{-2\lambda(\tau-t)})$. As $\tau \to \infty$ the expectation tends to 0 and the variance to σ^2. This process was considered by Ornstein and Uhlenbeck from an entirely different point of view. Its connection with diffusion will be discussed in X,4. ▶

9. PROBLEMS FOR SOLUTION

1. Let Ω be the region of the plane (of area $\frac{1}{2}$) bounded by the quadrilateral with vertices $(0, 0)$, $(1, 1)$, $(0, \frac{1}{2})$, $(\frac{1}{2}, 1)$ and the triangle with vertices $(\frac{1}{2}, 0)$, $(1, 0)$, $(1, \frac{1}{2})$. (The unit square is the union of Ω and the region symmetric to Ω with respect to the bisector.) Let $(\mathbf{X}, \mathbf{Y})$ be distributed uniformly in Ω. Prove that the marginal distributions are uniform and that $\mathbf{X} + \mathbf{Y}$ has the same density as if $\mathbf{X}$ and $\mathbf{Y}$ were independent.[14]

---

[14] In other words, the distribution of a sum may be given by the convolution even if the variables are dependent. This intuitive example is due to H. E. Robbins. For another freak of the same type see II,(4.*e*).

Hint: A diagram renders calculations unnecessary.

2. *Densities with normal marginal densities.* Let u be an *odd* continuous function on the line, vanishing outside $\overline{-1, 1}$. If $|u| < (2\pi e)^{-\frac{1}{2}}$ then

$$\mathfrak{n}(x)\,\mathfrak{n}(y) + u(x)\,u(y)$$

represents a bivariate density which *is not normal, but whose marginal densities are both normal.* (E. Nelson.)

3. *A second example.* Let φ_1 and φ_2 be two bivariate normal densities with unit variances but different correlation coefficients. The mixture $\frac{1}{2}(\varphi_1 + \varphi_2)$ is *not normal, but its two marginal densities coincide with* $\mathfrak{n}$.

Note. In the sequel all random variables are in $\mathcal{R}^1$. *Vector variables are indicated by pairs* $(\mathbf{X}_1, \mathbf{X}_2)$, *etc.*

4. Let $\mathbf{X}_1, \ldots, \mathbf{X}_n$ be independent random variables with the common density f and distribution function F. If $\mathbf{X}$ is the smallest and $\mathbf{Y}$ the largest among them, the joint density of the pair $(\mathbf{X}, \mathbf{Y})$ is given by

$$n(n-1)\,f(x)\,f(y)[F(y) - F(x)]^{n-2}.$$

5. Show that the Cauchy distribution in $\mathcal{R}^3$ [defined in (1.21)] corresponds to a random vector whose length has the density $v(r) = 4\pi^{-1}r^2(1+r^2)^{-2}$ for $r > 0$. [*Hint:* Use polar coordinates and either (1.15) or else the general relation I,(10.4) for projections.]

6. Let $a > 0$ and $f(x, y) = [(1+ax)(1+ay) - a]e^{-x-y-axy}$ for $x > 0$, $y > 0$ and $f(x, y) = 0$ elsewhere.

(*a*) Prove that f is a density of a pair $(\mathbf{X}, \mathbf{Y})$. Find the marginal densities and the distribution function.

(*b*) Find the conditional density $u_x(y)$ and $\mathbf{E}(\mathbf{Y} \mid \mathbf{X})$, $\mathrm{Var}(\mathbf{Y} \mid \mathbf{X})$. (E. J. Gumbel.)

7. Let f be a density concentrated on $\overline{0, \infty}$. Put $u(x, y) = f(x+y)/(x+y)$ for $x > 0$, $y > 0$ and $u(x, y) = 0$ otherwise. Prove that u is a density in $\mathcal{R}^2$ and find its covariance matrix.

8. Let $\mathbf{X}_1, \mathbf{X}_2, \mathbf{X}_3$ be mutually independent and distributed uniformly over $\overline{0, 1}$. Let $\mathbf{X}_{(1)}, \mathbf{X}_{(2)}, \mathbf{X}_{(3)}$ be the corresponding order statistics. Find the density of the pair

$$\left(\frac{\mathbf{X}_{(1)}}{\mathbf{X}_{(2)}}, \frac{\mathbf{X}_{(2)}}{\mathbf{X}_{(3)}}\right)$$

and show that the two ratios are independent. Generalize to n dimensions.

9. Let $\mathbf{X}_1, \mathbf{X}_2, \mathbf{X}_3$ be independent with a common exponential distribution. Find the density of $(\mathbf{X}_2 - \mathbf{X}_1, \mathbf{X}_3 - \mathbf{X}_1)$.

10. A particle of mass m is split into two fragments whose masses are $\mathbf{X}m$ and $(1-\mathbf{X})m$. Here $\mathbf{X}$ is a random variable with a density $f(x) > 0$ for $0 < x < 1$ and $f(x) = 0$ elsewhere; for reasons of symmetry $f(x) = f(1-x)$. Assume that the two fragments are split independently in the same manner. Find (*a*) the joint density of the smallest and the largest of the four fragments; (*b*) the marginal density of the smallest of the four fragments.

11. Let $\mathbf{X}_1, \mathbf{X}_2, \ldots$ be independent with the common normal density $\mathfrak{n}$, and $\mathbf{S}_k = \mathbf{X}_1 + \cdots + \mathbf{X}_k$. If $m < n$ find the joint density of $(\mathbf{S}_m, \mathbf{S}_n)$ and the conditional density for $\mathbf{S}_m$ given that $\mathbf{S}_n = t$.

12. In the preceding problem find the conditional density of $\mathbf{X}_1^2 + \cdots + \mathbf{X}_m^2$ given $\mathbf{X}_1^2 + \cdots + \mathbf{X}_n^2$.

13. Let $(\mathbf{X}, \mathbf{Y})$ have a bivariate normal density centered at the origin with $\mathbf{E}(\mathbf{X}^2) = \mathbf{E}(\mathbf{Y}^2) = 1$, and $\mathbf{E}(\mathbf{XY}) = \rho$. In polar coordinates $(\mathbf{X}, \mathbf{Y})$ becomes $(\mathbf{R}, \mathbf{\Phi})$ where $\mathbf{R}^2 = \mathbf{X}^2 + \mathbf{Y}^2$. Prove that $\mathbf{\Phi}$ has a density given by

$$\frac{\sqrt{1-\rho^2}}{2\pi(1 - 2\rho \sin \varphi \cos \varphi)} \qquad 0 < \varphi < 2\pi$$

and is uniformly distributed iff $\rho = 0$. Conclude

$$\mathbf{P}\{\mathbf{XY} > 0\} = \tfrac{1}{2} + \pi^{-1} \arcsin \rho \quad \text{and} \quad \mathbf{P}\{\mathbf{XY} < 0\} = \pi^{-1} \arccos \rho.$$

14. Let f be the uniform density for the triangle with vertices (0, 0), (0, 1), (1, 0) and g the uniform density for the symmetric triangle in the third quadrant. Find $f \star f$, and $f \star g$.

Warning. A tedious separate consideration of individual intervals is required.

15. Let f be the uniform density in the unit disk. Find $f \star f$ in polar coordinates.

16. Let u and v be densities in $\mathcal{R}^2$ of the form

$$u(x, y) = f(\sqrt{x^2 + y^2}), \qquad v(x, y) = g(\sqrt{x^2 + y^2}).$$

Find $u \star v$ in polar coordinates.

17. Find the general normal stationary process satisfying

(*a*) $\mathbf{X}_{n+2} + \mathbf{X}_n = 0$

(*b*) $\mathbf{X}_{n+2} - \mathbf{X}_n = 0$

(*c*) $\mathbf{X}_{n+3} - \mathbf{X}_{n+2} + \mathbf{X}_{n+1} - \mathbf{X}_n = 0.$

18. *A servo-stochastic process.* (H. D. Mills.) A servomechanism is exposed to random shocks, but corrections may be introduced at any time. Thus the *error* $\mathbf{Y}_n$ at time n is (in proper units) of the form $\mathbf{Y}_{n+1} = \mathbf{Y}_n + \mathbf{C}_n + \mathbf{X}_{n+1}$, where $\mathbf{C}_n$ is the correction and the $\mathbf{X}_n$ are independent normal variables, $\mathbf{E}(\mathbf{X}_n) = 0$, $\mathbf{E}(\mathbf{X}_n^2) = 1$. The $\mathbf{C}_n$ are, in principle, arbitrary functions of the past observations, that is, of $\mathbf{Y}_k$ and $\mathbf{X}_k$ for $k \le n$. One wishes to choose them so as to minimize $\mathrm{Var}(\mathbf{Y}_n)$ (which is a measure of how *well* the mechanism works), and $\mathrm{Var}(\mathbf{C}_n)$ (which is a measure of how *hard* it works).

(*a*) Discuss the covariance function of $\{\mathbf{Y}_n\}$ and show that $\mathrm{Var}(\mathbf{Y}_n) > 1$.

(*b*) Assuming that $\mathrm{Var}(\mathbf{C}_n) \to \alpha^2$, $\mathrm{Var}(\mathbf{Y}_n) \to \sigma^2$ (tendency to stationarity) show that $\sigma > \frac{1}{2}(\alpha + \alpha^{-1})$.

(*c*) Consider, in particular, the *linear device* $\mathbf{C}_n = a - p(\mathbf{Y}_n - b)$, $0 < p \le 1$. Find the covariance function and a representation of the form (7.8) for $\mathbf{Y}_n$.

19. *Continuation.* If there is a *time lag* in information or adjustment the model is essentially the same except that $\mathbf{C}_n$ is to be replaced by $\mathbf{C}_{n+N}$. Discuss this situation.

CHAPTER IV

Probability Measures and Spaces

As stated in the introduction, very little of the technical apparatus of measure theory is required in this volume, and most of the book should be readable without the present chapter.[1] It is nevertheless desirable to give a brief account of the basic concepts which form the theoretical background for this book and, for reference, to record the main theorems. The underlying ideas and facts are not difficult, but proofs in measure theory depend on messy technical details. For the beginner and outsider access is made difficult also by the many facets and uses of measure theory; excellent introductions exist, but of necessity they dwell on great generality and on aspects which are not important in the present context. The following survey concentrates on the needs of this volume and omits many proofs and technical details.[2] (It is fair to say that the simplicity of the theory is deceptive in that much more difficult measure theoretic problems arise in connection with stochastic processes depending on a continuous time parameter. The treatment of conditional expectations is deferred to V, 10; that of the Radon-Nikodym theorem to V,3.)

Formulas relating to Cartesian (or Euclidean) spaces $\mathfrak{R}^r$ are independent of the number of dimensions provided x is read as abbreviation for $(x_1, \ldots, x_r)$.

---

[1] This applies to readers acquainted with the rudiments of measure theory as well as to readers interested primarily in results and facts. For the benefit of the latter the definition of integrals is repeated in V,1. Beyond this they may rely on their intuition, because in effect measure theory justifies simple formal manipulations.

[2] An excellent source for Baire functions and Lebesgue–Stieltjes integration is found in E. J. McShane and T. A. Botts, *Real analysis*, D. Van Nostrand, Princeton, 1959. Widely used are presentations of general measure theory in P. R. Halmos, *Measure theory*, D. Van Nostrand, Princeton, 1950 and in N. Bourbaki, *Eléments de mathématiques* [livre VI, chapters 3–5] Hermann, Paris, 1952 and 1956. For presentations for the specific purposes of probability see the books of Doob, Loève, Neveu, and Hennequin-Tortrat.

1. BAIRE FUNCTIONS

We shall have to decide on a class of sets for which probabilities are defined and on a class of functions acceptable as random variables. The two problems are not only related but their treatment is unified by a streamlined modern notation. We begin by introducing it and by recalling the definition of convergence in terms of monotone limits.

The *indicator*[3] *of a set* A is the function which assumes the value 1 at all points of A and the value 0 at all points of the complement A'. It will be denoted by $\mathbf{1}_A$: thus $\mathbf{1}_A(x) = 1$ if $x \in A$ and $\mathbf{1}_A(x) = 0$ otherwise. Every set has an indicator, and every function assuming only the values 1 and 0 is the indicator of some set. If f is an arbitrary function, the product $\mathbf{1}_A f$ is the function that equals f on A and vanishes elsewhere.

Consider now the intersection $C = A \cap B$ of two sets. Its indicator $\mathbf{1}_C$ equals 0 wherever either $\mathbf{1}_A$ or $\mathbf{1}_B$ vanishes, that is, $\mathbf{1}_C = \inf(\mathbf{1}_A, \mathbf{1}_B)$ equals the smaller of the two functions. To exploit this parallelism one writes $f \cap g$ instead of $\inf(f, g)$ for the function which at each point x equals the smaller of the values of $f(x)$ and $g(x)$. Similarly $f \cup g = \sup(f, g)$ denotes the larger of the two values.[4] The operators $\cap$ and $\cup$ are called *cap* and *cup* respectively. They apply to arbitrary numbers of functions, and one writes

$$f_1 \cap \cdots \cap f_n = \bigcap_{k=1}^{n} f_k, \qquad f_1 \cup \cdots \cup f_n = \bigcup_{k=1}^{n} f_k. \tag{1.1}$$

To repeat, at each point x these functions equal, respectively, the minimum and the maximum among the n values $f_1(x), \ldots, f_n(x)$. If f_k is the indicator of a set A_k then (1.1) exhibits the indicators of the intersection $A_1 \cap \cdots \cap A_n$ and of the union $A_1 \cup \cdots \cup A_n$.

Consider now an *infinite* sequence $\{f_n\}$. The functions defined in (1.1) depend monotonically on n, and hence the limits $\cap_{k=1}^{\infty} f_k$ and $\cup_{k=1}^{\infty} f_k$ are well defined though possibly infinite. For fixed j

$$w_j = \bigcap_{k=j}^{\infty} f_k \tag{1.2}$$

is the limit of the monotone sequence of functions $f_j \cap \cdots \cap f_{j+n}$, and the sequence $\{w_j\}$ itself is again monotone, that is, $w_n = w_1 \cup \cdots \cup w_n$. With our notations $w_n \to \cup_{k=1}^{\infty} w_k$. By definition $w_n(x)$ is the greatest

[3] This term was introduced by Loève. The older term "characteristic function" is confusing in probability theory.

[4] Many writers prefer the symbols $\vee$ and $\wedge$ for functions and reserve $\cap$ and $\cup$ for sets. Within our context there is no advantage in the dual notation.

lower bound (the infimum) of the numerical sequence $f_n(x), f_{n+1}(x), \ldots$. Hence the limit of w_n is the same as lim inf f_n and thus

$$(1.3) \qquad \liminf f_n = \bigcup_{j=1}^{\infty} \bigcap_{k=j}^{\infty} f_k.$$

In this way the lim inf is obtained by a succession of two passages to the limit in *monotone* sequences. For lim sup f_n one gets (1.3) with $\cap$ and $\cup$ interchanged.

All these considerations carry over to sets. In particular, we write $A = \lim A_n$ iff $\mathbf{1}_A = \lim \mathbf{1}_{A_n}$. In words, the sequence $\{A_n\}$ of sets converges to the set A iff each point of A belongs to *all* A_n with finitely many exceptions, and each point of the complement A' belongs at most to finitely many A_n.

Example. (*a*) *The set* $\{A_n \text{ i. o.}\}$. As a probabilistically significant example of limiting operations among sets consider the event A defined as "the realization of infinitely many among a given sequence of events $A_1, A_2, \ldots$." [Special cases were considered in **1**; VIII (Borel-Cantelli lemmas) and in **1**; XIII (recurrent events).] More formally, given a sequence $\{A_n\}$ of sets, a point x belongs to A iff it belongs to infinitely many A_k. Since 0 and 1 are the only possible values of indicators this definition is equivalent to saying that $\mathbf{1}_A = \limsup \mathbf{1}_{A_n}$. In standard notation we should therefore write $A = \limsup A_n$, but the notation $\{A_n \text{ i. o.}\}$ (read "A_n infinitely often") is more suggestive and flexible. It is due to Chung and is now generally used in probability theory. ►

Our next problem is to delimit the class of functions[5] in $\mathfrak{R}^r$ with which we propose to deal. The notion of an arbitrary function is far too broad to be useful for our purposes, and a modernized version of Euler's notion of a function is more appropriate. Taking continuous functions as given, the only effective way of constructing new functions depends on taking limits. As it turns out, all our needs will be satisfied if we know how to deal with functions that are limits of sequences $\{f_n\}$ of continuous functions, or limits of sequences where each f_n is such a limit, and so on. In other words, we are interested in a class $\mathfrak{B}$ of functions with the

[5] We are, in principle, interested only in finite-valued functions, but it is sometimes convenient to permit $\pm\infty$ as values. For example, the simple theorem that every monotone sequence has a limit is false for finite-valued functions and without it many formulations become clumsy. For this reason we adhere to the usual convention that all functions are to the extended real line, that is, their values are numbers or $\pm\infty$. In practice the values $\pm\infty$ will play no role. To make sure that the sum and product of two functions are again functions one introduces for their values the conventions $\infty + \infty = \infty$, $\infty - \infty = 0$, $\infty \cdot \infty = \infty$, $0 \cdot \infty = 0$, etc.

following properties: (1) every continuous function belongs to $\mathfrak{B}$, and (2) if $f_1, f_2, \ldots$ belong to $\mathfrak{B}$ and a limit $f(x) = \lim f_n(x)$ exists for all x, then f belongs to $\mathfrak{B}$. Such a class is said to be *closed* under pointwise limits. There is no doubt that such classes exist, the class of *all* functions being one. The intersection of all such classes is itself a closed family, and obviously is the smallest such class. Prudence requires us to limit our considerations to this smallest class.

The smallest closed class of functions containing all continuous functions is called the Baire class and will be denoted by $\mathfrak{B}$. The functions in $\mathfrak{B}$ are called Baire functions.[6]

We shall use this notion not only for functions defined in the whole space but also for functions defined only on a subset (for example, $\sqrt{x}$ or $\log x$ in $\mathfrak{R}^1$).

It is obvious from the definition that the sum and the product of two Baire functions are again Baire functions, but much more is true. If w is a continuous function in r variables and $f_1, \ldots, f_r$ are Baire functions, then $w(f_1, \ldots, f_r)$ is again a Baire function. Replacing w by w_n and passing to a limit it can be shown that more generally *every Baire function of Baire functions is again a Baire function.* Fixing the value of one or more variables leads again to a Baire function, and so on. In short, none of the usual operations on Baire functions will lead outside the class, and therefore the class $\mathfrak{B}$ is a natural object for our analysis. It will turn out that no simplifications are possible by considering smaller classes.

2. INTERVAL FUNCTIONS AND INTEGRALS IN $\mathfrak{R}^r$

We shall use the word *interval*, and the indicated notation, for sets of points satisfying a double inequality of one of the following four types:

$$\overline{a, b}: \quad a < x < b \qquad\qquad \overline{a, b\rvert}: \quad a < x \le b$$

$$\overline{\lvert a, b\rvert}: \quad a \le x \le b \qquad\qquad \overline{\lvert a, b}: \quad a \le x < b.$$

In one dimension this covers all possible intervals, including the degenerate interval of length zero. In two dimensions the inequalities are interpreted coordinate-wise, and intervals are (possibly degenerate) rectangles parallel to the axes. Other types of partial closure are possible but are herewith *excluded.* The limiting case where one or more coordinates

[6] This definition depends on the notion of continuity but not on other properties of Cartesian spaces. It is therefore applicable to arbitrary topological spaces.

of either a or b are replaced by $\pm\infty$ is admitted; in particular, the whole space is the interval $\overline{-\infty, \infty}$.

A point function f assigns a value $f(x)$ to individual points. A *set function* F assigns values to sets or regions of the space. The volume in $\mathfrak{R}^3$, area in $\mathfrak{R}^2$, or length in $\mathfrak{R}^1$ are typical examples but there are many more, probabilities representing a special case of primary concern to us. We shall be interested only in set functions with the property that if a set A is partitioned into two sets A_1 and A_2, then $F\{A\} = F\{A_1\} + F\{A_2\}$. Such functions are called additive.[7]

As we have seen, it occurs frequently that probabilities $F\{I\}$ are assigned to all intervals of the r-dimensional space $\mathfrak{R}^r$ and it is desired to extend this assignment to more general sets. The same problem occurs in elementary calculus, where the area (content) is originally defined only for rectangles and it is desired to define the area of a more general domain A. The simplest procedure is first to define integrals for functions of two variables and then to equate "the area of A" with the integral of the indicator $\mathbf{1}_A$ (that is the function that equals 1 in A and vanishes outside A). In like manner we shall define the integral

$$\mathbf{E}(u) = \int_{\mathfrak{R}^r} u(x)\, F\{dx\} \tag{2.1}$$

of a point function u with respect to the interval function F. The probability of A will then be defined by $\mathbf{E}(\mathbf{1}_A)$. In the construction of the integral (2.1) the interpretation of F plays no role, and we shall actually describe the general notion of a Lebesgue-Stieltjes integral. With this program in mind we now start anew.

Let F be a function assigning to each interval I a finite value $F\{I\}$. Such a function is called (finitely) *additive* if for every partition of an interval I into finitely many non-overlapping intervals $I_1, \ldots, I_n$.

$$F\{I\} = F\{I_1\} + \cdots + F\{I_n\}. \tag{2.2}$$

Examples. (*a*) *Distributions in* $\mathfrak{R}^1$. In volume **1** we considered discrete probability distributions attributing probabilities $p_1, p_2, \ldots$ to the points $a_1, a_2, \ldots$. Here $F\{I\}$ is the sum of the weights p_n of all points a_n contained in I, and $\mathbf{E}(u) = \Sigma u(a_n)p_n$.

If G is any continuous monotone function increasing from 0 at $-\infty$ to 1 at ∞ one may define $F\{\overline{a, b}\} = G(b) - G(a)$.

---

[7] Empirical examples for additive functions are the mass and amount of heat in a region, the land value, the wheat acreage and the number of inhabitants of a geographical region, the yearly coal production, the passenger miles flown or the kilowatt hours consumed during a period, the number of telephone calls, etc.

(*b*) *Random vectors*. A vector of unit length issues from the origin in a random direction. The probability that its endpoint lies in a two-dimensional interval I is proportional to the length of the intersection of I with the unit circle. This defines a continuous probability distribution without density. The distribution is *singular* in the sense that the whole probability is carried by a circle. One may think that such distributions are artificial and that the circle rather than the plane should serve as natural sample space. The objection is untenable because the sum of two independent random vectors is capable of all lengths between 0 and 2 and has a positive density within the disk of radius 2 [see example V,(4.*e*)]. For some problems involving random unit vectors the plane is therefore the natural sample space. Anyhow, the intention was only to show by a simple example what happens in more complicated situations.

(*c*) We conclude with an example illustrating the contingency that will be *excluded* in the sequel. In $\mathcal{R}^1$ put $F\{I\} = 0$ for any interval $I = \overline{a, b}$ with $b < \infty$ and $F\{I\} = 1$ when $I = \overline{a, \infty}$. This interval function is additive but weird because it violates the natural continuity requirement that $F\{\overline{a, b}\}$ should tend to $F\{\overline{a, \infty}\}$ as $b \to \infty$. ►

The last example shows the desirability of strengthening the requirement (2.2) of finite additivity. We shall say that *an interval function F is countably additive, or σ-additive, if for every partitioning of an interval I into countably many intervals $I_1, I_2, \ldots$,*

$$F\{I\} = \sum F\{I_k\}. \tag{2.3}$$

["Countably many" means finitely or denumerably many. The term completely additive is synonymous with countably additive. The condition (2.3) is manifestly violated in the last example.]

We shall restrict our attention entirely to countably additive set functions. This is justified by the success of the theory, but the restriction can be defended a priori on heuristic or pragmatic grounds. In fact, if $A_n = I_1 \cup \cdots \cup I_n$ is the union of the first n intervals, then $A_n \to I$. One could argue that "for n sufficiently large A_n is practically indistinguishable from I." If $F\{I\}$ can be found by experiments, $F\{A_n\}$ must be "practically indistinguishable" from $F\{I\}$, that is, $F\{A_n\}$ must tend to $F\{I\}$. The countable additivity (2.3) expresses precisely this requirement.

Being interested principally in probabilities we shall consider only non-negative interval functions F normed by the condition that $F\{\overline{-\infty, \infty}\} = 1$. This norming imposes no serious restriction when $F\{\overline{-\infty, \infty}\} < \infty$, but it excludes interval functions such as length in $\mathcal{R}^1$ or area in $\mathcal{R}^2$. To make use of the following theory in such cases it suffices to partition the line or the plane into unit intervals and treat them separately. This procedure is so obvious and so well known that it requires no further explanation.

A function on $\mathcal{R}^r$ is called a *step function* if it assumes only finitely many values, each on an interval. For a step function u assuming the values $a_1, \ldots, a_n$ on intervals $I_1, \ldots, I_n$ (that is, with probabilities $F\{I_1\}, \ldots, F\{I_n\}$), respectively we put

$$\mathbf{E}(u) = a_1 F\{I_1\} + \cdots + a_n F\{I_n\} \tag{2.4}$$

in analogy with the definition of expectation of discrete random variables. [It is true that the partitioning of the space into intervals on which u is constant is not unique, but just as in the discrete case the definition (2.4) is easily seen to be independent of the partition.] This expectation $\mathbf{E}(u)$ satisfies the following conditions:

(*a*) *Additivity* for linear combinations:

$$\mathbf{E}(\alpha_1 u_1 + \alpha_2 u_2) = \alpha_1 \mathbf{E}(u_1) + \alpha_2 \mathbf{E}(u_2). \tag{2.5}$$

(*b*) *Positivity:*

$$u \geq 0 \quad \textit{implies} \quad \mathbf{E}(u) \geq 0. \tag{2.6}$$

(*c*) *Norming:* For the constant function

$$\mathbf{E}(1) = 1. \tag{2.7}$$

The last two conditions are equivalent to the *mean value theorem:* $\alpha \leq u \leq \beta$ implies $\alpha \leq \mathbf{E}(u) \leq \beta$ and so the function $\mathbf{E}(u)$ represents a sort of *average*.[8]

The problem is to extend the definition of $\mathbf{E}(u)$ to larger classes of functions preserving the properties (*a*)–(*c*). The classical Riemann integration utilizes the fact that to each continuous function u on $\overline{0, 1}$ there exists a sequence of step functions u_n such that $u_n \to u$ uniformly on $\overline{0, 1}$. By definition then $\mathbf{E}(u) = \lim \mathbf{E}(u_n)$. It turns out that the uniformity of the convergence is unnecessary and the same definition for

[8] When F represents probabilities $\mathbf{E}(u)$ may be interpreted as the expected gain of a gambler who can gain the amounts $a_1, a_2, \ldots$. To grasp the intuitive meaning in other situations consider three examples in which $u(x)$ represents, respectively, the temperature at time x, the number of telephone conversations at time x, the distance of a mass point from the origin, while F represents, respectively, the duration of a time interval, the value (cost of conversation) of a time interval, and mechanical mass. In each case integration will be extended over a finite interval only and $\mathbf{E}(u)$ will represent the accumulated "temperature hours," the accumulated gain, and a static moment. These examples will show our integration with respect to arbitrary set functions to be simpler and more intuitive than Riemann integration where the independent variable plays more than one role and the "area under the curve" is of no help to the beginner. One should beware of the idea that the concept of expectation occurs only in probability theory.

$\mathbf{E}(u)$ can be used whenever $u_n \to u$ pointwise. In this way it is possible to extend $\mathbf{E}(u)$ to *all bounded Baire functions*, and the extension is *unique*. When it comes to unbounded functions divergent integrals are unavoidable, but at least for *positive* Baire functions it is possible to define $\mathbf{E}(u)$ either as a number or as the symbol ∞ (indicating divergence). No trouble arises in this respect because the Lebesgue theory considers only absolute integrability. Roughly speaking, starting from the definition (2.4) for expectations of simple functions it is possible to define $\mathbf{E}(u)$ for general Baire functions by obvious approximations and passages to the limit. The number $\mathbf{E}(u)$ so defined is the Lebesgue-Stieltjes integral of u with respect to F. (The term expectation is preferable when the underlying function F remains fixed so that no ambiguity arises). We state here without proof[9] the basic fact of the Lebesgue theory; its nature and scope will be analyzed in the following sections. [A constructive definition of $\mathbf{E}(u)$ is given in section 4.]

Main theorem. *Let F be a countably additive interval function in $\mathcal{R}^r$ with $F\{\overline{-\infty, \infty}\} = 1$. There exists a unique Lebesgue-Stieltjes integral* $\mathbf{E}(u)$ *on the class of Baire functions such that:*

If $u \geq 0$ then $\mathbf{E}(u)$ *is a non-negative number or* ∞. *Otherwise* $\mathbf{E}(u)$ *exists iff either* $\mathbf{E}(u^+)$ *or* $\mathbf{E}(u^-)$ *is finite; in this case* $\mathbf{E}(u) = \mathbf{E}(u^+) - \mathbf{E}(u^-)$. *A function u is called integrable if* $\mathbf{E}(u)$ *is finite. Then*

(i) *If u is a step function,* $\mathbf{E}(u)$ *is given by* (2.4).

(ii) *Conditions* (2.5)–(2.7) *hold for all integrable functions.*

(iii) (*Monotone convergence principle*). *Let $u_1 \leq u_2 \leq \cdots \to u$ where u_n is integrable. Then* $\mathbf{E}(u_n) \to \mathbf{E}(u)$.

The change of variables $v_n = u_{n+1} - u_n$ leads to a restatement of the last principle in terms of series:

If v_n is integrable and $v_n \geq 0$, then

$$\sum \mathbf{E}(v_n) = \mathbf{E}\left(\sum v_n\right) \tag{2.8}$$

in the sense that both sides are meaningful (finite) or neither is. It follows in particular that if $v \geq u \geq 0$ and $\mathbf{E}(u) = \infty$ then also $\mathbf{E}(v) = \infty$.

What happens if in (iii) the condition of monotonicity is dropped? The answer depends on an important lemma of wide applicability.

Fatou's lemma. *If $u_n \geq 0$ and u_n is integrable, then*

$$\mathbf{E}(\liminf u_n) \leq \liminf \mathbf{E}(u_n). \tag{2.9}$$

In particular, if $u_n \to u$ then $\liminf \mathbf{E}(u_n) \geq \mathbf{E}(u)$.

[9] The method of proof is indicated in section 5. As usual, u^+ and u^- denote the positive and negative parts of u, that is, $u^+ = u \cup 0$ and $-u^- = u \cap 0$. Thus $u = u^+ - u^-$.

Proof. Put $v_n = u_n \cap u_{n+1} \cap \cdots$. Then $v_n \leq u_n$ and hence

$$\mathbf{E}(v_n) \leq \mathbf{E}(u_n).$$

But (as we saw in section 1) v_n tends monotonically to lim inf u_n, and so $\mathbf{E}(v_n)$ tends to the left side in (2.9) and the lemma is proved. [Note that each side in (2.9) can represent ∞.] ▶

As example (*d*) will show, the condition of positivity cannot be dropped, but it can be replaced by the formally milder condition that there exists an integrable function U such that $u_n \geq U$. (It suffices to replace u_n by $u_n - U$.) Changing u_n into $-u_n$ we see that *if* $u_n < U$ *and* $\mathbf{E}(U) < \infty$, *then*

$$\limsup \mathbf{E}(u_n) \leq \mathbf{E}(\limsup u_n). \tag{2.10}$$

For convergent sequences the extreme members in (2.9) and (2.10) coincide and the two relations together yield the important

Dominated convergence principle. *Let* u_n *be integrable and* $u_n \to u$ *pointwise. If there exists an integrable* U *such that* $|u_n| \leq U$ *for all* n, *then* u *is integrable and* $\mathbf{E}(u_n) \to \mathbf{E}(u)$.

This theorem relates to the only place in the Lebesgue theory where a naïve formal manipulation may lead to a wrong result. The necessity of the condition $|u_n| \leq U$ is illustrated by

Example. (*d*) Consider the gamma densities $u_n(x) = n^2 x e^{-nx}$ $(x > 0)$ differing from each other only by a scale parameter. Here $1 = \mathbf{E}(u_n) \to 1$ but $u_n(x) \to 0$ for all $x > 0$. Replacing u_n by $-u_n$, we see that Fatou's inequality (2.9) does not necessarily hold for non-positive functions. ▶

We mention without proof a rule of ordinary calculus applicable more generally.

Fubini's theorem *for repeated integrals. If* $u \geq 0$ *is a Baire function and* F *and* G *are probability distributions then*

$$\int_{-\infty}^{+\infty} F\{dx\} \int_{-\infty}^{+\infty} u(x, y)\, G\{dy\} = \int_{-\infty}^{+\infty} G\{dy\} \int_{-\infty}^{+\infty} u(x, y)\, F\{dx\} \tag{2.11}$$

with the obvious interpretation in case of divergence. Here x and y may be interpreted as points in $\mathcal{R}^m$ and $\mathcal{R}^n$, and the theorem includes the assertion that the two inner integrals are Baire functions. (This theorem applies to arbitrary product spaces and a better version is given in section 6.) ▶

Mean approximation theorem. *To each integrable* u *and* $\epsilon > 0$ *it is possible to find a step function* v *such that* $\mathbf{E}(|u - v|) < \epsilon$.

Note on Notations. The notation $\mathbf{E}(u)$ emphasizes the dependence on u and is practical in contexts where the interval function F is fixed. When

F varies or the dependence on F is to be emphasized, the integral notation (2.1) is preferable. It applies also to integrals extended over a subset A, for the integral of u extended over A is (by definition) the same as the integral of the product $\mathbf{1}_A u$ extended over the whole space. We write

$$\int_A u(x)\, F\{dx\} = \mathbf{E}(\mathbf{1}_A u)$$

(assuming, of course, that the indicator $\mathbf{1}_A$ is a Baire function). The two sides mean exactly the same thing, the left side emphasizing the dependence on F. When $A = \overline{a, b}$ is an interval the notation $\int_a^b$ is sometimes preferred, but to render it unambiguous it is necessary to indicate whether the endpoints belong to the interval. This may be done by writing $a+$ or $a-$.

In accordance with the program outlined at the beginning of this section we now define the probability of a set A to equal $\mathbf{E}(\mathbf{1}_A)$ whenever $\mathbf{1}_A$ is a Baire function; for other sets no probabilities are defined. The consequences of this definition will now be discussed in the more general context of arbitrary sample spaces. ▶

3. PROBABILITY MEASURES AND SPACES

The basic properties of the probabilities which we have introduced in $\mathfrak{R}^r$ are so satisfactory that we may use them for an axiomatic treatment of probabilities in arbitrary sample spaces. To be sure, no analogue to intervals need exist in an arbitrary sample space and the actual assignment of probabilities varies from case to case. (Two typical situations are described in sections 5 and 6.) In general it is necessary to reverse the procedure of section 2 and to define expectations in terms of a given probability measure. (This procedure is described in section 5.) Here we are concerned with the primary notion of a probability measure (or distribution).

A set A in $\mathfrak{R}^r$ whose indicator $\mathbf{1}_A$ is a Baire function is called a *Borel set*. For Borel sets we defined

$$\mathbf{P}\{A\} = \mathbf{E}(\mathbf{1}_A). \tag{3.1}$$

Intervals being Borel sets,[10] this definition is consistent with the requirement

[10] To see that an *open* interval I is a Borel set choose a continuous function v which vanishes outside I and is strictly positive in I. Then $\sqrt[n]{v} \to \mathbf{1}_I$. A closed or half-closed interval I is the limit of a descending sequence of open intervals I_n and hence $\mathbf{1}_I = \lim \mathbf{1}_{I_n}$ is again a Baire function. (Since every continuous function is the limit of step functions it follows that the Baire functions can be characterized as the smallest class closed under limits and containing all step functions.)

that $\mathbf{P}\{I\} = F\{I\}$ for each interval I. Furthermore (2.8) shows that for every countable collection of non-overlapping Borel sets A_n

$$\mathbf{P}\{\cup A_n\} = \sum_n \mathbf{P}\{A_n\}. \tag{3.2}$$

This is the property of complete additivity, and the discussion of the last section shows that (3.1) is the *only* assignment of probabilities to Borel sets such that (3.2) holds and $\mathbf{P}\{I\} = F\{I\}$ for intervals.

We have assigned probabilities only to Borel sets, but the class of Borel sets is so large that all standard operations can be performed within it. In fact, the complement A' of a Borel set is a Borel set, and so are the unions and intersections of countable collections of Borel sets. As was shown in section 1 this implies that the upper and lower limits of any sequence $\{A_n\}$ are again Borel sets. Families of sets with similar properties are of extremely wide use and we formalize their notion by a definition applicable in *arbitrary sample spaces*, and not only in $\mathfrak{R}^n$.

Definition 1. *A σ-algebra*[11] *is a family* $\mathfrak{A}$ *of subsets of a given set* $\mathfrak{S}$ *such that:* (i) *If* A *is in* $\mathfrak{A}$ *so is its complement* $A' = \mathfrak{S} - A$. (ii) *If* $\{A_n\}$ *is any countable collection of sets in* $\mathfrak{A}$ *then also their union* $\cup A_n$ *and their intersection* $\cap A_n$ *belong to* $\mathfrak{A}$.

In short, a σ-algebra is a system of sets closed under complementation and the formation of countable unions and intersections. Being the union of A and A', the whole space always belongs to the σ-algebra.

Examples. The *largest* σ-algebra in a space $\mathfrak{S}$ is the family of *all* subsets. This algebra served us well in discrete sample spaces but is too large to be useful in general. The other extreme is represented by the trivial algebra containing only the whole space and the empty set. For a non-trivial example consider the sets on the line $\mathfrak{R}^1$ with the property that if $x \in A$ then all points $x \pm 1, x \pm 2, \ldots$ belong to A (periodic sets). Obviously the family of such sets forms a σ-algebra. ▶

We have considered the particular case of Cartesian spaces $\mathfrak{R}^r$ and have shown how probabilities can be assigned to the σ-algebra of Borel sets. This procedure serves as model for the following more general probabilistic setup.

Definition 2. *A probability measure* $\mathbf{P}$ *on a σ-algebra* $\mathfrak{A}$ *in a space* $\mathfrak{S}$ *is a function assigning a value* $\mathbf{P}\{A\} \geq 0$ *to each set* $A \in \mathfrak{A}$ *such that* $\mathbf{P}\{\mathfrak{S}\} = 1$

[11] The definition of an algebra of sets is obtained on replacing the word countable by finite. A σ-algebra is sometimes called Borel algebra, but this term is better reserved for the smallest σ-algebra containing all open sets of a topological space $\mathfrak{S}$. For $\mathfrak{S} = \mathfrak{R}^r$ this coincides with our family of Borel sets.

and the addition rule (3.2) *holds for every countable collection of mutually non-overlapping sets* A_n *in* $\mathfrak{A}$.

A probability space[12] *is a triple* $(\mathfrak{S}, \mathfrak{A}, \mathbf{P})$ *of a sample space* $\mathfrak{S}$, *a* σ-*algebra* $\mathfrak{A}$ *of sets in it, and a probability measure* $\mathbf{P}$ *on* $\mathfrak{A}$.

Naturally this definition provides only the background for a general setup, and in individual cases it is necessary to choose an appropriate σ-algebra and to construct a probability measure on it. The procedure will be illustrated by the example of a "sequence of independent random variables" (section 6). It is true that an arbitrary "probability space" is not necessarily an interesting object but the definition embodies all that is required for the formal setting of a theory following the pattern of the first volume, and it would be sterile to discuss in advance the types of sample spaces that may turn up in some probabilistic context.

Approximation of Borel sets by intervals. Let us return to the important special case of the Cartesian space $\mathcal{R}^r$ and the σ-algebra of Borel sets. Starting from a completely additive interval function probabilities are defined by $\mathbf{P}\{A\} = \mathbf{E}(\mathbf{1}_A)$. By the mean approximation theorem (section 2) there exists a step function v such that $\mathbf{E}(|\mathbf{1}_A - v|) < \frac{1}{2}\epsilon$. Consider the function w such that $w(x) = 1$ where $v(x) > \frac{1}{2}$ and $w(x) = 0$ where $v(x) \leq \frac{1}{2}$. It is easily verified that $|\mathbf{1}_A(x) - w(x)| \leq 2\,|\mathbf{1}_A(x) - v(x)|$ for all x, and hence $|\mathbf{P}\{A\} - \mathbf{E}(w)| < \epsilon$. But w is a step function assuming only the values 0 and 1, and therefore $w = \mathbf{1}_B$ is an indicator. This proves that *to each Borel set A it is possible to find a set B consisting of finitely many rectangles such that*

$$|\mathbf{P}\{A\} - \mathbf{P}\{B\}| < \epsilon, \tag{3.3}$$

$\epsilon > 0$ being arbitrary. The meaning of this theorem becomes clear if one thinks of the area of a plane figure (such as the interior of a triangle or ellipse). It proves that the Borel sets are a natural object not too far removed from intervals.

4. RANDOM VARIABLES. EXPECTATIONS

(We are now working within the framework of an arbitrary probability space established in the last definition. The problem is to define random variables in analogy with the Baire functions of $\mathcal{R}^r$ and to define their expectations in terms of the underlying probability measure.)

Random variables are a common object of probability theory. Probabilities in discrete sample spaces are based on the σ-algebra of all sets,

---

[12] Condition $\mathbf{P}\{\mathfrak{S}\} = 1$ serves norming purposes only and nothing essential changes if it is replaced by $\mathbf{P}\{\mathfrak{S}\} < \infty$. One speaks in this case of a *finite measure space*. In probability theory the case $\mathbf{P}\{\mathfrak{S}\} < 1$ occurs in various connections and in this case we speak of a *defective probability measure*. Even the condition $\mathbf{P}\{\mathfrak{S}\} < \infty$ may be weakened by requiring only that $\mathfrak{S}$ be the union of countably many parts $\mathfrak{S}_n$ such that $\mathbf{P}\{\mathfrak{S}_n\} < \infty$. (Length and area are typical examples.) One speaks then of σ-*finite measures*.

and therefore an arbitrary real function on the sample space can serve as "random variable." In general, the minimal requirement on a random variable is that it have a distribution function. In other words, given a function u on a probability space we require that the set of points x where $u(x) \leq t$ should belong to our σ-algebra $\mathfrak{A}$ so that we can write

$$(4.1) \qquad F(t) = \mathbf{P}\{u \leq t\}.$$

Surprisingly enough it turns out that this innocuous requirement is sufficient to characterize a class of functions so large that we never need go beyond it. Accordingly we introduce the

Definition 1.[13] *A random variable is a function u on a probability space such that for each real t the set of points x where $u(x) \leq t$ belongs to the underlying σ-algebra $\mathfrak{A}$. The function F of* (4.1) *is called the distribution function of u.*

Some properties of random variables are almost self-evident. For example, the set where $u(x) < t$ is the union of the sets where $u(x) \leq t - n^{-1}$ for $n = 1, 2, \ldots$ and therefore belongs to $\mathfrak{A}$. The set where $a < u(x) \leq b$ is the difference of two sets in $\mathfrak{A}$ and hence again in $\mathfrak{A}$, and so forth. We now show more generally that—speaking very roughly—all sets that can be defined by a random variable belong to $\mathfrak{A}$ and all functions of u are random variables. In other words, no operations will lead outside the basic setup. To show this we give a characterization of random variables.

Definition 2. *A function is simple if it assumes only countably many values $a_1, a_2, \ldots$, each on a set belonging to the underlying σ-algebra $\mathfrak{A}$.*

By definition, every simple function is a random variable. Conversely, given a random variable u and $\epsilon > 0$ denote by A_n the set of all points x such that $(n-1)\epsilon < u(x) \leq n\epsilon$ (here $n = 0, \pm 1, \pm 2, \ldots$). These sets are obviously non-overlapping and we can define two simple functions $\underline{\sigma}$ and $\bar{\sigma}$ letting $\underline{\sigma}(x) = (n-1)\epsilon$ and $\bar{\sigma} = n\epsilon$ for $x \in A_n$. Then

$$(4.2) \qquad \underline{\sigma}(x) < u(x) \leq \bar{\sigma}(x) \quad \textit{and} \quad \bar{\sigma}(x) - \underline{\sigma}(x) = \epsilon.$$

[13] Given an *arbitrary* σ-algebra $\mathfrak{A}$ of sets in an arbitrary space, a function f is called $\mathfrak{A}$-*measurable* if for each t the set of points x where $f(x) \leq t$ belongs to $\mathfrak{A}$. (The term is misleading because no measure need be defined.) Definition 1 states that a function in a probability space is a random variable if it is measurable with respect to the underlying σ-algebra. The following discussion applies without change to the class of $\mathfrak{A}$-measurable functions for any σ-algebra $\mathfrak{A}$ (and this fact is used for conditional expectations in V,10). The restricted formulation of the text is chosen for simplicity and in order not to detract from the main point.

Thus every random variable can be approximated by a simple function with an error $\leq \epsilon$. Choosing $\epsilon = 1, \frac{1}{2}, \frac{1}{3}, \ldots$ we get two sequences of simple functions σ_n such that $\sigma_n \to u$ uniformly. Conversely, consider a non-decreasing sequence of simple functions σ_n and put $\lim \sigma_n(x) = v(x)$. If $v(x) < \infty$ for all x, denote by S_n and S the sets of points where $\sigma_n(x) > t$ and $v(x) > t$, respectively. Then $S_n \to S$ and therefore S belongs to $\mathfrak{A}$ so that v is a random variable. We have thus proved the

Lemma. *A function u is a random variable iff it is the pointwise limit of a monotone sequence of simple functions. In this case there exist two simple functions satisfying* (4.2) *with prescribed* $\epsilon > 0$.

The last argument shows more generally that if a monotone sequence $\{v_n\}$ of random variables tends to a finite limit v, this limit is again a random variable. The same is true of finite limits of arbitrary sequences $\{v_n\}$ of random variables because they can be represented as limits of monotone sequences (section 1). Furthermore, if $W(x_1, \ldots, x_n)$ is a continuous function of the real variables $x_1, \ldots, x_n$ and if $\sigma_1, \ldots, \sigma_n$ are simple functions in the sample space $\mathfrak{S}$, then $W(\sigma_1, \ldots, \sigma_n)$ is again a simple function in $\mathfrak{S}$. A simple passage to the limit shows that *every continuous function of random variables is a random variable.* Thus the class of random variables is closed under continuous operations and under passages to the limit. In particular, sums and products of random variables are again random variables. This statement suffices for our purposes but can be strengthened as follows. Consider a function W of n real variables with the property that $W(u_1, \ldots, u_n)$ is a random variable for every choice of random variables $u_1, \ldots, u_n$ in $\mathfrak{S}$. The class of such functions W is closed under passages to the limit, and it contains all continuous functions in $\mathfrak{R}^n$. It follows that this class contains all Baire functions in $\mathfrak{R}^n$, and we have thus proved

Theorem. *The class of random variables is closed under passages to the limit, and every Baire function of finitely many random variables is itself a random variable.*

Example. *Let the sample space be $\mathfrak{R}^r$, the σ-algebra $\mathfrak{A}$ coincide with the class of Borel sets and let* $\mathbf{P}\{A\} = \mathbf{E}(\mathbf{1}_A)$, the expectation being defined as in section 2. In this probability space *random variables, Baire functions, and Borel measurable functions are the same.* ►

Expectations

In the special case of the preceding example we started out by defining expectations and introduced probabilities as expectations of indicators. This procedure was convenient to introduce the various tools and concepts, but it is inapplicable when one starts from an arbitrary probability space. Fortunately a direct definition of expectations in terms of probabilities is simple and unique. For a simple function σ assuming the values $a_1, a_2, \ldots$ on sets $A_1, A_2, \ldots$ we must have under any circumstances

$$\mathbf{E}(\sigma) = \sum a_n \mathbf{P}\{A_n\}, \tag{4.3}$$

provided, of course, that the series converges absolutely. [Otherwise $\mathbf{E}(\sigma)$ remains undefined.] Every random variable u is the uniform limit of a sequence of simple functions σ_n. This means that for n and m sufficiently large $|\sigma_n(x) - \sigma_m(x)| < \epsilon$ and so either $\mathbf{E}(\sigma_n)$ exists for all n sufficiently large or for none. In the first case $|\mathbf{E}(\sigma_n) - \mathbf{E}(\sigma_m)| < \epsilon$ and hence $\{\mathbf{E}(\sigma_n)\}$ is a Cauchy sequence with a finite limit. As two approximating sequences can be combined into one, the limit is independent of the approximating sequence and we can define

$$\mathbf{E}(u) = \lim \mathbf{E}(\sigma_n). \tag{4.4}$$

In other words, the expectation of u *either does not exist or is the common limit of* $\mathbf{E}(\sigma_n)$ *for all sequences of simple functions* converging uniformly to u.

A computational definition of $\mathbf{E}(u)$ may clarify the situation. For given $\epsilon > 0$ and $n = 0, \pm 1, \pm 2, \ldots$ denote again by A_n the set of points x where $(n-1)\epsilon < u(x) \leq n\epsilon$. Consider again the simple functions $\underline{\sigma}$ and $\bar{\sigma}$ which assume on A_n the values $(n-1)\epsilon$ and $n\epsilon$, respectively. Then (4.2) is true and so either both

$$\mathbf{E}(\underline{\sigma}_n) = \epsilon \sum (n-1)\,\mathbf{P}\{A_n\} \qquad \text{and} \qquad \mathbf{E}(\bar{\sigma}_n) = \epsilon \sum n\,\mathbf{P}\{A_n\} \tag{4.5}$$

are finite, or neither expectation exists. In the latter case $\mathbf{E}(u)$ remains undefined while in the former

$$\mathbf{E}(\underline{\sigma}_n) \leq \mathbf{E}(u) \leq \mathbf{E}(\bar{\sigma}_n). \tag{4.6}$$

This yields $\mathbf{E}(u)$ with an error less than ϵ.

The random variable u maps our sample space $\mathfrak{S}$ into the real line, and its distribution function (4.1) induces a probability measure on the real line. Accordingly, we can view the random variable u either as function on the sample space $\mathfrak{S}$ or as coordinate variable on the line endowed with the probability distribution F. Now if F is the distribution of u and I_n the interval $(n-1)\epsilon < t \leq n\epsilon$, then

$$F\{I_n\} = \mathbf{P}\{(n-1)\epsilon < u \leq n\epsilon\} = \mathbf{P}\{A_n\}. \tag{4.7}$$

The simple functions $\underline{\sigma}_n$ and $\bar{\sigma}_n$ are mapped into simple functions on the line, and it is obvious that the expectation of the coordinate variable (as defined in section 2) satisfies the inequalities (4.6). Thus

$$\mathbf{E}(u) = \int_{-\infty}^{+\infty} t\, F\{dt\}. \tag{4.8}$$

In other words, *the expectation of a random variable may be defined (consistently) either directly in the original probability space or in terms of its distribution function.* (See **1**; IX for the analogous remark in discrete sample spaces.)

5. THE EXTENSION THEOREM

The usual starting point in the construction of probability spaces is that probabilities are assigned a priori to a restricted class of sets, and the domain of definition must be suitably extended. For example, in dealing with unending sequences of trials and recurrent events in volume **1** we were given the probabilities of all events depending on finitely many trials, but this domain of definition had to be enlarged to include events such as ruin, recurrence, and ultimate extinction. Again, the construction of measures in $\mathfrak{R}^r$ in section 2 proceeded from an assignment of probabilities $F\{I\}$ to intervals, and this domain of definition was extended to the class of all Borel sets. The possibility of such an extension is due to a theorem of much wider applicability, and many constructions of probability spaces depend on it. The procedure is as follows.

The additivity of F permits us to define without ambiguity

$$F\{A\} = \sum F\{I_k\} \tag{5.1}$$

for every set A which is the union of *finitely many non-overlapping intervals* I_k. Now these sets form an *algebra* $\mathfrak{A}_0$ (that is, unions, intersections, and complements of *finitely* many sets in $\mathfrak{A}_0$ belong again to $\mathfrak{A}_0$). From here on the nature of the underlying space $\mathfrak{R}^r$ plays no role, and we may consider an arbitrary algebra $\mathfrak{A}_0$ of sets in an arbitrary space $\mathfrak{S}$. There exists always a smallest algebra $\mathfrak{A}$ of sets containing $\mathfrak{A}_0$ which is closed also under *countable* unions and intersections. In other words, there exists a smallest σ-algebra $\mathfrak{A}$ containing $\mathfrak{A}_0$ (see definition 3.1). In the construction of measures in $\mathfrak{R}^r$ the σ-algebra $\mathfrak{A}$ coincided with the σ-algebra of all Borel sets. The extension of the domain of definition of probabilities from $\mathfrak{A}_0$ to $\mathfrak{A}$ is based on the general

Extension theorem. *Let $\mathfrak{A}_0$ be an algebra of sets in some space $\mathfrak{S}$. Let F be a set function defined on $\mathfrak{A}_0$ such that $F\{A\} \geq 0$ for all $A \in \mathfrak{A}_0$, that $F\{\mathfrak{S}\} = 1$, and that the addition rule* (5.1) *holds for any partition of A into countably many non-overlapping sets $I_k \in \mathfrak{A}_0$.*

There exists then a unique extension of F to a countably additive set function (that is, probability measure) on the smallest σ-algebra $\mathfrak{A}$ containing $\mathfrak{A}_0$.

A typical application will be given in the next section. Here we give a more general and more flexible version of the extension theorem which is more in line with the development in sections 2 and 3. We started from the expectation (2.4) for step functions (that is, functions assuming only finitely many values, each on an interval). The domain of definition of this expectation was then extended from the restricted class of step functions to a wider class including all bounded Baire functions. This extension leads directly to the Lebesgue-Stieltjes integral, and the measure of a set A is obtained as the expectation of its indicator $\mathbf{1}_A$. The corresponding abstract setup is as follows.

Instead of the algebra $\mathfrak{A}_0$ of sets we consider a class $\mathfrak{B}_0$ of functions closed under linear combinations and the operations $\cap$ and $\cup$. In other words, we suppose that if u_1 and u_2 are in $\mathfrak{B}_0$ so are the functions[14]

$$(5.2) \qquad \alpha_1 u_1 + \alpha_2 u_2, \qquad u_1 \cap u_2, \qquad u_1 \cup u_2.$$

This implies in particular that every function u of $\mathfrak{B}_0$ can be written in the form $u = u^+ - u^-$ as the difference of two non-negative functions, namely $u^+ = u \cup 0$ and $u^- = u \cap 0$. By a *linear functional on* $\mathfrak{B}_0$ is meant an assignment of values $\mathbf{E}(u)$ to all functions of $\mathfrak{B}_0$ satisfying the addition rule

$$(5.3) \qquad \mathbf{E}(\alpha_1 u_1 + \alpha_2 u_2) = \alpha_1 \mathbf{E}(u_1) + \alpha_2 \mathbf{E}(u_2).$$

The functional is *positive if* $u \geq 0$ implies $\mathbf{E}(u) \geq 0$. The *norm* of $\mathbf{E}$ is the least upper bound of $\mathbf{E}(|u|)$ for all functions $u \in \mathfrak{B}_0$ such that $|u| \leq 1$. If the constant function 1 belongs to $\mathfrak{B}_0$ the norm of $\mathbf{E}$ equals $\mathbf{E}(1)$. Finally, we say that $\mathbf{E}$ is *countably additive on* $\mathfrak{B}_0$ if

$$(5.4) \qquad \mathbf{E}\left(\sum_1^\infty u_k\right) = \sum_1^\infty \mathbf{E}(u_k)$$

whenever Σu_k happens to be in $\mathfrak{B}_0$. An *equivalent* condition is: if $\{v_n\}$ is a sequence of functions in $\mathfrak{B}_0$ converging *monotonically* to zero, then[15]

$$(5.5) \qquad \mathbf{E}(v_n) \to 0.$$

Given the class $\mathfrak{B}_0$ of functions there exists a *smallest class* $\mathfrak{B}$ *containing* $\mathfrak{B}_0$ *and closed under pointwise passages to the limit.* [It is automatically closed under the operations (5.2).] An alternative formulation of the

[14] Our postulates amount to requiring that $\mathfrak{B}_0$ be a linear lattice.

[15] To prove the equivalence of (5.4) and (5.5) it suffices to consider the case $u_k \geq 0$, $v_k \geq 0$. Then (5.4) follows from (5.5) with $v_n = u_{n+1} + u_{n+2} + \cdots$ and (5.5) follows from (5.4) on putting $u_k = v_k - v_{k+1}$ (that is, $\Sigma u_k = v_1$).

extension theorem is as follows.[16] *Every positive countably additive linear functional of norm* 1 *on* $\mathfrak{B}_0$ *can be uniquely extended to a positive countably additive linear functional of norm* 1 *on all bounded (and many unbounded) functions of* $\mathfrak{B}$.

As an example for the applicability of this theorem we prove the following important result.

F. Riesz representation theorem.[17] *Let* **E** *be a positive linear functional of norm* 1 *on the class of continuous functions on* $\mathcal{R}^r$ *vanishing at infinity.*[18] *There exists a measure* **P** *on the* σ*-algebra of Borel sets with* $\mathbf{P}\{\mathcal{R}^r\} = 1$ *such that* $\mathbf{E}(u)$ *coincides with the integral of* u *with respect to* **P**.

In other words, our integrals represent the most general positive linear functionals.

Proof. The crucial point is that if a sequence $\{v_n\}$ of continuous functions vanishing at infinity converges monotonically to zero, the convergence is automatically *uniform*. Assume $v_n \geq 0$ and put $\|v_n\| = \max v_n(x)$. Then $\mathbf{E}(v_n) \leq \|v_n\|$, and so the countable additivity condition (5.5) is satisfied. By the extension theorem **E** can be extended to all bounded Baire functions and putting $\mathbf{P}\{A\} = \mathbf{E}\{\mathbf{1}_A\}$ we get a measure on the σ-algebra of Borel sets. Given the measures $\mathbf{P}\{A\}$ we saw that the Lebesgue-Stieltjes integral is uniquely characterized by the double inequality (4.6) and this shows that for u continuous and vanishing at infinity this integral coincides with the given functional $\mathbf{E}(u)$. ▶

6. PRODUCT SPACES. SEQUENCES OF INDEPENDENT VARIABLES

The notion of combinatorial product spaces (**1**; V,4) is basic for probability theory and is used every time one speaks of repeated trials.

---

[16] The basic idea of the proof (going back to Lebesgue) is simple and ingenious. It is not difficult to see that if two sequences $\{u_n\}$ and $\{u_n'\}$ of functions in $\mathfrak{B}_0$ converge *monotonically* to the same limit u then $\mathbf{E}(u_n)$ and $\mathbf{E}(u_n')$ tend to the same limit. For such monotone limits u we can therefore define $\mathbf{E}(u) = \lim \mathbf{E}(u_n)$. Consider now the class $\mathfrak{B}_1$ of functions u such that to each $\epsilon > 0$ there exist two functions $\underline{u}$ and $\bar{u}$ which are either in $\mathfrak{B}_0$ or are monotone limits of sequences $\mathfrak{B}_0$ and such that $\underline{u} < u < \bar{u}$ and $\mathbf{E}(\bar{u}) - \mathbf{E}(\underline{u}) < \epsilon$. The class $\mathfrak{B}_1$ is closed under limits and for functions in $\mathfrak{B}_1$ the definition of $\mathbf{E}(u)$ is obvious since we must have $\mathbf{E}(\underline{u}) \leq \mathbf{E}(u) \leq \mathbf{E}(\bar{u})$.

The *tour de force* in this argument is that the class $\mathfrak{B}_1$ is usually greater than $\mathfrak{B}$ and the simple proof is made possible by proving more than is required. (For a comparison between $\mathfrak{B}$ and $\mathfrak{B}_1$ see section 7.)

[17] Valid for arbitrary locally compact spaces.

[18] u vanishes at infinity if for given $\epsilon > 0$ there exists a sphere (compact set) outside which $|u(x)| < \epsilon$.

Describing a point in the plane $\mathfrak{R}^2$ by two coordinates means that $\mathfrak{R}^2$ is taken as the combinatorial product of its two axes. Denote the two coordinate variables by **X** and **Y**. Considered as functions in the plane they are Baire functions, and if a probability measure **P** is defined on the σ-algebra of Borel sets in $\mathfrak{R}^2$ the two distribution functions $\mathbf{P}\{\mathbf{X} \leq x\}$ and $\mathbf{P}\{\mathbf{Y} \leq y\}$ exist. They induce probability measures on the two axes called the marginal distributions (or projections). In this description the plane appears as the primary notion, but frequently the inverse procedure is more natural. For example, when we speak of two independent random variables with given distributions, the two marginal distributions are the primary notion and probabilities in the plane are derived from it by "the product rule." The procedure is not more complicated in the general setup than for the plane.

Consider then two arbitrary probability spaces, that is, we are given two sample spaces $\mathfrak{S}^{(1)}$ and $\mathfrak{S}^{(2)}$, two σ-algebras $\mathfrak{A}^{(1)}$ and $\mathfrak{A}^{(2)}$ of sets in $\mathfrak{S}^{(1)}$ and $\mathfrak{S}^{(2)}$, respectively, and probability measures $\mathbf{P}^{(1)}$ and $\mathbf{P}^{(2)}$ defined on them. The combinatorial product $(\mathfrak{S}^{(1)}, \mathfrak{S}^{(2)})$ is the set of all ordered pairs $(x^{(1)}, x^{(2)})$ where $x^{(i)}$ is a point in $\mathfrak{S}^{(i)}$. Among the sets in this product space we consider the "rectangles," that is, the combinatorial products $(A^{(1)}, A^{(2)})$ of sets $A^{(i)} \in \mathfrak{A}^{(i)}$. With sets of this form we wish to associate probabilities by the product rule

$$\mathbf{P}\{(A^{(1)}, A^{(2)})\} = \mathbf{P}^{(1)}\{A^{(1)}\}\, \mathbf{P}^{(2)}\{A^{(2)}\}. \tag{6.1}$$

Now sets which are unions of finitely many non-overlapping rectangles form an algebra $\mathfrak{A}_0$, and (6.1) defines in a unique way a countably[19] additive function on it. Accordingly, by the extension theorem *there exists a unique probability measure* **P** *defined on the smallest σ-algebra containing all rectangles and such that the probabilities of rectangles are given by the product rule* (6.1). *This smallest σ-algebra containing all rectangles will be denoted by $\mathfrak{A}^{(1)} \times \mathfrak{A}^{(2)}$, and the measure will be called product measure.*

Of course, other probability measures can be defined on the product space, for example in terms of conditional probabilities. Under any circumstances the underlying σ-algebra $\mathfrak{A}$ of sets will be at least as large

[19] In fact, if $(A^{(1)}, A^{(2)})$ is the union of the non-overlapping rectangles $(A_p^{(1)}, A_p^{(2)})$, consider all intersections $A_j^{(i)} \cap A_k^{(i)}$ (where i = 1, 2). Among them one can choose a sequence $B_1^{(i)}, B_2^{(i)}, \ldots$ of non-overlapping sets such that each $A_p^{(i)}$ is the union of some $B_k^{(i)}$. Then $(A^{(1)}, A^{(2)})$ is the union of the non-overlapping rectangles $(B_j^{(1)}, B_k^{(2)})$ and $\sum_p \mathbf{P}^{(1)}\{A_p^{(1)}\} \cdot \mathbf{P}^{(2)}\{A_p^{(2)}\} = \sum_{j,k} \mathbf{P}^{(1)}\{B_j^{(1)}\}\, \mathbf{P}^{(2)}\{B_k^{(2)}\}$. The last double sum equals the product of

$$\sum_j \mathbf{P}^{(1)}\{B_j^{(1)}\} = \mathbf{P}\{A^{(1)}\} \quad \text{and} \quad \sum_k \mathbf{P}^{(2)}\{B_k^{(2)}\} = \mathbf{P}\{A^{(2)}\}.$$

as $\mathfrak{A}^{(1)} \times \mathfrak{A}^{(2)}$, and it is rarely necessary to go beyond this algebra. The following discussion of random variables is valid whenever the underlying algebra $\mathfrak{A}$ is given by $\mathfrak{A} = \mathfrak{A}^{(1)} \times \mathfrak{A}^{(2)}$.

The notion of random variable (measurable function) is relative to the underlying σ-algebra and with our setup for product spaces we must distinguish between random variables in the product space and those on $\mathfrak{S}^{(1)}$ and $\mathfrak{S}^{(2)}$. The relationship between these three classes is fortunately extremely simple. If u and v are random variables on $\mathfrak{S}^{(1)}$ and $\mathfrak{S}^{(2)}$ we consider in the product space the function w which at the point $(x^{(1)}, x^{(2)})$ takes on the value

$$w(x^{(1)}, x^{(2)}) = u(x^{(1)}) \cdot v(x^{(2)}). \tag{6.2}$$

We show that *the class of random variables in the product space* $(\mathfrak{S}^{(1)}, \mathfrak{S}^{(2)})$ *is the smallest class of finite-valued functions closed under pointwise passages to the limit and containing all linear combinations of functions of the form* (6.2).

To begin with, it is clear that each factor on the right in (6.2) is a random variable even when considered as a function on the product space. It follows that w is a random variable, and hence the class of random variables in $(\mathfrak{S}^{(1)}, \mathfrak{S}^{(2)})$ is at least as extensive as claimed. On the other hand, the random variables form the smallest class of functions that is closed under passages to the limit and contains all linear combinations of indicators of rectangles. Such indicators are of the form (6.2) and therefore the class of random variables cannot be larger than claimed.

The special case of the product of two spaces $\mathfrak{R}^m$ and $\mathfrak{R}^n$ with probability measures F and G occurred indirectly in connection with Fubini's theorem (2.12) concerning repeated integrals. We can now state the more general theorem, which is *not* restricted to $\mathfrak{R}^r$.

Fubini's theorem for product measures. *For arbitrary non-negative Baire functions u, the integral of u with respect to the product measure equals the repeated integrals in* (2.12).

(It is understood that the integrals may diverge. The theorem is obvious for simple functions and follows in general by the approximation procedure employed repeatedly.) The generalization to product spaces with three or more factors is too obvious to require comment.

We turn to the problem of *infinite sequences of random variables*, which we encountered in volume **1** in connection with unlimited sequences of Bernoulli trials, random walks, recurrent events, etc., and again in chapter III in connection with normal stochastic processes. Nothing need be said when infinitely many random variables are defined on a given probability space. For example, the real line with the normal distribution is a probability space and $\{\sin nx\}$ is an infinite sequence of random variables on it. We are here concerned only with the situation when the probabilities are to be defined in terms of the given random variables. More precisely, our problem is as follows.

Let $\mathfrak{R}^\infty$ denote the space whose points are infinite sequences of real numbers $(x_1, x_2, \ldots)$, (that is, $\mathfrak{R}^\infty$ is a denumerable combinatorial product of real lines). We denote the nth coordinate variable by $\mathbf{X}_n$ (that is, $\mathbf{X}_n$ is the function in $\mathfrak{R}^\infty$ which at the point $x = (x_1, x_2, \ldots)$ assumes the value x_n). We suppose that we are given the probability distributions for $\mathbf{X}_1, (\mathbf{X}_1, \mathbf{X}_2), (\mathbf{X}_1, \mathbf{X}_2, \mathbf{X}_3), \ldots$ and wish to define appropriate probabilities in $\mathfrak{R}^\infty$. Needless to say, the given distributions must be mutually consistent in the sense that the distributions of $(\mathbf{X}_1, \ldots, \mathbf{X}_n)$ appear as marginal distributions for $(\mathbf{X}_1, \ldots, \mathbf{X}_{n+1})$, and so on.

Let us now formalize the intuitive notion of an "event determined by the outcome of finitely many trials." We agree to say that *a set A in $\mathfrak{R}^\infty$ depends only on the first r coordinates iff there exists a Borel set A_r in $\mathfrak{R}^r$ such that $x = (x_1, x_2, \ldots)$ belongs to A iff $(x_1, \ldots, x_r)$ belongs to A_r.* The standard situation in probability is that the probabilities for such sets are prescribed, and we face the problem of extending this domain of definition. We state without proof the basic theorem derived (in slightly greater generality) by A. Kolmogorov in his now classical axiomatic foundation of probability theory (1933). It anticipated and stimulated the development of modern measure theory.

Theorem 1. *A consistent system of probability distributions for* $\mathbf{X}_1$, $(\mathbf{X}_1, \mathbf{X}_2), (\mathbf{X}_1, \mathbf{X}_2, \mathbf{X}_3), \ldots$ *admits of a unique extension to a probability measure on $\mathfrak{A}$, the smallest σ-algebra of sets in $\mathfrak{R}^\infty$ containing all sets depending only on finitely many coordinates.*[20]

The important point is that all probabilities are defined by successive passages to the limit starting with finite-dimensional sets. *Every set A in $\mathfrak{A}$ can be approximated by finite-dimensional sets* in the following sense. Given $\epsilon > 0$ there exists for each n a set A_n depending only on the first n coordinates and such that

$$\mathbf{P}\{A - A \cap A_n\} < \epsilon, \qquad \mathbf{P}\{A_n - A \cap A_n\} < \epsilon. \tag{6.3}$$

In other words, the set of those points that belong to either A or A_n but not to both has probability $< 2\epsilon$. It follows that the sets A_n can be chosen

[20] The theorem applies more generally to products of locally compact spaces; for example, the variables $\mathbf{X}_n$ may be interpreted as vector variables (points in $\mathfrak{R}^r$).

such that

$$(6.4) \qquad \mathbf{P}\{A_n\} \to \mathbf{P}\{A\}.$$

Theorem 1 enables us to speak of *an infinite sequence of mutually independent random variables with arbitrarily prescribed distributions.* Such sequences did in fact occur in volume **1**, but we had to be careful to define the probabilities in question by specific passsages to the limit, whereas theorem 1 provides the desirable freedom of motion. This point is well illustrated by the following two important theorems due, respectively, to A. Kolmogorov (1933) and to E. Hewitt and L. J. Savage (1955). They are typical for probabilistic arguments and play a central role in many contexts.

Theorem 2. (*Zero-or-one law for tail events.*) *Suppose that the variables* $\mathbf{X}_k$ *are mutually independent and that for each n the event A is independent of*[21] $\mathbf{X}_1, \ldots, \mathbf{X}_n$. *Then either* $\mathbf{P}\{A\} = 0$ *or* $\mathbf{P}\{A\} = 1$.

Proof. In principle the variables $\mathbf{X}_k$ can be defined in an arbitrary probability space, but they map this space into the product space $\mathcal{R}^\infty$ in which they serve as coordinate variables. There is therefore no loss of generality in departing from the setup described in this section. With the notations used in (6.3) the sets A and A_n are independent and so these relations imply that $\mathbf{P}\{A\} = \mathbf{P}^2\{A\}$. ▶

Example. (*a*) The series $\Sigma\mathbf{X}_n$ converges with probability zero or one. Similarly, the set of those points where $\limsup \mathbf{X}_n = \infty$ has either probability zero or one. ▶

Theorem 3. (*Zero-or-one law for symmetric events.*) *Suppose that the variables* $\mathbf{X}_k$ *are mutually independent and have a common distribution. If the set A is invariant under finite permutations of the coordinates*[22] *then either* $\mathbf{P}\{A\} = 0$ *or* $\mathbf{P}\{A\} = 1$.

Proof. As in the last proof we use the $\mathbf{X}_k$ as coordinate variables and refer to the sets A_n occurring in (6.3). Let B_n be the set obtained from A_n by reversing the first $2n$ coordinates and leaving the others fixed. By hypothesis then (6.3) remains valid also when A_n is replaced by B_n. It

[21] More precisely, A is independent of every event defined in terms of $\mathbf{X}_1, \ldots, \mathbf{X}_n$. In other words, the indicator of A is a random variable independent of $\mathbf{X}_1, \ldots, \mathbf{X}_n$.

[22] More precisely, if $(a_1, a_2, \ldots)$ is a point of A and n_1 and n_2 are two arbitrary integers it is supposed that A contains also the point obtained by exchanging a_{n_1} and a_{n_2} while leaving all other coordinates fixed. This condition extends automatically to permutations involving k coordinates.

follows that the set of points belonging to either A or $A_n \cap B_n$ but not to both has probability $< 4\epsilon$, and therefore

$$\mathbf{P}\{A_n \cap B_n\} \to \mathbf{P}\{A\}. \tag{6.5}$$

Furthermore A_n depends only on the first n coordinates and hence B_n depends only on the coordinates number $n + 1, \ldots, 2n$. Thus A_n and B_n are independent and from (6.5) we conclude again that $\mathbf{P}\{A\} = \mathbf{P}^2\{A\}$. ►

Example. (*b*) Put $\mathbf{S}_n = \mathbf{X}_1 + \cdots + \mathbf{X}_n$ and let A be the event $\{\mathbf{S}_n \in I \text{ i. o.}\}$ where I is an arbitrary interval on the line. Then A is invariant under finite permutations. [For the notation see example (1.*a*).] ►

7. NULL SETS. COMPLETION

Usually a set of probability zero is negligible and two random variables differing only on such a null set are "practically the same." More formally they are called *equivalent*. This means that all probability relations remain unchanged if the definition of a random variable is changed on a null set, and hence we can permit a random variable not to be defined on a null set. A typical example is the epoch of the first occurrence of a recurrent event: with unit probability it is a number, but with probability zero it remains undefined (or is called ∞). Thus we are frequently dealing with classes of equivalent random variables rather than with individual variables, but it is usually simplest to choose a convenient representative rather than to speak of equivalence classes.

Null sets give rise to the only point where our probabilistic setup goes against intuition. The situtation is the same in all probability spaces, but it suffices to describe it on the line. With our setup, probabilities are defined only for Borel sets, and in general a Borel set contains many subsets that are not Borel sets. Consequently, a null set may contain sets for which no probability is defined, contrary to the natural expectation that every subset of a null set should be a null set. The discrepancy has no serious effects and it is easily remedied. In fact, suppose we introduce the *postulate: if* $A \subset B$ *and* $\mathbf{P}\{B\} = 0$, *then* $\mathbf{P}\{A\} = 0$. It compels us to enlarge the σ-algebra $\mathfrak{A}$ of Borel sets (at least) to the smallest σ-algebra $\mathfrak{A}_1$ containing all sets of $\mathfrak{A}$ and all subsets of null sets. A direct description is as follows. A set A belongs to $\mathfrak{A}_1$ iff it differs only by a null set[23] from some Borel set A^0. The domain of definition can be extended from $\mathfrak{A}$ to $\mathfrak{A}_1$ simply by putting $\mathbf{P}\{A\} = \mathbf{P}\{A^0\}$. It is almost trivial that this definition is unique and leads to a completely additive measure on $\mathfrak{A}_1$.

[23] More precisely, it is required that both $A - A \cap A^0$ and $A^0 - A \cap A^0$ be contained in a null set.

By this device we have obtained a probability space satisfying our postulate and in which the probabilities of Borel sets remain unchanged.

The construction so described is called the *Lebesgue completion* (of the given probability space). In fact, the Lebesgue construction alluded to in section 5 leads to the completed σ-algebra $\mathfrak{A}_1$ rather than to the Borel algebra $\mathfrak{A}$. This completion is natural in problems concerned with a unique basic probability distribution. For this reason the length of intervals on $\mathfrak{R}^1$ is usually completed to a Lebesgue measure which is not restricted to Borel sets. But the completion would invite trouble when one deals with families of distributions (for example with infinite sequences of Bernoulli trials with unspecified probability p). In fact, $\mathfrak{A}_1$ depends on the underlying distribution, and so a random variable with respect to $\mathfrak{A}_1$ may stop being a random variable when the probabilities are changed.

Example. Let $a_1, a_2, \ldots$ be a sequence of points on $\mathfrak{R}^1$ carrying probabilities $p_1, p_2, \ldots$ where $\Sigma\, p_k = 1$. The complement of $\{a_j\}$ has probability zero and so $\mathfrak{A}_1$ *contains all sets* of $\mathfrak{R}^1$. Every bounded function u is now a random variable with expectation $\Sigma\, p_k u(a_k)$ but it would be dangerous to deal with "arbitrary functions" when the underlying distribution is not discrete. ►

CHAPTER V

Probability Distributions in $\mathfrak{R}^r$

This chapter develops the notion of probability distribution in the r-dimensional space $\mathfrak{R}^r$. Conceptually the notion is based on the integration theory outlined in the last chapter, but in fact no sophistication is required to follow the development because the notions and formulas are intuitively close to those familiar from volume **1** and from the first three chapters.

The novel feature of the theory is that (in contrast to discrete sample spaces) not *every* set carries a probability and not *every* function serves as random variable. Fortunately this theoretical complication is not noticeable in practice because we can start from intervals and continuous functions, respectively, and restrict our attention to sets and functions that can be derived from them by elementary operations and (possibly infinitely many) passages to the limit. This delimits the classes of Borel sets and Baire functions. Readers interested in facts rather than logical connections need not worry about the precise definitions (given in chapter IV). Rather they should rely on their intuition and assume that all sets and functions are "nice." The theorems are so simple[1] that elementary calculus should suffice for an understanding. The exposition is rigorous under the convention that *the words set and function serve as abbreviations for Borel set and Baire function.*

An initial reading should be restricted to sections 1–4 and 9. Sections 5–8 contain tools and inequalities to which one may refer when occasion arises. The last sections develop the theory of conditional distributions

[1] It should be understood that this simplicity cannot be achieved by any theory restricted to the use of continuous functions or any other class of "nice" functions. For example, in II,(8.3) we defined a density φ by an infinite series. To establish conditions for φ to be nice would be tedious and pointless, but the formula is obvious in simple cases and the use of Baire functions amounts to a substitute for a vague "goes through generally."—Incidentally, the few occasions where the restriction to Baire functions is not trivial will be pointed out. (The theory of convex functions in 8.*b* is an example.)

and expectations more fully than required for the present volume where the results are used only incidentally for martingales in VI,11 and VII,7.

1. DISTRIBUTIONS AND EXPECTATIONS

Even the most innocuous use of the term random variable may contain an indirect reference to a complicated probability space or a complex conceptual experiment. For example, the theoretical model may involve the positions and velocities of 10^{28} particles, but we concentrate our attention on the temperature and energy. These two random variables map the original sample space into the plane $\mathcal{R}^2$, carrying with them their probability distributions. In effect we are dealing with a problem in two dimensions and the original sample space looms dimly in the background. The finite-dimensional Cartesian spaces $\mathcal{R}^r$ therefore represent the most important sample spaces, and we turn to a systematic study of the appropriate probability distributions.

Let us begin with the line $\mathcal{R}^1$. The intervals defined by $a < x < b$ and $a \leq x \leq b$ will be denoted by $\overline{a, b}$ and $|\overline{a, b}|$. (We do not exclude the limiting case of a closed interval reducing to a single point. Half-open intervals are denoted by $\overline{a, b}|$ and $|\overline{a, b}$. In one dimension all random variables are functions of the coordinate variable $\mathbf{X}$ (that is, the function which at the place x assumes the value x). All probabilities are therefore expressible in terms of the distribution function

$$F(x) = \mathbf{P}\{\mathbf{X} \leq x\}, \qquad -\infty < x < \infty. \tag{1.1}$$

In particular, an interval $I = \overline{a, b}|$ carries the probability

$$\mathbf{P}\{I\} = F(b) - F(a).$$

The flexible standard notation $\mathbf{P}\{\ \}$ is impractical when we are dealing with varying distributions. A new letter would be uneconomical, and the notation $\mathbf{P}_F\{\ \}$ to indicate the dependence on F is too clumsy. It is by far the simplest to *use the same letter F both for the point function* (1.1) *and for the corresponding interval function*, and we shall write $F\{I\}$ instead of $\mathbf{P}\{I\}$. In other words, the use of braces $\{\ \}$ will indicate that the argument in $F\{A\}$ is an interval or set, and that F appears as a function of intervals (or measure). When parentheses are used the argument in $F(a)$ is a point. The relationship between the point function $F(\ )$ and the interval function $F\{\ \}$ is indicated by

$$F(x) = F\{\overline{-\infty, x}|\}, \qquad F\{\overline{a, b}|\} = F(b) - F(a). \tag{1.2}$$

Actually the notion of the point function $F(x)$ is redundant and serves merely for the convenience of analytical and graphical representation. The primary notion is the assignment of probabilities to *intervals*. The point function $F(\ )$ is called the *distribution function* of the interval function $F\{\ \}$. The symbols $F(\ )$ and $F\{\ \}$ refer to the same thing in two languages, and no confusion can arise by references to "the probability distribution F." One should get used to thinking in terms of *interval* functions or measures and using the distribution function only for graphical descriptions.[2]

Definition. *A point function F on the line is a distribution function if*

(i) *F is non-decreasing, that is, $a < b$ implies $F(a) \leq F(b)$*

(ii) *F is right continuous,*[3] *that is, $F(a) = F(a+)$*

(iii) *$F(-\infty) = 0$ and $F(\infty) < \infty$.*

F is a probability distribution function if it is a distribution function and $F(\infty) = 1$. Furthermore, F is defective if $F(\infty) < 1$.

We proceed to show that every distribution function induces an assignment of probabilities to all sets on the line. The first step consists in assigning probabilities to intervals. Since F is monotone a left limit $F(a-)$ exists for each point a. We define an interval function $F\{I\}$ by

$$(1.3)\qquad \begin{array}{ll} F\{\overline{|a, b|}\} = F(b) - F(a-), & F\{\overline{a, b}\} = F(b-) - F(a) \\ F\{\overline{a, b|}\} = F(b) - F(a), & F\{\overline{|a, b}\} = F(b-) - F(a-). \end{array}$$

For the interval $\overline{|a, a|}$ reducing to the single point a we have

$$F\{\overline{|a, a|}\} = F(a) - F(a-)$$

which is the jump of F at the point a. (It will be seen presently that F is continuous "almost everywhere.")

To show that the assignment of values (1.3) to intervals satisfies the requirements of probability theory we prove a simple lemma (which readers may accept as being intuitively obvious).

Lemma 1. (*Countable additivity.*) *If an interval I is the union of countably many non-overlapping intervals $I_1, I_2, \ldots$, then*

$$(1.4)\qquad F\{I\} = \sum F\{I_k\}.$$

---

[2] Pedantic care in the use of notations seems advisable for an introductory book, but it is hoped that readers will *not* indulge in this sort of consistency and will find the courage to write $F(I)$ and $F(x)$ indiscriminately. No confusion will result and it is (fortunately) quite customary in the best mathematics to use the same symbol (in particular 1 and =) on the same page in several meanings.

[3] As usual we denote by $f(a+)$ the limit, if it exists, of $f(x)$ as $x \to a$ in such a way that $x > a$, and by $f(\infty)$ the limit of $f(x)$ as $x \to \infty$. Similarly for $f(a-)$ and $f(-\infty)$. This notation carries over to higher dimensions.

Proof. The assertion is trivial in the special case $I = \overline{a, b}\rceil$ and $I_1 = \overline{a, a_1}\rceil$, $I_2 = \overline{a_1, a_2}\rceil, \dots, I_n = \overline{a_{n-1}, b}\rceil$. The most general *finite* partition of $I = \overline{a, b}\rceil$ is obtained from this by redistributing the endpoints a_k from one subinterval to another, and so the addition rule (1.4) holds for finite partitions.

In considering the case of infinitely many intervals I_k it suffices to assume I closed. In consequence of the right continuity of the given distribution function F it is possible to find an open interval $I_k^{\#}$ containing I_k and such that $0 \leq F\{I_k^{\#}\} - F\{I_k\} \leq \epsilon \cdot 2^{-k}$ for preassigned $\epsilon > 0$. Now there exists a finite collection $I_{k_1}^{\#}, \dots, I_{k_n}^{\#}$ covering I and hence

$$(1.5) \qquad F\{I\} \leq F\{I_{k_1}^{\#}\} + \cdots + F\{I_{k_n}^{\#}\} \leq F\{I_1\} + \cdots + F\{I_n\} + \epsilon.$$

Thus

$$(1.6) \qquad F\{I\} \leq \sum F\{I_k\}.$$

But the reversed inequality is also true since to each n there exists a *finite* partition of I containing $I_1, \dots, I_n$. This concludes the proof. ▶

As explained in IV,2 it is now possible to define

$$(1.7) \qquad F\{A\} = \sum F\{A_k\}$$

for every set A consisting of finitely or denumerably many disjoint intervals A_k. Intuition leads one to expect that every set can be approximated by such unions of intervals, and measure theory justifies this feeling.[4] Using the natural approximations and passages to the limit it is possible to extend the definition of F to all sets in such a way that the countable additivity property (1.7) is preserved. This extension is unique, and the resulting assignment is called a probability distribution or measure.

Note on terminology. In the literature the term distribution is used loosely in various meanings, and so it is appropriate here to establish the usage to which we shall adhere.

A *probability distribution*, or *probability measure*, is an assignment of numbers $F\{A\} \geq 0$ to sets subject to condition (1.7) of countable additivity and the norming $F\{\overline{-\infty, \infty}\} = 1$. More general measures (or mass distributions) are defined by dropping the norming condition; the Lebesgue measure (or ordinary length) is the most notable example.

As will be recalled from the theory of recurrent events in volume **1**, we have sometimes to deal with measures attributing to the line a total mass $p = F\{\overline{-\infty, \infty}\} < 1$. Such a measure will be called *defective*

[4] The convention that the words set and function serve as abbreviations for *Borel set* and *Baire function* should be borne in mind.

probability measure with *defect* $1 - p$. For stylistic clarity and emphasis we shall occasionally speak of *proper* probability distributions, but the adjective proper is redundant.

The argument of a measure $m\{A\}$ is a set and is indicated by braces. With every bounded measure m there is associated its *distribution function*, that is, a point function defined by $m(x) = m\{\overline{-\infty, x}|\}$. It will be denoted by the same letter with the argument in parentheses. The dual use of the same letter can cause no confusion, and by the same token the term distribution may stand as abbreviation both for a probability distribution and its distribution function. ►

In **1**; IX a *random variable* was defined as a real function on the sample space, and we continue this usage. When the line serves as sample space every real function becomes a random variable. The coordinate variable **X** is basic, and all other random variables can be expressed as functions of it. The distribution function of the random variable u is defined by $\mathbf{P}\{u(\mathbf{X}) \leq x\}$ and can be expressed in terms of the distribution F of the coordinate variable **X**. For example, $\mathbf{X}^3$ has the distribution function given by $F(\sqrt[3]{x})$.

A function u is called *simple* if it assumes only countably many values $a_1, a_2, \ldots$. If A_n denotes the set on which u equals a_n we define the *expectation* $\mathbf{E}(u)$ by

$$\mathbf{E}(u) = \sum a_k\, F\{A_k\} \tag{1.8}$$

provided the series converges absolutely. In the contrary case u is said not to be integrable with respect to F. Thus u has an expectation iff $\mathbf{E}(|u|)$ exists. Starting from the definition (1.8) we can define the expectation for an arbitrary bounded function u as follows. Choose $\epsilon > 0$, and denote by A_n the set of those points x at which $(n-1)\epsilon < x \leq n\epsilon$. With any reasonable definition of $\mathbf{E}(u)$ we must have

$$\sum (n-1)\epsilon \cdot F\{A_n\} \leq \mathbf{E}(u) \leq \sum n\epsilon \cdot F\{A_n\}. \tag{1.9}$$

(The extreme members represent the expectations of two approximating simple functions $\underline{\sigma}$ and $\bar{\sigma}$ such that $\underline{\sigma} \leq u \leq \bar{\sigma}$ and $\bar{\sigma} - \underline{\sigma} = \epsilon$.) Because of the assumed boundedness of u the series in (1.9) contain only finitely many non-zero terms, and their difference equals $\epsilon \sum F\{A_n\} = \epsilon$. Replacing ϵ by $\frac{1}{2}\epsilon$ will increase the first term in (1.9) and decrease the last. It is therefore not difficult to see that as $\epsilon \to 0$ the two extreme members in (1.9) tend to the same limit, and this limit defines $\mathbf{E}(u)$. For unbounded u the same procedure applies provided the two series in (1.9) converge *absolutely*; otherwise $\mathbf{E}(u)$ remains undefined (u is not integrable with respect to F).

The expectation defined in this simple way is called the *Lebesgue-Stieltjes integral of u* with respect to F. When it is desirable to emphasize the dependence of the expectation on F the integral notation is preferable and we write alternatively

$$\mathbf{E}(u) = \int_{-\infty}^{+\infty} u(x)\, F\{dx\} \tag{1.10}$$

with x appearing as dummy variable. Except on rare occasions we shall be concerned only with piecewise continuous or monotone integrands such that the sets A_n will reduce to unions of finitely many intervals. The sums in (1.9) are then simple rearrangements of the upper and lower sums used in the elementary definition of ordinary integrals. The general Lebesgue-Stieltjes integral shares the basic properties of the ordinary integral and has the additional advantage that formal operations and passages to the limit require less care. Our use of expectations will be limited to situations so simple that no general theory will be required to follow the individual steps. The reader interested in the theoretical background and the basic facts is referred to chapter IV.

Examples. (*a*) Let F be a discrete distribution attributing weights $p_1, p_2, \ldots$ to the points $a_1, a_2, \ldots$. Then clearly $\mathbf{E}(u) = \Sigma\, u(a_k)p_k$ whenever the series converges absolutely. This is in agreement with the definition in **1**; IX.

(*b*) For a distribution defined by a continuous density

$$\mathbf{E}(u) = \int_{-\infty}^{+\infty} u(x) f(x)\, dx \tag{1.11}$$

provided the integral converges absolutely. For the general notion of density see section 3. ▶

The generalization to higher dimensions can be described in a few words. In $\mathfrak{R}^2$ a point x is a pair of real numbers, $x = (x_1, x_2)$. Inequalities are to be interpreted coordinate-wise;[5] thus $a < b$ means $a_1 < b_1$ and $a_2 < b_2$ (or "a lies southwest of b"). This induces only a partial ordering, that is, two points a and b need not stand in either of the two relations $a < b$ or $a \geq b$. We reserve the word *interval* for the sets defined by the four possible types of double inequalities $a < x < b$, etc. They are rectangles parallel to the axes which may degenerate into segments or points.

The only novel feature is that the two-dimensional interval $\overline{a, c}\rvert$ with $a < b < c$ is not the union of $\overline{a, b}\rvert$ and $\overline{b, c}\rvert$. Corresponding to an interval

[5] This notation was introduced in III,5.

function assigning the value $F\{I\}$ to the interval I we may introduce its distribution function defined as before by $F(x) = F\{\overline{-\infty, x|}\}$, but an expression of $F\{\overline{a, b|}\}$ in terms of this distribution function involves all four vertices of the interval. If $\alpha = (\alpha_1, \alpha_2)$ is the vertex with coordinates $\alpha_1 = a_1$ and $\alpha_2 = b_2$ the difference $\overline{-\infty, b|} - \overline{-\infty, \alpha|}$ is a semi-infinite ("vertical") strip of width $b_1 - a_1$, and $I = \overline{a, b|}$ is the difference of two such strips. Thus for $a \leq b$

$$(1.12)\qquad F\{\overline{a, b|}\} = F(b_1, b_2) - F(a_1, b_2) - F(b_1, a_2) + F(a_1, a_2).$$

For a distribution function $F(x) = F(x_1, x_2)$ the "*mixed differences*" appearing on the right are non-negative. This implies that $F(x_1, x_2)$ depends monotonically on x_1 and x_2, but such monotonicity does not guarantee the positivity of (1.12).

Example. (*c*) Let $F(x) = 0$ for $x < 0$ and $F(x) = 1$ for all other points. Obviously F depends monotonically on each coordinate, but for $a < 0$, $b > 0$ the quantity (1.12) takes on the negative value -1. ►

The limited value of the use of distribution functions in higher dimensions is apparent: were it not for the analogy with $\mathfrak{R}^1$ all considerations would probably be restricted to interval functions. Formally the definition of distribution functions in $\mathfrak{R}^1$ carries over to $\mathfrak{R}^2$ if the condition of monotonicity (i) is replaced by the condition that for $a \leq b$ the mixed difference in (1.12) be non-negative. Such a distribution function induces an interval function as in (1.3) except that again the mixed differences take over the role of the simple differences in $\mathfrak{R}^1$. Lemma 1 and its proof remain valid.[6]

A simple, but conceptually important, property of expectations is sometimes taken for granted. Any function $u(\mathbf{X}) = u(\mathbf{X}_1, \mathbf{X}_2)$ of the two coordinate variables is a random variable and as such it has a distribution function G. The expectation $\mathbf{E}(u(\mathbf{X}))$ is now defined in two ways; namely, as the integral of $u(x_1, x_2)$ with respect to the given probability in the plane, but also by

$$(1.13)\qquad \mathbf{E}(u) = \int_{-\infty}^{\infty} y\, G\{dy\}$$

[6] The proof utilized the fact that in a *finite* partition of a one-dimensional interval the subintervals appear in a natural order from left to right. An equally neat arrangement characterizes the *checkerboard partitions* of a two-dimensional interval $\overline{a, b|}$, that is, partitions into mn subintervals obtained by subdividing separately the two sides of $\overline{a, b|}$ and drawing parallels to the axes through all points of the subdivisions. The proof of the finite additivity requires no change for such checkerboard partitions, and to an arbitrary partition there corresponds a checkerboard refinement. The passage from finite to denumerable partitions is independent of the number of dimensions.

in terms of the distribution function G of u. The two definitions are equivalent by the very definition of the former integral by the approximating sums IV,(4.6).[7] The point is that the expectation of a random variable **Z** (if it exists) has an intrinsic meaning although **Z** may be considered as a function either on the original probability space $\mathfrak{S}$ or on a space obtained by an appropriate mapping of $\mathfrak{S}$; in particular, **Z** itself maps $\mathfrak{S}$ on the line where it becomes the coordinate variable.

From this point on there is no difference between the setups in $\mathfrak{R}^1$ and $\mathfrak{R}^2$. In particular, the definition of expectations is independent of the number of dimensions.

To summarize formally, *any distribution function induces a probability measure on the σ-algebra of Borel sets in* $\mathfrak{R}^r$, *and thus defines a probability space*. Restated more informally, we have shown that the probabilistic setup of discrete sample spaces carries over without formal changes just as in the case of densities, and we have justified the probabilistic terminology employed in the first three chapters. If we speak of r random variables $\mathbf{X}_1, \ldots, \mathbf{X}_r$ it is understood that they are defined in the same probability space so that a joint probability distribution of $(\mathbf{X}_1, \ldots, \mathbf{X}_r)$ exists. We are then free to interpret the $\mathbf{X}_k$ as coordinate variables in the sample space $\mathfrak{R}^r$.

It is hardly necessary to explain the continued use of terms such as *marginal distribution* (see III,1 and **1**; IX,1), or *independent variables*. The basic facts concerning such variables are the same as in the discrete case, namely:

(i) Saying that **X** and **Y** are independent random variables with (one-dimensional) distributions F and G means that the joint distribution function of $(\mathbf{X}, \mathbf{Y})$ is given by the products $F(x_1)\,G(x_2)$. This statement may refer to two variables in a given probability space or may be an abbreviation for the statement that we introduce a plane with **X** and **Y** as coordinate variables and *define* probabilities by the product rule. This remark applies equally to pairs or triples of random variables, etc.

(ii) If the m-tuple $(\mathbf{X}_1, \ldots, \mathbf{X}_m)$ is independent of the n-tuple $(\mathbf{Y}_1, \ldots, \mathbf{Y}_n)$ then $u(\mathbf{X}_1, \ldots, \mathbf{X}_m)$ and $v(\mathbf{Y}_1, \ldots, \mathbf{Y}_n)$ are independent (for any pair of functions u and v).

(iii) If **X** and **Y** are independent, then $\mathbf{E}(\mathbf{XY}) = \mathbf{E}(\mathbf{X})\,\mathbf{E}(\mathbf{Y})$ whenever the expectations of **X** and **Y** exist (that is, if the integrals converge absolutely).

We conclude this section by a simple result[8] of frequent use.

---

[7] A special case is covered by theorem **1**; IX,2.1. See also problem 1.

[8] It is contained in IV,5 and repeated in view of the simplicity of the proof. For the reader interested in the general theory it may be remarked that our development depended heavily on intervals. In more general situations there exist no such distinguished sets and it is often preferable to *start* from expectations of continuous functions and define measures in terms of them. The argument of the next proof is then used in reverse.

Lemma 2. *A probability distribution F is uniquely determined by the knowledge of* $\mathbf{E}(u)$ *for every continuous function u vanishing outside some finite interval.*

Proof. Let I be a finite open interval and v a continuous function that is positive in I and zero outside I. Then $\sqrt[n]{v(x)} \to 1$ at each point $x \in I$, and hence $\mathbf{E}(\sqrt[n]{v}) \to F\{I\}$. Thus the knowledge of the expectations of our continuous functions uniquely determines the values $F\{I\}$ for all open intervals, and these uniquely determine F. ►

Note on independence and correlation. Statistical correlation theory goes back to a time when a formalization of the theory was impossible and the notion of stochastic independence was necessarily tinged with mystery. It was understood that the independence of two bounded random variables with zero expectation implies $\mathbf{E}(\mathbf{XY}) = 0$, but this condition was at first thought also to be sufficient for the independence of $\mathbf{X}$ and $\mathbf{Y}$. The discovery that this was not so led to a long search for conditions under which the vanishing of correlations would imply stochastic independence. As frequently happens, the history of the problem and the luster of partial results easily obscured the fact that the solution is extremely simple by modern methods. The following theorem contains various results proved in the literature by laborious methods.

Theorem. *The random variables* $\mathbf{X}$ *and* $\mathbf{Y}$ *are independent iff*

$$\mathbf{E}(u(\mathbf{X}) \cdot v(\mathbf{Y})) = \mathbf{E}(u(\mathbf{X})) \cdot \mathbf{E}(v(\mathbf{Y})) \tag{1.14}$$

for all continuous functions u and v vanishing outside a finite interval.

Proof. The necessity of the condition is obvious. To prove the sufficiency it suffices to show that for every bounded continuous function $\mathbf{E}(w)$ agrees with the expectation of w with respect to a pair of *independent* variables distributed as $\mathbf{X}$ and $\mathbf{Y}$. Now (1.14) states this to be the case whenever w is of the form $w(\mathbf{X}, \mathbf{Y}) = u(\mathbf{X})\, v(\mathbf{Y})$. Every bounded continuous function w can be uniformly approximated[9] by linear combinations of the form $\Sigma c_k u_k(\mathbf{X})\, v_k(\mathbf{Y})$, and by passing to the limit we see the assertion to be true for arbitrary bounded continuous w. ►

2. PRELIMINARIES

This section is devoted largely to the introduction of a terminology for familiar or obvious things concerning distribution functions in $\mathcal{R}^1$.

Just as in the case of discrete variables we define the kth *moment* of a random variable $\mathbf{X}$ by $\mathbf{E}(\mathbf{X}^k)$, provided the integral exists. By this we mean that the integral

$$\mathbf{E}(\mathbf{X}^k) = \int_{-\infty}^{\infty} x^k\, F\{dx\} \tag{2.1}$$

converges absolutely, and so $\mathbf{E}(\mathbf{X}^k)$ exists iff $\mathbf{E}(|\mathbf{X}|^k) < \infty$. The last quantity is called the kth *absolute moment* of X (and is defined also for non-integral $k > 0$). Since $|x|^a \le |x|^b + 1$ when $0 < a < b$, the existence

[9] See problem 10 in VIII,10.

of an absolute moment of order b implies the existence of all absolute moments of orders $a < b$.

If $\mathbf{X}$ has an expectation m, the second moment of $\mathbf{X} - m$ is called the *variance* of $\mathbf{X}$:

$$\text{Var}(\mathbf{X}) = \mathbf{E}((\mathbf{X}-m)^2) = \mathbf{E}(\mathbf{X}^2) - m^2. \tag{2.2}$$

Its properties and significance are the same as in the discrete case. In particular, if $\mathbf{X}$ *and* $\mathbf{Y}$ *are independent*

$$\text{Var}(\mathbf{X}+\mathbf{Y}) = \text{Var}(\mathbf{X}) + \text{Var}(\mathbf{Y}) \tag{2.3}$$

whenever the variances on the right exist.

[Two variables satisfying (2.3) are said to be *uncorrelated.* It was shown in **1**; IX,5 that two dependent variables may be uncorrelated.]

It will be recalled how often we have replaced a random variable $\mathbf{X}$ by the "reduced variable" $\mathbf{X}^* = (\mathbf{X}-m)/\sigma$ where $m = \mathbf{E}(\mathbf{X})$ and $\sigma^2 = \text{Var}(\mathbf{X})$. The physicist would say that $\mathbf{X}^*$ is "expressed in dimensionless units." More generally a change from $\mathbf{X}$ to $(\mathbf{X}-\beta)/\alpha$ with $\alpha > 0$ amounts to a change of the origin and the unit of measurement. The distribution function of the new variable is given by $F(\alpha x+\beta)$, and in many situations we are actually dealing with the whole class of distributions of this form rather than with an individual representative. For convenience of expression we introduce therefore

Definition 1. *Two distributions F_1 and F_2 in $\mathfrak{R}^1$ are said to differ only by location parameters if $F_2(x) = F_1(\alpha x+\beta)$ with $\alpha > 0$. We say, alternatively, that F_1 and F_2 are of the same type.*[10] *We refer to α as scale factor, β as centering constant.*

This definition permits the use of clauses such as "F is centered to zero expectation" or "centering does not affect the variance."

A *median* ξ of a distribution F is defined as a number such that $F(\xi) \geq \frac{1}{2}$ and $F(\xi-) \leq \frac{1}{2}$. It is not necessarily defined uniquely; if $F(x) = \frac{1}{2}$ for all x of an interval $\overline{a, b}$ then every such x is a median. It is possible to center a distribution so that 0 becomes a median.

Except for the median these notions carry over to higher dimensions or vector variables of the form $\mathbf{X} = (\mathbf{X}_1, \ldots, \mathbf{X}_n)$; the appropriate vector notation was introduced in III,5, and requires no modification. The expectation of $\mathbf{X}$ is now a vector, the variance a matrix.

The first things one notices looking at the graph of a distribution function are the discontinuities and the intervals of constancy. It is

[10] The notion was introduced by Khintchine who used the German term *Klasse*, but in English "a class of functions" has an established meaning.

frequently necessary to say that a point is not in an interval of constancy. We introduce the following convenient terminology applicable in all dimensions.

Definition 2. *A point x is an atom if it carries a positive mass.*[11] *It is a point of increase of F iff $F\{I\} > 0$ for every open interval I containing x.*

The distribution F is concentrated on the set A if the complement A' has probability $F\{A'\} = 0$.

The distribution F is atomic if it is concentrated on the set of its atoms.

Example. Order the rationals in $\overline{0, 1}$ in a sequence $r_1, r_2, \ldots$ with increasing denominators. Let F attribute probability 2^{-k} to r_k. Then F is purely atomic. Note, however, that every point of the closed interval $\overline{|0, 1|}$ is a point of increase of F. ▶

Because of the countable additivity (1.7) the sum of the weights of the atoms cannot exceed unity and so at most one atom carries a weight $>\frac{1}{2}$, at most two atoms carry weights $>\frac{1}{3}$, etc. It is therefore possible to arrange the atoms in a simple sequence $a_1, a_2, \ldots$ such that the corresponding weights decrease: $p_1 \geq p_2 \geq \cdots$. In other words, *there exist at most denumerably many atoms.*

In the absence of atoms a distribution is called *continuous.* If there are atoms, denote their weights by $p_1, p_2, \ldots$ and let $p = \Sigma p_k > 0$ be their sum. Put

$$F_a(x) = \frac{1}{p} \sum_{a_k \leq x} p_k, \tag{2.4}$$

the summation extending over all atoms in the interval $\overline{-\infty, x|}$. Obviously F_a is again a distribution function, and it is called the *atomic component* of F. If $p = 1$ the distribution F is atomic. Otherwise let $q = 1 - p$. It is easily seen that $[F - pF_a]/q = F_c$ is a *continuous* distribution, and so

$$F = pF_a + qF_c \tag{2.5}$$

is a linear combination of two distribution functions of which F_a is atomic, F_c continuous. If F is atomic (2.5) is true with $p = 1$ and F_c arbitrary; in the absence of atoms (2.5) holds with $p = 0$. We have thus the

Jordan decomposition theorem. *Every probability distribution is a mixture of the form* (2.5) *of an atomic and a continuous distribution; here* $p \geq 0, q \geq 0, p + q = 1$.

[11] This is, of course, short for "the set consisting of the single point x has positive probability."

Among the atomic distributions there is a class which sometimes encumbers simple formulation by trite exceptions. Its members differ only by an arbitrary scale factor from distributions of integral-valued random variables, but they occur so often that they deserve a name for reference.

Definition 3. *A distribution F in* $\mathfrak{R}^1$ *is arithmetic*[12] *if it is concentrated on a set of points of the form* $0, \pm\lambda, \pm 2\lambda, \ldots$. *The largest* λ *with this property is called the span of F.*

3. DENSITIES

The first two chapters were devoted to probability distributions in $\mathfrak{R}^1$ such that

$$F\{A\} = \int_A \varphi(x)\, dx \tag{3.1}$$

for all intervals (and therefore all sets). The distributions of chapter III are of the same form, the integration being with respect to the Lebesgue measure (area or volume) in $\mathfrak{R}^r$. If the density φ in (3.1) is concentrated on the interval $\overline{0,1}$ then (3.1) takes on the form

$$F\{A\} = \int_A \varphi(x)\, U\{dx\} \tag{3.2}$$

where U stands for the uniform distribution in $\overline{0,1}$. The last formula makes sense for an arbitrary probability distribution U, and whenever $F\{\overline{-\infty, \infty}\} = 1$ it defines a new probability distribution F. In this case we shall say that *φ is the density of F with respect to U.*

In (3.1) the measure U is infinite whereas in (3.2) we have $U\{\overline{-\infty, \infty}\} = 1$. The difference is not essential since the integral in (3.1) can be broken up into integrals of the form (3.2) extended over finite intervals. We shall use (3.2) only when U is either a probability distribution or the Lebesgue measure as in (3.1) but the following definition is general.

Definition. *The distribution F is absolutely continuous with respect to the measure U if it is of the form* (3.2). *In this case* φ *is called a density*[13] *of F with respect to U.*

The special case (3.1) where U is the Lebesgue measure is of course the most important and we say in this case that φ is an "*ordinary*" *density.*

[12] The term *lattice distribution* is, perhaps, more usual but its usage varies: according to some authors a lattice distribution may be concentrated on a set of points a, $a\pm\lambda$, $a\pm 2\lambda, \ldots$ with a arbitrary. (The binomial distribution with atoms at ± 1 is arithmetic with span 1 in our terminology, but a lattice distribution with span 2 according to the alternative definition.)

[13] The definition is standard in measure theory and φ is called a Radon-Nikodym derivative of F with respect to U.

We now introduce the *abbreviation*

$$F\{dx\} = \varphi(x)\, U\{dx\}. \tag{3.3}$$

This is merely a shorthand notation to indicate the validity of (3.2) for all sets and no meaning must be attached to the symbol dx. With this notation we would abbreviate (3.1) to $F\{dx\} = \varphi(x)\, dx$ and if U has an ordinary density u then (3.2) is the same as $F\{dx\} = \varphi(x)\, u(x)\, dx$.

Examples. (*a*) Let U be a probability distribution in $\mathcal{R}^1$ with second moment m_2. Then

$$F\{dx\} = \frac{1}{m_2}\, x^2\, U\{dx\}$$

is a new probability distribution. In particular, if U is the uniform distribution in $\overline{0, 1}$ then $F(x) = x^3$ for $0 < x < 1$, and if U has density e^{-x} $(x > 0)$ then F is the gamma distribution with ordinary density $\frac{1}{2}x^2e^{-x}$.

(*b*) Let U be atomic, attaching weights $p_1, p_2, \ldots$ to the atoms $a_1, a_2, \ldots$ (where $\Sigma p_k = 1$). A distribution F has a density φ with respect to U iff it is purely atomic and its atoms are among $a_1, a_2, \ldots$. If F attributes weight q_j to a_j the density φ is given by $\varphi(a_k) = q_k/p_k$. The value of φ at other points plays no role and it is best to leave φ undefined except at the atoms. ►

In theory the integrand φ in (3.2) is not uniquely determined, for if N is a set such that $U\{N\} = 0$ then φ may be redefined on N in an arbitrary manner without affecting (3.2). However, this is the only indeterminacy and *a density is uniquely determined up to values on a null set.*[14] In practice a unique choice is usually dictated by continuity conditions, and for this reason one speaks usually of "the" density although "a" density would be more correct.

For any bounded function v the relation (3.3) implies obviously[15]

$$v(x)\, F\{dx\} = v(x)\, \varphi(x)\, U\{dx\}. \tag{3.4}$$

---

[14] In fact, if both φ and φ_1 are densities of F with respect to U consider the set A of all points x such that $\varphi(x) > \varphi_1(x) + \epsilon$. From

$$F\{A\} = \int_A \varphi(x)\, U\{dx\} = \int_A \varphi_1(x)\, U\{dx\}$$

it follows that $U\{A\} = 0$, and since this holds for every $\epsilon > 0$ we see that $\varphi(x) = \varphi_1(x)$ except on a set N such that $U\{N\} = 0$.

[15] Readers who feel uneasy about the new integrals should notice the triviality of (3.4) when F and U have continuous densities. The following proof in the general case uses a standard argument applicable in more general situations. Formula (3.4) is trivial when v is simple, that is, assumes only finitely many values. For every bounded v there exist two simple functions of this nature such that $\underline{v} < v \leq \bar{v}$ and $\bar{v} - \underline{v} < \epsilon$, and so the validity of (3.4) for all simple functions implies its truth in general.

In particular, if φ is bounded away from 0 we can choose $v = \varphi^{-1}$ to obtain the *inversion formula* for (3.2):

$$U\{dx\} = \frac{1}{\varphi(x)} F\{dx\}. \tag{3.5}$$

A useful criterion for absolute continuity is contained in a basic theorem of measure theory which we accept without proof.

Radon-Nikodym theorem.[16] *F is absolutely continuous with respect to U iff*

$$F\{A\} = 0 \qquad \textit{whenever} \qquad U\{A\} = 0. \tag{3.6}$$

This expression may be rephrased by the statement that U-null sets are also F-null sets. We give an important corollary although it will not be used explicitly in this book.

Criterion. *F is absolutely continuous with respect to U iff to each $\epsilon > 0$ there corresponds a $\delta > 0$ such that for any collection of non-overlapping intervals $I_1, \ldots, I_n$*

$$\sum_1^n U\{I_k\} < \delta \quad \textit{implies} \quad \sum_1^n F\{I_k\} < \epsilon. \tag{3.7}$$

An important special case arises when

$$F\{I\} \leq a \cdot U\{I\} \tag{3.8}$$

for all intervals. Then (3.7) is trivially true with $\delta = \epsilon/a$, and it is easily seen that in this case F has a density φ with respect to U such that $\varphi \leq a$.

*3a. Singular Distributions

The condition (3.6) of the Radon-Nikodym theorem leads one to the study of the extreme counterpart to absolutely continuous distributions.

Definition. *The probability distribution F is singular with respect to U if it is concentrated on a set N such that $U\{N\} = 0$.*

The Lebesgue measure $U\{dx\} = dx$ plays a special role and the word "singular" without further qualification refers to it. Every atomic distribution is singular with respect to dx, but the *Cantor distribution* of example I,(11.*d*) shows that there exist *continuous* distributions in $\mathfrak{R}^1$ that are singular with respect to dx. Such distributions are not tractable

---

* Although conceptually of great importance, singular distributions appear in this book only incidentally.

[16] Often called Lebesgue-Nikodym theorem. The relation (3.6) may be taken as a *definition* of absolute continuity, in which case the theorem asserts the existence of a density.

by the methods of calculus and explicit representations are in practice impossible. For analytic purposes one is therefore forced to choose a framework which leads to absolutely continuous or atomic distributions. Conceptually, however, singular distributions play an important role and many statistical tests depend on their existence. This situation is obscured by the cliché that "in practice" singular distributions do not occur.

Examples. (*a*) *Bernoulli trials.* It was shown in example I,(11.*c*) that the sample space of sequences $SS \cdots F \cdots$ can be mapped onto the unit interval by the simple device of replacing the symbols S and F by 1 and 0, respectively. The unit interval then becomes the sample space, and the outcome of an infinite sequence of trials is represented by the random variable $\mathbf{Y} = \Sigma\, 2^{-k}\mathbf{X}_k$ where the $\mathbf{X}_k$ are independent variables assuming the values 1 and 0 with probabilities p and q. Denote the distribution of $\mathbf{Y}$ by F_p. For symmetric trials $F_{\frac{1}{2}}$ is the *uniform* distribution and the model becomes attractive because of its simplicity. In fact, the equivalence of symmetric Bernoulli trials with "a random choice of a point in $\overline{0, 1}$" has been utilized since the beginnings of probability theory. Now by the law of large numbers the distribution F_p is concentrated on the set N_p consisting of points in whose dyadic expansion the frequency of the digit 1 tends to p. When $p \neq \alpha$ the set N_α has probability zero and hence *the distributions F_p are singular with respect to each other;* for $p \neq \frac{1}{2}$ the distribution F_p is singular with respect to the uniform distribution dx. An explicit representation of F_p is impractical and, accordingly, the model is not in common use when $p \neq \frac{1}{2}$. Two points deserve attention.

First, consider what would happen if the special value $p = \frac{1}{3}$ presented a particular interest or occurred frequently in applications. We would replace the dyadic representation of numbers by triadic expansions and introduce a new scale such that now $F_{\frac{1}{3}}$ would coincide with the uniform distribution. "In practice" we would again deal only with absolutely continuous distributions, but the reason for this lies in our choice of tools rather than in the nature of things.

Second, whether a coin is, or is not, biased can be tested statistically and practical certainty can be reached after finitely many trials. This is possible only because what is likely under the hypothesis $p = \frac{1}{2}$ is extremely unlikely under the hypothesis $p = \frac{1}{3}$. A little reflection along these lines reveals that the possibility of a decision after finitely many trials is due to the fact that F_p is singular with respect to $F_{\frac{1}{2}}$ (provided $p \neq \frac{1}{2}$). The existence of singular distributions is therefore essential to statistical practice.

(*b*) *Random directions.* The notion of a unit vector in $\mathcal{R}^2$ with random direction was introduced in I,10. The distribution of such a vector is concentrated on the unit circle and is therefore singular with respect to the Lebesgue measure (area) in the plane. One might object that in this case the circle should serve as sample space, but practical problems sometimes render this choice impossible. [See example (4.*e*).] ▶

Returning to the general theory, suppose that F is a probability distribution which is not absolutely continuous with respect to the measure U. To simplify the language a set N with $U\{N\} = 0$ will be called nullset. Let p be the least upper bound (the sup) of $F\{N\}$ for all nullsets N. To each n there exists a nullset N_n such that $F\{N_n\} > p - \frac{1}{n}$. Then $F\{A\} \leq \frac{1}{n}$ for any nullset A in the complement N_n'. For the union $N = \bigcup N_n$ this implies $U\{N\} = 0$ and $F\{N\} = p$, and hence no nullset in the complement N' can carry positive probability. Put $q = 1 - p$ and define two new measures by

$$p \cdot F_s\{a\} = F\{AN\}, \qquad q \cdot F_{ac}\{A\} = F\{AN'\}. \tag{3.9}$$

If $q = 0$ then $F = F_s$; otherwise both F_s and F_{ac} have total mass 1 and are therefore probability distributions. By construction F_s is singular with respect to U whereas $U\{B\} = 0$ implies $F_{ac}\{B\} = 0$. Adding the two formulas in (3.9) we therefore obtain the

Lebesgue decomposition theorem. *Every probability distribution F is a mixture of the form*

$$F = p \cdot F_s + q \cdot F_{ac} \tag{3.10}$$

(where $p \geq 0$, $q \geq 0$, $p+q = 1$) *of two probability distributions such that F_s is singular and F_{ac} absolutely continuous with respect to the given measure U.*

The Jordan decomposition (2.5) applies to F_s and hence F can be written as a mixture of three probability distributions of which the first is atomic, the second absolutely continuous with respect to $U\{dx\}$, the third continuous but singular.

4. CONVOLUTIONS

It is difficult to exaggerate the importance of convolutions in many branches of mathematics. We shall have to deal with convolution in two ways: as an operation between distributions and as an operation between a distribution and a continuous function.

For definiteness we refer explicitly to distributions in $\mathfrak{R}^1$, but with the vector notation of section 1 the formulas are independent of the number of dimensions. The definition of *convolutions on a circle* follows the pattern described in II,8 and requires no comment. (More general convolutions can be defined on arbitrary groups.)

Let F be a probability distribution and φ a bounded point function. (In our applications φ will be either continuous or a distribution function.) A new function u is then defined by

$$u(x) = \int_{-\infty}^{+\infty} \varphi(x-y)\, F\{dy\}. \tag{4.1}$$

If F has a density f (with respect to dx) then

$$u(x) = \int_{-\infty}^{+\infty} \varphi(x-y)\, f(y)\, dy. \tag{4.2}$$

The condition that φ be bounded is unnecessarily restrictive, but for badly behaved integrands the integrals may become senseless.

Definition 1. *The convolution of a function φ with a probability distribution F is the function defined by* (4.1). *It will be denoted by $u = F \bigstar \varphi$. When F has a density f we write alternatively $u = f * \varphi$.*

Note that the order of the terms is important: the symbol $\varphi \bigstar F$ is in general meaningless. On the other hand, (4.2) makes sense for arbitrary integrable f and φ (also if f is not non-negative), and the symbol $*$ is used in this generalized sense. Needless to say, the boundedness of φ was assumed only for simplicity and is not necessary.

Examples. (*a*) When F is the uniform distribution in $\overline{0, a}$ then

$$u(x) = \frac{1}{a} \int_{x-a}^{x} \varphi(s)\, ds. \tag{4.3}$$

It follows that u is continuous; if φ is continuous u has a continuous derivative, etc. Generally speaking u will behave better than φ, and so the convolution serves as *smoothing operator*.

(*b*) The convolution formulas for the exponential and the uniform distributions [I,(3.6) and I,(9.1)] are special cases. For examples in $\mathfrak{R}^2$ see III,(1.22) and problems 14–16 of chapter III. ►

Theorem 1. *If φ is bounded and continuous, so is $u = F \bigstar \varphi$; if φ is a probability distribution function, so is u.*

Proof. If φ is bounded and continuous, then $\varphi(x+h-y) \to \varphi(x-y)$ as $h \to 0$, and so $u(x+h) \to u(x)$ by the dominated convergence principle. If φ is a distribution function the same is true when h approaches 0 from the positive side. Thus u is right-continuous and as u goes monotonically from 0 to 1 it is indeed a probability distribution function. ▶

The next theorem gives an interpretation of $F \bigstar \varphi$ when φ is a distribution function.

Theorem 2. *Let* **X** *and* **Y** *be independent random variables with distributions F and G. Then*

$$\mathbf{P}\{\mathbf{X}+\mathbf{Y} \leq t\} = \int_{-\infty}^{+\infty} G(t-x)\, F\{dx\}. \tag{4.4}$$

Proof.[17] Choose $\epsilon > 0$ and denote by I_n the interval $n\epsilon < x \leq (n+1)\epsilon$; here $n = 0, \pm 1, \ldots.$ The event $\{\mathbf{X}+\mathbf{Y} \leq t\}$ occurs if $\{\mathbf{X} \in I_{n-1}, \mathbf{Y} \leq t - n\epsilon\}$ for some n. The latter events are mutually exclusive, and as **X** and **Y** are independent we have therefore

$$\mathbf{P}\{\mathbf{X}+\mathbf{Y} \leq t\} \leq \sum G(t-n\epsilon) \cdot F\{I_n\}. \tag{4.5}$$

On the right we have the integral of the step function G_ϵ assuming in I_n the value $G(t-n\epsilon)$. Since $G_\epsilon(y) \leq G(t+\epsilon-y)$ we have

$$\mathbf{P}\{\mathbf{X}+\mathbf{Y} \leq t\} \leq \int_{-\infty}^{+\infty} G(t+\epsilon-x)\, F\{dx\}. \tag{4.6}$$

The same argument leads to the reversed inequality with ϵ replaced by $-\epsilon$. Letting $\epsilon \to 0$ we get (4.4). ▶

Example. (*c*) Let F and G be concentrated on the integers 0, 1, 2, ... and denote the weights of k by p_k and q_k. The integral in (4.4) then reduces to the sum $\Sigma G(t-k)p_k$. This is a function vanishing for $t < 0$ and constant in each interval $n-1 < t < n$. The jump at $t = n$ equals

$$\sum_{k=0}^{n} q_{n-k}p_k = q_np_0 + q_{n-1}p_1 + \cdots + q_0p_n \tag{4.7}$$

in agreement with the convolution formula **1**; XI,(2.1) for integral-valued random variables. ▶

Each of the preceding theorems shows that for two distribution functions the convolution operation $F \bigstar G$ yields a new distribution function U. The commutativity of the addition $\mathbf{X}+\mathbf{Y}$ implies that $F \bigstar G = G \bigstar F$. A perfect system might introduce a new symbol for such convolutions

---

[17] (4.4) is a special case of Fubini's theorem IV,(2.11) but the proof is given for purposes of illustration. The converse of theorem 2 is false: we saw in II,(4.*e*), and again in problem 1 of III,9, that in exceptional cases formula (4.4) may hold for a pair of dependent variables **X**, **Y**.

among distribution functions, but this would hardly be helpful.[18] Of course, one should think of U as an interval function or measure: for each interval $I = \overline{a, b}$ obviously

$$U\{I\} = \int_{-\infty}^{+\infty} G\{I-y\}\, F\{dy\} \tag{4.8}$$

where, as usual, $I - y$ denotes the interval $\overline{a-y, b-y}$. (This formula automatically carries over to arbitrary sets.) Because of the commutativity the roles of F and G in (4.8) may be interchanged.

Consider now three distributions F_1, F_2, F_3. The associative law of addition for random variables implies that $(F_1 \bigstar F_2) \bigstar F_3 = F_1 \bigstar (F_2 \bigstar F_3)$ so that we can dispense with the parentheses and write $F_1 \bigstar F_2 \bigstar F_3$. We summarize this in theorems 3 and 4.

Theorem 3. *Among distributions the convolution operation $\bigstar$ is commutative and associative.*

Theorem 4. *If G is continuous (= free of atoms), so is $U = F \bigstar G$. If G has the ordinary density φ, then U has the ordinary density u given by* (4.1).

(Because of symmetry the roles of F and G can be interchanged.)

Proof. The first assertion is contained in theorem 1. If φ is the density of G then an integration of (4.1) over the interval I leads to (4.8), and so u is indeed the density of the distribution U defined by (4.8).[19] ▶

Sums $\mathbf{S}_n = \mathbf{X}_1 + \cdots + \mathbf{X}_n$ of n mutually independent random variables with a common distribution F occur so frequently that a special

---

[18] In other words, the symbol $A \bigstar B$ is used when the integration is with respect to the measure A. This convolution is a point function or measure according as B is a point function [as in (4.1)] or a measure [as in (4.6)]. The asterisk $*$ is used for an operation between two functions, the integration being with respect to Lebesgue measure. In our context this type of convolution is restricted almost exclusively to probability densities.

A more general definition of a convolution between two functions may be defined by

$$f * g(x) = \int_{-\infty}^{+\infty} f(x-y)\, g(y)\, m\{dy\}$$

where m stands for an arbitrary measure. Sums of the form (4.7) represent the special case when m is concentrated on the positive integers and attributes unit weight to each. In this sense the use of the asterisk for the convolutions between sequences in **1**;XI,2 is consistent with our present usage.

[19] The criterion (3.7) shows directly that if G is absolutely continuous with respect to a measure V so is U; indeed, it satisfies the criterion with the same δ.

notation is in order. The distribution of $\mathbf{S}_n$ is the *n-fold convolution of F with itself.* It will be denoted by $F^{n\bigstar}$. Thus

$$F^{1\bigstar} = F, \qquad F^{(n+1)\bigstar} = F^{n\bigstar} \bigstar F \tag{4.9}$$

A sum with no terms is conventionally interpreted as 0, and for consistency we define $F^{0\bigstar}$ as the atomic distribution concentrated at the origin. Then (4.9) holds also for $n = 0$.

If F has a density f then $F^{n\bigstar}$ has the density $f * f * \cdots * f$ (n times). *We denote it by* f^{n*}. These notations are consistent with the notation introduced in I,2.

We conclude with two simple lemmas[20] to be used mainly in connection with renewal theory and random walks.

Lemma 1. *If a and b are points of increase for the distributions F and G, then $a + b$ is a point of increase for $F \bigstar G$. If a and b are atoms, the same is true of $a + b$. Furthermore, all atoms of $F \bigstar G$ are of this form.*

Proof. If $\mathbf{X}$ and $\mathbf{Y}$ are independent then

$$\mathbf{P}\{|\mathbf{X} + \mathbf{Y} - a - b| < \epsilon\} \geq \mathbf{P}\{|\mathbf{X}-a| < \tfrac{1}{2}\epsilon\} \cdot \mathbf{P}\{|\mathbf{Y}-b| < \tfrac{1}{2}\epsilon\}.$$

The right side is positive for every $\epsilon > 0$ if a and b are points of increase, and so $a + b$ is again a point of increase.

Denote by F_a and G_a the atomic components of F and G in the Jordan decomposition (2.5). The atomic component of $F \bigstar G$ is obviously identical with the convolution $F_a \bigstar G_a$, and hence all atoms of $F \bigstar G$ are of the form $a+b$, where a and b are atoms of F and G, respectively. ▶

The intrinsic simplicity of the next lemma suffers by the special role played on one hand by arithmetic distributions, on the other hand by distributions of *positive* variables.

Lemma 2. *Let F be a distribution in $\mathfrak{R}^1$ and Σ the set formed by the points of increase of $F, F^{2\bigstar}, F^{3\bigstar}, \ldots$.*

(*a*) *If F is not concentrated on a half-axis then Σ is dense in $\overline{-\infty, \infty}$ for F not arithmetic, and $\Sigma = \{0, \pm\lambda, \pm 2\lambda, \ldots\}$ for F arithmetic with span λ.*

(*b*) *Let F be concentrated on $\overline{0, \infty}$ but not at the origin. If F is not arithmetic then Σ is "asymptotically dense at ∞" in the sense that for given $\epsilon > 0$ and x sufficiently large the interval $\overline{x, x+\epsilon}$ contains points of Σ. If F is arithmetic with span λ then Σ contains all points $n\lambda$ for n sufficiently large.*

[20] The remainder of this section should be omitted at first reading.

Proof. Let a and b be two points in the set Σ with $0 < a < b$. From lemma 1 it is clear that the set Σ contains all linear combinations $ma + nb$ with $m, n = 0, 1, \ldots$. The $m + 1$ points ma, $(m-1)a+b, \ldots, mb$ are regularly spaced $b - a$ units apart. For $mb > (m+1)a$ it follows that every subinterval of $\overline{ma, (m+1)a}$ of length $\rho > b-a$ contains a point of Σ. In other words, if Σ contains a pair of points $a > 0, b > 0$ at a distance $<\rho$ then for sufficiently large x each interval $\overline{x, x + \rho}$ contains a point of Σ. Accordingly, either Σ is asymptotically dense at ∞ or else the points of Σ in $\overline{0, \infty}$ form a simple sequence $a_1 < a_2 < \cdots$ such that $a_{n+1} - a_n \to \delta > 0$. But for an arbitrary a in Σ the points $a_n + a$ belong to Σ, and so a must be a (positive or negative) multiple of δ. It follows that Σ is contained in the set of points $0, \pm\delta$, $\pm 2\delta, \ldots$, and hence F is arithmetic with a span $\lambda = k\delta$ where k is an integer. But then Σ is automatically contained in the set of points 0, $\pm\lambda, \pm 2\lambda, \ldots$, and hence $\delta = \lambda$. In this case, then, Σ contains all points $n\lambda$ with n sufficiently large. This proves part (*b*) of the theorem.

If Σ contains both positive and negative points the argument applies to the left half-axis as well, and hence for non-arithmetic F the set Σ is asymptotically dense both at $+\infty$ and $-\infty$. Now if a and b are points of Σ lying, respectively, in ϵ-neighborhoods of $x + \frac{1}{2}t$ and $-x + \frac{1}{2}t$, then $a + b$ lies in a 2ϵ-neighborhood of t, and hence every neighborhood of an arbitrary point t contains points of Σ. In the arithmetic case the same argument shows that all multiples of λ belong to Σ, and this concludes the proof. ▶

A special case of this theorem commands interest. Every number $x > 0$ can be represented uniquely in the form $x = m + \xi$ as the sum of an integer m and a number $0 \le \xi < 1$. This ξ is called the fractional part of x. Consider now a distribution F concentrated on the two points -1 and $\alpha > 0$. The set Σ contains all points of the form $n\alpha - m$ and hence the fractional parts of $\alpha, 2\alpha, \ldots$. This F is arithmetic if $\alpha = p/q$ where p and q are positive integers without common divisors, and in this case the span of F equals $1/q$. We have thus the following corollary (to be sharpened in the equidistribution theorem of VIII,6).

Corollary. *For* $\alpha > 0$ *irrational the fractional parts of* $\alpha, 2\alpha, 3\alpha, \ldots$ *form a set dense in* $\overline{0, 1}$.

(If $\alpha = p/q$ the set of fractional parts consists of the numbers 0, $1/q, \ldots, (q-1)/q$.) ▶

The following examples show that *the convolution of two singular distributions can have a continuous density*. They show also that an effective calculation of convolutions need not be based on the defining formula.

Examples. (*d*) *The uniform distribution in $\overline{0,1}$ is the convolution of two Cantor-type singular distributions.* In fact, let $\mathbf{X}_1, \mathbf{X}_2, \ldots$ be mutually independent random variables assuming the values 0 and 1 with probability $\frac{1}{2}$. We saw in example I,(11.*c*) that the variable $\mathbf{X} = \Sigma\, 2^{-k}\mathbf{X}_k$ has a uniform distribution. Denote the contributions of the even and odd terms by $\mathbf{U}$ and $\mathbf{V}$, respectively. Obviously $\mathbf{U}$ and $\mathbf{V}$ are independent and $\mathbf{X} = \mathbf{U} + \mathbf{V}$. The uniform distribution is therefore the convolution of the distributions of $\mathbf{U}$ and $\mathbf{V}$. But obviously $\mathbf{U}$ has the same distribution as $2\mathbf{V}$, and the variable $\mathbf{V}$ differs only notationally from the variable $\frac{1}{3}\mathbf{Y}$ of example I,(11.*d*). In other words, the distributions of $\mathbf{U}$ and $\mathbf{V}$ differ only by scale factors from the Cantor distribution of that example.

(*e*) *Random walk in $\mathcal{R}^2$.* The distribution of a unit vector with random direction (see I,10) is concentrated on the unit circle and therefore singular with respect to the Lebesgue measure in the plane. Nevertheless, the resultant of two independent vectors *has a length* $\mathbf{L}$ *which is a random variable with the density* $\frac{2}{\pi}\frac{1}{\sqrt{4-r^2}}$ concentrated on $\overline{0,2}$. In fact, by the law of the cosines $\mathbf{L} = \sqrt{2 - 2\cos\omega} = |2\sin\frac{1}{2}\omega|$ where $\pi - \omega$ is the angle between the two vectors. As ω is distributed uniformly in $\overline{0, 2\pi}$ we have

$$\mathbf{P}\{\mathbf{L} \le r\} = \mathbf{P}\{|2\sin\tfrac{1}{2}\omega| \le r\} = \frac{2}{\pi}\arcsin\tfrac{1}{2}r, \qquad 0 < r < 2 \tag{4.10}$$

which proves the assertion. ►

5. SYMMETRIZATION

If the random variable $\mathbf{X}$ has the distribution F we shall denote the distribution of $-\mathbf{X}$ by ${}^-F$. At points of continuity we have

$$^-F(x) = 1 - F(-x) \tag{5.1}$$

and this defines ${}^-F$ uniquely. The distribution F is called *symmetric* if ${}^-F = F$. [When a density f exists this means that $f(-x) = f(x)$.]

Let $\mathbf{X}_1$ and $\mathbf{X}_2$ be independent with the common distribution F. Then $\mathbf{X}_1 - \mathbf{X}_2$ has the symmetric distribution ${}^0F$ given by

$$^0F = F \bigstar {}^-F. \tag{5.2}$$

Using the symmetry property ${}^0F(x) = 1 - {}^0F(-x)$ it is readily seen that

$$^0F(x) = \int_{-\infty}^{+\infty} F(x+y)\, F\{dy\}. \tag{5.3}$$

We shall say that ${}^0F$ is obtained by *symmetrization* of F.

Examples. (*a*) Symmetrization of the exponential leads to the bilateral exponential [II,4(*a*)]; the uniform distribution on $\overline{0,1}$ leads to the triangular distribution τ_2 of II,(4.1).

(*b*) The distribution with atoms of weight $\frac{1}{2}$ at ± 1 is symmetric, but not the result of a symmetrization procedure.

(*c*) Let F be atomic, attributing weights $p_0, p_1, \ldots$ to $0, 1, \ldots$. The symmetrized distribution ${}^0F$ is atomic and attributes weight q_n to $\pm n$ where

$$q_n = \sum_{k=0}^{\infty} p_k p_{k+n}, \qquad n \geq 0, \tag{5.4}$$

$q_{-n} = q_n$. When F is the *Poisson* distribution we get for $n \geq 0$

$$q_n = e^{-2\alpha} \sum_{k=0}^{\infty} \frac{\alpha^{n+2k}}{k!(n+k)!} = e^{-2\alpha} I_n(2\alpha) \tag{5.5}$$

where I_n is the *Bessel function* defined in II,(7.1). (See problem 9.) ▶

Many messy arguments can be avoided by symmetrization. In this connection it is important that the tails of F and ${}^0F$ are of comparable magnitude, a statement made more precise by the following inequalities. Their meaning appears clearer when expressed in terms of random variables rather than the distribution itself.

Lemma 1. *Symmetrization inequalities. If* $\mathbf{X}_1$ *and* $\mathbf{X}_2$ *are independent and identically distributed, then for* $t > 0$

$$\mathbf{P}\{|\mathbf{X}_1 - \mathbf{X}_2| > t\} \leq 2\mathbf{P}\{|\mathbf{X}_1| > \tfrac{1}{2}t\}. \tag{5.6}$$

If $a \geq 0$ *is chosen so that* $\mathbf{P}\{\mathbf{X}_i \geq a\} \leq 1 - p$ *and* $\mathbf{P}\{\mathbf{X}_i \leq -a\} \leq 1 - p$ *then*

$$\mathbf{P}\{|\mathbf{X}_1 - \mathbf{X}_2| \geq t\} \geq p\,\mathbf{P}\{|\mathbf{X}_1| > t + a\}. \tag{5.7}$$

In particular, if 0 *is a median for* $\mathbf{X}_j$

$$\mathbf{P}\{|\mathbf{X}_1 - \mathbf{X}_2| \geq t\} \geq \tfrac{1}{2}\mathbf{P}\{|\mathbf{X}_1| > t\}. \tag{5.8}$$

Proof. The event on the left in (5.6) cannot occur unless either $|\mathbf{X}_1| > \frac{1}{2}t$ or $|\mathbf{X}_2| > \frac{1}{2}t$ and hence (5.6) is true. The event on the left in (5.7) occurs if $\mathbf{X}_1 > t + a$, $\mathbf{X}_2 \leq a$, and also if $\mathbf{X}_1 < -t - a$ and $\mathbf{X}_2 \geq -a$. This implies (5.7). ▶

Symmetrization is frequently used for the estimation of sums of independent random variables. In this connection the following inequality is particularly useful.

Lemma 2. *If* $\mathbf{X}_1, \ldots, \mathbf{X}_n$ *are independent and have symmetric distributions then* $\mathbf{S}_n = \mathbf{X}_1 + \cdots + \mathbf{X}_n$ *has a symmetric distribution and*

$$\mathbf{P}\{|\mathbf{X}_1 + \cdots + \mathbf{X}_n| > t\} \geq \tfrac{1}{2}\mathbf{P}\{\text{Max}\,|\mathbf{X}_j| > t\}. \tag{5.9}$$

If the $\mathbf{X}_j$ have a common distribution F then at all points of continuity

$$\mathbf{P}\{\text{Max}\,|\mathbf{X}_j| \leq t\} = (F(t) - F(-t))^n \leq e^{-n[1-F(t)+F(-t)]} \tag{5.10}$$

and hence (5.9) implies that for all $t > 0$

$$(5.11)\qquad \mathbf{P}\{|\mathbf{X}_1 + \cdots + \mathbf{X}_n| \geq t\} \geq \tfrac{1}{2}(1 - e^{-n[1-F(t)+F(-t)]}).$$

Proof. Let the random variable $\mathbf{M}$ equal the first term among $\mathbf{X}_1, \ldots, \mathbf{X}_n$ that is greatest in absolute value and put $\mathbf{T} = \mathbf{S} - \mathbf{M}$. The pair $(\mathbf{M}, \mathbf{T})$ is symmetrically distributed in the sense that the four combinations $(\pm\mathbf{M}, \pm\mathbf{T})$ have the same distribution. Clearly

$$(5.12)\qquad \mathbf{P}\{\mathbf{M} > t\} \leq \mathbf{P}\{\mathbf{M} > t, \mathbf{T} \geq 0\} + \mathbf{P}\{\mathbf{M} > t, \mathbf{T} \leq 0\}.$$

The two terms on the right have equal probabilities, and so

$$(5.13)\qquad \mathbf{P}\{\mathbf{S} > t\} = \mathbf{P}\{\mathbf{M} + \mathbf{T} > t\} \geq \mathbf{P}\{\mathbf{M} > t, \mathbf{T} \geq 0\} \geq \tfrac{1}{2}\mathbf{P}\{\mathbf{M} > t\}$$

which is the same as (5.9). ►

6. INTEGRATION BY PARTS. EXISTENCE OF MOMENTS

The familiar formula for integration by parts can be used also for arbitrary expectations in $\mathcal{R}^1$. *If u is bounded and has a continuous derivative u′, then*

$$(6.1)\qquad \int_a^{b+} u(x)\, F\{dx\} = u(b)\, F(b) - u(a)\, F(a) - \int_a^b u'(x)\, F(x)\, dx.$$

Consider the difference between the two sides as a function of the upper limit t and denote it by $\varphi(t)$. A simple rearrangement of terms shows that for $h > 0$

$$(6.2)\qquad \begin{aligned} &\varphi(t+h) - \varphi(t) = \\ &= \int_t^{(t+h)+} [u(x) - u(t+h)]\, F\{dx\} - \int_t^{t+h} u'(x)[F(t) - F(x)]\, dx. \end{aligned}$$

This implies that $\varphi(t+h) - \varphi(t) = o(h)$ as $h \to 0$. In fact, if $|u'| < m$ the first integrand is in absolute value less than mh, and hence the integral itself is $o(h)$; in the second integral the term within brackets tends to zero and hence this integral is $o(h)$ also. A similar reasoning applies to $h < 0$ and we conclude that at t the function φ has a derivative equal to 0. But t being arbitrary, this proves that the difference of the two sides in (6.1) does not depend on the upper limit, and hence is zero identically.

As an application we derive a frequently used formula [generalizing **1**; XI,(1.8)].

Lemma 1. *For any* $\alpha > 0$

$$(6.3)\qquad \int_0^\infty x^\alpha\, F\{dx\} = \alpha \int_0^\infty x^{\alpha-1}[1 - F(x)]\, dx$$

in the sense that if one side converges so does the other.

Proof. Because of the infinite interval of integration (6.1) does not apply directly, but for every $b < \infty$ we have after a trivial rearrangement

$$\int_0^{b+} x^\alpha F\{dx\} = -b^\alpha[1 - F(b)] + \alpha \int_0^b x^{\alpha-1}[1 - F(x)]\,dx. \tag{6.4}$$

Suppose first that the integral on the left converges as $b \to \infty$. The contribution of $\overline{b, \infty}$ to the infinite integral is $\geq b^\alpha[1 - F(b)]$, and this quantity therefore tends to zero. In this case the passage to the limit $b \to \infty$ leads from (6.4) to (6.3). On the other hand, the integral on the left is smaller than the integral on the right and hence the convergence of the second entails the convergence of the former, and hence (6.3). ►

An analogue to (6.3) holds for the left tail. Combining the two formulas we get

Lemma 2. *The distribution F possesses an absolute moment of order $\alpha > 0$ iff $|x|^{\alpha-1}[1 - F(x) + F(-x)]$ is integrable over $\overline{-\infty, \infty}$.*

As an application we prove

Lemma 3. *Let $\mathbf{X}$ and $\mathbf{Y}$ be independent random variables, and $\mathbf{S} = \mathbf{X}+\mathbf{Y}$. Then $\mathbf{E}(|\mathbf{S}|^\alpha)$ exists iff both $\mathbf{E}(|\mathbf{X}|^\alpha)$ and $\mathbf{E}(|\mathbf{Y}|^\alpha)$ exist.*

Proof. Since the variables $\mathbf{X}$ and $\mathbf{X}-c$ possess exactly the same moments there is no loss of generality in assuming that 0 is a median for both $\mathbf{X}$ and $\mathbf{Y}$. But then $\mathbf{P}\{|\mathbf{S}| > t\} \geq \frac{1}{2}\mathbf{P}\{|\mathbf{X}| > t\}$, and by the last lemma $\mathbf{E}(|\mathbf{S}|^\alpha) < \infty$ implies $\mathbf{E}(|\mathbf{X}|^\alpha) < \infty$. This proves the "only if" part of the assertion. The "if" part follows from the inequality $|\mathbf{S}|^\alpha \leq 2^\alpha(|\mathbf{X}|^\alpha + |\mathbf{Y}|^\alpha)$ which is valid, because at no point can $|\mathbf{S}|$ exceed the larger of $2|\mathbf{X}|$ and $2|\mathbf{Y}|$. ►

7. CHEBYSHEV'S INEQUALITY

Chebyshev's inequality is among the most frequently used tools in probability. Both the inequality and its proof are the same as in the discrete case (**1**; IX,6) and we repeat it mainly for reference. Interesting applications will be given in VII,1.

Chebyshev's inequality. *If* $\mathbf{E}(\mathbf{X}^2)$ *exists*

$$\mathbf{P}\{|\mathbf{X}| \geq t\} \leq \frac{1}{t^2}\mathbf{E}(\mathbf{X}^2) \qquad t > 0. \tag{7.1}$$

In particular, if $\mathbf{E}(\mathbf{X}) = m$ *and* $\mathrm{Var}(\mathbf{X}) = \sigma^2$,

$$\mathbf{P}\{|\mathbf{X} - m| \geq t\} \leq \frac{1}{t^2}\sigma^2. \tag{7.2}$$

Proof. If F stands for the distribution of $\mathbf{X}$,

$$\mathbf{E}(\mathbf{X}^2) \geq \int_{|x|\geq t} x^2\, F\{dx\} \geq t^2 \int_{|x|\geq t} F\,\{dx\}$$

which is the same as (7.1). ▶

The usefulness of Chebyshev's inequality depends (not on sharp numerical estimates but) on its simplicity and the fact that it is specially adapted to sums of random variables. Many generalizations are possible, but they do not share these desirable properties. (Most of them are so simple that it is better to derive them as occasion arises. For example, a useful combination of Chebyshev's inequality with truncation procedures is described in VII,7.)

A fairly general method for deriving non-trivial inequalities may be described as follows. If $u \geq 0$ everywhere and $u(x) > a > 0$ for all x in an interval I then

$$F\{I\} \leq a^{-1}\mathbf{E}(u(\mathbf{X})). \tag{7.3}$$

On the other hand, if $u \leq 0$ outside I and $u \leq 1$ in I we get the reversed inequality $F\{I\} \geq \mathbf{E}(u(\mathbf{X}))$. Choosing for u polynomials we obtain inequalities depending only on the moments of F.

Examples. (*a*) Let $u(x) = (x + c)^2$ with $c > 0$. Then $u(x) \geq 0$ for all x and $u(x) \geq (t + c)^2$ for $x \geq t > 0$. Therefore

$$\mathbf{P}\{\mathbf{X} > t\} \leq \frac{1}{(t + c)^2}\mathbf{E}((\mathbf{X} + c)^2). \tag{7.4}$$

If $\mathbf{E}(\mathbf{X}) = 0$ and $\mathbf{E}(\mathbf{X}^2) = \sigma^2$ the right side assumes its minimum for $c = \sigma^2/t$ and we get the *general inequality*

$$\mathbf{P}\{\mathbf{X} > t\} \leq \frac{\sigma^2}{\sigma^2 + t^2}, \qquad t > 0 \tag{7.5}$$

discovered independently by many authors.

(*b*) Let $\mathbf{X}$ be positive (that is, $F(0) = 0$) and $\mathbf{E}(\mathbf{X}) = 1$, $\mathbf{E}(\mathbf{X}^2) = b$. The polynomial $u(x) = h^{-2}(x - a)(a + 2h - x)$ is positive only for $a < x < a + 2h$, and $u(x) \leq 1$ everywhere. When $0 < a < 1$ it is readily seen that $\mathbf{E}(u(\mathbf{X})) \geq [2h(1-a) - b]h^{-2}$. Choosing $h = b(1 - a)^{-1}$ we get by the remark preceding these examples

$$\mathbf{P}\{\mathbf{X} > a\} \geq (1-a)^2 b^{-1}. \tag{7.6}$$

(*c*) If $\mathbf{E}(\mathbf{X}^2) = 1$ and $\mathbf{E}(\mathbf{X}^4) = M$, the last inequality applied to $\mathbf{X}^2$ shows that for $0 < t < 1$

$$\mathbf{P}\{|\mathbf{X}| > t\} \geq (1 - t^2)^2 M^{-1}. \tag{7.7}$$ ▶

For Kolmogorov's generalization see VII,8.

8. FURTHER INEQUALITIES. CONVEX FUNCTIONS

The inequalities collected in this section are of widespread use and are by no means typical for probability. Most common is Schwarz' inequality. The others are given mainly because of their use in stochastic processes and statistics. (This section is meant for reference rather than for reading.)

(a) Schwarz' Inequality

In its probabilistic version this inequality states that for two arbitrary random variables φ and ψ defined on the same space

$$(\mathbf{E}(\varphi\psi))^2 \leq \mathbf{E}(\varphi^2)\,\mathbf{E}(\psi^2) \tag{8.1}$$

whenever these expectations exist. Furthermore, the equality sign holds only if a linear combination $a\varphi + b\psi$ is zero with probability one. More generally, if F is an arbitrary measure on the set A then

$$\left(\int_A \varphi(x)\,\psi(x)\,F\{dx\}\right)^2 \leq \int_A \varphi^2(x)\,F\{dx\}\cdot\int_A \psi^2(x)\,F\{dx\} \tag{8.2}$$

for arbitrary functions for which the integrals on the right exist. Taking for F the purely atomic measure attaching unit weight to integers we get *Schwarz' inequality for sums* in the form

$$(\sum \varphi_i\psi_i)^2 \leq \sum \varphi_i^2 \sum \psi_i^2. \tag{8.3}$$

In view of the importance of (8.1) we give two proofs pointing to different generalizations. The same proofs apply to (8.2) and (8.3).

First proof. We may assume $\mathbf{E}(\psi^2) > 0$. Then

$$\mathbf{E}(\varphi + t\psi)^2 = \mathbf{E}(\varphi^2) + 2t\,\mathbf{E}(\varphi\psi) + t^2\,\mathbf{E}(\psi^2) \tag{8.4}$$

is a quadratic polynomial in t which, being non-negative, has either two complex roots or a double root λ. The standard solution for quadratic equations shows in the first case that (8.1) holds with strict inequality. In the second case $\mathbf{E}(\varphi + t\psi)^2 = 0$ and so $\varphi + t\psi = 0$ except on a set of probability zero.

Second proof. As we are free to replace φ and ψ by constant multiples $a\varphi$ and $b\psi$ it suffices to consider the case $\mathbf{E}(\varphi^2) = \mathbf{E}(\psi^2) = 1$. Then (8.1) follows trivially taking expectations in the inequality $2\,|\varphi\psi| \leq \varphi^2 + \psi^2$. ►

(b) Convex Functions. Jensen's inequality

Let u be a function defined on an open interval I, and $P = (\xi, u(\xi))$ a point on its graph. A line L passing through P is said to *support* u *at* ξ if the graph of u lies entirely above or on L. (This excludes vertical lines.) In analytical terms it is required that

$$u(x) \geq u(\xi) + \lambda\cdot(x - \xi) \tag{8.5}$$

for all x in I, where λ is the slope of L. The function u *is called convex in* I *if a supporting line exists at each point* x of I. (The function u is *concave*, if $-u$ is convex.)

We proceed to show that this definition implies the various properties intuitively associated with convexity as exemplified by convex polygonal lines.

Let F be an arbitrary probability distribution concentrated on I and suppose that the expectation $\mathbf{E}(\mathbf{X})$ exists. Choosing $\xi = \mathbf{E}(\mathbf{X})$ and taking expectations in (8.5) we get

$$\mathbf{E}(u) \geq u(\mathbf{E}(\mathbf{X})) \tag{8.6}$$

whenever the expectation on the left exists. This statement is known as *Jensen's inequality.*

By far the most important is the case where F is concentrated at two points x_1 and x_2 and attributes weights $1 - t$ and t to them. Then (8.6) takes on the form

$$(1-t)\, u(x_1) + t\, u(x_2) \geq u((1-t)x_1 + tx_2). \tag{8.7}$$

This inequality admits of a simple geometric interpretation which we state in the following.

Theorem 1. *The function u is convex iff all its chords lie above or on the graph of u.*

Proof. (i) *Necessity.* Let u be convex and consider the chord over an arbitrary interval $\overline{x_1, x_2}$. Then (8.7) holds for $0 \leq t \leq 1$. As t runs from 0 to 1 the point $(1-t)x_1 + tx_2$ runs through the interval $\overline{x_1, x_2}$ and the left side in (8.7) is the ordinate of the corresponding point on the chord. Thus (8.7) states that the points of the chord lie above or on the graph.

(ii) *Sufficiency.* Assume that u has the stated property and consider the triangle formed by three points P_1, P_2, P_3 on the graph of u with abscissas $x_1 < x_2 < x_3$. Then P_2 lies below the chord P_1P_3, and among the three sides of the triangle P_1P_2 has the smallest slope, P_2P_3 the largest. Outside the interval $\overline{x_2, x_3}$ the graph of u therefore lies above the line P_2P_3. Now consider x_3 as a variable and let $x_3 \to x_2+$. The slope of P_2P_3 decreases monotonically but is bounded from below by the slope of P_1P_2. Thus the lines P_2P_3 tend to a line L through P_2. Outside $\overline{x_2, x_3}$ the graph of u is above the line P_2P_3, and hence the whole graph lies above or on L. Thus L supports u at x_2, and as x_2 is arbitrary, this proves the convexity of u. ▶

Being the limit of chords, the line L is a right tangent. In the limiting process the abscissa x_3 of P_3 tends to x_2, and P_3 to a point on L. Thus $P_3 \to P_2$. The same argument applies for an approach from the left, and we conclude that the graph of u is continuous and possesses right and left tangents at each point. Furthermore, these tangents are supporting lines and their slopes vary monotonically. Since a monotone function has at most denumerably many discontinuities we have proved

Theorem 2. *A convex function possesses right and left derivatives at all points, and these are non-decreasing functions. They are the same except possibly at countably many points.*

Obviously this theorem again expresses necessary and sufficient conditions for convexity. In particular, if a second derivative exists, u is convex iff $u'' \geq 0$.

Usually (8.7) is taken as definition of convexity. For $t = \frac{1}{2}$ we get the inequality

$$u\left(\frac{x_1+x_2}{2}\right) \leq \tfrac{1}{2}u(x_1) + \tfrac{1}{2}u(x_2) \tag{8.8}$$

stating that the *midpoint* of the chord lies above or on the graph of u. If u is continuous this property guarantees that the graph can never cross a chord and hence that u is convex. It can be shown more generally that *any Baire function*[21] *satisfying* (8.8) *is convex.*

(c) Moment Inequalities

We prove that for any random variable **X**

$$u(t) = \log \mathbf{E}(|\mathbf{X}|^t), \qquad t \geq 0, \tag{8.9}$$

is a convex function of t in every interval in which the integral exists. In fact, by Schwarz' inequality (8.1)

$$\mathbf{E}^2(|\mathbf{X}|^t) \leq \mathbf{E}(|\mathbf{X}|^{t+h})\, \mathbf{E}(|\mathbf{X}|^{t-h}), \qquad 0 \leq h \leq t, \tag{8.10}$$

provided the integrals converge. Putting $x_1 = t-h$ and $x_2 = t+h$ we see that (8.8) holds and so u is convex as asserted.

Since $u(0) \leq 0$ the slope $t^{-1} u(t)$ of the line joining the origin to $(t, u(t))$ varies monotonically and hence $(\mathbf{E}(|\mathbf{X}|^t))^{1/t}$ *is a non-decreasing function of* $t > 0$.

(d) Hölder's Inequality

Let $p > 1, q > 1$ *and* $p^{-1}+q^{-1} = 1$. *Then for* $\varphi \geq 0, \psi \geq 0$

$$\mathbf{E}(\varphi\psi) \leq (\mathbf{E}(\varphi^p))^{1/p}\, (\mathbf{E}(\psi^q))^{1/q} \tag{8.11}$$

whenever the integrals exist.

(Schwarz' inequality (8.1) is the special case $p = q = \frac{1}{2}$, and (8.2) and (8.3) generalize similarly.)

---

[21] *Every u* satisfying (8.8) is either convex, or else its oscillations in *every* interval range from $-\infty$ to ∞. See G. H. Hardy, J. E. Littlewood, and G. Pólya, *Inequalities*, Cambridge, England, 1934, in particular p. 91.

Proof. For $x > 0$ the function $u = \log x$ is concave, that is, it satisfies (8.7) with the inequality reversed. Taking antilogarithms we get for $x_1, x_2 > 0$

$$x_1^{1-t}x_2^t \leq (1 - t)x_1 + tx_2 \tag{8.12}$$

As in the second proof of Schwarz' inequality it suffices to consider integrands normed by $\mathbf{E}(\varphi^p) = \mathbf{E}(\psi^q) = 1$. Let $t = q^{-1}$ and $1 - t = p^{-1}$. The assertion $\mathbf{E}(\varphi\psi) \leq 1$ then follows directly taking expectations in (8.12) with $x_1 = \varphi^p$ and $x_2 = \psi^p$.

(e) Kolmogorov's Inequality

This inequality was derived in **1**; IX,7, and the proof holds without change for arbitrary distributions. It is repeated in VII,8 in a stronger version (for martingales).

9. SIMPLE CONDITIONAL DISTRIBUTIONS. MIXTURES

In III,2 we introduced a "conditional density of a random variable **Y** for a given value of another variable **X**" in the case where the joint distribution of **X** and **Y** has a continuous density. Without any attempt at generality we proceed to define an analogous concept for a wider class of distributions. (A systematic theory is developed in sections 10 and 10*a*.)

For any pair of intervals A and B on the line put

$$Q(A, B) = \mathbf{P}\{\mathbf{X} \in A, \mathbf{Y} \in B\}. \tag{9.1}$$

With this notation the *marginal distribution for* **X** is given by

$$\mu\{A\} = Q(A, \mathcal{R}^1). \tag{9.2}$$

If $\mu\{A\} > 0$ the conditional probability of the event $\{\mathbf{Y} \in B\}$ given $\{\mathbf{X} \in A\}$ is

$$\mathbf{P}\{\mathbf{Y} \in B \mid \mathbf{X} \in A\} = \frac{Q(A, B)}{\mu\{A\}}. \tag{9.3}$$

(If $\mu\{A\} = 0$ this conditional probability is not defined.) We use this formula when A is the interval $A_h = \overline{x, x + h}$ and let $h \to 0+$. Under appropriate regularity conditions the limit

$$q(x, B) = \lim_{h \to 0} \frac{Q(A_h, B)}{\mu\{A_h\}} \tag{9.4}$$

will exist for all choices of x and B. Following the procedure and reasoning used in III,2 we write in this case

$$q(x, B) = \mathbf{P}\{\mathbf{Y} \in B \mid \mathbf{X} = x\} \tag{9.5}$$

and call q *"the conditional probability of the event* $\{\mathbf{Y} \in B\}$ *given that* $\mathbf{X} = x$." This constitutes an extension of the notion of conditional probabilities to situations in which the "hypothesis" has zero probability. No difficulties arise when q is sufficiently regular, but we shall not analyze the appropriate regularity conditions because a general procedure will be discussed in the next section. This naïve approach usually suffices in individual cases, and the form of the conditional distribution can frequently be derived by intuitive reasoning.

Example. (*a*) Let $\mathbf{X}$ and $\mathbf{Y}$ be independent random variables with distributions F and G, respectively. For simplicity we assume that $\mathbf{X} > 0$ [that is, $F(0) = 0$]. Consider the product $\mathbf{Z} = \mathbf{XY}$. Then

$$\mathbf{P}\{\mathbf{Z} \leq t \mid \mathbf{X} = x\} = G\left(\frac{t}{x}\right) \tag{9.6}$$

and the distribution function U of $\mathbf{Z}$ is obtained by integrating (9.6) with respect to F. [See II,(3.1). The assertion is a special case of formula (9.8) below.] In particular, when $\mathbf{X}$ is distributed uniformly over $\overline{0, 1}$

$$U(t) = \int_0^1 G\left(\frac{t}{x}\right) dx. \tag{9.7}$$

This formula can be used as a convenient starting point for the theory of unimodal distributions.[22]

For a further example see problems 13–14. ►

[22] A distribution function U is called *unimodal* with the mode at the origin iff the graph of U is *convex* in $\overline{-\infty, 0}$ and *concave* in $\overline{0, \infty}$ [see (8.*b*)]. The origin may be a point of discontinuity, but apart from this unimodality requires that there exist *a density u which is monotone in* $\overline{-\infty, 0}$ *and in* $\overline{0, \infty}$. (Intervals of constancy are not excluded.)

A much quoted characterization of unimodal distributions is due to A. Khintchine. As L. Shepp observed, (9.7) represents a simplified version of Khintchine's formula admitting of a simple probabilistic intrepretation.

Theorem. *U is unimodal iff it is of the form* (9.7), *that is, iff it is the distribution of the product* $\mathbf{Z} = \mathbf{XY}$ *of two independent variables such that* $\mathbf{X}$ *is distributed uniformly in* $\overline{0, 1}$.

Proof. Choose $h > 0$ and denote by U_h the distribution function whose graph is the polygonal line agreeing with U at the points $0, \pm h, \ldots$. [In other words, $U_h(nh) = U(nh)$ and U_h is linear in the interval between nh and $(n+1)h$.] It is obvious from the definition that U is unimodal iff all U_h are unimodal. Now U_h has a density u_h which is a step function, and every step function with discontinuities at the points nh can be written in the form

$$\Sigma p_n \cdot \frac{1}{|n|\, h} f\left(\frac{x}{nh}\right) \tag{*}$$

where $f(x) = 1$ for $0 < x < 1$ and $f(x) = 0$ elsewhere. The function (*) is monotone in $\overline{0, \infty}$ and in $\overline{-\infty, 0}$ iff $p_n \geq 0$ for all n, and it is a density if $\Sigma p_n = 1$. But in this

Under appropriate regularity conditions $q(x, B)$ will for fixed x represent a probability distribution in B and for fixed B a continuous function in x. Then

$$(9.8) \qquad Q(A, B) = \int_A q(x, B)\,\mu\{dx\}$$

In fact, the right side obviously represents a probability distribution in the plane, and the differentiation described in (9.4) leads to $q(x, B)$. Formula (9.8) shows how a given distribution in $\mathcal{R}^2$ can be expressed in terms of a conditional and a marginal distribution. In the terminology of II,5 it represents the given distribution as a *mixture* of the family of distributions $q(x, B)$ depending on the parameter x with μ serving as the distribution of the randomized parameter.

In practice the procedure is frequently reversed. One *starts* from a "*stochastic kernel*" q, that is a function $q(x, B)$ of a point x and a set B such that for fixed x it is a probability distribution and for fixed B a Baire function. Given an arbitrary probability distribution μ the integral in (9.8) defines probabilities for plane sets of the form (A, B) and hence a probability distribution in the plane. Usually (9.8) is expressed in terms of point functions. Consider a family of distribution functions $G(\theta, y)$ depending on a parameter θ, and a probability distribution μ. A new distribution function is then defined by

$$(9.9) \qquad U(y) = \int_{-\infty}^{+\infty} G(x, y)\,\mu\{dx\}.$$

[This formula represents the special case of (9.8) when $A = \overline{-\infty, \infty}$ and $q(x, \overline{-\infty, y}|) = G(x, y)$.]

Such mixtures occur in **1**; V and are discussed in II,5. In the next section it will be shown that q can always be interpreted as a conditional probability distribution.

Examples. (*b*) If F_1 and F_2 are distributions $pF_1 + (1-p)F_2$ is a mixture $(0 < p < 1)$ and represents a special case of (9.9) when μ is concentrated on two atoms.

(*c*) *Random sums.* Let $\mathbf{X}_1, \mathbf{X}_2, \ldots$ be independent random variables

---

case (*) is the density of the product $\mathbf{Z}_h = \mathbf{X}\mathbf{Y}_h$ of two independent variables such that $\mathbf{X}$ is distributed uniformly in $\overline{0, 1}$ and $\mathbf{P}\{\mathbf{Y}_h = nh\} = p_n$. We have thus proved that U_h is unimodal iff it is of the form (9.7) with G replaced by an arithmetic distribution G_h concentrated on the points $0, \pm h, \ldots$. Letting $h \to 0$ we get the theorem by monotone convergence.

(See problems 20–21 and problem 8 in XV,9.)

with a common distribution F. Let $\mathbf{N}$ be a random variable independent of the $\mathbf{X}_j$ and assuming the values $0, 1, \ldots$ with positive probabilities $p_0, p_1, \ldots$. We are interested in the random variable $\mathbf{S_N} = \mathbf{X}_1 + \cdots + \mathbf{X_N}$. The conditional distribution of $\mathbf{S_N}$ given that $\mathbf{N} = n$ is $F^{n\star}$, and so the distribution of $\mathbf{S_N}$ is given by

$$U = \sum_{n=0}^{\infty} p_n F^{n\star}, \tag{9.10}$$

which is a special case of (9.9). In this case each hypothesis $\mathbf{N} = n$ carries a positive probability p_n and so we have conditional probability distributions in the strict sense. A variety of other examples is found in II,5–7. (See problems 16 and 19.)

*10. CONDITIONAL DISTRIBUTIONS

It would be pointless to investigate the precise conditions under which conditional probabilities q can be defined by the differentiation process in (9.4). The main properties of conditional probabilities are embodied in the relation (9.8) expressing probabilities of sets in terms of conditional probabilities, and it is simplest to use (9.8) as *definition* of conditional probabilities. It will not determine q uniquely because if for each set B we have $q(x, B) = \bar{q}(x, B)$ except on a set of μ-measure zero, then (9.8) will remain true with q replaced by $\bar{q}$. This indeterminacy is unavoidable, however. For example, if μ is concentrated on an interval I no natural definition of q is possible for x outside I. By the very nature of things we are really dealing with the whole class of equivalent conditional probabilities and should refer to *a* rather than *the* conditional probability distribution q. In individual cases there usually exists a natural choice dictated by regularity requirements.

For definiteness we consider only events specified by conditions of the form $\mathbf{X} \in A$ and $\mathbf{Y} \in B$, where $\mathbf{X}$ and $\mathbf{Y}$ are given random variables and A, B are Borel sets on the line. Let us begin by examining the different meanings that may be attached to the phrase "conditional probability of the event $\{\mathbf{Y} \in B\}$ for given $\mathbf{X}$." The given value of $\mathbf{X}$ may be either a fixed number or indeterminate. With the second interpretation we have a function of $\mathbf{X}$, that is, a random variable. It will be denoted by $\mathbf{P}\{B \mid \mathbf{X}\}$ or $q(\mathbf{X}, B)$, etc. For the value at a fixed point x we write for emphasis $\mathbf{P}\{\mathbf{Y} \in B \mid \mathbf{X} = x\}$ or $q(x, B)$.

Definition 1. *Let the set B be fixed. By* $\mathbf{P}\{\mathbf{Y} \in B \mid \mathbf{X}\}$ *(in words, "a conditional probability of the event* $\{\mathbf{Y} \in B\}$ *for given* $\mathbf{X}$*") is meant a function*

* This section should be omitted at first reading.

$q(\mathbf{X}, B)$ such that for every set A in $\mathfrak{R}^1$

$$\mathbf{P}\{\mathbf{X} \in A, \mathbf{Y} \in B\} = \int_A q(x, B)\, \mu\{dx\} \tag{10.1}$$

where μ is the marginal distribution of $\mathbf{X}$.

When x happens to be an atom the hypothesis $\mathbf{X} = x$ has positive probability and $\mathbf{P}\{\mathbf{Y} \in B \mid \mathbf{X} = x\}$ is already defined by (9.3) with A consisting of the single point x. But in this case (10.1) reduces to (9.3) and our definitions and notations are consistent.

It follows from the Radon-Nikodym theorem (section 3) that a conditional probability $\mathbf{P}\{\mathbf{Y} \in B \mid \mathbf{X}\}$ *always exists*. In fact, consider

$$\mathbf{P}\{\mathbf{X} \in A, \mathbf{Y} \in B\}$$

for fixed B as a function of the set A. It differs only by a norming factor from a probability distribution. It is absolutely continuous with respect to μ because the weight $\mathbf{P}\{\mathbf{X} \in A, \mathbf{Y} \in B\}$ can never exceed $\mu\{A\}$. It follows that our distribution has a density q with respect to μ, which means that (10.1) is true.

So far the set B was fixed, but the notation $q(x, B)$ was chosen with a view to vary B. In other words, we wish to consider q as a function of two variables, a point x and a set B on the line. It is desired that for fixed x the set function q be a probability measure, which requires that $q(x, \mathfrak{R}^1) = 1$ and that for any sequence of non-overlapping sets $B_1, B_2, \ldots$ with union B

$$q(x, B) = \sum q(x, B_k). \tag{10.2}$$

Now if the terms on the right represent conditional probabilities for B_k this sum yields *a* conditional probability for B, but there is an additional consistency requirement that (10.2) be true for our choice of q and *all* x. [Note that definition 1 does not exclude the absurd choice $q(x, B) = 17$ at an individual point x.] It is not difficult to see that it is possible to choose $q(x, B)$ so as to satisfy these conditions.[23] This means that there

[23] It is easiest to choose *directly* only the values $q(x, B)$ when B is an interval in a dyadic subdivision of $\mathfrak{R}^1$. For example, let $B_1 = \overline{0, \infty}$ and $B_2 = \overline{-\infty, 0|}$. Choose for $q(x, B_1)$ any conditional probability for B_1 subject to the trite condition $0 \leq q(x, B_1) \leq 1$. Then $q(x, B_2) = 1 - q(x, B_1)$ is automatically a legitimate choice. Partition B_1 into B_{11} and B_{12} and choose $q(x, B_{11})$ subject to $0 \leq q(x, B_{11}) \leq q(x, B_1)$. Put $q(x, B_{12}) = q(x, B_1) - q(x, B_{11})$ and proceed in like manner refining the subdivision indefinitely. The additivity requirement (10.2) then defines $q(x, B)$ for all open sets B and hence for all Borel sets.

This construction depends only on the existence of a so-called *net*, namely a partition of the space into finitely many non-overlapping sets each of which is partitioned in like manner and the procedure is continued in such a way that each point of the space is the unique limit of a contracting sequence of sets appearing in the successive partitions. The assertion is therefore true in $\mathfrak{R}^r$ and in many other spaces.

exists a conditional probability distribution of **Y** *for given* **X** *in the sense* of the following.

Definition 2. *By a conditional probability distribution of* **Y** *for given* **X** *is meant a function q of two variables, a point x and a set B, such that*

(i) *for a fixed set B*

$$q(\mathbf{X}, B) = \mathbf{P}\{\mathbf{Y} \in B \mid \mathbf{X}\} \tag{10.3}$$

is a conditional probability of the event $\{\mathbf{Y} \in B\}$ for given **X**.

(ii) *q is for each x a probability distribution.*

In effect a conditional probability distribution is a family of ordinary probability distributions and so the whole theory carries over without change. Thus *when q is given*[24] the following definition introduces a new notation rather than a new concept.

Definition 3. *A conditional expectation* $\mathbf{E}(\mathbf{Y} \mid \mathbf{X})$ *is a function of* **X** *assuming at x the value*

$$\mathbf{E}(\mathbf{Y} \mid x) = \int_{-\infty}^{+\infty} y\, q(x, dy) \tag{10.4}$$

provided the integral converges (except possibly on an x-set of probability zero).

$\mathbf{E}(\mathbf{Y} \mid \mathbf{X})$ is a function of **X**, that is a random variable. For clarity it is occasionally preferable to denote its value at an individual point x by $\mathbf{E}(\mathbf{Y} \mid \mathbf{X} = x)$. From the very definition we get

$$\mathbf{E}(\mathbf{Y}) = \int_{-\infty}^{+\infty} \mathbf{E}(\mathbf{Y} \mid x)\, \mu\{dx\}. \tag{10.5}$$

Higher Dimensions. Iterated Expectations

The simplifying assumption that **X** is a one-dimensional random variable played no serious role in the foregoing considerations, and we may replace it by a vector variable in $\mathcal{R}^n$. For $n = 2$ we are lead to the conditional expectation $\mathbf{E}(\mathbf{Z} \mid \mathbf{X}, \mathbf{Y})$.

This is a random variable in two dimensions and we may take its conditional expectation for given **X**, that is, $\mathbf{E}(\mathbf{E}(\mathbf{Z} \mid \mathbf{X}, \mathbf{Y}) \mid \mathbf{X})$. It is plausible that this iterated expectation should be identical with $\mathbf{E}(\mathbf{Z} \mid \mathbf{X})$; that this is so follows directly from the streamlined definition (10.6). For the special case of the normal distribution these formulas are discussed in chapter III.

---

[24] For a more flexible general definition see section 10*a*.

*10a. Conditional Expectations

We have defined the conditional expectation in terms of a conditional probability distribution, and this is satisfactory as long as one deals with one fixed pair of random variables **X** and **Y**. The theory of stochastic processes, however, is concerned with a whole family of random variables, and the non-uniqueness of the individual conditional distributions leads to serious difficulties. It turns out that a more flexible theory can be developed by defining conditional expectations independently of conditional distributions. To understand this theory it is best to begin with a closer scrutiny of (10.5).

Let A be a Borel set *on the line* and $\mathbf{1}_A(\mathbf{X})$ the random variable that equals one whenever $\mathbf{X} \in A$ and zero otherwise. By (10.5)

$$\mathbf{E}(\mathbf{Y} \cdot \mathbf{1}_A(X)) = \int_A \mathbf{E}(\mathbf{Y} \mid x)\, \mu\{dx\}. \tag{10.6}$$

Since every bounded function v can be approximated uniformly by linear combinations of indicators a passage to the limit leads from (10.6) to the more general formula

$$\mathbf{E}(\mathbf{Y} \cdot v(\mathbf{X}) \mid \mathbf{X}) = v(\mathbf{X}) \cdot \mathbf{E}(\mathbf{Y} \mid \mathbf{X}). \tag{10.7}$$

Intuitively speaking this means that for given **X** the factor $v(\mathbf{X})$ acts as a constant and can be pulled out of the integral.

Formula (10.6) embodies the essential properties of the conditional expectation. Starting from it as *definition* we can entirely dispense with the more complicated notion of conditional distribution. It is possible to go a step further and render the notion more flexible by dispensing even with the conditioning variable **X**. In fact, **X** served mainly to specify events $\{\mathbf{X} \in A\}$ where A is a Borel set on the line. As long as we are concerned with the pair of variables $(\mathbf{X}, \mathbf{Y})$ there is no loss of generality in taking the plane as sample space and **X**, **Y** as coordinate variables. The event $\{a < \mathbf{X} < b\}$ is then an infinite strip, and $\{\mathbf{X} \in A\}$ is a set consisting of parallels to the y-axis. The class of all such sets in the plane forms a σ-algebra $\mathfrak{B}$ contained in the σ-algebra of all plane Borel sets. It is the smallest σ-algebra containing all sets of the form $\{\mathbf{X} \leq a\}$ and is called the σ-algebra *generated by the variable* **X**. (This definition applies to all random variables.) If we put $B = \{\mathbf{X} \in A\}$ the product $\mathbf{Y} \cdot \mathbf{1}_A(\mathbf{X})$ is the same as $\mathbf{Y} \cdot \mathbf{1}_B$. Formula (10.6) now states that the random variable $\mathbf{U} = \mathbf{E}(\mathbf{Y} \mid \mathbf{X})$ satisfies the relation

$$\mathbf{E}(\mathbf{Y} \cdot \mathbf{1}_B) = \mathbf{E}(\mathbf{U} \cdot \mathbf{1}_B) \tag{10.8}$$

for every set B in the σ-algebra generated by **X**.

---

* The theory of this section will be used only in connection with martingales in VI,12 and VII,8.

So far we have only restated (10.6), which was derived by integration with respect to a conditional probability distribution. But (10.8) makes sense more generally, and we can use it to *define* a conditional expectation of an arbitrary variable $\mathbf{Y}$ with respect to an arbitrary σ-algebra $\mathfrak{B}$ of sets. This conditional expectation is a random variable which will be denoted by $\mathbf{E}(\mathbf{Y} \mid \mathfrak{B})$. Our setup is as follows.

We start from an arbitrary probability space. Let $\mathfrak{A}$ be the underlying σ-algebra of sets and $\mathfrak{B}$ an arbitrary σ-algebra of sets *contained in* $\mathfrak{A}$. *Let* $\mathbf{Y}$ *be a random variable with expectation. A random variable* $\mathbf{U}$ *is called a conditional expectation of* $\mathbf{Y}$ *relative to* $\mathfrak{B}$ *if it is* $\mathfrak{B}$*-measurable*[25] *and* (10.8) *holds for every set* $B \in \mathfrak{B}$. *In this case we write* $\mathbf{U} = \mathbf{E}(\mathbf{Y} \mid \mathfrak{B})$.

The condition of $\mathfrak{B}$-measurability replaces the previous condition that $\mathbf{U}$ be a function of $\mathbf{X}$. If $\mathfrak{B}$ is the algebra generated by $\mathbf{X}$ the present definition agrees with (10.6), but even so it has the advantage of applying in arbitrary probability spaces without necessitating a mapping into the plane.

Examples. If $\mathfrak{B} = \mathfrak{A}$ we may take $\mathbf{U} = \mathbf{Y}$. If $\mathfrak{B}$ contains only the whole space and the empty set, then $\mathbf{U} = \mathbf{E}(\mathbf{Y})$. If $\mathbf{Y}$ is $\mathfrak{B}$-measurable we can take $\mathbf{U} = \mathbf{Y}$. ▶

The variable $\mathbf{U}$ can be changed on a set $N \in \mathfrak{B}$ of probability zero and the notation $\mathbf{E}(\mathbf{Y} \mid \mathfrak{B})$ usually refers to an arbitrary, but fixed, representative of the class of all conditional expectations.

The *existence* of a conditional expectation is easily established. If $\mathbf{Y}$ is a positive variable the left side in (10.8) defines a measure $\Phi(B)$ on $\mathfrak{B}$, and it is obvious that $\Phi(B) = 0$ whenever $\mathbf{P}\{B\} = 0$. An abstract version of the Radon-Nikodym theorem therefore implies that the measure Φ has a density U, and (10.8) expresses precisely this fact. This argument applies to arbitrary $\mathbf{Y}$ by the usual decomposition into positive and negative parts.

Just as (10.6) led to (10.7), so (10.8) leads to the general formula

$$\mathbf{E}(\mathbf{YZ} \mid \mathfrak{B}) = \mathbf{Z} \cdot \mathbf{E}(\mathbf{Y} \mid \mathfrak{B}), \tag{10.9}$$

valid whenever $\mathbf{Z}$ is $\mathfrak{B}$-measurable and the expectations exist. In particular $\mathbf{E}(\mathbf{Z} \mid \mathfrak{B}) = \mathbf{Z}$ whenever $\mathbf{Z}$ is $\mathfrak{B}$-measurable.

A further important property of conditional expectations is the following. If $\mathfrak{B}_0$ is a σ-algebra contained in $\mathfrak{B}$ and $\mathbf{U}_0 = \mathbf{E}(\mathbf{Y} \mid \mathfrak{B}_0)$ then $\mathbf{E}(\mathbf{Y} \cdot \mathbf{1}_B) = \mathbf{E}(\mathbf{U} \cdot \mathbf{1}_B) = \mathbf{E}(\mathbf{U}_0 \mathbf{1}_B)$ for $B \in \mathfrak{B}_0$. Thus by the very definition, *if* $\mathfrak{B}_0 \subset \mathfrak{B}$ *then* $\mathbf{E}(\mathbf{Y} \mid \mathfrak{B}_0) = \mathbf{E}(\mathbf{E}(\mathbf{Y} \mid \mathfrak{B}) \mid \mathfrak{B}_0)$. Since $\mathbf{U}_0$ is $\mathfrak{B}$-measurable we have also $\mathbf{E}(\mathbf{Y} \mid \mathfrak{B}_0) = \mathbf{E}(\mathbf{E}(\mathbf{Y} \mid \mathfrak{B}_0) \mid \mathfrak{B})$.

---

[25] That is, the sets $\{\mathbf{U} \leq a\}$ belong to $\mathfrak{B}$; see IV,4.

The main properties of ordinary expectations such as linearity and the basic inequalities generalize trivially to conditional expectations.

The foundations of the general theory of conditional distributions and expectations are due to Kolmogorov. The theory has been perfected by Doob, to whom the last definitions are due.

11. PROBLEMS FOR SOLUTION

1. Let $\mathbf{X}$ and $\mathbf{Y}$ be independent variables with distribution functions F and G. Find the distribution functions of[26] (*a*) $\mathbf{X} \cup \mathbf{Y}$, (*b*) $\mathbf{X} \cap \mathbf{Y}$, (*c*) $2\mathbf{X} \cup \mathbf{Y}$, (*d*), $\mathbf{X}^3 \cup \mathbf{Y}$.

2. *Mixtures.* Let $\mathbf{X}, \mathbf{Y}, \mathbf{Z}$ be independent; $\mathbf{X}$ and $\mathbf{Y}$ have distributions F and G, while $\mathbf{P}\{\mathbf{Z} = 1\} = p$, $\mathbf{P}\{\mathbf{Z} = 0\} = q$ $(p + q = 1)$. Find the distribution functions of (*a*) $\mathbf{ZX} + (1-\mathbf{Z})\mathbf{Y}$, (*b*) $\mathbf{ZX} + (1-\mathbf{Z})(\mathbf{X} \cup \mathbf{Y})$, (*c*) $\mathbf{ZX} + (1-\mathbf{Z})(\mathbf{X} \cap \mathbf{Y})$.

3. If F is a continuous distribution function show that

$$\int_{-\infty}^{+\infty} F(x)\, F\{dx\} = \int_0^1 y\, dy = \tfrac{1}{2}$$

(*a*) from the very definition of the first integral (partitioning $\overline{-\infty, \infty}$ into subintervals) and (*b*) from the interpretation of the left side as $\mathbf{E}(F(\mathbf{X}))$ where $F(\mathbf{X})$ has a uniform distribution. More generally, putting $G(x) = F^n(x)$,

$$\int_{-\infty}^{+\infty} F^k(x)\, G\{dx\} = \frac{n}{n+k}.$$

4. *Prescribed marginal distributions.*[27] Let F and G be distribution functions in $\mathcal{R}^1$ and

$$U(x, y) = F(x)\, G(y)[1 + \alpha(1-F(x))(1-G(y))]$$

where $|\alpha| \leq 1$. Prove that U is a distribution function in $\mathcal{R}^2$ with marginal distributions F, G and that U has a density iff F and G have densities.

Hint: If $w(x, y) = u(x)\, v(y)$, the mixed differences of w [defined in (1.12)] are of the form $\Delta u\, \Delta v$. Note also that $\Delta(F^2) \leq 2\, \Delta F$.

5. Within the unit square put $U(x, y) = x$ if $x \leq y$ and $U(x, y) = y$ if $x \geq y$. Show that U is a distribution function concentrated at the bisector (hence singular).

6. *Fréchet's maximal distribution with given marginal distributions.* Let F and G be distribution functions in $\mathcal{R}^1$ and $U(x, y) = F(x) \cap G(y)$. Prove: (*a*) U is a distribution function with marginal distributions F and G. (*b*) If V is any other distribution function with this property, then $V \leq U$. (*c*) U is concentrated on

[26] If a and b are numbers, $a \cup b = \max(a, b)$ denotes the larger of the two, $a \cap b = \min(a, b)$ the smaller. For functions $f \cup g$ denotes the function which at the point x assumes the value $f(x) \cup g(x)$ (see IV,1). Thus $\mathbf{X} \cup \mathbf{Y}$ and $\mathbf{X} \cap \mathbf{Y}$ are random variables.

[27] This problem contains a new example for a *non-normal distribution with normal marginal distributions* (see problems 2 and 3 in III,9). It is due to E. J. Gumbel.

the curve defined by $F(x) = G(y)$, and hence singular. (Problem 4 contains a special case.)

7. Denote by U the uniform distribution in $\overline{-h, 0}$ and by T the triangular distribution in $\overline{-h, h}$ [see II, 4(*b*)]. Then $F \bigstar U$ and $F \bigstar T$ have the *densities*

$$h^{-1}[F(x+h) - F(x)] \quad \text{and} \quad h^{-2}\int_0^h [F(x+y) - F(x-y)]\,dy.$$

8. Let F have atoms $a_1, a_2, \ldots$ with weights $p_1, p_2, \ldots$. Denote by p the maximum of $p_1, p_2, \ldots$. Using lemma 1 of section 4 prove

(*a*) The atoms of $F \bigstar F$ have weights strictly less than p except if F is concentrated at finitely many atoms of equal weight.

(*b*) For the symmetrized distribution ${}^0F$ the origin is an atom of weight $p' = \Sigma p_\nu^2$. The weights of the other atoms are strictly less than p'.

9. If **X** and **Y** have Poisson distributions with expectations α and β

$$\mathbf{P}\{\mathbf{X} - \mathbf{Y} = k\} = e^{-\alpha-\beta}\sqrt{\left(\frac{\alpha}{\beta}\right)^k}\, I_{|k|}(2\sqrt{\alpha\beta})$$

where I_k is the Bessel function defined in II,(7.1).

10. For a distribution function F such that

$$\varphi(\alpha) = \int_{-\infty}^{+\infty} e^{\alpha x}\, F\{dx\}$$

exists for $-a < \alpha < a$ we define a new distribution $F^{\#}$ by $\varphi(\alpha)F^{\#}\{dx\} = e^{\alpha x}\,F\{dx\}$. Let F_1 and F_2 be two distributions with this property and $F = F_1 \bigstar F_2$. Prove that (with obvious notations) $\varphi(\alpha) = \varphi_1(\alpha)\,\varphi_2(\alpha)$ and $F^{\#} = F_1^{\#} \bigstar F_2^{\#}$.

11. Let **X** and **Y** have densities f and g such that $f(x) \geq g(x)$ for $x < a$ and $f(x) \leq g(x)$ for $x > a$. Prove that $\mathbf{E}(\mathbf{X}) \leq \mathbf{E}(\mathbf{Y})$. Furthermore, if $f(x) = g(x) = 0$ for $x < 0$ then $\mathbf{E}(\mathbf{X}^k) \leq \mathbf{X}(\mathbf{Y}^k)$ for all k.

12. Let $\mathbf{X}_1, \mathbf{X}_2, \ldots$ be mutually independent with the common distribution F. Let **N** be a positive integral-valued random variable with generating function $P(s)$. If **N** is independent of the $\mathbf{X}_j$ then $\max[\mathbf{X}_1, \ldots, \mathbf{X}_\mathbf{N}]$ has the distribution $P(F)$.

13. Let $\mathbf{X}_1, \ldots, \mathbf{X}_n$ be mutually independent with a continuous distribution F. Let $\mathbf{X} = \max[\mathbf{X}_1, \ldots, \mathbf{X}_n]$ and $\mathbf{Y} = \min[\mathbf{X}_1, \ldots, \mathbf{X}_n]$. Then

$$\mathbf{P}\{\mathbf{X} \leq x, \mathbf{Y} > y\} = (F(x) - F(y))^n \quad \text{for} \quad y < x$$

and

$$\mathbf{P}\{\mathbf{Y} > y \mid \mathbf{X} = x\} = \frac{n-1}{n}[F(x) - F(y)]^{n-1}.$$

14. Using the same notations one has for each fixed $k \leq n$

$$\mathbf{P}\{\mathbf{X}_k \leq x \mid \mathbf{X} = t\} = \begin{cases} \dfrac{n-1}{n}\dfrac{F(x)}{F(t)} & \text{for} \quad x \leq t \\ 1 & \text{for} \quad x \geq t. \end{cases}$$

Derive this (*a*) by an intuitive argument considering the event $\{\mathbf{X}_k = \mathbf{X}\}$, and (*b*) formally from (9.4).

15. *Continuation.* Prove that

$$\mathbf{E}(\mathbf{X}_k \mid \mathbf{X} = t) = \frac{n-1}{n} \frac{1}{F(t)} \int_{-\infty}^{t} y\, F\{dy\} + \frac{t}{n}.$$

16. *Random sums.* In example (9.*c*) let $\mathbf{X}_k$ equal 1 and -1 with probabilities p and $q = 1 - p$. If $\mathbf{N}$ is a Poisson variable with expectation α

$$\mathbf{P}\{\mathbf{S_N} = k\} = e^{-\alpha} \sqrt{\left(\frac{p}{q}\right)^k}\, I_{|k|}(2\alpha\sqrt{pq})$$

where I_k is the Bessel function defined in II,(7.1).

17. *Mixtures.* Let the distribution G in (9.9) have expectation $m(x)$ and variance $\sigma^2(x)$. Prove that the mixture U has expectation and variance

$$a = \int_{-\infty}^{+\infty} m(x)\, \mu\{dx\}, \qquad b = \int_{-\infty}^{+\infty} \sigma^2(x)\, \mu\{dx\} + \int_{-\infty}^{\infty} (m^2(x) - a^2)\, \mu\{dx\}.$$

18. With obvious notations $\mathbf{E}(\mathbf{E}(\mathbf{Y} \mid \mathbf{X})) = \mathbf{E}(\mathbf{Y})$ but

$$\mathrm{Var}(\mathbf{Y}) = \mathbf{E}(\mathrm{Var}(\mathbf{Y} \mid \mathbf{X})) + \mathrm{Var}(\mathbf{E}(\mathbf{Y} \mid \mathbf{X})).$$

Problem 17 is a special case.

19. *Random sums.* In example (9.*c*), $\mathbf{E}(\mathbf{S_N}) = \mathbf{E}(\mathbf{N})\,\mathbf{E}(\mathbf{X})$,

$$\mathrm{Var}(\mathbf{S_N}) = \mathbf{E}(\mathbf{N})\mathrm{Var}(\mathbf{X}) + (\mathbf{E}(\mathbf{X}))^2\, \mathrm{Var}(\mathbf{N}).$$

Prove this directly and show that it is contained in the last two problems.

Note. The following problems refer to *convolutions of unimodal distributions* defined in footnote 22 of section 9. It has been conjectured that the convolution of two such distributions is again unimodal. One counterexample is due to K. L. Chung, and problem 20 contains another. Problem 21 shows the conjecture to be valid for *symmetric*[28] distributions. This result is due to A. Wintner.

20. Let $u(x) = 1$ for $0 < x < 1$ and $u(x) = 0$ elsewhere. Put

$$v(x) = \frac{\epsilon}{a}\, u\left(\frac{x}{a}\right) + \frac{1-\epsilon}{b}\, u\left(\frac{x}{b}\right)$$

where $0 < a < b$. If ϵ and a are small and b large, then $w = v \star v$ is not unimodal although v is.

Hint to avoid calculations: The convolution of two uniform densities is the triangular density and hence $w(a) > \epsilon^2 a^{-1}$ and $w(b) > \epsilon^2 b^{-1}$ and the integral of w from b to $2b$ is $> \frac{1}{2}(1 - \epsilon)^2$. It follows that w must have a minimum between a and b.

21. Let F be a uniform distribution and G unimodal. If both F and G are symmetric show by simple differentiation that the convolution $F \bigstar G$ is unimodal. Conclude (without further calculations) that the statement remains true when F is any fixture of symmetric uniform distributions, and hence that *the convolution of symmetric unimodal distributions is unimodal.*

[28] For the difficulties arising in the unsymmetric case see I. A. Ibragimov, Theory of Probability and Its Applications, vol. 1(1956) pp. 255–260.

CHAPTER VI

A Survey of Some Important Distributions and Processes

This chapter is the product of the deplorable need to avoid repetition and cross references between chapters intended for independent reading. For example, the theory of stable distributions will be developed independently by semi-group methods (IX), by Fourier analysis (XVII), and—at least partly—by Laplace transforms (XIII). Giving the definitions and examples at a neutral place is economical and makes it possible to scrutinize some basic relations without regard to purity of methods.

The miscellaneous topics covered in this chapter are not necessarily logically connected: the queuing process has little to do with martingale theory or stable distributions. The chapter is not intended for consecutive reading; the individual sections should be taken up as occasion arises or when their turn comes up. Sections 6–9 are somewhat interrelated, but independent of the rest.

1. STABLE DISTRIBUTIONS IN $\mathcal{R}^1$

Stable distributions play a constantly increasing role as a natural generalization of the normal distribution. For their description it is convenient to introduce the short-hand notation

$$\mathbf{U} \stackrel{d}{=} \mathbf{V} \tag{1.1}$$

to indicate that the random variables **U** and **V** have the same distribution. Thus $\mathbf{U} \stackrel{d}{=} a\mathbf{V} + b$ means that the distributions of **U** and **V** differ only by location parameters. [See definition 1 in V,2.] Throughout this section $\mathbf{X}, \mathbf{X}_1, \mathbf{X}_2, \ldots$ denote mutually independent random variables with a common distribution R and $\mathbf{S}_n = \mathbf{X}_1 + \cdots + \mathbf{X}_n$.

Definition 1. *The distribution R is stable (in the broad sense) if for each n there exist constants $c_n > 0$, γ_n such that*[1]

$$\mathbf{S}_n \stackrel{d}{=} c_n\mathbf{X} + \gamma_n \tag{1.2}$$

and R is not concentrated at the origin. R is stable in the strict sense if (1.2) holds with $\gamma_n = 0$.

Examples will be found in section 2. An elementary derivation of some basic properties of stable distributions is so instructive that we proceed with it at the cost of some repetition. The systematic theory developed in chapters IX and XVII does not depend on the following discussion.

Theorem 1. *Only the norming constants $c_n = n^{1/\alpha}$ are possible.*

It will be seen presently that $0 < \alpha \leq 2$. The constant α is called the *characteristic exponent* of the distribution R.

Proof. The argument is greatly simplified by symmetrization. If R is stable so is the distribution ${}^0R$ of $\mathbf{X}_1 - \mathbf{X}_2$ and the norming constants c_n are the same. It suffices therefore to prove the assertion for a *symmetric* stable R.

We start from the simple remark that $\mathbf{S}_{m+n}$ is the sum of the *independent* variables $\mathbf{S}_m$ and $\mathbf{S}_{m+n} - \mathbf{S}_m$ distributed, respectively, as $c_m\mathbf{X}$ and $c_n\mathbf{X}$. Thus for symmetric stable distributions

$$c_{m+n}\mathbf{X} \stackrel{d}{=} c_m\mathbf{X}_1 + c_n\mathbf{X}_2. \tag{1.3}$$

Similarly, the sum $\mathbf{S}_{rk}$ can be broken up into r independent blocks of k terms each, whence $c_{rk} = c_rc_k$ for all r and k. For subscripts of the form $n = r^\nu$ we conclude by induction that

$$\textit{if} \quad n = r^\nu \quad \textit{then} \quad c_n = c_r^{\,\nu}. \tag{1.4}$$

We next prove that *the sequence $\{c_n\}$ is monotone.* The variables in (1.3) being symmetric, we have for $x > 0$

$$\mathbf{P}\{c_{m+n}\mathbf{X} > c_mx\} \geq \tfrac{1}{2}\mathbf{P}\{c_m\mathbf{X}_1 > c_mx\} = \tfrac{1}{2}\mathbf{P}\{\mathbf{X}_1 > x\}. \tag{1.5}$$

For fixed x the right side is a positive constant and hence the ratio c_m/c_{m+n} must remain bounded when $m \to \infty$ and $n \to \infty$ in an arbitrary manner. We apply this result to $m = r^\nu$ and $m + n = (r + 1)^\nu$, where r is fixed and $\nu \to \infty$. In view of (1.4) it follows that $(c_r/c_{r+1})^\nu$ remains bounded, whence $c_r \leq c_{r+1}$ as asserted.

---

[1] It will be shown that the following (apparently more restrictive) definition is equivalent. R is stable iff to arbitrary constants c_1, c_2 there exist constants c and γ such that $c_1\mathbf{X}_1 + c_2\mathbf{X}_2 \stackrel{d}{=} c\mathbf{X} + \gamma$.

Consider now an arbitrary pair of integers j, k. To each ν there exists a unique λ such that

$$j^\lambda \leq k^\nu < j^{\lambda+1}. \tag{1.6}$$

On account of the monotonicity of $\{c_r\}$ and (1.4) this implies

$$c_j^{\,\lambda} \leq c_k^{\,\nu} < c_j^{\lambda+1}. \tag{1.7}$$

It follows that $c_j > 1$, and passing to logarithms we get

$$\frac{\lambda}{\lambda+1}\frac{\log j}{\log c_j} < \frac{\log k}{\log c_k} < \frac{\lambda+1}{\lambda}\frac{\log j}{\log c_j}. \tag{1.8}$$

As λ can be made arbitrarily large the ratio $(\log k)/(\log c_k) = \alpha$ must be independent of k, that is, $c_k = k^{1/\alpha}$. ▶

It turns out that all stable distributions have smooth densities but this will be proved only in XVII,6. Here we must be satisfied with

Lemma 1. *All (broad sense) stable distributions are continuous.*

Proof. Suppose that R has one or more atoms and denote by p the maximum of their weights. For stable distributions the atoms of $R \bigstar R$ differ from those of R only by their location, but not by their weights. Thus $R \bigstar R$ has again an atom of weight p, which contradicts the easily established fact that under convolutions the maximal weight of atoms decreases (problem 8 of V,11). ▶

Theorem 2. *If R is strictly stable with characteristic exponent α then for arbitrary positive s and t,*

$$s^{1/\alpha}\mathbf{X}_1 + t^{1/\alpha}\mathbf{X}_2 \stackrel{d}{=} (s+t)^{1/\alpha}\mathbf{X}. \tag{1.9}$$

Proof. For strictly stable distributions (1.3) holds. Since $c_n = n^{1/\alpha}$ this relation implies the truth of (1.9) for all rational s and t, and hence by continuity for arbitrary s and t. ▶

For the normal distribution $\alpha = 2$ and (1.9) merely restates the addition rule for the variances. In general (1.9) implies that *all linear combinations $a_1\mathbf{X}_2 + a_2\mathbf{X}_2$ belong to the same type.*

We show next that the restriction to strictly stable distributions is less serious than might appear, because every stable distribution with exponent $\alpha \neq 1$ can be centered so as to become strictly stable. The exponent $\alpha = 1$ presents an exception that is most annoying since it is of no particular interest.[2]

[2] For $\alpha = 1$ it turns out that with an appropriate centering the constants γ_n in (1.2) are of the form $\gamma_n = \gamma n \log n$. The analogue to (1.9) takes on the form

$$s(\mathbf{X}_1 + \gamma \log s) + t(\mathbf{X}_2 + \gamma \log t) \stackrel{d}{=} (s+t)(\mathbf{X} + \gamma \log(s+t)).$$

Theorem 3. *If R is stable with exponent $\alpha \neq 1$ there exists a constant b such that $R(x + b)$ is strictly stable.*

Proof. The variables $\mathbf{X}_k' = \mathbf{X}_k - b$ satisfy (1.2) with γ_n replaced by $\gamma_n' = \gamma_n + (c_n - n)\gamma$. When $\alpha \neq 1$ it is therefore possible to choose b such that $\gamma_2' = 0$. We now drop the primes and suppose $\gamma_2 = 0$ and $\alpha \neq 1$, that is, $c_2 \neq 2$. Then $\mathbf{S}_{2n}$ is the sum of n independent summands distributed as $\mathbf{X}_1 + \mathbf{X}_2$ and also the sum of two independent variables distributed as $\mathbf{S}_n$. Thus

$$\mathbf{S}_{2n} \stackrel{d}{=} c_2(\mathbf{X}_1 + \cdots + \mathbf{X}_n) \stackrel{d}{=} c_2 c_n \mathbf{X} + c_2 \gamma_n$$

and also

$$\mathbf{S}_{2n} \stackrel{d}{=} (c_n \mathbf{X}_1 + \gamma_n) + (c_n \mathbf{X}_2 + \gamma_n) \stackrel{d}{=} c_n c_2 \mathbf{X} + 2\gamma_n.$$

It follows that we must have $c_2\gamma_n = 2\gamma_n$ and hence $\gamma_n = 0$ as asserted. ►

The importance of the normal distribution $\mathfrak{N}$ is due largely to the central limit theorem. Let $\mathbf{X}_1, \ldots, \mathbf{X}_n$ be mutually independent variables with a common distribution F having zero expectation and unit variance. Put $\mathbf{S}_n = \mathbf{X}_1 + \cdots + \mathbf{X}_n$. The central limit theorem asserts that the distribution of $\mathbf{S}_n n^{-\frac{1}{2}}$ tends to $\mathfrak{N}$. For distributions without variance the norming constants must be chosen differently, but a limit may still exist. The interesting point is that all stable distributions and no others occur as such limits. The following terminology will facilitate the discussion of this problem.

Definition 2. *The distribution F of the independent random variables $\mathbf{X}_k$ belongs to the domain of attraction of a distribution R if there exist norming constants $a_n > 0$, b_n such that the distribution of $a_n^{-1}(\mathbf{S}_n - b_n)$ tends to R.*

Our last statement can now be reformulated to the effect that *a distribution R possesses a domain of attraction iff it is stable.* Indeed, by the very definition each stable R belongs to its own domain of attraction. That no other distribution appears as limit becomes plausible by the argument used in theorem 1. For subscripts of the form $n = rk$ we normalize the sums $\mathbf{S}_n$ in two ways, namely

$$\text{(1.10)} \qquad \mathbf{Y}_n = \frac{1}{a_n}(\mathbf{S}_n - b_n) \quad \textit{and} \quad \mathbf{Z}_n = \frac{1}{a_r}(\mathbf{S}_n - kb_r).$$

Keep k fixed and let $n = rk \to \infty$. By assumption the distribution of $\mathbf{Y}_n$ tends to R. On the other hand, $\mathbf{Z}_n$ is the sum of k independent variables each distributed as $a_r^{-1}(\mathbf{S}_r - b_r)$. The last distribution tends to R, and so it is intuitively clear that the distribution of $\mathbf{Z}_n$ tends to $R^{k\star}$. As the distributions of $\mathbf{Y}_n$ and $\mathbf{Z}_n$ differ only by location parameters, the same must be true of the limit distributions R and $R^{k\star}$ and this means precisely that R is stable. (The conclusions are justified in VIII,2 and theorem 2 of VIII,3.)

It can be shown by elementary methods (problem 3) that *a stable distribution with characteristic exponent* α *has absolute moments of all orders* $<\alpha$. A distribution with variance belongs to the domain of attraction of the normal distribution and hence *the exponents* α *are necessarily* ≤ 2. The proof that stable distributions with exponent $\alpha < 2$ actually exist is not simple.

Our results have important and surprising consequences. Consider, for example, a stable distribution satisfying (1.9) with $\alpha < 1$. The *average* $(\mathbf{X}_1 + \cdots + \mathbf{X}_n)/n$ has the same distribution as $\mathbf{X}_1 n^{-1+1/\alpha}$, and the last factor tends to ∞. Roughly speaking, we can say that the average of n variables is likely to be considerably larger than any given component $\mathbf{X}_k$. This is possible only if *the maximal term* $\mathbf{M}_n = \max[\mathbf{X}_1, \ldots, \mathbf{X}_n]$ is likely to grow exceedingly large and to receive a preponderating influence on the sum $\mathbf{S}_n$. A closer analysis bears out this conclusion. In the case of positive variables the expectation of the ratio $\mathbf{S}_n/\mathbf{M}_n$ tends to $(1-\alpha)^{-1}$, and this is true also for any sequence $\{\mathbf{X}_n\}$ whose distribution belongs to the domain of attraction of our stable distribution. (See problem 20 of XIII,11.)

Note on history. The general theory of stable distributions was initiated[3] by P. Lévy (1924), who found the Fourier transforms of all strictly stable distributions. (The others were originally called quasi-stable. As we have seen, they play a role only when $\alpha = 1$, and this case was analyzed jointly by Lévy and Khintchine.) A new and simpler approach to the whole theory was made possible by the discovery of infinitely divisible distributions. This new approach (still based on Fourier analysis) is also due to P. Lévy (1937). The interest in the theory was stimulated by A. Doblin's masterful analysis of the domains of attraction (1939). His criteria were the first to involve regularly varying functions. The modern theory still carries the imprint of this pioneer work although many authors have contributed improvements and new results. Chapter XVIII contains a streamlined treatment of the theory by the now classical Fourier methods, while chapter IX presents the same theory by a direct approach which is more in line with modern methods in Markov processes. Great simplifications and a unification of many criteria were made possible by the systematic exploitation of Karamata's theory of regularly varying functions. An improved version of this theory is presented in VIII,8–9.

[3] The Fourier transforms of *symmetric* stable distributions were mentioned by Cauchy, but it was not clear that they really corresponded to probability distributions. This point was settled by Pólya for the case $\alpha < 1$. The Holtsmark distribution of example (2.*c*) was known to astronomers, but not to mathematicians.—Readers interested in the historical development and in the older literature should consult P. Lévy [1925] and [1937].

2. EXAMPLES

(*a*) *The normal distribution* centered to zero expectation is strictly stable with $c_n = \sqrt{n}$.

(*b*) *The Cauchy distribution* with arbitrary location parameters has density

$$\frac{1}{\pi} \frac{c}{c^2 + (x-\gamma)^2}.$$

It is stable in the strict sense with characteristic exponent 1. [See II,(4.*e*).]

(*c*) *Stable distribution with* $\alpha = \frac{1}{2}$. The distribution

$$(2.1) \qquad F(x) = 2\left[1 - \mathfrak{N}\left(\frac{1}{\sqrt{x}}\right)\right], \qquad x > 0$$

with density

$$(2.2) \qquad f(x) = \frac{1}{\sqrt{2\pi x^3}}\, e^{-1/(2x)}, \qquad x > 0$$

[and $f(x) = 0$ for $x < 0$] is strictly stable with norming constants $c_n = n^2$.

A computational verification by elementary methods is possible but tedious, and it is preferable to derive the fact from a limit theorem. In a symmetric random walk let $\mathbf{X}_k$ denote the number of trials between the $(k - 1)$st and the kth return to the origin. We know that the $\mathbf{X}_k$ are mutually independent; their distribution is given in **1**; III,(4.2). Now $\mathbf{S}_k = \mathbf{X}_1 + \cdots + \mathbf{X}_k$ is the epoch of the kth return to the origin and the event $\{\mathbf{S}_r > k\}$ is the same as "fewer than r returns in k steps." Therefore by the limit theorem **1**; III,6.2

$$(2.3) \qquad \mathbf{P}\{\mathbf{S}_r \leq r^2 t\} \to F(t), \qquad r \to \infty.$$

Thus F has a domain of attraction and is therefore stable. [Continued in example (*e*).]

(*d*) *The gravitational field of stars* (*Holtsmark distribution*). In astronomical terms the problem is to calculate the x-component of the gravitational force exercised by the stellar system at a randomly chosen point O. The underlying idea is that the stellar system appears as a "random aggregate" of points with "randomly varying masses." These notions could be made precise in terms of Poisson distributions, etc., but fortunately no subtleties are required for the problem at hand.

Let us agree to treat the density of the stellar system as a free parameter and to let $\mathbf{X}_\lambda$ stand for the x-component of the gravitational force of a stellar system with density λ. We seek the conceivable types of such distributions. Now the intuitive notion of a "random aggregate of stars" presupposes that two independent aggregates with densities s and t may be combined into a single aggregate of density $s + t$. Probabilistically this amounts to the postulate that the sum of two independent variables distributed as $\mathbf{X}_s$ and $\mathbf{X}_t$ should have the same distribution as $\mathbf{X}_{s+t}$. We indicate this symbolically by

$$\mathbf{X}_s + \mathbf{X}_t \stackrel{d}{=} \mathbf{X}_{s+t}. \tag{2.4}$$

Considering that a change of density from 1 to λ amounts to a change of the unit of length from 1 to $1/\sqrt[3]{\lambda}$ and that the gravitational force varies inversely with the square of the distance we see that $\mathbf{X}_t$ must have the same distribution as $t^{\frac{2}{3}}\mathbf{X}_1$. This means that the distributions of $\mathbf{X}_t$ differ only by a scale parameter and (2.4) reduces to (1.9) with $\alpha = \frac{3}{2}$. In other words, $\mathbf{X}_\lambda$ *has a symmetric stable distribution with exponent* $\frac{3}{2}$. It will turn out that (up to the trivial scale parameter) there exists exactly one such distribution, and so we have solved our problem without appeal to deeper theory. The astronomer Holtsmark obtained an equivalent answer by other methods (see problem 4) and, remarkably, before P. Lévy's work.

(*e*) *First-passage times in Brownian motion.* We start from the notion of a one-dimensional diffusion process, that is, we suppose that the increments $\mathbf{X}(s+t) - \mathbf{X}(s)$ for non-overlapping time intervals are independent and have a symmetric normal distribution with variance t. We assume as known that the paths depend *continuously* on time. If $\mathbf{X}(0) = 0$ there exists an epoch $\mathbf{T}_a$ *at which the particle reaches the position* $a > 0$ *for the first time.* To derive the distribution function $F_a(t) = \mathbf{P}\{\mathbf{T}_a \leq t\}$ we observe that the notion of an additive process presupposes a complete lack of after-effect (the strong Markov property). This means that the increment $\mathbf{X}(t+\mathbf{T}_a) - a$ of the abscissa between epochs $\mathbf{T}_a$ and $\mathbf{T}_a + t$ is independent of the process before $\mathbf{T}_a$. Now to reach a position $a+b > a$ the particle must first reach a, and we conclude that the residual waiting time $\mathbf{T}_{a+b} - \mathbf{T}_a$ before reaching $a + b$ is independent of $\mathbf{T}_a$ and has the same distribution as $\mathbf{T}_b$. In other words, $F_a \star F_b = F_{a+b}$. But the transition probabilities depend only on the ratio x^2/t and therefore $\mathbf{T}_a$ must have the same distribution as $a^2\mathbf{T}_1$. This means that the distributions F_a differ only by a scale parameter and hence they are *stable with exponent* $\alpha = \frac{1}{2}$.

This argument, based on dimensional analysis, proves the stability of the first-passage distribution but does not lead to an explicit form. To show that F *coincides with the distribution of example* (*c*) we use a reasoning based on symmetry. Because of the assumed continuity of paths the event $\{\mathbf{X}(t) > a\}$ can occur only if the level a has been crossed at some epoch $\mathbf{T}_a < t$. Given that $\mathbf{T}_a = \tau < t$ we have $\mathbf{X}(\tau) = a$, and for reasons of symmetry the probability that $\mathbf{X}(t) - \mathbf{X}(\tau) > 0$ is $\frac{1}{2}$. We conclude that

$$\mathbf{P}\{\mathbf{T}_a < t\} = 2\mathbf{P}\{\mathbf{X}(t) > a\} = 2\left[1 - \mathfrak{N}\left(\frac{a}{\sqrt{t}}\right)\right] \tag{2.5}$$

which is equivalent with (2.1). Our symmetry argument is sometimes referred to as the method of Desiré André or the reflection principle.

(*f*) *Hitting points in two-dimensional Brownian motion.* A two-dimensional Brownian motion is formed by a pair $(\mathbf{X}(t), \mathbf{Y}(t))$ of independent one-dimensional Brownian motions. We are interested in the point $(a, \mathbf{Z}_a)$ at which the path first reaches the line $x = a > 0$. As in the preceding example we note that the path can reach the line $x = a+b > a$ only after crossing the line $x = a$; taking $(a, \mathbf{Z}_a)$ as new origin we conclude that $\mathbf{Z}_{a+b}$ has the same distribution as the sum of two independent variables distributed as $\mathbf{Z}_a$ and $\mathbf{Z}_b$. Now an obvious similarity consideration shows that $\mathbf{Z}_a$ has the same distribution as $a\mathbf{Z}_1$ and we conclude that $\mathbf{Z}_a$ has a symmetric stable distribution with exponent $\alpha = 1$. Only the Cauchy distribution fits this description, and so *the hitting point* $\mathbf{Z}_a$ *has a Cauchy distribution.*

This instructive dimensional analysis does not determine the scale parameter. For an explicit calculation note that $\mathbf{Z}_a = \mathbf{Y}(\mathbf{T}_a)$ where $\mathbf{T}_a$ is the epoch when the line $x = a$ is first reached. Its distribution is given in (2.5) while $\mathbf{Y}(t)$ has normal density with variance t. It follows that $\mathbf{Z}_a$ has a density given by[4]

$$(2.6) \qquad \int_0^\infty \frac{1}{t^{\frac12}\sqrt{2\pi}}\, e^{-\frac12 x^2/t} \cdot \frac{a}{t^{\frac32}\sqrt{2\pi}}\, e^{-\frac12 a^2/t} \cdot dt = \frac{a}{\pi(a^2 + x^2)}\,.$$

[We have here an example for the subordination of processes to which we shall return in X,7.]

(*g*) *Stable distributions in economics.* Arguments related to the dimensional analysis in the last two examples have been used by B. Mandelbrot to show that various economic processes (in particular income distributions) should be subject to stable (or "Lévy-Pareto") distributions. So far the strength of this interesting theory, which has attracted attention among economists, resides in the theoretical argument rather than observations. [For the apparent fit of the tails of the distribution to many empirical phenomena from city size to word frequency see II,(4.*h*).]

(*h*) *Products.* There exist many curious relations between stable distributions of different exponents. The most interesting may be stated in the form of the following proposition. Let $\mathbf{X}$ and $\mathbf{Y}$ be independent strictly stable variables with characteristic exponents α and β respectively. Assume $\mathbf{Y}$ to be a positive variable (whence $\beta < 1$). The *product* $\mathbf{X}\mathbf{Y}^{1/\alpha}$ *has a stable distribution with exponent* $\alpha\beta$. In particular, the product of a normal variable and the square root of the stable variable of example (*c*) is a Cauchy variable.

---

[4] The substitution $y = \frac12(x^2+a^2)/t$ reduces the integrand to e^{-y}.

We shall not prove the proposition here because it follows as a simple corollary to a theorem concerning subordinated processes[5] [example X,(7.*c*)]. Furthermore, it is easily verified by Fourier analysis [problem 8 of XVII, 12] and, for positive variables, also by Laplace transforms [XIII,(7.*e*) and problem 13].

3. INFINITELY DIVISIBLE DISTRIBUTIONS IN $\mathcal{R}^1$

Definition 1. *A distribution F is infinitely divisible if for every n there exists a distribution F_n such that $F = F_n^{n\star}$.*

In other words,[6] F is infinitely divisible iff for each n it can be represented as the distribution of the sum

$$\mathbf{S}_n = \mathbf{X}_{1,n} + \cdots + \mathbf{X}_{n,n} \tag{3.1}$$

of n independent random variables with a common distribution F_n.

This definition is valid in any number of dimensions, but for the present we shall limit our attention to one-dimensional distributions. It should be noted that infinite divisibility is a property of the *type*, that is, together with F all distributions differing from F only by location parameters are infinitely divisible. *Stable* distributions are infinitely divisible and distinguished by the fact that F_n differs from F only by location parameters.

Examples. (*a*) On account of the convolution property II,(2.3) all *gamma* distributions (including the *exponential*) are infinitely divisible. That the same is true of their discrete counterpart, the "*negative binomial*" (including the *geometric*) distributions was shown in **1**; XII, 2.

(*b*) The Poisson and the compound Poisson distributions are infinitely divisible. It will turn out that all infinitely divisible distributions are *limits* of compound Poisson distributions.

(*c*) The distribution II,(7.13) connected with *Bessel* functions is infinitely divisible but this is by no means obvious. See example XIII,(7.*d*).

---

[5] For a direct verification requiring a minimum of calculations calculate the distribution of $\mathbf{Z} = \mathbf{X}_1\sqrt[\alpha]{\mathbf{Y}_1} + \mathbf{X}_2\sqrt[\alpha]{\mathbf{Y}_2}$ by first calculating the conditional distribution of $\mathbf{Z}$ given that $\mathbf{Y}_1 = y_1$ and $\mathbf{Y}_2 = y_2$. It is a function of the sum $y_1 + y_2$ and the change of variables $u = y_1 + y_2$, $v = y_1 - y_2$ shows that the distribution of $\mathbf{Z}$ differs only by a scale factor from that of the two summands. The same calculation works for sums of n similar terms.

[6] It should be understood that the random variables $\mathbf{X}_{k,n}$ serve merely to render notations simpler and more intuitive. For fixed n the variables $\mathbf{X}_{1,n}, \ldots, \mathbf{X}_{n,n}$ are supposed to be mutually independent, but the variables $\mathbf{X}_{j,m}$ and $\mathbf{X}_{k,n}$ with $m \neq n$ need not be defined on the same probability space. (In other words, a joint distribution for $\mathbf{X}_{k,m}$ and $\mathbf{X}_{k,n}$ need not exist.) This remark applies to triangular arrays in general.

(*d*) *A distribution F carried by a finite interval is not infinitely divisible* except it if is concentrated at one point. Indeed, if $|\mathbf{S}_n| < a$ with probability one then $|\mathbf{X}_{k,n}| < an^{-1}$ and so $\text{Var}(\mathbf{X}_{k,n}) < a^2n^{-2}$. The variance of F is therefore $<a^2n^{-1}$ and hence zero. ▶

Returning to definition 1 let us consider what happens if we drop the requirement that the $\mathbf{X}_{k,n}$ have the same distribution and require only that for each n there exist n distributions $F_{1,n}, \ldots, F_{n,n}$ such that

$$F = F_{1,n} \bigstar \cdots \bigstar F_{n,n}. \tag{3.2}$$

Such generality leads to a new phenomenon best illustrated by examples.

Examples. (*e*) If F is infinitely divisible and U arbitrary, $G = U \bigstar F$ can be written in the form (3.2) with $G_{1,n} = U$ and all other $G_{k,n}$ equal to F_{n-1}. Here the first component plays an entirely different role from all other components.

(*f*) Consider a convergent series $\mathbf{X} = \Sigma \mathbf{X}_k$ of mutually independent random variables. The distribution F of $\mathbf{X}$ is the convolution of the distributions of $\mathbf{X}_1, \mathbf{X}_2, \ldots, \mathbf{X}_{n-1}$ and the remainder $(\mathbf{X}_n + \mathbf{X}_{n+1} + \cdots)$ and so F is of the form (3.2). Such distributions will be studied under the name of *infinite convolutions*. Example I,(11.*c*) shows the uniform distribution to be among them. ▶

The distinguishing feature of these examples is that the contribution of an individual component $\mathbf{X}_{1,n}$ to $\mathbf{S}_n$ is essential, whereas in the case of equally distributed components the contribution of each tends to zero. We wish to connect infinitely divisible distributions to the typical limit theorems involving "many small components." It is then necessary to supplement our scheme by the requirement that the individual components $\mathbf{X}_{k,n}$ become asymptotically negligible in the sense that for each $\epsilon > 0$.

$$\mathbf{P}\{|\mathbf{X}_{k,n}| > \epsilon\} < \epsilon, \qquad (k = 1, \ldots, n) \tag{3.3}$$

for n sufficiently large. In the terminology of VIII,2 this means that the $\mathbf{X}_{k,n}$ *tend in probability to zero uniformly in* $k = 1, \ldots, n$. Systems of variables of this type appear so often that it is convenient to give them a name.

Definition 2. *By a triangular array is meant a double sequence of random variables* $\mathbf{X}_{k,n}$ $(k = 1, 2, \ldots, n;\ n = 1, 2, \ldots)$ *such that the variables* $\mathbf{X}_{1,n}, \ldots, \mathbf{X}_{n,n}$ *of the* n*th row are mutually independent.*

The array is a null array (or has asymptotically negligible components) if (3.3) *holds.*

More generally one may consider arrays with r_n variables in the nth row with $r_n \to \infty$. The gain is generality is slight.[7]

Example. (*g*) Let $\{\mathbf{X}_j\}$ be a sequence of identically distributed independent random variables and $\mathbf{S}_n = \mathbf{X}_1 + \cdots + \mathbf{X}_n$. The normalized sequence $\mathbf{S}_n a_n^{-1}$ represents the nth row sum of a triangular array in which $\mathbf{X}_{k,n} = \mathbf{X}_k a_n^{-1}$. This array is a null array if $a_n \to \infty$. An array of a different sort was considered in the derivation of the Poisson distribution in **1**; VI,6. ▶

In chapters IX and XVII we shall prove the remarkable fact that *a limit distribution of the row sums* $\mathbf{S}_n$ *of a triangular null array* (*if it exists*) *is infinitely divisible.* As long as the asymptotic negligibility condition (3.3) holds it does not matter whether or not the components $\mathbf{X}_{k,n}$ have a common distribution, and in (3.2) we may replace the equality sign by a limit: the class of infinitely divisible distributions coincides with the class of limit distributions of the row sums of triangular null arrays.

Examples for applications. (*h*) *The shot effect in vacuum tubes.* Variants and generalizations of the following stochastic process occur in physics and in communication engineering.

We propose to analyze the fluctuations in electrical currents due to the chance fluctuations of the numbers of electrons arriving at an anode. It is assumed that the arrivals form a Poisson process, and that an arriving electron produces a current whose intensity x time unit later equals $I(x)$. The intensity of the current at epoch t is then formally a random variable

$$\mathbf{X}(t) = \sum_{k=1}^{\infty} I(t-\mathbf{T}_k), \tag{3.4}$$

where the $\mathbf{T}_k$ represent the epochs of past electron arrivals. (In other words, the variables $t-\mathbf{T}_1, \mathbf{T}_2-\mathbf{T}_1, \mathbf{T}_3-\mathbf{T}_2, \ldots$ are mutually independent and have a common exponential distribution.)

A direct analysis of the sum (3.4) by the methods of stochastic processes is not difficult, but the simple-minded approach by triangular arrays may serve as an aid to intuition. Partition the interval $\overline{-\infty, t}$ into small

[7] That the greater generality is a mere illusion can be seen as follows. We can increase the number of variables in each row by adding dummy variables that are identically zero. There is therefore no loss of generality in assuming that the number r_n of variables in the nth row increases with n. Given such an array $\mathfrak{A}$ we construct a new one as follows. The first r_1 lines are arbitrary. Then the first line of $\mathfrak{A}$ is repeated $r_2 - r_1$ times, next the second line of $\mathfrak{A}$ is repeated $r_3 - r_2$ times, and so on. In the new array the nth row contains at most n terms and we again increase the number of terms to n by adding zeros. The sequence $\{\mathbf{S}_n'\}$ of row sums in the new array differs from $\{\mathbf{S}_n\}$ merely by possible repetitions, and the asymptotic behavior is the same.

subintervals with endpoints $t_k = t - kh$ (where $k = 0, 1, \ldots$). By the very definition of the Poisson process the contribution of the interval $\overline{t_k, t_{k-1}}$ to the sum in (3.4) is comparable to a binomial random variable assuming the value 0 with probability $1 - \alpha h$ and $I(t - t_k)$ with probability αh. The expectation of this variable is $\alpha h\, I(kh)$, its variance $\alpha h(1-\alpha h)\, I^2(kh)$. We take $h = 1/\sqrt{n}$ and construct the triangular array in which $\mathbf{X}_{k,n}$ is the contribution of the kth interval. The row sums have then expectation $\alpha h\, \Sigma I(kh)$ and variance $\alpha h(1-\alpha h)\, \Sigma I^2(kh)$. If any meaning can be attached to the series (3.4) the distributions of the row sums must tend to the distribution of $\mathbf{X}(t)$ and so we must have

$$(3.5) \qquad \mathbf{E}(\mathbf{X}(t)) = \alpha \int_0^\infty I(s)\, ds, \qquad \operatorname{Var}(\mathbf{X}(t)) = \alpha \int_0^\infty I^2(s)\, ds.$$

These conclusions are easily confirmed by the theory of triangular arrays. (See problem 6 of XVII,12, and problem 22 of VIII,10). The relations (3.5) are well known as *Campbell's theorem*. From our point of view it does not appear deep, but it was proved in 1909 decades ahead of a systematic theory. It was rightly considered remarkable and various proofs have been given for it.

(*i*) *Busy trunklines.* A variant of the preceding example may illustrate the types of possible generalizations. Consider a telephone exchange with infinitely many trunklines. The incoming calls form a Poisson process, and an arriving call is directed to a free trunkline. The ensuing holding times have a common distribution F; as usual, they are assumed independent of the arrival process and of each other. The number of busy lines at epoch t is a random variable $\mathbf{X}(t)$ whose distribution can be derived by the method of the preceding example. In the present case the variables $\mathbf{X}_{k,n}$ of the triangular array assume only the values 0 and 1, the latter with probability $\alpha h[1 - F(kh)]$. The conclusion is that *the number of busy lines has expectation*

$$(3.6) \qquad \mathbf{E}(\mathbf{X}(t)) = \alpha \int_0^\infty [1 - F(s)]\, ds.$$

Note that the integral equals the expectation of the holding times. ►

Historical note. The notion of infinite divisibility goes back to B. de Finetti (1929). The Fourier transforms of infinitely divisible distributions with finite variance were found by A. Kolmogorov (1932), and those of the general infinitely divisible distributions by P. Lévy (1934), who also treated the problem from the point of view of stochastic processes. All subsequent investigations were strongly influenced by his pioneer work. The first purely analytical derivations of the general formula were given in 1937 independently by Feller and Khintchine. These authors proved also that the limit distributions of null arrays are infinitely divisible.

4. PROCESSES WITH INDEPENDENT INCREMENTS

Infinitely divisible distributions are intimately connected with stochastic processes with independent increments. By this we mean a *family of random variables* $\mathbf{X}(t)$ *depending on the continuous time parameter* t *and such that the increments* $\mathbf{X}(t_{k+1}) - \mathbf{X}(t_k)$ *are mutually independent for any finite set* $t_1 < t_2 < \cdots < t_n$. At this juncture we require no theory of stochastic processes; we argue simply that *if* certain phenomena can be described probabilistically, the theory will lead to infinitely divisible distributions. In this sense we have considered special processes with independent increments in **1**; XVII,1 and in example III,(8.*a*). We limit our attention to numerical variables $\mathbf{X}(t)$ although the theory carries over to vector variables.

The process has *stationary increments* if the distribution of $\mathbf{X}(s+t) - \mathbf{X}(s)$ depends only on the length t of the interval but not on s.

Let us partition the interval $\overline{s, s+t}$ by $n+1$ equidistant points $s = t_0 < t_1 < \cdots < t_n = s+t$ and put $\mathbf{X}_{k,n} = \mathbf{X}(t_k) - \mathbf{X}(t_{k-1})$. The variable $\mathbf{X}(s+t) - \mathbf{X}(s)$ of a process with stationary independent increments is the sum of the n independent variables $\mathbf{X}_{k,n}$ with a common distribution and hence $\mathbf{X}(s+t) - \mathbf{X}(s)$ *has an infinitely divisible distribution.* We shall see that the *converse* is also true. In fact, a one-parametric family of probability distributions Q_t defined for $t > 0$ can serve as the distribution of $\mathbf{X}(s+t) - \mathbf{X}(s)$ in a process with stationary independent increments iff

$$Q_{s+t} = Q_s \star Q_t \qquad s, t > 0. \tag{4.1}$$

A family of distributions satisfying (4.1) is said to form a semi-group (see VIII,3). Every infinitely divisible distribution can be taken as element Q_t (with $t > 0$ arbitrary) of such a semi-group.

Before passing to the non-stationary case let us consider typical examples.

Examples. (*a*) *The compound Poisson process.* With an arbitrary probability distribution F and $\alpha > 0$

$$Q_t = e^{-\alpha t} \sum_{k=0}^{\infty} \frac{(\alpha t)^k}{k!} F^{k\star} \tag{4.2}$$

defines a compound Poisson distribution, and it is easily verified that (4.1) holds. Suppose now that Q_t represents the distribution of $\mathbf{X}(t) - \mathbf{X}(0)$ in a stochastic process with stationary independent increments. When F is concentrated at the point 1 this process reduces to an ordinary *Poisson process* and (4.2) to

$$\mathbf{P}\{\mathbf{X}(t) - \mathbf{X}(0) = n\} = e^{-\alpha t}\frac{(\alpha t)^n}{n!}. \tag{4.3}$$

The general model (4.2) may be interpreted in terms of this special Poisson process as follows. Let $\mathbf{Y}_1, \mathbf{Y}_2, \ldots$ be independent variables with the common distribution F, and let $\mathbf{N}(t)$ be the variable of a pure Poisson process with $\mathbf{P}\{\mathbf{N}(t) = n\} = e^{-\alpha t}(\alpha t)^n/n!$, and independent of the $\mathbf{Y}_k$. Then (4.2) represents the distribution of the random sum $\mathbf{Y}_1 + \cdots + \mathbf{Y}_{\mathbf{N}(t)}$. In other words, with the nth jump of the Poisson process there is associated an effect $\mathbf{Y}_n$, and $\mathbf{X}(t) - \mathbf{X}(0)$ represents the sum of the effects occurring during $\overline{0, t}$. The *randomized random* walk studied in II,7 is a compound Poisson process with $\mathbf{Y}_k$ assuming the values ± 1 only. Empirical applications are illustrated at the end of this section.

(*b*) *Brownian motion* or the Wiener-Bachelier process. Here $\mathbf{X}(0) = 0$ (the process starts at the origin) and the increments $\mathbf{X}(t+s) - \mathbf{X}(s)$ have a normal distribution with zero expectation and variance t. Wiener and Lévy have shown that the sample functions of this process are *continuous* with probability one, and this property characterizes the normal distribution among all infinitely divisible distributions.

(*c*) *Stable processes.* The relation (1.9) for a strictly stable distribution merely paraphrases (4.1) with $Q_t(x) = R(t^{-1/\alpha}x)$. Thus this distribution defines transition probabilities in a process with stationary independent increments; for $\alpha = 2$ it reduces to Brownian motion. ▶

The main theorem of the theory (see IX and XVII) states that the *most general solution of* (4.1)—*and hence the most general infinitely divisible distribution—may be represented as a limit of an appropriate sequence of compound Poisson distributions.* This result is surprising in view of the great formal difference between examples (*a*) and (*b*).

Even in *non-stationary* processes with independent increments the distribution of $\mathbf{X}(t+s) - \mathbf{X}(t)$ appears as the distribution of the row sums of our triangular array $\{\mathbf{X}_{k,n}\}$, but a slight continuity condition must be imposed on the process to assure that (3.3) holds. Example (*e*) will explain this necessity. Under a slight restriction *only infinitely divisible distributions appear as distributions of* $\mathbf{X}(t+s) - \mathbf{X}(t)$.

Examples. (*d*) *Operational time.* A simple change of the time scale will frequently reduce a general process to a more tractable stationary process. Given any continuous increasing function φ we may switch from the variable $\mathbf{X}(t)$ to $\mathbf{Y}(t) = \mathbf{X}(\varphi(t))$. The property of independent increments is obviously preserved, and with an appropriate choice of φ the new process may also have stationary increments. In practice the choice is usually dictated by the nature of things. For example, at a *telephone exchange* nobody would compare an hour at night with the busy hour of the day, while it is natural to measure time in variable units such that the expected number of calls per unit remains constant. Again, in a growing *insurance* business claims will occur at an accelerated rate but this departure from stationarity is removed by the simple expedient of introducing an operational time measuring the frequency of claims.

(*e*) *Fixed discontinuities.* Let $\mathbf{X}_1, \mathbf{X}_2, \ldots$ be mutually independent random variables and $\mathbf{S}_n = \mathbf{X}_1 + \cdots + \mathbf{X}_n$. A process with (non-stationary) independent increments is defined by letting $\mathbf{X}(t) = \mathbf{S}_n$ for $n \leq t < n+1$ and in it all changes occur at the epochs $1, 2, 3, \ldots$. It follows that some sort of continuity condition is necessary to insure that the distributions of the increments be infinitely divisible. This example illustrates intuitively the possibility of discontinuities at fixed epochs. In the Poisson process the sample functions as such are discontinuous but for each *fixed* t the probability that no change occurs within the time interval $\overline{t, t+h}$ is $e^{-\alpha h}$ and tends to certainty as $h \to 0$. In other words, even though the number of telephone calls changes by jumps, a jump in a small time interval is unlikely. By contrast, in the present example a discontinuity is guaranteed at $t = 1, 2, \ldots$. ▶

Examples *for empirical applications.* An unending variety of practical problems can be reduced to compound Poisson processes. Here are a few typical examples. (i) The accumulated *damage* due to automobile accidents, fire, lightning, etc. For applications to *collective risk* theory see example (5.*a*). (ii) The total catch by a fishery boat in search of schools of fish (J. Neyman). (iii) The content of water *reservoirs* due to rainfall and demand. Other *storage facilities* are treated in like manner. (iv) A *stone at the bottom of a river* lies at rest for such long periods that its successive displacements are practically instantaneous. The total displacement within time $\overline{0, t}$ may be treated as a compound Poisson process. (First treated by different methods by Albert Einstein Jr. and G. Pólya.) (v) *Telephone calls*, or customers, arriving at a server require service. Under appropriate conditions the total service time caused by arrivals within the time interval $\overline{0, t}$ represents a compound Poisson process. The remarkable feature of this process is the fact that the value of $\mathbf{X}(t)$ *is not observable at epoch* t because it depends on service times that still lie in the future. (vi) For energy changes of physical particles due to *collisions* see example X,(1.*b*).

*5. RUIN PROBLEMS IN COMPOUND POISSON PROCESSES

Let $\mathbf{X}(t)$ be the variable of a compound Poisson process, that is, the increment $\mathbf{X}(t+s) - \mathbf{X}(s)$ over any time interval of duration t has the

* This section treats a special topic. It is of great practical interest, but will not be referred to in the present book except for examples.

probability distribution Q_t of (4.2). Let $c > 0$ and $z > 0$ be fixed. By *ruin* we mean the event

$$\{\mathbf{X}(t) > z + ct\}. \tag{5.1}$$

We regard c as a constant and $z > 0$ as a free parameter, *and we denote by $R(z)$ the probability that no ruin will ever occur.* We shall argue formally that if the whole problem makes sense $R(z)$ must be a non-increasing solution of the functional equation (5.2). First a few examples may indicate the surprising variety of practical situations to which our problem is applicable.

Examples. (*a*) *Collective risk theory.*[8] Here $\mathbf{X}(t)$ stands for the accumulated amount of claims within the time interval $\overline{0, t}$ against an insurance company. It is assumed that the occurrence of claims is subject to a Poisson process and that the individual claims have the distribution F. In principle these "claims" may be positive or negative. (For example, a death may free the company of an obligation and increase the reserves.) In this example z represents the company's initial reserve at epoch 0 and c the rate of increase of the reserves[9] in the absence of claims. The company's total reserve at epoch t is then represented by the random variable $z + ct - \mathbf{X}(t)$, and "ruin" stands for a negative reserve, that is, failure.

(*b*) *Storage facilities.* An idealized water reservoir is being filled by rivers and rainfall at a constant rate c. At random intervals the reservoir is tapped by amounts $\mathbf{X}_1, \mathbf{X}_2, \ldots$. The compound Poisson model applies and if z stands for the initial content at epoch 0 then $z + ct - \mathbf{X}(t)$ is the theoretical content at time t except that ruin can occur before t. In this problem F is concentrated on $\overline{0, \infty}$. For the huge literature on related problems see the monographs listed at the end of the book.

(*c*) *Scheduling of patients.*[10] We agree to treat the times devoted by a doctor to his patients as independent random variables with an exponential distribution and mean duration α^{-1}. As long as treatments continue

[8] A huge literature is devoted to this theory (inaugurated by F. Lundberg) and our ruin problem in particular. For a relatively recent survey see H. Cramér, *On some questions connected with mathematical risk*, Univ. Calif. Publications in Statistics, vol. 2, no. 5 (1954) pp. 99–125. Note that Cramér's asymptotic estimates (obtained by deep Wiener–Hopf techniques) are obtained in an elementary manner in examples XI,(7.*a*) and XII,(5.*d*).

[9] In practice a growing company will use the accumulated sum of premiums received as operational time [see example (4.*d*)].

[10] R. Pyke, *The supremum and infimum of the Poisson process*, Ann. Math. Statist., vol. 30 (1959) pp. 568–576. Pyke treats the ruin problem only for the pure Poisson process but he obtains more precise results (by different methods).

without interruption the departures of treated patients are subject to an *ordinary Poisson process*. Let $\mathbf{X}(t)$ stand for the number of such departures within $\overline{0, t}$. Suppose that z patients are waiting at epoch 0 (the beginning of the office hours) and that thereafter new patients arrive at epochs $c^{-1}, 2c^{-1}, 3c^{-1}, \ldots$. The doctor will not be idle as long as $\mathbf{X}(t) \leq z + ct$. ▶

The following formal argument leads to an equation determining the probability of ruin R. Suppose that the *first* jump of the sample function occurs at epoch τ and has magnitude x. For no ruin ever to occur it is necessary that $x \leq z + c\tau$ and that for all $t > \tau$ the increments $\mathbf{X}(t) - x$ be $\leq z - x + ct$. Such increments being independent of the past the latter event has probability $R(z-x+c\tau)$. Summing over all possible τ and x we get

$$(5.2) \qquad R(z) = \int_0^\infty \alpha e^{-\alpha\tau}\, d\tau \int_{-\infty}^{z+c\tau} R(z+c\tau-x)\, F\{dx\}.$$

This is the desired equation, but it can be simplified. The change of variable $s = z + c\tau$ shows that

$$(5.3) \qquad R(z) = \frac{\alpha}{c}\int_z^\infty e^{-(\alpha/c)(s-z)}\, ds \int_{-\infty}^{s} R(s-x)\, F\{dx\}.$$

Consequently R is differentiable, and a simple differentiation leads to the final *integro-differential equation*

$$(5.4) \qquad R'(z) = \frac{\alpha}{c} R(z) - \frac{\alpha}{c}\int_{-\infty}^{z} R(z-x)\, F\{dx\}.$$

Note that by definition $R(s) = 0$ for $s < 0$ so that the integral on the right is the *convolution* $F \bigstar R$. We shall return to (5.4) in examples (9.*d*), XI,(7.*a*) and XII,(5.*d*).

6. RENEWAL PROCESSES

The basic notions of renewal theory were introduced in **1**; XIII in connection with recurrent events. It will be seen that the introduction of a continuous time parameter depends on notational, rather than conceptual, changes. The salient feature of recurrent events is that the successive waiting times $\mathbf{T}_k$ are mutually independent random variables with a common distribution F; the epoch of the nth occurrence is given by the sum

$$(6.1) \qquad \mathbf{S}_n = \mathbf{T}_1 + \cdots + \mathbf{T}_n.$$

By convention $\mathbf{S}_0 = 0$ and 0 counts as occurrence number zero.

Even in stochastic processes depending on a continuous time parameter it is frequently possible to discover one or more sequences of epochs of the form (6.1). In such cases surprisingly sharp results are obtainable by simple methods. Analytically we are concerned merely with sums of independent positive variables, and the only excuse for introducing the term "renewal process" is its frequent occurrence in connection with *other* processes and the tacit implication that the powerful tool of the renewal equation is used.[11]

Definition 1. *A sequence of random variables* $\mathbf{S}_n$ *constitutes a renewal process if it is of the form* (6.1) *where the* $\mathbf{T}_k$ *are mutually independent variables with a common distribution F such that*[12] $F(0) = 0$.

The variables being positive there is no danger in writing $\mu = \mathbf{E}(\mathbf{T}_k)$ even if the integral diverges (in which case we write $\mu = \infty$). The expectation μ will be called *mean recurrence time*. As usual in similar situations, it is irrelevant for our present analysis whether the variables $\mathbf{T}_k$ occur in some stochastic process or whether the sequence $\{\mathbf{T}_j\}$ itself defines our probability space.

In most (but not all) applications the $\mathbf{T}_j$ can be interpreted as "waiting times" and the $\mathbf{S}_n$ are then referred to as *renewal* (*or regeneration*) epochs.

It seems intuitively obvious that for a fixed finite interval $I = \overline{a, b}$ the number of renewal epochs $\mathbf{S}_n$ falling within I is finite with probability one and hence a well-defined random variable $\mathbf{N}$. If the event $\{\mathbf{S}_n \in I\}$ is called "success" then $\mathbf{N}$ is the total number of successes in infinitely many trials and its expectation equals

$$U\{I\} = \sum_{n=0}^{\infty} \mathbf{P}\{\mathbf{S}_n \in I\} = \sum_{n=0}^{\infty} F^{n\star}\{I\}. \tag{6.2}$$

For integral-valued random variables such sums were considered in **1**; XIII in connection with recurrent events. There, however, it sufficed to consider intervals reducing to a single integer and so the events $\{\mathbf{S}_n \in I\}$ were mutually exclusive. For this reason it was possible to speak of the probability u_k that one among the sums $\mathbf{S}_n$ equals k rather than of the expected numbers of such sums. In the present situation it is not obvious that the series in (6.2) converges. To see that this is so we have to show that for each x

$$U(x) = \sum_{n=0}^{\infty} F^{n\star}(x) \tag{6.3}$$

[11] For a more sophisticated generalization of the recurrent events see J. F. C. Kingman, *The stochastic theory of regenerative events*, Zeit. Wahrscheinlichkeitstheorie, vol. 2 (1964) pp. 180–224.

[12] We could permit an atom at the origin, but nothing would be gained and we would have to exclude the case of a distribution F concentrated at the origin.

is finite. Then $U\{\overline{a, b}|\} = U(b) - U(a)$ defines a measure concentrated on $|\overline{0, \infty}$ with a unit atom at the origin.

We prove the assertion in conjunction with an application of U to the *renewal equation*

$$Z = z + F \bigstar Z \tag{6.4}$$

where z and Z are functions vanishing on $\overline{-\infty, 0}$. Spelled out explicitly (6.4) reads[13]

$$Z(x) = z(x) + \int_0^x Z(x-y)\, F\{dy\}, \qquad x > 0. \tag{6.5}$$

This is the analogue to the renewal equation studied in **1**; XIII and will turn up in many connections.

Theorem 1.[14] *$U(x) < \infty$ for all x. If z is bounded and vanishes for $x < 0$ the convolution $Z = U \bigstar z$ defined by*

$$Z(x) = \int_0^x z(x-y)\, U\{dy\} \tag{6.6}$$

represents a solution of the renewal equation (6.5). *There exists no other solution vanishing on $\overline{-\infty, 0}$ and bounded on finite intervals.*

Proof. The event $\{\mathbf{S}_n \leq x\}$ cannot occur unless $\mathbf{T}_j \leq x$ for $j = 1, \ldots, n$ and hence $\mathbf{P}\{\mathbf{S}_n \leq x\} \leq F^n(x)$. This implies that (6.3) converges geometrically at each x such that $F(x) < 1$. But for *every* x there exists an integer r such that $F^{r\bigstar}(x) < 1$, and since $F^{k\bigstar}(x)$ depends monotonically on k we have

$$U(x) \leq r \sum_{k=0}^{\infty} F^{rk\bigstar}(x) < \frac{r}{1 - F^{r\bigstar}(x)} < \infty. \tag{6.7}$$

Taking the convolution of (6.3) with z it is seen that Z satisfies the renewal equation. The difference V of two solutions satisfies $V = F \bigstar V$ and hence $V = F^{n\bigstar} \bigstar V$ for all n. But $F^{n\bigstar}(x) \to 0$ for all x and hence $V(x) = 0$. ►

It should be noted that $Z(x) = U(x)$ is a solution of the renewal equation (6.5) with $z(x) = 1$ for $x > 0$. This can be seen directly by the following argument.

The expected number of renewal epochs in the closed interval $|\overline{0, x}|$ is one plus the expected number in the half-open interval $\overline{0, x}|$. This interval contains renewal epochs only if $\mathbf{T}_1 \leq x$; given that $\mathbf{T}_1 = y \leq x$, the

[13] The limits of integration are indicated for convenience only; the convolution integral is the same as if the integration were extended over the whole line.

[14] A more systematic theory is developed in section 10.

expected number of renewal epochs in $\overline{0, x}|$ is $U(x-y)$. Summing over y we get (6.5). This is the standard "*renewal argument*" to be used time and again for the derivation of various distributions and expectations.

Two obvious generalizations of a renewal process are useful. First we consider *terminating processes* where the process can stop at any renewal epoch, this event being independent of the past and having a fixed probability $0 < q < 1$. (This is the analogue to transient recurrent events.) Abstractly speaking, the sample space is enlarged by a point called *death* and $\mathbf{S}_n$ is either a positive number or "dead." The distribution F is now the conditional probability distribution of the recurrence times T_j *if* the process does not stop. The absolute distribution is $(1-q)F$. We now change the notation and write F instead of $(1-q)F$ with the understanding that $F(\infty) < 1$ so that F is a *defective distribution.* Then all above formulas apply without change. For ease of reference we put on record the informal

Definition 2.[15] *A terminating or transient renewal process is an ordinary renewal process except that F is defective. The defect $q = 1 - F(\infty)$ is interpreted as probability of termination.*

For consistency 0 is counted as renewal epoch number zero. The probability that the process effectively survives the renewal epoch number n equals $(1 - q)^n$ and tends to 0 as $n \to \infty$. Thus *with probability one a terminating process terminates at a finite time.* The total mass of $F^{n\star}$ is $(1 - q)^n$ and so *the expected number of renewal epochs is $U(\infty) = q^{-1} < \infty$.* This is, so to speak, the expected number of generations attained by the process. The probability that $\mathbf{S}_n \leq x$ and the process dies with this nth renewal epoch is $qF^{n\star}(x)$. We have thus the

Theorem 2. *In a terminating renewal process, qU is the proper probability distribution of the duration of the process (age at time of death).*

A second generalization consists in permitting the *initial* waiting time to have a different distribution. In such cases we begin the numbering of the $\mathbf{T}_j$ with $j = 0$ so that now $\mathbf{S}_0 = \mathbf{T}_0 \neq 0$.

Definition 3. *A sequence $\mathbf{S}_0, \mathbf{S}_1, \ldots$ forms a delayed renewal process if it is of the form* (6.1) *where the $\mathbf{T}_k$ are mutually independent strictly positive (proper or defective) variables and $\mathbf{T}_1, \mathbf{T}_2, \ldots$ (but not $\mathbf{T}_0$) have a common distribution.*

For example, a proper renewal process becomes delayed when considered only beyond an epoch τ.

[15] See example 7(f) for an illustration and problem 10 for a generalization.

7. EXAMPLES AND PROBLEMS

Examples such as self-renewing aggregates, counters, and population growth carry over from the discrete case in an obvious manner. A special problem, however, will lead to interesting questions to be treated later on.

Example. (*a*) *Inspection paradox.* In the theory of self-renewing aggregates a piece of equipment, say an electric battery, is installed and serves until it breaks down. Upon failure it is instantly replaced by a like battery and the process continues without interruption. The epochs of renewal form a renewal process in which $\mathbf{T}_k$ is the lifetime of the kth battery.

Suppose now that the actual lifetimes of batteries in operation were to be tested by systematic or sampling inspection. We take a sample of batteries in operation at epoch $t > 0$ and observe their total lifetimes. Since F is the distribution of the lifetimes for *all* batteries one expects that this applies also to the inspected specimen. But this is not so. In fact, for an exponential distribution F the situation differs only verbally from the waiting time paradox in I,4 where the lifetime of the inspected item has an entirely different distribution. *The fact that the item was inspected at epoch t changes its lifetime distribution and doubles its expected duration.* We shall see in XI,(3.6) that this situation is typical of all renewal processes. The practical implications are serious. We see that an apparently unbiased inspection plan may lead to false conclusions because *what we actually observe need not be typical of the population* as a whole. Once noticed the phenomenon is readily understood (see I,4), but it reveals nevertheless the possible pitfalls of observations and the necessary interplay between theory and practice. Incidentally, no trouble arises if one decides to test the first item installed after epoch t. ▶

This is a good occasion to introduce three random variables of interest in renewal theory. In the example all three refer to the item in operation at epoch $t > 0$ and may be described by the self-explanatory terms: residual lifetime, spent lifetime, and total lifetime. The formal definition is as follows.

To given $t > 0$ there corresponds a unique (chance-dependent) subscript $\mathbf{N}_t$ such that $\mathbf{S}_{\mathbf{N}_t} \leq t < \mathbf{S}_{\mathbf{N}_t+1}$. Then:

(*a*) *The residual waiting time* is $\mathbf{S}_{\mathbf{N}_t+1} - t$, the time from t to the next renewal epoch.

(*b*) *The spent waiting time* is $t - \mathbf{S}_{\mathbf{N}_t}$, the time elapsed since the last renewal epoch.

(*c*) Their sum $\mathbf{S}_{\mathbf{N}_t+1} - \mathbf{S}_{\mathbf{N}_t} = \mathbf{T}_{\mathbf{N}_t+1}$ is the length of the recurrence interval covering the epoch t.

The terminology is not unique and varies with the context. For example, in random walk our residual waiting time is called *point of first entry* or *hitting point* for the interval $\overline{t, \infty}$. In the preceding example the word lifetime was used for waiting time. We shall investigate the three variables in XI,3 and XIV,3.

The *Poisson process* was defined as a renewal process with an exponential distribution for the recurrence times $\mathbf{T}_j$. In many server and counter problems it is natural to assume that the incoming traffic forms a Poisson process. In certain other processes the interarrival times are constant. To combine these two cases it has become fashionable in queuing theory to admit general renewal processes with arbitrary interarrival times.[16]

We turn to problems of a fairly general character connected with renewal processes. The distribution underlying the process is again denoted by F.

We begin with what could be described roughly as the "*waiting time* $\mathbf{W}$ *for a large gap*." Here a renewal process with recurrence times $\mathbf{T}_j$ is stopped at the first occurrence of a time interval of duration ξ free of renewal epochs, whereupon the process stops. The definition of a terminating renewal process could be phrased so as to cover this process (see problem 10), but we use a direct argument to derive a renewal equation for the *distribution* V *of the waiting time* $\mathbf{W}$. As the latter necessarily exceeds ξ we have $V(t) = 0$ for $t < \xi$. For $t \geq \xi$ consider the mutually exclusive possibilities that $\mathbf{T}_1 > \xi$ and $\mathbf{T}_1 = y \leq \xi$. In the first case the waiting time $\mathbf{W}$ equals ξ. In the second case the process starts from scratch and, given that $\mathbf{T}_1 = y$, the (conditional) probability of $\{\mathbf{W} \leq t\}$ is $V(t-y)$. Summing over all possibilities we get

$$V(t) = 1 - F(\xi) + \int_0^{\xi+} V(t-y)\, F\{dy\}, \qquad t \geq \xi, \tag{7.1}$$

and, of course, $V(t) = 0$ for $t < \xi$. This function V satisfies the standard renewal equation

$$V = z + G \star V \tag{7.2}$$

with the defective distribution G defined by

$$G(x) = \begin{cases} F(x) & x \leq \xi \\ F(\xi) & x \geq \xi \end{cases} \tag{7.3}$$

[16] The generality is somewhat deceptive because it is hard to find practical examples besides the bus running without schedule along a circular route. The illusion of generality detracts from the sad fact that a non-Poissonian input is usually also non-Markovian.

and

$$(7.4) \qquad z(x) = \begin{cases} 0 & x < \xi \\ 1-F(\xi) & x \geq \xi. \end{cases}$$

The most important special case is that of *gaps in a Poisson* process where $F(t) = 1 - e^{-ct}$ and the solution V is related to the covering theorems of I,9 [see problem 12 and example XIV,(2.*a*)].

Examples *for empirical applications.* (*b*) *Crossing a stream of traffic.*[17] Cars move in a single lane at constant speed, the successive passages forming a sample from a Poisson process (or some other renewal process). A pedestrian arriving at the curb—or a car arriving at an intersection—will start crossing as soon as he observes that no car will pass during the next ξ seconds, namely the time required for his crossing. Denote by $\mathbf{W}$ the time required to effect the crossing, that is, the waiting time at the curb plus ξ. The distribution V of $\mathbf{W}$ satisfies (7.1) with $F(t) = 1 - e^{-ct}$. [Continued in examples XI,(7.*b*) and XIV,(2.*a*).]

(*c*) *Type* II *Geiger counters.* Arriving particles constitute a Poisson process and each *arriving* particle (whether registered or not) locks the counter for a fixed time ξ. If a particle is registered, the counter remains "dead" until the occurrence of an interval of duration ξ without new arrivals. Our theory now applies to the distribution V of the *duration of the dead period.* [See **1**; XIII,11, problem 10.]

(*d*) *Maximal observed recurrence time.* In a primary renewal process denote by $\mathbf{Z}_t$ the maximum of $\mathbf{T}_j$ observed[18] up to epoch t. The event $\{\mathbf{Z}_t \leq \xi\}$ occurs iff up to epoch t no time interval of duration ξ was free of renewal epochs, and so in our notations $\mathbf{P}\{\mathbf{Z}_t > \xi\} = V(t)$. ►

A great many renewal processes occurring in applications may be described as *two stage processes.*

Using the terminology of counters we describe the typical process in terms of "free" and "dead" periods although in some physical applications the term "excited" would be more appropriate than "dead." In the process free and dead periods alternate, and a full cycle constitutes a recurrence time.

Examples (*e*) *Failures followed by delays.* The simplest example is given by actual replacements of a piece of equipment if each failure is followed by a delay (to be interpreted as time for discovery or repair). The successive

---

[17] For the older literature and variants (treated by different methods) see J. C. Tanner, *The delay to pedestrians crossing a road,* Biometrika, vol. 38 (1951) pp. 383–392.

[18] More precisely, if n is the (chance-dependent) index for which $\mathbf{S}_{n-1} \leq t < \mathbf{S}_n$ then $\mathbf{Z}_t = \max\,[\mathbf{T}_1, \ldots, \mathbf{T}_{n-1}, \xi]$. Variables of this nature were studied systematically by A. Lamperti.

service times $\mathbf{T}_1, \mathbf{T}_2, \ldots$ alternate with the successive dead periods $\mathbf{Y}_1, \mathbf{Y}_2, \ldots$ and we get a proper renewal process with recurrence times $\mathbf{T}_j + \mathbf{Y}_j$. The same process may be viewed as *delayed* renewal process with the first renewal epoch at $\mathbf{T}_1$, and recurrence times $\mathbf{Y}_j + \mathbf{T}_{j+1}$.

(*f*) *Lost calls.* Consider a single telephone trunkline such that the incoming calls form a Poisson process with interarrival distribution $F(t) = 1 - e^{-ct}$ while the durations of the ensuing conversations are independent random variables with the common distribution G. The trunkline is free or dead, and calls arriving during dead periods are lost. We have here a two stage process in which the distribution of the recurrence times is $F \bigstar G$.

We seek the distribution V of *the waiting time* $\mathbf{W}$ *for the first lost call* assuming that at epoch 0 the trunkline was free. By far simplest is the method of terminating processes. Suppose we stop our primary process at the epoch of the first lost call. In the derived process free and dead periods alternate, but a dead period may now terminate by the arrival of a new call. Under these circumstances the duration of a dead period equals the smaller of two independent random variables with distributions F and G, respectively. The defective distribution of the dead period is given by the product $H = FG$, and we are concerned with a terminating process with the defective recurrence time distribution $F \bigstar H$. The waiting time for the first lost call is identical with the life time of our terminating process; for the appropriate renewal equation and asymptotic estimates see XI,6.[19]

(*g*) *Last come first served.* In a data-processing machine the time required for processing new information is taken as a random variable with distribution G and the obvious independence assumption. The processing starts as soon as new data arrive provided the machine is free. In certain situations only the latest information is of interest; in such cases a new arrival is being processed immediately, whereas the effect of previous arrivals is entirely annulled. Again we get a renewal process in which free and dead periods alternate, but the distribution of the dead periods must be calculated by a method analogous to that of example (*c*). (Problem 13.)

(*h*) *Random impulses.* The first model of the preceding example may be generalized by other assumptions concerning the dead periods. We start from an arbitrary primary renewal process with an "arrival" at epoch

[19] It is instructive to compare this with the usual approach. By considering all possibilities up to the epoch of the termination of the first dead period it is possible to derive a renewal equation for V which is similar to, but more complicated than, the equation in problem 13. A good further exercise in formal manipulations is to prove the equivalence of this equation with the simpler equation suggested in the text.

0 during a free period. A dead period commences; after its expiration we wait for the next arrival in the primary process and suppose that the process starts from scratch. In other words, the secondary process is a subsequence of the primary process; its recurrence time consists of a dead period followed by the waiting time to the next primary renewal epoch. That the secondary process is a renewal process must be assumed or proved. It suffices that the durations of the successive dead periods be random variables $\mathbf{Y}_1, \mathbf{Y}_2, \ldots$ independent of the primary process as well as of each other and that they have a common distribution F. Such independence is not necessary, however. [Example (*i*).]

(*i*) *Geiger counters.* In type I counters each *registration* is followed by a dead period of fixed duration ξ and arrivals within the dead period have no effect. The process is the same as described in example (*e*), the $\mathbf{T}_j$ having an exponential distribution, the $\mathbf{Y}_j$ being equal to ξ. In type II counters also the unregistered arrivals produce locking and the situation is the same except that the distributions of the $\mathbf{Y}_j$ *depend on the primary process* and must be calculated as such. The method for doing this is described in example (*c*).

8. RANDOM WALKS

Let $\mathbf{X}_1, \mathbf{X}_2, \ldots$ be mutually independent random variables with a common distribution F and, as usual,

$$(8.1) \qquad \mathbf{S}_0 = 0, \qquad \mathbf{S}_n = \mathbf{X}_1 + \cdots + \mathbf{X}_n.$$

We say that $\mathbf{S}_n$ is the position, at epoch n, of a particle performing a general random walk. No new theoretical concepts are introduced,[20] but merely a terminology for a short and intuitive description of the process $\{\mathbf{S}_n\}$. For example, if I is any interval (or other set), the event $\{\mathbf{S}_n \in I\}$ is called a *visit to I*, and the study of the successive visits to a given interval I reveals important characteristics of the fluctuations of $\mathbf{S}_1, \mathbf{S}_2, \ldots$. The index n will be interpreted as time parameter and we shall speak of the "epoch n." In this section we describe some striking features of random walks in terms of the successive record values. The usefulness of the results will be shown by the applications in section 9. A second (independent) approach is outlined in section 10.

[20] Sample spaces of infinite random walks were considered also in volume **1**, but there we had to be careful to justify notions such as "probability of ruin" by the obvious limiting processes. Now these obvious passages to the limit are justified by measure theory. (See IV,6.)

Imbedded Renewal Processes

A record value occurs at epoch $n > 0$ if

$$\mathbf{S}_n > \mathbf{S}_j \qquad j = 0, 1, \ldots, n-1. \tag{8.2}$$

Such indices may not exist for a given sample path; if they do exist they form a finite or infinite ordered sequence. It is therefore legitimate to speak of the first, second, . . . , occurrence of (8.2). Their epochs are again random variables, but possibly defective. With these preparations we are now in a position to introduce the important random variables on which much of the analysis of random walks will be based.

Definition. *The* kth *(ascending) ladder index is the epoch of the* kth *occurrence of* (8.2). *The* kth *ladder height is the value of* $\mathbf{S}_n$ *at the* kth *ladder epoch. (Both random variables are possibly defective.)*

The descending ladder variables are defined in like manner with the inequality in (8.2) *reversed.*[21]

The term *ascending* will be treated as redundant and used only for emphasis or clarity.

In the graph of a sample path $(\mathbf{S}_0, \mathbf{S}_1, \ldots)$ the ladder points appear as the points where the graph reaches an unprecedented height (record value). Figure 1 represents a random walk $\{\mathbf{S}_n\}$ drifting to $-\infty$ with the last positive term at $n = 31$. The 5 ascending and 18 descending ladder points are indicated by ● and ○, respectively. For a random walk with Cauchy variables see figure 2.

Example. (*a*) In the "ordinary" random walk F has the atoms 1 and -1 with weights p and q. The ascending ladder variables are defective if $q > p$, the defect being p/q [see **1**; XI,(3.9)]. The kth ladder height necessarily equals k and for this reason was not mentioned in volume **1**. The kth ladder index is the epoch of the *first visit* to the point k. Its distribution was found in **1**; XI,3 and in the special case $p = \frac{1}{2}$ already in **1**; III,4. ▶

The *first* ladder index $\mathcal{T}_1$ is the epoch of the first entry into $\overline{0, \infty}$, and the *first* ladder height $\mathcal{H}_1$ equals $\mathbf{S}_{\mathcal{T}_1}$. The continuation of the random walk beyond epoch $\mathcal{T}_1$ is a probabilistic replica of the entire random walk, and hence the number of trials between the first ladder index and the second is a random variable $\mathcal{T}_2$ which is independent of $\mathcal{T}_1$ and has the

[21] Replacing the defining strict inequalities by $\geq$ and $\leq$ one gets the *weak* ladder indices. This troublesome distinction is unnecessary when the underlying distribution is continuous. In figure 1 weak ladder points are indicated by the letter w.

same distribution. In this way it is seen more generally that the kth *ladder index and the* kth *ladder height may be written in the form*

$$\mathcal{T}_1 + \cdots + \mathcal{T}_k, \qquad \mathcal{H}_1 + \cdots + \mathcal{H}_k$$

where the $\mathcal{T}_j$ *and* $\mathcal{H}_j$ *are mutually independent random variables distributed, respectively, as* $\mathcal{T}_1$ *and* $\mathcal{H}_1$. In other words, the ladder indices and heights form (possibly terminating) *renewal processes.*

For terminating processes it is intuitively obvious that $\mathbf{S}_n$ drifts to $-\infty$, and with probability one $\mathbf{S}_n$ reaches a finite maximum. The next section will show that the ladder variables provide a powerful tool for the analysis of a class of processes of considerable practical interest.

Example. (*b*) *Explicit expressions.* Let F have the density

$$(8.3) \qquad f(x) = \begin{cases} \dfrac{ab}{a+b}\, e^{ax} & x < 0 \\[2ex] \dfrac{ab}{a+b}\, e^{-bx} & x > 0. \end{cases}$$

This random walk has the rare distinction that all pertinent distributions can be calculated explicitly. It is of great interest in queuing theory because f is the convolution of two exponential densities concentrated on $\overline{0, \infty}$ and $\overline{-\infty, 0}$, respectively. This means that $\mathbf{X}_j$ may be written as the difference $\mathbf{X}_j = \mathcal{B}_j - \mathcal{A}_j$ of two *positive exponentially distributed random variables.* Without loss of generality we assume $a \leq b$.

It will be shown in example XII,(4.*b*), that the *ascending ladder height* $\mathcal{H}_1$ *has the density* ae^{-bx}; this variable is defective iff $a < b$, in which case its defect equals $(b-a)/b$. It will be shown in XVIII,3 that the *ascending ladder epoch* $\mathcal{T}_1$ has the generating function $b^{-1}p(s)$ where

$$(8.4) \qquad 2p(s) = a + b - \sqrt{(a+b)^2 - 4abs}.$$

The defect is again $(b-a)/b$.

The descending ladder height $\mathcal{H}_1^-$ has density ae^{ax} for $x < 0$, the descending ladder epoch $\mathcal{T}_1^-$ has the generating function[22] $a^{-1}p(s)$.

If $a < b$ the ascending ladder process is terminating. Then

$$\mathbf{M} = \max[0, \mathbf{S}_1, \mathbf{S}_2, \ldots]$$

exists with probability one. Obviously the probability of the event $\{\mathbf{M} = 0\}$ equals the defect of the ladder variables, namely $1 - a/b$. It will be shown in XII,5 that for $x > 0$ the distribution of $\mathbf{M}$ has density

[22] When $a = b$ the generating function reduces to $1 - \sqrt{1-s}$ known from the ordinary random walk (or coin tossing).

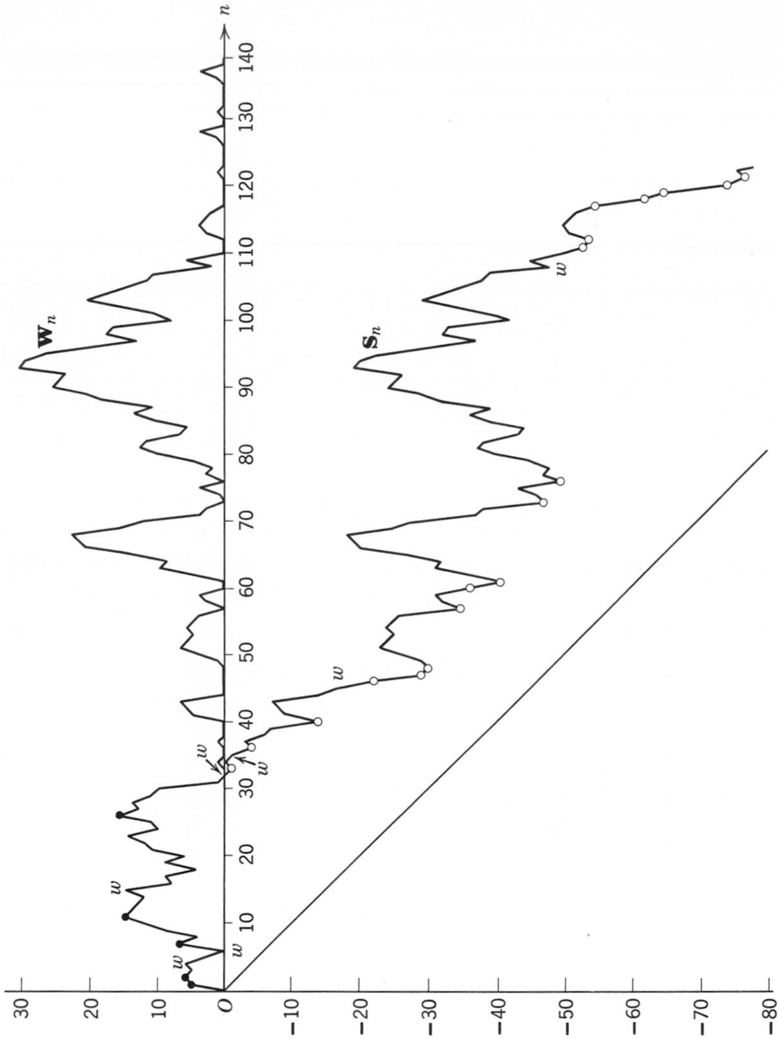

$\mathbf{W}_n$
$\mathbf{S}_n$
n
w
O
30
20
10
−10
−20
−30
−40
−50
−60
−70
−80
10
20
30
40
50
60
70
80
90
100
110
120
130
140

$\frac{b-a}{b} ae^{-(b-a)x}$. *The position (index) of this maximum has the generating function* $\frac{b-a}{b-p(s)}$. [This follows from the joint transform derived in example XVIII,(3.*e*).]

9. THE QUEUING PROCESS

An incredibly voluminous literature[23] has been devoted to a variety of problems connected with servers, storage facilities, waiting times, etc. Much progress has been made towards a unification, but the abundance of small variants obscures the view so that it is difficult to see the forest for

[23] For references consult the specialized books listed in the bibliography. It would be difficult to give a brief outline of the development of the subject with a proper assignment of credits. The most meritorious papers responsible for new methods are now rendered obsolete by the progress which they initiated. [D. V. Lindley's integral equation of queuing theory (1952) is an example.] Other papers are noteworthy by their treatment of (sometimes very intricate) special problems, but they find no place in a skeleton survey of the general theory. On the whole, the prodigal literature on the several subjects emphasizes examples and variants at the expense of general methods. An assignment of priorities is made difficult also by the many duplications. [For example, the solution of a simple integral equation is mentioned in passing in a thesis of 1939 and credited to unpublished lectures by the author in 1934. This solution has now been rediscovered in different contexts by several authors.] The readers interested in the history are referred to two survey papers by D. G. Kendall which themselves have influenced the subsequent development (see, for example, the problem in XIV,4). They are: *Some problems in the theory of queues*, and *Some problems in the theory of dams*, J. Roy. Statist. Soc., Series B, vol. 13 (1951) pp. 151–185, and vol. 19 (1957) pp. 207–233.

←—— *Figure* 1. *Random Walk and the Associated Queuing Process*

The variables $\mathbf{X}_n$ of the random walk $\{\mathbf{S}_n\}$ have expectation -1 and variance 16. Ascending and descending ladder points are indicated by ● and ○, respectively. The seventh ladder point is (26, 16) and represents with high probability the maximum of the entire random walk.

[The letter w indicates where a record value is assumed for a second or third time; these are the *weak* ladder points defined by (8.2) when the strict inequality is replaced by $\geq$.]

Throughout the graph $\mathbf{S}_n$ *exceeds its expected value* $-n$. In fact, $n = 135$ *is the first index such that* $\mathbf{S}_n \leq -n$ (namely $\mathbf{S}_{135} = -137$). This accords with the fact that the expectation of such n is infinite.

The variables $\mathbf{X}_n$ are of the form $\mathbf{X}_n = \mathscr{B}_n - \mathscr{A}_n$, where the variables $\mathscr{B}_n$ and $\mathscr{A}_n$ are mutually independent and uniformly distributed over 1, 3, 5, 7, 9 and 2, 4, 6, 8, 10, respectively. In example (9.*a*) the variable $\mathbf{W}_n$ represents the total waiting time of the nth customer if the interarrival times assume the values 2, 4, 6, 8, 10 with equal probabilities while the service times equal 1, 3, 5, 7 or 9, each with probability $\frac{1}{5}$. The distribution of $\mathbf{X}_n$ attributes probability $(5-k)/25$ to the points $\pm 2k - 1$, where $k = 0, 1, 2, 3, 4$.

the trees. The power of new and general methods is still underrated. We begin by a formal introduction of a stochastic process defined by a recursive scheme that at first sight appears artificial. Examples will illustrate the wide applicability of the scheme; later on we shall see that sharp results can be obtained by surprisingly simple methods. (See XII,5.)

Definition 1. *Let* $\mathbf{X}_1, \mathbf{X}_2, \ldots$ *be mutually independent random variables with a common (proper) distribution* F. *The induced queuing process is the sequence of random variables* $\mathbf{W}_0, \mathbf{W}_1, \ldots$ *defined recursively by* $\mathbf{W}_0 = 0$ *and*

$$\mathbf{W}_{n+1} = \begin{cases} \mathbf{W}_n + \mathbf{X}_{n+1} & \mathbf{W}_n + \mathbf{X}_{n+1} \geq 0 \\ 0 & \mathbf{W}_n + \mathbf{X}_{n+1} \leq 0 \end{cases} \tag{9.1}$$

$(n = 0, 1, \ldots)$. *In short,* $\mathbf{W}_{n+1} = (\mathbf{W}_n + \mathbf{X}_{n+1}) \cup 0$.

For an illustration see figure 1.

Examples. (*a*) *The one-server queue.* Suppose that "customers" arrive at a "server" the arrivals forming a proper renewal process with *interarrival times*[24] $\mathscr{A}_1, \mathscr{A}_2, \ldots$ (the epochs of arrivals are $0, \mathscr{A}_1, \mathscr{A}_1 + \mathscr{A}_2, \ldots$ and the customers are labeled $0, 1, 2, \ldots$). With the nth customer there is associated a *service time* $\mathscr{B}_n$, and we assume that the $\mathscr{B}_n$ are independent of the arrivals and of each other and subject to a common distribution. The server is either "free" or "busy"; it is free at the initial epoch 0. The sequel is regulated by the following rule. If a customer arrives at an epoch where the server is free, his service commences without delay. Otherwise he joins a waiting line (queue) and the server continues uninterruptedly to serve customers in the order of their arrival[25] until the waiting line disappears and the server becomes "free." By *queue length* we mean the number of customers present including the customer being served. The *waiting time* $\mathbf{W}_n$ of the nth customer is the time from his arrival to the epoch where his service *commences*; the total time spent by the customer at the server is $\mathbf{W}_n + \mathscr{B}_n$. (For example, if the first few service times are 4, 4, 1, 3, ... and the interarrival times are 2, 3, 2, 3, ... , customers number 1, 2, ... *join* queues of length 1, 1, 2, 1, ... , respectively, and have waiting times 2, 3, 2, 2, ...).

To avoid trite ambiguities such as when a customer arrives at the epoch of another's departure we shall assume that the distributions A and B of

[24] Normally the interarrival times will be constant or exponentially distributed; see footnote 16 to section 7.

[25] This "queue discipline" is totally irrelevant to queue length, duration of busy periods, and similar problems. Only the individual customer feels the effect of the several disciplines, among which "first come first served," "first come last served," and "random choice" are the extremes. The whole picture would change if departures were permitted.

the variables $\mathscr{A}_n$ and $\mathscr{B}_n$ are continuous. Then the queue length at any epoch is well defined.

We proceed to devise a scheme for calculating the waiting times $\mathbf{W}_n$ recursively. By definition customer number 0 arrives at epoch 0 at a free server and so his waiting time is $\mathbf{W}_0 = 0$. Suppose now that the nth customer arrives at epoch t and that we know his waiting time $\mathbf{W}_n$. His service time commences at epoch $t + \mathbf{W}_n$ and terminates at epoch $t + \mathbf{W}_n + \mathscr{B}_n$. The *next* customer arrives at time $t + \mathscr{A}_{n+1}$. He finds the server free if $\mathbf{W}_n + \mathscr{B}_n < \mathscr{A}_{n+1}$ and has a waiting time $\mathbf{W}_{n+1} = \mathbf{W}_n + \mathscr{B}_n - \mathscr{A}_{n+1}$ if this quantity is ≥ 0. In other words, *the sequence* $\{\mathbf{W}_n\}$ *of waiting times coincides with the queuing process induced by the independent random variables*

$$\mathbf{X}_n = \mathscr{B}_{n-1} - \mathscr{A}_n, \qquad n = 1, 2, \ldots \tag{9.2}$$

(*b*) *Storage and inventories.* For an intuitive description we use water *reservoirs* (or dams), but the model applies equally to other storage facilities or inventories. The content depends on the input and the output. The input is due to supplies by rivers and rainfall, the output is regulated by demand except that this demand can be satisfied only when the reservoir contains water.

Consider now the water contents[26] $0, \mathbf{W}_1, \mathbf{W}_2, \ldots$ at epochs $0, \tau_1, \tau_2, \ldots$. Denote by $\mathbf{X}_n$ the actual supply minus the theoretical (ideal) demand during $\overline{\tau_{n-1}, \tau_n}$ and let us pretend that all changes are instantaneous and concentrated at the epochs $\tau_1, \tau_2, \ldots$. We start with $\mathbf{W}_0 = 0$ at epoch 0. In general the change $\mathbf{W}_{n+1} - \mathbf{W}_n$ should equal $\mathbf{X}_{n+1}$ except when the demand exceeds the contents. For this reason the $\mathbf{W}_n$ must satisfy (9.1) and so the *successive contents are subject to the queuing process induced by* $\{\mathbf{X}_k\}$ provided the theoretical net changes $\mathbf{X}_k$ are independent random variables with a common distribution.

The problem (for the mathematician if not for the user) is to find conditions under which the $\mathbf{X}_k$ will appear as independent variables with a common distribution F and to find plausible forms for F. In practice the τ_k will be equidistant or else a sample from a Poisson process, but it suffices for our purposes to assume that the τ_k form a *renewal process* with interarrival times $\mathscr{A}_1, \mathscr{A}_2, \ldots$. The most frequently used models fall into one of the following two categories:

(i) The input is at a constant rate c, the demand $\mathscr{B}_n$ arbitrary. Then $\mathbf{X}_n = c\mathscr{A}_n - \mathscr{B}_n$. We must suppose this $\mathbf{X}_n$ to be independent of the

[26] For simplicity we start with an empty reservoir. An adjustment to arbitrary initial conditions causes no difficulties [see example (*c*).]

"past" $\mathbf{X}_1, \ldots, \mathbf{X}_{n-1}$. (The usual assumption that $\mathscr{A}_n$ and $\mathscr{B}_n$ be independent is superfluous: there is no reason why the demand $\mathscr{B}_n$ should not be correlated with the duration $\mathscr{A}_n$.)

(ii) The output is at a constant rate, the input arbitrary. The description is the same with the roles of $\mathscr{A}_n$ and $\mathscr{B}_n$ reversed.

(*c*) *Queues for a shuttle train.*[27] A shuttle train with r places for passengers leaves a station every hour on the hour. Prospective passengers appear at the station and wait in line. At each departure the first r passengers in line board the train, and the others remain in the waiting line. We suppose that the number of passengers arriving between successive departures are independent random variables $\mathscr{A}_1, \mathscr{A}_2, \ldots$ with a common distribution. Let $\mathbf{W}_n$ be the number of passengers in line just after the nth departure, and assume for simplicity $\mathbf{W}_0 = 0$. Then $\mathbf{W}_{n+1} = \mathbf{W}_n + \mathscr{A}_{n+1} - r$ if this quantity is positive, and $\mathbf{W}_{n+1} = 0$ otherwise. Thus $\mathbf{W}_n$ *is the variable of a queuing process* (9.1) *generated by the* random walk with variables $X_n = \mathscr{A}_n - r$. ►

We turn to a description of the queuing process $\{\mathbf{W}_n\}$ in terms of the random walk generated by the variables $\mathbf{X}_k$. As in section 8 we put $\mathbf{S}_0 = 0$, $\mathbf{S}_n = \mathbf{X}_1 + \cdots + \mathbf{X}_n$ and adhere to the notation for the ladder variables. For ease of description we use the terminology appropriate for the server of example (*a*).

Define ν as the subscript for which $\mathbf{S}_1 \geq 0, \mathbf{S}_2 \geq 0, \ldots, \mathbf{S}_{\nu-1} \geq 0$, but $\mathbf{S}_\nu < 0$. In this situation customers number $1, 2, \ldots, \nu-1$ had positive waiting times $\mathbf{W}_1 = \mathbf{S}_1, \ldots, \mathbf{W}_{\nu-1} = \mathbf{S}_{\nu-1}$, and customer number ν was the first to find the server free (the first lucky customer). At the epoch of his arrival the process starts from scratch as a replica of the whole process. Now ν is simply the index of the first negative sum, that is, ν is the first descending ladder index, and we denote it consistently by $\mathscr{T}_1^-$. We have thus reached the *first conclusion: The descending ladder indices correspond to the lucky customers who find the server free.* Put differently, the epochs of arrival of the lucky customers constitute a renewal process with recurrence times distributed as $\mathscr{T}_1^-$.

In practical cases the variable $\mathscr{T}_1^-$ must not be defective, for its defect p would equal the probability that a customer never finds the server free and with probability one there would be a last lucky customer followed by an unending queue. It will turn out that $\mathscr{T}_1^-$ is proper whenever $\mathbf{E}(\mathscr{B}_k) < \mathbf{E}(\mathscr{A}_k)$.

---

[27] P. E. Boudreau, J. S. Griffin Jr., and Mark Kac, *An elementary queuing problem*, Amer. Math. Monthly, vol. 69 (1962) pp. 713–724. The purpose of this paper is didactic, that is, it is written for outsiders without knowledge of the subject. Although a different mode of description is used, the calculations are covered by those in example XII,(4.*c*).

Suppose now that customer number $\nu - 1$ arrives at epoch τ. His waiting time was $\mathbf{W}_{\nu-1} = \mathbf{S}_{\nu-1}$ and so the epoch of his departure is $\tau + \mathbf{W}_{\nu-1} + \mathscr{B}_{\nu-1}$. The first lucky customer (number ν) arrives at epoch $\tau + \mathscr{A}_\nu$ when the server was free for

$$\mathscr{A}_\nu - \mathbf{W}_{\nu-1} - \mathscr{B}_{\nu-1} = -\mathbf{S}_{\nu-1} - \mathbf{X}_\nu = -\mathbf{S}_\nu$$

time units. But by definition $\mathbf{S}_\nu$ is the first descending latter height $\mathscr{H}_1^-$. As the process starts from scratch we have reached the *second conclusion: The durations of the free periods are independent random variables with the same distribution as* $-\mathscr{H}_1^-$ (the recurrence time for the descending ladder heights). In other words, customer number $\mathscr{T}_1^- + \cdots + \mathscr{T}_r^-$ is the rth customer who finds the server free. At the epoch of his arrival the server has been free for $-\mathscr{H}_r^-$ time units.

It should now be clear that between successive ladder epochs *the segments of the graph for the queuing process* $\{\mathbf{W}_n\}$ *are congruent to those for the random walk* but displayed vertically so as to start at a point of the time axis (figure 1). To describe this analytically denote for the moment by $[n]$ the *last* descending ladder index $\leq n$; in other words, $[n]$ is a (random) index such that $[n] \leq n$ and

$$\mathbf{S}_{[n]} \leq \mathbf{S}_j \qquad j = 0, 1, \ldots, n. \tag{9.3}$$

This defines $[n]$ uniquely with probability 1 (the distribution of $\mathbf{X}_i$ being continuous). Clearly

$$\mathbf{W}_n = \mathbf{S}_n - \mathbf{S}_{[n]}. \tag{9.4}$$

This relation leads to the most important conclusion if we look at the variables $\mathbf{X}_1, \ldots, \mathbf{X}_n$ in *reverse order*. Put for abbreviation $\mathbf{X}_1' = \mathbf{X}_n, \ldots, \mathbf{X}_n' = \mathbf{X}_1$. The partial sums of these variables are $\mathbf{S}_k' = \mathbf{X}_1' + \cdots + \mathbf{X}_k' = \mathbf{S}_n - \mathbf{S}_{n-k}$, and (9.4) shows that the maximal term of the sequence $0, \mathbf{S}_1', \ldots, \mathbf{S}_n'$ has subscript $n - [n]$ and equals $\mathbf{W}_n$. But the distribution of $(\mathbf{X}_1', \ldots, \mathbf{X}_n')$ is identical with that of $(\mathbf{X}_1, \ldots, \mathbf{X}_n)$. We have thus the basic

Theorem.[28] *The distribution of the queuing variable* $\mathbf{W}_n$ *is identical with the distribution of the random variable*

$$\mathbf{M}_n = \max[0, \mathbf{S}_1, \ldots, \mathbf{S}_n] \tag{9.5}$$

in the underlying random walk $\{\mathbf{X}_k\}$.

The consequences of this theorem will be discussed in chapter XII.

[28] Apparently first noticed by F. Pollaczek in 1952 and exploited (in a different context) by F. Spitzer, *The Wiener–Hopf equation whose kernel is a probability density*, Duke Math. J., vol. 24 (1957) pp. 327–344. For Spitzer's proof see problem 16.

Here we show that it permits us to reduce certain ruin problems to queuing processes despite the dissimilarity of the appearance.

Example. (*d*) *Ruin problems.* Let $\mathbf{X}(t)$ be the variable of a compound Poisson process whose increments have the distribution (4.2) with an arbitrary distribution F. In section 5 *ruin* was defined as the event $\{\mathbf{X}(t) > z + ct\}$ for some t where z and c are fixed positive numbers. Denote the epochs of the successive jumps by $\tau_1, \tau_2, \ldots$. If ruin occurs at all it occurs also at some epoch τ_k and it suffices therefore to consider the probability that $\mathbf{S}_n = \mathbf{X}(\tau_n) - c\tau_n > z$ for some n. But by the definition of a compound Poisson process $\mathbf{X}(\tau_n)$ is the sum of n independent variables $\mathbf{Y}_k$ with the common distribution F, while τ_n is the sum of n independent exponentially distributed variables $\mathscr{A}_k$. Accordingly we are in effect dealing with the random walk generated by the variables $\mathbf{X}_k = \mathbf{Y}_k - c\mathscr{A}_k$ whose probability *density* is given by the convolution

$$\frac{\alpha}{c}\int_x^\infty e^{(\alpha/c)(x-y)}\,F\{dy\}. \tag{9.6}$$

Ruin occurs iff in the random walk the event $\{\mathbf{S}_n \geq z\}$ takes place for some n. To find the probability of ruin amounts therefore to finding the distributions of the variables $\mathbf{W}_n$ in the associated queuing process.

(*e*) *A numerical illustration.* The most important queuing process arises when *the interarrival and service times are exponentially distributed* with expectations $1/a$ and $1/b$, respectively, where $a < b$. The characteristics of this process were described in example (8.*b*). The *waiting time of the* nth *customer has a limit distribution W with an atom of weight $1 - a/b$ at the origin and density* $\dfrac{b-a}{b}\,ae^{-(b-a)x}$ for $x > 0$. The expectation equals $\dfrac{a}{b(b-a)}$. The *free periods* of the counter have the same density as the first descending ladder height, that is, ae^{-at}. In this case the free periods and the interarrival times have the same distribution (but this is not so in other queuing processes).

The number $\mathbf{N}$ *of the first customer to find the counter empty has the generating function $p(s)/a$* with p defined in (8.4). Consider now the *busy period* commencing at epoch 0, that is, the time interval to the first epoch when the server becomes free. This period being initiated by customer number 0, *the random variable* $\mathbf{N}$ *also equals the number of customers during the initial busy period.* An easy calculation shows that its expectation equals $b/(b-a)$ its variance $ab(a+b)/(b-a)^3$.

Finally, let $\mathbf{T}$ be the duration of the busy period. Its density is given explicitly by XIV, (6.15) with $cp = a$ and $cq = b$. This formula involving a Bessel function does not lend itself to easy calculations, but the moments of **T** can be calculated from its Laplace transform derived by different methods in examples XIV,(4.*a*) and XIV,(6.*b*). The result is

$$\mathbf{E}(\mathbf{T}) = \frac{1}{(b-a)} \quad \text{and} \quad \mathrm{Var}(\mathbf{T}) = (a+b)\frac{1}{(b-a)^3}\,.$$

In the queuing process busy periods alternate with free periods, and their expectations are $1/(b-a)$ and $1/a$, respectively. Thus $(b-a)/a$ is a measure of the *fraction of the time during which the server is idle.*

Table 1

		$b = 1$					
		$a = 0.5$	$a = 0.6$	$a = 0.7$	$a = 0.8$	$a = 0.9$	$a = 0.95$
Waiting time (steady state)	Expectation	1	1.5	2.3	4	9	19
	Variance	3	5.3	10	24	99	399
Busy period	Expectation	2	2.5	3.3	5	10	399
	Variance	12	25	63	225	1900	16,000
No. of customers per busy period	Expectation	2	2.5	3.3	5	10	399
	Variance	6	15	44	200	1700	15,200

In the table the expected service time is taken as unit, and so a represents the *expected number of customers arriving during one service time.* The table shows the huge variances of the busy periods. It follows that *fantastic fluctuations of the busy period must be expected.* One sees that the customary reliance on expectations is very dangerous in practical applications. For a busy period with variance 225 the expectation 5 has little practical significance.

The multidimensional analogue to our queuing process is analytically much more intricate. The foundations for its theory were laid in a basic paper by J. Kiefer and J. Wolfowitz [*On the theory of queues with many servers*, Trans. Amer. Math. Soc., vol. 78 (1955) pp. 1–18].

10. PERSISTENT AND TRANSIENT RANDOM WALKS

We proceed to a classification of random walks which is independent of section 8 and closely related to the renewal theory of section 6. Given a distribution function F on the line we introduce formally an interval function defined by

$$U\{I\} = \sum_{k=0}^{\infty} F^{k\star}\{I\}. \tag{10.1}$$

The series is the same as in (6.2), but when F is not concentrated on a half-line the series may diverge even when I is a finite interval. It will be shown that the convergence or divergence of (10.1) has a deep significance. The basic facts are simple, but the formulations suffer from the unfortunate necessity of a special treatment for arithmetic distributions.[29]

For abbreviation we let I_h stand for the interval $-h < x < h$ and $I_h + t$ for $t-h < x < t+h$.

Theorem 1. (i) *If F is non-arithmetic either $U\{I\} < \infty$ for every finite interval or else $U\{I\} = \infty$ for all intervals.*

(ii) *If F is arithmetic with span λ either $U\{I\} < \infty$ for every finite interval or else $U\{I\} = \infty$ for every interval containing a point of the form $n\lambda$.*

(iii) *If $U\{I\} < \infty$ then*

$$U\{I_h + t\} \leq U\{I_{2h}\} \tag{10.2}$$

for all t and $h > 0$.

For ease of reference to the two cases we introduce a definition (in which F receives an adjective rightfully belonging to the corresponding random walk).

Definition. *F is transient if $U\{I\} < \infty$ for all finite intervals, and persistent otherwise.*

Besides its probabilistic significance the theorem has a bearing on the integral equation

$$Z = z + F \star Z \tag{10.3}$$

which is the analogue to the renewal equation (6.4). We use this integral equation as starting point and prove theorem 1 together with

Theorem 2. *Let z be continuous, and $0 \leq z(x) \leq \mu_0$ for $|x| < h$ and $z(x) = 0$ outside I_h.*

If F is transient then

$$Z(x) = \int_{-\infty}^{+\infty} z(x-y)\, U\{dy\} \tag{10.4}$$

is a uniformly continuous solution of (10.3) *with*

$$0 \leq Z(x) \leq \mu_0 \cdot U\{I_{2h}\}. \tag{10.5}$$

Z assumes its maximum at a point in I_h.

---

[29] F is arithmetic if all its points of increase are among the points of the form $0, \pm\lambda, \pm 2\lambda, \ldots$. The largest λ with this property is called the *span* of F. (See V,2.)

Proof *of the two theorems.* (i) Assume that $U\{I_\alpha\} < \infty$ for some $\alpha > 0$. Choose $h < \frac{1}{2}\alpha$ and let z vanish outside I_h but not identically. We try to solve (10.3) by successive approximations putting $Z_0 = z$ and, recursively,

$$Z_n(x) = z(x) + \int_{-\infty}^{+\infty} Z_{n-1}(x-y)\, F\{dy\}. \tag{10.6}$$

With U_n defined by

$$U_n\{I\} = F^{0\star}\{I\} + \cdots + F^{n\star}\{I\} \tag{10.7}$$

we have obviously

$$Z_n(x) = \int_{-\infty}^{+\infty} z(x-y)\, U_n\{dy\}, \tag{10.8}$$

(the integration extending in effect over an interval of length $\leq 2h$). The function Z_n so defined is continuous, and we prove by induction that it assumes its maximum μ_n at a point ξ_n such that $z(\xi_n) > 0$. This is trivially true for $Z_0 = z$. If it is true for Z_{n-1} one sees from (10.6) that $z(x) = 0$ implies $Z_n(x) \leq \mu_{n-1}$ whereas $\mu_n \geq Z_n(\xi_{n-1}) > Z_{n-1}(\xi_{n-1}) = \mu_{n-1}$.
It follows that the interval $I_h + \xi_n$ is contained in I_{2h} and so by (10.8)

$$\mu_n \leq \mu_0 \cdot U\{I_{2h}\} \tag{10.9}$$

which proves that the functions Z_n remain uniformly bounded. Since $Z_0 \leq Z_1 \leq \cdots$ it follows that $Z_n \to Z$ with Z satisfying (10.5). If we choose z such that $z(x) = \mu_0$ for $|x| < \eta < h$, we get

$$Z_n(x) \geq \mu_0\, U_n\{I_\eta + x\} \tag{10.10}$$

and hence $U\{I\} < \infty$ for every interval of length $< h$. By the obvious partitioning it follows that $U\{I\} < \infty$ for every finite interval. Thus F is transient, and we can drop the restriction on h. Clearly (10.9) implies (10.2), and taking differences in (10.4) it is seen that

$$|Z(x+\delta) - Z(x)| \leq U\{I_{2h}\} \cdot |z(x+\delta) - z(x)|.$$

Accordingly, Z is uniformly continuous and all assertions concerning transient F are proved.

(ii) There remains the case where $U\{I_\alpha\} = \infty$ for *every* $\alpha > 0$. When $z \geq \mu_0$ in I_η we have (10.10) and hence $Z_n(x) \to \infty$ for all x in a neighborhood of the origin. If t is a point of increase of F it follows from (10.6) that $Z_n(x) \to \infty$ for all x in a neighborhood of t. By induction the same is true of each point of increase of $F^{2\star}$, $F^{3\star}$, ... Assume F non-arithmetic. If F were concentrated on a half-line we would have $U\{I_\alpha\} < \infty$ (section 6). By theorem 3 of V,4 therefore the points of increase of $F^{2\star}$, $F^{3\star}$, ... are dense on the line and so $Z_n(x) \to \infty$ everywhere. This implies $U_n\{I\} \to \infty$, for all intervals. With the obvious modification this argument applies also to arithmetic distributions, and so the theorems are proved. ▶

Corollary. *Let $Z \geq 0$ be a bounded solution of the renewal equation* (10.3). *If $z \geq 0$ and $z \geq \mu > 0$ in some interval I then F is transient.*

Proof. We have proved the assertion when I contains the origin. The general case follows by changing x into $x - a$ which does not effect the renewal equation. ▶

Note *on uniqueness.* The difference ζ of two bounded solutions of the renewal equation (10.3) satisfies the convolution equation $\zeta = F \bigstar \zeta$. It will be shown in XI,2 that in this case $\zeta =$ const when F is non-arithmetic, and that ζ is periodic with period λ when F is arithmetic with span λ. Apart from this trite indeterminacy the solution is therefore unique. As we have seen, the particular solution given by (10.4) is *minimal* and hence uniquely characterized by the property that $\liminf_{|x| \to \infty} Z(x) = 0$ whenever z vanishes at infinity.

In XI,2 and XI,9 we shall return to the renewal equation (10.3), but now we turn to the implications of theorem 1 for random walks. Let $\mathbf{X}_1$, $\mathbf{X}_2, \ldots$ be independent random variables with the common distribution F, and put $\mathbf{S}_n = \mathbf{X}_1 + \cdots + \mathbf{X}_n$. By "visit to I at epoch $n = 1, 2, \ldots$" is meant the event that $\mathbf{S}_n \in I$.

Theorem 3.[30] *If F is transient the number of visits to a finite interval I is finite with probability one, and the expected number of such visits equals $U\{I\}$.*

If F is persistent and non-arithmetic every interval I is visited infinitely often with probability one. If F is persistent and arithmetic with span λ then every point $n\lambda$ is visited infinitely often with probability one.

Proof. Assume F transient. The probability of a visit to I after epoch n does not exceed the nth remainder of the series in (10.1) and so for n sufficiently large the probability of more than n visits is $< \epsilon$. This proves the first assertion.

Assume now F persistent and non-arithmetic. Denote by $\rho_h(t)$ the probability of a visit to $I_h + t$. If suffices to prove that $\rho_h(t) = 1$ for all

[30] For a different proof see K. L. Chung and W. H. J. Fuchs, *On the distribution of values of sums of random variables*, Memoirs Amer. Math. Soc., no. 6 (1950) pp. 1–12. The theorem is also an immediate consequence of the second zero-or-one law in IV,6. If $\varphi(I + t)$ is the probability of entering $I + t$ infinitely often then for fixed I the function φ can assume only the values 0 or 1. On the other hand, considering the first step in the random walk one sees that $\varphi = F \bigstar \varphi$ and hence $\varphi =$ const (see XI,2). The proof of the text is given because it is instructive and it renders this section self-contained.

$h > 0$ and all t, for this obviously implies the certainty of any number of visits to each interval. Considering the possible values of $\mathbf{S}_1$ it is seen that

$$(10.11) \qquad \rho_h(t) = F\{I_h + t\} + \int_{|y-t|\geq h} \rho_h(t-y)\, F\{dy\}.$$

This can be put into the form of the renewal equation $\rho_h = z_h + F \bigstar \rho_h$ where

$$(10.12) \qquad z_h(t) = \int_{|y-t|<h} [1 - \rho_h(t-y)]\, F\{dy\}.$$

Now for $|x| < \alpha$ the interval $I_h + x$ is contained in $I_{\alpha+h}$ and hence $\rho_h(x) \leq \rho_{h+\alpha}(0)$. The integrand in (10.12) is therefore $\geq 1 - \rho_{3h}(0)$ and if this quantity were positive $z_h(t)$ would be bounded away from 0 in some neighborhood of every point of increase of F. This is impossible in consequence of the last corollary and so $\rho_\alpha(0) = 1$ for every $\alpha > 0$.

Assume now that $\rho_\alpha(-x) < 1$ for some $x \neq 0$. For $|y+x| < \frac{1}{3}\alpha$ and $h < \frac{1}{3}\alpha$ the interval I_{h+y} is contained in $I_{\alpha-x}$, and so $\rho_h(y) \leq \rho_\alpha(-x)$. This means that for h sufficiently small $1 - \rho_h$ is strictly positive in a neighborhood of $-x$. Consider then (10.10) for the particular value $t = 0$. If x were a point of increase of F the right side would be less than 1 whereas the left equals 1. Thus $\rho_\alpha(-x) = 1$ for every $\alpha > 0$ whenever x is a point of increase of F. By the density argument used in the second part of the last proof this implies $\rho_\alpha(x) = 1$ for all x and this accomplishes the proof for non-arithmetic F. With the obvious change the proof applies also to arithmetic F. ►

In testing the character of a distribution it is sometimes difficult to establish directly that $U\{I_h\} = \infty$ and it is advisable to rely on the following criterion: *if F is transient the ratios $t^{-1}U\{I_t\}$ remain bounded as $t \to \infty$.* This is an immediate consequence of (10.2) (the bound being $U\{I_1\}$). The method is illustrated by

Theorem 4. *A distribution with expectation μ is transient if $\mu \neq 0$, persistent if $\mu = 0$.*

Proof.[31] Let $\mu > 0$. By the strong law of large numbers with probability one $n^{-1}\mathbf{S}_n > \frac{1}{2}\mu$ for all n sufficiently large, and hence the probability of entering $\overline{-\infty, 0}$ infinitely often is zero.

Let $\mu = 0$. By the weak law of large numbers $\mathbf{P}\{|\mathbf{S}_n| < \epsilon n\} > \frac{1}{2}$ for

[31] Due to K. L. Chung and D. Ornstein. Using the central limit theorem instead of the law of large numbers one can prove by the same method that a two-dimensional random walk with zero expectations and finite variances is persistent. For an alternative proof see XVIII,7.

$n > n_\epsilon$. It follows that $F^{k\star}\{\overline{-a,\ a}\} > \frac{1}{2}$ for $n_\epsilon < k < \epsilon^{-1}a$, and so $a^{-1}U\{\overline{-a,\ a}\} > \frac{1}{2}(\epsilon^{-1} - n_\epsilon a^{-1})$. As $a \to \infty$ the right side tends to $\frac{1}{2}\epsilon^{-1}$, and since ϵ is arbitrary, the random walk cannot be transient. ▶

In a persistent process the sequence $\{\mathbf{S}_n\}$ necessarily changes sign infinitely often and so the ascending and descending ladder processes are persistent. It may come as a surprise that the converse is false. *Even in a transient random walk* $\{\mathbf{S}_n\}$ *may change signs infinitely often.* Since a finite interval $\overline{-a,\ a}$ will be visited only finitely often this implies (very roughly speaking) that the changes of signs are due to occasional jumps of fantastic magnitude: $|\mathbf{S}_n|$ is likely to grow over all bounds, but the fantastic inequality $\mathbf{X}_{n+1} < -\mathbf{S}_n - a$ will occur infinitely often however large the constant a.

Figure 2 illustrates the occurrence of large jumps but is not fully representative of the phenomenon because it was necessary to truncate the distribution in order to obtain a finite graph.

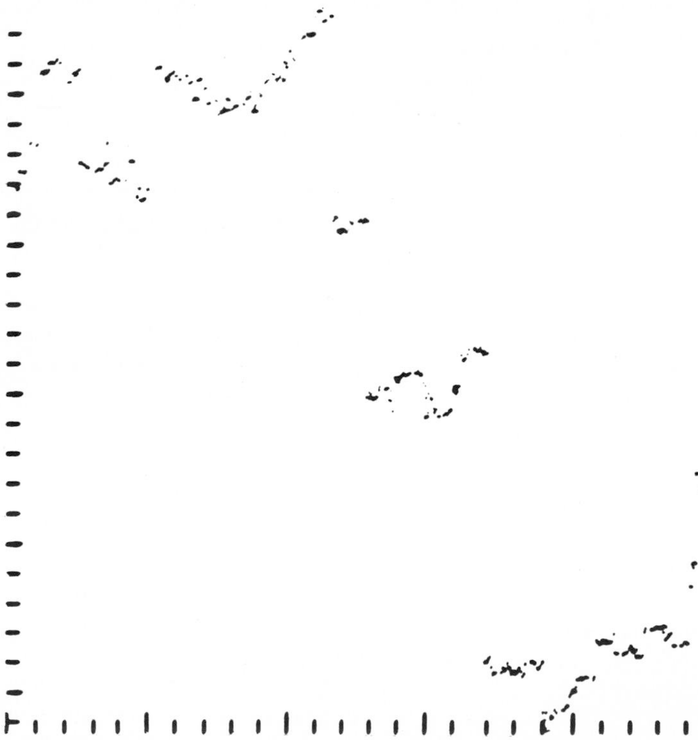

Figure 2. *Random Walk Generated by the Cauchy Distribution.* (The distribution was truncated so as to eliminate jumps of the magnitude of the graph.)

Example. *Symmetric stable distributions.* For such distributions $F^{n\star}(n^{1/\alpha}x) = F(x)$. We consider the case $\alpha < 1$ and take as known that F has a density f such that $f(0) > 0$. (See XVII,6.) Then

$$F^{n\star}\{\overline{-a, a}\} \approx 2a\, f(0) n^{-1/\alpha}$$

and so $U\{\overline{-a, a}\} < \infty$. Hence F is *transient.* It is easily seen that not both the ascending and the descending ladder processes can terminate, and in the present case for reasons of symmetry both processes are *persistent.*

11. GENERAL MARKOV CHAINS

The generalization of the discrete Markov chains of **1**; XV to Cartesian (and more general) spaces is rather obvious. In the discrete case the transition probabilities were given by a stochastic matrix with elements p_{ij} whose rows were probability distributions. Now we shall have to consider transitions from a point x to an arbitrary interval or set Γ in $\mathcal{R}^n$; we shall denote the probability of this transition by $K(x, \Gamma)$. The novel feature is that we must impose some mild regularity conditions to ensure that the necessary integrations can be performed. Continuity would do for most practical purposes, but nothing is gained by restricting the full generality.

Definition 1. *A stochastic kernel K is a function of two variables, a point and a set, such that $K(x, \Gamma)$ is* (i) *for a fixed x a probability distribution in Γ, and* (ii) *for any interval Γ a Baire function in x.*

This definition applies in any number of dimensions (and more generally).

It is *not* required that K be defined on the whole space. If x and Γ are restricted to a set Ω we say that *K is concentrated on Ω.* Sometimes it is necessary to admit *defective* distributions and we speak then of *sub-stochastic* kernels. Frequently K will be of the form

$$K(x, \Gamma) = \int_\Gamma k(x, y)\, dy \tag{11.1}$$

and in this case k is called a *stochastic density kernel.* Following the convention of V,(3.3) we indicate (11.1) by the shorthand notation

$$K(x, dy) = k(x, y)\, dy.$$

[Strictly speaking, k represents densities with respect to Lebesgue measure or length; densities with respect to an arbitrary measure m would be denoted by $K(x, dy) = k(x, y)\, m\{dy\}$.]

Before giving a formal definition of Markov chains we can assemble the appropriate analytical apparatus by analogy with the discrete case. The probability of a transition from x to Γ in *two* steps is defined by

$$K^{(2)}(x, \Gamma) = \int_{\Omega} K(x, dy)\, K(y, \Gamma), \tag{11.2}$$

the integration extending over the whole space or the set Ω on which K is concentrated. Relation (11.2) expresses, of course, that the first step leads from x to some point y and the second from y to Γ. The crucial assumption is that, given the intermediate point y, the past history in no way influences the further transitions. A similar argument holds for the higher transition probabilities $K^{(n)}$. If we put $K^{(1)} = K$ we must have for arbitrary positive integers

$$K^{(m+n)}(x, \Gamma) = \int K^{(m)}(x, dy) K^{(n)}(y, \Gamma), \tag{11.3}$$

which reduces to (11.2) when $m = n = 1$. Keeping $m = 1$ and letting $n = 1, 2, 3, \ldots$ we get an *inductive definition for* $K^{(n)}$. For consistency we define $K^{(0)}$ to stand for the probability distribution concentrated at the point x (the so-called *Kronecker delta* kernel). Then (11.3) is valid for $m \geq 0, n \geq 0$. The operation (11.3) between two kernels occurs frequently also outside probability theory and is known as *composition of kernels.* It is in all respects similar to matrix multiplication.

It is hardly necessary to emphasize that the kernels $K^{(n)}$ are stochastic. If K has a density, the same is true of $K^{(n)}$ and the *composition formula* for densities is

$$k^{(m+n)}(x, z) = \int_{\Omega} k^{(m)}(x, y)\, k^{(n)}(y, z)\, dy, \tag{11.4}$$

Examples. (*a*) *Convolutions.* If $k(x, y) = f(y-x)$, where f is a probability density, the composition (11.4) reduces to ordinary convolutions. The same is true generally if K is *homogeneous* in the sense that

$$K(x, \Gamma) = K(x+s, \Gamma+s)$$

where $\Gamma + s$ is the set obtained by translating Γ through s. For convolutions on the circle see theorem 3 in VIII,7.

(*b*) *Energy losses under collisions.* In physics successive collisions of a particle are usually treated as a chance process such that if the energy (or mass) before collision equals $x > 0$ the resulting energy (mass) is a random variable $\mathbf{Y}$ such that $\mathbf{P}\{\mathbf{Y} \in \Gamma\} = K(x, \Gamma)$ where K is a stochastic kernel. The standard assumption is that only losses are possible, and that the ratio $\mathbf{Y}/x$ has a distribution function G independent of x; then $\mathbf{P}\{\mathbf{Y} \leq y\} = G(y/x)$ which defines a stochastic kernel.

In a related problem in stellar radiation [example X,(2.*b*)] Ambarzumian considered the special case $G(y) = y^\lambda$ for $0 \le y \le 1$ where λ is a positive constant. This corresponds to a density kernel $\lambda y^{\lambda-1} x^{-\lambda}$ concentrated on $0 < y < x$ and it is easily verified that the higher densities are given by

$$(11.5) \qquad k^{(n)}(x, y) = \frac{\lambda^n}{(n-1)!} \frac{y^{\lambda-1}}{x^\lambda} \left(\log \frac{x}{y}\right)^{n-1}, \qquad 0 < y < x.$$

The particular value $\lambda = 1$ corresponds to a uniform distribution (the *fraction lost* is "randomly distributed") and (11.5) then reduces to I,(8.2). [Continued in example X,(1.*a*).]

(*c*) *Random chains.* Consider a chain (or polygonal line) in $\mathcal{R}^3$ whose links have unit length and where the angles between adjacent links depend on a chance mechanism. Many (frequently rather involved) situations like this occur in polymer chemistry, but we consider only the case where the successive angles are independent random variables.

By *length* of a chain with endpoints A and B we mean the distance between A and B. Addition of a unit link to a chain of length x results in a chain length $\sqrt{x^2 + 1 - 2x \cos \theta}$ where θ is the angle between the new link and the line through A and B. We treat θ as a random variable and consider in particular two distributions that are of special interest in chemistry.

(i) Let θ equal 60° or 120° with probabilities $\frac{1}{2}$ each. Then $\cos \theta = \pm\frac{1}{2}$ and the length of the prolonged chain is subject to the stochastic kernel $K(x, \Gamma)$ attributing probabilities $\frac{1}{2}$ to the two points $\sqrt{x^2 \pm x + 1}$. For fixed x the distribution $K^{(n)}$ is concentrated on 2^n points.

(ii) Let the direction of the new link be chosen "at random," that is, suppose $\cos \theta$ to be uniformly distributed in $\overline{-1, 1}$. [See I,10.] The length of the prolonged chain is $\le y$ iff $\cos \theta \ge [x^2 + 1 - y^2]/2x$, and because of the uniform distribution of $\cos \theta$ this means that the length is determined by the stochastic density kernel

$$k(x, y) = y/2x \qquad |x-1| < y < x + 1.$$

The length L_{n+1} of a chain with $n+1$ links has density $k^{(n)}(1, y)$. (See problem 18.)

(*d*) *Discrete Markov chains.* A stochastic matrix (p_{ij}) may be considered as a stochastic density $k(i, j) = p_{ij}$ defined on the set Ω of positive integers and with respect to the measure m attributing unit weight to each integer. The definition can be extended to the whole line if we put $K(i, dy) = m\{dy\}$, where m attributes measure 0 to the complement Ω'. For $x \notin \Omega$ the values $K(x, \Gamma)$ may be defined arbitrarily, for example by linear interpolation. ►

Absolute and Stationary Probabilities

Saying that a sequence $\mathbf{X}_0, \mathbf{X}_1, \ldots$ is subject to the transition probabilities $K^{(n)}$ means that $K^{(n)}(x, \Gamma)$ is the conditional probability of the event $\{\mathbf{X}_{m+n} \in \Gamma\}$ given that $\mathbf{X}_m = x$. If the probability distribution of $\mathbf{X}_0$ is γ_0 *the probability distribution of* $\mathbf{X}_n$ *is given by*

$$\gamma_n(\Gamma) = \int_\Omega \gamma_0\{dx\}\, K^{(n)}(x, \Gamma). \tag{11.6}$$

Definition 2. *The distribution* γ_0 *is a stationary distribution for* K *if* $\gamma_n = \gamma_0$ *for all* n, *that is, if*

$$\gamma_0\{\Gamma\} = \int_\Omega \gamma_0\{dx\}\, K(x, \Gamma). \tag{11.7}$$

The basic facts concerning stationary distributions are the same as in the case of discrete Markov chains. Under mild regularity conditions on K *there exists a unique stationary distribution and it represents the asymptotic distribution of* $\mathbf{X}_n$ *under any initial distribution.* In other words, the influence of the initial state fades away and the system tends to a *steady state* governed by the stationary solution. This is one form of the ergodic theorem. (See VIII,7.)

Examples. (*e*) *The queuing process* $\{\mathbf{W}_n\}$ defined in (9.1) is a Markov process concentrated on the closed interval $\overline{0, \infty}$. The transition probabilities are defined only for $x, y \geq 0$ and there $K(x, \overline{0, y}) = F(y-x)$. The existence of a stationary measure will be proved in VIII,7.

(*f*) Let $\mathbf{X}_1, \mathbf{X}_2, \ldots$ be mutually independent positive variables with a continuous density f concentrated on $\overline{0, \infty}$. Define a sequence of random variables $\mathbf{Y}_k$ recursively by

$$\mathbf{Y}_1 = \mathbf{X}_1, \qquad \mathbf{Y}_{n+1} = |\mathbf{Y}_n - \mathbf{X}_{n+1}|. \tag{11.8}$$

Then $\{\mathbf{Y}_n\}$ is a Markov chain concentrated on $\overline{0, \infty}$ with transition densities

$$k(x, y) = \begin{cases} f(x-y) + f(x+y) & 0 < y < x \\ f(x+y) & y > x > 0. \end{cases} \tag{11.9}$$

The defining equation for a stationary density g is

$$g(y) = \int_0^\infty g(x+y)\, f(x)\, dx + \int_0^\infty g(x)\, f(x+y)\, dx. \tag{11.10}$$

Denote the distribution function of f by F and suppose that it has a finite expectation μ. Then

$$g(y) = \mu^{-1}[1 - F(y)] \tag{11.11}$$

is a *stationary probability density*. In fact, a simple integration by parts will show that g satisfies[32] (11.10) and we know from V,(6.3) that g is a probability density. (See problem 17.)

(*g*) *A technical application.*[33] A long transmission line consists of individual pieces of cable whose characteristics are subject to statistical fluctuations. We treat the deviations from the ideal value as independent random variables $\mathbf{Y}_1, \mathbf{Y}_2, \ldots$ and suppose that their effect is additive. Reversing the cable changes the sign of the contribution. Assume that the deviations $\mathbf{Y}_k$ are symmetric and put $\mathbf{X}_k = |\mathbf{Y}_k|$. An efficient construction of a long transmission line now proceeds by the following inductive rule: the $(n + 1)$st piece of cable is attached in that position which gives its error a sign opposite to the sign of the accumulated error of the preceding n pieces. The accumulated errors then follow the rule (10.8), and (11.11) is not only a stationary density but actually a limiting distribution: *the error of a line consisting of n pieces is (for large n) distributed approximately with density* (11.11). On the other hand, if the pieces of cable were combined randomly, the central limit theorem would apply and the variance of the error would increase linearly with n, that is, with the length of the cable. The simple procedure of testing the sign of the error thus permits us to keep it in bounds ►

In the preceding examples a Markovian sequence $\mathbf{X}_0, \mathbf{X}_1, \ldots$ was defined in terms of an initial distribution γ_0 and the transition probabilities K. The joint distribution of $(\mathbf{X}_0, \mathbf{X}_1, \ldots, \mathbf{X}_n)$ is of the form

$$\gamma_0\{dx_0\}\, K(x_0, dx_1) \ldots K(x_{n-1}, dx_n)$$

discussed in III,8 and **1**; XV,1. We have here a typical example of the advantage of defining absolute probabilities in terms of conditional ones. A more systematic way would be to start from the postulate

$$\mathbf{P}\{\mathbf{X}_{n+1} \in \Gamma \mid \mathbf{X}_0 = x_0, \ldots, \mathbf{X}_n = x_n\} = K(x_n, \Gamma) \tag{11.12}$$

as definition. Here the *Markov property* is expressed by the fact that the right side is independent of $x_0, x_1, \ldots, x_{n-1}$ so that the "past history" has no effect. The disadvantage of this definition is that it would involve us in useless talk about existence of conditional probabilities, their uniqueness, etc.

[32] How does one discover such a thing? Assuming hopefully that g and f have derivatives we may differentiate (11.10) formally. An integration by parts leads to a cancellation of the integrals and to the relation $g'(y) = -g(0)f(y)$ showing that g must be of the form (11.11). Direct verification then proves the validity of (11.11) without differentiability conditions.

[33] Adapted from a discrete model used by H. von Schelling, Elektrische Nachr.-Technik, vol. 20 (1943) pp. 251–259.

(For Markov processes depending on a continuous time parameter see chapter X.)

*12. MARTINGALES

For a first orientation we may consider a stochastic process $\{\mathbf{X}_n\}$ such that the joint distribution of $(\mathbf{X}_0, \ldots, \mathbf{X}_n)$ has a strictly positive continuous density p_n $(n = 0, 1, \ldots)$. Conditional densities and expectations are then defined everywhere in the elementary way of III,2. The variables $\mathbf{X}_n$ and $\mathbf{Y}_n$ are supposed to have expectations.

The sequence $\{\mathbf{X}_n\}$ will be called *absolutely fair* if for $n = 1, 2, \ldots$

$$\mathbf{E}(\mathbf{X}_1) = 0, \qquad \mathbf{E}(\mathbf{X}_{n+1} \mid \mathbf{X}_1, \ldots, \mathbf{X}_n) = 0. \tag{12.1}$$

A sequence $\{\mathbf{Y}_n\}$ is a *martingale* if

$$\mathbf{E}(\mathbf{Y}_{n+1} \mid \mathbf{Y}_0, \ldots, \mathbf{Y}_n) = \mathbf{Y}_n. \tag{12.2}$$

(A more flexible definition will be given presently.)

The connection between the two types is simple. Given an absolutely fair sequence $\{\mathbf{X}_n\}$ put

$$\mathbf{Y}_n = \mathbf{X}_1 + \cdots + \mathbf{X}_n + c \tag{12.3}$$

where c is a constant, $n = 1, 2, \ldots$. Then

$$\mathbf{E}(\mathbf{Y}_{n+1} \mid \mathbf{X}_1, \ldots, \mathbf{X}_n) = \mathbf{Y}_n. \tag{12.4}$$

The conditioning variables $\mathbf{X}_j$ may be replaced by the $\mathbf{Y}_k$, and so (12.4) is equivalent to (12.2). On the other hand, given a martingale $\{\mathbf{Y}_n\}$ put $\mathbf{X}_1 = \mathbf{Y}_1 - \mathbf{E}(\mathbf{Y}_1)$ and $\mathbf{X}_{n+1} = \mathbf{Y}_{n+1} - \mathbf{Y}_n$. Then $\{\mathbf{X}_n\}$ is absolutely fair and (12.3) holds with $c = \mathbf{E}(\mathbf{Y}_1)$. Thus $\{\mathbf{Y}_n\}$ *is a martingale iff it is of the form* (12.3) *with* $\{\mathbf{X}_n\}$ *absolutely fair.*

The concept of martingales is due to P. Lévy, but it was J. L. Doob who realized its unexpected potentialities and developed the theory.[34] It will be shown in VII,8 that under mild boundedness conditions the variables $\mathbf{Y}_k$ of a martingale converge to a limit; this fact is important for the modern theory of stochastic processes.

Examples. (*a*) Classical gambling is concerned with independent variables $\mathbf{X}_n$ with $\mathbf{E}(\mathbf{X}_n) = 0$. Such a game is absolutely fair[35] and the

---

* Martingales are treated because of their great importance, but they are not used as a tool in this book.

[34] For a fuller treatment see the books by Doob or Loève.

[35] The practical limitations of this notion are discussed in **1**; X,3. It will be recalled that there exist "fair" games in which with probability $>1 - \epsilon$ the gambler's gain at the nth trial exceeds, say, $n/\log n$.

partial sums $\mathbf{S}_n = \mathbf{X}_1 + \cdots + \mathbf{X}_n$ constitute a martingale. Consider now an ordinary coin-tossing game in which the gambler chooses his stakes according to some rule involving his success in previous trials. The successive gains cease to be independent random variables but the game remains absolutely fair. The idea of a fair game is that the knowledge of the past should not enable the gambler to improve on his fortunes. Intuitively this means that an absolutely fair game should remain absolutely fair under any system of gambling, that is, under rules of skipping individual trials. We shall see that this is so.

(*b*) *Polya's urn scheme of* [**1**; V,(2.*c*)]. An urn contains b black and r red balls, A ball is drawn at random. It is replaced and, moreover, c balls of the color drawn are added. Let $\mathbf{Y}_0 = \dfrac{b}{b+r}$ and let $\mathbf{Y}_n$ be the proportion of black balls attained by the nth drawing. Then $\{\mathbf{Y}_n\}$ is a martingale. In this case the convergence theorem guarantees the existence of a limit distribution [see examples VII,(4.*a*) and VII,(8.*a*)].

(*c*) *Concordant*[36] *functions*. Let $\{\mathbf{X}_n\}$ be a Markov chain with transition probabilities given by the stochastic kernel K. Nothing is assumed concerning the expectations of $\mathbf{X}_n$. The function u is called concordant with respect to K if

$$u(x) = \int K(x, dy)\, u(y). \tag{12.5}$$

Define random variables $\mathbf{Y}_k$ by $\mathbf{Y}_k = u(\mathbf{X}_k)$ and assume that all expectations exist (for example, that u is bounded). The relation (12.5) is the same as $\mathbf{E}(\mathbf{Y}_{k+1} \mid \mathbf{X}_k = x) = u(x)$, and thus $\mathbf{E}(\mathbf{Y}_{k+1} \mid \mathbf{X}_k) = \mathbf{Y}_k$. Since $\{\mathbf{X}_k\}$ is Markovian this implies (12.4), and since $\mathbf{Y}_k$ is a function of $\mathbf{X}_k$, this in turn implies (12.2) [see V,10.*a*]. Thus $\{\mathbf{Y}_n\}$ *is a martingale*. This result is of great value in the boundary theory for Markov chains because the existence of a limit for $\mathbf{Y}_n$ usually implies the existence of a limit for the given sequence $\{\mathbf{X}_n\}$. [See examples (*f*) and VII,(8.*c*).]

(*d*) *Likelihood ratios*. Suppose it known that in a stochastic process $\mathbf{X}_1, \mathbf{X}_2, \ldots$ the joint densities of $(\mathbf{X}_1, \ldots, \mathbf{X}_n)$ are either p_n or q_n, but we do not know which. To reach a decision statisticians introduce the new random variables

$$\mathbf{Y}_n = \frac{q_n(\mathbf{X}_1, \ldots, \mathbf{X}_n)}{p_n(\mathbf{X}_1, \ldots, \mathbf{X}_n)}. \tag{12.6}$$

Under sufficient regularity conditions it is plausible that if the true densities are p_n the observed values of $\mathbf{X}_1, \ldots, \mathbf{X}_n$ will on the average cluster around points where p_n is relatively large. If this is so $\mathbf{Y}_n$ is likely

[36] This term was introduced by G. Hunt.

to be small or large according as the true density is p_n or q_n. The asymptotic behavior of $\{\mathbf{Y}_n\}$ is therefore of interest in statistical decision theory.

For simplicity we assume that the densities p_n are strictly positive and continuous. If the p_n represent the true densities, then the conditional density of $\mathbf{X}_{n+1}$ for given $\mathbf{X}_1, \ldots, \mathbf{X}_n$ equals the ratio p_{n+1}/p_n, and hence

$$\begin{aligned}(12.7)\qquad &\mathbf{E}(\mathbf{Y}_{n+1} \mid \mathbf{X}_1 = x_1, \ldots, \mathbf{X}_n = x_n) = \\ &\qquad = \int_{-\infty}^{+\infty} \frac{q_{n+1}(x_1, \ldots, x_n, y)}{p_{n+1}(x_1, \ldots, x_n, y)} \cdot \frac{p_{n+1}(x_1, \ldots, x_n, y)}{p_n(x_1, \ldots, x_n)}\, dy.\end{aligned}$$

The factors p_{n+1} cancel. The second denominator is independent of y, and the integral of q_{n+1} is given by the marginal density q_{n+1}. Thus (12.7) reduces to q_n/p_n and so (12.4) is true. Accordingly, under the present conditions the likelihood ratios $\mathbf{Y}_n$ form a martingale. ►

The conditioning used in (12.2) is not particularly fortunate because one has frequently to replace the conditioning variables $\mathbf{Y}_1, \ldots, \mathbf{Y}_n$ by some functions of them. [Such was the case in (12.4).] A greater defect is revealed by example (*a*). The underlying process (say coin tossing or roulette) is represented by a sequence of random variables $\mathbf{Z}_n$, and the gambler's gain at the $(n + 1)$st trial is some function of $\mathbf{Z}_1, \ldots, \mathbf{Z}_{n+1}$ and, perhaps, other variables. The observable past is represented by $(\mathbf{Z}_1, \ldots, \mathbf{Z}_n)$, which may provide more information than the past gains. For example, if the gambler skips trials number 1, 3, 5, . . . the knowledge of his gains up to epoch $2n$ is at best equivalent to the knowledge of $\mathbf{Z}_2, \mathbf{Z}_4, \ldots, \mathbf{Z}_{2n}$. Here the additional knowledge of $\mathbf{Z}_1, \mathbf{Z}_3, \ldots$ could in principle imply an advantage, and absolute fairness in this case must be based on conditioning by $\mathbf{Z}_1, \ldots, \mathbf{Z}_n$. Thus conditioning with respect to various sets of random variables may be necessary, and to take care of all situations it is best to use the conditioning with respect to arbitrary σ-algebras of events.

Consider then a sequence $\{\mathbf{Y}_n\}$ of random variables in an arbitrary probability space and denote by $\mathfrak{A}_n$ the σ-algebra of events generated by $(\mathbf{Y}_1, \ldots, \mathbf{Y}_n)$ [see V,10*a*]. The defining relation (12.2) is now the same as $\mathbf{E}(\mathbf{Y}_{n+1} \mid \mathfrak{A}_n) = \mathbf{Y}_n$. We want to take this as the defining relation but replace the σ-algebra $\mathfrak{A}_n$ by a larger σ-algebra $\mathfrak{B}_n$. In most cases $\mathfrak{B}_n$ will be generated by $\mathbf{Y}_1, \ldots, \mathbf{Y}_n$ and additional random variables depending on the past. The idea is that any random variable depending on the past must be measurable with respect to $\mathfrak{B}_n$, and in this sense $\mathfrak{B}_n$ represents the information contained in the past history of the process. As this information grows richer with time we shall suppose that the $\mathfrak{B}_n$ increase, that is,

$$(12.8)\qquad \mathfrak{B}_1 \subset \mathfrak{B}_2 \subset \cdots.$$

Definition. *Let* $\mathbf{Y}_1, \mathbf{Y}_2, \ldots$ *be random variables with expectations. Let* $\mathfrak{B}_1, \mathfrak{B}_2, \ldots$ *be* σ*-algebras of events satisfying* (12.8).

The sequence $\{\mathbf{Y}_n\}$ *is a martingale with respect to* $\{\mathfrak{B}_n\}$ *iff*

$$\mathbf{E}(\mathbf{Y}_{n+1} \mid \mathfrak{B}_n) = \mathbf{Y}_n. \tag{12.9}$$

[Because of the non-uniqueness of the conditional expectations, (12.9) should be read "there exists a version of the conditional probability for which (12.9) is true." This remark applies in the sequel.] Note that (12.9) implies that $\mathbf{Y}_n$ is $\mathfrak{B}_n$-measurable and so $\mathfrak{B}_n$ contains the σ-algebra $\mathfrak{A}_n$ generated by $\mathbf{Y}_1, \ldots, \mathbf{Y}_n$. Therefore $\{\mathbf{Y}_n\}$ *is a martingale also with respect to* $\{\mathfrak{A}_n\}$, that is, (12.2) holds.

Example. (*e*) Let the σ-algebras $\mathfrak{B}_n$ satisfy (12.8) and let $\mathbf{Y}$ be an arbitrary random variable with expectation. Put $\mathbf{Y}_n = \mathbf{E}(\mathbf{Y} \mid \mathfrak{B}_n)$. Then $\mathbf{Y}_n$ is $\mathfrak{B}_n$-measurable and hence (12.9) is true. Thus $\{\mathbf{Y}_n\}$ *is a martingale.* ►

Returning to example (*a*) it is now easy to prove the impossibility of systems of a fairly general type. Let $\{\mathbf{Y}_n\}$ be a martingale with respect to $\{\mathfrak{B}_n\}$. To describe the gambler's freedom to skip the nth trial we introduce a *decision function* $\boldsymbol{\epsilon}_n$; this is a $\mathfrak{B}_{n-1}$-measurable[37] random variable assuming only the values 0 and 1. In the event $\boldsymbol{\epsilon}_n = 0$ the gambler skips the nth trial; in the event $\boldsymbol{\epsilon}_n = 1$ he bets and in this case his gain at the nth trial is $\mathbf{Y}_n - \mathbf{Y}_{n-1}$. Denoting his accumulated gain up to and including the nth trial by $\mathbf{Z}_n$ we have

$$\mathbf{Z}_n = \mathbf{Z}_{n-1} + \boldsymbol{\epsilon}_n[\mathbf{Y}_n - \mathbf{Y}_{n-1}]. \tag{12.10}$$

By induction it is seen that $\mathbf{Z}_n$ has an expectation. Furthermore, $\mathbf{Z}_{n-1}$, $\boldsymbol{\epsilon}_n$, and $\mathbf{Y}_{n-1}$ are $\mathfrak{B}_{n-1}$-measurable and hence [see V,(10. 8)]

$$\mathbf{E}(\mathbf{Z}_n \mid \mathfrak{B}_{n-1}) = \mathbf{Z}_{n-1} + \boldsymbol{\epsilon}_n[\mathbf{E}(\mathbf{Y}_n \mid \mathfrak{B}_{n-1}) - \mathbf{Y}_{n-1}]. \tag{12.11}$$

Since $\{\mathbf{Y}_n\}$ is a martingale the expression within brackets vanishes, and so $\{\mathbf{Z}_n\}$ is a martingale. We have thus proved a theorem due to Halmos proving the

Impossibility of systems. *Every sequence of decision functions* $\boldsymbol{\epsilon}_1, \boldsymbol{\epsilon}_2, \ldots$ *changes the martingale* $\{\mathbf{Y}_n\}$ *into a martingale* $\{\mathbf{Z}_n\}$.

By far the most important special case concerns *optional stopping*. By this is meant a system where the first $\mathbf{N}$ trials are accepted and all

[37] This condition guarantees that the decision is made on the basis of past history of observations. No mathematical theory can disprove prescience of the future, we must exclude it from our models.

succeeding ones skipped; the **N**th trial is the last. Here **N** (*the stopping epoch*) is a random variable such that the event $\{\mathbf{N} > k\}$ is in $\mathfrak{B}_k$. (In the notation of the theorem $\epsilon_k = 1$ for $\mathbf{N} > k - 1$ and $\epsilon_k = 0$ for $\mathbf{N} \le k - 1$.) We have thus the

Corollary. *Optional stopping does not affect the martingale property.*

Examples. (*f*) A simple random walk on the line starts at the origin; the particle moves with probability p one step to the right, with probability $q = 1 - p$ to the left. If $\mathbf{S}_n$ is the position of the particle at epoch n it is easily seen that $\mathbf{Y}_n = (q/p)^{\mathbf{S}_n}$ constitutes a martingale with $\mathbf{E}(\mathbf{Y}_n) = 1$ and $\mathbf{E}(\mathbf{Y}_0) = 1$. [This is a special case of example (*c*).]

In the ruin problem the random walk is stopped when it first reaches one of the positions $-a$ or b, where a and b are positive integers. In this modified process $-a \le \mathbf{S}_n \le b$ and with probability one $\mathbf{S}_n$ is ultimately fixed at b or at $-a$. Denote the corresponding probabilities by x and $1 - x$. Since $\mathbf{S}_n$ is bounded

$$\mathbf{E}(\mathbf{S}_n) \to x \cdot \left(\frac{q}{p}\right)^b + (1-x)\left(\frac{q}{p}\right)^{-a}$$

But $\mathbf{E}(\mathbf{S}_n) = 1$ because the expected value of the martingale remains constant. The right side, therefore, equals 1, and this linear equation determines x. We have thus found the probability x of termination at b derived by different methods in **1**; XIV,2. The formula breaks down when $p = q$, but in this case $\{\mathbf{S}_n\}$ is a martingale and the same argument shows that $x = a/(a+b)$. Although the result is elementary and known, the argument illustrates the possible uses of martingale theory.

(*g*) *On systems.* Consider a sequence of independent random variables $\mathbf{X}_n$ where $\mathbf{X}_n$ assumes the value $\pm 2^n$ with probability $\frac{1}{2}$ each. A gambler tosses a coin to decide whether he takes the nth bet. The probability that his first try occurs at epoch n is 2^{-n} and in this case his gain is $\pm 2^n$. Thus *the gambler's gain at his first try is a random variable without expectation.* The system theorem therefore depends on the fact that we have not changed the time parameter. ►

It is frequently necessary to work with absolute values and inequalities, and for such purposes the notion of submartingale is important. The sequence $\{\mathbf{Y}_n\}$ is a *submartingale*[38] if it satisfies the conditions of the last definition with the equality sign in (12.9) replaced by $\ge$. In gambling terminology we replace absolutely fair games by absolutely favorable ones. If $\{\mathbf{Y}_n\}$ is a martingale then $\{|\mathbf{Y}_n|\}$ is a submartingale. This follows from the more general

[38] This term is now generally preferred to the older lower semi-martingale.

Lemma. *If u is a convex function and* $\{\mathbf{Y}_n\}$ *a martingale, then* $\{u(\mathbf{Y}_n)\}$ *is a submartingale provided the expectation of* $u(\mathbf{Y}_n)$ *exists.*

The proof is immediate from Jensen's inequality [V,(8.6)] which applies to conditional expectations as well as to ordinary ones. It states that

$$\mathbf{E}(u(\mathbf{Y}_{n+1}) \mid \mathfrak{B}_n) \geq u(\mathbf{E}(\mathbf{Y}_{n+1} \mid \mathfrak{B}_n)), \tag{12.12}$$

and the right side equals $u(\mathbf{Y}_n)$.

The same proof shows that if $\{\mathbf{Y}_n\}$ is a submartingale and u a convex *non-decreasing* function, then $\{u(\mathbf{Y}_n)\}$ is again a submartingale, provided $u(\mathbf{Y}_n)$ has an expectation

13. PROBLEMS FOR SOLUTION

1. For F to be stable it suffices that (1.2) holds for $n = 2$ and 3. (P. Lévy)
Hint: Products of the form $c_1{}^j c_2{}^k$ where $j, k = 0, \pm 1, \pm 2, \ldots$ are either dense in $\overline{0, \infty}$ or powers of a fixed number c. The latter must be shown to be impossible in the present case.

Note. Curiously enough it does *not* suffice that (1.2) holds for $n = 2$. See example XVII,(3.*f*) and problem 9 of IX,10.

2. If F and G are stable with the same exponent α so is $F \bigstar G$. Find the appropriate norming constants γ_n.

3. For a symmetric stable distribution R the symmetrization inequality V,(5.8) implies that $n[1 - R(c_n x)]$ remains bounded. Conclude that *R has absolute moments of order* $<\alpha$. [Use V,(6.3).] By symmetrization the last statement carries over to unsymmetric R.

4. *Alternative derivation of the Holtsmark distribution.* Consider a ball of radius r about the origin and n stars (points) placed independently and randomly in it. Let each star have unit mass. Let $\mathbf{X}_1, \ldots, \mathbf{X}_n$ be the x-components of the gravitational force due to the individual stars, and $\mathbf{S}_n = \mathbf{X}_1 + \cdots + \mathbf{X}_n$. Let $r \to \infty$, $n \to \infty$ so that $\frac{4}{3}r^3\pi n^{-1} \to \lambda$. Show that the distribution of $\mathbf{S}_n$ tends to the symmetric stable distribution with characteristic exponent $\frac{3}{2}$.

5. Show that the preceding problem is not essentially modified if the mass of a star is assumed to be a random variable with unit expectation provided the masses of the stars are mutually independent and also independent of the position of the stars.

6. *Holtsmark distribution, four dimensions.* The four-dimensional analogue to the Holtsmark distribution is a symmetric stable distribution with characteristic exponent $\frac{4}{3}$. (In four dimensions the gravitational force varies inversely as the third power of the distance.)

7. Let $\{\mathbf{X}_{k,n}\}$ be a triangular null array with a common distribution F_n for $\mathbf{X}_{1,n}, \ldots, \mathbf{X}_{n,n}$. Does $\mathbf{P}\{\max(|\mathbf{X}_{1,n}|, \ldots, |\mathbf{X}_{n,n}|) > \epsilon\}$ tend to zero?

8. Find the density for the renewal function U of (6.3) if F has the density (*a*) $f(x) = e^{-x}$, and (*b*) $f(x) = xe^{-x}$.

9. In a terminating process F has density pce^{-ct}. Find the distributions of the lifetime and of the number of renewal epochs.

10. *Generalized terminating renewal process.* Instead of assuming that with probability q the process terminates instantaneously we let it (with probability q) continue for a random duration with a proper distribution F_0 and *then* stop. In other words, the renewal epochs are of the form $\mathbf{T}_1 + \cdots + \mathbf{T}_n + \mathbf{Y}$ where the *last* variable has a different distribution. Show that the distribution V of the *duration* of the process satisfies the renewal equation

$$(*) \qquad V = qF_0 + F \bigstar V \qquad (F(\infty) = 1 - q).$$

11. Show that the waiting time problem for large gaps reduces to a special case of the process described in the last problem. Put (7.1) into the form (*).

12. *Poisson process and covering theorems.* We recall from example III,(3.*d*) that if in a Poisson process n renewal epochs occur in $\overline{0, t}$ their (conditional) distribution is *uniform*. The probability $1 - V(t)$ that no gap of length ξ appears follows therefore from the covering theorem 3 in I,9 in the form

$$(\dagger) \qquad 1 - V(t) = e^{-cx} \sum_{n=1}^{\infty} \frac{(ct)^{n-1}}{(n-1)!} \theta_n(t).$$

(*a*) Verify that this is indeed a solution of (7.1) when $F(x) = 1 - e^{-cx}$.

(*b*) Given (†) is the unique solution of (7.1), derive the covering theorem from it. [This is an instance of a proof by randomization. See **1**; XII, problem 5.]

13. Let V be the distribution of the waiting time in example (7.*g*) ("last come first served"). Show that V satisfies the renewal equation $V(t) = A(t) + B \bigstar V(t)$ where A and B are defective distributions given by $A\{dx\} = e^{-cx}\, G\{dx\}$, and $B\{dx\} = [1 - G(x)]ce^{-cx}\, dx$. (Show that we are concerned with a generalized terminating process in the sense of problem 10: a renewal process generated by B is followed by an undisturbed dead period, the latter having a distribution proportional to A.)

14. *Small gaps in a Poisson process.*[39] A "coincidence" is said to occur if two renewal epochs $\mathbf{S}_n$ and $\mathbf{S}_{n+1}$ with $n > 0$ are at a distance $\leq \xi$. Express the waiting time distribution in terms of the distribution V, of the preceding problem.

15. *Generalization of the small gap problem* 14.[40] In the standard renewal process find a renewal equation for the waiting time to the first occurrence of the event $\{\mathbf{T}_n \leq \mathbf{Y}_n\}$, where the $\mathbf{Y}_k$ are independent of the process and of each other and have common distribution G.

16. Let $a_1, \ldots, a_n$ be arbitrary numbers and $m = \max[0, a_1, a_1+a_2, \ldots, a_1 + \cdots + a_n]$. Put recursively $v_1 = a_n \cup 0$, $v_2 = (v_1 + a_{n-1}) \cup 0, \ldots,$

$$v_n = (v_{n-1} + a_1) \cup 0.$$

Prove by induction that $v_n = m$. Show that this implies the truth of the theorem in section 9.

---

[39] For variants (treated differently) see E. N. Gilbert and H. O. Pollak, *Coincidences in Poisson patterns*, Bell System Technical J., vol. 36 (1957) pp. 1005–1033.

[40] The "large gap" problem admits of a similar generalization with an analogous answer.

17. In example (11.f) assume that $f(x) = 1$ for $0 < x < 1$. Prove that $g(y) = 2(1-y)$ is a stationary density and that $k^{(n)}(x, y) = g(y)$ for $n \geq 2$. If $f(x) = \alpha e^{-\alpha x}$ then $g(x) = f(x)$.

18. Define a stochastic density kernel concentrated on 0, 1 by

$$k(x, y) = \tfrac{1}{2}(1-x)^{-1} \quad \text{if} \quad 0 < x < y < 1$$

and

$$k(x, y) = \tfrac{1}{2}x^{-1} \quad \text{if} \quad 0 < y < x < 1.$$

Find a stationary density. (It satisfies a simple differential equation.) Interpret probabilistically.

19. A Markov chain on $\overline{0, 1}$ is such that if $\mathbf{X}_n = x$ then $\mathbf{X}_{n+1}$ is uniformly distributed on $1-x, 1$. Show that a stationary density is given by $2x$. (T. Ugaheri.)

CHAPTER VII

Laws of Large Numbers. Applications in Analysis

In the first part of this chapter it is shown that some famous and deep theorems of analysis can be derived with surprising ease by probabilistic arguments. Section 7 treats variants of the laws of large numbers. Section 8 contains a restricted version of the martingale convergence theorem and stands somewhat apart from the remainder.

1. MAIN LEMMA AND NOTATIONS

By way of preparation consider a one-dimensional distribution G with expectation θ and variance σ^2. If $\mathbf{X}_1, \ldots, \mathbf{X}_n$ are independent variables with the distribution G, their arithmetic mean $\mathbf{M}_n = (\mathbf{X}_1 + \cdots + \mathbf{X}_n)n^{-1}$ has expectation θ and variance $\sigma^2 n^{-1}$. For large n this variance is small and $\mathbf{M}_n$ is likely to be close to θ. It follows that for every continuous function $u(\mathbf{M}_n)$ is likely to be close to $u(\theta)$. This remark constitutes the weak law of large numbers. It is slightly generalized in the following lemma, which despite its simplicity will prove a source of valuable information.

For $n = 1, 2, \ldots$ consider a family of distributions $F_{n,\theta}$ with expectation θ and variance $\sigma_n^2(\theta)$; here θ is a parameter varying in a finite or infinite interval. For expectations we use the notation

$$\mathbf{E}_{n,\theta}(u) = \int_{-\infty}^{+\infty} u(x)\, F_{n,\theta}\{dx\}. \tag{1.1}$$

Lemma 1. *If* $\sigma_n^2(\theta) \to 0$ *then*

$$\mathbf{E}_{n,\theta}(u) \to u(\theta) \tag{1.2}$$

for every bounded continuous function u. The convergence is uniform in every subinterval in which $\sigma_n^2(\theta) \to 0$ *uniformly and u is uniformly continuous.*

Proof. Obviously

$$(1.3)\qquad |\mathbf{E}_{n,\theta}(u) - u(\theta)| \le \int_{-\infty}^{+\infty} |u(x) - u(\theta)|\, F_{n,\theta}\{dx\}.$$

There exists a neighborhood $|x - \theta| < \delta$ of θ in which the integrand is $<\epsilon$. Outside this neighborhood the integrand is less than some constant M, and by Chebyshev's inequality V,(7.2) the probability carried by the region $|x - \theta| > \delta$ is less than $\sigma_n^2(\theta)\delta^{-2}$. Thus the right side cannot exceed $\epsilon + M\sigma_n^2(\theta)\delta^{-2}$, and this quantity is $<2\epsilon$ for n sufficiently large. ▶

The next three examples are important and useful. In each case $F_{n,\theta}$ is the distribution of an average $(\mathbf{X}_1 + \cdots + \mathbf{X}_n)n^{-1}$. In example (*a*) the $\mathbf{X}_j$ assume the values 0 and 1 only, in (*b*) they have a Poisson distribution, in (*c*) a gamma distribution.

Examples. (*a*) If $F_{n,\theta}$ is a binomial distribution $\sigma_n^2(\theta) = \theta(1-\theta)n^{-1} \to 0$ and so

$$(1.4)\qquad \sum_{k=0}^{n} u\left(\frac{k}{n}\right)\binom{n}{k}\theta^k(1-\theta)^{n-k} \to u(\theta)$$

uniformly in $0 \le \theta \le 1$. The implications are discussed in section 2.

(*b*) If $F_{n,\theta}$ attaches probability $e^{-n\theta}(n\theta)^k/k!$ to the point k/n, we have $\sigma_n^2(\theta) = \theta/n$ and so

$$(1.5)\qquad e^{-n\theta}\sum_{k=0}^{\infty} u\left(\frac{k}{n}\right)\frac{(n\theta)^k}{k!} \to u(\theta)$$

uniformly in every finite θ-interval. This formula is valid also for non-integral n. (Continued in sections 5 and 6.)

(*c*) Taking for $F_{n,\theta}$ a gamma distribution we get

$$(1.6)\qquad \frac{1}{(n-1)!}\int_0^{\infty} u(x)\cdot\left(\frac{nx}{\theta}\right)^{n-1} e^{-nx/\theta}\,\frac{n\,dx}{\theta} \to u(\theta)$$

uniformly in every finite interval. Again this formula holds for non-integral n provided $(n-1)!$ is replaced by $\Gamma(n)$. It will be shown in section 6 that (1.6) is an inversion formula for Laplace transforms.

(*d*) Statisticians frequently face the situation described at the beginning of this section but consider the expectation θ an unknown parameter to be estimated from observations. In statistical language the relation (1.2) then states that $u(\mathbf{M}_n)$ is an *asymptotically unbiased estimator* for the unknown parameter $u(\theta)$. [The estimator would be unbiased if the two sides in (1.2) were equal.]

Notations for Differences

In the following applications use will be made of the basic notions and relations of the calculus of finite differences. Given a sequence $c_0, c_1, \ldots$ the *differencing operator* Δ is defined by $\Delta c_n = c_{n+1} - c_n$. Applying the operator Δ to the sequence $\{\Delta c_n\}$ we get a new sequence $\{\Delta^2 c_n\}$, and so forth. The higher differences Δ^r are thus defined recursively by the relation $\Delta^r = \Delta(\Delta^{r-1})$ where $\Delta^1 = \Delta$. For consistency we define $\Delta^0 c_n = c_n$ for all n.

Simple induction shows that

$$\Delta^r c_\nu = \sum_{k=0}^{r} \binom{r}{k} (-1)^{r+k} c_{\nu+k}. \tag{1.7}$$

This formula can be inverted to express the c_0 in terms of the differences on the left. In fact, $c_\nu = -\Delta c_\nu + c_{\nu+1}$. Applying this representation to Δc_ν and $c_{\nu+1}$ we get $c_\nu = \Delta^2 c_\nu - 2\,\Delta c_{\nu+1} + c_{\nu+2}$. Proceeding in like manner we get the identities

$$c_\nu = \sum_{k=0}^{r} \binom{r}{k} (-1)^{r-k} \Delta^{r-k} c_{\nu+k}, \qquad r = 1, 2, \ldots. \tag{1.8}$$

We shall apply the operators Δ^r to sequences with terms $c_n = f(x+nh)$ obtained from a function f by fixing a point x and a span $h > 0$. In such cases it is more convenient to replace Δ by the *difference ratio* $\underset{h}{\Delta} = h^{-1}\Delta$. Thus for fixed $h > 0$

$$\underset{h}{\Delta} f(x) = \frac{f(x+h) - f(x)}{h}. \tag{1.9}$$

The higher difference ratios are again defined recursively by $\underset{h}{\Delta}^{r+1} = \underset{h}{\Delta}\underset{h}{\Delta}^r$ where $\underset{h}{\Delta}^1 = \underset{h}{\Delta}$ and $\underset{h}{\Delta}^0 f(x) = f(x)$. Formula (1.7) is equivalent to

$$\underset{h}{\Delta}^r f(x) = h^{-r} \sum_{k=0}^{r} \binom{r}{k} (-1)^{r+k} f(x+kh). \tag{1.10}$$

2. BERNSTEIN POLYNOMIALS. ABSOLUTELY MONOTONE FUNCTIONS

Every linear combination of polynomials of the form $\binom{n}{k}\theta^k(1-\theta)^{n-k}$ is called a *Bernstein polynomial*. For a function u defined for $0 \le \theta \le 1$ we introduce the Bernstein polynomial of degree n

$$B_{n,u}(\theta) = \sum_{k=0}^{n} u(kh) \binom{n}{k} \theta^k (1-\theta)^{n-k}, \qquad h = \frac{1}{n}. \tag{2.1}$$

The following theorem merely restates (1.4).

Theorem 1. *If u is continuous in the closed interval $\overline{0, 1}$ the Bernstein polynomials $B_{n,u}(\theta)$ tend uniformly to $u(\theta)$.*

In other words, for given $\epsilon > 0$

$$|B_{n,u}(\theta) - u(\theta)| < \epsilon, \qquad 0 \leq \theta \leq 1, \tag{2.2}$$

for all n sufficiently large. The famous *Weierstrass approximation theorem* asserts the possibility of uniform approximation by some polynomials. The present theorem is sharper inasmuch as it exhibits the approximating polynomials. The above proof is due to S. Bernstein.

To rewrite the polynomial (2.1) in the standard form according to powers of θ we expand $(1 - \theta)^{n-k}$ by the binomial theorem and observe that for fixed j the coefficient of θ^j in (2.1) equals

$$\sum_k u(kh)\binom{n}{k}\binom{n-k}{j-k}(-1)^{j-k} = \binom{n}{j} h^j \underset{h}{\Delta^j} u(0) \tag{2.3}$$

[the last form follows from (1.10)]. We have thus

Theorem 2. *The Bernstein polynomial* (2.1) *is identical with*

$$B_{n,u}(\theta) = \sum_{j=0}^{n}\binom{n}{j}(h\theta)^j \underset{h}{\Delta^j} u(0), \qquad h = \frac{1}{n}. \tag{2.4}$$

We use this representation for a simple proof of a criterion for probability generating functions. A function u defined for $0 \leq x \leq 1$ is a *probability generating function if*

$$u(x) = u_0 + u_1 x + u_2 x^2 + \cdots \tag{2.5}$$

where $u_j \geq 0$ and $\Sigma\, u_j = 1$. Such a function possesses positive derivatives $u^{(n)}$ of all orders, but the converse is far from obvious when considered out of the present context.

Lemma. *The following three statements are equivalent.*

(i) *u is a probability generating function.*

(ii) *For $0 < x < 1$ and all n the derivatives $u^{(n)}$ exist and $u^{(n)}(x) \geq 0$. Furthermore $u(x) \to 1$ as $x \to 1$.*

(iii) *u is continuous for $0 < x \leq 1$ and*

$$\underset{h}{\Delta^r} u(0) \geq 0, \qquad h = \frac{1}{n}, \tag{2.6}$$

for $r \leq n$ and $n = 1, 2, \ldots$. Furthermore $u(1) = 1$.

Proof. Obviously (i) implies (ii). The monotonicity of the derivatives $u^{(n)}$ implies that $\underset{h}{\Delta} u$ has positive derivatives of all orders, and so by induction (2.6) is true. Thus (ii) implies (iii). If (2.6) holds, the coefficients of the polynomial $B_{n,u}$ in (2.4) are non-negative and they add to $B_{n,u}(1)$. From the representation (2.1) it is seen that $B_{n,u}(1) = u(1) = 1$ and so $B_{n,u}$ *is a probability generating function.* By the continuity theorem of **1**; XI,6 (or below VIII,7) the limit $u = \lim B_{n,u}$ is again a probability generating function, and this concludes the proof. ▶

Dropping the artificial restriction $u(1) = 1$ leads to the following definition used widely outside probability theory.

Definition. *The function u is absolutely monotone in $\overline{a, b}$ if $u^{(n)}(x) \geq 0$ for $a < x < b$.*

The example $u(x) = (1 - x)^{-1}$ shows that an unbounded function can be absolutely monotone in $\overline{0, 1}$. Put, however, $v(x) = u(\alpha x)/u(\alpha)$, where $0 < \alpha < 1$. If u is absolutely monotone in $\overline{0, 1}$, then v is a probability generating function and so u possesses a power series converging for $0 < x < \alpha$. As α can be taken arbitrarily close to 1 we have proved

Theorem 3. *The function u is absolutely monotone in $\overline{0, 1}$ iff it possesses a power series with non-negative coefficients converging for $0 < x < 1$.*

This theorem has important applications to Laplace transforms. It was first proved (by very different methods) by S. Bernstein.

3. MOMENT PROBLEMS

Let F be a probability distribution concentrated on the *closed* interval $\overline{0, 1}$ and denote by $\mathbf{E}(u)$ the integral of u with respect to F. The kth *moment* μ_k of F is defined by

$$\mu_k = \mathbf{E}(\mathbf{X}^k) = \int_0^1 x^k \, F\{dx\}, \tag{3.1}$$

it being understood that the interval of integration is *closed*. (As usual, $\mathbf{X}$ denotes the coordinate variable.) Taking differences it is seen that $-\Delta\mu_k = \mathbf{E}(\mathbf{X}^k(1 - \mathbf{X}))$, and by induction

$$(-1)^r \Delta^r \mu_k = \mathbf{E}(\mathbf{X}^k(1 - \mathbf{X})^r). \tag{3.2}$$

The expectation of the Bernstein polynomial (2.1) is therefore given by

$$\mathbf{E}(B_{n,u}) = \sum_{k=0}^{n} u(kh) \cdot \binom{n}{k} \cdot (-1)^{n-k} \Delta^{n-k} \mu_k. \tag{3.3}$$

For the coefficients appearing on the right we write

$$p_k^{(n)} = \binom{n}{k} (-1)^{n-k} \Delta^{n-k} \mu_k, \qquad k = 0, \ldots, n. \tag{3.4}$$

It follows from (3.2) that $p_k^{(n)} \geq 0$. For the constant function $u = 1$ we have $B_{n,u}(\theta) = 1$ for all θ, and (3.3) shows that for fixed n the coefficients $p_k^{(n)}$ add up to unity. We can therefore introduce the *atomic probability distribution* F_n *attributing weight* $p_k^{(n)}$ *to the atom* k/n *(where* $k = 0, 1, \ldots, n$*)*. Denote expectations with respect to F_n by $\mathbf{E}_n$. The quantity (3.3) is then identical with $\mathbf{E}_n(u)$, and the approximation theorem of the last section states that *if u is continuous in the closed interval* $\overline{0, 1}$, *then as* $n \to \infty$

$$\mathbf{E}_n(u) \to \mathbf{E}(u). \tag{3.5}$$

This relation makes it plausible that the distribution F itself can be expressed in terms of the distributions F_n. The following theorem shows that this is indeed so.

Theorem 1. *Inversion formula. At each point of continuity of F*

$$F_n(t) = \sum_{k \leq nt} \binom{n}{k} (-1)^{n-k} \Delta^{n-k} \mu_k \to F(t). \tag{3.6}$$

Proof. Introduce the step function u_t defined for fixed t by

$$u_t(\theta) = \begin{cases} 1 & \text{for } \theta \leq t \\ 0 & \text{for } \theta > t. \end{cases} \tag{3.7}$$

The two sides in (3.6) equal $\mathbf{E}_n(u_t)$ and $\mathbf{E}(u_t)$, respectively, and so (3.6) is formally a special case of (3.5). Some caution is necessary because (3.5) depends on the approximation theorem, which was proved only for continuous functions. The same proof shows, however, that

$$B_{n,u_t}(\theta) \to u_t(\theta)$$

in any closed interval excluding the point t where u_t is discontinuous. Taking expectations it follows that all possible limit values of the left side in (3.6) lie between $F(t-\epsilon)$ and $F(t+\epsilon)$, with $\epsilon > 0$ arbitrary. Letting $\epsilon \to 0$ we see that (3.6) is valid at every point t where F is continuous. ▶

By extraordinary good luck it is possible to restate this argument so as to yield a simple proof of the following celebrated and important theorem due to F. Hausdorff.

Theorem 2. *A sequence of numbers* $\mu_0, \mu_1, \ldots$ *represents the moments (3.1) of some probability distribution F concentrated on* $\overline{0, 1}$ *iff*

$$(-1)^{-r}\Delta^r \mu_k \geq 0, \qquad \mu_0 = 1. \tag{3.8}$$

Proof. Moments of a distribution satisfy (3.2) and hence (3.8) is necessary. Assume (3.8) to hold and define $p_k^{(n)}$ by (3.4). Using the inversion formula (1.8) for differences with $r = n - \nu$ we get the identity

$$\sum_{k=0}^{n} \binom{k}{\nu} p_k^{(n)} = \binom{n}{\nu} \mu_\nu. \tag{3.9}$$

For $\nu = 0$ we conclude that the $p_k^{(n)}$ add up to $\mu_0 = 1$, and so we may again define an atomic probability distribution F_n attributing weight $p_k^{(n)}$ to the atom k/n. The left side in (3.9) is the expectation of $\binom{n\mathbf{X}}{\nu}$ with respect to this distribution F_n. Multiplying (3.9) by $\nu! n^{-\nu}$ we see therefore that as $n \to \infty$ the expectation of $\mathbf{X}^\nu$ converges to μ_ν. The sequence $\{\mu_\nu\}$ thus appears as a limit of moment sequences $\{\mathbf{E}_n(\mathbf{X}^\nu)\}$ and is therefore itself a moment sequence by a simple theorem whose proof is postponed to example VIII,(1.*d*) in order to avoid repetition. This concludes the proof and shows at the same time that *the distribution* F *with moments* μ_ν *is given by* (3.6). ▶

A sequence $\{\mu_n\}$ such that $(-1)^r\Delta^r\mu_k \geq 0$ for all combinations r, k is called *completely monotone*. Although confusing, this term is well established. We shall return to completely monotone sequences and functions in XIII,4 and 11.

To avoid misconceptions it should be pointed out that the situation is radically different for distributions that are not concentrated on some finite interval. In fact, in general *a distribution is not uniquely determined by its moments.*

Example. Elementary, though tedious, integrations by parts show that for $n = 0, 1, \ldots$

$$\int_0^\infty x^n \cdot e^{-\sqrt[4]{x}} \sin \sqrt[4]{x}\, dx = 0. \tag{3.10}$$

If $0 < \alpha < 1$ it follows that $\varphi_\alpha(x) = \frac{1}{24} e^{-\sqrt[4]{x}}(1 - \alpha \sin \sqrt[4]{x})$ represents a probability density concentrated on $\overline{0, \infty}$, and *all these densities have identical moment sequences.* Letting $\varphi(x) = \frac{1}{2}\varphi_\alpha(x)$ when $x > 0$ and $\varphi(x) = \frac{1}{2}\varphi_\beta(-x)$ when $x < 0$ we get a density which *is not an even function even though all its odd moments vanish.* ▶

This negative result should not give rise to undue pessimism, for suitable regularity conditions can remove the source of trouble. The best result is a theorem of Carleman to the effect that a distribution F on $\overline{-\infty, \infty}$ *is uniquely determined by its moments if*

$$\sum \mu_{2n}^{-1/(2n)} = \infty, \tag{3.11}$$

that is, if the series on the left diverges. In this book we shall prove only the weaker statement that F is uniquely determined by its moments whenever the power series $\Sigma\, \mu_{2n} t^n/(2n)!$ converges in some interval. (Section 6 and XV,4.) Both criteria put restrictions on the rate of growth of μ_{2n}. Even in the most general situation the knowledge of finitely many moments $\mu_0, \mu_1, \ldots, \mu_n$ leads to useful inequalities for F similar to those derived in V,7 from the knowledge of μ_0 and μ_1.[1]

[1] The first sharp results were obtained by Markov and Stieltjes around 1884. The recent literature on the subject is inexhaustible. See, for example, A. Wald, Trans. Amer. Math. Soc., vol. 46 (1939) pp. 280–306; H. L. Royden, Ann. Math. Statist., vol. 24 (1953) pp. 361–376 [gives bounds on $F(x) - F(-x)$]. For a general survey see the monograph by J. A. Shohat and J. D. Tamarkin, *The problem of moments*, New York, 1943 (Math. Surveys No. 1). See also S. Karlin and W. Studden (1966).

*4. APPLICATION TO EXCHANGEABLE VARIABLES

We proceed to derive a beautiful result due to B. de Finetti which may serve as a typical example of the ease with which theorem 3.2 leads to surprising results.

Definition. *The random variables* $\mathbf{X}_1, \ldots, \mathbf{X}_n$ *are exchangeable*[2] *if the* $n!$ *permutations* $(\mathbf{X}_{k_1}, \ldots, \mathbf{X}_{k_n})$ *have the same n-dimensional probability distribution. The variables of an infinite sequence* $\{\mathbf{X}_n\}$ *are exchangeable if* $\mathbf{X}_1, \ldots, \mathbf{X}_n$ *are exchangeable for each n.*

As the examples will show, there is an essential difference between finite and infinite sequences. We consider here the special case of an *infinite sequence* $\{\mathbf{X}_n\}$ *of exchangeable variables assuming the values* 0 *and* 1 *only.* The next theorem asserts that *the distribution of such a process* $\{\mathbf{X}_n\}$ *are obtained by randomization of the binomial distribution.* As usual we put $\mathbf{S}_n = \mathbf{X}_1 + \cdots + \mathbf{X}_n$ and interpret the event $\{\mathbf{X}_k = 1\}$ as success.

Theorem. *To every infinite sequence of exchangeable variables* $\mathbf{X}_n$ *there corresponds a probability distribution F concentrated on* $\overline{0, 1}$ *such that*

$$\mathbf{P}\{\mathbf{X}_1 = 1, \ldots, \mathbf{X}_k = 1, \mathbf{X}_{k+1} = 0, \ldots, \mathbf{X}_n = 0\} = \int_0^1 \theta^k(1-\theta)^{n-k}\, F\{d\theta\} \tag{4.1}$$

$$\mathbf{P}\{\mathbf{S}_n = k\} = \binom{n}{k}\int_0^1 \theta^k(1-\theta)^{n-k}\, F\{d\theta\}. \tag{4.2}$$

Proof. Put $\mu_0 = 1$ and for $n = 1, 2, \ldots$

$$\mathbf{P}\{\mathbf{X}_1 = 1, \ldots, \mathbf{X}_n = 1\} = \mu_n. \tag{4.3}$$

Then for $n \geq 0$

$$\mathbf{P}\{\mathbf{X}_1 = 1, \ldots, \mathbf{X}_{n-1} = 1, \mathbf{X}_n = 0\} = \mu_{n-1} - \mu_n = -\Delta\mu_{n-1} \tag{4.4}$$

whence

$$\mathbf{P}\{\mathbf{X}_1 = 1, \ldots, \mathbf{X}_{n-1} = 1, \mathbf{X}_n = 0, \mathbf{X}_{n+1} = 0\} = -\Delta\mu_{n-1} + \Delta\mu_n = (-1)^2\Delta^2\mu_{n-1}. \tag{4.5}$$

Continuing in this way it is seen that the left side in (4.1) is identical with $(-1)^{n-k}\Delta^{n-k}\mu_k$. It follows that these quantities are non-negative. Hence theorem 3.2 guarantees that μ_k is the kth moment of a probability

* Not used in the sequel.

[2] The term *symmetrically dependent* is also in use.

distribution F. The assertion (4.1) is now contained in (3.2), and (4.2) is equivalent with (4.1) because there are $\binom{n}{k}$ ways in which k successes can occur in n trials. ▶

Generalizations. The theorem carries over in an obvious way to random variables assuming a *finite* number of values only. For example, if the $\mathbf{X}_j$ range over the values a_1, a_2, a_3, we may define new variables by $\mathbf{Y}_j = 0$ if $\mathbf{X}_j$ equals a_1 and $\mathbf{Y}_j = 1$ otherwise. The theorem applies to $\{\mathbf{Y}_j\}$, and a repeated application of this procedure leads to an analogue of (4.1). This argument leads to the conjecture that the most general symmetrically dependent sequence $\{\mathbf{X}_j\}$ is obtained by randomization of a parameter from a sequence of independent variables. Individual cases are not difficult to treat, but the general problem presents the inherent difficulty that "parameters" are not well defined and may be chosen in weird ways. A version of the theorem has been proved nevertheless in very great generality.[3]

The theorem makes it possible to apply laws of large numbers and the central limit theorem to exchangeable variables. (See problem 17 in VIII,10.)

The next example shows that in individual cases the theorem may lead to surprising results. The other examples show that the theorem fails for finite sequences.

Examples. (*a*) *In Polya's urn model* of **1**; V,2 an urn contains originally b black and r red balls. After each drawing the ball is returned and c balls of the color drawn are added to the urn. Thus the probability of a black ball in each of the first n drawings equals

$$(4.6)\quad \mu_n = \frac{b(b+c)\cdots(b+(n-1)c)}{(b+r)\cdots(b+r+(n-1)c)} = \frac{\Gamma\left(\frac{b}{c}+n\right)\Gamma\left(\frac{b+r}{c}\right)}{\Gamma\left(\frac{b+r}{c}+n\right)\Gamma\left(\frac{b}{c}\right)}.$$

Put $\mathbf{X}_n = 1$ or 0 according as the nth drawing results in black or red. The easy calculation in **1**; V,2 shows that these variables are exchangeable and hence μ_n represents the nth moment of a distribution F. The appearance of (4.6) reminds one of the beta integral II,(2.5), and inspection shows that *F is the beta distribution* II,(4.2) *with parameters* $\mu = b/c$ and $\nu = r/c$. Again using the beta integral it is seen that (4.1) agrees with **1**; V,(2.3), and (4.2) with **1**; V,(2.4).

[3] E. Hewitt and L. J. Savage, *Symmetric measures on Cartesian products*, Trans. Amer. Math. Soc., vol. 80 (1956) pp. 470–501. A martingale treatment is found in Loève (1963). See also H. Bühlmann, *Austauschbare stochastische Variabeln und ihre Grenzwertsätze*, Univ. of California Publications in Statistics, vol. 3, No. 1 (1960) pp. 1–36.

(*b*) Consider the 6 distinguishable distributions of 2 balls in 3 cells and attribute probability $\frac{1}{6}$ to each. Let $\mathbf{X}_i$ equal 1 or 0 according as the cell number i is occupied or empty. The variables are exchangeable but the theorem does not apply. Indeed, from (4.3) we get $\mu_0 = 1$, $\mu_1 = \frac{1}{2}$, $\mu_2 = \frac{1}{6}$, $\mu_3 = 0$ and here the sequence stops. If it were the beginning of a completely monotone sequence $\{\mu_n\}$ we would have $\mu_4 = \mu_5 = \cdots = 0$. But then $\Delta^4\mu_1 = -\frac{1}{6} < 0$ against the rule.

(*c*) Let $\mathbf{X}_1, \ldots, \mathbf{X}_n$ be independent with a common distribution and $\mathbf{S}_n = \mathbf{X}_1 + \cdots + \mathbf{X}_n$. Put $\mathbf{Y}_k = \mathbf{X}_k - n^{-1}\mathbf{S}_n$ for $k = 1, \ldots, n-1$. The variables $(\mathbf{Y}_1, \ldots, \mathbf{Y}_{n-1})$ are exchangeable but their joint distribution is not of the form suggested by de Finetti's theorem. ▶

*5. GENERALIZED TAYLOR FORMULA AND SEMI-GROUPS

We saw that the Bernstein polynomials appearing in example (1.*a*) may be rewritten in the form (2.4) using finite differences. A similar rearrangement in example (1.*b*) leads to a fascinating version (due to E. Hille) of Taylor's formula which may serve as an illustration for certain basic facts in semi-group theory. We start from formula (1.5), stating that for any bounded continuous function u on $\overline{0, \infty}$

$$e^{-\lambda\theta}\sum_{k=0}^{\infty} u\left(\frac{k}{\lambda}\right)\frac{(\lambda\theta)^k}{k!} \to u(\theta) \tag{5.1}$$

as $\lambda \to \infty$, uniformly in every finite interval. Expanding $e^{-\lambda\theta}$ into a power series we get for the left side of (5.1) the double series

$$\sum\sum \frac{(\lambda\theta)^{j+k}}{(j+k)!}\binom{j+k}{k}(-1)^j\, u\left(\frac{k}{\lambda}\right). \tag{5.2}$$

It converges absolutely and hence we are free to reorder its terms. Take $j + k = r$ as new summation index and put $\lambda^{-1} = h$. With the notation (1.10) the terms within the bracket add up to $h^r \underset{h}{\Delta^r}\, u(0)$ and thus (5.1) is recast in the form

$$\sum_{r=0}^{\infty} \frac{\theta^r}{r!} \underset{h}{\Delta^r}\, u(0) \to u(\theta) \tag{5.3}$$

where $h \to 0+$. Replacing $u(\theta)$ by $u(t+\theta)$ leads to the relation

$$\sum_{r=0}^{\infty} \frac{\theta^r}{r!} \underset{h}{\Delta^r}\, u(t) \to u(t+\theta), \qquad h \to 0 \tag{5.4}$$

* This section may be omitted at first reading.

which is a replica of Taylor's expansion except that the derivatives are replaced by differences. We considered only values $h > 0$, $\theta > 0$ but the argument applies equally when both h and θ are negative. As the domain of definition of any continuous u may be extended to the whole line we have proved the following

Theorem. *If u is bounded and continuous* (5.4) *holds provided h remains of the same sign as θ. For fixed t the convergence is uniform in every θ finite interval.*

For analytic functions the left side approaches the Taylor series but the theorem applies also to non-differentiable functions. In this sense (5.4) represents a generalization of the Taylor expansion and reveals a new side of its nature.

There is another way of looking at (5.4) which leads to the so-called exponential formula of semi-group theory.[4] (See theorem 2 in X,9.) The left side of (5.4) contains the formal exponential series and it is natural to use it to define an operator $\exp \theta \underset{h}{\Delta}$. The relation (5.4) is then abbreviated to

$$\exp \theta \underset{h}{\Delta}\, u(t) \to u(t+\theta). \tag{5.5}$$

To write it more consistently in terms of operators we introduce the *translation operator*[5] $T(\theta)$ sending u into the function u_t defined by $u_\theta(t) = u(t+\theta)$. Then $T(0) = 1$ is the identity operator and

$$\underset{h}{\Delta} = h^{-1}[T(h) - 1]. \tag{5.6}$$

In operator language (5.4) [or (5.5)] now becomes

$$e^{\theta h^{-1}[T(h)-1]} \to T(\theta). \tag{5.7}$$

The main information conveyed by this formula is that the whole family of operators $T(\theta)$ is determined by the behavior of $T(h)$ for small h.

In retrospect it is now clear that our derivation of (5.7) applies to a much more general class of operators. The left side in (5.1) is simply a linear combination of values of u and may be interpreted as an interpolation formula for u. An analogous interpolatory expression is meaningful for *every* family of operators $\{T(\theta)\}$ defined for $\theta > 0$. Indeed, for fixed θ and $h > 0$ the operator

$$A_h(\theta) = e^{-\theta h^{-1}} \sum_{k=0}^{\infty} \frac{1}{k!}\left(\frac{\theta}{h}\right)^k T(kh) \tag{5.8}$$

[4] The remainder of this section may be omitted at first reading.

[5] In the standard notation of the calculus of finite differences $T(\theta) = E^\theta$, but we conform to the notation used in X,8 for general semi-groups.

is a weighted linear combination of operators $T(kh)$. The weights are given by the Poisson distribution and are such that as $h \to 0$ a neighborhood of θ preponderates, the complement carrying a weight tending to 0. This makes it at least plausible that with any reasonable notion of convergence and continuity we shall have $A_h(\theta) \to T(\theta)$ *for any continuous family of operators* $T(\theta)$. In particular, if the operators $T(\theta)$ form a *semi-group*, one has $T(kh) = (T(h))^k$ and the interpolatory operator $A_h(\theta)$ is the same as appears on the left in (5.7). It is therefore not surprising that the "exponential formula" (5.7) *is generally valid for continuous semi-groups of bounded operators.* We shall return to the proof[6] in X,9.

6. INVERSION FORMULAS FOR LAPLACE TRANSFORMS

As was emphasized repeatedly, the approximation formula (5.1) [see example (1.*b*)] has the following probabilistic content. If **X** is a random variable with a Poisson distribution of expectation $\lambda\theta$ then for large λ the probability of the event $|\mathbf{X} - \lambda\theta| > \lambda\epsilon$ is small. For $\mathbf{P}\{\mathbf{X} \leq \lambda x\}$ we get therefore as $\lambda \to \infty$

$$e^{-\lambda\theta} \sum_{k \leq \lambda x} \frac{(\lambda\theta)^k}{k!} \to \begin{matrix} 0 \\ 1 \end{matrix} \qquad \text{if} \quad \begin{matrix} \theta > x \\ \theta < x. \end{matrix} \tag{6.1}$$

This formula is valid for fixed positive θ and x, and is contained in (5.1) when u is a step function. Its use in analysis will now be illustrated by an application to Laplace transforms, a topic treated systematically in chapter XIII.

Let F be a probability distribution concentrated on $\overline{0, \infty}$. The Laplace transform of F is the function φ defined for $\lambda > 0$ by

$$\varphi(\lambda) = \int_0^\infty e^{-\lambda\theta}\, F\{d\theta\}. \tag{6.2}$$

Obviously the derivatives $\varphi^{(k)}(\lambda)$ exist and are obtained by formal differentiation:

$$(-1)^k\, \varphi^{(k)}(\lambda) = \int_0^\infty e^{-\lambda\theta}\, \theta^k\, F\{d\theta\}. \tag{6.3}$$

[6] This is the proof, due to M. Riesz, given (in slightly greater generality) in E. Hille and R. S. Phillips, *Functional analysis and semi-groups*, AMS Colloquium Publications, vol. 31 (1957) p. 314. Understandably the authors did not consider it helpful to refer to the linear interpolation (5.8) as a Poisson *randomization of the semi-group* parameter or to take Chebyshev's inequality for granted. The probabilistic content was noted by D. G. Kendall. It is fully exploited in K. L. Chung, *On the exponential formulas of semi-group theory*, Math. Scandinavica, vol. 10 (1962) pp. 153–162.

From this identity and (6.1) one sees that at every point of continuity of F

$$\sum_{k\leq\lambda x} \frac{(-1)^k}{k!} \lambda^k \varphi^{(k)}(\lambda) \to F(x). \tag{6.4}$$

This is an *inversion formula* of great use. It shows, in particular, that *a distribution F is uniquely determined by its Laplace transform.*

The same argument leads to a great variety of related inversion formulas applicable under various circumstance. In fact, (1.6) is an inversion formula for Laplace integrals of the form

$$w(\lambda) = \int_0^\infty e^{-\lambda x} u(x)\, dx. \tag{6.5}$$

Formal differentiation can be performed as in (6.3), and (1.6) states that *if u is bounded and continuous, then*

$$\frac{(-1)^{n-1}}{(n-1)!}\left(\frac{n}{\theta}\right)^n w^{(n-1)}\left(\frac{n}{\theta}\right) \to u(\theta) \tag{6.6}$$

uniformly in every finite interval.

[These inversion formulas hold under much wider conditions, but it seemed undesirable at this juncture to weigh down the simplicity of the argument by the ballast of new terminology. An abstract version of (6.6) appears in XIII,9.]

If the distribution F possesses moments $\mu_1, \ldots, \mu_{2n}$ its *Laplace transform satisfies the inequalities*

$$\sum_{k=0}^{2n-1} \frac{(-1)^k \mu_k \lambda^k}{k!} \leq \varphi(\lambda) \leq \sum_{k=0}^{2n} \frac{(-1)^k \mu_k \lambda^k}{k!} \tag{6.7}$$

which are of frequent use. To verify them we start from the well-known inequalities[7]

$$\sum_{k=0}^{2n-1} \frac{(-1)^k t^k}{k!} < e^{-t} < \sum_{k=0}^{2n} \frac{(-1)^k t^k}{k!}, \qquad t > 0. \tag{6.8}$$

Replacing t by λt and integrating with respect to F one gets (6.7). It follows, in particular, that

$$\varphi(\lambda) = \sum_{k=0}^{\infty} \frac{(-1)^k \mu_k \lambda^k}{k!} \tag{6.9}$$

in any interval $0 \leq \lambda < \lambda_0$ *in which the series on the right converges.* It is known from analytic function theory that in this case the series in (6.9) uniquely determines $\varphi(\lambda)$ for *all* $\lambda > 0$, and hence *the moments* $\mu_1, \mu_2, \ldots$ *determine the distribution F uniquely whenever the series in* (6.9) *converges in some interval* $|\lambda| < \lambda_0$. This useful criterion holds also for distributions not concentrated on $\overline{0, \infty}$, but the proof depends on the use of characteristic functions (see XV,4).

[7] Simple differentiation shows by induction that the difference between any two members in (6.8) is a *monotone* function of t.

*7. LAWS OF LARGE NUMBERS FOR IDENTICALLY DISTRIBUTED VARIABLES

Throughout this section we use the notation $\mathbf{S}_n = \mathbf{X}_1 + \cdots + \mathbf{X}_n$. The oldest version of the law of large numbers states that if the $\mathbf{X}_k$ are independent and have a common distribution with expectation μ and finite variance then[8] for fixed $\epsilon > 0$ as $n \to \infty$

$$\mathbf{P}\left\{\left|\frac{\mathbf{S}_n}{n} - \mu\right| > \epsilon\right\} \to 0. \tag{7.1}$$

This chapter started from the remark that (7.1) is contained in Chebyshev's inequality. To obtain sharper results we derive a variant of Chebyshev's inequality applicable even when no expectation exists. Define new random variables $\mathbf{X}_k'$ by truncation of $\mathbf{X}_k$ at an arbitrary, but fixed, level $\pm s$. Thus

$$\mathbf{X}_k' = \begin{matrix} \mathbf{X}_k \\ 0 \end{matrix} \quad \textit{when} \quad \begin{matrix} |\mathbf{X}_k| \leq s \\ |\mathbf{X}_k| > s. \end{matrix} \tag{7.2}$$

Put

$$\mathbf{S}_n' = \mathbf{X}_1' + \cdots + \mathbf{X}_n', \qquad m_n' = \mathbf{E}(\mathbf{S}_n'). \tag{7.3}$$

Then obviously

$$\mathbf{P}\{|\mathbf{S}_n - m_n'| > t\} \leq \mathbf{P}\{|\mathbf{S}_n' - m_n'| > t\} + \mathbf{P}\{\mathbf{S}_n \neq \mathbf{S}_n'\} \tag{7.4}$$

because the event on the left cannot occur unless one of the events on the right occurs. The inequality (7.4) is generally applicable even when the $\mathbf{X}_k$ are not independent. Useful versions are obtained by applying Chebyshev's inequality to the first term on the right. Most important is the special case where the $\mathbf{X}_k$ are independent and identically distributed. Since the variance never exceeds the second moment we get in this case

$$\mathbf{P}\{|\mathbf{S}_n - m_n'| > t\} \leq \frac{n}{t^2}\,\mathbf{E}(\mathbf{X}_j'^2) + n\mathbf{P}\{|\mathbf{X}_j| > s\}. \tag{7.5}$$

The fact that (7.1) holds whenever $\mu = \mathbf{E}(\mathbf{X}_j)$ exists, is an easy consequence of this inequality. This is Khintchine's *law of large numbers*

---

* The topics of this section are related to the oldest probabilistic theory but are of no particular significance in the remainder of this book. They are treated for their historical and methodological interest and because many papers are devoted to a converse of the law of large numbers.

[8] With the notation introduced in VIII,2 the relation (7.1) simplifies to

$$n^{-1}\mathbf{S}_n - \mu \xrightarrow{\mathrm{p}} 0,$$

where $\xrightarrow{\mathrm{p}}$ signifies "tends in probability to."

proved essentially in this form in **1**; X,2. Instead of repeating the proof we give a stronger version that includes the necessary and sufficient condition (7.6) which is obviously satisfied whenever $\mu = \mathbf{E}(\mathbf{X}_j)$ exists.

Theorem 1. (*Weak law of large numbers.*) *Let the* $\mathbf{X}_k$ *be independent with a common distribution F. In order that there exist constants* μ_n *such that*

$$\mathbf{P}\left\{\left|\frac{\mathbf{S}_n}{n} - \mu_n\right| > \epsilon\right\} \to 0 \tag{7.6}$$

it is necessary and sufficient that as $t \to \infty$

$$t[1 - F(t) + F(-t)] \to 0 \qquad t > 0. \tag{7.7}$$

In this case (7.6) *holds with*

$$\mu_n = \int_{-n}^{n} x\, F\{dx\}. \tag{7.8}$$

Proof. (*a*) *Sufficiency*. We use (7.5) with a truncation level $s = n$ and $t = n\epsilon$. Then $m_n' = n\mu_n$ and the probabilities on the left in (7.6) and (7.4) are identical. Denote now the left side in (7.7) by $\tau(t)$. An integration by parts shows that the right side in (7.5) is

$$\leq \frac{4}{n\epsilon^2}\int_0^n \tau(x)\, dx + \tau(n)$$

and (7.7) assures that this quantity tends to zero for every fixed $\epsilon > 0$.

(*b*) *Necessity*. Assume first that F is symmetric. By the symmetrization inequality V,(5.11) in this case

$$\mathbf{P}\{|\mathbf{S}_n| \geq \eta n\} \geq \tfrac{1}{2}(1 - e^{-\tau(\eta n)/\eta}).$$

Because of symmetry we need consider (7.6) only with $\mu_n = 0$. Then the left side must tend to 0 as $n \to \infty$ and thus (7.7) is necessary when F is symmetric. If F is unsymmetric the symmetrization inequality V,(5.6) shows that (7.6) holds also for the symmetrized distribution ${}^0F$ and hence $t[1 - {}^0F(t) + {}^0F(t)] \to 0$. The symmetrization inequality V,(5.7) shows that this implies (7.7) and the theorem is proved. ▶

Example. Let F be a symmetric distribution. The law of large numbers does *not* hold if $1 - F(x) \sim x^{-1}$ (as in the Cauchy distribution) but *does* hold if $1 - F(x) \sim (x \log x)^{-1}$. ▶

When F has an expectation μ then $\mu_n \to \mu$ and (7.6) is equivalent with (7.1). On the other hand, $\mu = \lim \mu_n$ can exist also in the absence of an expectation; for example, $\mu_n \to 0$ whenever F is symmetric. Thus *the weak law in its classical form* (7.1) *applies also to certain variables without expectation.* In such cases the left side in (7.1) will be small for each individual large number n, but we show that nevertheless the sequence of averages $\mathbf{S}_n/n$ is certain to contain infinitely many terms falling outside any preassigned finite interval. This observation (due to Kolmogorov) proves that the character of the chance fluctuations is strongly influenced by the existence of an expectation.

Theorem 2. (*Strong law of large numbers and converse.*) *Let the* $\mathbf{X}_k$ *be independent with a common distribution F. If they have an expectation* μ *then* $n^{-1}\mathbf{S}_n \to \mu$ *with probability one. Otherwise the sequence* $\{n^{-1}\mathbf{S}_n\}$ *is unbounded with probability one.*

Proof. (*a*) For discrete distributions the first part is contained in the theorem of **1**; X,7. The same proof applies to arbitrary distributions and will be repeated in a strengthened version in the next section.

(*b*) If the numbers a_n remain bounded, the same is true of their differences $a_n - a_{n-1}$. For the second part of the theorem it suffices therefore to prove that in the absence of an expectation there is probability one that with arbitrary $a > 0$ the event $\{|\mathbf{X}_n| > an\}$ will take place for infinitely many n. By the second Borel-Cantelli lemma [see **1**; VIII,3] this is the case iff

$$\sum_{n=1}^{\infty} \mathbf{P}\{|\mathbf{X}_n| > an\} = \infty. \tag{7.9}$$

For fixed k the interval $ak < x < a(k+1)$ contributes to the left side only if $n \le k$; the series on the left therefore equals

$$\sum_{k=1}^{\infty} k \int_{ak<|x|\le a(k+1)} F\{dx\} \ge \frac{1}{2a}\sum_{k=1}^{\infty}\int_{ak<|x|<a(k+1)} |x|\, F\{dx\} = \frac{1}{2a}\int_{|x|>a} |x|\, F\{dx\}.$$

The last integral diverges by assumption, and so (7.9) is true. ►

The law of large numbers is violated in the *St. Petersburg game* of **1**; X,4, and yet a slightly modified law was seen to apply. The following theroem generalizes this example and has the same intuitive interpretation.

Theorem 3. *Let the* $\mathbf{X}_k$ *be independent positive variables with a common distribution F [such that* $F(0) = 0$*]. In order that there exist constants* a_n *such that*

$$\mathbf{P}\left\{\left|\frac{\mathbf{S}_n}{a_n} - 1\right| > \epsilon\right\} \to 0 \tag{7.10}$$

it is necessary and sufficient that[9] *as* $t \to \infty$

$$\frac{1}{t[1-F(t)]}\int_0^t x\, F\{dx\} \to \infty. \tag{7.11}$$

Needless to say, (7.10) implies $a_n \to \infty$.

[9] It will be seen in VIII,8 that (7.11) is equivalent to *regular variation of* $1 - F(x)$ *with exponent* -1. (The use of this would simplify the proofs.) The relation (7.10) states that $a_n^{-1}S_n \xrightarrow{p} 1$.

Proof. (*a*) *Sufficiency.* For arbitrary η_n with $0 < \eta_n < 1$ define first ρ_n and then a_n by

$$\eta_n = n[1 - F(\rho_n)], \qquad a_n = n\int_0^{\rho_n} x\, F\{dx\}. \tag{7.12}$$

Assuming (7.11) we have $\eta_n \rho_n a_n^{-1} \to 0$ and hence it is possible to choose $\eta_n \to 0$ such that $a_n \rho_n^{-1} \to \infty$. With this sequence we use the truncation (7.2) at the level $s = \rho_n$ and get from (7.5)

$$\begin{aligned} \mathbf{P}\{|\mathbf{S}_n - a_n| > \epsilon a_n\} &\le \frac{n}{\epsilon^2 a_n^{\ 2}} \int_0^{\rho_n} x^2\, F\{dx\} + n[1 - F(\rho_n)] \\ &\le \frac{\rho_n}{\epsilon^2 a_n} + \eta_n \to 0 \end{aligned} \tag{7.13}$$

and so (7.10) is true.

(*b*) Assume (7.10) and put

$$\eta_n = n[1 - F(2a_n)], \qquad \mu_n = n\int_0^{2a_n} x\, F\{dx\}. \tag{7.14}$$

We use the truncation (7.2) with $s = 2a_n$. From (7.5) we get then by the estimates used in (7.13)

$$\mathbf{P}\{|\mathbf{S}_n - \mu_n| > \epsilon a_n\} < \frac{2}{\epsilon^2}\frac{\mu_n}{a_n} + \eta_n. \tag{7.15}$$

The variables $\mathbf{X}_k$ being positive, the relation (7.10) cannot hold unless the probability $F^n(2a_n)$ that all n variables $\mathbf{X}_1, \ldots, \mathbf{X}_n$ be $\le 2a_n$ tends to 1. This implies that $\eta_n \to 0$. It is now obvious that (7.15) would contradict the assumption (7.10) if the ratios μ_n/a_n did not remain bounded away from 0. Thus the ratios $\mu_n/(a_n\eta_n)$ tend to infinity which means that (7.11) holds when t runs through $a_1, a_2, \ldots$. But from (7.10) it is easily seen that $a_{n+1}/a_n \to 1$ and hence (7.11) holds for any approach $t \to \infty$. ▶

*8. STRONG LAWS FOR MARTINGALES

The strong law of large numbers for discrete random variables was discussed at length in **1**; X,7, and the arguments used carry over without change to the present more general situation. Rather than indulge in a mechanical repetition of the theory we shall extend it from sums of independent variables to martingales. This complicates the situation conceptually, but it simplifies the calculations and yields better results.

Assume that $\mathbf{E}(\mathbf{X}_j) = 0$ exists and put

$$\mathbf{S}_n = \mathbf{X}_1 + \cdots + \mathbf{X}_n. \tag{8.1}$$

$$\mathbf{M}_n = \max\,[|\mathbf{S}_1|, \ldots, |\mathbf{S}_n|]. \tag{8.2}$$

* Not used in the sequel.

It will be recalled that the analysis of **1**; X,7 depended largely on Kolmogorov's inequality. For independent variables with zero expectations and finite variances this inequality states that

$$\mathbf{P}\{\mathbf{M}_n > t\} \le \frac{\mathbf{E}(\mathbf{S}_n^{\,2})}{t^2}, \qquad t > 0. \tag{8.3}$$

This is a considerable strengthening of Chebyshev's inequality which gives the same estimate for the tail of the distribution of $|\mathbf{S}_n|$. A perusal of the proof in **1**; IX,7 shows that it does not use the independence of the variables $\mathbf{X}_j$ but only the fact that the sequence $\{\mathbf{X}_n\}$ is *absolutely fair*, that is,

$$\mathbf{E}(\mathbf{X}_n \mid \mathbf{X}_1, \ldots, \mathbf{X}_{n-1}) = 0 \tag{8.4}$$

for $n = 2, 3, \ldots$. As was shown in VI,12 the partial sums $\{\mathbf{S}_n\}$ of such a sequence form a *martingale*, and all martingales are obtained in this way. We now state

Kolmogorov's inequality for martingales. *If* $\{\mathbf{X}_n\}$ *is absolutely fair and* $\mathbf{S}_n$ *is defined by* (8.1), *then the inequality* (8.3) *holds.*

We can go a step further and note that the proof does not even depend on $\{\mathbf{S}_n\}$ being a strict martingale. All that really matters is that the variables $\mathbf{Y}_n = \mathbf{S}_n^{\,2}$ form a *submartingale*, that is, the inequalities

$$\mathbf{E}(\mathbf{Y}_n \mid \mathbf{Y}_1, \ldots, \mathbf{Y}_{n-1}) \ge \mathbf{Y}_{n-1} \tag{8.5}$$

are satisfied.[10] We now prove a version of Kolmogorov's inequality for arbitrary submartingales. (It is an instructive exercise to verify that the following proof differs only notationally from the proof in **1**; IX,7.)

Kolmogorov's inequality for submartingales. *Let* $\{\mathbf{Y}_n\}$ *be a sequence of variables for which* (8.5) *holds and* $\mathbf{Y}_j \ge 0$ *for all* j. *Then for* $x > 0$

$$\mathbf{P}\{\max\,[\mathbf{Y}_1, \ldots, \mathbf{Y}_n] > x\} \le \frac{\mathbf{E}(\mathbf{Y}_n)}{x}. \tag{8.6}$$

(The martingale inequality (8.3) is obtained by letting $\mathbf{Y}_j = \mathbf{S}_j^{\,2}$ and $x = t^2$.)

---

[10] $u(x) = x^2$ is a convex function, and therefore $\{\mathbf{S}_n^{\,2}\}$ is a submartingale whenever $\{\mathbf{S}_n\}$ is a martingale. In the special case of independent variables with $\mathbf{E}(\mathbf{X}_j) = 0$, $\mathbf{E}(\mathbf{X}_j^{\,2}) = \sigma_j^{\,2}$ we have trivially

$$\mathbf{E}(\mathbf{S}_n^{\,2} \mid \mathbf{S}_1^{\,2}, \ldots, \mathbf{S}_{n-1}^2) = \mathbf{E}((\mathbf{X}_n + \mathbf{S}_{n-1})^2) \mid \mathbf{S}_{n-1}^2) = \sigma_n^{\,2} + \mathbf{S}_{n-1}^2.$$

Proof. For fixed $x > 0$ denote by $\mathbf{K}$ the *smallest* subscript $j \leq n$ such *that* $\mathbf{Y}_j > x$, and put $\mathbf{K} = 0$ if no such event occurs. Then $\mathbf{K}$ is a random variable with possible values $0, 1, \ldots, n$ and

$$\mathbf{P}\{\max[\mathbf{Y}_1, \ldots, \mathbf{Y}_n] > x\} = \mathbf{P}\{\mathbf{K} \neq 0\} = \sum_{j=1}^{n} \mathbf{P}\{\mathbf{K} = j\}. \tag{8.7}$$

Now

$$\mathbf{E}(\mathbf{Y}_n) = \sum_{j=0}^{n} \mathbf{E}(\mathbf{Y}_n \mid \mathbf{K} = j) \cdot \mathbf{P}\{\mathbf{K} = j\}. \tag{8.8}$$

The jth term equals the integral of $\mathbf{Y}_n$ extended over the event $\{\mathbf{K} = j\}$ (integration being with respect to the distribution of $(\mathbf{Y}_1, \ldots, \mathbf{Y}_n)$). For $j > 0$ the event $\{\mathbf{K} = j\}$ depends only on $\mathbf{Y}_1, \ldots, \mathbf{Y}_j$, and so the integrand $\mathbf{Y}_n$ may be replaced by $\mathbf{E}(\mathbf{Y}_n \mid \mathbf{Y}_1, \ldots, \mathbf{Y}_j)$ by the very definition of conditional expectations. This integrand is $\geq \mathbf{Y}_j > x$ in consequence of (8.5) and the definition of $\mathbf{K}$. Thus for $j > 0$ the jth term of the last sum is at least $x \cdot \mathbf{P}\{\mathbf{K} = j\}$, and the truth of (8.6) is now evident on comparing (8.7) with (8.8). ▶

As a first application we prove a theorem of surprisingly wide applicability. It covers partial sums (8.1) of arbitrary absolutely fair sequences $\{\mathbf{X}_n\}$.

Theorem 1. *Martingale convergence theorem.*[11] *Let* $\{\mathbf{S}_n\}$ *be a martingale defined on some probability space. If* $\mathbf{E}(\mathbf{S}_n^2) \leq \mathbf{M} < \infty$ *for all* n *there exists a random variable* $\mathbf{Y}$ *such that* $\mathbf{S}_n \to \mathbf{Y}$ *on a set of probability one.*

Proof. We begin by observing that on account of the submartingale property the sequence of expectations $\mathbf{E}(\mathbf{S}_n^2)$ is non-decreasing. The boundedness assumption is therefore equivalent to

$$\mathbf{E}(\mathbf{S}_n^2) \to \mu < \infty. \tag{8.9}$$

By Kolmogorov's inequality for martingales

$$\begin{aligned} &\mathbf{P}\{|\mathbf{S}_{m+k} - \mathbf{S}_m| > t \textit{ for some } k \leq n\} \leq \\ &\qquad \leq \frac{\mathbf{E}((\mathbf{S}_{m+n} - \mathbf{S}_m)^2)}{t^2} = \frac{\mathbf{E}(\mathbf{S}_{m+n}^2) - \mathbf{E}(\mathbf{S}_m^2)}{t^2}. \end{aligned} \tag{8.10}$$

[11] The theorem remains true under the sole assumption that $\mathbf{E}(|\mathbf{S}_n|)$ remains bounded. See the books by Doob, Loève, or Neveu.

[For the last equality recall that $\mathbf{E}(\mathbf{S}_{m+n}\mathbf{S}_m \mid \mathbf{S}_m) = \mathbf{S}_m^2$.] In view of (8.9) the right side in (8.10) is $<\epsilon$ for $m > m_0$ and all n. We may therefore let $n \to \infty$ in (8.10) and conclude that the set of points in sample space at which $|\mathbf{S}_{m+k} - \mathbf{S}_m| > t$ for some k and $m > m_0$ has probability $<\epsilon/t^2$. As ϵ is arbitrary it follows that the set of points at which $\{\mathbf{S}_m\}$ is not a Cauchy sequence has probability zero. ►

Examples. (*a*) *Polya's urn scheme* was treated in examples VI,(12.*b*) and above in (4.*a*). If $\mathbf{Y}_n$ is the proportion of black balls at the nth trial it was shown that $\{\mathbf{Y}_n\}$ is a martingale and we see now that a limit $\mathbf{Y} = \lim \mathbf{Y}_n$ exists with probability one. On the other hand, the probability of a black ball at the nth trial is obtained by randomization of the binomial distribution. Thus, if $\mathbf{S}_n$ is the total number of black balls drawn in the first n trials the distribution of $n^{-1}\mathbf{S}_n$ tends to the beta distribution F found in example (4.*a*). It follows that the limit variable $\mathbf{Y}$ has the beta distribution F.

(*b*) *Branching processes.* In the branching process described in **1**; XII,5 the population size $\mathbf{X}_n$ in the nth generation has the expectation $\mathbf{E}(\mathbf{X}_n) = \mu^n$ [see **1**; XII,(5.3)]. Given that the $(n-1)$th generation consisted of ν individuals, the (conditional) expectation of $\mathbf{X}_n$ becomes $\mu\nu$, and this independently of the size of the preceding generations. Thus, if we put $\mathbf{S}_n = \mathbf{X}_n/\mu^n$ the sequence $\{\mathbf{S}_n\}$ forms a martingale. It is not difficult to establish that if $\mathbf{E}(\mathbf{X}_1^2) < \infty$ then $\mathbf{E}(\mathbf{S}_n^2)$ remains bounded (see problem 7 of **1**; XII,6). We thus have the striking result that $\mathbf{S}_n$ converges with probability one to a limit $\mathbf{S}_\infty$. This implies, in particular, that the distribution of $\mathbf{S}_n$ tends to the distribution of $\mathbf{S}_\infty$. These results are due to T. E. Harris.

(*c*) *Harmonic functions.* For clarity we describe a specific example, although the following argument applies to more general Markov chains and concordant functions [example VI,(12.*c*)].

Let D denote the unit disk of points $x = (x_1, x_2)$ such that $x_1^2 + x_2^2 \leq 1$. For any point $x \in D$ let C_x be the largest circle centered at x and contained in D. We consider a Markov process $\{\mathbf{Y}_n\}$ in D defined as follows. Given that $\mathbf{Y}_n = x$ the variable $\mathbf{Y}_{n+1}$ is uniformly distributed on the circle C_x; the initial position $\mathbf{Y}_0 = y$ is assumed known. The transition probabilities are given by a stochastic kernel K which for fixed x is concentrated on C_x and reduces there to the uniform distribution. A function u in D is concordant if $u(x)$ equals the average of the value of u on C_x. Consider now a harmonic function u that is continuous on the *closed* disk D. Then $\{u(\mathbf{Y}_n)\}$ is a bounded martingale and hence $\mathbf{Z} = \lim u(\mathbf{Y}_n)$ exists with probability one. Since the coordinate variables x_j are harmonic functions it follows that with probability one $\mathbf{Y}_n$ tends to a limit $\mathbf{Y} \in D$.

It is easily seen that the process cannot converge to an interior point of D, and hence with probability one $\mathbf{Y}_n$ *tends to a point* $\mathbf{Y}$ *on the boundary of* D.

An extension of arguments of this sort is used for the study of asymptotic properties of Markov processes, and also to prove general theorems concerning harmonic functions, such as Fatou's theorem concerning the existence almost everywhere of radial boundary values.[12] ►

The next theorem generalizes the Kolmogorov criterion of **1**; X,7 in two directions; it applies to martingales rather than to independent variables and it uses arbitrary coefficients b_k.

Theorem 2. *Let* $\{\mathbf{X}_k\}$ *satisfy* (8.4) *and define the* $\{\mathbf{S}_n\}$ *by* (8.1). *If* $b_1 < b_2 < \cdots \to \infty$ *and*

$$\sum b_k^{-2}\,\mathbf{E}(\mathbf{X}_k^2) < \infty \tag{8.11}$$

then with probability one,

$$b_n^{-1}\,\mathbf{S}_n \to 0 \tag{8.12}$$

and the variables

$$\mathbf{Y}_n = \sum_{k=1}^{n} b_k^{-1}\mathbf{X}_k. \tag{8.13}$$

converge.

Proof. Clearly $\{\mathbf{Y}_n\}$ is a martingale and the analogue to the estimate applied for the right side in (8.10) shows that $\mathbf{E}(\mathbf{Y}_n^2)$ is bounded by the series in (8.11). By theorem 1, therefore, the sequence $\{\mathbf{Y}_n\}$ converges with probability one, and the relation (8.12) is true at each point of the sample space where $\{\mathbf{Y}_n\}$ converges.[13] This completes the proof. ►

As a corollary we get the *law of large numbers for martingales: if* $\Sigma n^{-2}\mathbf{E}(\mathbf{X}_n^2) < \infty$ *then* $n^{-1}\mathbf{S}_n \to 0$ *with probability one.* In the special case of independent random variables $\mathbf{X}_k$ with a common distribution the truncation described in **1**; X,7 leads to the stronger result that $n^{-1}\mathbf{S}_n \to 0$ *with probability one whenever* $\mathbf{E}(\mathbf{X}_k) = 0$.

---

[12] M. Brelot and J. L. Doob, *Limites angulaires et limites fines*, Ann. Inst. Fourier, vol. 13(1963) pp. 395–415.

[13] This assertion is known as *Kronecker's lemma*. It asserts that the convergence of $\Sigma\, b_k^{-1}x_k$ implies that $(x_1 + \cdots + x_n)b_n^{-1} \to 0$. For a proof denote the remainders of the series by ρ_n. Then $x_n = b_n(\rho_{n-1} - \rho_n)$ and hence

$$\frac{x_1 + \cdots + x_n}{b_n} = -\rho_n + \frac{1}{b_n}\sum_{k=0}^{n-1} \rho_k(b_{k+1} - b_k). \tag{*}$$

Suppose $|\rho_k| < \epsilon$ for $k \geq r$. Since $b_n \to \infty$ the contribution of the first r terms tends to 0. Because of the monotonicity of $\{b_n\}$ the terms with $k > r$ contribute $< \epsilon(b_n - b_r)b_n^{-1} \leq \epsilon$.

9. PROBLEMS FOR SOLUTION

1. If u is bounded and continuous on $\overline{0, \infty}$ then as $n \to \infty$

$$\sum_{k=0}^{\infty} \binom{n+k}{k} \frac{t^k}{(1+t)^{n+k+1}} u\left(\frac{k}{n+1}\right) \to u(t)$$

uniformly in every finite interval.

Hint: Remember the "negative binomial" distribution of **1**; VI,8. No calculation necessary.

2. If u has a continuous derivative u', the derivative $B'_{n,u}$ of $B_{n,u}$ tends uniformly to u'.

3. *Bernstein polynomials in* $\mathfrak{R}^2$. If $u(x, y)$ is continuous in the triangle $x \geq 0$, $y \geq 0$, $x+y \leq 1$, then uniformly

$$\sum u\left(\frac{j}{n}, \frac{k}{n}\right) \frac{n!}{j!\,k!\,(n-j-k)!} x^j y^k (1-x-y)^{n-j-k} \to u(x, y).$$

4. A function u continuous in $\overline{0, 1}$ can be uniformly approximated by polynomials of even degree. If $u(0) = 0$ the same is true for polynomials of odd degree.[14]

5. If u is continuous in the interval $\overline{0, \infty}$ and $u(\infty)$ exists, it can be approximated uniformly by linear combinations of e^{-nx}.

6. For the three moment sequences given below find the probabilities $p_k^{(n)}$ of (3.4). Find the corresponding probability distribution F using the limit relation (3.6).

(*a*) $\mu_n = p^n$ where $0 < p < 1$, (*b*) $\mu_n = \dfrac{1}{n+1}$,

(*c*) $\mu_n = \dfrac{2}{n+2}$.

7.[15] Let p be a polynomial of degree ν. Show that $\underset{h}{\Delta}^n p$ vanishes identically when $n > \nu$. Conclude that $B_{n,p}$ is a polynomial of degree $\leq \nu$ (despite its formal appearance as polynomial of degree $n > \nu$).

8. Show that when F has a density (6.4) can be derived by integration from (6.6).

---

[14] A famous theorem due to Müntz asserts that uniform approximation is possible in terms of linear combinations of $1, x^{n_1}, x^{n_2}, \ldots$ iff $\Sigma\, n_k^{-1}$ diverges.

[15] The use of this result leads to a considerable simplification of the classical solution of the moment problem (for example in the book by Shohat and Tamarkin). This solution is as follows. For a polynomial $p(x) = p_0 + \cdots + p_\nu x^\nu$ put $\mathbf{E}(p) = p_0\mu_0 + \cdots + p_\nu\mu_\nu$ where μ_k are the presumed moments. This $\mathbf{E}(p)$ is a linear functional on the polynomials in $\overline{0,1}$. Problem 7 shows easily that $0 \leq p \leq 1$ implies $0 \leq \mathbf{E}(p) \leq 1$ and hence the functional $\mathbf{E}$ can be extended to all continuous functions by uniform convergence. The Riesz representation theorem of IV,5 now shows that the μ_k are indeed moments of a probability distribution.

9. *Law of large numbers for stationary sequences.* Let $\{\mathbf{X}_k\}$ $(k = 0, \pm 1, \pm 2, \ldots)$ be a stationary sequence and define the $\mathbf{X}_k'$ by truncation as in (7.2). If $\mathbf{E}(\mathbf{X}_k) = 0$ and $\mathbf{E}(\mathbf{X}_0'\mathbf{X}_n') \to 0$ as $n \to \infty$ then $\mathbf{P}\{n^{-1}\,|\mathbf{X}_1 + \cdots + \mathbf{X}_n| > \epsilon\} \to 0$.

10. The $\mathbf{X}_k$ are independent with distributions F_k and have their medians at the origin. Define $\mathbf{X}_k'$ by truncation [as in (7.2)] at the level $s = a_n$. If

$$\sum_1^n \mathbf{P}\{\,|\mathbf{X}_k| > a_n\} \to 0$$

and

$$\sum_1^n \mathbf{E}(\mathbf{X}_k') \to 0$$

then

$$\mathbf{P}\left\{\left|\, \mathbf{S}_n - \sum_1^n \mathbf{E}(\mathbf{X}_k') \right| > \epsilon\right\} \to 0.$$

11. Generalize the variant of Chebyshev's inequality in example V,(7.*a*) to martingales.[16]

[16] A. W. Marshall, *A one-sided analog of Kolmogorov's inequality*, Ann. Math. Statist., vol. 31(1960) pp. 483–487.

CHAPTER VIII

The Basic Limit Theorems

The main results of this chapter are found in sections 1, 3, and 6. Sections 4, 5, and 7 may be considered as sources of interesting examples. These are chosen because of their importance in other contexts.

The last two sections are devoted to regularly varying functions in the sense of Karamata. This interesting theory steadily gains in importance, but it is not accessible in textbooks and has not been adapted to distribution functions. A tremendous amount of disconnected calculation in probability can be saved by exploiting the asymptotic relations in section 9. They are of a technical nature in contrast to the simple section 8.

1. CONVERGENCE OF MEASURES

The following theory is independent of the number of dimensions. For convenience of expression the text refers to one-dimensional distributions, but with the conventions of III, 5 the formulas apply without change in higher dimensions.

Two examples are typical for the phenomena with which we have to cope.

Examples. (*a*) Consider an arbitrary probability distribution F and put $F_n(x) = F(x-n^{-1})$. At a point x at which F is continuous we have $F_n(x) \to F(x)$, but at points of discontinuity $F_n(x) \to F(x-)$. We shall nevertheless agree to say that the sequence $\{F_n\}$ converges to F.

(*b*) This time we put $F_n(x) = F(x+n)$ where F is a continuous distribution function. Now $F_n(x) \to 1$ for all x: a limit exists, but is not a probability distribution function. Similarly, if $F_n(x) = F(n^{-1}x)$, then $F_n(x) \to F(0)$. In such cases we shall speak of improper convergence.

(*c*) In theorem 1 of VII,3 we had to deal with distribution functions F_n and F such that $F_n(x) \to F(x)$ at each point x where F is continuous, but not necessarily at other points. Formula VII,(6.1) exhibits the same phenomenon with F concentrated at a single point.

Basic Notions and Notations

It will be necessary to distinguish three classes of continuous functions. In one dimension[1] $C(-\infty, \infty)$ is the class of all bounded continuous functions; $C[-\infty, \infty]$ is the subclass of functions with finite limits $u(-\infty)$ and $u(\infty)$; finally, $C_0(-\infty, \infty)$ is the subclass of functions "*vanishing at infinity*," that is, where $u(\pm\infty) = 0$.

We shall say that I is an *interval of continuity* for the probability distribution F if I is open and its endpoints are not atoms.[2] The whole line counts as an interval of continuity. Throughout this section we use the abbreviations

$$(1.1) \qquad \mathbf{E}_n(u) = \int_{-\infty}^{+\infty} u(x)\, F_n\{dx\}, \qquad \mathbf{E}(u) = \int_{-\infty}^{+\infty} u(x)\, F\{dx\}.$$

Except for section 9 we shall in this chapter consider only sequences of probability distributions, but the following definition applies to arbitrary measures[3] F_n.

Definition 1. *We say that the sequence $\{F_n\}$ converges to F, and write $F_n \to F$, iff*

$$(1.2) \qquad F_n\{I\} \to F\{I\}$$

for every bounded interval of continuity of F.

Suppose that the F_n are proper probability distributions and $F_n \to F$. Then $F\{I\} \leq 1$ for every bounded interval and hence F is a proper or defective probability distribution. For a defective distribution F the relation (1.2) does not hold when I is the entire line. On the other hand, if the limit F is proper then (1.2) holds also for every unbounded interval of continuity I. Indeed, under any circumstances

$$(1.3) \qquad \liminf F_n\{I\} \geq F\{I\}$$

[1] For the analogue in higher dimensions note that in one dimension $C[-\infty, \infty]$ is simply the class of continuous functions on the compactified line obtained by adding $\pm\infty$ to $\mathcal{R}^1$. For $C[-\infty, \infty]$ in $\mathcal{R}^2$ both axes are so extended, and this requires the existence of limits $u(x, \pm\infty)$ and $u(\pm\infty, x)$ for each number x. In itself this class is not very interesting, but distribution functions belong to it. For $C_0(-\infty, \infty)$ it is required that $u(x, \pm\infty) = u(\pm\infty, x) = 0$.

[2] In higher dimensions it is required that the boundary of I has probability zero.

[3] For readers interested in general measure theory we remark the following. The definitions and the theorem of this section apply without change to arbitrary locally compact spaces provided "interval of continuity" is replaced by "open set whose boundary has measure zero." To bounded intervals there correspond subsets of compacts sets. Finally, C_0 is the class of continuous functions vanishing at infinity, that is, $u \in C_0$ iff u is continuous and $|u| < \epsilon$ outside some compact set. The other classes play no role in this section.

(which becomes obvious on replacing I by a bounded subinterval of continuity J such that $F\{J\}$ differs from $F\{I\}$ by less than a preassigned ϵ). When F is proper the relation (1.3) for the complement I' of I states that

$$\limsup F_n\{I\} \leq F\{I\}, \tag{1.4}$$

and so (1.2) is true. We combine this important result with

Definition 2. *The sequence* $\{F_n\}$ *of probability distributions converges properly to* F *iff* $F_n \to F$ *and* F *is a proper probability distribution.*

This is the case iff (1.2) *holds for every* (*bounded or unbounded*) *interval of continuity for* F.

Choosing $I = \overline{-\infty, x}$ it is seen that[4] *if* $F_n \to F$ *properly then* $F_n(x) \to F(x)$ *at each point of continuity of* F.

Instead of $F_n \to F$ we write also $F = \lim F_n$. For stylistic clarity we speak sometimes of *improper convergence* to indicate that the limit F is defective.

The following theorem is basic. It restates the definition of convergence in terms of expectations and, at the same time, it provides a criterion for the convergence of a sequence of distributions.

Theorem. *Let* $\{F_n\}$ *be a sequence of proper probability distributions.*

(*a*) *In order that there exists a proper or defective distribution* F *such that* $F_n \to F$ *it is necessary and sufficient that the sequence of expectations* $\mathbf{E}_n(u)$ *converges for each* $u \in C_0(-\infty, \infty)$. *In this case*

$$\mathbf{E}_n(u) \to \mathbf{E}(u) \tag{1.5}$$

for $u \in C_0(-\infty, \infty)$.

(*b*) *If the convergence is proper* (1.5) *holds for all* $u \in C(-\infty, \infty)$.

Note on terminology. If (1.5) holds for all u of a certain class one says that F_n converges to F weakly with respect to that class. Thus our $F_n \to F$ can be described as weak convergence with respect to $C_0(-\infty, \infty)$. This definition of convergence has the advantage that it applies also in arbitrary probability spaces, but our elementary definition is more intuitive. [Needless to say, all these notions apply to arbitrary bounded measures and the norming is introduced only for convenience.]

Proof. (i) Let u be a bounded continuous function, say $|u| \leq 1$. Suppose $F_n \to F$ *properly*. To given $\epsilon > 0$ choose a bounded interval of continuity

---

[4] With improper convergence the sequence $\{F_n(x)\}$ need not converge for any x. For example, if $F_n(x) = F(x + (-1)^n n)$, then $F_{2k}(x) \to 1$ and $F_{2k+1}(x) \to 0$ for all x, but $F_n\{I\} \to 0$ for all bounded intervals. A restricted type of improper convergence may be defined by requiring that $F_n(x) \to F(x)$ at all points of continuity.

A for F so large that $F\{A\} > 1 - \epsilon$. Partition A by intervals $I_1, \ldots, I_r$ of continuity so small, that within each u oscillates by less than ϵ. There exists then a function σ vanishing outside A and assuming a constant value on I_k such that $|u(x)-\sigma(x)| < \epsilon$ for $x \in A$. In the complement A' of A we have $|u(x) - \sigma(x)| = |u(x)| \leq 1$. Hence

$$(1.6) \qquad |\mathbf{E}_n(u) - \mathbf{E}_n(\sigma)| \leq \epsilon + F_n\{A'\}$$

$$(1.7) \qquad |\mathbf{E}(u) - \mathbf{E}(\sigma)| \leq \epsilon + F\{A'\} < 2\epsilon.$$

Now $\mathbf{E}_n(\sigma)$ is a fixed linear combination of values $F_n\{I_j\}$, and hence $\mathbf{E}_n(\sigma) \to \mathbf{E}(\sigma)$. Furthermore $F_n\{A'\} \to F\{A'\}$. It follows then from (1.6) and (1.7) that $|\mathbf{E}_n(u) - \mathbf{E}(u)| < 10\epsilon$ for n sufficiently large, and hence (1.5) holds for all $u \in C(-\infty, \infty)$.

In the case of *improper* covergence the argument breaks down because, the complement A' being unbounded, $F_n\{A'\}$ need not converge to $F\{A\}$. In this case, however, we consider only functions vanishing at infinity and we can choose A so large that $|u(x)| < \epsilon$ for $x \in A'$. Then $|u - \sigma| < \epsilon$ everywhere and the left sides in (1.6) and (1.7) are $< \epsilon$. Therefore $\mathbf{E}_n(u) \to \mathbf{E}(u)$ at least for $u \in C_0(-\infty, \infty)$.

(ii) For the sufficiency we anticipate the selection theorem 1 of section 6. (It is quite elementary, but it seemed preferable to discuss it together with variants and other applications.)

According to this theorem every sequence $\{F_n\}$ of probability distributions contains a subsequence converging properly or improperly to a limit F. From (1.5) and the first part of the theorem we conclude that $\mathbf{E}(u)$ coincides with the expectation of u with respect to the limit F. If (1.5) holds no subsequence of $\{F_n\}$ can converge to another limit, and hence $F_n \to F$ as asserted. ▶

Examples. (*d*) *Convergence of moments.* If the distributions F_n are concentrated on $\overline{0, 1}$ the definition of u outside this interval is immaterial and in the wording of the theorem it suffices to assume u continuous in $\overline{0, 1}$. Every such function can be approximated uniformly by polynomials (see VII,2) and hence the theorem may be restated as follows. *A sequence of distributions F_n concentrated on $\overline{0, 1}$ converges to a limit F iff for each k the sequence of moments $\mathbf{E}_n(\mathbf{X}^k)$ converges to a number μ_k. In this case $\mu_k = \mathbf{E}(\mathbf{X}^k)$ is the* kth *moment of F and the convergence is proper because $\mu_0 = 1$.* (See VI,3.)

(*e*) *Convergence of moments* (continued). In general the expectations of F_n need not converge even if $F_n \to F$ properly. For example, if F_n attributes weight n^{-1} to n^2 and weight $1 - n^{-1}$ to the origin, then $\{F_n\}$ converges to the distribution concentrated at the origin, but $\mathbf{E}_n(\mathbf{X}) \to \infty$. We have however, the following useful *criterion. If $F_n \to F$ and for some $\rho > 0$ the expectations $\mathbf{E}_n(|\mathbf{X}|^\rho)$ remain bounded, then F is a proper probability distribution.* Indeed, the contribution of the region $|x| \geq a$ to $\mathbf{E}_n(|\mathbf{X}|^\rho)$ is $\geq a^\rho(1 - F_n\{\overline{-a, a}\})$ and this quantity tends to a limit $\geq a^\rho \eta$ where η is the defect of F. Since a can be chosen arbitarily large we must have $\eta = 0$. A slight sharpening of this argument shows that *the absolute moments $\mathbf{E}_n(|\mathbf{X}|^\alpha)$ of order $\alpha < \rho$ converge to $\mathbf{E}(|\mathbf{X}|^\alpha)$.*

(*f*) *Convergence of densities.* If the probability distributions F_n have densities f_n the latter need not converge even if $F_n \to F$ and F has a continuous density. As an example let $f_n(x) = 1 - \cos 2n\pi x$ for $0 < x < 1$ and $f_n(x) = 0$ elsewhere. Here F_n converges to the uniform distribution with density $f(x) = 1$ for $0 < x < 1$, but f_n does not converge to f. On the other hand, *if $f_n \to f$ and f is a probability density then $F_n \to F$* where F is the proper distribution with density f. Indeed, Fatou's lemma [IV,(2.9)] implies (1.3), and we saw that this in turn implies (1.4) and hence (1.2). ►

In dealing with functions u_t such as $\sin tx$ or $v(t+x)$ depending on a parameter t, it is often useful to know that for n sufficiently large the relation $|\mathbf{E}_n(u_t) - \mathbf{E}(u_t)| < \epsilon$ holds simultaneously for all t. We prove that this is so if the family of functions u_t is *equicontinuous.*[5]

Corollary. *Suppose that $F_n \to F$ properly. Let $\{u_t\}$ be a family of equicontinuous functions depending on the parameter t and such that $|u_t| < M < \infty$ for some M and all t. Then $\mathbf{E}_n(u_t) \to \mathbf{E}(u_t)$ uniformly in t.*

Proof. The proof of (1.5) depended on partitioning the interval A into intervals within each of which u varies by less than ϵ. In the present situation this partition may be chosen independently of t and the assertion becomes obvious. ►

Example. (*g*) Let $u_t(x) = \sin tx$. By the mean value theorem

$$|u_t(x_2) - u_t(x_1)| \leq |t| \cdot |x_2 - x_1|,$$

and so the family is equicontinuous provided t is restricted to a finite interval $\overline{-a, a}$. Therefore $\mathbf{E}_n(u_t) \to \mathbf{E}(u_t)$ uniformly in every finite t-interval. ►

2. SPECIAL PROPERTIES

According to definition 1 of V,2 two distributions U and V are of the same *type* if they differ only by location parameters, that is, if

$$V(x) = U(Ax + B), \qquad A > 0. \tag{2.1}$$

[5] The family is *equicontinuous* if to each $\epsilon > 0$ there corresponds a δ independent of t such that $|u_t(x_2) - u_t(x_1)| < \epsilon$ whenever $|x_2 - x_1| < \delta$.

We now show that convergence is a property of types in the sense that a change of location parameters does not affect the type of the limit distribution. It is this fact which makes it legitimate to speak of an "asymptotically normal sequence" without specifying the appropriate parameters. More precisely we prove

Lemma 1. *Let U and V be two probability distributions neither of which is concentrated at one point. If for a sequence $\{F_n\}$ of probability distributions and constants $a_n > 0$ and $\alpha_n > 0$*

$$F_n(a_nx + b_n) \to U(x), \qquad F_n(\alpha_nx + \beta_n) \to V(x) \tag{2.2}$$

at all points of continuity, then

$$\frac{\alpha_n}{a_n} \to A \neq 0, \qquad \frac{\beta_n - b_n}{a_n} \to B \tag{2.3}$$

and (2.1) *is true. Conversely, if* (2.3) *holds then each of the two relations* (2.2) *implies the other and* (2.1).

[It is essential that none of the distributions be concentrated at one point. For example, let V be concentrated at the origin and $F_n = U$ for all n. The first relation in (2.2) holds with $a_n = 1$ and $b_n = 0$, the second if $\alpha_n \to \infty$ and the β_n remain bounded. Obviously (2.3) need not hold.]

Proof. We begin with the converse part of the lemma. Assume (2.3) and put $y = Ax + B$. Given $\epsilon > 0$ we have for n sufficiently large

$$F_n(a_n(y-\epsilon) + b_n) \leq F_n(\alpha_nx + \beta_n) \leq F_n(a_n(y+\epsilon) + b_n) \tag{2.4}$$

because the arguments satisfy the analogous strict inequalities. It follows that the first relation in (2.2) implies the second, and the same argument applies also in the opposite direction.

Next assume that both relations (2.2) hold. Choose two points of continuity of V such that $x' < x''$ and $0 < V(x') \leq V(x'') < 1$. Then there exist points of continuity of U such that $U(y') < V(x')$ and $U(y'') > V(x'')$. For n sufficiently large we conclude from (2.2)

$$a_ny' + b_n \leq \alpha_nx' + \beta_n \leq \alpha_nx'' + \beta_n \leq a_ny'' + b_n.$$

Hence $\alpha_n(x'' - x') \leq a_n(y'' - y')$ and so the ratios α_n/a_n and $(\beta_n - b_n)/a_n$ remain bounded. For reasons of symmetry the ratios a_n/α_n must also remain bounded, and so we can find a sequence $n_1, n_2, \ldots$ such that (2.3) holds when n runs through it. By the converse part of the lemma this implies (2.1). Now the constants A and B in (2.1) are obviously uniquely determined and so our limits are independent of the sequence $\{n_k\}$. Thus (2.3) holds for an arbitrary approach $n \to \infty$ and this concludes the proof. ▶

Two types of sequences $\{F_n\}$ of probability distributions occur so frequently that they deserve names. For notational clarity we state the definitions formally in terms of random variables $\mathbf{X}_n$, but the notions really refer only to their distributions F_n. The definitions are therefore meaningful without reference to any probability space.

Definition 1. *If*

$$\mathbf{P}\{|\mathbf{X}_n| > \epsilon\} \to 0 \tag{2.5}$$

for any $\epsilon > 0$ *we shall say that* $\mathbf{X}_n$ *converges in probability to zero, and indicate this by* $\mathbf{X}_n \xrightarrow{\mathrm{p}} 0$.

By extension $\mathbf{X}_n \xrightarrow{\mathrm{p}} \mathbf{X}$ *means the same as* $\mathbf{X}_n - \mathbf{X} \xrightarrow{\mathrm{p}} 0$.

Note that (2.5) holds iff the distributions F_n tend to the distribution concentrated at the origin. In general, however, $F_n \to F$ implies nothing about the convergence of $\mathbf{X}_1, \mathbf{X}_2, \ldots.$ For example, if the $\mathbf{X}_j$ are independent with a common distribution F then $F_n \to F$ but the sequence $\{\mathbf{X}_n\}$ does not converge in probability.

The following simple lemma is of frequent use but not always mentioned explicitly. (For example, the truncation method used in **1**; X depends implicitly on it.)

Lemma 2. *Denote the distributions of* $\mathbf{X}_n$ *and* $\mathbf{Y}_n$ *by* F_n *and* G_n. *Suppose that* $\mathbf{X}_n - \mathbf{Y}_n \xrightarrow{\mathrm{p}} 0$ *and* $G_n \to G$. *Then also* $F_n \to G$.

In particular, if $\mathbf{X}_n \xrightarrow{\mathrm{p}} \mathbf{X}$ then $F_n \to F$ where F is the distribution of $\mathbf{X}$.

Proof. If $\mathbf{X}_n \leq x$ then either $\mathbf{Y}_n \leq x + \epsilon$ or $\mathbf{X}_n - \mathbf{Y}_n \leq -\epsilon$. The probability of the latter event tends to 0 and hence $F_n(x) \leq G_n(x+\epsilon) + \epsilon$ for all n sufficiently large. The same argument leads to an analogous inequality in the opposite direction. ▶

Definition 2. *The sequences* $\{\mathbf{X}_n\}$ *and* $\{F_n\}$ *are said to be stochastically bounded if for each* $\epsilon > 0$ *there exists an* a *such that*

$$\mathbf{P}\{|\mathbf{X}_n| > a\} < \epsilon \tag{2.6}$$

for all n sufficiently large.

This notion applies equally to distributions in higher dimensions and vector variables $\mathbf{X}_n$.

A properly convergent sequence is obviously stochastically bounded whereas improper convergence excludes stochastic boundedness. We have therefore the trite but useful *criterion*: If the distributions F_n converge, then the limit F is a proper distribution iff $\{F_n\}$ is stochastically bounded.

If $\{\mathbf{X}_n\}$ and $\{\mathbf{Y}_n\}$ are stochastically bounded, so is $\{\mathbf{X}_n + \mathbf{Y}_n\}$. Indeed, the event $|\mathbf{X}_n + \mathbf{Y}_n| > 2a$ cannot occur unless either $|\mathbf{X}_n| > a$ or $|\mathbf{Y}_n| > a$ and therefore

$$\mathbf{P}\{|\mathbf{X}_n + \mathbf{Y}_n| > 2a\} \leq \mathbf{P}\{|\mathbf{X}_n| > a\} + \mathbf{P}\{|\mathbf{Y}_n| > a\}. \tag{2.7}$$

The following simple lemma can be proved in many ways (see problem 4) and is given here chiefly to illustrate the use of the preceding lemmas.

Lemma 3. *Let $\mathbf{X}_1, \mathbf{X}_2, \ldots$ be independent random variables with a common distribution F and $\mathbf{S}_n = \mathbf{X}_1 + \cdots + \mathbf{X}_n$. Let the variables $a_n^{-1}\mathbf{S}_n - b_n$ have a proper limit distribution U not concentrated at one point. If $a_n > 0$ then*

$$a_n \to \infty, \qquad \frac{a_n}{a_{n-1}} \to 1. \tag{2.8}$$

Proof. If $a_n \to \infty$ then $a_n^{-1}\mathbf{X}_n \xrightarrow{\mathrm{p}} 0$ and so by the last lemma the distribution of $a_n^{-1}\mathbf{S}_{n-1} - b_n$ tends to U. The variables $a_n^{-1}\mathbf{S}_{n-1} - b_n$ and $a_{n-1}^{-1}\mathbf{S}_{n-1} - b_{n-1}$ have therefore the same limit distribution U, and by lemma 1 this implies that $\dfrac{a_n}{a_{n-1}} \to 1$. To prove that $a_n \to \infty$ we show that in the contrary case sequence $\{a_n^{-1}\mathbf{S}_n - b_n\}$ cannot remain stochastically bounded. By symmetrization it suffices to prove this assertion for *symmetric* distributions F and $b_n = 0$. By the inequality V,(5.9)

$$\mathbf{P}\{|\mathbf{S}_n| > t\} \geq \tfrac{1}{2}\,\mathbf{P}\{\mathrm{Max}[|\mathbf{X}_1|, \ldots, |\mathbf{X}_n|] > t\}. \tag{2.9}$$

If F is not concentrated on a finite interval the last probability tends to 1 for every fixed $t > 0$, and so $\{a_n^{-1}\mathbf{S}_n\}$ cannot remain stochastically bounded unless $a_n \to \infty$. This argument can be strengthened to cover also distributions concentrated on a finite interval, but we shall presently see that such distributions obey the central limit theorem and therefore for them $a_n \sim a\sqrt{n}$ by lemma 1. ►

3. DISTRIBUTIONS AS OPERATORS

The convolution $U = F \bigstar u$ of a point function u and a probability distribution F was defined in V,4. If we define a family of functions u_t by $u_t(x) = u(t-x)$ we can express the value $U(t)$ as an expectation

$$U(t) = \int_{-\infty}^{+\infty} u(t-y)\, F\{dy\} = \mathbf{E}(u_t). \tag{3.1}$$

We use this to derive a criterion for proper convergence. It is based on the class $C[-\infty, \infty]$ of continuous functions with limits $u(\pm\infty)$ because such functions are uniformly continuous.

Theorem 1. *A sequence of probability distributions F_n converges properly to a probability distribution F iff for each $u \in C[-\infty, \infty]$ the convolutions $U_n = F_n \bigstar u$ converge uniformly to a limit U. In this case $U = F \bigstar u$.*

Proof. The condition is necessary because the uniform continuity of u implies that the family $\{u_t\}$ is equicontinuous and so by the last corollary $U_n \to F \bigstar u$ uniformly. Conversely, the condition of the theorem entails the convergence of the expectations $\mathbf{E}_n(u)$. We saw in section 1 that this implies the convergence $F_n \to F$, but it remains to show that F is proper. Let u be a continuous monotone function increasing from 0 to 1. Then $U_n(-\infty) = 0$ for each n. Restricting the interval of integration in (3.1) to $\overline{-\infty, -2x}$ shows that $U_n(-x) \geq u(x)F_n(-2x)$. Since $U_n \to U$ uniformly this implies that $F_n(-2x) < \epsilon$ for all x sufficiently large. Thus $F(-\infty) = 0$ and by the same reasoning $1 - F(\infty) = 0$. ►

A significant application may illustrate the usefulness of this criterion.

Example. (*a*) *Approximation theorems.* Let G be an arbitrary probability distribution and $G_h(x) = G(h^{-1}x)$. As $h \to 0+$ the distribution G_h tends to the distribution concentrated at the origin and hence $G_h \bigstar u \to u$ *for each $u \in C[-\infty, \infty]$, the convergence being uniform.*[6]

If G has a density g, the values of $G_h \bigstar u$ are given by

$$G_h \bigstar u(t) = \int_{-\infty}^{+\infty} u(y)\, g\left(\frac{t-y}{h}\right) \frac{1}{h}\, dy. \tag{3.2}$$

When g has a bounded derivative the same is true of G_h and (3.2) may be differentiated under the integral. Taking for g the normal density we get the following *approximation lemma*: *to each $u \in C[-\infty, \infty]$ there exists an infinitely differentiable $v \in C[-\infty, \infty]$ such that $|u(x) - v(x)| < \epsilon$ for all x.*

These results are frequently used even outside probability theory but the proof is particularly simple in the present setting. A typical application is found in problem 10. ►

---

[6] This can be verified directly from the defining formula

$$G_h \bigstar u(t) - u(t) = \int_{-\infty}^{+\infty} [u(t-y) - u(t)]G\{dy/h\}.$$

Assume $|u(x)| \leq 1$. To given $\epsilon > 0$ find δ such that within each interval of length 2δ, u oscillates by less than ϵ. The contribution of $|y| > \delta$ is less than $2[1 - G(h^{-1}\delta) + G(-h^{-1}\delta)]$, which tends to 0 as $h \to 0$. Therefore the integral tends to 0 uniformly in t.

In the present context it is desirable to replace the clumsy convolution symbol $\bigstar$ by a simpler notation emphasizing that in (3.1) the distribution F serves as an operator sending u into U. This operator will be denoted by the German letter $\mathfrak{F}$ and we agree that $U = \mathfrak{F}u$ means exactly the same as $U = F \bigstar u$. The true advantage of this apparent pedantry will become visible only when other types of operators appear in the same context. It will then be convenient to see at a glance whether a distribution plays its original probabilistic role or serves merely as an analytic operator (even though this fine distinction may lead to schizophrenia among the distributions themselves). With this explanation we introduce the

Notational convention. *With each probability distribution F we associate the operator $\mathfrak{F}$ from $C[-\infty, \infty]$ to itself which associates with the function u the transform $\mathfrak{F}u = F \bigstar u$. As far as possible distributions and the associated operators will be denoted by corresponding Latin and German letters.*

As usual in operator notation $\mathfrak{F}\mathfrak{G}u$ denotes the result of $\mathfrak{F}$ operating on $\mathfrak{G}u$, and so $\mathfrak{F}\mathfrak{G}$ *denotes the operator associated with the convolution* $F \bigstar G$ of two probability distributions. In particular, $\mathfrak{F}^n$ *is the operator associated with* $F^{n\bigstar}$, the n-fold convolution of F with itself.

Example. (*b*) If H_a denotes the atomic distribution concentrated at a, then $\mathfrak{H}_a$ is the *translation* operator $\mathfrak{H}_a u(x) = u(x-a)$. In particular, $\mathfrak{H}_0$ serves as the *indentity* operator: $\mathfrak{H}_0 u = u$. ►

We use the notation[7]

$$\|u\| = \sup |u(x)| \tag{3.3}$$

and note the easily verified *triangle inequality* $\|u + v\| \leq \|u\| + \|v\|$. Then $\|u_n - u\| \to 0$ means *uniform* convergence.

An operator T is called bounded if there exists a constant a such that $\|Tu\| \leq a \cdot \|u\|$. The smallest number with this property is called the *norm* of T and is denoted by $\|T\|$. With these notations the principal properties of the linear operators associated with distribution functions are:

They are positive, that, is, $u \geq 0$ implies $\mathfrak{F}u \geq 0$. They have norm 1, which implies

$$\|\mathfrak{F}u\| \leq \|u\|. \tag{3.4}$$

Finally, they commute, that is, $\mathfrak{F}\mathfrak{G} = \mathfrak{G}\mathfrak{F}$.

---

[7] $\|u\|$ is the *norm* of u as element of the usual Banach space $C[-\infty, \infty]$, but we shall not appeal to that theory.

Definition.[8] *If* $\mathfrak{F}_n$ *and* $\mathfrak{F}$ *are operators associated with probability distributions* F_n *and* F *we write* $\mathfrak{F}_n \to \mathfrak{F}$ *iff*

$$\|\mathfrak{F}_n u - \mathfrak{F}u\| \to 0 \tag{3.5}$$

for each $u \in C[-\infty, \infty]$.

Theorem 1 may now be restated as follows.

Theorem 1a. $F_n \to F$ *properly iff* $\mathfrak{F}_n \to \mathfrak{F}$.

The next lemma is basic. It has the form of an algebraic inequality and illustrates the suggestive power of the new notation.

Lemma 1. *For operators associated with probability distributions*

$$\|\mathfrak{F}_1\mathfrak{F}_2 u - \mathfrak{G}_1\mathfrak{G}_2 u\| \leq \|\mathfrak{F}_1 u - \mathfrak{G}_1 u\| + \|\mathfrak{F}_2 u - \mathfrak{G}_2 u\|. \tag{3.6}$$

Proof. The operator on the left equals $(\mathfrak{F}_1 - \mathfrak{G}_1)\mathfrak{F}_2 + (\mathfrak{F}_2 - \mathfrak{G}_2)\mathfrak{G}_1$ and (3.6) follows from the triangle inequality and the fact that $\mathfrak{F}_2$ and $\mathfrak{G}_1$ have norms ≤ 1. Notice that this proof applies also to defective probability distributions. ►

An immediate consequence of (3.6) is

Theorem 2. *Let the sequences* $\{F_n\}$ *and* $\{G_n\}$ *of probability distributions converge properly to* F *and* G *respectively. Then*

$$F_n \star G_n \to F \star G. \tag{3.7}$$

(The convergence is proper by the definition of $F \star G$. The theorem remains valid for improper convergence, but the proof breaks down. See problem 9.)

As a second application we prove that theorem 1 remains valid if the class of functions u is restricted to the particularly pleasing functions with derivatives of all orders. In this way we obtain the more flexible

Criterion 1. *Let the* F_n *be probability distributions. If for each infinitely differentiable*[9] $v \in C[-\infty, \infty]$ *the sequence* $\{\mathfrak{F}_n v\}$ *converges uniformly, then there exists a proper probability distribution* F *such that* $F_n \to F$.

---

[8] In Banach space terminology (3.5) is described as *strong convergence*. Note that it does *not* imply $\|\mathfrak{F}_n - \mathfrak{F}\| \to 0$. For example, if F_n is concentrated at $1/n$ and $\mathfrak{F}$ is the identity operator, then $\mathfrak{F}_n u(x) - \mathfrak{F}u(x) = u(x-n^{-1}) - u(x)$ and (3.5) is true but $\|\mathfrak{F}_n - \mathfrak{F}\| = 2$, because there exist functions $|v| \leq 1$ such that $v(0) = 1$ and $v(-n^{-1}) = -1$.

[9] By this is meant that all derivatives exist and belong to $C[-\infty, \infty]$.

Proof. It was shown in example (*a*) that to given $u \in C[-\infty, \infty]$ and $\epsilon > 0$ there exists an infinitely differentiable v such that $\|u - v\| < \epsilon$. By the triangle inequality

$$\|\mathfrak{F}_n u - \mathfrak{F}_m u\| \leq \|\mathfrak{F}_n u - \mathfrak{F}_n v\| + \\ + \|\mathfrak{F}_n v - \mathfrak{F}_m v\| + \|\mathfrak{F}_m v - \mathfrak{F}_m u\|. \tag{3.8}$$

The first and last terms on the right are $<\epsilon$, and by assumption the middle term is $< \epsilon$ for all n, m sufficiently large. Thus $\{\mathfrak{F}_n u\}$ converges uniformly and $F_n \to F$ by theorem 1. ▶

Using the notations (1.1) the same argument yields

Criterion 2. *Let F_n and F be proper probability distributions. If $\mathbf{E}_n(v) \to \mathbf{E}(v)$ for each infinitely differentiable v vanishing at infinity then $F_n \to F$.*

The basic inequality (3.6) extends by induction to convolutions with more than two terms; for ease of reference we record the obvious result in

Lemma 2. *Let $\mathfrak{U} = \mathfrak{F}_1 \cdots \mathfrak{F}_n$ and $\mathfrak{V} = \mathfrak{G}_1 \cdots \mathfrak{G}_n$ where the $\mathfrak{F}_j$ and $\mathfrak{G}_j$ are associated with probability distributions. Then*

$$\|\mathfrak{U}u - \mathfrak{V}u\| \leq \sum_{j=1}^{n} \|\mathfrak{F}_j u - \mathfrak{G}_j u\|. \tag{3.9}$$

In particular

$$\|\mathfrak{F}^n u - \mathfrak{G}^n u\| \leq n \cdot \|\mathfrak{F}u - \mathfrak{G}u\|. \tag{3.10}$$

(For applications see problems 14–15.)

4. THE CENTRAL LIMIT THEOREM

The central limit theorem establishes conditions under which sums of independent random variables are asymptotically normally distributed. Its role and meaning has been partly explained in **1**; X,1 and we have applied it on several occasions [last in example VI,(11.*g*)]. It occupies a place of honor in probability theory acquired by its age and by the fruitful role which it played in the development of the theory and still plays in applications. It is therefore appropriate to use the central limit theorem as a test case to compare the scope of the various tools at our disposal. For this reason we shall give several proofs. A more systematic treatment (including necessary and sufficient conditions) will be found in chapters IX, XV, and XVI. The present discussion sidetracks us from the development of our main theme; its purpose is to illustrate the advantages of the operator terminology by a striking and significant example. Also, many readers will welcome an easy access to the central limit theorem in its simplest setting. At the cost of some repetitions we begin by a special case.

Theorem 1. (*Identical distributions in* $\mathcal{R}^1$.) *Let* $\mathbf{X}_1, \mathbf{X}_2, \ldots$ *be mutually independent random variables with a common distribution* F. *Assume*

$$\mathbf{E}(\mathbf{X}_k) = 0, \qquad \operatorname{Var}(\mathbf{X}_k) = 1. \tag{4.1}$$

As $n \to \infty$ *the distribution of the normalized sums*

$$\mathbf{S}_n^* = \frac{\mathbf{X}_1 + \cdots + \mathbf{X}_n}{\sqrt{n}} \tag{4.2}$$

tends to the normal distribution $\mathfrak{N}$ *with density* $\mathfrak{n}(x) = e^{-\frac{1}{2}x^2}/\sqrt{2\pi}$.

In purely analytical terms: for a distribution F with zero expectation and unit variance

$$F^{n\star}(x\sqrt{n}) \to \mathfrak{N}(x). \tag{4.3}$$

We show that this theorem is an immediate consequence of the following.

Lemma. *If* $\mathfrak{F}_n$ *is the operator associated with* $F_n(x) = F(x\sqrt{n})$ *then for each* $u \in C[-\infty, \infty]$ *with three bounded derivatives*

$$n[\mathfrak{F}_n u - u] \to \tfrac{1}{2}u'' \tag{4.4}$$

uniformly on the line.

Proof *of theorem* 1. Let $\mathfrak{G}$ be the operator associated with the normal distribution $\mathfrak{N}$ and $\mathfrak{G}_n$ with $\mathfrak{N}(x\sqrt{n})$. Since (4.4) holds also for $\mathfrak{G}_n$ we have by the basic inequality (3.10)

$$\|\mathfrak{F}_n{}^n u - \mathfrak{G}u\| = \|\mathfrak{F}_n{}^n u - \mathfrak{G}_n{}^n u\| \le n\,\|\mathfrak{F}_n u - \mathfrak{G}_n u\| \to 0, \tag{4.5}$$

and hence $\mathfrak{F}_n{}^n \to \mathfrak{G}$ by criterion 1. ►

Proof *of the lemma.* We introduce the proper probability distribution $F_n{}^\#$ defined by

$$F_n{}^\#\{dy\} = ny^2\, F_n\{dy\} = ny^2\, F\{\sqrt{n}\, dy\}. \tag{4.6}$$

The change of variables $\sqrt{n}\, y = s$ shows that $F_n{}^\#$ tends to the distribution concentrated at the origin. In view of (4.1) we have for the difference of the two sides in (4.4)

$$\begin{aligned} &n[\mathfrak{F}_n u(x) - u(x)] - \tfrac{1}{2}u''(x) = \\ &\quad = \int_{-\infty}^{+\infty} \left[\frac{u(x-y) - u(x) + yu'(x)}{y^2} - \tfrac{1}{2}u''(x)\right] F_n{}^\#\{dy\}. \end{aligned} \tag{4.7}$$

The Taylor development of the numerator shows that for $|y| < \epsilon$ the integrand is dominated by $\frac{1}{6}|y| \cdot \|u'''\| < \epsilon \cdot \|u'''\|$, and for all y by $\|u''\|$. Since $F_n^{\#}$ tends to concentrate near the origin it follows that for n sufficiently large the quantity is in absolute value less than $\epsilon(\|u''\| + \|u'''\|)$, and so the left side tends uniformly to zero. ▶

Example. (*a*) *Central limit theorem with infinite variances.* It is of methodological interest to note that the proof of theorem 1 applies without change to certain distributions without variance, provided appropriate norming constants are chosen. For example, if the $\mathbf{X}_k$ have a density such that $f(x) = 2\,|x|^{-3} \log |x|$ for $|x| \geq 1$ and $f(x) = 0$ for $|x| \leq 1$, then $(\mathbf{X}_1 + \cdots + \mathbf{X}_n)/(\sqrt{n} \log n)$ has a normal limit distribution. (The proof requires only obvious changes.) Necessary and sufficient conditions for a normal limit are given in IX,7. ▶

The method of proof is of wide applicability. Problem 16 may serve as a good exercise. Here we use the method to prove the central limit theorem in more general settings, The following theorem refers formally to two dimensions but is valid in $\mathcal{R}^r$.

Theorem 2. (*Multivariate case*). *Let* $\{\mathbf{X}_n\}$ *stand for a sequence of mutually independent two-dimensional random variables with a common distribution* F. *Suppose that the expectations are zero and that the covariance matrix is given by*

$$C = \begin{pmatrix} \sigma_1^2 & \rho\,\sigma_1\sigma_2 \\ \rho\,\sigma_1\sigma_2 & \sigma_2^2 \end{pmatrix}. \tag{4.8}$$

As $n \to \infty$ *the distribution of* $(\mathbf{X}_1 + \cdots + \mathbf{X}_n)/\sqrt{n}$ *tends to the bivariate normal distribution with zero expectation and covariance matrix* C.

Proof. The proof requires no essential change if the matrix notation of III,5 is used. Since subscripts are already overtaxed we denote the points of the plane by row vectors $x = (x^{(1)}, x^{(2)})$. Then $u(x)$ denotes a function of the two variables and we denote its partial derivatives by subscripts. Thus $u' = (u_1, u_2)$ is a row vector, and $u'' = (u_{jk})$ is a symmetric two by two matrix. With this notation the Taylor expansion takes on the form

$$u(x-y) = u(x) - yu'(x) + \tfrac{1}{2}yu''(x)y^T + \cdots \tag{4.9}$$

where y^T is the transpose of y, namely the column vector with components $y^{(1)}, y^{(2)}$. In analogy with (4.6) we define a proper probability distribution by

$$F_n^{\#}\{dy\} = nq(y)\,F\{\sqrt{n}\,dy\} \quad \text{where} \quad 2q(y) = \frac{y_1^2}{\sigma_1^2} + \frac{y_2^2}{\sigma_2^2}.$$

As in the last proof $F_n^\#$ tends to the probability distribution concentrated at the origin. To (4.7) there corresponds the identity

$$(4.10)\qquad \begin{aligned} &n[\mathfrak{F}_n u(x) - u(x)] - \tfrac{1}{2}\, m(x) = \\ &\qquad = \int_{\mathcal{R}^2} \frac{u(x-y) - u(x) + yu'(x) - \tfrac{1}{2}\, yu''(x)y^T}{q(y)} \cdot F_n^\#\{dy\} \end{aligned}$$

where[10]

$$(4.11)\quad m(x) = \mathbf{E}(yu''(x)y^T) = u_{11}(x)\sigma_1^{\,2} + 2u_{12}(x)\rho\sigma_1\sigma_2 + u_{22}(x)\sigma_2^{\,2}.$$

(Here $\mathbf{E}$ denotes expectations with respect to F). In view of (4.9) the integrand tends to zero and as in the preceding lemma it is seen that $n[\mathfrak{F}_n u - u] \to mu$ uniformly, and the proof of the theorem requires no change. ▶

Example. (*b*) *Random walks in d dimensions.* Let $\mathbf{X}_1, \mathbf{X}_2, \ldots$ be independent random vectors with a common distribution that may be described as follows. The direction of $\mathbf{X}_k$ is random (I,10) and the length $\mathbf{L}$ is a random variable with $\mathbf{E}(\mathbf{L}^2) = 1$. For reasons of symmetry the covariance matrix C is the diagonal matrix with elements $\sigma_j^{\,2} = 1/d$. The distribution of the normalized sum $\mathbf{S}_n/\sqrt{n}$ tends to the normal distribution with covariance matrix C. The distribution of the *length of the vector* $\mathbf{S}_n/\sqrt{n}$ therefore tends to the distribution of the sum of squares of independent normal variables. It was shown in II,3 that this limit has the density

$$(4.12)\qquad w_d(r) = \frac{d^{\frac{1}{2}d}}{2^{\frac{1}{2}d-1}\Gamma(\frac{1}{2}d)}\, e^{-\frac{1}{2}dr^2} r^{d-1}.$$

This result shows the influence of the number of dimensions and applies, in particular, to the random flight example I,(10.*e*).

(*c*) *Random dispersal of populations.* As an empirical application of the foregoing example consider the spread of a population of oak trees in prehistoric times. If new plants were due only to seeds dropped by mature trees, then seedlings would be located near mature trees and the distance of an nth generation tree from its progenitor would be approximately normally distributed. Under these conditions the area covered by the descendants of a tree would be roughly proportional to the age of the tree. Observations show that the actual development is inconsistent with this hypothesis. Biologists conclude that the actual dispersal was strongly influenced by birds carrying the seeds long distances.[11] ▶

[10] Obviously $m(x)$ is the trace (sum of the diagonal elements) of the product Cu''. This is true in all dimensions. [In one dimension $m(x) = u''(x)$.]

[11] J. G. Skellam, Biometrika, vol. 38(1951) pp. 196–218.

We turn to a generalization of theorem 1 to variable distributions. The conditions give the impression that they are introduced artificially with the sole purpose of making the same proof work. Actually it turns out that the conditions are also necessary for the validity of the central limit theorem with the classical norming used in (4.17). (See XV,6.)

Theorem 3. (*Lindeberg*).[12] *Let* $\mathbf{X}_1, \mathbf{X}_2, \ldots$ *be mutually independent one-dimensional random variables with distributions* $F_1, F_2, \ldots$. *Assume*

$$\mathbf{E}(\mathbf{X}_k) = 0, \qquad \operatorname{Var}(\mathbf{X}_k) = \sigma_k^2, \tag{4.13}$$

and put

$$s_n^2 = \sigma_1^2 + \cdots + \sigma_n^2. \tag{4.14}$$

Assume that for each $t > 0$

$$\frac{1}{s_n^2} \sum_{k=1}^{n} \int_{|y| \geq ts_n} y^2 \, F_k\{dy\} \to 0 \tag{4.15}$$

or, what amounts to the same, that

$$\frac{1}{s_n^2} \sum_{k=1}^{n} \int_{|y| < ts_n} y^2 \, F_k\{dy\} \to 1. \tag{4.16}$$

Then the distribution of the normalized sum

$$\mathbf{S}_n^* = \frac{\mathbf{X}_1 + \cdots + \mathbf{X}_n}{s_n} \tag{4.17}$$

tends to the normal distribution $\mathfrak{N}$ *with zero expectation and unit variance.*

The Lindeberg condition (4.15) guarantees that the individual variances σ_k^2 are small as compared to their sum s_n^2 in the sense that for given $\epsilon > 0$ and all n sufficiently large

$$\frac{\sigma_k}{s_n} < \epsilon, \qquad k = 1, \ldots, n. \tag{4.18}$$

---

[12] J. W. Lindeberg, Math. Zeit., vol. 15 (1922) pp. 211–235. Special cases and variants had been known before, but Lindeberg gave the first general form containing theorem 1. The necessity of Lindeberg's condition with the classical norming was proved by Feller, *Ibid.*, vol. 40(1935). (See XV,6.)

Lindeberg's method appeared intricate and was in practice replaced by the method of characteristic functions developed by P. Lévy. That streamlined modern techniques permit presenting Lindeberg's method in a simple and intuitive manner was shown by H. F. Trotter, Archiv. der Mathematik, vol. 9 (1959) pp. 226–234. Proofs of this section utilize Trotter's idea.

In fact, obviously σ_k^2/s_n^2 is less than t^2 plus the left side in (4.15), and taking $t = \frac{1}{2}\epsilon$ we see that (4.15) implies (4.18).

Theorem 3 generalizes to higher dimensions in the way indicated by theorem 2. See also problems 17–20.

Proof. To each distribution F_k we make correspond a normal distribution G_k with zero expectation and the same variance σ_k^2. The distribution $F_k(xs_n)$ of $\mathbf{X}_k/s_n$ now depends on both k and n, and we denote the associated operator by $\mathfrak{F}_{k,n}$. Similarly $\mathfrak{G}_{k,n}$ is associated with the normal distribution $G_k(xs_n)$. By (3.9) it suffices to prove that

$$\sum_{k=1}^{n} \|\mathfrak{F}_{k,n}u - \mathfrak{G}_{k,n}u\| \to 0 \tag{4.19}$$

for every $u \in C[-\infty, \infty]$ with three bounded derivatives. We proceed as in theorem 1, but (4.7) is now replaced by the n relations

$$\begin{aligned} \mathfrak{F}_{k,n}u(x) - u(x) - \frac{\sigma_k^2}{2s_n^2}u''(x) &= \\ = \int_{-\infty}^{+\infty}\left[\frac{u(x-y) - u(x) + yu'(x)}{y^2} - \frac{1}{2}u''(x)\right] &\cdot y^2F_k\{s_n\,dy\}. \end{aligned} \tag{4.20}$$

Splitting the interval of integration into $|y| \leq \epsilon$ and $|y| > \epsilon$ and using the same estimates as in (4.7) we obtain

$$\left\|\mathfrak{F}_{k,n}u - u - \frac{\sigma_k^2}{2s_n^2}u''\right\| \leq \epsilon\,\|u'''\|\,\frac{\sigma_k^2}{s_n^2} + \|u''\|\cdot\int_{|y|>\epsilon} y^2\,F_k\{s_n\,dy\}. \tag{4.21}$$

The Lindeberg condition (4.15) with $t = \epsilon$ now guarantees that for n sufficiently large

$$\sum_{k=1}^{n}\left\|\mathfrak{F}_{k,n}u - u - \frac{\sigma_k^2}{2s_n^2}u''\right\| \leq \epsilon(\|u'''\| + \|u''\|). \tag{4.22}$$

For our normal distributions G_k the Lindeberg condition (4.15) appears as a simple consequence of (4.18), and therefore the inequality (4.22) remains valid with $\mathfrak{F}_{k,n}$ replaced by $\mathfrak{G}_{k,n}$. Adding these two inequalities we obtain (4.19), and this concludes the proof. ▶

Examples. (*d*) *Uniform distributions.* Let $\mathbf{X}_k$ be uniformly distributed [with density $1/(2a_k)$] between $-a_k$ and a_k. Then $\sigma_k^2 = \frac{1}{3}a_k^2$. It is easily seen that the conditions of the theorem are satisfied if the a_k remain bounded and $a_1^2 + \cdots + a_n^2 \to \infty$; indeed, in this case the sum (4.15) vanishes identically for all n sufficiently large. On the other hand, if $\Sigma\, a_k^2 < \infty$ then s_n remains bounded and (4.15) cannot hold: in this case the central limit theorem does *not* apply. (Instead we get an example of an infinite convolution to be studied in section 5.)

A less obvious case where the central limit theorem does *not* hold is $a_k^2 = 2^k$. Then $3s_n^2 = 2^{n+1} - 2 < 2a_n^2$ and obviously the left side of (4.15) is $> \frac{1}{2}$ if, say, $t < \frac{1}{100}$. These examples show that (4.15) serves to insure that the individual $\mathbf{X}_k$ will be asymptotically negligible: the probability that *any* term $\mathbf{X}_k$ will be of the same order of magnitude as the sum $\mathbf{S}_n$ must tend to zero.

(*e*) *Bounded variables.* Assume that the $\mathbf{X}_k$ are uniformly bounded, that is, that all the distributions F_k are carried by some finite interval $\overline{-a, a}$. The Lindeberg condition (4.15) is then satisfied iff $s_n \to \infty$. ►

It is of methodological interest to observe that the same method of proof works even for certain sequences of random variables *without expectations*, but the norming factors are, of course, different. We shall return to this problem in XV,6 where we shall also further analyze the nature of the Lindeberg condition. (See problems 19–20.)

We conclude this excursion by a version of the central limit theorem for *random sums*. The idea is as follows. If in theorem 1 we replace the fixed number n of terms by a Poisson variable $\mathbf{N}$ with expectation n it is plausible that the distribution of $\mathbf{S_N}$ will still tend to $\mathfrak{N}$. Similar situations arise in statistics and physics when the number of observations is not fixed in advance.

We consider only sums of the form $\mathbf{S_N} = \mathbf{X}_1 + \cdots + \mathbf{X_N}$ where the $\mathbf{X}_j$ and $\mathbf{N}$ are mutually independent random variables. We suppose that the $\mathbf{X}_j$ have a common distribution F with zero expectation and variance 1. Using the notation of section 2 we have

Theorem 4.[13] (*Random sums*) *Let* $\mathbf{N}_1, \mathbf{N}_2, \ldots$ *be positive integral-valued random variables such that*

$$\frac{\mathbf{N}_n}{n} \xrightarrow{\text{P}} 1. \tag{4.23}$$

Then the distribution of $\mathbf{S}_{\mathbf{N}_n}/\sqrt{n}$ *tends to* $\mathfrak{N}$.

The interesting feature is that $\dfrac{1}{\sqrt{n}}\mathbf{S}_{\mathbf{N}_n}$ is *not* normalized to unit variance. In fact, the theorem applies to cases with $\mathbf{E}(\mathbf{N}_n) = \infty$ and even when expectations exist,

[13] For generalizations to mutually dependent $\mathbf{X}_j$ see P. Billingsley, *Limit theorems for randomly selected partial sums*, Ann. Math. Statist., vol. 33 (1963) pp. 85–92. When (4.20) is dropped one gets limit theorems of a novel form. See H. E. Robbins, *The asymptotic distribution of the sum of a random number of random variables*, Bull. Amer. Math. Soc. vol. 54 (1948) pp. 1151–1161.

For generalizations of the central limit theorem to other types of dependent variables the reader is referred to the book by Loève. (For Markov chains see **1**; XV,11; for exchangeable variables, problem 21.)

(4.23) does *not* imply that $\frac{1}{n}\,\mathbf{E}(\mathbf{N}_n) \to 1$. Normalization to unit variance may be impossible, and when possible it complicates the proof.

Proof. To avoid double subscripts we write $\mathbf{P}\{\mathbf{N}_n = k\} = a_k$ with the understanding that the a_k depend on n. The operator associated with $\mathbf{S}_{\mathbf{N}_n}$ is given by the formal power series $\Sigma\, a_k \mathfrak{F}^k$. As in the proof of theorem 1 let $\mathfrak{F}_n$ be the operator associated with $F(x\sqrt{n})$. Since $F_n^{n\star} \to \mathfrak{N}$ it suffices to prove that

$$(4.24) \qquad \sum_{k=1}^{\infty} a_k \mathfrak{F}_n^{\,k} u - \mathfrak{F}_n^{\,n} u \to 0$$

uniformly for each $u \in C[-\infty, \infty]$ with three bounded derivatives.

Using the obvious factoring and the basic inequality (3.10) it is seen that

$$(4.25) \qquad \|\mathfrak{F}_n^{\,k} u - \mathfrak{F}_n^{\,n} u\| \leq \|\mathfrak{F}_n^{|k-n|} u - u\| \leq |k - n| \cdot \|\mathfrak{F}_n u - u\|.$$

Because of (4.23) the sum of the coefficients a_k with $|k - n| > \epsilon n$ is $< \epsilon$ for all n sufficiently large. For such n the norm of the left side in (4.24) is

$$(4.26) \qquad \leq \sum_{k=1}^{\infty} a_k \|\mathfrak{F}_n^{\,k} u - \mathfrak{F}_n^{\,n} u\| \leq 2\epsilon \cdot \|u\| + 2\epsilon \cdot n\, \|\mathfrak{F}_n u - u\|.$$

By the lemma the right side is $\leq 2\epsilon\|u\| + 3\epsilon\|u''\|$ for all n sufficiently large, and so (4.24) holds uniformly. ▶

*5. INFINITE CONVOLUTIONS

The following theorem is given for its intrinsic interest and because it is a good example for the working of our criteria. Stronger versions are found in IX,9 and XVII,10.

We denote by $\mathbf{X}_1, \mathbf{X}_2, \ldots$ mutually independent variables with distributions $F_1, F_2, \ldots$. It is assumed that $\mathbf{E}(\mathbf{X}_j) = 0$ and $\sigma_k^2 = \mathbf{E}(\mathbf{X}_k^2)$ exist.

Theorem. *If* $\sigma^2 = \Sigma\, \sigma_k^2 < \infty$ *the distributions*[14] G_n *of the partial sums* $\mathbf{X}_1 + \cdots + \mathbf{X}_n$ *tend to a probability distribution* G *with zero expectation and variance* σ^2.

Proof. To establish the existence of a proper limit G it suffices (theorem 1 of section 3) to show that for infinitely differentiable $u \in C[-\infty, \infty]$

* This section is not used in the sequel.

[14] The martingale convergence theorem 1 of VII,8 applies and shows that *the random variables* $\mathbf{S}_n$ *themselves converge to a limit.*

the sequence of functions $\mathfrak{F}_1\mathfrak{F}_2 \cdots \mathfrak{F}_n u$ converges uniformly as $n \to \infty$. Now for $n > m$ by the obvious factorization

(5.1) $$\|\mathfrak{F}_1 \cdots \mathfrak{F}_n u - \mathfrak{F}_1 \cdots \mathfrak{F}_m u\| \leq \|\mathfrak{F}_{m+1} \cdots \mathfrak{F}_n u - u\|.$$

Since $\mathbf{E}(\mathbf{X}_k) = 0$ we have the identity

(5.2) $$\mathfrak{F}_k u(x) - u(x) = \int_{-\infty}^{+\infty} [u(x-y) - u(x) + yu'(x)]\, F_k\{dy\}.$$

By the second-order Taylor expansion the integrand is in absolute value $\leq \|u''\| \cdot y^2$ and therefore $\|\mathfrak{F}_k u - u\| \leq \sigma_k^2 \cdot \|u''\|$. By the basic inequality (3.9) the quantity (5.1) is therefore $\leq (\sigma_{m+1}^2 + \cdots + \sigma_n^2) \cdot \|u''\|$ and thus there exists a proper distribution G such that $G_n \to G$. Since G_n has variance $\sigma_1^2 + \cdots + \sigma_n^2$ the second moment of G exists and is $\leq \sigma^2$. By the criterion of example (1.*e*) this implies that G has zero expectation. Finally, G is the convolution of G_n and the limit distribution of $\mathbf{X}_{n+1} + \cdots + \mathbf{X}_{n+k}$, and hence the variance of G cannot be smaller than that of G_n. This concludes the proof. ►

Examples. (*a*) In example I,(11.*c*) a random choice of a point between 0 and 1 is effected by a succession of coin tossings. In the present terminology this means representing the uniform distribution as an infinite convolution. Example I,(11.*d*) shows that the infinite convolution of the corresponding even-numbered terms is a singular distribution.

(*b*) Let the $\mathbf{Y}_k$ be independent with $\mathbf{E}(\mathbf{Y}_k) = 0$ and $\mathbf{E}(\mathbf{Y}_k^2) = 1$. Then the distributions of the partial sums of $\Sigma b_k \mathbf{Y}_k$ converge if $\Sigma b_k^2 < \infty$. This fact was exploited in the discussion of normal stochastic processes in III,7.

(*c*) *Application to birth processes.* Let $\mathbf{X}_n$ be a positive variable with density $\lambda_n e^{-\lambda_n t}$. Then $\mathbf{E}(\mathbf{X}_n) = \mathrm{Var}(\mathbf{X}_n) = \lambda_n^{-1}$ and in case $m = \Sigma \lambda_n^{-1} < \infty$ our theorem applies to the centered variables $\mathbf{X}_n - \lambda_n^{-1}$. This observation leads to a probabilistic interpretation of the divergent *pure birth process* described in **1**; XVII,3–4. A "particle" moves by successive jumps, the sojourn times $\mathbf{X}_1, \mathbf{X}_2, \ldots$ being independent exponentially distributed variables. Here $\mathbf{S}_n = \mathbf{X}_1 + \cdots + \mathbf{X}_n$ represents the epoch of the nth jump. If $\lim \mathbf{E}(\mathbf{S}_n) = m < \infty$, the distribution of $\mathbf{S}_n$ tends to a proper limit G. Then $G(t)$ is the probability that infinitely many jumps will occur before epoch t.

(*d*) For applications to shot noise, trunking problems, etc., see problem 22. ►

6. SELECTION THEOREMS

A standard method of proving the convergence of a numerical sequence consists in proving first the existence of at least one point of accumulation and then its uniqueness. A similar procedure is applicable to distributions, the analogue to a point of accumulation being provided by the following important theorem usually ascribed to Helly. As all theorems of this section, it is independent of the number of dimensions. (A special case was used in **1**; XI,6.)

Theorem 1. (i) *Every sequence* $\{F_k\}$ *of probability distributions in* $\mathfrak{R}^r$ *possesses a subsequence* $F_{n_1}, F_{n_2}, \ldots$ *that converges (properly or improperly) to a limit* F.

(ii) *In order that all such limits be proper it is necessary and sufficient that* $\{F_n\}$ *be stochastically bounded. (See definition* 2.2.)

(iii) *In order that* $F_n \to F$ *it is necessary and sufficient that the limit of every convergent subsequence equals* F.

The proof is based on the following.

Lemma. *Let* $a_1, a_2, \ldots$ *be an arbitrary sequence of points. Every sequence* $\{u_n\}$ *of numerical functions contains a subsequence* $u_{n_1}, u_{n_2}, \ldots$ *that converges at all points* a_j *(possibly to* $\pm\infty$).

Proof. We use G. Cantor's "diagonal method." It is possible to find a sequence $\nu_1, \nu_2, \ldots$ such that the sequence of values $u_{\nu_k}(a_1)$ converges. To avoid multiple indices we put $u_k^{(1)} = u_{\nu_k}$ so that $\{u_k^{(1)}\}$ is a subsequence of $\{u_n\}$ and converges at the particular point a_1. Out of this subsequence we extract a further subsequence $u_1^{(2)}, u_2^{(2)}, \ldots$ that converges at the point a_2. Proceeding by induction we construct for each n a sequence $u_1^{(n)}, u_2^{(n)}, \ldots$ converging at a_n and contained in the preceding sequence. Consider now the diagonal sequence $u_1^{(1)}, u_2^{(2)}, u_3^{(3)}, \ldots$. Except for its first $n-1$ terms this sequence is contained in the nth sequence $u_1^{(n)}, u_2^{(n)}, \ldots$ and hence it converges at a_n. This being true for each n, the diagonal sequence $\{u_n^{(n)}\}$ converges at all points $a_1, a_2, \ldots$ and the lemma is proved. ►

Proof *of theorem* 1. Choose for $\{a_j\}$ a sequence that is everywhere dense. By the preceding lemma there exists a subsequence $\{F_{n_k}\}$ converging at all points a_j. Denote the limit at a_j by $G(a_j)$. We may extend the definition of G to all x by letting $G(x)$ equal the greatest lower bound of all $G(a_j)$ for $a_j > x$. Then G is monotone and $0 \leq G(x) \leq 1$ for all x. If x is a point of continuity of G there exist a_i and a_j such that $a_i < x < a_j$ and $G(a_j) - G(a_i) < \epsilon$. Then $F_{n_k}(a_i) \leq F_{n_k}(x) \leq F_{n_k}(a_j)$, and as $k \to \infty$ the extreme members tend to $G(a_i)$ and $G(a_j)$, respectively. The upper and lower limits of the sequence $\{F_{n_k}(x)\}$ can therefore not differ by more than ϵ, and so $F_{n_k}(x) \to G(x)$ at all points of continuity of G. This proves (i).

Next we recall that a convergent sequence of distributions converges properly iff it is stochastically bounded. Given (i) the remaining assertions are therefore almost tautological. ▶

The selection theorem is extremely important. The following famous theorem in number theory may give an idea of its amazing power and may also serve as a reminder that our probabilistic terminology must not be allowed to obscure the much wider scope of the theory developed.

Examples. (*a*) *An equidistribution theorem in number theory.*[15] *Let* α *be an irrational number and* α_n *the fractional part of* $n\alpha$. *Denote by* $N_n(x)$ *the number of terms among* $\alpha_1, \alpha_2, \ldots, \alpha_n$ *that are* $\leq x$. *Then* $n^{-1}N_n(x) \to x$ *for all* $0 < x < 1$.

Proof. We consider distributions and functions on the *circle* of unit length; in other words, additions of coordinates are reduced modulo 1. The idea was explained in II,8. (The convenient tool of distribution functions becomes meaningless on the circle, but distributions in the sense of measures are meaningful.) Let F_n be the atomic distribution concentrated on the n points $\alpha, 2\alpha, \ldots, n\alpha$ and assigning probability $1/n$ to each. By the selection theorem there exists a sequence $n_1, n_2, \ldots$ such that $F_{n_k} \to F$, where F is a *proper* probability distribution (the circle being bounded). Taking convolutions with an arbitrary continuous function u we get

$$\frac{1}{n_k}\,[u(x-\alpha) + u(x-2\alpha) + \cdots + u(x-n_k\alpha)] \to v(x). \tag{6.1}$$

Now it is obvious that replacing x by $x-\alpha$ does not affect the asymptotic behavior of the left side, and hence $v(x) = v(x-\alpha)$ for all x. This in turn implies $v(x) = v(x-k\alpha)$ for $k = 1, 2, \ldots$. By the corollary to lemma V,4.2 the points $\alpha, 2\alpha, \ldots$ lie everywhere dense, and hence $v = \text{const}$. We have thus shown that for each continuous u the convolution $F \bigstar u$ is a constant. It follows that F must attribute the same value to intervals of equal length, and so $F\{I\}$ equals the length of the interval I. The impossibility of other limits proves that the whole sequence $\{F_n\}$ converges to this distribution, and this proves the theorem. We call F *the uniform distribution* on the circle.

(*b*) *Convergence of moments.* Let F_n and F be probability distributions with finite moments of all orders, which we denote by $\mu_k^{(n)}$ and μ_k, respectively. We know (VI,3) that different distribution functions can have the same moment sequence and it is therefore not always possible from

[15] Usually attributed to H. Weyl although discovered independently by Bohl and by Sierpiński. See G. H. Hardy and E. M. Wright, *Theory of numbers*, Oxford, 1945, pp. 378–381, to appreciate the difficulties of the proof in its original setting.

the behavior of $\mu_k^{(n)}$ to conclude that $F_n \to F$. However, *if F is the only distribution with the moments $\mu_1, \mu_2, \ldots$ and if $\mu_k^{(n)} \to \mu_k$ for $k = 1, 2, \ldots$ then $F_n \to F$.* In fact, the result of example (1.*e*) shows that every convergent subsequence of $\{F_n\}$ converges to F.

(*c*) *Separability*. For abbreviation call a distribution rational if it is concentrated at finitely many rational points and attributes a rational weight to each. An arbitrary distribution F is the limit of a sequence $\{F_n\}$ of rational distributions, and we may choose F_n with zero expectation since this can be achieved by the addition of an atom and adjustment of the weights by arbitrarily small amounts. But there are only denumerably many rational distributions and they may be ordered into a simple sequence $G_1, G_2, \ldots$. Thus *there exists a sequence $\{G_n\}$ of distributions with zero expectations and finite variances such that every distribution F is the limit of some subsequence $\{G_{n_k}\}$.*

(*d*) The proof that $F^{n\star} \to 0$ outlined in problem 23 depends on the selection theorem. ►

Theorem 1 was formulated in the form most useful for probability but is unnecessarily restrictive. The proof depended on the fact that a sequence $\{F_n\}$ of monotone functions with $F_n(-\infty) = 0$, $F_n(\infty) = 1$ contains a convergent subsequence. Now this remains true also when the condition $F_n(\infty) = 1$ is replaced by the less stringent requirement that the numerical sequence $\{F_n(x)\}$ be bounded for each fixed x. The limit F will then be finite but possibly unbounded; the induced measure will be finite on intervals $\overline{-\infty, x}|$ but possibly infinite for $\overline{-\infty, \infty}$. A similar relaxation is possible for $-\infty$ and we are led to the following generalization of theorem 1, in which the symbol $\mu_n \to \mu$ is used in the obvious sense that the relation holds in finite intervals.

Theorem 2. *Let $\{\mu_n\}$ be a sequence of measures such that the numerical sequence of measures $\mu_n\{\overline{-x, x}\}$ is bounded for each x. There exists a measure μ and a sequence $n_1, n_2, \ldots$ such that $\mu_{n_k} \to \mu$.*

Variants of the selection theorem hold for many classes of functions. Particularly useful is the following theorem, usually called after either Ascoli or Arzelà.

Theorem 3. *Let $\{u_n\}$ be an equicontinuous*[16] *sequence of functions $|u_n| \leq 1$. There exists a subsequence $\{u_{n_k}\}$ converging to a continuous limit u. The convergence is uniform in every finite interval.*

---

[16] That is, to each $\epsilon > 0$ there corresponds a $\delta > 0$ such that $|x' - x''| < \delta$ implies $|u_n(x') - u_n(x'')| < \epsilon$ for all n.

Proof. Choose again a dense sequence of points a_j and a subsequence $\{u_{n_k}\}$ converging at $a_1, a_2, \ldots$. Denote the limit at a_j by $u(a_j)$. Consider an arbitrary point x. By the definition of equicontinuity there exists a point a_j such that $|u_n(x) - u_n(a_j)| < \epsilon$ for all n and hence the upper and lower limits of the sequence $\{u_{n_k}(x)\}$ differ by at most 2ϵ. As ϵ is arbitrary it follows that $\{u_{n_k}(x)\}$ converges to a limit $u(x)$. Moreover, we have $|u_{n_k}(x) - u(x)| < 4\epsilon$ for all k such that $|u_{n_k}(a_j) - u(a_j)| < \epsilon$. For a given $\epsilon > 0$ finitely many points a_j will serve for all x of a finite closed interval I, and hence the convergence is uniform in I. This implies the continuity of the limit u. ►

*7. ERGODIC THEOREMS FOR MARKOV CHAINS

Let K be a stochastic kernel concentrated on a finite or infinite interval Ω. (By definition 1 of VI,11 this means: K is a function of two variables, a point x and a set Γ, which for fixed Γ reduces to a Baire function of x and for fixed $x \in \Omega$ a probability distribution concentrated on Ω.) In higher dimensions the interval Ω may be replaced by more general regions and the theory requires no change.

It was shown in VI,11 that there exist Markov chains $(\mathbf{X}_0, \mathbf{X}_1, \ldots)$ with transition probabilities K. The distribution γ_0 of the initial variable $\mathbf{X}_0$ may be chosen arbitrarily and the distributions of $\mathbf{X}_1, \mathbf{X}_2, \ldots$ are then given recursively by

$$\gamma_n(\Gamma) = \int_\Omega \gamma_{n-1}(dx)\, K(x, \Gamma). \tag{7.1}$$

In particular, if γ_0 is concentrated at a point x_0 then $\gamma_n(\Gamma) = K^{(n)}(x_0, \Gamma)$ coincides with the transition probability from x_0 to Γ.

Definition 1. *A measure α is strictly positive in Ω if $\alpha\{I\} > 0$ for each open interval $I \subset \Omega$. The kernel K is strictly positive if $K(x, I) > 0$ for each x and each open interval in Ω.*

Definition 2. *The kernel is ergodic if there exists a strictly positive probability distribution α such that $\gamma_n \to \alpha$ independently of the initial probability distribution γ_0.*

This amounts to saying that

$$K^{(n)}(x, I) \to \alpha(I) > 0 \tag{7.2}$$

for each interval of continuity for α. The definition is the same as in the

* This material is treated because of its importance and as a striking example for the use of the selection theorems. It is not used explicitly in the sequel.

discrete case (**1**; XV); its meaning has been discussed and clarified by examples in VI,10.

The most general stochastic kernels are subject to various pathologies, and we wish to restrict the theory to kernels depending in a continuous manner on x. The simplest way of expressing this is by considering the transformations on continuous functions induced by K. Given a function u which is bounded and continuous in the underlying interval Ω we define $u_0 = u$ and, by induction,

$$u_n(x) = \int_\Omega K(x, dy)\, u_{n-1}(y). \tag{7.3}$$

This transformation on functions is dual to the transformation (7.1) on measures. Note that in both cases throughout this section indices serve to indicate the effect of a transformation induced by K.

The regularity property that we wish to impose on K is, roughly speaking, that u_1 should not be worse than u_0. The following definition expresses exactly our needs but looks formal. The examples will show that it is trivially satisfied in typical situations.

Definition 3. *The kernel K is regular if the family of transforms u_k is equicontinuous*[17] *whenever u_0 is uniformly continuous in Ω.*

Examples. (*a*) *Convolutions* represent a special case of transformations induced by a regular stochastic kernel.

(*b*) Let Ω be the unit interval and let K be defined by a density k which is continuous in the closed unit square. Then

$$|u_n(x') - u_n(x'')| \le \int_0^1 |k(x', y) - k(x'', y)| \cdot |u_{n-1}(y)|\, dy. \tag{7.4}$$

By induction it is seen that if $|u_0| < M$ also $|u_n| < M$ for all n. Because of the uniform continuity of k there exists a δ such that

$$|k(x', y) - k(x'', y)| < \epsilon/M \qquad \text{whenever} \qquad |x' - x''| < \delta,$$

and then $|u_n(x') - u_n(x'')| < \epsilon$ independently of n. ▶

The condition of strict positivity in the following theorems is unnecessarily restrictive. Its main function is to eliminate the nuisance of decomposable and periodic chains with which we had to cope in **1**; XV.

Theorem 1. *Every strictly positive regular kernel K on a bounded closed interval Ω is ergodic.*

This theorem fails when Ω is unbounded, for the limit in (7.2) can be identically zero. A universal criterion may be formulated in terms of

---

[17] See the last footnote. Our "regularity" is analogous to "complete continuity" as used in Hilbert space theory.

stationary measures. We recall that a measure α is called stationary for K if $\alpha_1 = \alpha_2 = \cdots = \alpha$, that is, if all its transforms (7.1) are identical.

Theorem 2. *A strictly positive regular kernel K is ergodic iff it possesses a strictly positive stationary probability distribution α.*

Proof *of theorem* 1. Let v_0 be a continuous function and v_1 its transform (7.3). The proof depends on the obvious fact that for a strictly positive kernel K the maximum of the transform v_1 is strictly less than the maximum of v_0 except if v_0 is a constant.

Consider now the sequence of transforms u_n of a continuous function u_0. Since Ω is closed, u_0 is uniformly continuous on Ω and so there exists a subsequence $\{u_{n_k}\}$ converging uniformly to a continuous function v_0 (theorem 6.3). Then u_{n_k+1} converges to the transform v_1 of v_0. Now the numerical sequence of the maxima m_n of u_n is monotone, and hence $m_n \to m$. Because of the uniform convergence both v_0 and v_1 have the maximum m, and hence $v_0(x) = m$ for all x. This limit being independent of the subsequence $\{u_{n_k}\}$ we conclude that $u_n \to m$ uniformly.

Let γ_0 be an arbitrary probability distribution on Ω and denote by $\mathbf{E}_n$ expectations with respect to its transform γ_n defined in (7.1). A comparison of (7.1) and (7.3) shows that

$$\mathbf{E}_n(u_0) = \mathbf{E}_0(u_n) \to \mathbf{E}_0(m) = m.$$

The convergence of $\mathbf{E}_n(u_0)$ for arbitrary continuous u_0 implies the existence of a probability measure α such that $\gamma_n \to \alpha$. (See the theorem of section 1; the convergence is proper since the distributions γ_n are concentrated on a finite interval.) From (7.1) it follows that α is stationary. The strict positivity of α is an immediate consequence of the strict positivity of K. ►

Proof *of theorem* 2. Denote by $\mathbf{E}$ expectations with respect to the given stationary probability distribution α. For an arbitrary $u_0 \in C[-\infty, \infty]$ and its transforms u_k we have on account of the stationarity

$$\mathbf{E}(u_0) = \mathbf{E}(u_1) = \cdots.$$

Furthermore, $\mathbf{E}(|u_k|)$ decreases with k and so $\lim \mathbf{E}(|u_k|) = m$ exists.

As in the preceding proof we choose a subsequence such that $u_{n_k} \to v_0$ and $u_{n_k+1} \to v_1$, where v_1 is the transform of v_0. By bounded convergence this entails $\mathbf{E}(u_{n_k}) \to \mathbf{E}(v_0)$ and $\mathbf{E}(|u_{n_k}|) \to \mathbf{E}(|v_0|)$. Thus

$$\mathbf{E}(v_1) = \mathbf{E}(v_0) = \mathbf{E}(u_0) \quad \text{and} \quad \mathbf{E}(|v_1|) = \mathbf{E}(|v_0|) = m.$$

In view of the strict positivity of K the last equality implies that the continuous function v_0 cannot change signs. When $\mathbf{E}(u_0) = 0$ we have therefore $v_0(x) = 0$ identically. It follows that for arbitrary initial u_0 we have $v_0(x) = \mathbf{E}(u_0)$ for all x. This proves that $u_n(x) \to \mathbf{E}(u_0)$ which is the same as $K^{(n)}(x, \Gamma) \to \alpha(\Gamma)$ at all intervals of continuity. ▶

We now apply this theory to *convolutions on the circle* of circumference 1, that is, to transformations of the form

$$u_{n+1}(x) = \int_0^1 u_n(x-y)\, F\{dy\} \tag{7.5}$$

where F is a probability distribution on the circle and addition is modulo 1. [See II,8 and example (6.*a*).] This transformation may be written in the form (7.3) with $\Omega = \overline{0, 1}$ and $K^{(n)}(x, \Gamma) = F^{n\star}\{x - \Gamma\}$. Theorem 1 applies directly if F is strictly positive, but we prove the following more general analogue to the central limit theorem.

Theorem 3.[18] *Let F be a probability distribution on the circle and suppose that it is not concentrated on the vertices of a regular polygon. Then $F^{n\star}$ tends to the distribution with constant density.*

Proof. It suffices to show that for an arbitrary continuous function u_0 the transforms u_n tend to a constant m (depending on u_0). Indeed, as the second part of the proof of theorem 1 shows, this implies that $F^{n\star}$ converges to a probability distribution α on the circle, and since $\alpha \star u_0$ is constant for every continuous function u_0 it follows that α coincides with the uniform distribution.

To show that $u_n \to m$ we use the first part of the proof of theorem 1 except that we require a new proof for the proposition that the maximum of the transform v_1 of a continuous function v_0 is strictly less than the maximum of v_0 except if v_0 is a constant. To prove the theorem it suffices therefore to establish the following proposition. *If v_0 is a continuous function such that $v_0 \leq m$ and $v_0(x) < m$ for all x of an internal I of length $\lambda > 0$, then there exists an r such that $v_r(x) < m$ for all x.*

Since rotations do not affect the maxima there is no loss of generality in assuming that 0 is a point of increase of F. If b is another point of increase then $0, b, 2b, \ldots, rb$ are points of increase of $F^{r\star}$, and it is possible to choose b and r such that every interval of length λ contains at least one among these points (see lemma 1 and the corollary in V,4). By definition

$$v_r(x) = \int_0^1 v_0(x-y)\, F^{r\star}\{dy\}. \tag{7.6}$$

[18] For the analogue on the open line see problems 23 and 24. For generalizations to variable distributions see P. Lévy, Bull. Soc. Math. France, vol. 67(1939) pp. 1–41; A. Dvoretzky and J. Wolfowitz, Duke Math. J., vol. 18(1951) pp. 501–507.

To every point x it is possible to find a point y of increase of $F^{r\bigstar}$ such that $x - y$ is contained in I. Then $v_0(x-y) < m$, and hence $v_r(x) < m$. Since x is arbitrary this proves the assertion. ▶

Note. The proof is easily adapted to show that *if F is concentrated on the vertices of a regular polygon with one vertex at* 0, *then $F^{n\bigstar}$ tends to an atomic distribution with atoms of equal weight.* Convergence need *not* take place if 0 is not among the atoms.

Example. (*c*) Let F be concentrated on the two irrational points a and $a + \frac{1}{2}$. Then $F^{n\bigstar}$ is concentrated on the two points na and $na + \frac{1}{2}$, and convergence is impossible. ▶

8. REGULAR VARIATION

The notion of regular variation (introduced by J. Karamata in 1930) proved fruitful in many connections, and finds an ever increasing number of applications in probability theory. The reason for this is partly explained in the next lemma, which is basic despite its simplicity. The examples of this section contain interesting probabilistic results, and problem 31 contains a famous result concerning stable distributions which follow from the lemma in an elementary way.

We have frequently to deal with monotone functions U obtained from a probability distribution F by integrating $y^p\, F\{dy\}$ over $\overline{0, x}$ or $\overline{x, \infty}$. [See, for example, (4.6), (4.15), (4.16).] The usual changes of parameters lead from such a function U to the family of functions of the form $a_t\, U(tx)$, and we have to investigate their asymptotic behavior as $t \to \infty$. If a limit $\psi(x)$ exists, it suffices to consider norming factors of the form $a_t = \psi(1)/U(t)$ provided $\psi(1) > 0$. The next lemma is therefore wider in scope than appears at first sight. It shows that the class of possible limits is surprisingly restricted.

Lemma 1. *Let U be a positive monotone function on $\overline{0, \infty}$ such that*

$$\frac{U(tx)}{U(t)} \to \psi(x) \leq \infty \qquad t \to \infty \tag{8.1}$$

at a dense set A of points. Then

$$\psi(x) = x^\rho \tag{8.2}$$

where $-\infty \leq \rho \leq \infty$.

The senseless symbol x^∞ is introduced only to avoid exceptions. It is, of course, to be interpreted as ∞ for $x > 1$ and as 0 for $x < 1$. Similarly $x^{-\infty}$ is ∞ or 0 according as $x < 1$ or $x > 1$. (See problem 25.)

Proof. The identity

$$(8.3)\qquad \frac{U(tx_1x_2)}{U(t)} = \frac{U(tx_1x_2)}{U(tx_2)} \cdot \frac{U(tx_2)}{U(t)}$$

shows that if in (8.1) a finite positive limit exists for $x = x_1$ and $x = x_2$, then also for $x = x_1x_2$, and

$$(8.4)\qquad \psi(x_1x_2) = \psi(x_1)\,\psi(x_2).$$

Suppose first that $\psi(x_1) = \infty$ for some point x_1. Then by induction $\psi(x_1^{\,n}) = \infty$ and $\psi(x_1^{-n}) = 0$ for all n. Since ψ is monotone this implies that either $\psi(x) = x^{\infty}$ or $\psi(x) = x^{-\infty}$. It remains to prove the lemma for finite valued ψ. (See problem 25.) Because of the assumed monotonicity we may define ψ everywhere by right-continuity. Then (8.4) holds at all points x_1, x_2. Now this equation differs only notationally from the equation which we have used repeatedly to characterize the exponential distribution. In fact, letting $x = e^{\xi}$ and $\psi(e^{\xi}) = u(\xi)$ the relation (8.4) is transformed into $u(\xi_1 + \xi_2) = u(\xi_1)\,u(\xi_2)$. We know from **1**; XVII,6 that all solutions that are bounded in finite intervals[19] are of the form $u(\xi) = e^{\rho\xi}$. This, however, is the same as $\psi(x) = x^{\rho}$. ▶

Example. (*a*) All powers of $|\log x|$ satisfy (8.1)–(8.2) with $\rho = 0$. Similarly, if $U(x)$ approaches a *positive finite* limit as $x \to \infty$ then (8.1)–(8.2) hold with $\rho = 0$. The functions $(1 + x^2)^p$ and e^x satisfy (8.1)–(8.2) with $\rho = 2p$ and $\rho = \infty$, respectively. The function $2 + \sin x$ does not satisfy (8.1). ▶

For a positive function U satisfying (8.1)–(8.2) with a *finite* ρ we put

$$(8.5)\qquad U(x) = x^{\rho}\, L(x).$$

Then for each $x > 0$ as $t \to \infty$

$$(8.6)\qquad \frac{L(tx)}{L(t)} \to 1,$$

and so L satisfies (8.1)–(8.2) with $\rho = 0$. The following definition is *not* restricted to monotone functions.

Definition. *A positive function L defined on* $\overline{0, \infty}$ *varies slowly at infinity iff* (8.6) *is true. U varies regularly with exponent* ρ *iff* (8.5) *holds with* $-\infty < \rho < \infty$ *and L varying slowly.*

By definition the property of regular variation is independent of the

[19] More generally, a finite Baire function satisfying (8.4) is of the form x^{ρ}. It follows that lemma 1, with exclusion of the case $\rho = \pm\infty$, remains valid for arbitrary (not necessarily monotone) functions U provided that (8.1) holds at *all* points.

behavior of U in finite intervals. For ease of reference we rephrase lemma 1 in the form of the basic

Theorem. *A monotone function U varies regularly at infinity iff* (8.1) *holds on a dense set and the limit ψ is finite and positive in some interval.*

The following lemma provides a useful *criterion.*

Lemma 2. *Suppose that*

$$\frac{\lambda_{n+1}}{\lambda_n} \to 1, \qquad a_n \to \infty. \tag{8.7}$$

If U is a monotone function such that

$$\lim \lambda_n\, U(a_n x) = \chi(x) \leq \infty \tag{8.8}$$

exists on a dense set, and χ is finite and positive in some interval, then U varies regularly and $\chi(x) = cx^\rho$ where $-\infty < \rho < \infty$.

Proof. We may assume that $\chi(1) = 1$ and that (8.8) is true for $x = 1$ (because this can be achieved by a trivial change of scale). For given t define n as the *smallest* integer such that $a_{n+1} > t$. Then $a_n \leq t < a_{n+1}$ and for a non-decreasing U

$$\frac{U(a_n x)}{U(a_{n+1})} \leq \frac{U(tx)}{U(t)} \leq \frac{U(a_{n+1}x)}{U(a_n)}\,; \tag{8.9}$$

for a non-increasing U the reversed inequalities hold. Since $\lambda_n\, U(a_n) \to 1$ the extreme members tend to $\chi(x)$ at each point where (8.8) holds. The assertion is therefore contained in the last theorem. ►

As typical applications we derive first a well-known theorem due to R. A. Fisher and B. V. Gnedenko, and next a new result.

Examples. (*b*) *Distribution of maxima.* Let the variables $\mathbf{X}_k$ be mutually independent and have a common distribution F. Put

$$\mathbf{X}_n^* = \max\,[\mathbf{X}_1, \ldots, \mathbf{X}_n].$$

We ask whether there exist scale factors a_n such that the variables $\mathbf{X}_n^*/a_n$ have a limit distribution G. We exclude two cases on account of their triviality. If F has a largest point of increase ξ then the distribution of $\mathbf{X}_n^*$ trivially tends to the distribution concentrated at ξ. On the other hand, it is always possible to choose scale factors a_n increasing so rapidly that $\mathbf{X}_n^*/a_n$ tends to 0 in probability. The remaining cases are covered by the following *proposition.*

Let $F(x) < 1$ for all x. In order that with appropriate scale factors a_n the distributions G_n of $\mathbf{X}_n^*/a_n$ tend to a distribution G not concentrated at 0 *it is necessary and sufficient that* $1 - F$ *varies regularly with an exponent* $\rho < 0$. *In this case,*

$$G(x) = e^{-cx^{\rho}} \tag{8.10}$$

for $x > 0$ *and* $G(x) = 0$ *for* $x < 0$. *(Clearly* $c > 0$.*)*

Proof. If a limit distribution G exists we have

$$F^n(a_n x) \to G(x) \tag{8.11}$$

at all points of continuity. Passing to logarithms and remembering that $\log(1-z) \sim -z$ as $z \to 0$ we get

$$n[1 - F(a_n x)] \to -\log G(x). \tag{8.12}$$

Since $0 < G(x) < 1$ in some interval the last lemma guarantees the regular variation of $1 - F$. Conversely, if $1 - F$ varies regularly it is possible to determine a_n such that $n[1 - F(a_n)] \to 1$, and in this case the left side in (8.12) tends to x^{ρ}. (See problem 26.)

(*c*) *Convolutions.* As a further example we prove the following *proposition.*

Let F_1 *and* F_2 *be two distribution functions such that as* $x \to \infty$

$$1 - F_i(x) \sim \frac{a_i}{x^{\rho}} L(x) \tag{8.13}$$

with L *varying slowly. Then the convolution* $G = F_1 \star F_2$ *has a regularly varying tail such that*

$$1 - G(x) \sim \frac{a_1 + a_2}{x^{\rho}} L(x). \tag{8.14}$$

Proof. Let $\mathbf{X}_1$ and $\mathbf{X}_2$ be independent random variables with the distributions F_1 and F_2. For $t > 1$, $\epsilon > 0$ trivially

$$\begin{aligned}\mathbf{P}\{\mathbf{X}_1 + \mathbf{X}_2 > t\} \geq \mathbf{P}\{\mathbf{X}_1 > t(1+\epsilon)\} \cdot \mathbf{P}\{|\mathbf{X}_2| < t\epsilon\} &+ \\ + \mathbf{P}\{\mathbf{X}_2 > t(1+\epsilon)\} \cdot \mathbf{P}\{|\mathbf{X}_1| < t\epsilon\}&.\end{aligned} \tag{8.15}$$

Since $\mathbf{P}\{|\mathbf{X}_i| < t\epsilon\} \to 1$ as $t \to \infty$ we get

$$\liminf_{t\to\infty} \frac{1 - G(t)}{t^{-\rho}L(t)} \geq \frac{a_1 + a_2}{(1 + \epsilon)^{\rho}}. \tag{8.16}$$

On the other hand, the event $\mathbf{X}_1 + \mathbf{X}_2 > t$ cannot occur unless either one of the variables $\mathbf{X}_i$ is $> t(1-\epsilon)$ or else both are $> t\epsilon$. Hence

$$\begin{aligned}\mathbf{P}\{\mathbf{X}_1 + \mathbf{X}_2 > t\} \leq \mathbf{P}\{\mathbf{X}_1 > t(1-\epsilon)\} + \mathbf{P}\{\mathbf{X}_2 > t(1-\epsilon)\} &+ \\ + \mathbf{P}\{\mathbf{X}_1 > t\epsilon\} \cdot \mathbf{P}\{\mathbf{X}_2 > t\epsilon\}&.\end{aligned} \tag{8.17}$$

Dividing by $t^{-\rho}L(t)$ and letting $t \to \infty$ we get a dual to (8.16) and the two inequalities together imply (8.14). ►

By induction on r one gets the interesting

Corollary.[20] *If* $1 - F \sim x^{-\rho} L(x)$ *then* $1 - F^{r\star}(x) \sim rx^{-\rho} L(x)$.

When applicable, this theorem supplements the central limit theorem by providing information concerning the tails.

*9. ASYMPTOTIC PROPERTIES OF REGULARLY VARYING FUNCTIONS

The purpose of this section is to investigate the relations between the tails and the truncated moments of distributions with regularly varying tails. The main result is that if $1 - F(x)$ and $F(-x)$ vary regularly so do all the truncated moments. This is asserted by theorem 2, which contains more than what we shall need for the theory of stable distributions. It could be proved directly, but it may also be considered a corollary to theorem 1 which embodies Karamata's[21] striking characterization of regular variation. It seems therefore best to give a complete exposition of the theory in particular since the arguments can now be significantly simplified.[22]

We introduce the formal abbreviations

$$(9.1) \qquad Z_p(x) = \int_0^x y^p\, Z(y)\, dy, \qquad Z_p^*(x) = \int_x^\infty y^p\, Z(y)\, dy.$$

It will now be shown that in the case of a regularly varying Z these functions are asymptotically related to Z just as in the simple case $Z(x) = x^a$.

The asymptotic behavior of Z_p at infinity is not affected by the behavior of Z near the origin. Without loss of generality we may therefore assume that Z vanishes identically in some neighborhood of 0 and so the integral defining Z_p will be meaningful for all p.

Lemma. *Let* $Z > 0$ *vary slowly. The integrals in* (9.1) *converge at* ∞ *for* $p < -1$, *diverge for* $p > -1$.

If $p \geq -1$ *then* Z_p *varies regularly with exponent* $p + 1$. *If* $p < -1$

* This section is used only for the theory of stable distributions, but the use of theorem 2 would simplify many lengthy calculations in the literature.

[20] This was noticed with a different proof by S. C. Port assuming that F has a regularly varying density and that $F(0) = 0$.

[21] J. Karamata, *Sur un mode de croissance regulière*, Mathematica (Cluj), vol. 4 (1930) pp. 38–53. Despite frequent references to this paper, no newer exposition seems to exist.

[22] Although new, our proof of theorem 1 uses Karamata's ideas.

then Z_p^* varies regularly with exponent $p + 1$, and this remains true for $p + 1 = 0$ if Z_{-1}^* exists.

Proof. For $x > 0$ and $0 < \eta < t$

$$Z_p(tx) = Z_p(\eta x) + x^{p+1} \int_\eta^t y^p Z(xy)\, dy. \tag{9.2}$$

As Z varies slowly we can choose η (depending on x) such that for $y > \eta$

$$(1 - \epsilon) Z(y) < Z(xy) < (1 + \epsilon) Z(y).$$

Then by (9.2)

$$x^{p+1}[Z_p(t) - Z_p(\eta)](1 - \epsilon) \le Z_p(tx) \le Z_p(\eta x) + x^{p+1} Z_p(t)(1 + \epsilon). \tag{9.3}$$

Keeping t and η fixed and letting $x \to \infty$ it is seen that $p+1 > 0$ implies divergence of Z_p, whereas $p+1 < 0$ implies convergence of Z_p. When $p+1 = 0$, both contingencies are possible.

Consider first the case $p+1 \ge 0$. Convergence of Z_p implies slow variation, and so nothing is to be proved in this case. If $Z_p(\infty) = \infty$, divide both sides in (9.3) by $Z(t)$ and let $t \to \infty$. Since ϵ is arbitrary we see that[23]

$$\frac{Z_p(tx)}{Z_p(t)} \to x^{p+1}. \tag{9.4}$$

Thus Z_p varies regularly with exponent $p+1$ as asserted. The same argument applies to Z_p^* (which is meaningful iff Z_p converges). ▶

Theorem 1. (i) *If Z varies regularly with exponent γ then*

$$\frac{t^{p+1} Z(t)}{Z_p(t)} \to p + \gamma + 1 \qquad p + \gamma + 1 \ge 0. \tag{9.5}$$

Similarly

$$\frac{t^{p+1} Z(t)}{Z_p^*(t)} \to |p + \gamma + 1| \qquad p + \gamma + 1 < 0, \tag{9.6}$$

and also if $p + \gamma + 1 = 0$ in case $Z_{-\gamma-1}^*$ exists.

(ii) *Conversely, if the left side in either* (9.5) *or* (9.6) *approaches a limit $\lambda > 0$ then Z varies regularly with exponent $\gamma = \lambda - p - 1$ [and so* (9.5) *and* (9.6) *are true for all admissible p].*

Proof. Put

$$\frac{y^p Z(y)}{Z_p(y)} = \frac{\eta(y)}{y}. \tag{9.7}$$

---

[23] When Z is continuous the relation follows directly from L'Hospital's rule.

Assume that Z varies regularly with exponent γ, and let $p + \gamma + 1 \geq 0$. Then $y^p Z(y)$ varies regularly with exponent $p + \gamma$ and by the preceding lemma Z_p varies regularly with exponent $p + \gamma + 1$. It follows that the quantity (9.7) varies regularly with exponent -1, and hence η is *slowly varying*. The numerator on the left being (almost everywhere) the derivative of the denominator we can integrate (9.7) between the limits t and tx to obtain

$$\log \frac{Z_p(tx)}{Z_p(t)} = \int_1^x \eta(ts) \cdot \frac{ds}{s} = \eta(t) \int_1^x \frac{\eta(ts)}{\eta(t)} \frac{ds}{s}. \tag{9.8}$$

Since Z_p varies regularly the left side tends to $(p+\gamma+1) \log x$. Let t run through a sequence $t_n \to \infty$ such that the last integral on the right approaches a limit $c \leq \infty$. In view of the slow variation of η the integrand tends to s^{-1} and so $c \geq \log x$ by Fatou's theorem [IV,(2.9)]. Hence $\eta(t_n)$ approaches a finite limit $a < p+\gamma+1$. The fact that for no sequence $\{t_n\}$ does $\eta(t_n)$ tend to ∞ means that our η is *bounded* at infinity. Now $\eta(t_n) \to a$ implies $\eta(t_n s) \to a$ for each s. As the convergence is bounded, the middle term of (9.8) tends to $a \log x$, and thus regular variation of Z implies (9.5).

The converse is easier. If the left side of (9.5) approaches $\lambda \geq 0$ then $\eta(t) \to \lambda$. Therefore the middle term in (9.8) approaches $\lambda \log x$ which implies that Z_p varies regularly with exponent λ. The assumption $Z(x) \sim \lambda x^{-p-1} Z_p(x)$ now shows that Z varies regularly with exponent $\lambda - p - 1$ as asserted. The same argument applies to Z_p^* and concludes the proof. ►

Although we shall not use it we mention the following interesting

Corollary. *A function Z varies slowly iff it is of the form*

$$Z(x) = a(x) \exp\left(\int_1^x \frac{\epsilon(y)}{y}\, dy \right) \tag{9.9}$$

where $\epsilon(x) \to 0$ and $a(x) \to c < \infty$ as $x \to \infty$.

Proof. The "if" part is trivially verified from the very definition. For the converse use (9.8) with $t = 1$ and substitute back into (9.7) to obtain an explicit expression of Z in terms of the auxiliary function η. In the present case $p = 0$, and $\eta(x) \to 1$. Putting $\epsilon(x) = \eta(x) - 1$ we get (9.9). ►

In applications of this theorem to distribution functions the two tails may be considered separately and it suffices to study distributions concentrated on $\overline{0, \infty}$.

Theorem 2. *Let F be a probability distribution concentrated on* $\overline{0, \infty}$ *and*

$$U_\zeta(x) = \int_0^x y^\zeta \, F\{dy\}, \tag{9.10}$$

where $\zeta > 0$ *is fixed and* $U_\zeta(\infty) = \infty$.

(i) *If either* U_ζ *or* $1 - F$ *varies regularly, there exists a limit*

$$\lim_{t\to\infty} \frac{t^\zeta[1 - F(t)]}{U_\zeta(t)} = c, \qquad 0 \leq c \leq \infty. \tag{9.11}$$

(ii) *Conversely, if* (9.11) *holds with* $0 < c < \infty$, *we write it in the form*

$$c = \frac{\zeta - \alpha}{\alpha}. \tag{9.12}$$

Then

$$U_\zeta(x) \sim x^{\zeta-\alpha} \, L(x), \qquad 1 - F(x) \sim \frac{\zeta - \alpha}{\alpha} \, x^{-\alpha} \, L(x), \tag{9.13}$$

with L slowly varying.

Furthermore, (9.11) *with* $c = 0$ *implies slow variation of* U_ζ, *and with* $c = \infty$ *that of* $1 - F$.

(Slow variation of U_ζ does not imply regular variation of $1 - F$; see problem 29.)

Proof. The theorem is symmetric in U_ζ and $1 - F$ and the proof is the same both ways. We prove the assertion concerning U_ζ. (The other is not used in this book.)

Starting from

$$1 - F(x) = \int_x^\infty y^{-\zeta} \, U_\zeta\{dy\} \tag{9.14}$$

we get by formal integration by parts

$$1 - F(x) = -x^{-\zeta} \, U_\zeta(x) + \zeta \int_x^\infty y^{-\zeta-1} \, U_\zeta(y) \, dy. \tag{9.15}$$

[The procedure is justified, for if applied to the contribution from $\overline{x, t}$ it becomes obvious that the integral in (9.15) converges. From (9.10) it is seen that $x^{-\zeta} \, U_\zeta(x) \to 0$ as $x \to \infty$.] Rewrite (9.15) in the form

$$\frac{x^\zeta[1 - F(x)]}{U_\zeta(x)} = -1 + \zeta \frac{1}{x^{-\zeta} \, U_\zeta(x)} \int_x^\infty y^{-\zeta-1} \, U_\zeta(y) \, dy. \tag{9.16}$$

If U_ζ varies regularly, its exponent is necessarily $\leq \zeta$ and we may call it $\gamma = \zeta - \alpha$. Using (9.6) with $Z = U_\zeta$ and $p = -\zeta - 1$ we see that the right side in (9.16) then tends to $-1 + \zeta/\alpha$ (to ∞ if $\alpha = 0$) which proves (9.11)–(9.12). The first relation in (9.13) is true by definition, and when $\alpha < \zeta$ the second follows from it and (9.11). Conversely, if (9.11) holds theorem 1 guarantees that U_ζ varies regularly with an exponent γ such that $\zeta/(\zeta - \gamma) = c + 1$. ►

(For an apparently more general form see problem 30.)

10. PROBLEMS FOR SOLUTION

1. *Alternative definition of convergence.* Let F_n and F be probability distributions. Show that $F_n \to F$ (properly) iff for given $\epsilon > 0$, $h > 0$ and t there exists an $N(\epsilon, h, t)$ such that for $n > N(\epsilon, h, t)$

$$F(t-h) - \epsilon < F_n(t) < F(t+h) + \epsilon. \tag{10.1}$$

2. *Improper convergence.* If F is a defective distribution then (10.1) implies that $F_n \to F$ improperly. The converse is *not* true. Show that *proper* convergence may be *defined* by requiring that (10.1) holds for $n \geq N(\epsilon, h)$, independently of t.

3. Let $\{F_n\}$ converge properly to a limit that is not concentrated at one point. The sequence $\{F_n(a_nx + b_n)\}$ converges to the distribution concentrated at the origin iff $a_n \to \infty$, $b_n = o(a_n)$.

4. *Alternative proof for lemma* 2.3. Using theorem 3.2 show that $a_{2n}/a_n \to \lambda$. Conclude that $a_n \to \infty$ and that *the limit distribution is necessarily stable* (see VI,1). (*Hint:* It suffices to consider symmetric F.)

5. Let $\{u_n\}$ be a sequence of bounded monotone functions converging pointwise to a bounded *continuous* limit (which is automatically monotone). Prove that the convergence is uniform. (*Hint:* Partition the axis into subintervals within each of which u varies by less than ϵ.)

6. (To theorem 3.1). Let F_n be concentrated at n^{-1} and $u(x) = \sin(x^2)$. Then $F_n \bigstar u \to u$ pointwise, but not uniformly.

7. (*a*) If the joint distribution of $(\mathbf{X}_n, \mathbf{Y}_n)$ converges to that of $(\mathbf{X}, \mathbf{Y})$, then the distribution of $\mathbf{X}_n + \mathbf{Y}_n$ tends to that of $\mathbf{X} + \mathbf{Y}$.

(*b*) Show that theorem 3.2 is a special case.

(*c*) The conclusion does not hold in general if it is only known that the marginal distributions for $\mathbf{X}_n$ and $\mathbf{Y}_n$ converge.

8. Let $F_n \to F$ where F is defective. If $u \in C_0(-\infty, \infty)$ then

$$F_n \bigstar u \to F \bigstar u$$

uniformly *in every finite interval.* (This generalizes theorem 3.1.)

9. Prove that if $F_n \to F$ and $G_n \to G$ *improperly* then $F_n \bigstar G_n \to F \bigstar G$. (This generalizes theorem 3.2.)

Hint: If $\mathbf{E}_n$ and $\mathbf{E}$ denote expectations with respect to F_n and F it follows easily from the last problem that $\mathbf{E}_n(G_n \bigstar u) \to \mathbf{E}(G \bigstar u)$ provided u vanishes at infinity. Use the theorem of section 1.

10. In the plane every continuous function vanishing at infinity can be approximated uniformly by finite linear combinations $\Sigma\, c_k\, \varphi_k(x)\, \psi_k(y)$ with infinitely differentiable φ_k and ψ_k.

Hint: Use the approximation theorem of example (3.*a*) choosing

$$G_k(x, y) = \mathfrak{N}_k(x)\mathfrak{N}_k(y)$$

where $\mathfrak{N}$ is the normal density.

Metrics. A function ρ is called a *distance function* for probability distributions if $\rho(F, G)$ is defined for every pair F, G of probability distributions and has the following three properties: $\rho(F, G) \geq 0$ and $\rho(F, G) = 0$ iff $F = G$; next $\rho(F, G) = \rho(G, F)$; and finally, ρ satisfies the triangle inequality

$$\rho(F_1, F_2) \leq \rho(F_1, G) + \rho(F_2, G).$$

11. *P. Lévy metric.* For two proper distributions F and G define $\rho(F, G)$ as the infimum of all $h > 0$ such that

$$F(x-h) - h \leq G(x) \leq F(x+h) + h \tag{10.2}$$

for all x. Verify that ρ is a distance function. Show that $F_n \to F$ properly iff $\rho(F_n, F) \to 0$.

12. *Distance "in variation."* Put $\rho(F, G) = \sup \|\mathfrak{F}u - \mathfrak{G}u\|$ where $u \in C_0$ and $\|u\| = 1$. Show that ρ is a distance function.[24] If F and G are atomic and attribute weights p_k and q_k to the point a_k, then

$$\rho(F, G) = \sum |p_k - q_k|. \tag{10.3}$$

If F and G have densities f and g

$$\rho(F, G) = \int_{-\infty}^{\infty} |f(x) - g(x)|\, dx. \tag{10.4}$$

[It suffices to prove (10.4) for continuous f and g. The general case follows by approximation.]

13. *Continuation.* Show that $\rho(F_n, G) \to 0$ implies proper convergence $F_n \to G$. To see that the converse is false consider the normal distribution functions $\mathfrak{N}(nx)$ and the distribution F_n concentrated at n^{-1}.

14. *Continuation.* If $U = F_1 \bigstar \cdots \bigstar F_n$ and $V = G_1 \bigstar \cdots \bigstar G_n$ show that

$$\rho(U, V) \leq \sum_{k=1}^{n} \rho(F_k, G_k). \tag{10.5}$$

This generalizes the basic inequality (3.9). [*Hint:* Use (3.9) and a test function u such that $\|\mathfrak{U}u - \mathfrak{V}u\|$ is close to $\rho(U, V)$.]

15. *Approximation by the Poisson distribution.*[25] Let F attribute weight p to the point 1 and $q = 1 - p$ to the point 0. If G is the Poisson distribution with expectation p show that $\rho(F, G) \leq \frac{9}{4}p^2$, where ρ is the distance defined in (10.3). Conclude: If F is the distribution of the number of successes in n Bernoulli trials with probabilities $p_1, \ldots, p_n$ and if G is the Poisson distribution with expectation $p_1 + \cdots + p_n$ then $\rho(F, G) \leq \frac{9}{4}(p_1^2 + \cdots + p_n^2)$.

---

[24] The definition can be extended to differences of arbitrary finite measures and defines the "*norm topology*" for measures. Problem 13 shows that the resulting notion of convergence is not natural for probability theory.

[25] Suggested by inequalities in L. LeCam, *An approximation theorem for the Poisson binomial distribution*, Pacific J. Math., vol. 10(1960) pp. 1181–1197.

16. The law of large numbers proved in chapter VII states that if the $\mathbf{X}_k$ are independent and identically distributed, and if $\mathbf{E}(\mathbf{X}_k) = 0$, then

$$(\mathbf{X}_1 + \cdots + \mathbf{X}_n)/n \xrightarrow{\text{p}} 0.$$

Prove this by the method used for theorem 4.1.

17. The Lindeberg condition (4.15) is satisfied if $\alpha_k = \mathbf{E}(|\mathbf{X}_k^{2+\delta}|)$ exists for some $\delta > 0$ and $\alpha_1 + \cdots + \alpha_n = o(s_n^{2+\delta})$ (Ljapunov's condition).

18. Let F_k be symmetric and $1 - F_k(x) = \dfrac{1}{2x^{2+k^{-1}}}$ for $x > 1$. Show that the Lindeberg condition (4.15) is satisfied.

19. Let $\mathbf{X}_k = \pm 1$ with probability $\frac{1}{2}(1 - k^{-2})$ and $\mathbf{X}_k = \pm k$ with probability $\frac{1}{2}k^{-2}$. By simple truncation prove that $\mathbf{S}_n/\sqrt{n}$ behaves asymptotically in the same way as if $\mathbf{X}_k = \pm 1$ with probability $\frac{1}{2}$. Thus *the distribution of* $\mathbf{S}_n/\sqrt{n}$ *tends to* $\mathfrak{N}$ *but* $\text{Var}(\mathbf{S}_n/\sqrt{n}) \to 2$.

20. Construct variants of the preceding problem where $\mathbf{E}(\mathbf{X}_k^2) = \infty$ and yet the distribution of $\mathbf{S}_n/\sqrt{n}$ tends to $\mathfrak{N}$.

21.[26] *Central limit theorem for exchangeable variables.* For fixed θ let F_θ be a distribution with zero expectation and variance $\sigma^2(\theta)$. A value θ is chosen according to the probability distribution G and one considers mutually independent variables $\mathbf{X}_n$ with the common distribution F_θ. If a^2 is the expectation of σ^2 with respect to G show that the distribution of $\mathbf{S}_n/(a\sqrt{n})$ tends to the distribution with density

$$\int_{-\infty}^{+\infty} \mathfrak{n}\left(\frac{x}{\sigma(\theta)}\right) G\{d\theta\}.$$

It is not normal unless G is concentrated at one point.

22. *Shot noise in vacuum tubes, etc.* Consider the stochastic process of example VI,(3.*h*) with discretized time parameter. Assuming that at epoch kh an arrival occurs with probability αh show that the intensity of the current in the discrete model is given by an *infinite convolution.* The passage to the limit $h \to 0$ leads to Campbell's theorem VI,(3.5).

Do the same for the busy-trunkline example VI,(3.*i*). Generalize the model to the situation where the after-effect at epoch kh is a random variable assuming the values 1, 2, . . . with probabilities $p_1, p_2, \ldots$.

23. *For any probability distribution not concentrated at the origin* $F^{n\bigstar} \to 0$. *Hint:* Consider a convergent subsequence and denote the total mass of the limit by p. Using problem 8 conclude that $p^2 = p$. The impossibility of a *proper* limit is easily established in many ways. (For example, from the impossibility of $G^{r\bigstar} = G$ or the symmetrization inequalities.)

24. *Continuation.* It is nevertheless possible that for every x

$$\limsup_{n\to\infty} F^{n\bigstar}(x) = 1, \qquad \liminf_{n\to\infty} F^{n\bigstar}(x) = 0.$$

In fact, it is possible to choose two extremely rapidly increasing sequences of

---

[26] J. R. Blum, H. Chernoff, M. Rosenblatt, and H. Teicher, *Central limit theorems for interchangeable processes*, Canadian J. Math., vol. 10(1958) pp. 222–229.

integers a_k and n_k such that

$$(-1)^k \frac{1}{a_k} \mathbf{S}_{n_k} \xrightarrow{\mathrm{p}} 1.$$

Hint: Consider the distribution $\mathbf{P}\{\mathbf{X} = (-1)^k a_k\} = p_k$. With an appropriate choice of the constants there is an overwhelming probability that one among the terms $\mathbf{X}_1, \ldots, \mathbf{X}_{n_k}$ will equal $(-1)^k a_k$ and none will exceed a_k in absolute value. Then for k even $\mathbf{S}_{n_k} > a_k - n_k a_{k-1}$. Show that

$$n_k = (2k)!, \qquad p_k \sim \frac{1}{(2k-1)!}, \qquad a_k \sim (n_k)^k$$

will do.

25. In the proof of lemma 8.1 it suffices to assume that the set A is dense in some open interval.

26. *Distribution of maxima.* Let $\mathbf{X}_1, \ldots, \mathbf{X}_n$ be independent with the common distribution F and $\mathbf{X}_n^* = \max(\mathbf{X}_1, \ldots, \mathbf{X}_n)$. Let G_n be the distribution of $a_n^{-1}\mathbf{X}_n^*$.

(*a*) If $F(x) = 1 - e^{-x}$ and $a_n = n$ then G_n tends to the distribution concentrated at the point 1. Show directly that no choice of a_n leads to more discriminating results.

(*b*) If F is the Cauchy distribution with density $\dfrac{1}{\pi(1+x^2)}$ and $a_n = n/\pi$, then $G_n(x) \to e^{-x^{-1}}$ for $x > 0$.

27. If $\mathbf{X}$ and $\mathbf{Y}$ have a common distribution F such that $1 - F(x) \sim x^{-\rho} L(x)$ with L slowly varying, then

$$\mathbf{P}\{\mathbf{X} > t \mid \mathbf{X} + \mathbf{Y} > t\} \to \tfrac{1}{2}$$

as $t \to \infty$. Roughly speaking, a large value for the sum is likely to be due to the contribution of one of the two variables.[27]

28. Let $v > 0$ and $a > 0$ on $\overline{0, \infty}$ and suppose that

$$\lim_{t\to\infty} [a(t)\, v(tx) + b(t)x] = z(x)$$

exists and depends continuously on x. For fixed $x_0 > 0$ prove that $\dfrac{v(x_0x)}{x_0x} - \dfrac{v(x)}{x}$ varies regularly. Conclude that either $z(x) = cx^\alpha$ or $z(x) = cx + c_1 x \log x$.

29. Let F be atomic with weight proportional to $n^{-1}2^{-2n}$ at the point 2^n. Show that U_2, as defined in (9.10), is slowly varying and $U_2(\infty) = \infty$, but that $1 - F$ does not vary regularly.

Hint: For the last statement it suffices to consider the magnitude of the jumps.

30. For a probability distribution F concentrated on $\overline{0, \infty}$ define U_ζ as in (9.10) and

$$(*) \qquad V_\sigma(x) = \int_x^\infty y^{-\sigma} F\{dy\}.$$

Theorem 9.2 generalizes as follows. Let F possess moments of orders $<\alpha$, but not of orders $>\alpha > 0$. Then either U_ζ and V_σ vary regularly for *all* $\zeta > \alpha$ and

[27] The phenomenon as such seems to have been noticed first by B. Mandelbrot.

all $\sigma > -\alpha$ or for no such value. In the first case the exponents are $\zeta - \alpha$ and $\sigma - \alpha$, and this case arises iff

$$(**) \qquad \frac{x^{\sigma+\zeta}\, V_\sigma(x)}{U^\zeta} \to \frac{\zeta - \alpha}{\sigma + \alpha}$$

$(0 < \alpha < \zeta)$. If U_ζ varies slowly, (**) holds with $\alpha = \zeta$; if V_σ varies slowly the left side tends to ∞. [The special case $\sigma = 0$ reduces to (9.11).]

Hint: The proof of theorem 2 carries over, but the assertions may be obtained from theorem 2 by a mere change of notations.

31. Let G be a symmetric stable distribution, that is, $G^{r\bigstar}(c_r x) = G(x)$ (see VI,1) From the last corollary in section 8 conclude that $1 - G(x) \sim x^{-\alpha} L(x)$ with $\alpha < 2$ unless $r[1 - G(c_r x)] \to 0$ in which case G is the normal distribution.

Hint: The sequence $r[1 - G(c_r x)]$ remains bounded by the symmetrization inequality V,(5.10). The remainder is easy.

32. Generalize to unsymmetric stable distributions.

CHAPTER IX

Infinitely Divisible Distributions and Semi-groups

The purpose of this chapter is to show that the basic theorems concerning infinitely divisible distributions, processes with independent increments, and stable distributions and their domains of attraction can be derived by a natural extension of the argument used to prove the central limit theorem. *The theory will be developed anew and amplified by methods of Fourier analysis*, and for this reason the present outline is limited to the basic facts. The interest in the chapter is largely methodological, to tie the present topics to the general theory of Markov processes; when applicable, the methods of Fourier analysis lead to sharper results. To provide easy access to important facts some theorems are proved twice. Thus the general structure theorem is first proved for semi-groups of distributions with variances. In this way sections 1–4 present a self-contained exposition of basic facts.

The semi-group operators in this chapter are convolutions. Other semi-groups will be considered independently in the next chapter by new methods.

1. ORIENTATION

The limit theorems of this chapter are a natural extension of the central limit theorem, and the infinitely divisible distributions are closely related to the normal distribution. To see this it is worthwhile to repeat the proof of theorem VIII,4.1 in a slightly different setting.

We consider this time an arbitrary triangular array $\{\mathbf{X}_{k,n}\}$ where for each n the n variables[1] $\mathbf{X}_{1,n}, \ldots, \mathbf{X}_{n,n}$ are independent and have a *common*

[1] Triangular arrays were defined in VI,3. It should be borne in mind that we are really dealing with distribution functions $F_{k,n}$; the random variables $\mathbf{X}_{k,n}$ serve merely to simplify notations. Accordingly, the variables of different rows need not be related in any way (and need not be defined on the same probability space).

distribution F_n. For the row sums we write $\mathbf{S}_n = \mathbf{X}_{1,n} + \cdots + \mathbf{X}_{n,n}$. In chapter VIII we dealt with the special case where $\mathbf{X}_{k,n} = \mathbf{X}_k a_n^{-1}$ and $F_n(x) = F(a_n x)$. There the row sums were denoted by $\mathbf{S}_n^*$.

Throughout this chapter we use the operational notation of VIII,3. Thus $\mathfrak{F}_n$ is the operator associated with F_n and $\mathfrak{F}_n{}^n$ is associated with the distribution of $\mathbf{S}_n$. Finally, $\|u\|$ denotes the maximum of the continuous function u.

Example. (*a*) *Central limit theorem.* Suppose that there exist numbers $\epsilon_n \to 0$ such that

$$(1.1) \qquad |\mathbf{X}_{1,n}| < \epsilon_n, \qquad \mathbf{E}(\mathbf{X}_{1,n}) = 0, \qquad n\mathbf{E}(\mathbf{X}_{1,n}^2) \to 1.$$

For a function u with three bounded derivatives we have the identity

$$(1.2) \quad n[\mathfrak{F}_n u(x) - u(x)] = \int_{-\epsilon_n}^{\epsilon_n} \frac{u(x-y) - u(x) + y\,u'(x)}{y^2} \cdot ny^2\, F_n\{dy\}.$$

The finite measure $ny^2\, F_n\{dy\}$ converges by assumption to the probability distribution concentrated at the origin. The fraction under the integral is a continuous function of y and differs from $\frac{1}{2}u''(x)$ by less than $\epsilon_n\|u'''\|$. Thus

$$(1.3) \qquad n[\mathfrak{F}_n u - u] \to \tfrac{1}{2}u''$$

uniformly in x.

Suppose now that $\{\mathfrak{G}_n\}$ is a second sequence of operators such that $n[\mathfrak{G}_n u - u]$ tends uniformly to $\frac{1}{2}u''$. Then

$$(1.4) \qquad n(\mathfrak{F}_n u - \mathfrak{G}_n u) \to 0$$

uniformly. By the basic inequality VIII,(3.10) (which will be used constantly in the sequel)

$$(1.5) \qquad \|\mathfrak{F}_n{}^n u - \mathfrak{G}_n{}^n u\| \le n\|\mathfrak{F}_n u - \mathfrak{G}_n u\|,$$

and the right side tends to zero in consequence of (1.4). As we have seen in the proof of theorem 1 in VIII,4, we may choose for $\mathfrak{G}_n$ the operator associated with the symmetric normal distribution with variance $1/n$. Then $\mathfrak{G}_n{}^n = \mathfrak{G}_1$ and hence $\mathfrak{F}_n{}^n \to \mathfrak{G}_1$. We have thus proved that *the distribution of* $\mathbf{S}_n$ *tends to the normal distribution* $\mathfrak{N}$. ▶

In scrutinizing the structure of this proof it is seen that the form of the right side in (1.3) played no role. Suppose we had an array such that (uniformly)

$$(1.6) \qquad n[\mathfrak{F}_n u - u] \to \mathfrak{A}u$$

where $\mathfrak{A}$ is an arbitrary, but fixed, operator. Our argument permits us to compare any two arrays satisfying (1.6) and to conclude that their row sums behave asymptotically in the same way. If for *one* such array the distributions of $\mathbf{S}_n$ tend to a limit G then the same will be true for *all* our arrays. We shall prove that this is always the case.

Example. (*b*) *Poisson distribution.* Suppose $\mathbf{X}_{1,n}$ equals 1 with probability p_n, and 0 with probability $1 - p_n$. If $np_n \to \alpha$

$$(1.7)\quad n[\mathfrak{F}_n u(x) - u(x)] = np_n[u(x-1) - u(x)] \to \alpha[u(x-1) - u(x)].$$

This time we take for $\mathfrak{G}_n$ the operator associated with the Poisson distribution with expectation α/n. An easy calculation shows that also $n[\mathfrak{G}_n u - u]$ tends to the right side in (1.7) and we conclude as before that $\mathfrak{F}_n{}^n u \to \mathfrak{G}_1$. Thus the distribution of $\mathbf{S}_n$ tends to the Poisson distribution with expectation α. [The right side in (1.7) illustrates one possible form for the operator $\mathfrak{A}$ in (1.6). For another example of a simple triangular array see problem 2.] ►

In the two examples we were fortunate in knowing the limit distribution in advance. In general the triangular array as such will serve to define the limit and in this way we shall derive new distribution functions. This procedure was used in **1**; VI to *define* the Poisson distribution as a limit of binomial distributions.

We recall from VI,3 that the limit distributions of the sums $\mathbf{S}_n$ are called *infinitely divisible*. We shall show that such a limit distribution exists whenever a relation of the form (1.6) holds, and that this condition is also necessary. Another approach to the problem depends on the study of the measures $ny^2\, F_n\{dy\}$. In both examples a limit measure existed; in example (*a*) it was concentrated at the origin, in (*b*) at the point 1. In general, the relation (1.6) is intimately connected with the existence of a measure Ω such that $ny^2\, F_n\{dy\} \to \Omega\{dy\}$, and infinitely divisible distributions will be characterized either by the operator $\mathfrak{A}$ or the measure Ω (which may be unbounded).

A third approach to the problem starts from the solution of the convolution equation

$$(1.8)\qquad Q_s \bigstar Q_t = Q_{s+t}$$

in which Q_t is a probability distribution depending on the parameter $t > 0$. [The normal and the Poisson distributions satisfy (1.8) with t proportional to the variance.] We get a triangular array by identifying F_n with $Q_{1/n}$ and the relation (1.6) is equivalent to

$$(1.9)\qquad \frac{1}{t}\,[Q_t \bigstar u - u] \to \mathfrak{A}u$$

as t runs through $\frac{1}{2}, \frac{1}{3}, \ldots$. One should expect that (1.9) will hold for an arbitrary approach $t \to 0+$.

Now (1.8) is the basic equation for processes with *stationary independent increments* (VI,4) and is closely connected with semi-group theory. In this context $\mathfrak{A}$ appears as a "generator." It turns out that this theory provides the easiest access to limit theorems and to infinitely divisible distributions, and hence we begin with it.

2. CONVOLUTION SEMI-GROUPS

For $t > 0$ let Q_t be a probability distribution in $\mathcal{R}^1$ satisfying (1.8) and $\mathfrak{Q}(t)$ the associated operator, that is,

$$\mathfrak{Q}(t)\, u(x) = \int_{-\infty}^{+\infty} u(x-y)\, Q_t\{dy\}. \tag{2.1}$$

Then (1.8) is equivalent to

$$\mathfrak{Q}(s+t) = \mathfrak{Q}(s)\, \mathfrak{Q}(t). \tag{2.2}$$

A family of operators satisfying (2.2) is called a *semi-group*. [It fails to be a group because in general $\mathfrak{Q}(t)$ has no inverse.] The operators of a semi-group may be of an arbitrary nature and it is convenient to have a word to indicate our requirement that $\mathfrak{Q}(t)$ be associated with a probability distribution.

Definition 1. *A convolution semi-group* $\{\mathfrak{Q}(t)\}$ (*where* $t > 0$) *is a family of operators associated with probability distributions and satisfying* (2.2).

We take $C_0[-\infty, \infty]$ as domain of definition. The operators $\mathfrak{Q}(t)$ are transition operators, that is, $0 \le u \le 1$ implies $0 \le \mathfrak{Q}(t)u \le 1$ and we have $\mathfrak{Q}(t)1 = 1$.

We shall have to deal with operators [such as d^2/dx^2 in (1.3)] which are not defined for all continuous functions. For our present purposes it is fortunately possible to avoid tedious discussions of the precise domain of definition of such operators since we need consider only the class of functions u such that $u \in C[-\infty, \infty]$ and u has derivatives of all orders belonging to $C[-\infty, \infty]$. Such functions will be called *infinitely differentiable*,[2] and their class will be denoted by C^∞. For the present we consider only operators $\mathfrak{A}$ defined for all $u \in C^\infty$ and such that $\mathfrak{A}u \in C^\infty$, and so all occurring operators may be taken as *operators from* C^∞ to C^∞.

[2] The class C^∞ is introduced only to avoid a new term. It could be replaced by the class of functions with (say) four bounded derivatives, or (simpler still) by the class of all linear combinations of normal distribution functions with arbitrary expectations and variances.

For operators associated with probability distributions we saw in VIII,3 that $\mathfrak{F}_n \to \mathfrak{F}$ iff $\mathfrak{F}_n u \to \mathfrak{F}u$ for $u \in C^\infty$. We now extend this definition of convergence consistently to arbitrary operators.

Definition 2. *Let $\mathfrak{A}_n$ and $\mathfrak{A}$ be operators from C^∞ to C^∞. We say that $\mathfrak{A}_n$ converges to $\mathfrak{A}$, in symbols $\mathfrak{A}_n \to \mathfrak{A}$, if*

$$\|\mathfrak{A}_n u - \mathfrak{A}u\| \to 0 \tag{2.3}$$

for each $u \in C^\infty$.

Now (2.3) states that $\mathfrak{A}_n u \to \mathfrak{A}u$ *uniformly*. Conversely, if for each $u \in C^\infty$ the sequence $\{\mathfrak{A}_n u\}$ converges uniformly to a limit $v \in C^\infty$ an operator $\mathfrak{A}$ is defined by $\mathfrak{A}u = v$, and clearly $\mathfrak{A}_n \to \mathfrak{A}$.

Definition 3. *The convolution semi-group $\{\mathfrak{Q}(t)\}$ is continuous if*

$$\mathfrak{Q}(h) \to \mathbf{1} \qquad h \to 0+ \tag{2.4}$$

where $\mathbf{1}$ is the identity operator. In this case we put $\mathfrak{Q}(0) = \mathbf{1}$.

Since $\|\mathfrak{Q}(t)u\| \leq \|u\|$ we get from the definition (2.2) for $h > 0$

$$\|\mathfrak{Q}(t+h)u - \mathfrak{Q}(t)u\| \leq \|\mathfrak{Q}(h)u - u\|. \tag{2.5}$$

For h sufficiently small the left side will be $< \epsilon$ independently of t, and in this sense a continuous convolution semi-group is *uniformly continuous.*

Definition 4. *An operator $\mathfrak{A}$ from C^∞ to C^∞ is said to generate the convolution semi-group $\{\mathfrak{Q}(t)\}$ if as $h \to 0+$*

$$\frac{\mathfrak{Q}(h) - \mathbf{1}}{h} \to \mathfrak{A}. \tag{2.6}$$

We say, equivalently, that $\mathfrak{A}$ is the generator.[3]

Obviously a semi-group with a generator is automatically continuous. It will be shown that all continuous convolution semi-groups possess generators, but this is by no means obvious.

Formally (2.6) defines $\mathfrak{A}$ as derivative of $\mathfrak{Q}(t)$ at $t = 0$. Its existence implies differentiability at $t > 0$ since

$$\frac{\mathfrak{Q}(t+h) - \mathfrak{Q}(t)}{h} = \frac{\mathfrak{Q}(h) - \mathbf{1}}{h}\mathfrak{Q}(t) \to \mathfrak{A}\mathfrak{Q}(t) \tag{2.7}$$

as $h \to 0+$ and similarly for $h \to 0-$.

The first four among the following examples will be used in the sequel.

---

[3] Since we restrict the domain of definition of $\mathfrak{A}$ to C^∞ our terminology departs slightly from canonical usage as developed in E. Hille and R. S. Phillips (1957).

Examples. (*a*) *Compound Poisson semi-groups.* Let

$$Q_t = e^{-\alpha t}\sum_{k=0}^{\infty}\frac{(\alpha t)^k}{k!}\,F^{k\star} \tag{2.8}$$

be a compound Poisson distribution. Here

$$\mathfrak{Q}(h)u - u = (e^{-\alpha h} - 1)u + \alpha h e^{-\alpha h}\left[\mathfrak{F}u + \frac{\alpha h}{2!}\,\mathfrak{F}^2 u + \cdots\right]. \tag{2.9}$$

Dividing by h we see that (2.6) holds with $\mathfrak{A} = \alpha(\mathfrak{F} - \mathbf{1})$. Thus *the compound Poisson semi-group* (2.8) *is generated by* $\alpha(\mathfrak{F} - \mathbf{1})$ *and we shall indicate its elements by the abbreviation* $\mathfrak{Q}(t) = e^{\alpha(\mathfrak{F}-1)t}$.

(*b*) *Translations.* Denote by T_a the distribution concentrated at a and by $\mathfrak{T}(a)$ the associated operator. For fixed $\beta > 0$ the semi-group property $T_{\beta s}\star T_{\beta t} = T_{\beta(t+s)}$ holds and $\mathfrak{T}(\beta t)\,u(x) = u(x-\beta t)$. The graph of $\mathfrak{T}(\beta t)u$ is obtained by a translation from that of u and we speak of a *translation semi-group. The generator is given by* $-\beta\,\dfrac{d}{dx}$. Note that this generator is the limit as $h \to 0$ of the generator $\alpha(\mathfrak{F} - \mathbf{1})$ when $\alpha = \beta/h$ and F is concentrated at h. Now $\alpha(\mathfrak{F} - \mathbf{1})$ is a difference operator, and the passage to the limit was studied in VI,5. It is suggestive to indicate this semi-group by $\mathfrak{T}(t) = \exp\left(-\beta t\,\dfrac{d}{dx}\right)$.

(*c*) *Addition of generators.* Let $\mathfrak{A}_1$ and $\mathfrak{A}_2$ generate the convolution semi-groups $\{\mathfrak{Q}_1(t)\}$ and $\{\mathfrak{Q}_2(t)\}$. Then $\mathfrak{A}_1 + \mathfrak{A}_2$ *generates the convolution semi-group of operators* $\mathfrak{Q}(t) = \mathfrak{Q}_1(t)\;\mathfrak{Q}_2(t)$. [Such $\mathfrak{Q}(t)$ is associated with the convolution of the distributions associated with $\mathfrak{Q}_1(t)$ and $\mathfrak{Q}_2(t)$; see theorem 2 of VIII,3.] The assertion is obvious from the simple rearrangement

$$\begin{aligned}\frac{\mathfrak{Q}_1(h)\,\mathfrak{Q}_2(h) - \mathbf{1}}{h} &= \frac{\mathfrak{Q}_1(h) - \mathbf{1}}{h} + \mathfrak{Q}_1(h)\,\mathfrak{A}_2 + \\ &\quad + \mathfrak{Q}_1(h)\left[\frac{\mathfrak{Q}_2(h) - \mathbf{1}}{h} - \mathfrak{A}_2\right].\end{aligned} \tag{2.10}$$

(*d*) *Translated semi-groups.* As a special case we get the rule: if $\mathfrak{A}$ generates the semi-group of operators $\mathfrak{Q}(t)$ associated with the distributions Q_t, then $\mathfrak{A} - \beta\,d/dx$ generates a semi-group $\{\mathfrak{Q}^{\#}(t)\}$ such that $Q_t^{\#}(x) = Q_t(x-\beta t)$.

(*e*) *Gamma distributions.* The distributions with densities $e^{-x}x^{t-1}/\Gamma(t)$ form a semi-group. Here

$$\frac{\mathfrak{Q}(t) - \mathbf{1}}{t}\,u(x) = \frac{1}{\Gamma(t+1)}\int_0^{\infty}\frac{u(x-y) - u(x)}{y^{1-t}}\,e^{-y}\,dy. \tag{2.11}$$

As $t \to 0$ we get

$$\mathfrak{A}u(x) = \int_0^\infty \frac{u(x-y) - u(x)}{y} e^{-y}\, dy. \tag{2.12}$$

The integral converges if u is a bounded continuously differentiable function, for in this case the integrand is (for fixed x) a continuous function assuming the value $-u'(x)$ at $y = 0$.

(For further examples see problems 3 and 4.)

Note *on the Fokker–Planck equation.* Consider the family of functions defined by $v(t, x) = \mathfrak{Q}(t)f(x)$. The relation (2.7) states that for smooth f

$$\frac{\partial v}{\partial t} = \mathfrak{A}v. \tag{2.13}$$

This is the Fokker–Planck equation of the process, and v is its unique solution satisfying the initial condition $v(0, x) = f(x)$. Equation (2.13) describes the process, and unnecessary complications are introduced by the traditional attempts to replace (2.13) by an equation for the transition probabilities Q_t themselves. Consider, for example, a translated compound Poisson semi-group generated by $\mathfrak{A} = \alpha(\mathfrak{F} - \mathbf{1}) - \beta \dfrac{d}{dx}$. The Fokker–Planck equation (2.13) holds whenever the initial function $f(x) = v(0, x)$ has a continuous derivative. Its formal analogue for the transition probabilities is given by

$$\frac{\partial Q_t}{\partial t} = -\beta \frac{\partial Q_t}{\partial x} - \alpha Q_t + \alpha F \bigstar Q_t. \tag{2.14}$$

This equation makes sense only if Q has a density and is therefore impossible for discrete processes. The usual reliance on (2.14) instead of (2.13) only causes trouble.

3. PREPARATORY LEMMAS

In this section we collect a few simple lemmas on which the whole theory depends. Despite its simplicity the following inequality is basic.

Lemma 1. *If* $\mathfrak{A}$ *and* $\mathfrak{A}^\#$ *generate the convolution semi-groups* $\{\mathfrak{Q}(t)\}$ *and* $\{\mathfrak{Q}^\#(t)\}$, *respectively, then for all* $t > 0$

$$\|\mathfrak{Q}(t)u - \mathfrak{Q}^\#(t)u\| \leq t\|\mathfrak{A}u - \mathfrak{A}^\#u\|. \tag{3.1}$$

Proof. From the semi-group property and the basic inequality (1.5) we get for $r = 1, 2, \ldots$

$$\begin{aligned} \|\mathfrak{Q}(t)u - \mathfrak{Q}^\#(t)u\| &\leq r \left\| \mathfrak{Q}\left(\frac{t}{r}\right)u - \mathfrak{Q}^\#\left(\frac{t}{r}\right)u \right\| \\ &= t \left\| \frac{\mathfrak{Q}(t/r) - \mathbf{1}}{t/r} u - \frac{\mathfrak{Q}^\#(t/r) - \mathbf{1}}{t/r} u \right\|. \end{aligned} \tag{3.2}$$

As $r \to \infty$ the right side tends to the right side in (3.1) and so this inequality is true. ►

Corollary. *Distinct convolution semi-groups cannot have the same generator.*

Lemma 2. (*Convergence*). *For each n let $\mathfrak{A}_n$ generate the convolution semi-group $\{\mathfrak{Q}_n(t)\}$.*

If $\mathfrak{A}_n \to \mathfrak{A}$, *then* $\mathfrak{A}$ *generates a convolution semi-group* $\{\mathfrak{Q}(t)\}$, *and* $\mathfrak{Q}_n(t) \to \mathfrak{Q}(t)$ *for each* $t > 0$.

Proof. For each $t > 0$ the sequence $\{\mathfrak{Q}_n(t)u\}$ converges uniformly, since by (3.1)

$$\|\mathfrak{Q}_n(t)u - \mathfrak{Q}_m(t)u\| \leq t\|\mathfrak{A}_n u - \mathfrak{A}_m u\|. \tag{3.3}$$

By criterion 1 of VIII,3 there exists therefore an operator $\mathfrak{Q}(t)$ associated with a probability distribution such that $\mathfrak{Q}_n(t) \to \mathfrak{Q}(t)$. Then

$$\mathfrak{Q}_n(s)\, \mathfrak{Q}_n(t) \to \mathfrak{Q}(s)\, \mathfrak{Q}(t)$$

(by theorem 2 of VIII,3) and so $\{\mathfrak{Q}(t)\}$ is a convolution semi-group. To show that it is generated by $\mathfrak{A}$ note that

$$\left\| \frac{\mathfrak{Q}(t) - \mathbf{1}}{t} u - \mathfrak{A}u \right\| \leq \left\| \frac{\mathfrak{Q}_n(t) - \mathbf{1}}{t} u - \mathfrak{A}u \right\| + \frac{\|\mathfrak{Q}(t)u - \mathfrak{Q}_n(t)u\|}{t}. \tag{3.4}$$

Letting $m \to \infty$ in (3.3) it is seen that

$$\|\mathfrak{Q}(t)u - \mathfrak{Q}_n(t)u\| \leq t\|\mathfrak{A}u - \mathfrak{A}_n u\|. \tag{3.5}$$

For fixed n as $t \to 0$ the upper limit of the left side in (3.4) is therefore $<2\|\mathfrak{A}u - \mathfrak{A}_n u\|$ which can be made $<\epsilon$ by choosing n sufficiently large. ▶

The next lemma makes it at least plausible that every continuous convolution semi-group has a generator.

Lemma 3. *Let* $\{\mathfrak{Q}(t)\}$ *be a continuous convolution semi-group. If for some sequence* $t_1, t_2, \ldots, \to 0$

$$\frac{\mathfrak{Q}(t_k) - \mathbf{1}}{t_k} \to \mathfrak{A}, \tag{3.6}$$

then $\mathfrak{A}$ *generates the semi-group.*

Proof. Call the left side $\mathfrak{A}_k$. As was shown in example (2.*a*) this $\mathfrak{A}_k$ generates a compound Poisson semi-group and by the last lemma there exists a semi-group $\{\mathfrak{Q}^{\#}(t)\}$ generated by $\mathfrak{A}$. To show that $\mathfrak{Q}^{\#}(t) = \mathfrak{Q}(t)$ we proceed as in (3.2) to obtain

$$\|\mathfrak{Q}(rt_k)u - \mathfrak{Q}^{\#}(rt_k)u\| \leq rt_k \left\| \mathfrak{A}_k u - \frac{\mathfrak{Q}^{\#}(t_k) - \mathbf{1}}{t_k} u \right\|. \tag{3.7}$$

Let $k \to \infty$ and $r \to \infty$ so that $rt_k \to t$. The right side tends to 0 and the left to $\|\mathfrak{Q}(t)u - \mathfrak{Q}^{\#}(t)u\|$ by virtue of (2.5). ▶

These are the lemmas that will be of immediate use. The next is recorded here because it is merely a variant of lemma 2 and the proof is nearly the same. We shall use only the special case $\nu_n = n$ and $t = 1$, which will serve as the connecting link between triangular arrays and convolution semi-groups.

Lemma 4. *For each n let $\mathfrak{F}_n$ be the operator associated with the probability distribution F_n. If*

$$n(\mathfrak{F}_n - \mathbf{1}) \to \mathfrak{A}, \tag{3.8}$$

then $\mathfrak{A}$ generates a convolution semi-group $\{\mathfrak{Q}(t)\}$. If $n \to \infty$ and $\frac{\nu_n}{n} \to t$ then

$$\mathfrak{F}_n^{\nu_n} \to \mathfrak{Q}(t). \tag{3.9}$$

In particular, $\mathfrak{F}_n{}^n \to \mathfrak{Q}(1)$. The lemma remains true if n is restricted to a sequence $n_1, n_2, \ldots$.

Proof. The left side in (3.8) generates a compound Poisson semi-group [example (2*a*)] and so $\mathfrak{A}$ is a generator by lemma 2. By the basic inequality (1.5)

$$\left\| \mathfrak{F}_n^{\nu_n} u - \mathfrak{Q}\left(\frac{\nu_n}{n}\right) u \right\| \leq \frac{\nu_n}{n} \left\| n[\mathfrak{F}_n u - u] - n\left[\mathfrak{Q}\left(\frac{1}{n}\right)u - u\right] \right\| \tag{3.10}$$

and for $u \in C^\infty$ each of the terms within the norm signs tends uniformly to $\mathfrak{A}u$. ▶

4. FINITE VARIANCES

Semi-groups of distributions with finite variances are of special importance and their theory is so simple that it deserves a special treatment. Many readers will not be interested in the more complicated general semi-groups, and for others this section will provide an interesting introductory example.

We consider a convolution semi-group $\{\mathfrak{Q}(t)\}$ and denote the associated probability distributions by Q_t. Suppose that Q_t has a finite variance $\sigma^2(t)$. Because of the semi-group property $\sigma^2(s+t) = \sigma^2(s) + \sigma^2(t)$ and the only positive solution of this equation[4] is of the form $\sigma^2(t) = ct$.

[4] The equation $\varphi(s+t) = \varphi(s) + \varphi(t)$ is called the Hamel equation. Putting $u(t) = e^{\varphi(t)}$ one gets $u(s+t) = u(s)\,u(t)$ in which form the equation was encountered several times and is treated in **1**; XVII,6. The expectation of Q_t is also a solution of the Hamel equation; it is therefore either of the form mt or exceedingly weird. See section 5*a*.

Suppose that Q_t is centered to zero expectation. We have then the identity

$$(4.1)\qquad \frac{\mathfrak{Q}(t)-\mathbf{1}}{t}\,u(x) = c\int_{-\infty}^{+\infty}\frac{u(x-y)-u(x)+y\,u'(x)}{y^2}\,\Omega_t\{dy\}$$

where Ω_t is the *probability distribution* defined by

$$(4.2)\qquad \Omega_t\{dy\} = \frac{1}{ct}\,y^2\,Q_t\{dy\}.$$

As we consider only $u \in C^\infty$ the integrand is (for fixed x) a continuous function of y vanishing at infinity. By the selection theorem there exists a sequence $t_1, t_2, \ldots \to 0$ such that as t runs through it $\Omega_t\{dy\} \to \Omega\{dy\}$ where Ω is a possibly defective probability distribution.

Define the operator $\mathfrak{A}$ by

$$(4.3)\qquad \mathfrak{A}u(x) = c\int_{-\infty}^{+\infty}\frac{u(x-y)-u(x)+y\,u'(x)}{y^2}\,\Omega\{dy\}.$$

When t runs through $t_1, t_2, \ldots$ the right side in (4.1) tends to $\mathfrak{A}u(x)$ and the convergence is uniform in x because the integrand is uniformly continuous and uniformly small at infinity. By lemma 3.3 therefore the semi-group $\{\mathfrak{Q}(t)\}$ has the generator $\mathfrak{A}$ defined by (4.3).

We have thus proved the existence of a generator and found the representation (4.3) for it. To see that it is unique note that for functions of the form

$$(4.4)\qquad u(x) = 1 + \frac{x^2}{1+x^2}f(-x)$$

one gets from (4.3)

$$(4.5)\qquad \mathfrak{A}u(0) = c\int_{-\infty}^{+\infty}\frac{f(y)}{1+y^2}\,\Omega\{dy\}.$$

The knowledge of $\mathfrak{A}u$ for all $u \in C^\infty$ therefore uniquely determines the measure $(1+y^2)^{-1}\,\Omega\{dy\}$ and hence Ω itself.

In consequence of this uniqueness the limit distribution Ω is independent of the sequence $\{t_k\}$ and hence $\Omega_t\{dy\} \to \Omega\{dy\}$ for any approach $t \to 0$.

We shall show that Ω is a proper probability distribution and that every operator of the form (4.3) is a generator. The proof depends on two special cases contained in the following

Examples. (*a*) *Normal semi-groups.* With $Q_t(x) = \mathfrak{N}(x/\sqrt{t})$ the distributions $\Omega_t\{dy\}$ tend to the probability distribution concentrated at the origin. For $y = 0$ the value of the integrand in (4.3) equals $\frac{1}{2}u''(x)$, and so in this case $\mathfrak{A} = \frac{1}{2}(d^2/dx^2)$.

(*b*) *Compound Poisson semi-groups.* Let c be a positive constant, and let Ω be a measure with total mass $\omega > 0$ concentrated on the two intervals $|y| > \eta > 0$. There exists then a unique probability measure F of the form $\alpha F\{dy\} = cy^{-2}\,\Omega\{dy\}$. Denote the first two moments of F by m_1 and m_2. The operator $\mathfrak{A}$ of (4.3) is identical with $\alpha(\mathfrak{F} - \mathbf{1}) + \alpha m_1 \dfrac{d}{dx}$. Now $\alpha(\mathfrak{F} - \mathbf{1})$ generates a semi-group of compound Poisson distributions with expectation $\alpha m_1 t$ and variance $\alpha m_2 t$. Adding $\alpha m_1 \dfrac{d}{dx}$ to the generator reduces the expectation to zero without affecting the variance [example (2.*d*)]. Thus under the stated conditions the operator $\mathfrak{A}$ of (4.3) generates a semi-group of distributions Q_t with zero expectation and variance $\alpha m_2 t = c\omega t$. ▶

We are now in a position to formulate the basic

Theorem. *Let Q_t have zero expectation and variance ct. The convolution semi-group $\{\mathfrak{Q}(t)\}$ has then a generator $\mathfrak{A}$ of the form* (4.3) *where Ω is a proper probability distribution. The representation* (4.3) *is unique. Conversely, every operator of this form generates a convolution semi-group of distributions with zero expectation and variance ct.*

Proof. We have shown the existence of a generator of the form (4.3) but have proved only that Ω has a total mass $\omega \leq 1$. It remains to prove that if Ω has a mass ω then the operator $\mathfrak{A}$ of (4.3) generates a semi-group such that Q_t has zero expectation and a variance $\leq c\omega t$.

Let $\mathfrak{A}_\eta$ be the operator obtained from (4.3) by restricting the integration to the intervals $|y| > \eta$ and the atom at the origin, if any. Then $\mathfrak{A}_\eta$ is the sum of two operators of the described types and by the addition rule for generators [example (2.*c*)] the operator $\mathfrak{A}_\eta$ generates a semi-group $\{\mathfrak{Q}_\eta(t)\}$ such that the associated distributions $Q_{t,\eta}$ have zero expectation and variance $\leq c\omega t$. Accordingly $\mathfrak{A}$ generates a semi-group $\{\mathfrak{Q}(t)\}$ such that $Q_{t,\eta} \to Q_t$. Since the second moments of $Q_{t,\eta}$ are bounded by $c\omega t$ it follows that Q_t has zero expectation and a variance $\leq c\omega t$ [example VIII,(1.*e*)]. This completes the proof. ▶

Example. (*c*) In example (2.*e*) we have $\Omega\{dy\} = ye^{-y}\,dy$. To put the operator of (2.12) into the canonical form (4.3) add the term $yu'(x)$ to the integrand and subtract $u'(x)$ outside the integral. It follows that Q_t has expectation t. ▶

5. THE MAIN THEOREMS

In this section $\{\mathfrak{Q}(t)\}$ stands for an arbitrary continuous convolution semi-group, and the associated distribution functions are again denoted by Q_t. The last proof depended on the existence of a measure Ω such that

$$\frac{1}{t}\, y^2\, Q_t\{dy\} \to \Omega\{dy\}. \tag{5.1}$$

Such a measure exists always, but it is not necessarily finite. Instead it satisfies the condition

$$\int_{-\infty}^{+\infty} \frac{1}{1+y^2}\,\Omega\{dy\} < \infty \tag{5.2}$$

which ensures that the measure $\Omega\{\overline{-x,\, x}\}$ does not increase too fast.

The existence of a limit in (5.1) is easily established assuming the existence of a generator (problem 8), but it is more difficult to prove that a generator does indeed exist. To prove this we return to the notations of section 1. For each n we consider the sum $\mathbf{S}_n = \mathbf{X}_{1,n} + \cdots + \mathbf{X}_{n,n}$ of n mutually independent variables with a common distribution F_n. Then $\mathfrak{F}_n{}^n$ is the operator associated with the distribution of $\mathbf{S}_n$. We are interested primarily in the case $\mathfrak{F}_n = \mathfrak{Q}(1/n)$ but arbitrary $\mathfrak{F}_n$ are used in connection with limit theorems. The problem is to investigate the asymptotic behavior of the operator $n[\mathfrak{F}_n - \mathbf{1}]$. We use a representation analogous to (4.1) but are compelled to use truncated expectations.

For fixed $s > 0$ the *truncation function* τ_s is defined by

$$\tau_s(x) = \begin{cases} x & |x| \le s \\ s \qquad \text{for} & x \ge s \\ -s & x \le -s. \end{cases} \tag{5.3}$$

Our starting point is the *identity*

$$\begin{aligned} &n(\mathfrak{F}_n - \mathbf{1})\, u(x) = \\ &\quad = \int_{-\infty}^{+\infty} \frac{u(x-y) - u(x) + u'(x)\,\tau_s(y)}{y^2}\, ny^2\, F_n\{dy\} - b_n\, u'(x) \end{aligned} \tag{5.4}$$

where

$$b_n = n \int_{-\infty}^{+\infty} \tau_s(y)\, F_n\{dy\}. \tag{5.5}$$

For the smooth functions u under consideration the fraction under the integral is (for fixed x) a continuous function of y assuming the value $\frac{1}{2}u''(x)$ at the origin. For $|y| < s$ the numerator is bounded by $y^2\|u''\|$, and for $|y| \ge s$ by $2\|u\| + s\|u'\|$.

The following lemma is an easy consequence of the compactness lemma for triangular arrays. We postpone the proof to section 7.

Lemma. *If the variables* $\{\mathbf{S}_n\}$ *have a proper limit distribution there exists a measure* Ω *satisfying* (5.2) *and a sequence* $n_1, n_2, \ldots$ *of integers such that as* n *runs through it*

$$ny^2\, F_n\{dy\} \to \Omega\{dy\}. \tag{5.6}$$

Furthermore, to each $\epsilon > 0$ *there corresponds a number a such that for all n*

$$n[1 - F_n(a) + F_n(-a)] < \epsilon. \tag{5.7}$$

Finally, the sequence $\{b_n\}$ *is bounded.*

Because of the boundedness of $\{b_n\}$ there is no loss of generality in assuming that as n runs through $n_1, n_2, \ldots$

$$b_n \to b. \tag{5.8}$$

Define an operator $\mathfrak{A}^{(0)}$ by

$$\mathfrak{A}^{(0)}u(x) = \int_{-\infty}^{+\infty} \frac{u(x-y) - u(x) + u'(x)\,\tau_s(y)}{y^2}\,\Omega\{dy\}. \tag{5.9}$$

[The integral converges because of (5.2) and the bounds on the integrand discussed after (5.5).] Under the conditions of the lemma the contribution of the region $|y| > a > s$ to the integral in (5.4) is $\leq 2\,\|u\|\epsilon + s\,\|u'\|\,\epsilon$ when a is sufficiently large; the contribution of $|y| \leq a$ tends to the corresponding integral with respect to Ω, at least if Ω has no atoms at $\pm a$. Letting $a \to \infty$ we see that

$$n[\mathfrak{F}_n - \mathbf{1}]u \to \mathfrak{A}^{(0)}u - bu' \tag{5.10}$$

the convergence being uniform. Both $\mathfrak{A}^{(0)}$ and b depend on the truncation constant s, but the left side is independent of s and therefore the effect of a change of s on $\mathfrak{A}^{(0)}$ is compensated by the effect on b.

Theorem 1. *A continuous convolution semi-group* $\{\mathfrak{Q}(t)\}$ *has a generator* $\mathfrak{A}$, *and* $\mathfrak{A}$ *is of the form*

$$\mathfrak{A} = \mathfrak{A}^{(0)} - b\frac{d}{dx} \tag{5.11}$$

with $\mathfrak{A}^{(0)}$ *defined by* (5.9) *where* Ω *is a measure satisfying* (5.2).

Conversely, every operator $\mathfrak{A}$ *of this form generates a convolution semi-group* $\{\mathfrak{Q}(t)\}$. *The measure* Ω *is unique.*

Proof. If $\mathfrak{F}_n = \mathfrak{Q}(1/n)$, the row sums $\mathbf{S}_n$ have the distribution Q_1 independent of n. Hence the lemma applies and (5.10) states that

$$\frac{1}{t}\,[\mathfrak{Q}(t) - \mathbf{1}] \to \mathfrak{A} \tag{5.12}$$

as t runs through the sequence $\frac{1}{n_1}, \frac{1}{n_2}, \ldots$. Accordingly, $\mathfrak{A}$ is the generator of $\{\mathfrak{Q}(t)\}$ by virtue of lemma 3.3.

We know already that $\mathfrak{A}$ generates a semi-group (with finite variances) whenever Ω is *finite*, and from the convergence lemma 3.2 we conclude that all our operators are generators. The uniqueness follows as in section 4 because for functions of the form (4.4) one gets (4.5) (without factor c). Therefore the knowledge of $\mathfrak{A}u$ determines Ω. This completes the proof. ►

We are now in a position to formulate the various characterizations of infinitely divisible distributions which serve as basis for the whole theory. We combine them in one theorem, of which part (iv) is by far the deepest and most unexpected. For the history see VI,3.

Theorem 2. *The following classes of probability distributions are identical.*

(i) *Distributions associated with operators* $\mathfrak{Q}(t)$ *of continuous convolution semi-groups* (*in other words, distributions of increments in processes with stationary independent increments*).

(ii) *Limits of sequences of compound Poisson distributions.*

(iii) *Infinitely divisible distributions and limits of such distributions.*

(iv) *Limit distributions of row sums* $\mathbf{S}_n$ *in triangular arrays* $\{\mathbf{X}_{k,n}\}$ *where* $\mathbf{X}_{1,n}, \mathbf{X}_{2,n}, \ldots$ *have a common distribution.*

Proof. By theorem 1 every continuous semi-group possesses a generator $\mathfrak{A}$, and by the very definition $\mathfrak{A}$ is the limit of operators $t^{-1}(\mathfrak{Q}(t) - \mathbf{1})$. As was shown in example (2.*a*) these operators generate compound Poisson semi-groups, and so the convergence lemma 3.2 guarantees that each element Q_t of a continuous semi-group is the limit of a sequence of compound Poisson distributions. Thus (i) is included in (ii), and (ii) is trivially included in (iii). Next, any infinitely divisible distribution $G^{(n)}$ may be taken as the distribution of the sum $\mathbf{S}_n = \mathbf{X}_{1,n} + \cdots + \mathbf{X}_{n,n}$ of n identically distributed independent random variables. It follows that the limit G of a sequence of infinitely divisible distributions $G^{(n)}$ is automatically the limit distribution of the row sums $\mathbf{S}_n$ of an appropriate triangular array, and so (iii) is contained in (iv). Finally, if the row sums $\mathbf{S}_n$ of a triangular array have a limit distribution G, then the last lemma asserts that (5.10) holds at least when n runs through an appropriate sequence $n_1, n_2, \ldots$. By lemma 3.4 the limit G coincides with the element Q_1 of the semi-group generated by operator on the right side in (5.10). Thus (iv) is included in (i), and this completes the proof. ►

It follows from theorem 1 that, up to an arbitrary centering, the semi-group $\{\mathfrak{Q}(t)\}$ is determined by the measure Ω which, in turn, is determined by (5.1). Sometimes it is more convenient to describe the semi-group in terms of the functions ψ^+ and ψ^- defined on the right and the left half-axes, respectively, by

$$(5.13) \qquad \psi^+(x) = \int_x^\infty \frac{1}{y^2}\,\Omega\{dy\}, \qquad \psi^-(-x) = \int_{-\infty}^{-x} \frac{1}{y^2}\,\Omega\{dy\}, \qquad x > 0.$$

(For definiteness we may take the intervals of integration closed.) These functions uniquely determine Ω except for a possible atom at the origin. The relation (5.1) implies that

$$(5.14) \qquad \frac{1}{t}[1 - Q_t(x)] \to \psi^+(x), \qquad \frac{1}{t}Q_t(-x) \to \psi^-(-x)$$

at all points of continuity. We record this result in the form of a

Corollary. *For every continuous convolution semi-group the relations* (5.1) *and* (5.14) *hold.*

Example. (*a*) *Cauchy semi-group.* Let Q_t have density $\pi^{-1}t[t^2 + x^2]^{-1}$. The semi-group property is satisfied, and obviously

$$\psi^+(x) = \psi^-(-x) = (\pi x)^{-1}.$$

The measure Ω is given by $\Omega\{dy\} = \pi^{-1}\,dy$. ▶

Application to stochastic processes. Let $\mathbf{X}(t)$ be the variable of a stochastic process with *stationary independent increments* (VI,4) and let us interpret Q_t as the distribution of the increment $\mathbf{X}(t+s) - \mathbf{X}(s)$. Consider a time interval $\overline{s,\ s+1}$ of unit length and subdivide it by the points $s = s_0 < s_1 < \cdots < s_n = s + 1$ into subintervals of length n^{-1}. Then $\mathbf{P}\{\mathbf{X}(s_k) - \mathbf{X}(s_{k-1}) > x\} = 1 - Q_{1/n}(x)$ and so $n[1 - Q_{1/n}(x)]$ equals the expected number of intervals $\overline{s_{k-1}, s_k}$ with increment $>x$. As $n \to \infty$ this expected number tends to $\psi^+(x)$. For simplicity of discussion suppose that the limits $\mathbf{X}(t+)$ and $\mathbf{X}(t-)$ exist for all t and that $\mathbf{X}(t)$ lies between them. Let $\overline{s_{k-1}, s_k}$ be the interval of our partition containing t. For n sufficiently large the increment $\mathbf{X}(s_k) - \mathbf{X}(s_{k-1})$ will be close to the jump $\mathbf{X}(t+) - \mathbf{X}(t-)$ and it is intuitively clear that the limit $\psi^+(x)$ *represents the expected number of epochs t per unit time at which* $\mathbf{X}(t+) - \mathbf{X}(t-) > x$. The argument may be justified rigorously but we shall not enter into details. It follows from this result that the expected number of discontinuities is zero only if $\psi^+(x) = 0$ and $\psi^-(-x) = 0$ for all $x > 0$. In this case Ω is concentrated at the origin, that is, the increments $\mathbf{X}(t+s) - \mathbf{X}(s)$ are normally distributed. For such a process the paths are continuous with probability one (theorem of P. Lévy and N. Wiener) and so *the paths are continuous with probability* 1 *iff the process is normal.*

As a second illustration consider the *compound Poisson process* (2.8). The expected number of jumps per unit time is α, and the probability of a jump exceeding $x > 0$ is $1 - F(x)$. Thus $\alpha[1 - F(x)]$ is the expected number of jumps $>x$ in full agreement with our intuitive argument.

*5a. Discontinuous Semi-groups

It is natural to ask whether there exist discontinuous semi-groups. The question is of no practical importance but the answer has some curiousity value: *Every convolution semi-group* $\{\mathfrak{Q}(t)\}$ *differs merely by centering from a continuous semi-group* $\{\mathfrak{Q}^{\#}(t)\}$. In particular, *if the distributions* Q_t *are symmetric the semi-group is necessarily continuous.* In the general case there exists a function φ such that the distributions $Q_t^{\#}$ defined by $Q_t(x + \varphi(t))$ *are associated with a continuous semi-group*. The function φ must obviously satisfy

$$\varphi(t+s) = \varphi(t) + \varphi(s). \tag{5.15}$$

This is the famous Hamel equation[4] whose only continuous solution is of the form ct. In fact, the only Baire function satisfying (5.15) is linear. The other solutions are weird indeed; for example, a non-linear solution assumes in *every* interval arbitrarily large and arbitrarily small values, and it is impossible to represent it analytically by limiting processes. In short, it is fair to ask in what precise sense it "exists."

To return to earth, consider an arbitrary convolution semi-group $\{\mathfrak{Q}(t)\}$ and the triangular array $\{\mathbf{X}_{k,n}\}$ associated with the distributions $Q_{1/n}$. The row sums $\mathbf{S}_n$ have the common distribution Q_1 and hence we can use the last lemma to extract a sequence $n_1, n_2, \ldots$ such that as n runs through it $n[\mathfrak{Q}(1/n) - 1] \to \mathfrak{A}^{\#}$ where $\mathfrak{A}^{\#}$ is the generator of a continuous semi-group $\{\mathfrak{Q}^{\#}(t)\}$. We may choose the n_k of the form $2^{+\nu}$. The inequality (3.5) now shows that $\mathfrak{Q}(t) = \mathfrak{Q}^{\#}(t)$ for all t that are multiples of $1/n_k$ for arbitrarily large k, that is, for all t of the form $t = a2^{-\nu}$ with a and ν integers. Thus *there exists always a continuous semi-group* $\{\mathfrak{Q}^{\#}(t)\}$ *such that* $\mathfrak{Q}(t) = \mathfrak{Q}^{\#}(t)$ *for all t of a dense set* Σ.

We are now in a position to prove the initial proposition. Choose $\epsilon_n > 0$ such that $t + \epsilon_n$ is in Σ. Then

$$\mathfrak{Q}^{\#}(t+\epsilon_n) = \mathfrak{Q}(t+\epsilon_n) = \mathfrak{Q}(t)\,\mathfrak{Q}(\epsilon_n). \tag{5.16}$$

As $\epsilon_n \to 0$ the left side tends to $\mathfrak{Q}^{\#}(t)$ and hence it suffices to show that if $\mathfrak{Q}(\epsilon_n) \to \mathfrak{F}$ then the distribution F is concentrated at a single point. Choose points h_n in Σ such that $0 < \epsilon_n < h_n$ and $h_n \to 0$. Then $\mathfrak{Q}^{\#}(h_n) = \mathfrak{Q}(h_n - \epsilon_n)\,\mathfrak{Q}(\epsilon_n)$. The left side tends to the identity operator, and so F can indeed have only one point of increase.

6. EXAMPLE: STABLE SEMI-GROUPS

A semi-group $\{\mathfrak{Q}(t)\}$ is called *stable* if its distributions are of the form

$$Q_t(x) = G(\lambda_t(x - \beta_t)) \tag{6.1}$$

where $\lambda_t > 0$ and β_t are constants depending continuously on t, and G is a fixed distribution. Obviously G is a stable distribution as defined in VI,1. The theory of stable semi-groups is here developed principally as an illustration for the results of the last section and to put on record the form of their generators. In an indirect way the results of this section are derived independently in section 8.

Because of the assumed continuity of λ_t and β_t the semi-group (if it

[4] See footnote 4 to section 4.

exists) is continuous. Furthermore $\lambda_t \to \infty$ and $\beta_t \to 0$ as $t \to 0$. The first relation in (5.14) takes on the form

$$\frac{1 - G(\lambda_t(x-\beta_t))}{t} \to \psi^+(x), \qquad x > 0. \tag{6.2}$$

Since G is monotone and $\beta_t \to 0$ this relation remains valid when β_t is dropped. But (6.2) without β_t reduces to the defining relation for regular variation, and so by the theorem of VIII,8,

$$\psi^+(x) = c^+ x^{-\alpha}, \tag{6.3}$$

where $c^+ \geq 0$ is a constant. Here $\alpha > 0$ because $\psi^+(\infty) = 0$. This implies $\Omega\{dy\} = c^+\alpha y^{-\alpha+1}\, dy$ for $y > 0$. Here $\alpha < 2$ because finite intervals have finite measures.

Consider now the canonical form (5.9) of generators. Disregarding for the moment the trivial centering it is clear that the contribution of the right half-axis is represented by the operator $c^+\mathfrak{A}_\alpha^+$ where

$$\mathfrak{A}_\alpha^+ u(x) = \alpha \int_0^\infty \frac{u(x-y) - u(x)}{y^{\alpha+1}}\, dy \tag{6.4}$$

if $0 < \alpha < 1$, and

$$\mathfrak{A}_\alpha^+ u(x) = \alpha \int_0^\infty \frac{u(x-y) - u(x) + y\, u'(x)}{y^{\alpha+1}}\, dy \tag{6.5}$$

if $1 < \alpha < 2$; finally when $\alpha = 1$

$$\mathfrak{A}_1^+ u(x) = \int_0^\infty \frac{u(x-y) - u(x) + u'(x)\tau_1(y)}{y^2}\, dy. \tag{6.6}$$

A relation of the form (6.2) holds also for the left tail and for the tail sum. It follows that the left tail gives rise to analogous operators $\mathfrak{A}_\alpha^-$ with the same α. To piece the tails together we now define the operator

$$\mathfrak{A}_\alpha = c^+\mathfrak{A}_\alpha^+ + c^-\mathfrak{A}_\alpha^-. \tag{6.7}$$

The functions ψ^+ and ψ^- determine the measure Ω up to an atom at the origin and we have shown that *the generators of stable semi-groups are necessarily of the form*

$$\mathfrak{A} = \mathfrak{A}_\alpha + \gamma \frac{d^2}{dx^2} + \beta \frac{d}{dx}. \tag{6.8}$$

For $c^+ = c^- = 0$ we get $\mathfrak{A}_\alpha = 0$ and $\mathfrak{A}$ generates a *normal semi-group*. It is easily seen (and it will be shown in section 8) that in all other cases necessarily $\gamma = 0$. Accordingly, apart from normal semi-groups and the arbitrary centering, (6.7) represents the most general possible generator.

It remains to show that the semi-groups generated by $\mathfrak{A}_\alpha$ are really stable.

We show that *if* $\alpha \neq 1$ *the operator* $\mathfrak{A}_\alpha$ *generates a strictly stable semi-group of the form*

$$Q_s(x) = G\left(\frac{x}{s^{1/\alpha}}\right) \tag{6.9}$$

and for $\alpha = 1$ *a stable semi-group of the form*[5]

$$Q_t(x) = G\left(\frac{x}{t} - (c^+ - c^-)\log t\right). \tag{6.10}$$

Put $Q_t^{\#}(x) = Q_t(x/\rho)$ where $\rho > 0$ is a constant. Then Q_t and $Q_t^{\#}$ differ only by scale factors and so $\{\mathfrak{Q}^{\#}(t)\}$ is again a continuous semi-group. Putting $u_\rho(x) = u(\rho x)$ we have $\mathfrak{Q}^{\#}(t)u(x) = \mathfrak{Q}(t)u_\rho(x/\rho)$ and hence the generator $\mathfrak{A}^{\#}$ is obtained simply by changing x to ρx in the integrals defining $\mathfrak{A}$. [Thus $u'(x) = \dfrac{du(x)}{dx}$ is replaced by $\dfrac{1}{\rho}u'(\rho x)$.] For $\alpha \neq 1$ the substitution $y = z/\rho$ shows that $\mathfrak{A}_\alpha^{\#} = \rho^\alpha \mathfrak{A}_\alpha$. Now this $\mathfrak{A}_\alpha^{\#}$ generates the semi-group $\{\mathfrak{Q}(\rho^\alpha t)\}$ and in view of the uniqueness of generators this implies that $\mathfrak{Q}^{\#}(\rho^{-\alpha}t) = \mathfrak{Q}(t)$ for all t. For $t = 1$ and $\rho^\alpha = s$ we get (6.9).

When $\alpha = 1$ the presence of the truncation term leads to the modified form $\mathfrak{A}_1^{\#} = \rho\mathfrak{A}_1 + \rho\,\gamma(\rho)\dfrac{d}{dx}$, where

$$\gamma(\rho) = (c^+ - c^-)\int_0^\infty [\rho\,\tau_1(y/\rho) - \tau_1(y)]y^{-2}dy = (c^+ - c^-)\int_1^\rho y^{-1}dy\,, \tag{6.11}$$

and the argument used for $\alpha \neq 1$ now leads to (6.10).

7. TRIANGULAR ARRAYS

For each n let $\mathbf{X}_{1,n}, \ldots, \mathbf{X}_{n,n}$ be mutually independent with a common distribution F_n and $\mathbf{S}_n = \mathbf{X}_{1,n} + \cdots + \mathbf{X}_{n,n}$. The limit theorems for the distributions of $\mathbf{S}_n$ depends on a compactness lemma which was used also in section 5. To derive it we use the *truncation function* τ_s of (5.3), and put

$$\mathbf{X}'_{k,n} = \tau_s(\mathbf{X}_{k,n}), \qquad \mathbf{X}_{k,n} = \mathbf{X}'_{k,n} + \mathbf{X}''_{k,n}. \tag{7.1}$$

The $\mathbf{X}'_{k,n}$ are the familiar variables obtained by truncation at the level $\pm s$, but the dependence on the parameter s is not emphasized. Together with $\{\mathbf{X}_{k,n}\}$ we study the auxiliary triangular arrays $\{\mathbf{X}'_{k,n}\}$ and $\{\mathbf{X}''_{k,n}\}$ whose row sums will be denoted by $\mathbf{S}_n'$ and $\mathbf{S}_n''$. Thus $\mathbf{S}_n = \mathbf{S}_n' + \mathbf{S}_n''$.

[5] These assertions follow from the results of section 8, but a direct verification is instructive.

Recall from VIII,2 that $\{\mathbf{S}_n\}$ is *stochastically bounded* if to each $\epsilon > 0$ there corresponds an a such that

$$\mathbf{P}\{|\mathbf{S}_n| \geq a\} < \epsilon \tag{7.2}$$

for all n. Stochastic boundedness is a necessary condition for *proper* convergence of the distributions of $\mathbf{S}_n$. For clarity we derive the required criterion first for symmetric distributions.

Lemma 1. (*Symmetric case*). *When the distributions F_n are symmetric, $\{\mathbf{S}_n\}$ is stochastically bounded iff there exist numbers M_s and a_ϵ such that*

$$n \operatorname{Var}(\mathbf{X}'_{j,n}) < M_s \tag{7.3}$$

and

$$n[1 - F_n(a) + F_n(-a)] < \epsilon, \qquad a > a_\epsilon. \tag{7.4}$$

Proof. By the inequality V,(5.11) the probability in (7.2) is $\geq \frac{1}{2}(1 - e^{-\eta})$ where η stands for the left side in (7.4). The condition (7.4) is therefore necessary for the stochastic boundedness of $\{\mathbf{S}_n\}$. From now on we assume that it is satisfied.

For $s > a$ the number of terms among the $\mathbf{X}''_{1,n}, \ldots, \mathbf{X}''_{n,n}$ that are different from 0 is a binomial variable with expectation $< \epsilon$, and hence $\{\mathbf{S}_n''\}$ is stochastically bounded. Under these circumstances $\{\mathbf{S}_n\}$ is stochastically bounded iff $\{\mathbf{S}_n'\}$ is.

Put $\sigma_n^2 = \operatorname{Var}(\mathbf{S}_n')$. If $\sigma_n \to \infty$ the central limit theorem of example (1.a) applies to the variables $\mathbf{X}'_{k,n}/\sigma_n$. In this case the distribution of $\mathbf{S}_n'/\sigma_n$ tends to $\mathfrak{N}$, and $\{\mathbf{S}_n'\}$ is *not* stochastically bounded. This argument applied to subsequences of $\{\mathbf{S}_n'\}$ shows that $\{\sigma_n\}$ must remain bounded. Accordingly (7.3) is necessary for $s > a$ and this implies the boundedness for all smaller s. Conversely, if (7.3) is true, then $\mathbf{P}\{|\mathbf{S}_n'| > c\} < \epsilon$ for $c^2 > M_s/\epsilon$ by Chebyshev's inequality, and hence $\{\mathbf{S}_n'\}$ is stochastically bounded. ►

From this we derive the following general criterion in which we use the abbreviation

$$\beta_n = \mathbf{E}(\mathbf{X}'_{1,n}). \tag{7.5}$$

Lemma 2. (*Compactness*). *Suppose that*[6] $\mathbf{X}_{1,n} \xrightarrow{\mathrm{P}} 0$. *In order that there exist constants b_n such that $\{\mathbf{S}_n - b_n\}$ remains stochastically bounded, it is necessary and sufficient that the conditions of lemma* 1 *be satisfied. In this case $\{\mathbf{S}_n - n\beta_n\}$ remains stochastically bounded, $\beta_n \to 0$, and therefore* $n^{-1}\mathbf{S}_n \xrightarrow{\mathrm{P}} 0$.

[6] This means $\mathbf{P}\{|\mathbf{X}_{1,n}| > \eta\} \to 0$ for every $\eta > 0$. See VIII,2.

Proof. As usual, we denote by ${}^0\mathbf{X}_{k,n}$ the variable obtained by symmetrization of $\mathbf{X}_{k,n}$. If $\{\mathbf{S}_n - b_n\}$ remains stochastically bounded, so do the row sums of the symmetrized array $\{{}^0\mathbf{X}_{k,n}\}$. Since $\mathbf{X}_{1,n} \xrightarrow{\text{P}} 0$ the condition (7.4) for $\{\mathbf{X}_{k,n}\}$ is fully equivalent to the same condition for $\{{}^0\mathbf{X}_{k,n}\}$, and hence it is necessary.

As in the preceding proof this condition ensures the stochastic boundedness of $\{\mathbf{S}_n''\}$. Thus if $\{\mathbf{S}_n - b_n\}$ is stochastically bounded, the same is true of $\{\mathbf{S}_n' - b_n\}$, and hence also of the row sums of the symmetrized array $\{{}^0\mathbf{X}'_{k,n}\}$. Since $\text{Var}({}^0\mathbf{X}'_{1,n}) = 2\,\text{Var}(\mathbf{X}'_{1,n})$ the boundedness condition (7.3) is again necessary. If it is satisfied, then by Chebyshev's inequality $\mathbf{S}_n' - \mathbf{E}(\mathbf{S}_n')$ remains stochastically bounded. This proves the first assertion. Obviously $\mathbf{X}_{1,n} \xrightarrow{\text{P}} 0$ implies $\mathbf{X}'_{1,n} \xrightarrow{\text{P}} 0$, and hence $\beta_n \to 0$. ►

Lemma 3. *If* $\{\mathbf{S}_n\}$ *is stochastically bounded, then* $\mathbf{X}_{1,n} \xrightarrow{\text{P}} 0$ *as* $n \to \infty$.

Proof. Assume that $\{\mathbf{S}_n\}$ is stochastically bounded, and let μ_n be a median for $\mathbf{X}_{1,n}$. The row sums of the symmetrized array $\{{}^0\mathbf{X}_{k,n}\}$ are stochastically bounded, and ${}^0\mathbf{X}_{k,n} \xrightarrow{\text{P}} 0$ by lemma 1. In view of the symmetrization inequality V,(5.8) this implies that $\mathbf{X}_{k,n} - \mu_n$ and hence lemma 2 applies to the array $\{\mathbf{X}_{k,n} - \mu_n\}$. Thus $n^{-1}\mathbf{S}_n - \mu_n \xrightarrow{\text{P}} 0$. Since also $n^{-1}\mathbf{S}_n \xrightarrow{\text{P}} 0$ the last relation implies $\mu_n \to 0$, which proves the assertion. ►

The condition (7.3) is rather unwieldy, but *if* $n\beta_n^2 \to 0$ *then it simplifies to*

$$n\int_{-s}^{s} y^2\, F_n\{dy\} < M_s. \tag{7.6}$$

Proof *of the lemma in section* 5. When $\{\mathbf{S}_n\}$ remains stochastically bounded the last two lemmas show that $n\beta_n$ remains bounded and hence (7.6) is true. By the second selection theorem in VIII,6 there exists therefore a measure Ω such that

$$ny^2\, F_n\{dy\} \to \Omega\{dy\} \tag{7.7}$$

as n runs through an appropriate sequence $\{n_k\}$. The integrability condition (5.2) is trivially satisfied, the tails of the integral being less than the limit of the quantity in (7.4). Finally, (7.4) is the same as (5.7) and thus all assertions of the lemma are verified. ►

We are now in a position to formulate the main limit theorem for triangular arrays. Suppose that a limit distribution for $\{\mathbf{S}_n\}$ exists. Then there exists a sequence $\{n_k\}$ such that as n runs through it (7.7) holds and $b_n = n\beta_n \to b$. We saw in section 5 that under these circumstances $n[\mathfrak{F}_n - \mathbf{1}] \to \mathfrak{A}$ where $\mathfrak{A}$ is the operator described in (5.9) and (5.11).

The limit distribution of $\mathbf{S}_n$ *is identical with the distribution* Q_1 *of the semi-group generated by* $\mathfrak{A}$.

It is conceivable that another choice of the subsequence $\{n_k\}$ might lead to a different pair $(\Omega^\#, b^\#)$ and hence to a different semi-group $\{\mathfrak{Q}^\#(t)\}$. In this case the limit distribution of $\mathbf{S}_n$ would be associated with both $\mathfrak{Q}(1)$ and $\mathfrak{Q}^\#(1)$ and we would have two distinct semi-groups such that $\mathfrak{Q}^\#(1) = \mathfrak{Q}(1)$. Such semi-groups do not exist, however. This assertion requires some proof, but it happens to be absolutely trivial in the Fourier representation and it really plays no role in the present context.[7] We accept it therefore without proof simply in order to avoid misleading formulations.

From a purely theoretical point of view we have solved the problem of describing the limit distribution of $\mathbf{S}_n$ (if any) by the generator of the related convolution semi-group. The result is often difficult to apply because it presupposes that the distribution of $\mathbf{S}_n$ actually converges. In practice the centering of the variables is flexible and the question is whether there exist constants b_n such that the distribution of $\mathbf{S}_n - b_n$ tends to a limit. We continue the practice of denoting by $\mathbf{X}'_{k,n}$ the variable obtained by truncating $\mathbf{X}_{k,n}$ at an arbitrary, but *fixed*, level $\pm s$. [See (7.1).] We recall that $\{\mathbf{X}_{k,n}\}$ is a *null array* if $\mathbf{X}_{1,n} \xrightarrow{\text{p}} 0$. Such an array can be centered so that as $n \to \infty$

$$(\mathbf{E}(\mathbf{X}'_{1,n}))^2 = o(\mathbf{E}(\mathbf{X}'^2_{1,n})). \tag{7.8}$$

This condition is harmless, and without it the criteria become so clumsy as to be useless. As in (7.5) we put $\beta_n = \mathbf{E}(\mathbf{X}'_{1,n})$.

Theorem. *Let* $\{\mathbf{X}_{k,n}\}$ *be a null array satisfying the centering condition* (7.8).

(*a*) *In order that there exist centering constants* b_n *such that the distribution of* $\mathbf{S}_n - b_n$ *tends to a proper limit it is necessary and sufficient that* (7.4) *and* (7.7) *hold.*

(*b*) *In this case the distribution of* $\mathbf{S}_n - n\beta_n$ *tends to the distribution* Q_1 *associated with the operator* $\mathfrak{Q}(1)$ *of the semi-group generated by the operator*

$$\mathfrak{A}^{(0)} = \lim n\left[\mathfrak{F}_n - \mathbf{1} + \beta_n \frac{d}{dx}\right] \tag{7.9}$$

described explicitly in (5.9).

Proof. Assuming (7.4) and (7.7) we have proved that the limit $\mathfrak{A}^{(0)}$ in (7.9) exists and is given by (5.9). We next show that in this case

$$\mathfrak{A}^{(0)} = \lim n[\mathfrak{F}_n^{(0)} - \mathbf{1}] \tag{7.10}$$

[7] It is used in the next section, but the uniqueness is obvious for stable semi-groups.

where $\mathfrak{F}_n^{(0)}$ is the operator associated with $\mathbf{X}_{k,n} - \beta_n$. Clearly

$$n[\mathfrak{F}_n u(x) - u(x) + \beta_n u'(x)] - n[\mathfrak{F}_n^{(0)} u(x-\beta_n) - u(x-\beta_n)] = \tag{7.11}$$
$$= n[u(x-\beta_n) - u(x) + \beta_n u'(x)].$$

In view of (7.8) we have $n\beta_n^2 \to 0$ and hence the right side tends uniformly to zero. The assertion of the theorem is now contained in lemma 3.4, and so the conditions are sufficient.

To prove their necessity note that lemma 2 applies. Because of (7.8) the variances in (7.3) may be replaced by the second moments and so the stochastic boundedness of $\{\mathbf{S}_n - b_n\}$ implies that (7.7) holds at least when n runs through an appropriate sequence $n_1, n_2, \ldots$. The first part of the proof now shows that the limit distribution of $\mathbf{S}_n - b_n$ can differ from Q_1 only by a centering. Because of the uniqueness of the semi-group the measure Ω is uniquely determined and we conclude that (7.7) holds for every passage to the limit $n \to \infty$. ►

Example. Let $\mathbf{X}_{k,n}$ have the normal distribution with expectation $1/\sqrt[3]{n^2}$ and variance $1/n$. Then $\mathbf{S}_n - \sqrt[3]{n}$ has the standard normal distriution $\mathfrak{N}$ even though the sequence $\{\mathbf{S}_n\}$ is not stochastically bounded. The theorem applies with $\mathfrak{A}^{(0)} = \dfrac{1}{2}\dfrac{d^2}{dx^2}$.

8. DOMAINS OF ATTRACTION

In this section $\mathbf{X}_1, \mathbf{X}_2, \ldots$ are independent variables with a common distribution F. By definition 2 of VI,1 the distribution F *belongs to the domain of attraction of* G if there exist constants $a_n > 0$ and b_n such that the distribution of $\dfrac{1}{a_n}(\mathbf{X}_1 + \cdots + \mathbf{X}_n) - b_n$ tends to G, where G is a proper distribution *not concentrated at a point.* Despite preliminary results in VI,1 and in section 6 we here develop the theory from scratch.

Throughout this section we use the notation

$$U(x) = \int_{-x}^{x} y^2 \, F\{dy\}, \qquad x > 0. \tag{8.1}$$

We recall from the theory of regular variation in VIII,8 that a positive function L defined on $\overline{0, \infty}$ *varies slowly* (at ∞) if[8] for all $x > 0$

$$\frac{L(sx)}{L(s)} \to 1 \qquad s \to \infty \tag{8.2}$$

[8] It may be helpful to keep in mind that $s^\epsilon L(s) \to \infty$ and $s^{-\epsilon} L(s) \to 0$ for every $\epsilon > 0$. When $x^{-\alpha} L(x)$ is monotone this assertion becomes clear by looking at the ratio $L(2x)/L(x)$. [For more general L the assertion is contained in VIII,(9.9), but no such functions will occur in this section.]

Theorem 1. *A distribution F belongs to the domain of attraction of some distribution G iff there exists a slowly varying L such that*

$$(8.3) \qquad U(x) \sim x^{2-\alpha} L(x) \qquad x \to \infty$$

with $0 < \alpha \leq 2$, *and when* $\alpha < 2$

$$(8.4) \qquad \frac{1 - F(x)}{1 - F(x) + F(-x)} \to p, \qquad \frac{F(-x)}{1 - F(x) + F(-x)} \to q.$$

(No subsidiary condition is required when $\alpha = 2$.)

Note that (8.3) holds with $\alpha = 2$ whenever a finite variance exists, but U may vary slowly also when no variance exists. We shall see that $\alpha = 2$ corresponds to attraction to the normal distribution.

By theorem VIII,9.2 *the relation* (8.3) *is fully equivalent to*[9]

$$(8.5) \qquad \frac{x^2[1 - F(x) + F(-x)]}{U(x)} \to \frac{2 - \alpha}{\alpha}$$

in the sense that the two relations imply each other.

When $0 < \alpha < 2$ we can rewrite (8.5) in the form

$$(8.6) \qquad 1 - F(x) + F(-x) \sim \frac{2 - \alpha}{\alpha} x^{-\alpha} L(x),$$

and conversely (8.6) implies (8.3) and (8.5). This leads us to a reformulation of the theorem which is more intuitive inasmuch as it describes the behavior of the individual tails. (For other alternatives see problem 14.)

Theorem 1a. (*Alternative form*). (i) *A distribution F belongs to the domain of attraction of the normal distribution iff U varies slowly.*

(ii) *It belongs to some other domain of attraction iff* (8.6) *and* (8.4) *hold for some* $0 < \alpha < 2$.

Proof. We shall apply the theorem of section 7 to the array of variables $\mathbf{X}_{k,n} = \mathbf{X}_k/a_n$ with distributions $F_n(x) = F(a_n x)$. The row sums of the array $\{\mathbf{X}_{k,n}\}$ are given by

$$(8.7) \qquad \mathbf{S}_n = \frac{\mathbf{X}_1 + \cdots + \mathbf{X}_n}{a_n}.$$

---

[9] Condition (8.4) requires a similar relation for each tail separately:

$$(*) \qquad \frac{x^2[1-F(x)]}{U(x)} \to p\,\frac{2-\alpha}{\alpha}, \qquad \frac{x^2 F(-x)}{U(x)} \to q\,\frac{2-\alpha}{\alpha}.$$

When $\alpha = 2$ these relations follow from (8.5), which explains the absence of a second condition when $\alpha = 2$. Theorem 1 could have been formulated more concisely (but more artificially) as follows: *F belongs to some domain of attraction iff* (*) *is true* with $0 < \alpha \leq 2, p \geq 0, q \geq 0, p + q = 1$.

With the abbreviation

$$(8.8) \qquad v(x) = \int_{-x}^{x} y\, F\{dy\}$$

the condition (7.8) takes on the form

$$(8.9) \qquad v^2(x) = o(U(x)).$$

It is satisfied automatically if F has no expectation,[10] and if an expectation exists we shall center F to *zero* expectation. Then $v(x) \to 0$ and (8.9) is true. Thus the theorem applies. Its two conditions (7.7) and (7.4) take on the form

$$(8.10) \qquad ny^2\, F_n\{dy\} \to \Omega\{dy\}$$

and

$$(8.11) \qquad n[1 - F_n(\eta) + F_n(-\eta)] < \epsilon$$

for η sufficiently large and all n.

(*a*) *Necessity.* Obviously (8.10) requires that

$$(8.12) \qquad \frac{n}{a_n^2}\, U(a_n x) \to \Omega\{\overline{-x, x}\}$$

at all points of continuity and Ω must not vanish identically (for otherwise the limit distribution would be concentrated at one point). By lemma 2 of VIII,8 therefore[11] U varies regularly and $\Omega\{-x, x\} = cx^{2-\alpha}$ with $0 < \alpha \leq 2$. If $\alpha = 2$ nothing more is to be proved. If $\alpha < 2$ the origin is not an atom for Ω and the argument applies separately to

$$(8.13) \qquad U^+(x) = \int_0^x y^2\, F\{dy\}$$

and the analogous function U^-. The condition (8.4) follows from the analogue to (8.5) for U^+ and U^-.

(*b*) *Sufficiency.* Assuming (8.3) it is possible to choose a_n such that

$$(8.14) \qquad \frac{n}{a_n^2}\, U(a_n) \to 1.$$

Then

$$(8.15) \qquad \frac{n}{a_n^2}\, U(a_n x) \to x^{2-\alpha}.$$

---

[10] By Schwarz' inequality $[v(x) - v(a)]^2 \leq U(x)[1 - F(a) + F(-a)]$ for $x > a$ and hence (8.9) is true whenever $U(x) \to \infty$.

[11] The condition $a_{n+1}/a_n \to 1$ is satisfied by lemma 3 of VIII,2.

If $\alpha = 2$ this implies (8.10) with Ω the probability distribution concentrated at the origin. If $\alpha < 2$ the auxiliary relation (8.4) ensures that $na_n^{-2}\, U^+(a_n x) \to px^{2-\alpha}$ and similarly for U^-. Thus (8.9) holds. Finally, (8.11) is a direct consequence of (8.5). ▶

This proof leads to additional information concerning the limit distribution. Suppose that F satisfies the conditions of the theorem for some fixed values of the parameters. It follows from (8.6) that for $\alpha > 1$ a finite expectation exists and in this case we suppose that F is centered to zero expectation. Letting $b_n = na_n^{-1}v(a_n)$ there exists a limit distribution for $\mathbf{S}_n - b_n$. Now theorem 2 of VIII,9 shows that when $\alpha \neq 1$ a finite limit $b = \lim b_n$ exists, and hence $\mathbf{S}_n$ itself has a limit distribution G. Thus when $\alpha \neq 1$

$$F^{n\star}(a_n x) \to G(x). \tag{8.16}$$

Our choice of norming constants a_n is given in (8.14). Other norming constants a_n' can be chosen, but they are necessarily of the form $a_n' \sim ca_n$ (lemma 1 of VIII,2) and lead to the limit $G(cx)$. This means that for a given limit G in (8.16) the norming constants a_n are essentially unique. Now $a_{rn}/a_n \to r^{1/\alpha}$ and hence

$$G^{r\star}(r^{1/\alpha}x) = G(x). \tag{8.17}$$

Thus G itself satisfies the conditions of the theorem with $a_n = n^{1/\alpha}$. These coefficients must satisfy (8.14). For $0 < \alpha < 1$ and $1 < \alpha < 2$ this implies, as we have seen, that as $x \to \infty$

$$x^\alpha[1 - G(x)] \to p\,\frac{2-\alpha}{\alpha}, \qquad x^\alpha\, G(-x) \to q\,\frac{2-\alpha}{\alpha}. \tag{8.18}$$

When $\alpha = 1$ the centering constants b_n need not remain bounded, but a trite modification of the argument shows that the limit distribution of $S_n - b_n$ satisfies (8.18). We have thus the following sharpening of theorem 1.

Theorem 2. *Let F satisfy the conditions of theorem* 1. *When $\alpha > 1$ suppose, moreover, that F is centered to zero expectation. Choose a_n in accordance with* (8.14).

(i) *If $0 < \alpha < 1$ or $1 < \alpha < 2$ then* (8.16) *holds. The limit G is stable and satisfies* (8.18).

(ii) *If $\alpha = 2$ then* (8.16) *holds with $G = \mathfrak{N}$, the standard normal distribution.*

(iii) *If $\alpha = 1$ the limit distribution of $\mathbf{S}_n - b_n$ is stable and satisfies* (8.18).

By the definition of stability (see VI,1) every stable distribution belongs to its own domain of attraction. A distribution satisfying (8.17) is strictly stable. The following theorem is therefore implied in the preceding.

Theorem 3. *For every choice of the parameters there exists exactly one type of stable distributions satisfying the conditions of theorem* 1.

For $\alpha = 2$ *the distributions are normal.*

When $\alpha < 1$, *there exists a choice of the scale factor such that* (8.18) *holds.*[12]

When $\alpha = 1$ *the class contains exactly one strictly stable distribution satisfying* (8.18).

Stable distributions determined by $\alpha = 1$ and $p \neq q$ satisfy (6.10) and are therefore *not* strictly stable.

Note on the central limit theorem. Theorem 2 contains a characterization of the domain of attraction of the normal distribution. To belong to it, F must have an expectation (and, indeed, finite absolute moments of all orders <2). If centered to zero expectation *F belongs to the domain of* $\mathfrak{N}$ *iff U varies slowly.* Of course, a finite second moment implies $U(\infty) < \infty$ and is a sufficient condition, but example VIII,(4.*a*) shows that it is not necessary. The appropriate norming constants are in each case dictated by (8.14).

(Concerning the so-called normal domain of attraction of a non-normal distribution see XVII,5.)

9. VARIABLE DISTRIBUTIONS. THE THREE-SERIES THEOREM

We turn very briefly to general triangular arrays $\{\mathbf{X}_{k,n}\}$ where the variables[13] $\mathbf{X}_{1,n}, \ldots, \mathbf{X}_{n,n}$ of the nth row are mutually independent, but have arbitrary distributions $F_{k,n}$. As explained in VI,3 in order to preserve the character of our limit theorems it is necessary to impose the condition that the $\mathbf{X}_{k,n}$ be in some sense individually small. Most satisfactory is the condition that for arbitrary $\eta > 0$ and $\epsilon > 0$

$$\mathbf{P}\{|\mathbf{X}_{k,n}| > \eta\} < \epsilon, \qquad k = 1, \ldots, n \tag{9.1}$$

for all n sufficiently large.

The notations used in section 7 require no change. For example, $\mathbf{X}'_{k,n}$ will again denote the variable obtained by truncating $\mathbf{X}_{k,n}$ at $\pm s$. The whole theory carries over with the sole change that expressions like $n \operatorname{Var}(\mathbf{X}'_{1,n})$ are replaced by the corresponding sums. The verification is a matter of simple routine and may be left to the reader. The following is a simple variant of the compactness lemma.

[12] (8.18) is independent of the centering.

[13] Concerning the number of variables in the nth row see footnote 7 to VI,3.

Theorem 1. (*Law of large numbers*). *If the condition* (9.1) *holds there exist constants* b_n *such that* $\mathbf{S}_n - b_n \xrightarrow{\text{p}} 0$ *iff*

$$(9.2) \qquad \sum_{k=1}^{n} \mathbf{P}\{|X_{k,n}| > \eta\} \to 0, \qquad \sum_{k=1}^{n} \text{Var}(X'_{k,n}) \to 0$$

for each $\eta > 0$ *and each truncation level* s. *In this case one may take* $b_n = \mathbf{E}(\mathbf{S}_n')$.

As a simple corollary we get the following theorem in which primes again denote the truncation (5.3) at $\pm s$. Special cases and examples were treated in VIII,5.

Theorem 2. (*Infinite convolutions*). *Let* $\mathbf{Y}_1, \mathbf{Y}_2, \ldots$ *be independent random variables with distributions* $G_1, G_2, \ldots$. *In order that the distributions* $G_1 \bigstar G_2 \cdots \bigstar G_n$ *of the sums* $\mathbf{T}_n = \mathbf{Y}_1 + \cdots + \mathbf{Y}_n$ *tend to a proper limit distribution* G *it is necessary and sufficient that for each* $s > 0$

$$(9.3) \qquad \sum \mathbf{P}\{|\mathbf{Y}_k| > s\} < \infty, \qquad \sum \text{Var}(\mathbf{Y}_k') < \infty$$

and

$$(9.4) \qquad \sum_{k=1}^{n} \mathbf{E}(\mathbf{Y}_k') \to m.$$

Proof. For a given increasing sequence of integers $\nu_1, \nu_2, \ldots$ and $k = 1, \ldots, n$ put $\mathbf{X}_{k,n} = \mathbf{Y}_{\nu_n+k}$. The distributions $G_1 \bigstar \cdots \bigstar G_n$ converge iff *all* triangular arrays of this type obey the law of large numbers with centering constants $b_n = 0$. From theorem 1 it is clear that the conditions (9.3) and (9.4) are necessary and sufficient for this. ▶

Just as in the case of equal components, *only infinitely divisible distributions occur as limit distributions for row sums of arrays satisfying* (9.1). (See problem 11.)

Theorem 2 may be reformulated more strikingly as follows.

Theorem 3. (*Kolmogorov's "three-series theorem"*). *The series* $\Sigma\, \mathbf{Y}_k$ *converges with probability one if* (9.3) *and* (9.4) *hold, and with probability zero otherwise.*

Proof. Assume (9.3) and (9.4). By theorem 2 of VII,8 the second condition in (9.3) guarantees that $\Sigma\, [\mathbf{Y}_k' - \mathbf{E}(\mathbf{Y}_k')]$ converges with probability one, and then (9.4) implies the same for $\Sigma\, \mathbf{Y}_k'$. By the Borel-Cantelli lemma (see **1**; VIII,3) the first condition in (9.3) entails that with probability one only finitely many $\mathbf{Y}_k$ differ from $\mathbf{Y}_k'$, and so $\Sigma\, \mathbf{Y}_k$ converges with probability one.

To prove the necessity of our conditions recall from IV,6 that the probability of convergence is either zero or one. In the latter case the distribution of the partial sums must converge, and so (9.3) and (9.4) hold. ▶

Inhomogeneous Processes

The semi-group theory developed in this chapter is the tool particularly adapted to processes with stationary independent increments. Without the condition of stationarity the increment $\mathbf{X}(t) - \mathbf{X}(\tau)$ will have a distribution depending on the two parameters t and τ, and we have to deal with a two-parametric family of operators $\mathfrak{Q}(\tau, t)$, $0 < \tau < t$ satisfying the convolution equation

$$\mathfrak{Q}(\tau, s)\mathfrak{Q}(s, t) = \mathfrak{Q}(\tau, t), \qquad \tau < s < t. \tag{9.5}$$

Are the distributions associated with such operators infinitely divisible? We can partition $\overline{\tau, t}$ into n intervals $\overline{t_{k-1}, t_k}$ and consider the variables $\mathbf{X}(t_k) - \mathbf{X}(t_{k-1})$, but to apply the theory of triangular arrays we require the condition (9.1) amounting to a uniform continuity of the distributions in their dependence on the two time parameters. But $\mathfrak{Q}(\tau, t)$ need not depend continuously on t. In fact, the partial sums of a sequence $\mathbf{X}_1, \mathbf{X}_2, \ldots$ of independent random variables represent a process with independent increments where all changes occur at integer-valued epochs and so the process is basically discontinuous. In a certain sense, however, this is the only type of essential discontinuity. The qualification "essential" is necessary, for it was shown in section 5*a* that even with ordinary semi-groups artificial centering can produce mischief which, though inconsequential, requires caution in formulations. For simplicity we stick therefore to symmetric distributions and prove

Lemma. *If the distributions associated with $\mathfrak{Q}(\tau, t)$ are symmetric, a one-sided limit $\mathfrak{Q}(\tau, t-)$ exists for each t.*

[A similar statement holds for other limits such as $(\tau+, t)$ etc.]

Proof. Let $\tau < t_1 < t_2 < \cdots$ and $t_n \to t$. The sequence of distributions associated with $\mathfrak{Q}(\tau, t_n)$ is stochastically bounded and so there exists a convergent subsequence. Dropping double subscripts we may suppose that $\mathfrak{Q}(\tau, t_n) \to \mathfrak{U}$ where $\mathfrak{U}$ is associated with a proper distribution U. It follows easily that $\mathfrak{Q}(t_n, t_{n+1}) \to 1$ and this implies $\mathfrak{Q}(t_n, s_n) \to 1$ for any sequence of epochs such that $t_n < s_n < t_{n+1}$. In view of (9.5) this means that $\mathfrak{Q}(\tau, s_n) \to \mathfrak{U}$, and so the limit $\mathfrak{U}$ is independent of the sequence $\{t_n\}$, and the lemma is proved. ▶

Following Paul Lévy, we call an epoch t a *fixed discontinuity* if the two limits $\mathfrak{Q}(\tau, t+)$ and $\mathfrak{Q}(\tau, t-)$ are different. It follows readily from theorem 2 on infinite convolutions that *the set of fixed discontinuities is at most denumerable*. Using symmetrization it follows also in the general case that, except for at most denumerably many epochs, discontinuities are due only to centering (and are removable by an adequate centering). The contribution $\mathfrak{Q}_d(\tau, t)$ of all fixed discontinuities to $\mathfrak{Q}(\tau, t)$ is an infinite convolution and it is possible to *decompose the process into a discrete and a continuous part*. For the triangular arrays arising from continuous processes it is not difficult to see (using theorem 2) that the uniformity condition (9.1) is automatically satisfied and we reach the conclusion that *the distributions associated with continuous processes are infinitely divisible*. P. Lévy has shown that the sample function of such processes are well-behaved in the sense that with probability one right and left limits exist at every epoch t.

10. PROBLEMS FOR SOLUTION

1. In example (1.*a*) show that $\Sigma\, \mathbf{X}_{k,n}^2 \xrightarrow{\text{P}} 1$ as $n \to \infty$. (*Hint:* Use variances.)

2. In an ordinary symmetric random walk let $\mathbf{T}$ be the epoch of the first passage through $+1$. In other words, $\mathbf{T}$ is a random variable such that

$$\mathbf{P}\{\mathbf{T} = 2r-1\} = \frac{1}{2r}\binom{2r}{r}\, 2^{-2r}.$$

Consider a triangular array in which $\mathbf{X}_{k,n}$ has the same distribution as $\mathbf{T}/n^2$. Using the elementary methods of section 1 show by direct calculation that

$$(*)\qquad n[\mathfrak{F}_n u(x) - u(x)] \to \frac{1}{\sqrt{2\pi}} \int_0^\infty \frac{u(x-y) - u(x)}{\sqrt{y^3}}\, dy.$$

Conclude that the distribution of the row sums tends to the stable distribution F_1 defined in II,(4.7) with the convolution property II,(4.9). Interpret the result in terms of a random walk in which the steps are $\pm 1/n$ and the times between successive steps $1/n^2$.

3. From II,(4.9) conclude that the distributions of II,(4.7) form a semi-group with a generator given by the right side of (*) in the preceding problem.

4. Let the distributions Q_t of a semi-group be concentrated on the integers and denote the weight of k by $q_k(t)$. Show that

$$\mathfrak{A}u(x) = -q'(0)\, u(x) + \sum_{k\neq 0} q_k'(0)\, u(x-k).$$

Compare with the canonical form (5.9). Interpret in this light the generating functions for infinitely divisible distributions obtained in **1**; XII,3.

5. Generalize the notions of section 2 to semi-groups with defective distributions. Show that if $\mathfrak{A}$ generates $\{\mathfrak{Q}(t)\}$ then $\mathfrak{A} - c\mathbf{1}$ generates $\{e^{-ct}\mathfrak{Q}(t)\}$.

6. The notation $e^{t(\mathfrak{F}-1)}$ for the compound Poisson semi-group tempts one to write in general $\mathfrak{Q}(t) = e^{t\mathfrak{A}}$. For the normal semi-group this leads to the formal operational equation

$$\exp\left(\frac{1}{2}\, t\, \frac{d^2}{dx^2}\right) u(x) = \sum \frac{1}{n!}\left(\frac{t}{2}\right)^n u^{(2n)}(x).$$

Show that it is valid whenever the Taylor series of u converges for all x. (*Hint:* Use the moments of the normal distribution.)

7. The distributions of a semi-group have finite expectations iff $\dfrac{1}{1+|x|}$ is integrable with respect to the measure Ω appearing in the generator.

8. Show directly that if $n[\mathfrak{F}_n - \mathbf{1}] \to \mathfrak{A}$, the operator $\mathfrak{A}$ is necessarily of the form of a generator. [Use the method of section 4 considering functions of the form (4.4) but do not use semi-group theory. The intention is to derive the general form of a generator without first proving its existence.]

9. Let F_k attach probabilities $\frac{1}{2}$ to the two points $\pm\mu^k$. Then

$$\sum_{k=-\infty}^{+\infty} 2^{-k}(\mathfrak{F}_k - \mathbf{1})$$

generates a semi-group such that $Q_{2t}(x) = Q_t(\frac{1}{2}x)$, but Q_t is not stable. (P. Lévy.)

10. For any distribution F and smooth u

$$\|(\mathfrak{F}-\mathbf{1})u\| \leq 100(\|u\| + \|u''\|)\int_{-\infty}^{+\infty} \frac{x^2}{1+x^2} F\{dx\} + \|u'\|.$$

11. *Continuation.* To the triangular array $\{\mathbf{X}_{k,n}\}$ with distributions F_n there corresponds another array $\{\mathbf{X}^{\#}_{k,n}\}$ with compound Poisson distributions

$$\mathfrak{F}_n{}^{\#} = e^{\mathfrak{F}_n - \mathbf{1}}.$$

Show that $n[\mathfrak{F}_n - \mathfrak{F}_n{}^{\#}] \to 0$ whenever $\{\mathbf{S}_n\}$ is stochastically bounded. This shows that *the row sums* $\mathbf{S}_n$ *and* $\mathbf{S}_n{}^{\#}$ *are asymptotically equivalent.* Since the distribution of $\mathbf{S}_n{}^{\#}$ is associated with $e^{[n\mathfrak{F}_n - \mathbf{1}]}$ this yields a second method for deriving the main theorems of section 5. This method can be used also for arrays with variable distributions.

12. With the notations of section 5 put $\mathbf{M}_n = \max[\mathbf{X}_{1,n}, \ldots, \mathbf{X}_{n,n}]$. If $\mathbf{S}_n$ has a limit distribution show that $\psi^+(x) = \lim \log \mathbf{P}\{\mathbf{M}_n > x\}$.

13. If $\mathbf{S}_n$ has a limit distribution so do the row sums of the array formed by the squares $\mathbf{X}^2_{k,n}$.

14. *Criteria for domains of attraction.* Theorem 8.1 uses the truncated second-moment function U only for reasons of tradition. (The factor $2 - \alpha$ is the result of this.) Theorem 2 of VIII,9 permits us to replace y^2 in (8.1) by $|y|^\rho$ with other exponents ρ, and for each ρ to replace (8.3) and (8.5) by equivalent relations.

15. Let $\mathbf{X}_1, \mathbf{X}_2, \ldots$ be independent variables with a common distribution F. If $1 - F(x) + F(-x)$ varies slowly deduce from the compactness lemma that a sequence $\mathbf{S}_{n_k}/a_k + b_k$ can have no proper limit distribution G except G concentrated at a point. (This may be expressed by saying that *F belongs to no domain of partial attraction.*)

CHAPTER X

Markov Processes and Semi-groups

This chapter starts out with an elementary survey of the most common types of Markov processes—or rather, of the basic equations governing their transition probabilities. From this we pass to Bochner's notion of subordination of processes and to the treatment of Markov processes by semi-groups. The so-called exponential formula of semi-group theory is the connecting link between these topics. The existence of generators will be proved only in chapter XIII. In theory the present exposition might have covered the processes and semi-groups of the last chapter as a special case, but the methods and uses are so different that the following theory is self-contained and *independent of chapter IX*. The results will be amplified in chapter XIII, but *the theory of Markov processes is not used* for the remaining topics in this book.

This chapter is largely in the nature of a survey, and no attempt is made at either generality or completeness.[1] Specifically, we shall not discuss properties of the sample functions, and throughout this chapter the existence of the processes will be taken for granted. Our interest centers entirely on the analytical properties of the transition probabilities and of the defining operators.

The theory of the induced semi-groups of transformations will be treated in fair generality in sections 8–9. In the earlier sections the basic space is an interval on the line or the whole line although parts of the theory apply more generally. To avoid special symbols it is therefore agreed that when no limits are indicated *integrals are taken over a fixed set* Ω *serving as the basic space.*

---

[1] The semi-group treatment of Markov processes is described in greater detail in Loève (1963). [Added in proof. The general theory of Markov processes and their connection with semi-groups of transformations is treated exhaustively in the basic monograph by E. B. Dynkin (1965). The new book by K. Yosida contains a succinct introduction to the analytic theory of semi-groups and their applications to diffusion and ergodic theory.]

1. THE PSEUDO-POISSON TYPE

Throughout this chapter we limit our discussion to Markov processes with *stationary transition probabilities* Q_t defined by

$$Q_t(x, \Gamma) = \mathbf{P}\{\mathbf{X}(t+\tau) \in \Gamma \mid \mathbf{X}(\tau) = x\} \tag{1.1}$$

and supposed to be independent of τ. (See VI,11.)

A simple generalization of the compound Poisson process leads to an important class of such processes from which all others can be derived by approximation. The theory of semi-groups hinges on an analytical counterpart to this situation (section 10).

Let K be a stochastic kernel and $\mathbf{S}_0, \mathbf{S}_1, \ldots$ a Markov chain induced by it. (For the definition and examples see VI,11.) Let $\mathbf{N}(t)$ denote the variable of a Poisson process that is independent of the chain $\{\mathbf{S}_k\}$. The variables $\mathbf{X}(t) = \mathbf{S}_{\mathbf{N}(t)}$ define a new stochastic process which can be described formally as follows. Between the jumps of the Poisson process the typical sample path remains constant. A transition from x to Γ can occur in 0, 1, 2, . . . steps, and hence

$$Q_t(x, \Gamma) = e^{-\alpha t}\sum_{n=0}^{\infty}\frac{(\alpha t)^n}{n!}\, K^{(n)}(x, \Gamma), \qquad t > 0. \tag{1.2}$$

This generalizes the compound Poisson distribution VI,(4.2) and reduces to it in the special case when Ω is the whole line and $\mathbf{S}_n$ is the sum of n independent random variables with a common distribution F.

The composition rule

$$Q_{t+\tau}(x, \Gamma) = \int Q_t(x, dy)\, Q_\tau(y, \Gamma) \tag{1.3}$$

($t, \tau > 0$) analogous to VI,(4.1) is easily verified analytically.[2] It is called the *Chapman-Kolmogorov* equation and states that a transition from x at epoch 0 to Γ at epoch $t + \tau$ occurs via a point y at epoch τ and that the subsequent change is independent of the past.[3] [See **1**; XVII,9 and also VI,(11.3).]

Examples. (*a*) *Particles under collision.* Let a particle travel at uniform speed through homogeneous matter occasionally scoring a collision. Each collision produces a change of energy regulated by a stochastic kernel K. The transition probabilities for the energy $\mathbf{X}(t)$ are of the form (1.2) if the number of collisions is regulated by a Poisson process. This will be

[2] Approximating Q_t and Q_τ by their partial sums with n terms shows that the right side in (1.3) is $\leq$ the left side but $\geq$ the nth partial sum of $Q_{t+\tau}$.

[3] It is sometimes claimed that (1.3) is a law either of nature or of compound probabilities, but it is *not* true for non-Markovian processes. See **1**; XV,10.

the case under the now familiar assumptions concerning homogeneity of space and lack of memory.

It is usually assumed that the *fraction of energy* lost at each collision is independent of the initial amount, which means that $K(x, dy) = V\{dy/x\}$ where V is a probability distribution concentrated on $\overline{0, 1}$. For later applications we consider the special case where $V(x) = x^\lambda$. Then K has a density given by

$$(1.4) \qquad k(x, y) = \lambda x^{-\lambda} y^{\lambda-1}, \qquad 0 < y < x.$$

For $\lambda = 1$ this implies that the fraction of energy lost is *uniformly distributed.*[4] The iterated kernels $k^{(n)}$ were calculated in VI,(11.5). Substituting into (1.2) it is seen that Q_t has an atom of weight $e^{-\alpha t}$ at the origin (accounting for the event of no collision) and for $0 < y < x$ the density

$$(1.5) \qquad q_t(x, y) = e^{-\alpha t}\sqrt{\lambda\alpha t}\, \frac{y^{\lambda-1}}{x^\lambda\sqrt{\log(x/y)}}\, I_1(2\sqrt{\alpha t\lambda \log(x/y)})$$

where I_1 is the Bessel function defined in II,(7.1). [See examples (2.*a*) and (2*b*).]

(*b*) *The energy loss of fast particles by ionization.*[5] An instructive variant of the last example is obtained by considering the extreme case of a particle whose energy may be considered infinitely large. The energy losses at successive collisions are then independent random variables with a common distribution V concentrated on $\overline{0, \infty}$. If $\mathbf{X}(t)$ is the total energy loss within the time interval $\overline{0, t}$ then $\mathbf{X}(t)$ is the variable of a *compound Poisson process*. Its transition probabilities are given by (1.2) with $K^{(n)}$ replaced by the convolutions $V^{n\star}$. [See VI,(4.2).]

(*c*) *Changes in direction.* Instead of the energy of a particle we may consider the direction in which it travels and derive a model analogous to example (*a*). The main difference is that a direction in $\mathcal{R}^3$ is determined by two variables, and so that the density kernel k now depends on four real variables.

(*d*) *The randomized random walk* of example II,(7.*b*) represents a pseudo-Poisson process restricted to the integers. For a fixed integer x the kernel K attributes weight $\frac{1}{2}$ to the two points $x \pm 1$. ▶

[4] This assumption is used by W. Heitler and L. Janossy, *Absorption of meson producing nucleons*, Proc. Physical Soc., Series A, vol. 62(1949) pp. 374–385, where the Fokker-Planck equation (1.8) is derived (but not solved).

[5] Title of a paper by L. Landau, J. Physics, USSR, vol. 8 (1944) pp. 201–205. Landau uses a different terminology, but his assumptions are identical with ours and he derives the forward equation (1.6).

From (1.2) one gets easily

$$\frac{\partial Q_t(x, \Gamma)}{\partial t} = -\alpha Q_t(x, \Gamma) + \alpha \int Q_t(x, dz)\, K(z, \Gamma). \tag{1.6}$$

This is *Kolmogorov's forward equation* which will be discussed in a more general setting in the following sections. It will be shown in the next section that (1.2) is its *only* solution satisfying the obvious probabilistic requirements. The equation (1.6) takes on a more familiar form when K has a density k. At the point x the distribution Q_t has an atom of weight $e^{-\alpha t}$ equal to the probability of no change; except for this atom Q_t has a density q_t satisfying the equation

$$\frac{\partial q_t(x, \xi)}{\partial t} = -\alpha\, q_t(x, \xi) + \alpha \int q_t(x, z)\, k(z, \xi)\, dz. \tag{1.6a}$$

If μ_0 is the probability distribution at epoch 0 the distribution at epoch t is given by

$$\mu_t\{\Gamma\} = \int \mu_0\{dx\}\, Q_t(x, \Gamma) \tag{1.7}$$

and (1.6) implies

$$\frac{\partial \mu_t\{\Gamma\}}{\partial t} = -\alpha \mu_t\{\Gamma\} + \alpha \int \mu_t\{dz\}\, K(z, \Gamma). \tag{1.8}$$

This version of (1.6) is known to physicists as the *Fokker-Planck* (or continuity) equation. Its nature will be analyzed in section 3. When K and the initial distribution μ_0 have densities, then also μ_t has a density m_t, and the Fokker-Planck equation reduces to

$$\frac{\partial m_t(\xi)}{\partial t} = -\alpha m_t(\xi) + \alpha \int m_t(z)\, k(z, \xi)\, dz. \tag{1.8a}$$

2. A VARIANT: LINEAR INCREMENTS

A simple variant of our process occurs in physics, queuing theory, and other applications. The assumptions concerning the jumps remain the same but *between jumps* $\mathbf{X}(t)$ *varies linearly at a rate* c. This means that $\mathbf{X}(t) - ct$ is the variable of the described pseudo-Poisson process; if Q_t stands for the transition probabilities of the new process, then $Q_t(x, \Gamma + ct)$ must satisfy (1.6). The resulting equation for Q_t is of an unfamiliar form, but if differentiable densities exist they satisfy familiar equations. For m_t we have to replace ξ in (1.8a) by $\xi + ct$. With the change of variables $y = \xi + ct$ we get the Fokker-Planck equation.[6]

$$(2.1)\qquad \frac{\partial m_t(y)}{\partial t} = -c\,\frac{\partial m_t(y)}{\partial y} - \alpha m_t(y) + \alpha \int m_t(z)\, k(z, y)\, dz.$$

The analogue to (1.6a) is obtained similarly by adding the term $-c\,\partial q_t/\partial y$ to the right side.

In connection with semi-group theory we shall cast the Fokker-Planck equation in a more flexible form quite independent of the unnatural differentiability conditions. [See example (10.b).]

Examples. (a) *Particles under collision.* In the physical literature example (1.a) occurs usually in a modified form where it is assumed that energy is dissipated at a constant rate due to absorption or friction. The model of (2.1) fits this situation. If the energy loss is proportional to the instantaneous energy, then the logarithm of the energy decreases at a constant rate and the model applies with this change of notation.

(b) *Stellar radiation.*[7] In this model the variable t stands for *distance* and $\mathbf{X}(t)$ for the intensity of a light ray traveling through space. It is assumed that (within the equatorial plane) each element of volume radiates at a constant rate and hence $\mathbf{X}(t)$ increases linearly. But the space also contains absorbing dark clouds which we treat as a Poissonian ensemble of points. On meeting a cloud each ray experiences a chance-determined loss and we have the exact situation that led us to (2.1). It is plausible (and it can be proved) that the density m_t of $\mathbf{X}(t)$ approaches a *steady state density* m which is independent of t and satisfies (2.1) with the left side replaced by 0.

Ambarzumian assumes specifically that the loss of intensity at an individual passage through a cloud is regulated by the transition kernel (1.4). In this case an explicit solution is available in (1.5) but it is of

[6] Many special cases of the Fokker-Planck equation (1.8) have been discovered independently, and much fuss has been made about the generalization (2.1). The general notion of Fokker-Planck equations was developed by Kolmogorov in his celebrated paper, *Über die analytischen Methoden in der Wahrscheinlichkeitsrechnung*, Math. Ann., vol. 104 (1931) pp. 415–458. In it Kolmogorov mentions the possibility of adding an arbitrary diffusion term

$$\gamma\,\frac{\partial^2 m_t}{\partial y^2} - c\,\frac{\partial m_t}{\partial y}$$

to the right side, and (2.1) is merely a special case of this. Even the first existence theorems covered the general equation in the non-stationary case. [Feller, Math. Ann., vol. 113 (1963).]

[7] The physical assumptions are taken from V. A. Ambarzumian, *On the brightness fluctuations in the Milky Way*, Doklady Akad. Nauk SSSR, vol. 44 (1944) pp. 223–226, where a version of (2.1) is derived by an indirect approach.

minor interest. More important (and easily verified) is the fact that (2.1) has a time-independent (or steady state) solution, namely the gamma density

$$m(y) = \left(\frac{\alpha}{c}\right)^{\lambda+1} \frac{1}{\Gamma(\lambda+1)}\, y^{\lambda} e^{-(\alpha/c)y}, \qquad y > 0. \tag{2.2}$$

This result shows that pertinent information can be derived from (2.1) even without finding explicit solutions. For example, it is readily verified by direct integration that the steady state solution has expectation $(\mu+c)/\alpha$ where μ is the expectation of the absorption distribution V.

(*c*) *The ruin problems* of VI,5 represent the special case where k is a convolution kernel. The variable of these processes is obtained by adding $-ct$ to the variable of a compound Poisson process. Analogous ruin problems can be formulated for arbitrary pseudo-Poissonian processes, and they lead to (2.1).

3. JUMP PROCESSES

In the pseudo-Poisson process the waiting time to the next jump has a fixed exponential distribution with expectation $1/\alpha$. A natural generalization consists in permitting this distribution to depend on the present value of the path function $\mathbf{X}(t)$. (In example (1.*a*) this amounts to assuming that the probability of scoring a hit depends on the energy of the particle.) The Markovian character of the process requires that the distribution be exponential, but its expectation α can depend on the present value of $\mathbf{X}(t)$. Accordingly, we start from the following

Basic postulates. *Given that* $\mathbf{X}(t) = x$, *the waiting time to the next jump has an exponential distribution with expectation* $1/\alpha(x)$ *and is independent of the past history. The probability that the following jump leads to a value in* Γ *equals* $K(x, \Gamma)$.

In analytical terms these postulates lead to an integral equation for the transition probabilities $Q_t(x, \Gamma)$ of the process (assuming that such a process does in fact exist). Consider a fixed point x and a fixed set Γ *not containing* x. The event $\{\mathbf{X}(t) \in \Gamma\}$ cannot occur unless the first jump from x has occurred at some epoch $s < t$. Given this, the conditional probability of $\{\mathbf{X}(t) \in \Gamma\}$ is obtained by integrating $K(x, dy)Q_{t-s}(y, \Gamma)$ over the set Ω of all possible y. Now the epoch of the first jump is a random variable with exponential density $\alpha(x)e^{-\alpha(x)s}$. Integrating with respect to it we get the probability of $\{\mathbf{X}(t) \in \Gamma\}$ in the form

$$Q_t(x, \Gamma) = \alpha(x)\int_0^t e^{-\alpha(x)s}\, ds \int_\Omega K(x, dy)\, Q_{t-s}(y, \Gamma). \tag{3.1a}$$

For a set Γ containing x we must add the probability that no jump occurs before t and thus we get

$$(3.1b)\quad Q_t(x, \Gamma) = e^{-\alpha(x)t} + \alpha(x)\int_0^t e^{-\alpha(x)s}\,ds\int_\Omega K(x, dy)\,Q_{t-s}(y, \Gamma).$$

These two equations, valid for $x \notin \Gamma$ and $x \in \Gamma$, respectively, are the analytic equivalent of the basic postulates. It is possible to replace this pair by a single integro-differential equation. Indeed, the change of variable $s = t - \tau$ makes differentiation with respect to t trivial and leads to

$$(3.2)\quad \frac{\partial Q_t(x, \Gamma)}{\partial t} = -\alpha(x)\,Q_t(x, \Gamma) + \alpha(x)\int_\Omega K(x, dy)\,Q_t(y, \Gamma).$$

This is *Kolmogorov's backward equation*, which serves as point of departure for the analytical development because it avoids the annoyance of distinguishing between two cases.

The backward equation (3.2) admits of a simple intuitive interpretation which may serve to reformulate the basic postulates in more practical terms. In terms of difference ratios (3.2) is equivalent to

$$(3.3)\quad \begin{aligned} Q_{t+h}(x, \Gamma) &= [1 - \alpha(x)h]\,Q_t(x, \Gamma) \\ &\qquad + \alpha(x)h\int_\Omega K(x, dy)\,Q_t(y, \Gamma) + o(h). \end{aligned}$$

For an intuitive interpretation of this relation consider the change within the time interval $\overline{0, t+h}$ as the result of the change within the initial short interval $\overline{0, h}$ and the subsequent interval $\overline{h, t+h}$ of duration t. Evidently then (3.3) states that if $\mathbf{X}(0) = x$, the probability of one jump within $\overline{0, h}$ is $\alpha(x)h + o(h)$; and the probability of more than one jump is $o(h)$; finally, if a jump does occur within $\overline{0, h}$, the conditional probabilities of the possible transitions are given by $K(x, dy)$. These three postulates lead to (3.3) and hence to (3.2). In essence they repeat the basic postulates.[8]

From a probabilistic point of view the backward equation is somewhat artificial inasmuch as in it the terminal state Γ plays the role of a parameter, and (3.2) describes the dependence of $Q_t(x, \Gamma)$ on the initial position x. Offhand it would seem more natural to derive an equation for Q_{t+h} by splitting up the interval $\overline{0, t+h}$ into a long initial interval $\overline{0, t}$ and the

[8] The differentiability of Q_t with respect to t and the fact that the probability of more than one jump is $o(h)$ are now stated as new postulates, whereas they are implied by the original more sophisticated formulation.

short terminal interval $\overline{t, t+h}$. Instead of (3.3) we get then *formally*

$$Q_{t+h}(x, \Gamma) = \int_\Gamma Q_t(x, dz)[1 - \alpha(z)h] + \int_\Omega Q_t(x, dz)\,\alpha(z)h\,K(z, \Gamma) + o(h) \tag{3.4}$$

and hence

$$\frac{\partial Q_t(x, \Gamma)}{\partial t} = -\int_\Gamma Q_t(x, dz)\,\alpha(z) + \int_\Omega Q_t(x, dz)\,\alpha(z)\,K(z, \Gamma). \tag{3.5}$$

This is *Kolmogorov's forward equation* (known to physicists as the *continuity or Fokker-Planck equation*). In the special case of a constant α is reduces to (1.6).

The formal character of the derivation was emphasized because the forward equation is really not implied by our basic postulates. This is because the term $o(h)$ in (3.3) depends on z and since z appears as variable of integration in (3.4), the term $o(h)$ should have appeared under the integral sign. But then the problem arises as to whether the integrals in (3.5) converge and whether the passage to the limit $h \to 0$ is legitimate. [No such problems occurred in connection with the backward equation because the initial value x was fixed and the integral in (3.2) exists in consequence of the boundedness of Q_t.]

It is possible to justify the forward equation by adding to our basic postulates an appropriate condition on the error term in (3.3), but such a derivation would lose its intuitive appeal and, besides, it seems impossible to formulate conditions which will cover all typical cases occurring in practice. Once unbounded functions α are admitted, the existence of the integrals in (3.5) is in doubt and the equation cannot be justified a priori. On the other hand, the backward equation is a necessary consequence of the basic assumptions, and it is therefore best to use it as a starting point and to investigate the extent to which the forward equation can be derived from it.

A solution of the backward equation is easily constructed using successive approximations with a simple probabilistic significance. Denote by $Q_t^{(n)}(x, \Gamma)$ the probability of a transition from $\mathbf{X}(0) = x$ to $\mathbf{X}(t) \in \Gamma$ *with at most n jumps*. A transition without jumps is possible only if $x \in \Gamma$, and since the sojourn time at x has an exponential distribution we have

$$Q_t^{(0)}(x, \Gamma) = e^{-\alpha(x)t}\,K^{(0)}(x, \Gamma) \tag{3.6}$$

(where the right side equals 1 or 0 according as x is, or is not, contained in Γ). Suppose next that the first jump occurs at epoch $s < t$ and leads from x to y. Summing over all possible s and y we get [as in (3.1)] the recursion formula

$$(3.7)\quad Q_t^{(n+1)}(x, \Gamma) = Q_t^{(0)}(x, \Gamma) + \int_0^t e^{-\alpha(x)s}\alpha(x)\, ds \int K(x, dy)\, Q_{t-s}^{(n)}(y, \Gamma)$$

valid for $n = 0, 1, \ldots$. Obviously $Q_t^{(0)} \leq Q_t^{(1)}$ and hence by induction $Q_t^{(1)} \leq Q_t^{(2)} \leq \cdots$. Furthermore, all these kernels are bounded by the constant 1. Indeed, this is trivial for $n = 0$. If it is true for n, the inner integral in (3.7) is ≤ 1, and hence the second term on the right is $\leq 1 - e^{-\alpha(x)t}$. In view of (3.6) this implies $Q_t^{(n+1)}(x, \Gamma) \leq 1$. It follows that the limit

$$(3.8)\qquad Q_t^{(\infty)}(x, \Gamma) = \lim_{n\to\infty} Q_t^{(n)}(x, \Gamma)$$

exists for every pair x, Γ, and that $Q_t^{(\infty)}$ is either a stochastic or a sub-stochastic kernel. Evidently $Q_t^{(\infty)}$ satisfies the backward equation[9] in the integral version (3.1), and any other positive solution Q_t is $> Q_s^{(\infty)}$. For this reason $Q_t^{(\infty)}$ is called the *minimal solution* of the backward equation.

When $Q_t^{(\infty)}$ is strictly stochastic, any other solution would have to attribute to the whole space a probability ≥ 1. It follows that *the solution is unique whenever the minimal solution is strictly stochastic.* The next example will show that the minimal solution can be defective. As will be shown in XIV,8, this corresponds to the case where infinitely many jumps can occur within a finite time interval. By its very construction the minimal solution $Q_s^{(\infty)}$ gives the probability of transitions in finitely many steps or—what amounts to the same—the transition probabilities up to the first point of accumulation of epochs of jumps. From this epoch on, the process can continue in various ways without violating our basic postulates.

To avoid duplications we postpone to XIV,7 the proof of the basic fact that *the minimal solution $Q_t^{(\infty)}$ of the backward equation automatically satisfies also the forward equation and is minimal also for the latter.* In this way the forward equation is established without additional hypotheses and, at the same time, it becomes understandable that a direct derivation is impossible. The argument establishing (3.4) depends on the consideration of a last jump prior to the given epoch $t + h$. Now our basic postulates imply the existence of a *first* jump following t, but not of a last jump before t. If infinitely many jumps occur there need not exist a last one. Whether this contingency does or does not occur in a given situation (for given α and K) must be decided by analysis and not by postulates.

[9] The details of this proof are given in a Laplace transform version in XIV,7, and there also the other assertions of the text are justified. The notation of Laplace transforms is more elegant, but the present proof has the advantage of working also for *non-stationary processes* (that is, when α and K depend on t). See W. Feller, Amer. Math. Soc., vol. 48 (1940) pp. 488–515 [*erratum*, vol. 58, p. 474].

Furthermore, surprisingly enough, there exist many processes in which infinitely many jumps do occur in finite time intervals and yet the forward equation is valid [although its derivation from (3.4) is absurd].

These considerations should be helpful for the understanding of the role of the backward equation in diffusion processes and in semi-group theory.

In conclusion note that (in contrast to the process of section 2 and to diffusion processes where derivatives with respect to x occur) the purely discontinuous process *in no way depends on the nature of the underlying space*, and our formulas apply whenever a stochastic kernel K is defined.

Example. *Denumerable sample spaces.* If the random variables $\mathbf{X}(t)$ are positive and integral-valued the underlying sample space consists of the integers 1, 2, ... It suffices now to know the transition probabilities $P_{ik}(t)$ from one integer to another; all other transition probabilities are obtained by summation over k. The theory of Markovian processes on the integers was outlined in **1**; XVII,9 where, however, also non-stationary transition probabilities were considered. To restrict that theory to the stationary case the coefficients c_i and probabilities p_{ik} must be assumed constant (independent of t). The assumptions are then identical with the present ones and the two systems of Kolmogorov equations derived in **1**; XVII,9 are easily seen to be the special cases of (3.2) and (3.5) [replacing $\alpha(i)$ by c_i and $K(i, j)$ by p_{ik}]. The divergent birth process of **1**; XVII,4 is an example of a process with infinitely many jumps within a finite time interval. We shall return to this process in XIV,8 to present the possibilities of various continuations.

4. DIFFUSION PROCESSES IN $\mathcal{R}^1$

Having considered processes in which all changes occur by jumps we turn to the other extreme where the sample functions are (with probability one) continuous. Their theory is surprisingly parallel to that developed in the last section, but the basic equations require more sophisticated analysis. We shall therefore be satisfied with a derivation of the backward equation and with a brief summary concerning the minimal solution and other problems. The prototype for diffusion processes is the Brownian motion (or Wiener process). This is the process with independent normally distributed increments. Its transition probabilities have densities $q_t(x, y)$ given by the normal density with expectation x and variance at, where $a > 0$ is a constant. These densities satisfy the standard diffusion equation,

$$(4.1) \qquad \frac{\partial q_t(x, y)}{\partial t} = \frac{1}{2} a \frac{\partial^2 q_t(x, y)}{\partial x^2}.$$

It will now be shown that other transition probabilities are governed by related partial differential equations. The object of this derivation is merely to give an idea concerning the types of processes and the problems involved and thus to serve as a first introduction; for this reason we shall not strive at generality or completeness.

From the nature of the normal distribution it is evident that in Brownian motion the increments during a short time interval of duration t have the following properties: (i) for fixed $\delta > 0$ the probability of a displacement exceeding δ is $o(t)$; (ii) the expected value of the displacement is zero; (iii) its variance is at. We retain the first condition, but adapt the others to an inhomogeneous medium; that is, we let a depend on x and permit a non-zero mean displacement. Under such circumstances the expectation and the variance of the displacement will not be strictly proportional to t and we can postulate only that given $\mathbf{X}(\tau) = x$ the displacement $\mathbf{X}(t+\tau) - \mathbf{X}(\tau)$ has an expectation $b(x)t + o(t)$ and variance $a(x)t + o(t)$. Moments do not necessarily exist, but in view of the first condition it is natural to consider truncated moments. These considerations lead us to the following

Postulates[10] *for the transition probabilities* Q_t. *For every* $\delta > 0$ *as* $t \to 0$

$$\frac{1}{t}\int_{|y-x|\geq\delta} Q_t(x, dy) \to 0 \tag{4.2}$$

$$\frac{1}{t}\int_{|y-x|<\delta} (y - x)\, Q_t(x, dy) \to b(x) \tag{4.3}$$

$$\frac{1}{t}\int_{|y-x|<\delta} (y - x)^2\, Q_t(x, dy) \to a(x). \tag{4.4}$$

Note that if (4.2) holds for *all* $\delta > 0$, the asymptotic behavior of the quantities in (4.3) and (4.4) is independent of δ; it is then permissible in the last two relations to replace δ by 1.

The first condition makes large displacements improbable and was introduced in 1936 in the hope that it is necessary and sufficient for the continuity of the sample functions.[11] It was named in honor of Lindeberg because of its similarity to his condition in the central limit theorem. It can be shown that under mild regularity conditions on the

[10] The original derivation of (4.1) from probabilistic assumptions is due to Einstein. The first systematic derivation of the backward equation (4.6) and forward equation (5.2) was given in Kolmogorov's famous paper of 1931 (see section 1). The improved postulates of the text are due to Feller (1936), who gave the first existence proof and investigated the relation between the two equations.

[11] This conjecture was verified by D. Ray.

transition probabilities the existence of the limits in (4.3) and (4.4) is really a consequence of the Lindeberg condition (4.2). We shall not discuss such details because we are not at this juncture interested in developing a systematic theory.[12] Our modest aim is to explain the nature and the empirical meaning of the diffusion equations in the simplest situation. For this purpose we show how certain differential equations can be derived formally from (4.2)–(4.4), but we shall not discuss under what conditions there exist solutions to these equations. The coefficients a and b may be therefore assumed as bounded continuous functions and $a(x) > 0$.

We take as our basic space a finite or infinite interval I on the line and continue the convention that when no limits are indicated, the integration is over the interval I. To simplify writing and to prepare for the applications of semi-group theory we introduce the transformations

$$u(t, x) = \int Q_t(x, dy)\, u_0(y) \tag{4.5}$$

changing (for fixed t) a bounded continuous "initial function" u_0 into a function[13] with values $u(t, x)$.

Clearly the knowledge of the left side in (4.5) for all initial u_0 uniquely determine Q_t. It will now be shown that under mild regularity conditions u must satisfy the *backward equation*

$$\frac{\partial u}{\partial t} = \frac{1}{2}\, a\, \frac{\partial^2 u}{\partial x^2} + b\, \frac{\partial u}{\partial x}, \tag{4.6}$$

generalizing the standard diffusion equation (4.1). We seek a function u satisfying it and such that $u(t, x) \to u_0(x)$ as $t \to 0$. In case of uniqueness this solution is necessarily of the form (4.5) and Q_t is called the Green function of the equation. Cases of non-uniqueness will be discussed in the next section.[14]

To derive the backward equation (4.6) we start from the identity

$$u(s+t, x) = \int Q_s(x, dy)\, u(t, y), \qquad s, t > 0 \tag{4.7}$$

[12] Modern semi-group theory enabled the author to derive the most general backward equation (generator) for Markov processes satisfying a Lindeberg type condition. The classical differential operators are replaced by a modernized version, in which a "natural scale" takes over the role of the coefficient b, and a "speed measure" the role of a. The study of such processes was the object of fruitful research by Dynkin and his school on one hand, by K. Ito and H. P. McKean on the other. The whole theory is developed in the books by these authors.

[13] In terms of the stochastic process, $u(t, x)$ is the conditional expectation of $u_0(\mathbf{X}(t))$ on the hypothesis that $\mathbf{X}(0) = x$.

[14] For the treatment of diffusion equations by Laplace transforms see XIV,5.

which is an immediate consequence of the Chapman-Kolmogorov equation (1.3). From it we get for $h > 0$

$$\frac{u(t+h,\, x)-u(t,\, x)}{h} = \frac{1}{h}\int Q_h(x,\, dy)[u(t,\, y)-u(t,\, x)]. \tag{4.8}$$

We now suppose that the transition probabilities Q_t are sufficiently regular to ensure that in (4.5) the transform u has two bounded continuous derivatives with respect to x, at least when u_0 is infinitely differentiable. To given given $\epsilon > 0$ and fixed x there corresponds then by Taylor's formula a $\delta > 0$ such that

$$\left| u(t,\, y) - u(t,\, x) - (y-x)\frac{\partial u(t,\, x)}{\partial x} - \tfrac{1}{2}(y-x)^2\frac{\partial^2 u(t,\, x)}{\partial x^2}\right| < \epsilon\, |y-x|^2 \tag{4.9}$$

for all $|y - x| \leq \delta$. With this δ consider in (4.8) separately the contributions of the domains $|y - x| > \delta$ and $|y - x| \leq \delta$. The former tends to 0 in consequence of the Lindeberg condition (4.2) and of the boundedness of u. Owing to the conditions (4.3) and (4.4) it is clear from (4.9) that for sufficiently small h the contribution of $|y - x| \leq \delta$ differs from the right side in (4.6) by less than $\epsilon \cdot a(x)$. Since ϵ is arbitrary, this means that as $h \to 0$ the right side in (4.8) tends to that of (4.6). Accordingly, at least a right-sided derivative $\partial u/\partial t$ exists and is given by (4.6). The principal result of the theory may be summarized roughly as follows. *If the transition probabilities of a Markov process satisfy the continuity condition* (4.2) *the process is determined by the two coefficients b and a.* This sounds theoretical, but in practical situations the coefficients b and a are given a priori from their empirical meaning and the nature of the process.

To explain the meaning of b and a let us forget that the definitions (4.3) and (4.4) use truncated moments. Consider the increment $\mathbf{X}(t+\tau) - \mathbf{X}(\tau)$ over a short time interval assuming that $\mathbf{X}(\tau) = x$. If the moments in (4.3) and (4.4) were complete, this increment would have the conditional expectation $b(x)t + o(t)$ and the conditional variance $a(x)t - b^2(x)t^2 + o(t) = a(x)t + o(t)$. Thus $b(x)$ is a measure for the local average rate of displacement (which may be zero for reasons of symmetry), and $a(x)$ for the variance. For want of a better word we shall refer to b as the *infinitesimal velocity* (or drift) and a as the *infinitesimal variance.*

The following examples illustrate the way in which these coefficients are determined in concrete situations.

Examples. (*a*) *Brownian motion.* If the x-axis is assumed homogeneous and symmetric, $a(x)$ must be independent of x and $b(x)$ must vanish. We are thus led to the classical diffusion equation (4.1).

(*b*) *The Ornstein-Uhlenbeck process* is obtained by subjecting the particles of a Brownian motion to an elastic force. Analytically this means a drift towards the origin of a magnitude proportional to the distance, that is, $b(x) = \rho x$. As this does not affect the infinitesimal variance, $a(x)$ remains a constant, say 1. The backward equation takes on the form

$$\frac{\partial u(t, x)}{\partial t} = \frac{1}{2}\frac{\partial^2 u(t, x)}{\partial x^2} - \rho x \frac{\partial u(t, x)}{\partial x}. \tag{4.10}$$

It is fortunately easy to solve this equation. Indeed, the change of variables

$$v(t, x) = u(t, xe^{\rho t})$$

reduces it to

$$e^{2\rho t}\frac{\partial v}{\partial t} = \frac{1}{2}\frac{\partial^2 v}{\partial x^2} \tag{4.11}$$

and the further change of variables

$$\tau = \frac{1 - e^{-2\rho t}}{2\rho} \tag{4.12}$$

changes (4.11) into the standard diffusion equation (4.1). It follows that *the transition densities $q_t(x, y)$ of the Ornstein-Uhlenbeck process coincide with the normal density centered at $xe^{-\rho t}$ and with variance τ given by* (4.12).

It was shown in example III,(8.*e*) that the Ornstein-Uhlenbeck process determined by (4.10) and an initial normal distribution is the only *normal Markovian process* with stationary transition probabilities. (Brownian motion is included as the special case $\rho = 0$.)

(*c*) *Diffusion in genetics.* Consider a population with distinct generations and a constant size N. (A cornfield represents a typical example.) There are $2N$ genes and each belongs to one of two genotypes. We denote by $\mathbf{X}_n$ the *proportion* of genes of type A. If no gene has a selection advantage and the possibility of mutations is disregarded, the genes in the $(n + 1)$st generation may be taken as a random sample of size $2N$ of the genes in the nth generation. The $\mathbf{X}_n$ process is then Markovian, $0 \leq \mathbf{X}_n \leq 1$, and given that $\mathbf{X}_n = x$ the distribution of $2N\mathbf{X}_{n+1}$ is binomial with mean $2Nx$ and variance $2Nx(1 - x)$. The change per generation has expectation 0 and variance proportional to $x(1 - x)$.

Suppose now that we look over a tremendous number of generations and introduce a time scale on which the development appears continuous. In this approximation we deal with a Markov process whose transition probabilities satisfy our basic conditions with $b(x) = 0$ and $a(x)$ proportional to $x(1 - x)$. The proportionality factor depends on the unit of time scale and may be normalized to 1. Then (4.6) takes on the form

$$\frac{\partial u(t, x)}{\partial t} = x(1-x)\frac{\partial^2 u(t, x)}{\partial x^2} \tag{4.13}$$

and this time the process is restricted to the finite interval $\overline{0, 1}$. Selection and mutation pressures would cause a drift and lead to an equation (4.13) with a first-order term added.

Although their starting points and their arguments were different, R. A. Fisher and S. Wright developed genetical models that are mathematically equivalent to ours.[15] The genetical implications are somewhat dubious because of the assumption of constant population size, the effect of which is not generally appreciated. The correct description[16] depends on an equation in two space variables (gene frequency and population size).

(*d*) *Population growth.* We wish to describe the growth of a large population in which the individuals are stochastically independent and the reproduction rate does not depend on the population size. For a very large population the process is approximately continuous, that is, governed by a diffusion equation. The independence of the individuals implies that the infinitesimal velocity and variance must be proportional to the population size. Thus the process is governed by the backward equation (4.6) with $a = \alpha x$ and $b = \beta x$. The constants α and β depend on the choice of the units of time and population size, and with appropriate units of measurement it is possible to achieve that $\alpha = 1$ and $\beta = 1$, -1, or 0 (depending on the net rate of growth).

In **1**; XVII,(5.7) the *same* population growth is described by a discrete model. Given $\mathbf{X}(\tau) = n$ it was assumed that the probabilities of the contingencies $\mathbf{X}(t+\tau) = n+1$, $n-1$, and n differ from λnt, μnt, and $1 - (\lambda+\mu)nt$, respectively, by terms $o(t^2)$, and so the infinitesimal velocity and variance are $(\lambda-\mu)n$ and $(\lambda+\mu)n$. The diffusion process is obtained by a simple passage to the limit, and it can be shown that its transition probabilities represent the limit of the transition probabilities for the discrete model.

Similar approximations of discrete processes by diffusion processes are often practical; the passage from ordinary random walks to diffusion processes described in **1**; XIV,6 provides a typical example. [Continued in example (5.*a*).]

(*e*) *Transformations.* A continuous increasing function Φ may be used to transform an arbitrary stochastic process $\{\mathbf{X}(t)\}$ into a new process

[15] For explicit solutions of (4.13) (due to M. Kimura) see A. T. Barucha-Reid (1960).

[16] W. Feller, Proc. Second Berkeley Symposium on Math. Statist. and Probability, 1951, pp. 227–246.

defined by $\mathbf{Y}(t) = \Phi(\mathbf{X}(t))$. If Φ is twice differentiable and the $\mathbf{X}$-process satisfies the conditions (4.2)–(4.4) used in the derivation of the backward equation, the same is true of the transformed process. The latter is therefore governed by a backward equation which can be written down without trouble.[17] This transformation can be used to represent some complicated diffusion processes in terms of the simple Brownian motion. In fact, using the modern generalized diffusion operators, no differentiability conditions need be imposed and it is possible to derive *all* diffusion processes by transformations from Brownian motion. The transformations are more delicate, however, and depend on the ingenious notion of chance-dependent local times introduced by P. Lévy. This method is fully exploited in the book by Ito and McKean.

5. THE FORWARD EQUATION. BOUNDARY CONDITIONS

As explained in the last section, an analytic characterization of the transition probabilities starts necessarily from the backward equation (4.6) even though it describes $Q_t(x, \Gamma)$ for fixed Γ in its dependence on the initial position x. In analyzing the dependence on the set Γ we assume for simplicity that Q_t possesses a probability density $q_t(x, y)$. Given the initial density v_0 of $\mathbf{X}(0)$, the density of $\mathbf{X}(s)$ is given by

$$v(s, y) = \int v_0(x)\, q_s(x, y)\, dx \tag{5.1}$$

[which relation is the "forward" analogue to (4.5)]. Many facts known about partial differential equations make it plausible that (under sufficient regularity conditions) v should satisfy the equation

$$\frac{\partial v(s, y)}{\partial s} = \frac{1}{2}\frac{\partial^2}{\partial y^2}[a(y)\, v(s, y)] - \frac{\partial}{\partial y}[b(y)\, v(s, y)]. \tag{5.2}$$

In probability theory this equation is known as the *forward* or *Fokker-Planck* equation.

Before proceeding let us illustrate the kind of information that can be derived from (5.2) more easily than from the backward equation.

Example. (*a*) *Population growth.* Example (4.*d*) leads to the forward equation

$$\frac{\partial v(s, y)}{\partial s} = \alpha\frac{\partial^2 y\, v(s, y)}{\partial y^2} - \beta\frac{\partial y\, v(s, y)}{\partial y}. \tag{5.3}$$

[17] From the Taylor formula for Φ it is seen that for given $\mathbf{Y}(t) = \Phi(\mathbf{X})$ the new infinitesimal velocity and acceleration are given by $\Phi'(x)\, b(x) + \frac{1}{2}\Phi''(x)\, a(x)$ and $\Phi'^2(x)\, a(x)$.

It can be proved that for a given initial density v_0 there exists a unique solution. Although explicit formulas are hard to come by, much relevant information can be obtained directly from the equation. For example, to calculate the expected population size $M(s)$ multiply (5.3) by y and integrate with respect to y from 0 to ∞. On the left we get the derivative $M'(s)$. Using integration by parts and assuming that v vanishes at infinity faster than $1/y^2$ it is seen that the right side equals $\beta M(s)$. Thus

$$M'(s) = \beta M(s)$$

and hence $M(s)$ is proportional to $e^{\beta s}$. Similar formal manipulations show that the variance is proportional to $2\alpha\beta^{-1}e^{\beta s}(e^{\beta s}-1)$. [Compare the analogous result in the discrete case, **1**; XVII,(5.10) and (11.9).] Admittedly the manipulations require justification, but the result has at least heuristic value and could not be obtained from the backward equation without explicit calculation of q_t. ▶

The problem is to decide to what extent the forward equation (5.2) really follows[18] from the backward equation (4.6). The theory is a close parallel to that for the jump processes described in section 3. We give a brief summary without proof.

Consider the backward equation (4.6) in an open interval $\overline{x_1, x_2}$ which may be finite or infinite. We assume, of course, $a > 0$ and that the coefficients a and b are sufficiently regular for (5.2) to make sense. Under these conditions there exists a *unique minimal solution* Q_t such that (4.5) yields a solution of the backward equation (4.6). The catch is that for fixed t and x the kernel $Q_t(x, \Gamma)$ may represent a *defective distribution*. Under any circumstances Q_t possesses densities and the function v of (5.1) satisfies the forward equation. In fact, this solution is again minimal in the obvious sense made precise in section 3. To this extent the forward equation is a consequence of the backward equation. However, these equations determine the process uniquely only when the minimal solution is not defective. In all other cases the nature of the process is determined by additional boundary conditions.

The nature of boundary conditions is best understood by analogy with the simple random walk on $\overline{0, \infty}$ discussed in **1**; XIV. Various conventions can be in effect when the origin is reached for the first time. In the *ruin problem* the process stops; in this case the origin is said to act as an

[18] More correctly, the problem is to find the true form of the forward equation that does follow from the backward equation. Note that the latter determines a process whenever $a > 0$ and b are continuous whereas the forward equation (5.2) requires the existence of derivatives of a and b. The true forward equation can be written down in all cases, but it depends on the generalized differential operators mentioned in footnote 12 of section 4.

absorbing barrier. On the other hand, when the origin acts as *reflecting barrier*, the particle is returned instantaneously to the position 1 and the process continues forever. The point is that boundary conditions appear iff a boundary point can be reached. The event "the boundary point x_2 has been reached before epoch t" is well defined in diffusion processes because of the continuity of the path functions. It is closely related to the event "infinitely many jumps have occurred before t" in jump processes.

In some diffusion processes with probability one no boundary point is ever reached. Such is the Brownian motion [example (4.*a*)]. Then the minimal solution stands for a proper probability distribution and no other solutions exist. In all other situations the minimal solution regulates the process until a boundary is reached. It corresponds to absorbing barriers, that is, it describes a process that stops when a boundary point is reached. This is the most important type of process not only because all other processes are extensions of it, but even more because all *first-passage* probabilities can be calculated by imposing artificial absorbing barriers. The method is generally applicable but will be explained by the simplest example. (It was used implicitly in random walks and elsewhere, for example in problem 15 of **1**; XVII.)

Examples. (*b*) *One absorbing barrier. First-passage times.* Consider Brownian motion on $\overline{0, \infty}$ with an absorbing barrier at the origin. More precisely, a Brownian motion starting at the point $x > 0$ at epoch 0 is stopped at the epoch of the first arrival at the origin. Because of symmetry both the backward and the forward equation take on the form of the classical diffusion equation

$$\frac{\partial u}{\partial t} = \frac{1}{2}\frac{\partial^2 u}{\partial x^2}. \tag{5.4}$$

The appropriate *boundary condition* is $q_t(0, y) = 0$ for all t, just as in the case of random walks. (The assertion can be justified either by the passage to the limit in **1**; XIV,6 or from the minimal character of the solution.)

For a given u_0 we seek a solution of (5.4) defined for $t \geq 0$, $x \geq 0$ and such that $u(0, x) = u_0(x)$ and $u(t, 0) = 0$. Its construction depends on *the method of images* due to Lord Kelvin.[19] We extend u_0 to the left half-line by $u_0(-x) = -u_0(x)$ and solve (5.4) with this initial condition in $\overline{-\infty, \infty}$. For reasons of symmetry the solution satisfies the condition $u(t, 0) = 0$, and restricting x again to $\overline{0, \infty}$ we have the desired solution. It is given by the integral of $u_0(y)\, q_t(x, y)$ over $\overline{0, \infty}$ where

$$q_t(x, y) = \frac{1}{\sqrt{2\pi t}}\left[\exp\left(-\frac{(y-x)^2}{2t}\right) - \exp\left(-\frac{(y+x)^2}{2t}\right)\right]. \tag{5.5}$$

[19] See problems 7–10 in **1**; XIV for the same method applied to difference equations.

Thus q_t *represents the transition probabilities of our process* ($t > 0, x > 0, y > 0$). It is easily seen that q_t is, for fixed y, a solution (5.4) satisfying the boundary condition $q_t(0, y) = 0$. [For a more systematic derivation see example XIV,(5.*a*).]

Integrating over y one gets the total probability mass at epoch t

$$\int_0^\infty q_t(x, y)\, dy = 2\mathfrak{N}\left(\frac{x}{\sqrt{t}}\right) - 1, \tag{5.6}$$

where $\mathfrak{N}$ stands for the standard normal distribution. In other words, (5.6) *is the probability that a path starting from* $x > 0$ *does not reach the origin before epoch* t. In this sense (5.6) represents the distribution of *first-passage times in a free Brownian motion.* Note that (5.6) may be characterized as the solution of the differential equation (5.4) defined for $x > 0$ and satisfying the initial condition $u(0, x) = 1$ together with the boundary condition $u(t, 0) = 0$.

[One recognizes in (5.6) the stable distribution with exponent $\alpha = \frac{1}{2}$; the same result was found in VI,2 by a passage to the limit from random walks.]

(*c*) *Two absorbing barriers.* Consider now a Brownian motion impeded by two absorbing barriers at 0 and $a > 0$. This means that for fixed $0 < y < a$ the transition densities q_t should satisfy the differential equation (5.4) together with the boundary conditions $q_t(0, y) = q_t(a, y) = 0$.

It is easily seen that the solution is given by[20]

$$q_t(x, y) = \frac{1}{\sqrt{2\pi t}} \sum_{k=-\infty}^{+\infty} \left\{ \exp\left(-\frac{(y - x + 2ka)^2}{2t}\right) - \exp\left(-\frac{(y + x + 2ka)^2}{2t}\right)\right\} \tag{5.7}$$

where $0 < x, y < a$. Indeed, the series is manifestly convergent, and the obvious cancellation of terms shows that $q_t(0, y) = q_t(a, y) = 0$ for all $t > 0$ and $0 < y < a$. [The Laplace transform of (5.7) is given in XIV,(5.17).]

Integrating (5.7) over $0 < y < a$ we get the total probability mass at epoch t in the form

$$\lambda_a(t, x) = \sum_{k=-\infty}^{\infty} \left\{ \mathfrak{N}\left(\frac{2ka + a - x}{\sqrt{t}}\right) - \mathfrak{N}\left(\frac{2ka - x}{\sqrt{t}}\right) - \mathfrak{N}\left(\frac{2ka + a + x}{\sqrt{t}}\right) + \mathfrak{N}\left(\frac{2ka + x}{\sqrt{t}}\right)\right\}. \tag{5.8}$$

[20] The construction depends on successive approximations by repeated reflections. In (5.5) we have a solution of the differential equation satisfying the boundary condition at 0, but not a. A reflection at a leads to a four-term solution satisfying the boundary condition at a, but not at 0. Alternating reflections at 0 and a lead in the limit to (5.7). The analogous solution for random walks is given in **1**; XIV,(9.1), and (5.7) could be derived from it by the passage to the limit described in **1**; XIV,6.

This is the probability that *a particle starting at x will not be absorbed before epoch t.*

The function λ_a is a solution of the differential equation tending to 1 as $t \to 0$ and satisfying the boundary conditions $\lambda_a(t, 0) = \lambda_a(t, a) = 0$. This solution can be obtained also by a routine application of the method of Fourier series in the form[21]

$$(5.9)\quad \lambda_a(t, x) = \frac{4}{\pi}\sum_{n=0}^{\infty} \frac{1}{2n+1} \cdot \exp\left(-\frac{(2n+1)^2\pi^2}{2a^2}\,t\right) \cdot \sin\frac{(2n+1)\pi x}{a}.$$

The possibility of expressing the solution λ_a in two ways is fortunate because the series in (5.8) converges rapidly for small t, and that in (5.9) for large t. The identity between (5.8) and (5.9) serves as a standard example for the Poisson summation formula [see XIX,(5.8)]. It has acquired historical luster, having been discovered originally in connection with Jacobi's theory of transformations of theta functions.[22]

For an alternative interpretation of λ_a consider the position $\mathbf{X}(t)$ of a particle in free Brownian motion starting at the origin. To say that during the time interval $\overline{0, t}$ the particle remained within $\overline{-\frac{1}{2}a, \frac{1}{2}a}$ amounts to saying that in a process with absorbing barriers at $\pm\frac{1}{2}a$ and starting at 0 no absorption took place before epoch t. Thus $\lambda_a(t, \frac{1}{2}a)$ *equals the probability that in an unrestricted Brownian motion starting at the origin* $|\mathbf{X}(s)| < \frac{1}{2}a$ *for all s in the interval* $0 < s < t$.

(*d*) *Application to limit theorems and Kolmogorov-Smirnov tests.* Let $\mathbf{Y}_1, \mathbf{Y}_2, \ldots$ be independent random variables with a common distribution and suppose that $\mathbf{E}(\mathbf{Y}_j) = 0$ and $\mathbf{E}(\mathbf{Y}_j^2) = 1$. Put $\mathbf{S}_n = \mathbf{Y}_1 + \cdots + \mathbf{Y}_n$ and $\mathbf{T}_n = \max\,[|\mathbf{S}_1|, \ldots, |\mathbf{S}_n|]$. In view of the central limit theorem it is plausible that the asymptotic behavior of $\mathbf{T}_n$ will be nearly the same as in the case where the $\mathbf{Y}_j$ are normal variables, and in the latter case the normed sums $(1/\sqrt{n})\mathbf{S}_k$ are comparable to the variables $\mathbf{X}(k/n)$, $k = 1, \ldots, n$ of a Brownian motion. The probability that these variables be constrained to the interval $\overline{-\frac{1}{2}a, \frac{1}{2}a}$ was shown to equal $\lambda_a(1, \frac{1}{2}a)$. Our plausibility argument would therefore lead us to the conjecture that as $n \to \infty$

$$(5.10)\qquad \mathbf{P}\{\mathbf{T}_n < z\} \to L(z)$$

where $L(z) = \lambda_{2z}(1, z)$ is obtained from (5.8) and (5.9):

$$(5.11)\qquad \begin{aligned} L(z) &= 2\sum_{k=-\infty}^{\infty} \{\mathfrak{N}((4k+1)z) - \mathfrak{N}((4k-1)z)\} = \\ &= \frac{4}{\pi}\sum_{n=0}^{\infty} \frac{(-1)^n}{2n+1} \exp\left(-\frac{(2n+1)^2\pi^2}{8z^2}\right). \end{aligned}$$

[21] The analogous formula for random walks is derived in **1**; XIV,5 where, however, the boundary conditions are $\lambda_a(t, 0) = 1$ and $\lambda_a(t, a) = 0$.

[22] See Satz 277 in E. Landau, *Verteilung der Primzahlen*, 1909.

This conjecture was proved in 1946 by P. Erdös and M. Kac, and the underlying idea has since become known as *invariance principle.* It states, roughly speaking, that the asymptotic distribution of certain functions of random variables is insensitive to changes of the distributions of these variables and may be obtained by considering an appropriate approximating stochastic process. This method has been perfected by M. Donsker, P. Billingsley, Yu. V. Prohorov, and others, and has become a powerful tool for proving limit theorems.

For similar reasons the distribution (5.11) plays a prominent part also in the vast literature on non-parametric tests of the type discussed in I,12.[23]

(*e*) *Reflecting barriers.* We return to Brownian motion. The boundary condition $\dfrac{\partial q_t(0, y)}{\partial y} = 0$ for a reflecting barrier at the origin is imposed by analogy with random walks. It is readily verified that the solution for the interval $\overline{0, \infty}$ is obtained by replacing the difference in (5.5) by a sum. The formal derivation by the method of images is the same, except that one puts $u_0(-x) = u_0(x)$. In this case q_t is a proper probability density. The solution for $\overline{0, a}$ with reflecting barriers at both 0 and a is obtained similarly by changing the minus sign to a plus in (5.7). (An alternative expression obtained by Fourier expansions or the Poisson summation formula is given in problem 11 of XIX,9.) ▶

Similar considerations for boundary conditions and first-passage times apply to diffusion processes governed by the general diffusion equation (4.6), but explicit solutions are usually hard to come by. For an approach to related problems by Laplace transforms see XIV,6.

6. DIFFUSION IN HIGHER DIMENSIONS

It is easy to generalize the foregoing theory to two dimensions. To avoid the nuisance of subscripts we denote the coordinate variables by $(\mathbf{X}(t), \mathbf{Y}(t))$ and the values of the transition *densities* by $q_t(x, y; \xi, \eta)$; here x, y is the initial point and q_t is a density in (ξ, η). The postulates are as in section 4 except that the infinitesimal velocity $b(x)$ is replaced by a

[23] The topic is relatively new, but the starting point of the much used identity (5.11) seems already to have fallen into oblivion so that modern workers could find no proof in the literature. [A. Renyi, *On the distribution function* $L(z)$. Selected Translations in Math. Statist. and Probability, vol. 4 (1963) pp. 219–224. Renyi's new proof depends on the classical argument involving theta functions, thus obscuring the simple probabilistic meaning of (5.11).]

vector, and the variance $a(x)$ by a covariance matrix. Instead of (4.6) we get for the *backward diffusion equation*

$$\frac{\partial u}{\partial t} = a_{11}\frac{\partial^2 u}{\partial x^2} + 2a_{12}\frac{\partial^2 u}{\partial x\,\partial y} + a_{22}\frac{\partial^2 u}{\partial y^2} + b_1\frac{\partial u}{\partial x} + b_2\frac{\partial u}{\partial y}, \tag{6.1}$$

the coefficients depending on x and y. In the case of two-dimensional Brownian motion we require rotational symmetry, and up to an irrelevant norming constant we must have

$$\frac{\partial u}{\partial t} = \frac{1}{2}\left[\frac{\partial^2 u}{\partial x^2} + \frac{\partial^2 u}{\partial y^2}\right]. \tag{6.2}$$

The corresponding transition densities are normal with variance t, centered at (x, y). The obvious factoring of this density shows that $\mathbf{X}(t)$ and $\mathbf{Y}(t)$ are stochastically independent.

The most interesting variable in this process is the distance $\mathbf{R}(t)$ from the origin ($\mathbf{R}^2 = \mathbf{X}^2 + \mathbf{Y}^2$). It is intuitively obvious that $\mathbf{R}(t)$ is the variable of a one-dimensional diffusion process and it is interesting to compare the various ways of getting at the diffusion equation for this process. In polar coordinates our normal transition densities for (6.2) take on the form

$$\frac{\rho}{2\pi t}\exp\left(-\frac{\rho^2 + r^2 - 2\rho r\cos(\theta-\alpha)}{2t}\right) \tag{6.3}$$

(with $x = r\cos\alpha$, etc.). Given the position r, α at epoch 0, the marginal density of $\mathbf{R}(t)$ is obtained by integrating (6.3) with respect to θ. The parameter α drops out and we get[24] for *the transition densities of the* $\mathbf{R}(t)$ *process*

$$w_t(r, \rho) = \frac{1}{t}\exp\left(-\frac{r^2 + \rho^2}{2t}\right)I_0\left(\frac{r\rho}{t}\right) \tag{6.4}$$

where I_0 is the Bessel function defined in II,(7.1). From the derivation it is clear that for fixed ρ the transition probabilities w_t must satisfy (6.2) in polar coordinates; that is to say, we must have

$$\frac{\partial w_t}{\partial t} = \frac{1}{2}\left(\frac{\partial^2 w_t}{\partial r^2} + \frac{1}{r}\frac{\partial w_t}{\partial r}\right). \tag{6.5}$$

This is the *backward equation for the* $\mathbf{R}(t)$ *process* and is obtained from (6.2) simply by requiring rotational symmetry.

[24] The integral is well known. For a routine verification expand $e^{\cos\theta}$ into a power series in $\cos\theta$.

From (6.5) it is seen that the infinitesimal variance of the $\mathbf{R}(t)$ process is the same as for $\mathbf{X}(t)$, but the infinitesimal velocity is $\frac{1}{2}r^{-1}$. This velocity can be explained (and even calculated) as follows. Consider a particle in plane Brownian motion starting at the point r of the x-axis. For reasons of symmetry its *abscissa* at epoch $h > 0$ is equally likely to be $>r$ or $<r$. In the first case certainly $\mathbf{R}(h) > r$, but this relation can occur also in the second case. Thus the relation $\mathbf{R}(h) > r$ has probability $>\frac{1}{2}$, and on the average $\mathbf{R}$ is bound to increase.

The same derivation of transition probabilities applies to three dimensions with one essential simplification: the Jacobian ρ in (6.3) is now replaced by $\rho^2 \sin \theta$, and an elementary integration is possible. Instead of (6.4) we get for the *transition densities of the* $\mathbf{R}(t)$ *process in three dimensions*

$$(6.6)\quad w_t(r, \rho) = \frac{1}{\sqrt{2\pi t}} \frac{\rho}{r}\left[\exp\left(-\frac{(\rho - r)^2}{2t}\right) - \exp\left(-\frac{(\rho + r)^2}{2t}\right)\right].$$

7. SUBORDINATED PROCESSES

Given a Markov process $\{\mathbf{X}(t)\}$ with stationary transition probabilities $Q_t(x, \Gamma)$ it is possible to derive from it a variety of new Markov processes by introducing what may be called a *randomized operational time*. For a first orientation consider a family of stochastic kernels

$$(7.1)\qquad P_t(x, \Gamma) = \sum_{n=0}^{\infty} e^{-\alpha t} \frac{(\alpha t)^n}{n!} Q_n(x, \Gamma)$$

obtained by treating the time parameter in Q_t as a Poisson variable.[25] If $\mathbf{T}(t)$ is the variable of a Poisson process and $\mathbf{X}(0) = x$ then (7.1) represents the distribution of the random variables $\mathbf{X}(\mathbf{T}(t))$. These variables define a new stochastic process in which the Poisson variables $\mathbf{T}(t)$ serve as operational time. A great variety of other processes $\{\mathbf{T}(t)\}$ may serve in this capacity, but in general $\{\mathbf{X}(\mathbf{T}(t))\}$ will not be Markovian. To avoid notational complications let us first suppose that $\mathbf{T}(t)$ is restricted to the multiples $0, h, 2h, \ldots$ of a fixed number $h > 0$, and put

$$\mathbf{P}\{\mathbf{T}(t) = nh\} = a_n(t).$$

[25] Note that (7.1) defines a pseudo-Poissonian process. A generalization in terms of operators will be introduced in section 9. There it will be shown that the simple application of the law of large numbers described in VII,5 leads to the so-called *exponential formula of semi-group theory* which states that every family Q_t may be approximated by transition probabilities of the form (7.1). The following considerations will show that the Poisson distribution in (7.1) may be replaced by others and that the notion of subordination leads to an understanding of the true nature of the exponential formula.

Given that $\mathbf{X}(0) = x$ the variable $\mathbf{X}(\mathbf{T}(t))$ has the distribution

$$P_t(x, \Gamma) = \sum_{k=0}^{\infty} a_k(t)\, Q_{kh}(x, \Gamma). \tag{7.2}$$

Since the kernels $\{Q_t\}$ satisfy the Chapman-Kolmogorov equation we have

$$\int_{-\infty}^{+\infty} P_s(x, dy)\, P_t(y, \Gamma) = \sum_{j,k} a_j(s)\, a_k(t) \cdot Q_{(j+k)h}(x, \Gamma), \tag{7.3}$$

and it is seen that the kernels P_t satisfy the Chapman-Kolmogorov equation whenever

$$a_0(s)\, a_n(t) + a_1(s)\, a_{n-1}(t) + \cdots + a_n(s)\, a_0(t) = a_n(s+t) \tag{7.4}$$

for all $s > 0$ and $t > 0$. This relation holds if $\{\mathbf{T}(t)\}$ *is a process with stationary independent increments*, and the most general solution of (7.4) was studied in **1**; XII,3.

Example. (*a*) The relation (7.4) holds if $\{a_n(t)\}$ has the generating function $\Sigma a_n(t)\zeta^n = (2-\zeta)^{-t}$. Then $a_n(t) = \binom{-t}{n}(-1)^n 2^{-n-t}$. ▶

We saw that (7.4) insures that the quantity (7.3) equals $P_{s+t}(x, \Gamma)$. This means that the distribution of $\mathbf{X}(\mathbf{T}(t+s))$ is obtained by integration of $P_t(y, \Gamma)$ with respect to the distribution of $\mathbf{X}(\mathbf{T}(s))$ and so

$$P_t(y, \Gamma) = \mathbf{P}\{\mathbf{X}(\mathbf{T}(t+s)) \in \Gamma \mid \mathbf{X}(\mathbf{T}(s)) = y\} \tag{7.5}$$

by the definition of conditional probabilities. A similar argument applies to higher transition probabilities and shows that *the process* $\{\mathbf{X}(\mathbf{T}(t))\}$ *is Markovian.*

A formal passage to the limit $h \to 0$ leads us now to the general situation. Suppose that the $\mathbf{T}(t)$ are the variables of a process with non-negative stationary independent increments. The distribution U_t of $\mathbf{T}(t)$ is then concentrated on $\overline{0, \infty}$ and satisfies the convolution equation

$$U_{t+s}(x) = \int_{0-}^{x} U_s(x-y)\, U_t\{dy\}, \qquad x > 0 \tag{7.6}$$

generalizing (7.4). The sum in (7.2) is an integral with respect to the distribution of $\mathbf{T}(t)$, and the general form of (7.2) is

$$P_t(x, \Gamma) = \int_{0-}^{\infty} Q_s(x, \Gamma)\, U_t\{ds\}. \tag{7.7}$$

Now every family of distributions U_t satisfying (7.6) may be obtained as the limit as $\nu \to \infty$ of a sequence of arithmetic distributions $\{a_n^{(\nu)}(t)\}$

satisfying (7.4). Under extremely weak continuity conditions[26] on Q_t we get therefore by a passage to the limit the following basic result:

Let $\{\mathbf{X}(t)\}$ be a Markov process with continuous transition probabilities Q_t and $\{\mathbf{T}(t)\}$ a process with non-negative independent increments [that is, with infinitely divisible transition probabilities U_t satisfying (7.6)]. *Then* $\{\mathbf{X}(\mathbf{T}(t))\}$ *is a Markovian process with transition probabilities* P_t *given by* (7.7). This process is said to be *subordinated*[27] *to* $\{\mathbf{X}(t)\}$ using the operational time $\mathbf{T}(t)$. The process $\{\mathbf{T}(t)\}$ is called the *directing process.*

The most interesting special case arises when also the $\mathbf{X}(t)$ process has independent increments. In this case the transition probabilities depend only on the differences $\Gamma - x$ and may be replaced by the equivalent distribution functions. Then (7.7) takes on the simpler form

$$P_t(x) = \int_0^\infty Q_s(x)\, U_t\{ds\}. \tag{7.8}$$

All our examples are of this type.

Examples. (*b*) *The Cauchy process is subordinated to Brownian motion.* Let $\{\mathbf{X}(t)\}$ be the Brownian motion (Wiener process) with transition *densities* given by $q_t(x) = (2\pi t)^{-\frac{1}{2}} e^{-\frac{1}{2}x^2/t}$. For $\{\mathbf{T}(t)\}$ we take the stable process with exponent $\frac{1}{2}$ with transition densities given by

$$u_t(x) = \frac{t}{\sqrt{2\pi}\,\sqrt{x^3}}\, e^{-\frac{1}{2}t^2/x}.$$

Passing in (7.8) to densities it is seen that the substitution $s = 1/y$ reduces the integral to an ordinary exponential and hence P_t has the density

$$p_t(x) = \frac{1}{\pi}\,\frac{t}{t^2 + x^2} \tag{7.9}$$

corresponding to a Cauchy process. [Compare example VI,(2.*f*).]

We know that U_t is the distribution of the first-passage time through a

---

[26] It suffices obviously that for each continuous function f vanishing at infinity $\int_{-\infty}^{+\infty} Q_t(x, dy)\, f(y)$ should depend continuously on t and x. That P_t is a stochastic kernel is trivial since it is obtained by randomization. (A *direct* verification requires a certain skill in manipulations and may prove embarrassing. Our passage to the limit yields this result rigorously at no extra cost and shows that the naïve approach may be the most sophisticated one.)

[27] The intriguing notion of subordination is due to S. Bochner, 1949. [A further developed theory is available in his book (1955).] The interpretation in terms of operational time was found by Nelson, Trotter, and Woll. [For a (high-level) systematic approach see E. Nelson, *A functional calculus using singular Laplace integrals*, Trans. Amer. Math. Soc., 88 (1958) pp. 400–413.]

fixed point $t > 0$ in ordinary Brownian motion and this enables us to *interpret the Cauchy process in terms of two independent Brownian motions* $\mathbf{X}(t)$, $\mathbf{Y}(t)$ *as follows.* The Cauchy variable $\mathbf{Z}(t)$ is the value of $\mathbf{X}$ at the epoch $\mathbf{T}(t)$ when $\mathbf{Y}(s)$ first attains the value t.

(*c*) *Stable processes.* The last example generalizes easily to arbitrary stable processes $\{\mathbf{X}(t)\}$ and $\{\mathbf{T}(t)\}$ with exponents α and β, respectively. Here $\alpha \leq 2$, but since $\mathbf{T}(t)$ must be positive we have necessarily $\beta < 1$. The transition probabilities Q_t and U_t are of the form $Q_t(x) = Q(xt^{-1/\alpha})$ and $U_t(x) = U(xt^{-1/\beta})$ where Q and U are fixed stable distributions. We show that *the subordinated process* $\mathbf{X}(\mathbf{T}(t))$ *is stable with exponent* $\alpha\beta$. This assertion is equivalent to the relation $P_{\lambda t}(x) = P_t(x^{-1/\alpha\beta})$. In view of the given form of Q_s and U_t this relation follows trivially from (7.8) by the substitution $s = y\lambda^{1/\beta}$.

[Our result is essentially equivalent to the product formula derived in example VI,(2.*g*). When $\mathbf{X}(t) > 0$ the formula can be restated in terms of Laplace transforms as in XIII,(7.*e*). For the Fourier version see problem 8 in XVII,12.]

(*d*) *Compound Poisson process directed by gamma process.* Let Q_t be the compound Poisson distribution generated by the probability distribution F and let U_t have the gamma density $e^{-x}x^{t-1}/\Gamma(t)$. Then (7.8) takes on the form

$$P_t = \sum_{n=0}^{\infty} a_n(t)\, F^{n\star} \tag{7.10}$$

where

$$a_n(t) = \int_0^\infty e^{-s}\frac{s^n}{n!}\cdot e^{-s}\frac{s^{t-1}}{\Gamma(t)}\,ds = \frac{\Gamma(n+t)}{n!\,\Gamma(t)}\cdot 2^{-n-t}. \tag{7.11}$$

Simple arithmetic shows that the $a_n(t)$ are the probabilities of example (*a*). In particular, if F is concentrated at the point 1 the process $\{\mathbf{X}(t)\}$ is the Poisson process with expectation t and we see that *the process of example* (*a*) *is subordinated to the Poisson process* using the gamma process for operational time,

(*e*) *Gamma process directed by the Poisson process.* Let us now consider the same distributions but with reversed roles. The operational time is then integral-valued and 0 has weight e^{-t}. It follows that the resulting distribution has an atom of weight e^{-t} at the origin. The continuous part has the density

$$\sum_{n=1}^{\infty} e^{-x}\frac{x^{n-1}}{(n-1)!}\cdot e^{-t}\frac{t^n}{n!} = e^{-t-x}\sqrt{\frac{t}{x}}\,I_1(2\sqrt{xt}), \tag{7.12}$$

where I_1 is the Bessel function of II,(7.1). It follows that this distribution is infinitely divisible, but a direct verification is not easy. ▶

8. MARKOV PROCESSES AND SEMI-GROUPS

Chapter VIII revealed the advantages of treating probability distributions as operators on continuous functions. The advantages of the operator approach to stochastic kernels are even greater, and the theory of semi-groups leads to a unified theory of Markov processes not attainable by other methods. Given a stochastic kernel K in $\mathfrak{R}^1$ and a bounded continuous function u the relation

$$(8.1) \qquad U(x) = \int_{-\infty}^{+\infty} K(x, dy)\, u(y)$$

defines a new function. Little generality is lost in assuming that the transform U is again continuous and we could proceed to study properties of the kernel K in terms of the induced transformation $u \to U$ on continuous functions. There are two main reasons for a more general setup. First, transformations of the form (8.1) make sense in arbitrary spaces, and it would be exceedingly uneconomical to develop a theory which does not cover the simplest and most important special case, namely processes with a denumerable state space [where (8.1) reduces to a matrix transformation]. Second, even in a theory restricted to continuous functions on the line various types of boundary conditions compel one to introduce special classes of continuous functions. On the other hand, the greater generality is bought at no expense. Readers so inclined are urged to ignore the generality and refer all theorems to one (or several) of the following typical situations. (i) The underlying space Σ is the real line and $\mathscr{L}$ the class of bounded continuous functions vanishing at infinity. (ii) the space Σ is a finite closed interval I in $\mathfrak{R}^1$ or $\mathfrak{R}^2$ and $\mathscr{L}$ the class of continuous functions on it. (iii) Σ consists of the integers and $\mathscr{L}$ of bounded sequences. In this case it is best to think of sequences as column vectors and of transformations as matrices.

As in chapter VIII the *norm* of a bounded real function u is defined by $\|u\| = \sup |u(x)|$. A sequence of functions u_n converges uniformly to u iff $\|u_n - u\| \to 0$.

From now on $\mathscr{L}$ *will denote a family of real functions on some set* Σ *with the following properties:* (i) If u_1 and u_2 belong to $\mathscr{L}$ then every linear combination $c_1u_1 + c_2u_2 \in \mathscr{L}$. (ii) If $u_n \in \mathscr{L}$ and $\|u_n - u\| \to 0$ then $u \in \mathscr{L}$. (iii) If $u \in \mathscr{L}$ then also u^+ and u^- belong to $\mathscr{L}$ (where $u = u^+ - u^-$ is the usual decomposition of u into its positive and negative parts.) In other words, $\mathscr{L}$ is closed under linear combinations, uniform limits, and absolute values. The first two properties make $\mathscr{L}$ a *Banach* space, the last a lattice.

The following definitions are standard. A linear transformation T

is an *endomorphism* on $\mathscr{L}$ if each $u \in \mathscr{L}$ has an image $Tu \in \mathscr{L}$ such that $\|Tu\| \leq m \|u\|$ where m is a constant independent of u. The smallest constant with this property is called the *norm* $\|T\|$ of T. The transformation T is *positive* if $u \geq 0$ implies $Tu \geq 0$. In this case $-Tu^- \leq Tu \leq Tu^+$. A *contraction* is a positive operator T with $\|T\| \leq 1$. If the constant function 1 belongs to $\mathscr{L}$ and T is a positive operator such that $T1 = 1$, then T is called a *transition operator*. (It is automatically a contraction.)

Given two endomorphisms S and T on $\mathscr{L}$, their *product* ST is the endomorphism mapping u into $S(Tu)$. Obviously $\|ST\| \leq \|S\| \cdot \|T\|$. In general $ST \neq TS$, in contrast to the particular class of convolution operators of VIII,3 which commuted with each other.

We are seriously interested only in transformations of the form (8.1) where K is a stochastic, or at least substochastic, kernel. Operators of this form are contractions or transition operators and they also enjoy the

Monotone convergence property: *if* $u_n \geq 0$ *and* $u_n \uparrow u$ (*with* u_n *and* u *in* $\mathscr{L}$) *then* $Tu_n \to Tu$ *pointwise.*

In practically all situations contractions with this property are of the form (8.1). Two examples will illustrate this point.

Examples. (*a*) Let Σ stand for the real line and $\mathscr{L} = C$ for the family of all bounded continuous functions on it. Let $C_0 \subset \mathscr{L}$ the subclass of functions vanishing at $\pm\infty$. If T is a contraction on $\mathscr{L}$ then for $u \in C_0$ the value $Tu(x)$ of Tu at a fixed x is a positive linear functional on $\mathscr{L}$. By the F. Riesz representation theorem there exists a possibly defective probability distribution F such that $Tu(x)$ is the expectation of u with respect to F. Since F depends on x we write $K(x, \Gamma)$ for $F(\Gamma)$. Then for $u \in C_0$

$$(8.2) \qquad Tu(x) = \int_{-\infty}^{+\infty} K(x, dy)\, u(y),$$

and when T has the monotone convergence property this relation automatically extends to all bounded continuous functions.

For fixed x, as a function of Γ, the kernel K is a measure. If Γ is an open interval and $\{u_n\}$ an increasing sequence of continuous functions such that $u_n(x) \to 1$ if $x \in \Gamma$ and $u_n(x) \to 0$ otherwise, then $K(x, \Gamma) = \lim Tu_n(x)$ by the basic properties of integrals. Since Tu_n is continuous it follows that for fixed Γ the kernel K is a Baire function of x and therefore K has all the properties required of stochastic or substochastic kernels. The same situation prevails when the line is replaced by an interval, or $\mathcal{R}^n$.

(*b*) Let Σ be the set of integers, and $\mathscr{L}$ the set of numerical sequences

$\{u_n\}$ with $\|u\| = \sup |u_n|$. In particular, let $e^{(n)} = (0, 0, \ldots, 0, 1, 0, \ldots)$ be the sequence with a single non-vanishing term at the nth place. For a contraction operator T denote the ith term of $Te^{(k)}$ by p_{ik}. If u has only finitely many non-zero terms it is a linear combination of finitely many $e^{(k)}$, and hence the ith term of Tu is given by

$$(8.3) \qquad (Tu)_i = \sum p_{ik}u_k,$$

the sum being only formally infinite. In consequence of the monotone convergence property the representation (8.3) applies evidently to all u. The fact that T is a contraction implies $p_{ik} \geq 0$ and that the row sums are ≤ 1. Thus the matrix (p_{ik}) is substochastic and it is strictly stochastic if T is a transition operator. ▶

These examples are typical[28] and it is actually difficult to find contractions not induced by a stochastic kernel. Anyhow, we are justified to proceed with the general theory of contractions with the assurance that applications to probabilistically significant problems will be obvious. (In fact, we shall never have to go beyond the scope of these examples.)

The transition probabilities of a Markov process form a one-parameter family of kernels satisfying the Chapman-Kolmogorov equation

$$(8.4) \qquad Q_{s+t}(x, \Gamma) = \int Q_s(x, dy)\, Q_t(y, \Gamma)$$

$(s > 0, t > 0)$, the integration extending over the underlying space. Each individual kernel induces a transition operator $\mathfrak{Q}(t)$ defined by

$$(8.5) \qquad \mathfrak{Q}(t)\, u(x) = \int Q_t(x, dy)\, u(y).$$

Obviously then (8.4) is equivalent with

$$(8.6) \qquad \mathfrak{Q}(s+t) = \mathfrak{Q}(s)\, \mathfrak{Q}(t), \qquad s > 0, t > 0.$$

A family of endomorphisms with this property is a *semi-group*. Clearly $\mathfrak{Q}(s)\, \mathfrak{Q}(t) = \mathfrak{Q}(t)\, \mathfrak{Q}(s)$, that is, the *elements of a semi-group commute with each other.*

A sequence of endomorphisms T_n on $\mathscr{L}$ is said to converge[29] *to the endomorphism T iff $\|T_n u - Tu\| \to 0$ for each $u \in \mathscr{L}$. In this case we write $T_n \to T$.*

---

[28] They depend only on the local compactness of Σ.

[29] This mode of convergence was introduced in VIII,3 and is called *strong*. It does *not* imply that $\|T_n - T\| \to 0$ (which type of convergence is called uniform). A weaker type of convergence is defined by the requirement that $T_n u(x) \to Tu(x)$ for each x, but not necessarily uniformly. See problem 6 in VIII,10.

From now on we concentrate on semi-groups of contraction operators and impose a regularity condition on them. Denote again by $\mathbf{1}$ the identity operator, $\mathbf{1}u = u$.

Definition. *A semi-group of contraction operators $\mathfrak{Q}(t)$ will be called continuous*[30] *if $\mathfrak{Q}(0) = \mathbf{1}$ and $\mathfrak{Q}(h) \to \mathbf{1}$ as $h \to 0+$.*

If $0 \leq t' < t''$ we have

$$\|\mathfrak{Q}(t'')u - \mathfrak{Q}(t')u\| \leq \|\mathfrak{Q}(t''-t')u - u\|. \tag{8.7}$$

For continuous semi-groups there exists a $\delta > 0$ such that the right side is $<\epsilon$ for $t'' - t' < \delta$. Thus not only is it true that $\mathfrak{Q}(t) \to \mathfrak{Q}(t_0)$ as $t \to t_0$, but (8.7) shows that $\mathfrak{Q}(t)u$ is a uniformly continuous function of t for each fixed u.[31]

The transformation (8.1) is, of course, the same as (4.5) and served as starting point for the derivation of the backward equation for diffusion processes. Now a family of Markovian transition probabilities induces also a semi-group of transformations of *measures* such that the measure μ is transformed into a measure $T(t)\mu$ attributing to the set Γ the mass

$$T(t)\mu(\Gamma) = \int \mu\{dx\}\, Q_t(x, \Gamma). \tag{8.8}$$

When the Q_t have a density kernel q_t this transformation is the same as (5.1) and was used for the forward equation. Probability theory being concerned primarily with measures, rather than functions, the question arises, why we do not start from the semi-group $\{T(t)\}$ rather than $\mathfrak{Q}(t)$? The answer is interesting and throws new light on the intricate relationship between the backward and forward equations.

The reason is that (as evidenced by the above examples) with the usual setup the continuous semi-groups of contractions on the function space $\mathscr{L}$ come from transition probabilities: studying our semi-groups $\mathfrak{Q}(t)$ is in practice the same as studying Markovian transition probabilities. For semi-groups of measures this is *not* true. There exist analytically very reasonable contraction semi-groups that are not induced by Markov processes. To get an example consider any Markovian semi-group of the form (8.8) on the line assuming only that an absolutely continuous μ is transformed into an absolutely continuous $T(t)\mu$ [for example, let $T(t)$ be the convolution with a normal distribution with variance t]. If $\mu = \mu_c + \mu_s$ is the decomposition of μ into its absolutely continuous and singular parts define a new semi-group $\{S(t)\}$ by

$$S(t)\mu = T(t)\mu_c + \mu_s. \tag{8.9}$$

This semi-group is continuous and $S(0) = \mathbf{1}$, but it is not difficult to see that it is not

[30] We use this word as abbreviation for the standard term "strongly continuous at the origin."

[31] There exist semi-groups such that $\mathfrak{Q}(h)$ tends to an operator $T \neq \mathbf{1}$, but they are pathological. For an example define an endomorphism T by $Tu(x) = \frac{1}{2}u(0)[1 + \cos x] + \frac{1}{2}u(\pi)[1 - \cos x]$ and put $\mathfrak{Q}(t) = T$ for all $t \geq 0$.

connected with any system of transition probabilities and that it is probabilistically absurd.

9. THE "EXPONENTIAL FORMULA" OF SEMI-GROUP THEORY

The pseudo-Poisson processes of section 1 are by far the simplest Markov processes, and it will now be shown that practically all Markov processes represent limiting forms of pseudo-Poisson processes.[32] An abstract version of the theorem plays a fundamental role in semi-group theory, and we shall now see that it is really a consequence of the law of large numbers.

If T is the operator induced by the stochastic kernel K, the operator $\mathfrak{Q}(t)$ induced by the pseudo-Poisson distribution (1.2) takes on the form

$$\mathfrak{Q}(t) = e^{-\alpha t} \sum_{n=0}^{\infty} \frac{(\alpha t)^n}{n!} T^n, \tag{9.1}$$

the series being defined as the limit of the partial sums. These operators form a semi-group by virtue of the Chapman-Kolmogorov equation (1.3). It is better, however, to start afresh and to prove the assertion for arbitrary contractions T.

Theorem 1. *If T is a contraction on $\mathscr{L}$, the operators* (9.1) *form a continuous semi-group of contractions. If T is a transition operator so is $\mathfrak{Q}(t)$.*

Proof. Obviously $\mathfrak{Q}(t)$ is positive and $\|\mathfrak{Q}(t)\| \leq e^{-\alpha t + \alpha t \|T\|} \leq 1$. The semi-group property is easily verified from the formal product of the series for $\mathfrak{Q}(s)$ and $\mathfrak{Q}(t)$ (see footnote 1 to section 1). The relation $\mathfrak{Q}(h) \to \mathbf{1}$ is obvious from (9.1). ▶

We shall abbreviate (9.1) to

$$\mathfrak{Q}(t) = e^{\alpha t(T-\mathbf{1})}. \tag{9.2}$$

Semi-groups of contractions of this form will be called pseudo-Poissonian[33] *and we shall say that $\{\mathfrak{Q}(t)\}$ is generated by $\alpha(T - \mathbf{1})$.*

Consider now an arbitrary continuous semi-group of contractions $\mathfrak{Q}(t)$. It behaves in many respects just as a real-valued continuous function and the approximation theory developed in chapter VII using the law of large numbers carries over without serious change. We use in particular the formula VII,(5.1) based on the Poisson distribution. For fixed $h > 0$

[32] The special case where the $\mathfrak{Q}(t)$ are convolution operators is treated in chapter IX.

[33] There exist contraction semi-groups of the form e^{tS} where S is an *endomorphism not* of the form $\alpha(T - \mathbf{1})$. Such are the semi-groups associated with the solutions of the jump processes of section 3 if $\alpha(x)$ remains bounded.

it introduces the operators

$$(9.3) \qquad \mathfrak{Q}_h(t) = e^{-th^{-1}} \sum_{n=0}^{\infty} \frac{(th^{-1})^n}{n!} \mathfrak{Q}(nh)$$

which could be described as obtained by randomization of the parameter t in $\mathfrak{Q}(t)$. Comparing with (9.1) is it seen that the $\mathfrak{Q}_h(t)$ form a pseudo-Poissonian semi-group generated by $[\mathfrak{Q}(h) - \mathbf{1}]/h$. We now prove that

$$(9.4) \qquad \mathfrak{Q}_h(t) \to \mathfrak{Q}(t), \qquad h \to 0.$$

The starting point is the identity

$$(9.5) \qquad \mathfrak{Q}_h(t)u - \mathfrak{Q}(t)u = e^{-th^{-1}} \sum_{n=0}^{\infty} \frac{(th^{-1})^n}{n!} [\mathfrak{Q}(nh)u - \mathfrak{Q}(t)u].$$

The Poisson distribution appearing in this formula has expectation and variance th^{-1}. By Chebyshev's inequality the norm of the sum of all terms with $|n - th^{-1}| > \eta th^{-1}$ is $\leq \eta^{-2}t^{-1}h \cdot 2\,\|u\|$. In consequence of the uniform continuity property (8.7) it is possible to choose η so small that

$$(9.6) \qquad \|\mathfrak{Q}(nh)u - \mathfrak{Q}(t)u\| \leq \epsilon \qquad \text{for} \quad |nh - t| < \eta t.$$

It follows then that the norm of (9.5) is $\leq \epsilon + 2\eta^{-2}t^{-1} \cdot \|u\| \cdot h$. Since ϵ is arbitrary it follows that as $h \to 0$ the norm of (9.5) tends to zero. We have thus proved a famous theorem known in semi-group theory as the "*exponential formula*."

Theorem 2. *Every continuous semi-group of contractions $\mathfrak{Q}(t)$ is the limit* (9.4) *of the pseudo-Poisson semi-group $\{\mathfrak{Q}_h(t)\}$ generated by the endomorphism h^{-1} $[\mathfrak{Q}(h) - \mathbf{1}]$.*

Equivalent variants of this section are obtained by letting other infinitely divisible distributions take over the role of the Poisson distribution. We know from **1**; XII,3 that the generating function of an infinitely divisible distribution $\{u_n(t)\}$ concentrated on the integers $n \geq 0$ is of the form

$$(9.7) \qquad \sum_0^{\infty} u_n(t)\zeta^n = \exp(t\alpha[p(\zeta)-1])$$

where

$$(9.8) \qquad p(\zeta) = p_0 + p_1\zeta + \cdots, \qquad p_j \geq 0,\ \Sigma p_j = 1.$$

Suppose that the distribution $\{u_n(t)\}$ has expectation bt and a finite variance. Replacing in (9.3) the Poisson distribution by $\{u_n(t/b)\}$ leads to the operator

$$(9.9) \qquad \mathfrak{Q}_h(t) = \sum u_n(t/bh)\mathfrak{Q}(nh) = \sum u_n(t/bh)\mathfrak{Q}^n(h).$$

It is not difficult to see that $\{\mathfrak{Q}_h(t)\}$ is (for fixed h) a pseudo-Poisson semi-group generated by the transition operator $\alpha b^{-1}h^{-1}[p(\mathfrak{Q}(h)) - \mathbf{1}]$. As in the preceding proof a simple application of the law of large numbers shows that $\mathfrak{Q}_h(t) \to \mathfrak{Q}(t)$ as $h \to 0$. In this way we get a substitute "exponential formula" in which $\{u_n(t)\}$ takes over the role of the Poisson distribution.[33]

[33] This was pointed out by K. L. Chung (see VII,5).

To see the probabilistic content and the possible generalizations of this argument, denote by $\mathbf{X}(t)$ the variables of the Markov process with the semi-group $\{\mathfrak{Q}(t)\}$, and by $\mathbf{T}(t)$ the variables of the process with independent increments subject to $\{u_n(t)\}$. The operators (9.9) correspond to the transition probabilities for the variables $\mathbf{X}(hT(t/bh))$. In other words, we have introduced a particular subordinated process; the law of large numbers for the $\mathbf{T}$-process makes it plausible that as $h \to 0$ the distributions of the new process tend to those of the initial Markov process. This approximation procedure is by no means restricted to integral valued variables $\mathbf{T}(t)$. Indeed, we may take for $\{\mathbf{T}(t)\}$ an arbitrary process with positive independent increments such that $\mathbf{E}(\mathbf{T}(t)) = bt$ and that variances exist.

The subordinated process with variables $\mathbf{X}(h\mathbf{T}(t/bh))$ *is of the pseudo-Poisson type. Its semi-group* $\{\mathfrak{Q}_h(t)\}$ *is generated by an endomorphism,*[34] *and* $\mathfrak{Q}_h(t) \to \mathfrak{Q}(t)$ *as* $h \to 0$.

10. GENERATORS. THE BACKWARD EQUATION

Consider a pseudo-Poisson semi-group $\{\mathfrak{Q}(t)\}$ of contractions generated by the operator $\mathfrak{A} = \alpha(T - \mathbf{1})$. This operator being an endomorphism, $\mathfrak{A}u = v$ is defined for all $u \in \mathscr{L}$, and

$$\frac{\mathfrak{Q}(h)-\mathbf{1}}{h}\,u \to v, \qquad h \to 0+. \tag{10.1}$$

It would be pleasant if the same were true of all semi-groups, but this is too much to expect. For example, for the semi-group associated with Brownian motion the diffusion equation (4.1) implies that for twice continuously differentiable u the left side in (10.1) tends to $\frac{1}{2}u''$, but no limit exists when u is not differentiable. The diffusion equation nevertheless determines the process uniquely because a semi-group is determined by its action on twice differentiable functions. We must therefore not expect that (10.1) will hold for *all* functions u, but for all practical purposes it will suffice if it holds for sufficiently many functions. With this in mind we introduce the

Definition. *If for some elements u, v in $\mathscr{L}$ the relation* (10.1) *holds* (*in the sense of uniform convergence*) *we put* $v = \mathfrak{A}u$. *The operator so defined is called the generator*[35] *of the semi-group* $\{\mathfrak{Q}(t)\}$.

Premultiplying (10.1) by $\mathfrak{Q}(t)$ we see that it implies

$$\frac{\mathfrak{Q}(t+h) - \mathfrak{Q}(t)}{h}\,u \to \mathfrak{Q}(t)v. \tag{10.2}$$

[34] For the generators of arbitrary subordinated processes see example XIII,(9.*b*).

[35] In the treatment of convolution semi-groups in the last chapter we restricted the consideration to infinitely differentiable functions with the result that all generators were defined on the same domain. No such convenient device is applicable for general semi-groups.

Thus, if $\mathfrak{A}u$ exists then all functions $\mathfrak{Q}(t)u$ are in the domain of the $\mathfrak{A}$ and

$$\frac{\mathfrak{Q}(t+h) - \mathfrak{Q}(t)}{h} u \to \mathfrak{Q}(t)\mathfrak{A}u = \mathfrak{A}\mathfrak{Q}(t)u. \tag{10.3}$$

This relation is essentially the same as the backward equation for Markov processes. In fact, with the notations of section 4 we should put

$$u(t, x) = \mathfrak{Q}(t)\, u_0(x),$$

where u_0 is the initial function. Then (10.3) becomes

$$\frac{\partial u(t, x)}{\partial t} = \mathfrak{A}u(t, x). \tag{10.4}$$

This is the familiar backward equation, but it must be interpreted properly. The transition probabilities of the diffusion processes in section 4 are so smooth that the backward equation is satisfied for *all* continuous initial functions u_0. This is not necessarily so in general.

Examples. (*a*) *Translations.* Let $\mathscr{L}$ consist of the continuous functions on the line vanishing at infinity and put $\mathfrak{Q}(t)\, u(x) = u(x+t)$. Obviously (10.1) holds iff u possesses a continuous derivative u' vanishing at infinity, and in this case $\mathfrak{A}u = u'$.

Formally the backward equation (10.4) reduces to

$$\frac{\partial u}{\partial t} = \frac{\partial u}{\partial x}. \tag{10.5}$$

The formal solution reducing for $t = 0$ to a given initial u_0 would be given by $u(t, x) = u_0(t+x)$. But this a true solution only if u_0 is differentiable.

(*b*) As in section 2 consider a pseudo-Poisson process with variables $\mathbf{X}(t)$ and another process defined by $\mathbf{X}^{\#}(t) = \mathbf{X}(t) - ct$. The corresponding semi-groups are in the obvious relationship that the value of $\mathfrak{Q}^{\#}(t)u$ at x equals the value of $\mathfrak{Q}(t)u$ at $x + ct$. For the generators this implies

$$\mathfrak{A}^{\#} = \mathfrak{A} - c\frac{d}{dx} \tag{10.6}$$

and so the domain of $\mathfrak{A}^{\#}$ is restricted to differentiable functions. The backward equation is satisfied whenever the initial function u_0 has a continuous derivative but not for arbitrary functions. In particular, the transition probabilities themselves need not satisfy the backward equation. This explains the difficulties of the old-fashioned theories [discussed in connection with IX,(2.14)] and also why we had to introduce unnatural regularity assumptions to derive the forward equation (2.1). ►

The usefulness of the notion of generator is due to the fact that *for each continuous*[36] *semi-group of contractions the domain of* $\mathfrak{A}$ *is dense in* $\mathscr{L}$ *and so the generator defines the semi-group uniquely.* A simple proof of this theorem will be given in XIII,9.

This theorem enables us to handle backward equations without unnecessary restrictions and greatly simplifies their derivation. Thus the most general form of diffusion operators alluded to in footnote 12 of section 4 could not have been derived without the a priori knowledge that a generator does in fact exist.

[36] In the sense of the definition in section 8.

CHAPTER XI

Renewal Theory

Renewal processes were introduced in VI,6 and illustrated in VI,7. We now begin with the general theory of the so-called renewal equation, which occurs frequently in various connections. A striking example for the applicability of the general renewal theorem is supplied by the limit theorem of section 8. Sections 6 and 7 contain an improved and generalized version of some asymptotic estimates originally derived laboriously by deep analytic methods. This illustrates the economy of thought and tools to be achieved by a general theoretical approach to hard individual problems. For a treatment of renewal problems by Laplace transforms see XIV,1–3.

Many papers and much ingenuity have been spent on the elusive problem of freeing the renewal theorem of the condition that the variables be positive. In view of this impressive history a new and greatly simplified proof of the general theorem is incorporated in section 9.

A general survey of literature, applications, and generalizations in the case of positive variables is contained in *Renewal theory and its ramifications* by W. L. Smith, J. Roy. Statist. Soc. (3), vol. 20 (1958) pp. 243–302. For new results see *A renewal theorem for random variables which are dependent or non-identically distributed*, by Y.S.Chow and H. E. Robbins, Ann. Math. Statist., vol. 34 (1963) pp. 390–401.

1. THE RENEWAL THEOREM

Let F be a distribution concentrated[1] on $\overline{0, \infty}$, that is, we suppose $F(0) = 0$. We do not require the existence of an expectation, but because of the assumed positivity we can safely write[2]

$$\mu = \int_0^\infty y\, F\{dy\} = \int_0^\infty [1 - F(y)]\, dy \tag{1.1}$$

[1] As shown in problem 1, no essential changes occur if one permits $F(0) > 0$ [provided $F(x) = 0$ for $x < 0$].

[2] For the identity of the two integrals in (1.1) see V,(6.3).

where $\mu \leq \infty$. When $\mu = \infty$ we agree to interpret the symbol μ^{-1} as 0.

In VI,6 we defined a pure renewal process induced by F. A dominant role in this process is played by the function

$$U = \sum_{n=0}^{\infty} F^{n\bigstar} \tag{1.2}$$

which was shown to be finite. The value $U(x)$ equals the expected number of renewal epochs in the interval $\overline{0, x}$, the origin counting as a renewal epoch. For the present we shall disregard this probabilistic content and proceed purely analytically to investigate the asymptotic behavior at infinity of the function U defined in (1.2).

It is best to think of U as a measure concentrated on $\overline{0, \infty}$, the interval $I = \overline{a, b}$ carrying measure $U\{I\} = U(b) - U(a)$. As usual we denote by $I + t$ the interval $\overline{a+t, b+t}$ obtained by translating I through t. Thus $U\{I+t\} = U(b+t) - U(a+t)$. Note that the origin is an atom of weight 1 contributed by the term $F^{0\bigstar}$ in the series (1.2).

Suppose first that all points of increase of F are among the multiples $\lambda, 2\lambda, \ldots$. According to definition 3 of V,2 such a distribution is called *arithmetic*, and the largest λ with the said property is called the *span* of F. By the renewal theory developed in **1**; XIII,4 in this case the measure U is purely atomic and if u_n is the weight of $n\lambda$ then $u_n \to \mu^{-1}\lambda$ as $n \to \infty$. The following theorem generalizes this result to arbitrary distributions[3] concentrated on $\overline{0, \infty}$. The case of arithmetic F is repeated for completeness.

Theorem 1. (*Renewal theorem.*) *If F is not arithmetic then as $t \to \infty$*

$$U(t) - U(t-h) \to \frac{h}{\mu} \tag{1.3}$$

for every fixed $h > 0$. If F is arithmetic the same is true when h is a multiple of the span λ.

Before proving the theorem[4] we examine some of its implications and variants. Let z be a bounded function vanishing in $\overline{-\infty, 0}$. Given that

[3] The discrete case was first proved by P. Erdös, W. Feller, and H. Pollard (1949). Their proof was generalized to arbitrary positive variables by D. Blackwell. The present proof is new.

[4] At first reading it is recommended to pass directly to section 3.

$U(x) < \infty$ for all x, the *convolution* $Z = U \star z$ is defined by the integral[5]

$$Z(x) = \int_0^x z(x-y)\, U\{dy\}, \tag{1.4}$$

which is meaningful even though the measure U is unbounded. For $x < 0$ we have $Z(x) = 0$. As was shown in VI,6–7, the importance of the function U derives largely from the fact that (1.4) represents the unique solution of the *renewal equation*

$$Z = z + F \star Z \tag{1.5}$$

reducing to 0 for $x < 0$. Explicitly this equation reads

$$Z(x) = z(x) + \int_0^x Z(x-y)\, F\{dy\}, \qquad x > 0. \tag{1.6}$$

When z is a continuous function vanishing outside a finite interval it is easy to show that theorem 1 implies

$$Z(t) \to \frac{1}{\mu} \int_0^\infty z(y)\, dy, \qquad t \to \infty \tag{1.7}$$

when F is non-arithmetic, and

$$Z(x+n\lambda) \to \frac{\lambda}{\mu} \sum_k z(x + k\lambda), \qquad n \to \infty \tag{1.8}$$

when F is arithmetic with span λ. This result does not hold for arbitrary continuous functions z because such functions can oscillate wildly at infinity. [Example (d).] Fortunately no trouble arises if one considers only functions z for which the integral in (1.7) is the limit of the familiar upper and lower sums in the following sense. For fixed $h > 0$ denote by $\underline{m}_n$ and $\bar{m}_n$, respectively, the minimum and maximum of z in the interval $(n-1)h \leq x \leq nh$. We assume that the two series

$$\underline{\sigma} = h \sum \underline{m}_n, \qquad \bar{\sigma} = h \sum \bar{m}_n \tag{1.9}$$

converge absolutely. They will be called the lower and upper Riemann sums for the given partition. We agree to say that the function z defined on $\overline{0, \infty}$ is *directly Riemann integrable*[6] if these upper and lower sums exist and if $\bar{\sigma} - \underline{\sigma} < \epsilon$ for h sufficiently small.

---

[5] The interval of integration is *closed* and is indicated only for clarity: because of the vanishing of z and U in $\overline{-\infty, 0}$ the integral is the same as if the limits were $-\infty$ and ∞. All the convolution integrals of the text should be interpreted in this spirit.

[6] The term is not standard, but the notion as such is known from N. Wiener's work on Tauberian theorems. For functions vanishing outside a finite interval $\overline{0, a}$ "direct" integrability is the same as ordinary Riemann integrability, but the Riemann integral over $\overline{0, \infty}$ is usually defined by a passage to the limit $a \to \infty$.

Examples. (*a*) Let $z \geq 0$ be bounded and continuous and denote by μ_n the maximum of z in $n-1 \leq x < n$. It is easily seen that z is directly integrable iff $\Sigma\, \mu_n < \infty$.

(*b*) Let z be non-increasing and $z(\infty) = 0$. Then $\Sigma\, (\bar{m}_n - \underline{m}_n) \leq z(0)$ and so either both series in (1.9) converge, or neither does. It follows that a monotone function z is directly integrable iff it is integrable in the ordinary sense.

(*c*) We give an example of an integrable continuous function that is *not* directly integrable. Let α be an irrational number, $0 < \alpha < 1$, and consider the triangles of unit height with bases on the x-axis centered about the points $k + n\alpha$ and so small that they do not overlap. (Here m and n are positive integers.) Choose the bases so small that the sum of the areas of the triangles is finite. Define z as the continuous function whose graph consists of the inclined sides of these triangles and a set of the x-axis. The total "area under the graph" being finite, z is integrable in the usual sense. On the other hand, there exist infinitely many intervals $(n-1)h \leq x < nh$ containing the basis of one of our triangles. For such intervals $\bar{m}_n = 1$ and hence the upper sum $\bar{\sigma}$ cannot converge.

(*d*) We use the last example to show that (1.7) need not hold when z is not directly integrable. Let F be concentrated on the two points 1 and $1 - \alpha$. Then U is concentrated on the set of points of the form $k - n\alpha$. If $x = r > 0$ is an integer the integrand $z(x-y)$ in $U \bigstar z$ equals 1 at all atoms of U and hence $Z(r) = U(r) - 1$. It follows that Z *is not even bounded.* ▶

Theorem 2. (*Alternative form for the renewal theorem.*)[7] *Let z be directly Riemann integrable, and $z(x) = 0$ for $x < 0$. Then* (1.7) *holds when F is not arithmetic, and* (1.8) *when F is arithmetic with span λ.*

Proof *of the equivalence of the two theorems.* Suppose F non-arithmetic. To derive (1.3) from (1.7) it suffices to let $z(x) = 1$ for $0 \leq x < h$ and $z(x) = 0$ for other x. For the converse we consider first the special case of step functions with equal steps.

For fixed $h > 0$ and $n \geq 1$ put $z_n(x) = 1$ when $(n-1)h \leq x < nh$ and $z_n(x) = 0$ elsewhere. Letting $Z_n = U \bigstar z_n$ we see from (1.3) that for fixed n as $t \to \infty$

$$(1.10) \qquad Z_n(t) = U(t - (n-1)h) - U(t - nh) \to \frac{h}{\mu}$$

[7] Despite its simplicity, theorem 2 seems to have passed unnoticed. Several restricted substitutes can be found in the literature and there is a good deal of confusion concerning their interdependence. Much trouble is caused by artificial restrictions on the distribution F.

and that there exists an upper bound M_h such that $Z_n(t) \le M_h$ for all n and t.

Let $a_k \ge 0$ and $\Sigma\, a_k < \infty$. The step function $z = \Sigma\, a_k z_k$ is then directly integrable and for $Z = U \bigstar z$ we have

$$(1.11) \qquad \sum_{k=1}^{n} a_k\, Z_k(t) \le Z(t) \le \sum_{k=1}^{n} a_k\, Z_k(t) + M_h \cdot \sum_{n+1}^{\infty} a_k.$$

This being true for arbitrary n we get as $t \to \infty$

$$(1.12) \qquad Z(t) \to \frac{h}{\mu} \sum_{1}^{\infty} a_k = \frac{1}{\mu} \int_0^{\infty} z(x)\, dx.$$

Thus (1.7) holds for step functions with equal steps. If z is an arbitrary directly integrable function we apply this result to the two step functions obtained by letting $a_k = \bar{m}_k$ and $a_k = \underline{m}_k$, respectively. It follows that the points of accumulation of $Z(t)$ lie between $\mu^{-1}\underline{\sigma}$ and $\mu^{-1}\bar{\sigma}$, and hence (1.7) is generally true.

With obvious modifications the same argument applies to arithmetic distributions, and this concludes the proof. ▶

Proof *of theorem* 1. When

$$(1.13) \qquad z(x) = 1 - F(x), \qquad x > 0$$

the solution (1.4) of the renewal equation satisfies $Z(x) = 1$ for $x > 0$. As z is monotone we conclude from (1.4) that $z(\alpha)[U(x) - U(x - \alpha)] < 1$, and so $U(x) - U(x - \alpha)$ remains bounded provided α is chosen sufficiently small. Now every interval can be partitioned into intervals of length $\le \alpha$, and hence $U\{I + t\}$ remains bounded for every fixed finite interval I. By the selection theorem 2 of VIII,6 there exists therefore a sequence of numbers $t_k \to \infty$ and a measure V such that $U\{t_k + dy\} \to V\{dy\}$. (Note that V is not concentrated on the positive half axis.)

Now let z be a continuous function vanishing outside a finite interval $\overline{0, a}$, and define Z again by (1.4). Then

$$(1.14) \qquad Z(t_k + x) = \int_{-\infty}^{\infty} z(x-s)\, U\{t_k + ds\} \to \int_{-\infty}^{\infty} z(x-s)\, V\{ds\},$$

the integration extending in effect over an interval of length $\le a$. The right side is a bounded continuous function of x which we denote by ζ. Then $Z(t_k + x) \to \zeta(x)$, and since Z satisfies the renewal equation (1.5) this implies

$$(1.15) \qquad \zeta(x) = \int_0^{\infty} \zeta(x-y)\, F\{dy\}.$$

Assume now F non-arithmetic. It will be shown in the next section that in this case ζ is necessarily a constant. This means that the limit in (1.14) is independent of x, and so the measure V must be proportional to the Lebesgue measure. In other words, we have proved that

$$U(t_k) - U(t_k - h) \to \alpha h \tag{1.16}$$

where α is independent of h. This relation differs from (1.3) only in that t is now restricted to the sequence $\{t_k\}$, but the argument of the preceding proof applies to the effect that

$$Z(t_k) \to \alpha \int_0^\infty z(x)\, dx \tag{1.17}$$

whenever z is directly integrable.

For the function z of (1.13) the left side equals 1. This function is directly integrable when $\mu < \infty$, and then $\alpha = \mu^{-1}$. When $\mu = \infty$ the integral on the right diverges and the boundedness of $Z(t_k)$ requires again that $\alpha = 0$. The constant α is therefore independent of the sequence $\{t_k\}$. But every sequence of numbers $t_k' \to \infty$ contains a subsequence $\{t_k\}$ that can serve in (1.16), and hence the theorem holds for all non-arithmetic F.

With trite changes this argument applies also to arithmetic distributions (but for them the renewal theorem was proved already in **1**; XIII). ►

*2. THE EQUATION $\zeta = F\bigstar\zeta$

The last proof used the fact that for non-arithmetic distributions F the only bounded continuous solutions of (1.15) are constants. We separate the proof because of its formal analytic character, and at the same time we prove the assertion also for distributions that are not concentrated on a half-line. This general result will be used for the renewal theorem in section 9.

Lemma.[8] *Let F be a probability distribution not concentrated at the origin, and let ζ be a bounded continuous solution of the convolution equation*

$$\zeta(x) = \int_{-\infty}^{+\infty} \zeta(x-y)\, F\{dy\}. \tag{2.1}$$

Then $\zeta(x) =$ const except if F is arithmetic. If F has span λ then ζ is periodic with period λ.

---

* Used only for the renewal theorems in sections 1 and 9.

[8] This lemma holds for distributions on arbitrary groups. See G. Choquet and J. Deny, C. R. Acad. Sci. Paris, vol. 250 (1960) pp. 799–801.

Proof. To begin with we assume F non-arithmetic and accept for the moment as known the following *proposition*:

"Let ζ be a uniformly continuous bounded solution of (2.1) with least upper bound $m > 0$; then there exist intervals $\overline{t, t+h}$ of arbitrary length h such that $\zeta(x) > \frac{1}{2}m$ for all $t < x < t+h$."

Consider then an arbitrary bounded continuous solution ζ of (2.1) and let η_ϵ be its convolution with a normal distribution with zero expectation and variance ϵ. The function η_ϵ and its derivative η_ϵ' are again solutions of the convolution equation (2.1), and our proposition applies to them. Put $q = \sup \eta_\epsilon'(x)$. If $q > 0$ there exists an interval $t < x < t + h$ of arbitrary length h in which $\eta_\epsilon'(x) > \frac{1}{2}q$. Integrating over x we get

$$\frac{1}{2}qh < \eta_\epsilon(t+h) - \eta_\epsilon(t) \le 2 \cdot \sup |\zeta(x)|. \tag{2.2}$$

Since h is arbitrary we conclude that $q = 0$, and so $\eta_\epsilon' \le 0$. But the same argument applies to $-\eta_\epsilon$, and hence η_ϵ is a constant. Letting $\epsilon \to 0$ it follows that ζ is indeed a constant.

To accomplish the proof we have to prove the proposition in quotation marks. We proceed in two steps.

(i) Suppose that the maximum m is attained, say at 0. The equation (2.1) represents $\zeta(0) = m$ as a weighted average of values $\zeta(-y) \le m$, and hence we must have $\zeta(-y) = m$ for each y that is a point of increase of F. But ζ satisfies also the convolution equations $\zeta = F^{r\star} \star \zeta$ for $r = 1, 2, \ldots$, and hence $\zeta(-y) = m$ whenever y is a point of increase for some $F^{r\star}$. In other words, if Σ stands for the set formed by the points of increase of $F, F^{2\star}, F^{3\star}, \ldots$ then $\zeta(-y) = m$ at all points $y \in \Sigma$. According to lemma 2 of V,4 the set Σ is dense except when F is concentrated on a half-axis, and denseness of Σ obviously implies $\zeta = \text{const}$. In the remaining case we may assume that F is concentrated in $\overline{0, \infty}$, but not at the origin. By the theorem quoted Σ is asymptotically dense at infinity, and so $\zeta(-y) \to m$ as $y \to \infty$. For large r the mass $F^{r\star}$ tends to be concentrated near infinity and letting $r \to \infty$ in $\zeta = F^{r\star} \star \zeta$ we see again that $\zeta(x) = m$ for all x.

(ii) It follows that a non-constant solution ζ cannot assume a maximum, and hence there exists a sequence $t_1, t_2, \ldots \to \pm\infty$ such that $\zeta(t_n) \to m$. Define functions ζ_n by $\zeta_n(x) = \zeta(t_n + x)$. Because of the assumed uniform continuity of ζ the sequence $\{\zeta_n\}$ is equicontinuous and contains a subsequence that converges uniformly in every finite interval [theorem 3 of VIII,6]. Dropping double subscripts we may suppose that $\zeta_n \to \eta$. Obviously $\eta = F \star \eta$ and η is uniformly continuous. By the definition of the upper bound we have $\eta(x) \le m$, but $\eta(0) = \lim \zeta(t_n) = m$. By the preceding result therefore $\eta(x) = m$ for all x. Thus $\zeta_n(x) \to m$ uniformly in $\overline{0, h}$, and hence for n sufficiently large $\zeta(s) > \frac{1}{2}m$ for $t_n < s < t_n + h$. This proves the lemma for non-arithmetic distributions.

For arithmetic F it is asserted that for fixed a the values $\zeta(a + n\lambda)$ are independent of n. The proof is the same, except that m is defined as the least upper bound of these values, and the derivative is replaced by differences. ▶

The lemma may be interpreted and proved probabilistically as follows. Let $\mathbf{X}_1, \mathbf{X}_2, \ldots$ be independent random variables with the common distribution F, and $\mathbf{S}_n = \mathbf{X}_1 + \cdots + \mathbf{X}_n$. The convolution equation (2.1) states that for fixed a the variables $\zeta(a - \mathbf{S}_n)$ form a *martingale* [see VI,12]. The martingale convergence theorem of VII,8 guarantees the existence of a random variable $\mathbf{U}_a$ such that $\zeta(a - \mathbf{S}_n) \to \mathbf{U}_a$ with probability one. The lemma asserts that neglecting a set of probability zero $\mathbf{U}_a$ is a constant. This is an easy consequence of the second zero- or one-law of IV,6.[9]

3. PERSISTENT RENEWAL PROCESSES

The renewal theorem will now be used to derive various limit theorems for the renewal processes introduced in VI,6. We are concerned with a sequence of mutually independent random variables $\mathbf{T}_1, \mathbf{T}_2, \ldots,$ the *interarrival times*, with a common distribution F. In this section we assume that F is a proper distribution and $F(0) = 0$. In addition to the $\mathbf{T}_k$ there may be defined a non-negative variable $\mathbf{S}_0$ with a proper distribution F_0. We put

$$\mathbf{S}_n = \mathbf{S}_0 + \mathbf{T}_1 + \cdots + \mathbf{T}_n. \tag{3.1}$$

The variables $\mathbf{S}_n$ are called *renewal epochs*. The renewal process $\{\mathbf{S}_n\}$ is called *pure* if $\mathbf{S}_0 = 0$ and *delayed* otherwise.

The *expected number of renewal epochs in* $\overline{0, t}$ equals

$$V(t) = \sum_{n=0}^{\infty} \mathbf{P}\{\mathbf{S}_n \leq t\}. \tag{3.2}$$

We adhere to the notation $U = \Sigma F^{n\bigstar}$ introduced in (1.2). Then

$$V = F_0 \bigstar U$$

(and $V = U$ in the pure renewal process). Thus[10] for $h > 0$

$$V(t+h) - V(t) = \int_0^{t+h} [U(t+h-y) - U(t-y)]\, F_0\{dy\}. \tag{3.3}$$

[9] J. L. Doob, J. L. Snell, and R. E. Williamson in Contributions to Probability and Statistics (Essays in Honor of H. Hotelling), Stanford, 1960.

[10] See footnote 5 to section 1.

If F is not arithmetic the integrand tends to $\mu^{-1}h$ as $t \to \infty$, and thus the basic theorem extends also to delayed processes: if F is non-arithmetic *the expected number of renewal epochs within* $\overline{t, t+h}|$ *tends to* $\mu^{-1}h$. This statement contains two equidistribution theorems; first, the renewal rate tends to a constant, and second, this constant rate is independent of the initial distribution. In this sense we have an analogue to the ergodic theorems for Markov chains in **1**; XV.

If $\mu < \infty$ it follows that $V(t) \sim \mu^{-1}t$ as $t \to \infty$. It is natural to ask whether F_0 can be chosen as to get the identity $V(t) = \mu^{-1}t$, meaning a constant renewal rate. Now V satisfies the renewal equation

$$V = F_0 + F \bigstar V \tag{3.4}$$

and thus $V(t) = \mu^{-1}t$ iff

$$F_0(t) = \frac{t}{\mu} - \frac{1}{\mu}\int_0^t (t-y)\, F\{dy\}. \tag{3.5}$$

Integration by parts shown this to be the same as

$$F_0(t) = \frac{1}{\mu}\int_0^t [1 - F(y)]\, dy. \tag{3.6}$$

This F_0 is a probability distribution and so the answer is affirmative: *with the initial distribution* (3.6) *the renewal rate is constant,* $V(t) = \mu^{-1}t$.

The distribution (3.6) appears also as the limit distribution of the residual waiting times, or hitting probabilities. To given $t > 0$ there corresponds a chance-dependent subscript $\mathbf{N}_t$ such that

$$\mathbf{S}_{\mathbf{N}_t} \leq t < \mathbf{S}_{\mathbf{N}_t+1}. \tag{3.7}$$

In the terminology introduced in VI,7 the variable $\mathbf{S}_{\mathbf{N}_t+1} - t$ is called *residual waiting time* at epoch t. We denote by $H(t, \xi)$ the probability that it is $\leq \xi$. In other words, $H(t, \xi)$ is the probability that the *first* renewal epoch following epoch t lies within $\overline{t, t+\xi}|$ or that the level t be overshot by an amount $\leq \xi$. This event occurs if some renewal epoch $\mathbf{S}_n$ equals $x \leq t$ and the following interarrival time lies between $t - x$ and $t - x + \xi$. In the case of a pure renewal process we get, summing over x and n,

$$H(t, \xi) = \int_0^t U\{dx\}[F(t-x+\xi) - F(t-x)]. \tag{3.8}$$

This integral contains ξ as a free parameter but is of the standard form $U \bigstar z$ with $z(t) = F(t+\xi) - F(t)$, which function is directly integrable.[11]

[11] The maximum of z in $\overline{n, n+1}$ is $\leq F(n+1+\xi) - F(n)$ and the series of these terms converges.

Assume F non-arithmetic. Since

$$(3.9)\quad \int_0^\infty z(t)\,dt = \int_0^\infty ([1 - F(t)] - [1 - F(t+\xi)])\,dt = \int_0^\xi (1 - F(s))\,ds$$

we have the *limit theorem*

$$(3.10)\qquad \lim_{t\to\infty} H(t, \xi) = \frac{1}{\mu}\int_0^\xi [1 - F(s)]\,ds.$$

(It is easily verified that this is true also for the delayed process regardless of the initial distribution F_0.) This limit theorem is remarkable in several respects.

If $\mu < \infty$ the right side coincides with the distribution in (3.6) and thus if $\mu < \infty$ *the residual waiting time has a proper limit distribution which* coincides with the distribution attaining a uniform renewal rate. In this pattern we recognize once more the tendency towards a "*steady state*."

The limit distribution of (3.10) has a finite expectation only if F has a variance. This indicates that, roughly speaking, *the entrance probabilities*[12] *behave worse than F.* Indeed, when $\mu = \infty$ we have

$$(3.11)\qquad H(t, \xi) \to 0$$

for all ξ: the probability tends to 1 that *the level t will be overshot by an arbitrarily large amount* ξ. (For the case of regularly varying tails more precise information is derived in XIV,3.)

Examples. (*a*) *Superposition of renewal processes.* Given n renewal processes, a new process can be formed by combining all their renewal epochs into one sequence. In general the new process is *not* a renewal process, but it is easy to calculate the waiting time W for the first renewal following epoch 0. We shall show that under fairly general conditions *the distribution of W is approximately exponential* and so the combined process is close to a Poisson process. This result explains why many processes (such as the incoming traffic at a telephone exchange) are of the Poisson type.

Consider n mutually independent renewal processes induced by the distributions of their interarrival times by $F_1, \ldots, F_n$ with expectations $\mu_1, \ldots, \mu_n$. Put

$$(3.12)\qquad \frac{1}{\mu_1} + \cdots + \frac{1}{\mu_n} = \frac{1}{\alpha}.$$

We require, roughly speaking, that the renewal epochs of each individual renewal process are extremely rare so that the cumulative effect is due to many small causes. To express this we assume that for fixed k and y the

---

[12] See VI,7.

probabilities $F_k(y)$ are small and μ_k large—an assumption that becomes meaningful in the form of a limit theorem.

Consider the "steady state" situation where the processes have been going on for a long time. For the waiting time $\mathbf{W}_k$ to the nearest renewal epoch in the kth process we have then approximately

$$\mathbf{P}\{\mathbf{W}_k \leq t\} \approx \frac{1}{\mu_k}\int_0^t (1 - F_k(y))\, dy \approx \frac{t}{\mu_k}. \tag{3.13}$$

[The last approximation is justified by the smallness of $F_k(y)$.] The waiting time $\mathbf{W}$ in the cumulative process is the smallest among the waiting times $\mathbf{W}_k$ and hence

$$\mathbf{P}\{\mathbf{W} > t\} \approx \left(1 - \frac{t}{\mu_1}\right)\cdots\left(1 - \frac{t}{\mu_n}\right) \approx e^{-t\alpha}. \tag{3.14}$$

This estimate is easily made precise, and under the indicated conditions the exponential distribution emerges as the limit distribution as $n \to \infty$.

(*b*) *Hitting probabilities in random walks.* Consider a sequence of independent random variables $\mathbf{X}_1, \mathbf{X}_2, \ldots$ and their partial sums

$$\mathbf{Y}_n = \mathbf{X}_1 + \cdots + \mathbf{X}_n.$$

For positive $\mathbf{X}_k$ the random walk $\{\mathbf{Y}_n\}$ reduces to a renewal process, but we consider arbitrary $\mathbf{X}_k$. Assume the random walk to be persistent so that for each $t > 0$ with certainty $\mathbf{Y}_n > t$ for some n. If $\mathbf{N}$ is the smallest index for which this is true $\mathbf{Y_N}$ is called the point of *first entry* into $\overline{t, \infty}$. The variable $\mathbf{Y_N} - t$ is the amount by which the t level is overshot at the first entry and corresponds to the residual waiting time in renewal processes. We put again $\mathbf{P}\{\mathbf{Y_N} \leq t + \xi\} = H(t, \xi)$, and show how the limit theorem for residual waiting times applies to this distribution.

Define $\mathbf{S}_1$ as the point of first entry into $\overline{0, \infty}$ and, by induction, $\mathbf{S}_{n+1}$ as the point of first entry into $\overline{\mathbf{S}_n, \infty}$. The sequence $\mathbf{S}_1, \mathbf{S}_2, \ldots$ coincides with the *ladder heights* introduced in VI,8 and forms a renewal process: the differences $\mathbf{S}_{n+1} - \mathbf{S}_n$ are evidently mutually independent and have the same distribution as $\mathbf{S}_0$. Thus $\mathbf{Y_N} - t$ is actually the residual waiting time in the renewal process $\{\mathbf{S}_n\}$, and so (3.10) applies. ▶

By the method used to derive (3.10) it can be shown that *the spent waiting time* $t - \mathbf{S}_{\mathbf{N}_t}$ *has the same limit distribution. For the length* $\mathbf{L}_t = \mathbf{S}_{\mathbf{N}_t+1} - \mathbf{S}_{\mathbf{N}_t}$ *of the interarrival time containing the epoch* t *we get*

$$\mathbf{P}\{\mathbf{L}_t < \xi\} = \int_{t-\xi}^{t} U\{dx\}[F(\xi) - F(t-x)] \tag{3.15}$$

and hence

$$\lim_{t\to\infty} \mathbf{P}\{\mathbf{L}_t \leq \xi\} = \frac{1}{\mu}\int_0^\xi [F(\xi) - F(y)]\, dy = \frac{1}{\mu}\int_0^\xi x\, F(dx). \tag{3.16}$$

The curious implications of this formula were discussed in connection with the inspection paradox in VI,7 and the waiting time paradox in I,4.

It is easily seen that the three families of random variables $t - \mathbf{S}_{\mathbf{N}_t}$, $\mathbf{S}_{\mathbf{N}_t+1} - t$, and $\mathbf{L}_t$ form Markov processes with stationary transition probabilities. Our three limit theorems therefore represent examples for ergodic theorems for Markov processes. (See also XIV,3.)

4. REFINEMENTS

In this section we show how regularity properties of the interarrival distribution F affect the behavior of the solutions of the renewal equation

$$(4.1) \qquad Z(t) = z(t) + \int_0^t Z(t-y)\, F\{dy\}.$$

The results are not exciting in themselves but are of importance in many applications, and a methodological interest attaches to their derivation. To avoid trivialities (and repetitions from **1**; XIII) we assume F *non-arithmetic.*

When $\mu < \infty$ the renewal theorem implies that $U(t) \sim t/\mu$. Our first goal is to estimate the difference

$$(4.2) \qquad Z(t) = U(t) - \frac{t}{\mu}$$

in the case when F has a variance σ^2. It follows from the derivation of (3.6), and it is easily verified directly, that this function satisfies (4.1) with

$$(4.3) \qquad z(t) = \frac{1}{\mu} \int_t^\infty [1 - F(y)]\, dy.$$

Integrating by parts we get

$$(4.4) \qquad \int_0^\infty z(t)\, dt = \frac{1}{2\mu} \int_0^\infty y^2\, F\{dy\} = \frac{\sigma^2 + \mu^2}{2\mu}.$$

Since z is monotone the second renewal theorem shows that *if F is non-arithmetic with variance σ^2 then*

$$(4.5) \qquad 0 \le U(t) - \frac{t}{\mu} \to \frac{\sigma^2 + \mu^2}{2\mu^2}.$$

This result is much sharper than the renewal theorem itself, and the asymptotic expansion of U may be further refined if F has moments of higher order. When $\mu < \infty$ but no variance exists, (4.5) still holds with the right side replaced by ∞.

Example. If F is the uniform distribution in $\overline{0, 1}$ one easily gets from the convolution formula for the uniform distribution

$$U(t) = \sum_{k=0}^{n}(-1)^k e^{t-k}\frac{(t-k)^k}{k!} \quad \text{for} \quad n \le t \le n+1. \tag{4.6}$$

This formula is frequently rediscovered in queuing theory, but it reveals little about the nature of U. The asymptotic formula $0 \le U(t) - 2t \to \frac{2}{3}$ is much more interesting. It appears trivial in the present context but less so outside of it [SIAM Rev., vol. 5 (1963) pp. 283–287]. ▶

From asymptotic properties we turn to properties of smoothness. Assume that F has a density f and consider the renewal equation

$$u(x) = f(x) + \int_0^x u(x-y)\,f(y)\,dy. \tag{4.7}$$

We know that its solution is unique. The integral Z of u satisfies (4.1) with $z = F$ and hence

$$U(t) = 1 + \int_0^t u(y)\,dy, \qquad t > 0. \tag{4.8}$$

Thus, except for the atom at the origin, U has a density u, and the renewal theorem applies to it whenever f behaves reasonably (for example, if f is ultimately monotone). Under such conditions *U has a density u such that $u(t) \to \mu^{-1}$.*

Densities that are not directly integrable will hardly occur in practice but certain conclusions are possible even for them. In fact, consider the density

$$f_2(t) = \int_0^t f(t-y)\,f(y)\,dy \tag{4.9}$$

of $F \star F$. In general f_2 will behave much better than f. For example, if $f < M$ we get from (4.9) for reasons of symmetry

$$f_2(t) < 2M[1 - F(\tfrac{1}{2}t)]. \tag{4.10}$$

The right side is monotone and integrable when $\mu < \infty$. Now $u - f$ is a solution of the renewal equation (4.1) corresponding to $z = f_2$, and thus

$$u(t) - f(t) \to \frac{1}{\mu}. \tag{4.11}$$

We have derived this asymptotic relation under the sole assumption that $\mu < \infty$ and that f is bounded. It follows that if the oscillations of f are wild, u will oscillate in a manner to compensate them. This type of argument is rather powerful and frequently applicable.

5. THE CENTRAL LIMIT THEOREM

For simplicity of expression consider a pure renewal process and denote by $\mathbf{N}_t$ the number of renewal epochs within $\overline{0, t}|$ (the origin is excluded). The event $\{\mathbf{N}_t \geq r\}$ is the same as that the renewal epoch number r occurred within $\overline{0, t}$, and so

$$\mathbf{P}\{\mathbf{N}_t \geq r\} = F^{r\star}(t). \tag{5.1}$$

In principle, therefore, the knowledge of $F^{r\star}$ permits us to calculate the distribution of $\mathbf{N}_t$. Exact calculations are cumbersome, but the knowledge of the asymptotic behavior of $F^{r\star}$ leads to asymptotic expressions for the distribution of $\mathbf{N}_t$. For the case where F has a finite expectation μ and variance σ^2 the calculations are performed in **1**; XIII,6. They do not depend on the arithmetic character of F and so we have the general result: If F has expectation μ and variance σ^2 then for large t *the number* $\mathbf{N}_t$ *of renewal epochs is approximately normally distributed with expectation* $t\mu^{-1}$ *and variance* $t\sigma^2\mu^{-3}$.

Example. (*a*) *Type* I *counters.* The incoming particles constitute a Poisson process. A particle reaching the counter when it is free is registered but locks the counter for a *fixed* duration ξ. Particles reaching the counter during a locked period have no effect whatever. For simplicity we start the process at an epoch when a new particle reaches a free counter. We have then *two* renewal processes. The primary process—the incoming traffic—is a Poisson process, that is, its interarrival times have an exponential distribution $1 - e^{-ct}$ with expectation c^{-1} and variance c^{-2}. The successive registrations form a secondary renewal process in which the interarrival times represent the sum of ξ and an exponential random variable. Their expectation is therefore $\xi + c^{-1}$, their variance c^{-2}. Thus *the number of registrations within the time interval* $\overline{0, t}$ *is approximately normally distributed with expectation* $tc(1 + c\xi)^{-1}$ *and variance* $tc(1 + c\xi)^{-3}$.

The discrepancy between these quantities shows that the registrations are not Poisson distributed. In the early days it was not understood that the registration process differs essentially from the primary process, and the observations led some physicists to the erroneous conclusion that cosmic ray showers do not conform to the Poisson pattern of "perfect randomness." ▶

A limit distribution for $\mathbf{N}_t$ exists iff F belongs to some domain of attraction. These domains of attraction are characterized in IX,8 and XVII,5 and it follows $\mathbf{N}_t$ *has a proper limit distribution iff*

$$1 - F(x) \sim x^{-\alpha} L(x), \qquad x \to \infty \tag{5.2}$$

where L is slowly varying and $0 < \alpha < 2$. The limit distribution for $\mathbf{N}_t$ is easily obtained and reveals the paradoxical properties of fluctuations. The behavior is radically different for $\alpha < 1$ and $\alpha > 1$.

Consider the case $0 < \alpha < 1$. If a_r is chosen so that

$$r[1 - F(a_r)] \to \frac{2 - \alpha}{\alpha} \tag{5.3}$$

then $F^{r\star}(a_r x) \to G_\alpha(x)$ where G_α is the one-sided stable distribution with $p = 1$, $q = 0$ described in IX,(8.18) [and again in XVII,(5.20) as well as in XIII,6]. Let r and t increase in such a manner that $t \sim a_r x$. Then from (5.2) and (5.3), on account of the slow variation of L,

$$r \sim \frac{2-\alpha}{\alpha}\,\frac{x^{-\alpha}}{1-F(t)} \tag{5.4}$$

whence from (5.1)

$$\mathbf{P}\left\{[1-F(t)]\mathbf{N}_t \geq \frac{2-\alpha}{\alpha}\,x^{-\alpha}\right\} \to G_\alpha(x). \tag{5.5}$$

This is an analogue to the central limit theorem. The special case $\alpha = \frac{1}{2}$ is covered in theorem 2 of **1**; XIII,6. The surprising feature is conveyed by the norming factor $1 - F(t)$ in (5.5). Very roughly $1 - F(t)$ is of the order of magnitude $t^{-\alpha}$ and so the probable order of magnitude of $\mathbf{N}_t$ is of the order t^α; the density of the renewal epochs must decrease radically (which agrees with the asymptotic behavior of the hitting probabilities).

When $1 < \alpha < 2$ the distribution F has an expectation $\mu < \infty$ and the same type of calculation shows that

$$\mathbf{P}\left\{\mathbf{N}_t \geq \frac{t - \lambda(t)x}{\mu}\right\} \to G_\alpha(x) \tag{5.6}$$

where $\lambda(t)$ satisfies

$$t[1 - F(\lambda(t))] \to \frac{2-\alpha}{\alpha}\,\mu. \tag{5.7}$$

In this case the expected number of renewal epochs increases linearly, but the norming $\lambda(t)$ indicates that the fluctuations about the expectation are extremely violent.

6. TERMINATING (TRANSIENT) PROCESSES

The general theory of renewal processes with a defective distribution F reduces almost to a triviality. The corresponding renewal equation, however, frequently appears under diverse disguises with accidental features obscuring the general background. A clear understanding of the basic facts will avoid cumbersome argument in individual applications. In particular, the asymptotic estimate of theorem 2 will yield results previously derived by special adaptations of the famous Wiener-Hopf techniques.

To avoid notational confusion we replace the underlying distribution F by L. Accordingly, in this section *L stands for a defective distribution with $L(0) = 0$ and $L(\infty) = L_\infty < 1$.* It serves as distribution of the (defective) interarrival times $\mathbf{T}_k$, the defect $1 - L_\infty$ representing the probability of a termination. The origin of the time axis counts as renewal epoch number zero, and $\mathbf{S}_n = \mathbf{T}_1 + \cdots + \mathbf{T}_n$ is the nth renewal epoch; it is a defective variable with distribution $L^{n\star}$ whose total mass equals $L^{n\star}(\infty) = L_\infty{}^n$. The defect $1 - L_\infty{}^n$ is the probability of extinction *before the* nth renewal epoch. We put again

$$U = \sum_{n=0}^{\infty} L^{n\star}. \tag{6.1}$$

As in the persistent process, $U(t)$ equals the *expected number of* renewal epochs within $\overline{0, t}$; this time, however, the expected number of renewal epochs ever occurring is finite, namely

$$U(\infty) = \frac{1}{1 - L_\infty}. \tag{6.2}$$

The probability that the nth renewal epoch $\mathbf{S}_n$ is the last and $\leq x$ equals $(1 - L_\infty)\, L^{n\star}(x)$. We have thus

Theorem 1. *A transient renewal process commencing at the origin terminates with probability one. The epoch of termination* $\mathbf{M}$ *(that is, the maximum attained by the sequence* $0, \mathbf{S}_1, \mathbf{S}_2, \ldots$*) has the proper distribution*

$$\mathbf{P}\{\mathbf{M} \leq x\} = (1 - L_\infty)\, U(x). \tag{6.3}$$

The probability that the nth renewal epoch is the last equals $(1 - L_\infty)L_\infty{}^n$, and so the number of renewal epochs has a geometric distribution.

It is possible to couch these results in terms of the (defective) *renewal equation*

$$Z(t) = z(t) + \int_0^t Z(t-y)\, L\{dy\}, \tag{6.4}$$

but with a defective L the theory is trite. Assuming again that $z(x) = 0$ for $x \leq 0$ the unique solution is given by

$$Z(t) = \int_0^t z(t-y)\, U\{dy\} \tag{6.5}$$

and evidently

$$Z(t) \to \frac{z(\infty)}{1 - L_\infty} \tag{6.6}$$

whenever $z(t) \to z(\infty)$ as $t \to \infty$.

Examples. (*a*) The event $\{\mathbf{M} \leq t\}$ occurs if the process terminates with $\mathbf{S}_0$, or else if $\mathbf{T}_1$ assumes some positive value $y \leq t$ and the residual process attains an age $\leq t - y$. Thus $Z(t) = \mathbf{P}\{\mathbf{M} \leq t\}$ *satisfies the renewal equation*

$$Z(t) = 1 - L_\infty + \int_0^t Z(t-y)\, L\{dy\}, \tag{6.7}$$

This is equivalent to (6.3).

(*b*) *Calculation of moments.* The last equation represents the proper distribution Z as the sum of two defective distributions, namely a convolution and the distribution with a single atom at the origin. To calculate the expectation of Z put

$$E_L = \int_0^\infty x\, L\{dx\} \tag{6.8}$$

and similarly for other distributions, whether defective or not. Since L is defective the convolution in (6.7) has expectation $L_\infty \cdot E_Z + E_L$. Thus $E_Z = E_L/(1 - L_\infty)$. For the more general equation (6.4) we get in like manner.

$$E_Z = \frac{E_z + E_L}{1 - L_\infty}. \tag{6.9}$$

Higher moments can be calculated by the same method. ▶

In applications it is important to obtain *asymptotic estimates for* $Z(\infty) - Z(t)$. This is easy whenever the defective distribution L has the property that

$$\int_0^\infty e^{\kappa y}\, L\{dy\} = 1 \tag{6.10}$$

for some number κ. The κ of this equation is evidently unique and $\kappa > 0$. We now define a *proper* probability distribution $L^\#$ by

$$L^\#\{dy\} = e^{\kappa y}\, L\{dy\} \tag{6.11}$$

and associate with each function f a new function $f^\#$ defined by

$$f^\#(x) = e^{\kappa x} f(x).$$

A glance at (6.4) shows that the renewal equation

$$Z^\#(t) = z^\#(t) + \int_0^t Z^\#(t-y)\, L^\#\{dy\} \tag{6.12}$$

holds, and to it the renewal theorems of section 1 apply. If $Z^\#(t) \to a > 0$ we conclude that $Z(t) \sim ae^{-\kappa t}$. If Z has a positive limit we apply the same argument to the difference $Z_1(t) = Z(\infty) - Z(t)$ which satisfies (6.4) with z replaced by

$$z_1(t) = z(\infty) - z(t) + z(\infty)\frac{L_\infty - L(t)}{1 - L_\infty}. \tag{6.13}$$

It is easily verified that the integral of $z_1{}^\#(t) = z_1(t)e^{\kappa t}$ equals the right side in (6.14) and thus we have

Theorem 2. *If* (6.10) *holds then the solution of the renewal equation satisfies*

$$\mu^\# e^{\kappa t}[Z(\infty) - Z(t)] \to \frac{z(\infty)}{\kappa} + \int_0^\infty e^{\kappa x}[z(\infty) - z(x)]\, dx \tag{6.14}$$

with

$$\mu^{\#} = \int_0^{\infty} e^{\kappa y} y \, L\{dy\} \tag{6.15}$$

provided $\mu^{\#} < \infty$ *and the integrand*[13] *in* (6.14) *is* $O(x^{-1-\epsilon})$ *for some* $\epsilon > 0$.

For the particular case (6.7) we get

$$\mathbf{P}\{\mathbf{M} > t\} \sim \frac{1 - L_{\infty}}{\kappa \mu^{\#}} e^{-\kappa t}. \tag{6.16}$$

The next section will show the surprising power of this estimate in applications.

The case $L_{\infty} > 1$. If $L_{\infty} > 1$ there exists a constant $\kappa < 0$ such that (6.10) is true and the transformation described reduces the integral equation (6.4) to (6.12). The renewal theorem therefore leads to precise estimates of the asymptotic behavior of $Z(t)e^{\kappa t}$. [The discrete case is covered in theorem 1 of **1**; XIII,4. For applications in demography see example **1**; XIII,(5.*c*). For a formulation in terms of Laplace transforms see XIII,(6.*c*).]

7. APPLICATIONS

As has been pointed out already the theory of the last section may be applied to problems which are conceptually not directly related to renewal processes. In this section we give two independent examples.

(*a*) *Cramér's estimates for ruin.* It was shown in VI,5 that the ruin problem in compound Poisson processes and problems connected with storage facilities, scheduling of patients, etc., depends on *a probability distribution R, concentrated on* $\overline{0, \infty}$, *and satisfying the integro-differential equation*

$$R'(z) = \frac{\alpha}{c} R(z) - \frac{\alpha}{c} \int_0^z R(z-x) \, F\{dx\} \tag{7.1}$$

where F is a proper distribution.[14] Integrating (7.1) over $\overline{0, t}$ and performing the obvious integration by parts one gets

$$R(t) - R(0) = \frac{\alpha}{c} \int_0^t R(t-x)[1 - F(x)] \, dx. \tag{7.2}$$

Here $R(0)$ is an unknown constant, but otherwise (7.2) is a renewal equation with a *defective* distribution L with density $\frac{\alpha}{c}[1 - F(x)]$.

[13] This condition serves only to insure the direct integrability condition of the second renewal theorem. With the obvious modification theorem 2 applies also when $\mu^{\#} = \infty$.

[14] This is the special case of VI,(5.4) when F is concentrated on $\overline{0, \infty}$. It will be treated by Laplace transforms in XIV,(2.*b*). The general situation will be taken up in XII,(5.*d*).

Denoting the expectation of F by μ the mass of L equals $L_\infty = \frac{\alpha\mu}{c}$. [The process is meaningful only if $L_\infty < 1$ for otherwise $R(t) = 0$ for all t.] Note that (7.2) is a special case of (6.4) and that $R(\infty) = 1$. Recalling (6.6) we conclude that

$$R(0) = 1 - \frac{\alpha\mu}{c}, \tag{7.3}$$

and with this value the integral equation (7.2) reduces to the form (6.7) for the distribution of the lifetime **M** of a terminating process with interarrival time distribution L. From (6.16) if follows that *if there exists a constant* κ *such that*

$$\frac{\alpha}{c}\int_0^\infty e^{\kappa x}[1 - F(x)]\, dx = 1 \tag{7.4}$$

and

$$\mu^\# = \frac{\alpha}{c}\int_0^\infty e^{\kappa x} x[1 - F(x)]\, dx < \infty \tag{7.5}$$

then as $t \to \infty$

$$1 - R(t) \sim \frac{1}{\kappa\mu^\#}\left(1 - \frac{\alpha\mu}{c}\right)e^{-\kappa t}. \tag{7.6}$$

This is Cramér's famous estimate. The moments of R may be calculated as indicated in example (6.*b*).

(*b*) *Gaps in Poisson processes.* In VI,7 we derived a renewal equation for the distribution V of the waiting time for the first gap of length $\geq \xi$ in a renewal process. When the latter is a Poisson process the interarrival times have an exponential distribution, and the renewal equation VI,(7.2) is of the standard form $V = z + V \bigstar L$ with

$$L(x) = \begin{cases} 1 - e^{-cx} & \textit{for} \quad x < \xi \\ 1 - e^{-c\xi} & \textit{for} \quad x \geq \xi \end{cases} \tag{7.7}$$

and

$$z(x) = \begin{cases} 0 & \textit{for} \quad x < \xi \\ e^{-c\xi} & \textit{for} \quad x \geq \xi. \end{cases} \tag{7.8}$$

Since $z(\infty) = 1 - L_\infty$ the solution V is a proper distribution as required by the problem.

The *moments* of our waiting time **W** are easily calculated by the method described in example (6.*b*). We get

$$\mathbf{E}(\mathbf{W}) = \frac{e^{c\xi} - 1}{c}, \qquad \mathrm{Var}(\mathbf{W}) = \frac{e^{2c\xi} - 1 - 2c\xi\, e^{c\xi}}{c^2}. \tag{7.9}$$

If we interpret **W** as the *waiting time for a pedestrian to cross a stream* *of traffic* these formulas reveal the effect of an increasing traffic rate. The average number of cars during a crossing time is $c\xi$. Taking $c\xi = 1, 2$ we get $\mathbf{E}(\mathbf{W}) \approx 1.72\xi$ and $\mathbf{E}(\mathbf{W}) \approx 3.2\xi$, respectively. The variance increases from about ξ^2 to $6\xi^2$. [For explicit solutions and connection with covering theorems see example XIV,(2.a)]. The asymptotic estimate of theorem 6.2 applies. If $c\xi > 1$ the determining equation (6.10) reduces to

$$ce^{(\kappa-c)\xi} = \kappa, \qquad 0 < \kappa < c \tag{7.10}$$

and by a routine calculation we get from (6.14)

$$1 - V(t) \sim \frac{1 - \kappa/c}{1 - \kappa\xi}\, e^{-\kappa t}. \tag{7.11}$$

▶

8. EXISTENCE OF LIMITS IN STOCHASTIC PROCESSES

Perhaps the most striking proof of the power of the renewal theorem is that it enables us without effort to derive the existence of a "steady state" in a huge class of stochastic processes. About the process itself we need assume only that the probabilities in question are well defined; otherwise the theorem is purely analytic.[15]

Consider a stochastic process with denumerably many states $E_0, E_1, \ldots$ and denote by $P_k(t)$ the probability of E_k at epoch $t > 0$. The following theorem depends on the existence of "recurrent events." that is, of epochs at which the process starts from scratch. More precisely, we assume that with probability one there exists an epoch $\mathbf{S}_1$ such that the continuation of the process beyond $\mathbf{S}_1$ is a probabilistic replica of the whole process commencing at epoch 0. This implies the existence of further epochs $\mathbf{S}_2, \mathbf{S}_3, \ldots$ with the same property. The sequence $\{\mathbf{S}_n\}$ forms a persistent renewal process, and we assume that the mean recurrence time $\mu = \mathbf{E}(\mathbf{S}_1)$ is finite. We denote by $P_k(t)$ the conditional probability of the state E_k at epoch $t + s$ given that $\mathbf{S}_1 = s$. It is assumed that these probabilities are independent of s. Under these conditions we prove the important

Theorem

$$\lim_{t\to\infty} P_k(t) = p_k \tag{8.1}$$

exists with $p_k \geq 0$ *and* $\Sigma p_k = 1$.

Proof. Let $q_k(t)$ be the probability of the joint event that $\mathbf{S}_1 > t$ and that at epoch t the system is in state E_k. Then

$$\sum_{k=0}^{\infty} q_k(t) = 1 - F(t) \tag{8.2}$$

[15] For more sophisticated results see V. E. Beneš, *A "renewal" limit theorem for general stochastic processes*, Ann. Math. Statist., vol. 33 (1962) pp. 98–113, or his book (1963).

where F is the distribution of the recurrence times $\mathbf{S}_{n+1} - \mathbf{S}_n$. By hypothesis

$$(8.3) \qquad P_k(t) = q_k(t) + \int_0^t P_k(t-y)\, F\{dy\}.$$

Since $1 - F$ is monotone and has a finite integral μ

$$(8.4) \qquad \lim_{t\to\infty} P_k(t) = \frac{1}{\mu}\int_0^\infty q_k(t)\, dt$$

by the second renewal theorem. Integration of (8.2) shows that these limits add to unity, and the theorem is proved. ▶

It is noteworthy that the *existence* of the limit (8.1) has been established without indication of a way to compute them.

Note. If F_0 is a proper distribution, then (8.1) implies that

$$(8.5) \qquad \int_0^t P_k(t-y)\, F_0\{dy\} \to p_k \qquad \text{as} \quad t \to \infty.$$

Thus the theorem also covers the case of a *delayed* renewal process $\{\mathbf{S}_n\}$ in which $\mathbf{S}_0$ has distribution F_0.

Examples. (*a*) *Queuing theory.* Consider an installation (telephone exchange, post office, or part of a computer) consisting of one or more "servers," and let the state E_k signify that there are k "customers" in the installation. In most models the process starts from scratch whenever an arriving customer finds the system in state E_0; in this case our limit theorem holds iff such an epoch occurs with probability one and the expectations are finite.[16]

(*b*) *Two-stage renewal process.* Suppose that there are two possible states E_1, E_2. Initially the system is in E_1. The successive sojourn times in E_1 are random variables $\mathbf{X}_j$ with a common distribution F_1. They alternate with sojourn times $\mathbf{Y}_j$ in E_2, having a common distribution F_2. Assuming, as usual, independence of all the variables we have an imbedded renewal process with interarrival distribution $F = F_1 \star F_2$. Our theorem applies if $\mathbf{E}(\mathbf{X}_j) = \mu_1 < \infty$ and $\mathbf{E}(\mathbf{Y}_j) = \mu_2 < \infty$. Clearly

$$q_1(t) = 1 - F_1(t)$$

and therefore as $t \to \infty$ the probabilities of E_k tend to the limits

$$(8.6) \qquad P_1(t) \to \frac{\mu_1}{\mu_1 + \mu_2}, \qquad P_2(t) \to \frac{\mu_2}{\mu_1 + \mu_2}.$$

This argument generalizes easily to multi-stage systems.

[16] For a typical application see the many-server model of Kiefer and Wolfowitz quoted in VI,9.

(*c*) The differential equations of **1**; XVII correspond to stochastic processes in which the successive returns to *any* state form a renewal process of the required type. Our theorem therefore guarantees the existence of limit probabilities. Their explicit form can be determined easily from equations that must be satisfied. [See, for example, **1**; XVII,(7.8). We shall return to this point more systematically in XIV,9. The same argument applies to the semi-Markov process described in problem 12 of XIV,10.]

*9. RENEWAL THEORY ON THE WHOLE LINE

In this section the renewal theory will be generalized to distributions that are not concentrated on a half-line. To avoid trivialities we assume that $F\{\overline{-\infty, 0}\} > 0$ and $F\{\overline{0, \infty}\} > 0$ and that F *is non-arithmetic*. The modifications necessary for arithmetic distributions will be obvious by analogy with section 1.

We recall from VI,10 that the distribution F is *transient* iff

$$U\{I\} = \sum_{n=0}^{\infty} F^{n\bigstar}\{I\} \tag{9.1}$$

is finite for all finite intervals.[17] For such distributions the question imposes itself: do the renewal theorems of section 1 carry over? This problem has intrigued many mathematicians, perhaps less because of its intrinsic importance than because of its unsuspected difficulties. Thus the renewal theorem was generalized step by step to various special classes of transient distributions by Blackwell, Chung, Chung and Pollard, Chung and Wolfowitz, Karlin, and Smith, but the general theorem was proved only in 1961 by Feller and Orey using probabilistic and Fourier analytic tools. The following proof is considerably simpler and more elementary. In fact, when F has a finite expectation the proof given in section 1 carries over without change.

If z is a continuous function vanishing identically outside a finite interval $-h < x < h$ the convolution $Z = U \bigstar z$ is well defined by

$$Z(x) = \int_{-\infty}^{+\infty} z(x-y)\, U\{dy\} \tag{9.2}$$

because the effective domain of integration is finite. According to theorem 2 of VI,10 this Z is a continuous function satisfying the *renewal equation*

$$Z = z + F \bigstar Z. \tag{9.3}$$

---

* Not used in the sequel.

[17] Otherwise $U\{I\} = \infty$ for *every* interval and F is called persistent.

By the lemma of section 2 the solution of (9.3) is determined up to an arbitrary additive constant.

Theorem 1. *If F has an expectation $\mu > 0$ then for every finite interval I of length $h > 0$*

$$U\{I + t\} \to \frac{h}{\mu} \qquad t \to \infty \tag{9.4}$$

$$U\{I + t\} \to 0 \qquad t \to -\infty. \tag{9.5}$$

This theorem may be reformulated by obvious analogy with theorem 2 of section 1. For asymptotic estimates see problem 13.

Proof. The proof of theorem 1 in section 1 started by showing that $U\{I + t\}$ remains bounded. This was done for completeness only, the fact being actually known from theorem 2 in VI,10. Otherwise the proofs of section 1 can be repeated literally with the obvious interpretation of (1.13) as

$$z(x) = F^{0\bigstar}(x) - F(x)\ ; \tag{9.6}$$

substitution into (9.2) yields $Z(x) = F^{0\bigstar}(x)$ (namely 1 or 0 according as $x \geq 0$ or $x < 0$). ▶

Theorem 2. *If F is transient and without expectation then $U\{I + t\} \to 0$ as $t \to \pm\infty$ for every finite interval I.*

The proof is more delicate and we preface it by a study of the asymptotic behavior of the function Z defined in (9.2).

Lemma. *Let $z \geq 0$ be continuous and vanish for $|x| > h$. Then*[18] *for fixed a*

$$Z(t+a) - Z(t) \to 0, \qquad t \to \pm\infty \tag{9.7}$$

$$Z(t)\, Z(-t) \to 0, \qquad t \to \pm\infty. \tag{9.8}$$

Proof. We know from theorem 2 of VI,10 that Z is uniformly continuous. By the selection theorem 3 of VIII,6 therefore every sequence of numbers $t_k' \to \pm\infty$ contains a subsequence $\{t_k\}$ such that $Z(t_k + x) \to \zeta(x)$ where ζ is a bounded continuous function. From the renewal equation (9.3) it follows that $\zeta = F \bigstar \zeta$, and hence $\zeta =$ const (as shown in section 2). This implies (9.7) for otherwise we could choose $\{t_k\}$ such that $\zeta(a) \neq \zeta(0)$.

---

[18] It is easily seen that (9.8) is equivalent to $U\{I + t\}\ U\{I - t\} \to 0$. If $\rho\{I\}$ stands for the probability that the random walk $\{\mathbf{S}_n\}$ governed by F enters I, then (9.8) is also equivalent to $\rho\{I + t\}\ \rho\{I - t\} \to 0$. If this were false the probability of coming near the origin *after a visit* to $I + t$ would not tend to 0, and F could not be transient.

To prove (9.8) we recall from VI,10 that liminf $Z(x) = 0$. To given $\epsilon > 0$ choose a such that $Z(a) < \epsilon$, and consider the family of functions V_τ defined by

$$V_\tau(x) = Z(x+a+\tau) - \gamma\, Z(x)\, Z(\tau) \tag{9.9}$$

where γ is a constant such that $\gamma' = 1 - \gamma \cdot \|Z\| > 0$. In view of the uniform continuity of Z and (9.7) there exists a τ_0 such that

$$Z(x+a+\tau) - Z(\tau) > -\epsilon\gamma' \quad \textit{for} \quad \tau > \tau_0, \quad |x| < h. \tag{9.10}$$

The function V_τ satisfies the renewal equation (9.3) with $z(x)$ replaced by $v(x) = z(x+a+\tau) - \gamma\, Z(\tau)\, z(x)$. Since $v(x) \geq 0$ for $|x| > h$ it follows from theorem 2[19] in VI,10 that if V_τ assumes negative values it attains its minimum at a point $|x| \leq h$. Because of (9.10) therefore for $\tau > \tau_0$

$$V_\tau(x) > -\epsilon\gamma' + \gamma' \cdot Z(\tau). \tag{9.11}$$

Thus for $\tau > \tau_0$ *either* $Z(\tau) < \epsilon$ *or else* $V_\tau(x) \geq 0$ *for all* x. For $x = -\tau$ we get in the latter case $\gamma\, Z(-\tau)\, Z(\tau) \leq Z(a) < \epsilon$. In either case the left side in (9.8) is $< \epsilon/\gamma$. ▶

Proof *of theorem* 2. In consequence of (9.8)

$$\limsup_{x\to\pm\infty} Z(x) = \limsup_{x\to\infty}\, [Z(x) + Z(-x)] = \eta. \tag{9.12}$$

Assume $\eta > 0$ because otherwise there is nothing to be proved. Consider the convolutions of Z and z with the uniform distribution $\overline{0, t}$, namely

$$W_t(x) = \frac{1}{t}\int_{x-t}^{x} Z(y)\, dy, \qquad w_t(x) = \frac{1}{t}\int_{x-t}^{x} z(y)\, dy. \tag{9.13}$$

Our next goal is to show that as $t \to \infty$ one of the relations

$$W_t(t) = \frac{1}{t}\int_0^t Z(y)\, dy \to \eta \quad \text{or} \quad W_t(0) = \frac{1}{t}\int_{-t}^{0} Z(y)\, dy \to \eta \tag{9.14}$$

must take place.

Because of (9.7) the upper bounds for $Z(x)$ and $W_t(x)$ (with t fixed) are the same, and hence the maximum of W_t is $\geq \eta$. On the other hand, W_t satisfies the renewal equation (9.3) with z replaced by w_t. As noted before, this implies that the maximum of W_t is attained at a point where w_t is positive, that is, between $-h$ and $t + h$. Now for $\frac{1}{2}t \leq x < t$

$$W_t(x) = \frac{1}{t}\int_{t-x}^{x} Z(y)\, dy + \frac{1}{t}\int_0^{t-x} [Z(y) + Z(-y)]\, dy. \tag{9.15}$$

[19] For simplicity of formulation this theorem refers to non-negative functions, but the argument remains unchanged for negative minima.

The combined length of the two intervals of integration is x and so it follows from (9.12) that for t sufficiently large $W_t(x) < \eta \frac{x}{t} + \epsilon$. Thus if $W_t(x) \geq \eta$ the point x must be close to t and $W_t(t)$ close to η. If the maximum of W_t is attained at a point $x \leq \frac{1}{2}t$ a similar argument shows that x must be close to 0 and $W_t(0)$ close to η.

We have now proved that for large t either $W_t(t)$ or $W_t(0)$ is close to η. But a glance at (9.14) shows that in view of (9.7)

$$\limsup\, [W_t(t) + W_t(0)] \leq \eta. \tag{9.16}$$

Because of the continuity of the two functions therefore either $W_t(t) \to \eta$ and $W_t(0) \to 0$, or else these relations hold with the limits interchanged.

For reasons of symmetry we may assume that $W_t(t) \to \eta > 0$. We return to the proof of the lemma and consider $\epsilon > 0$ and $\tau_0 > 0$ as given. For sufficiently large t it is now possible to choose $\tau > \tau_0$ such that both $Z(\tau) > \eta - \epsilon$ and $Z(t-\tau) > \eta - \epsilon$ [for otherwise one would have $W_t(t) < \eta - \epsilon$]. By the remark following (9.11) the function V_τ is positive and substituting $x = t - \tau$ in (9.9) we see that $Z(t+a) > \gamma(\eta-\epsilon)^2$. Thus liminf $Z(t) > 0$ and hence $Z(-t) \to 0$ as $t \to \infty$. It follows that for every bounded interval I

$$U\{I - t\} \to 0, \qquad t \to +\infty. \tag{9.17}$$

To complete the proof we use the result of example (3.*b*) concerning hitting probabilities in the random walk governed by F. Denote by $H(t, \xi)$ the probability that the first entry into $\overline{t, \infty}$ takes place between t and $t + \xi$. Relative to $t + x$ the interval $I + t$ occupies the same position as $I - x$ relative to t and hence

$$U\{I + t\} = \int_0^\infty H(t, d\xi)\, U\{I - \xi\}. \tag{9.18}$$

Two cases are possible. If the point of first entry into $\overline{0, \infty}$ (that is, the first ascending ladder height) has infinite expectation, then $H(t, \xi) \to 0$ as $t \to \infty$ for every ξ. In this case only large values of ξ play a role in the integral and $U\{I + t\} \to 0$ in consequence of (9.17). In the contrary case H tends to a probability distribution and hence $U\{I + t\} \to \eta' > 0$. But this is manifestly impossible when F has no expectation. In fact, considering the first step in the random walk one sees that

$$1 - H(0, \xi) \geq 1 - F(\xi),$$

and hence $1 - F(\xi)$ is integrable over $\overline{0, \infty}$. Thus F has expectation $-\infty$ (in the obvious sense of the word), and hence the random walk drifts to

$-\infty$. The analogue to (9.18) for the negative half-axis now leads to an obvious contradiction because the integrand tends to η' whereas the left side goes to 0. ▶

10. PROBLEMS FOR SOLUTION

(See also problems 8–15 in VI,13.)

1. Dropping the assumption $F(0) = 0$ amounts to replacing F by the distribution $F^\# = pH_0 + qF$ where H_0 is concentrated at the origin and $p + q = 1$. Then U is replaced by $U^\# = U/q$. Show that this is a probabilistically obvious consequence of the definition and verify the assertion formally (*a*) by calculating the convolutions, (*b*) from the renewal equation.

2. From (3.4) show that $Z(t) = V(t) - V(t-h)$ satisfies the standard renewal equation with $z(t) = F_0(t) - F_0(t-h)$. Derive the result $V(t) - V(t-h) \to h/\mu$ directly from theorem 1.2.

3. *Joint distribution for the residual and spent waiting times.* With the notation (3.7) prove that as $t \to \infty$

$$\mathbf{P}\{t - \mathbf{S}_{\mathbf{N}_t} > x,\ \mathbf{S}_{\mathbf{N}_t+1} - t > y\} \to \frac{1}{\mu}\int_{x+y}^{\infty} [1 - F(s)]\, ds.$$

(*Hint:* Derive a renewal equation for the left side.)

4. *Steady-state properties.* Consider a delayed renewal process with initial distribution F_0 given by (3.10). The probability that a renewal epoch $\mathbf{S}_n$ occurs between t and $t + \xi$ is given by $H^\#(t, \xi) = F_0(t + \xi) - F_0(t) + F_0 \bigstar H(t, \xi)$. Prove that $H^\#(t, \xi) = F_0(\xi)$ identically. (*Hint:* Verify by differentiation that $H^\#$ is independent of t.)

5. *Maximal observed lifetime.* In the standard persistent renewal process let $V(t, \xi)$ be the probability that the maximal interarrival time observed up to epoch t had a duration $>\xi$. Show that

$$V(t, \xi) = 1 - F(\xi) + \mathbf{M}\int_0^{\xi} V(t-y, \xi)\, F\{dy\}.$$

Discuss the character of the solution.

6. Let F be a proper distribution with expectation $\mu < \infty$, and $Z = z + F \bigstar Z$. If $z(t) \sim t^\alpha$ as $t \to \infty$ (with $\alpha > 0$) then $Z(t) \sim t^{\alpha+1}/\mu(\alpha+1)$.

7. If F is proper and a a constant, reduce the integro-differential equation

$$Z' = aZ - aZ \bigstar F \quad \text{to} \quad Z(t) = Z(0) + a\int_0^t Z(t-x)[1 - F(x)]\, dx.$$

8. *Generalized type* II *counters.* The incoming particles constitute a Poisson process. The nth arriving particle locks the counter for a duration $\mathbf{T}_j$ and *annuls the aftereffect* (if any) of its predecessors. The $\mathbf{T}_j$ are independent of each other and of the Poisson process and have the common distribution G. If $\mathbf{Y}$ is the duration of a locked interval and $Z(t) = \mathbf{P}\{\mathbf{Y} > t\}$, show that $\mathbf{Y}$ is a proper variable and

$$Z(t) = [1 - G(t)]e^{\alpha - t} + \int_0^t Z(t-x) \cdot [1 - G(x)]\alpha e^{-\alpha x}\, dx.$$

Show that this renewal process is terminating if and only if G has an expectation $\mu < \alpha^{-1}$. Discuss the applicability of the asymptotic estimates of section 6.

9. *Effect of a traffic island.* [Example (7.*b*).] A two-way traffic moves in two independent lanes, representing Poisson processes with equal densities. The expected time required to effect a crossing is 2ξ, and formulas (7.9) apply with this change. A traffic island, however, has the effect that the total crossing time is the sum of two independent variables with expectations and variances given in (7.9). Discuss the practical effect.

10. Arrivals at a counter constitute a persistent renewal process with distribution F. After each registration the counter is locked for a fixed duration ξ during which all arrivals are without effect. Show that the distribution of the time from the end of a locked period to the next arrival is given by

$$\int_0^\xi [F(\xi + t - y) - F(\xi - y)]\, U\{dy\}.$$

If F is exponential so is this distribution.

11. *Non-linear renewal.* A particle has an exponential lifetime at the expiration of which it has probability p_k to produce k independent replicas acting in the same manner ($k = 0, 1, \ldots$). The probability $F(t)$ that the whole process stops before epoch t satisfies the equation

$$F(t) = p_0(1 - e^{-\alpha t}) + \sum_{n=1}^{\infty} p_k \int_0^t \alpha e^{-\alpha(t-x)} F^k(x)\, dx.$$

(No general method for handling such equations is known.)

12. *Renewal theorem in* $\mathcal{R}^2$. Let the distribution of the pair $(\mathbf{X}, \mathbf{Y})$ be concentrated on the positive quadrant. Let I be the interval $0 \leq x,\ y \leq 1$. For an arbitrary vector $\mathbf{a}$ denote by $I + \mathbf{a}$ the interval obtained by translating I through $\mathbf{a}$. Lemma 1.3 generalizes as follows. For any fixed vectors $\mathbf{a}$ and $\mathbf{b}$

$$(*) \qquad U\{I + \mathbf{a} + t\mathbf{b}\} - U\{I + t\mathbf{b}\} \to 0$$

as $t \to \infty$.

(*a*) Taking this for granted show that the renewal theorem for the marginal distributions implies that $U\{I + t\mathbf{b}\} \to 0$.

(*b*) Show that the proof of lemma 1.3 carries over trivially.[20]

13. Let F be an arbitrary distribution in $\mathcal{R}^1$ with expectation $\mu > 0$ and finite second moment m_2. Show that

$$\sum_{n=0}^{\infty} F^{n\star}(x) - \frac{x_+}{\mu} \to \frac{m_2}{2\mu^2}$$

where, as usual, x_+ denotes the positive part of x. [*Hint:* If $Z(t)$ stands for the left side then Z satisfies the standard renewal equation with

$$z(x) = \begin{cases} \dfrac{1}{\mu}\displaystyle\int_{-\infty}^t F(x)\, dx, & t < 0 \\[2ex] \dfrac{1}{\mu}\displaystyle\int_t^\infty (1 - F(x))\, dx, & t > 0. \end{cases}$$

This method can be used for better estimates when higher moments exist.]

[20] A more appropriate formulation of renewal problems in the plane has been introduced recently by P. J. Bickel and J. A. Yahav, [*Renewal theory in the plane*, Ann. Math. Statist., vol. **36** (1965) pp. 946–955.]. They consider the expected number of visits to the region between circles of radii r and $r + a$, and let $r \to \infty$.

CHAPTER XII

Random Walks in $\mathfrak{R}^1$

This chapter treats random-walk problems with emphasis on combinatorial methods and the systematic use of ladder variables. Some of the results will be derived anew and supplemented in chapter XVIII by Fourier methods. (Other aspects of random walks were covered in VI,10.) In the main our attention will be restricted to two central topics. First, it will be shown that the curious results derived in **1**; III for fluctuations in coin tossing have a much wider validity and that essentially the same methods are applicable. The second topic is connected with first passages and ruin problems. It has become fashionable to relate such topics to the famous Wiener-Hopf theory, but the connections are not as close as they are usually made to appear. They will be discussed in sections 3*a* and XVIII,4.

E. Sparre Andersen's discovery in 1949 of the power of combinatorial methods in fluctuation theory put the whole theory of random walks into a new light. Since then progress has been extremely rapid, stimulated also by the unexpected discovery of the close connection between random walks and queuing problems.[1]

The literature is vast and bewildering. The theory presented in the following pages is so elementary and simple that the newcomer would never suspect how difficult the problems used to be before their natural setting was understood. For example, the elementary asymptotic estimates in section 5 cover a variety of practical results obtained previously by deep methods and sometimes with great ingenuity.

Sections 6–8 are nearly independent of the first part. It is hardly necessary to say that our treatment is one-sided and neglects interesting

[1] The first such connection seems to have been pointed out by D. V. Lindley in 1952. He derived an integral equation which would now be considered of the Wiener–Hopf type.

aspects of random walks such as connections with potential theory and group theory.[2]

1. NOTATION AND CONVENTIONS

Throughout this chapter $\mathbf{X}_1, \mathbf{X}_2, \ldots$ are independent random variables with a common distribution F such that $0 < F(0) < 1$. [Random walks with $F(0) = 0$ are covered by renewal theory.] They induce a "random walk" starting at the origin, that is, the sequence of random variables

$$\mathbf{S}_0 = 0, \qquad \mathbf{S}_n = \mathbf{X}_1 + \cdots + \mathbf{X}_n. \tag{1.1}$$

Sometimes we consider a section $(\mathbf{X}_{j+1}, \ldots, \mathbf{X}_k)$ of the given sequence $\{\mathbf{X}_j\}$; its partial sums $0, \mathbf{S}_{j+1}-\mathbf{S}_j, \ldots, \mathbf{S}_k-\mathbf{S}_j$ will be called a *section of the random walk*. The subscripts are treated in the usual manner as a time parameter. Thus an epoch n is said to divide the whole random walk into a *preceding* and a *residual section*.

The ladder variables were introduced in VI,8 but will now be defined anew. The definition depends on an inequality, and there exist therefore four types of ladder variables corresponding to the four possibilities $<, \leq, >, \geq$. This leads to a twofold classification to be described by the self-explanatory terms *ascending* and *descending*, *strict* and *weak*. The ascending and descending variables are related by the familiar symmetry between plus and minus, or maxima and minima. The distinction between strict and weak variables, however, puts a burden on description and notation. The simplest way out is to consider only continuous distributions F, for then the strict and weak variables are the same with probability one. Beginners are advised to proceed in this way and not to distinguish between strict and weak ladder variables, but this distinction is unavoidable for the general theory on one hand, and for examples such as the coin-tossing game on the other.

Consider the sequence of points $(n, \mathbf{S}_n)$ for $n = 1, 2, \ldots$ (the origin is excluded). The *first strict ascending ladder point* $(\mathscr{T}_1, \mathscr{H}_1)$ *is the first term in this sequence for which* $\mathbf{S}_n > 0$. In other words, $\mathscr{T}_1$ is the epoch of the first entry into the (strictly) positive half-axis defined by

$$\{\mathscr{T}_1 = n\} = \{\mathbf{S}_1 \leq 0, \ldots, \mathbf{S}_{n-1} \leq 0, \mathbf{S}_n > 0\}, \tag{1.2}$$

and $\mathscr{H}_1 = \mathbf{S}_{\mathscr{T}_1}$. The variable $\mathscr{T}_1$ is called first *ladder epoch*, $\mathscr{H}_1$ the first *ladder height*. These variables remain *undefined* if the event (1.2) does not take place, and hence both variables are possibly defective.[3]

[2] For other aspects see Spitzer's book (1964), although it is limited to arithmetic distributions. For combinatorial methods applicable to higher dimensions see C. Hobby and R. Pyke, *Combinatorial results in multidimensional fluctuation theory*, Ann. Math. Statist., vol. 34 (1963) pp. 402–404.

[3] Problems 3–5 provide illustrative exercises accessible without general theory.

For the joint distribution of $(\mathscr{T}_1, \mathscr{H}_1)$ we write

$$\mathbf{P}\{\mathscr{T}_1 = n, \mathscr{H}_1 \leq x\} = H_n(x). \tag{1.3}$$

The marginal distributions are given by

$$\mathbf{P}\{\mathscr{T}_1 = n\} = H_n(\infty), \qquad n = 1, 2, \ldots \tag{1.4}$$

$$\mathbf{P}\{\mathscr{H}_1 \leq x\} = \sum_{n=1}^{\infty} H_n(x) = H(x). \tag{1.5}$$

The two variables have the same defect, namely $1 - H(\infty) \geq 0$.

The section of the random walk following the first ladder epoch is a probabilistic replica of the whole random walk. Its first ladder point is the *second* point of the whole random walk with the property that

$$\mathbf{S}_n > \mathbf{S}_0, \ldots, \mathbf{S}_n > \mathbf{S}_{n-1}; \tag{1.6}$$

it will be called the second ladder point of the entire random walk. It is of the form $(\mathscr{T}_1 + \mathscr{T}_2, \mathscr{H}_1 + \mathscr{H}_2)$ where the pairs $(\mathscr{T}_1, \mathscr{H}_1)$ and $(\mathscr{T}_2, \mathscr{H}_2)$ are independent and identically distributed. Proceeding in this way we define the third, fourth, ... ladder points of our random walk. Thus *a point* $(n, \mathbf{S}_n)$ *is an ascending ladder point if it satisfies* (1.6). The rth ladder point (if it exists) is of the form $(\mathscr{T}_1 + \cdots + \mathscr{T}_r, \mathscr{H}_1 + \cdots + \mathscr{H}_r)$ where the pairs $(\mathscr{T}_k, \mathscr{H}_k)$ are mutually independent and have the common distribution (1.3). [See fig. 1 in VI,8.]

For economy of notation no new letters will be introduced for the sums $\mathscr{T}_1 + \cdots + \mathscr{T}_r$ and $\mathscr{H}_1 + \cdots + \mathscr{H}_r$. They form (possibly terminating) *renewal processes with "interarrival times"* $\mathscr{T}_k$ and $\mathscr{H}_k$. In the random walk, of course, only $\mathscr{T}_k$ is of the nature of a time variable. The ladder points themselves form a two-dimensional renewal process.

We shall denote by ψ_0 *the atomic distribution with unit mass* at the origin, and by

$$\psi = \sum_{n=0}^{\infty} H^{n\star} \tag{1.7}$$

the renewal measure for the ladder height process. (Here $H^{0\star} = \psi_0$.) Its improper distribution function given by $\psi(x) = \psi\{\overline{-\infty, x}\}$ vanishes when $x < 0$, while for x positive $\psi(x)$ *equals one plus the expected number of ladder points in the strip* $\overline{0, x}$ (no limitation on time). We know that $\psi(x) < \infty$ for all x and in the case of defective ladder variables

$$\psi(\infty) = \sum_{n=0}^{\infty} H^n(\infty) = \frac{1}{1 - H(\infty)}. \tag{1.8}$$

The *ascending weak ladder points are defined by* (1.6) *with* $>$ *replaced by* $\geq$. The corresponding variables and quantities will be indicated by bars; thus $\overline{\mathcal{T}}_1$ is the smallest index n such that $\mathbf{S}_1 < 0, \ldots, \mathbf{S}_{n-1} < 0$, but $\mathbf{S}_n \geq 0$. As was mentioned before, the tedious distinction between strict and weak variables becomes unnecessary when the distribution F is continuous. Even in the general situation it is easy to express the distribution $\bar{H}$ of weak ladder heights in terms of the distribution H, and this will enable us to confine our attention to the single distribution defined in (1.5). The event $\{\overline{\mathcal{H}}_1 = 0\}$ occurs iff the random walk returns to the origin before entering $\overline{0, \infty}$ and its probability is

$$(1.9) \qquad \zeta = \sum_{n=1}^{\infty} \mathbf{P}\{\mathbf{S}_1 < 0, \ldots, \mathbf{S}_{n-1} < 0, \mathbf{S}_n = 0\}.$$

[This event cannot occur if $\mathbf{X}_1 > 0$ and hence $0 \leq \zeta < F(0) < 1$.] With probability $1 - \zeta$ the first strict ladder point coincides with the first weak ladder point and hence

$$(1.10) \qquad \bar{H} = \zeta\psi_0 + (1-\zeta)H.$$

In words, the distribution of the first weak ladder height is a mixture of the distribution H and the atomic distribution concentrated at the origin.

The probability that prior to the first entry into $\overline{0, \infty}$ the random walk returns to the origin exactly k times equals $\zeta^k(1-\zeta)$. The expected number of such returns is $1/(1-\zeta)$ and this is also the expected multiplicity of each weak ladder height prior to the appearance of the next strict ladder points. Therefore

$$(1.11) \qquad \bar{\psi} = \frac{1}{1-\zeta}\,\psi.$$

(See problem 7.) The simplicity of these relations enables us to avoid explicit use of the distribution $\bar{H}$.

In the definition of the ascending ladder variables the positive direction was singled out. The *strict and weak descending ladder variables are defined by symmetry*, that is, by changing $>$ into $<$. On the rare occasions where a special notation will be required we shall denote descending order by the superscript minus. Thus the first strict descending ladder point is $(\mathcal{T}_1^-, \mathcal{H}_1^-)$, and so on.

From now on we take the ascending strict ladder variables as typical, and when no danger of confusion arises, we shall drop the qualifications "ascending" and "strict."

Example. *Simple random walk*. In the random walks studied in volume **1** the distribution F was atomic and attributed weights p and q to 1 and -1, respectively. The ladder times $\mathcal{T}_k$ were introduced in example **1**; XIII,(1.*d*) but the ladder heights were not mentioned because of their triviality: the ordinate of the rth ladder point (if it exists) is necessarily r.

The only unknown connected with the ladder height distribution H is the weight x it attributes to the single atom at 1. Now x is the probability that $\mathbf{S}_n = 1$ for some n and was calculated in **1**,XIII and XIV. The following calculation is more in the spirit of the calculations of the present chapter.

If the first step leads to -1 the (conditional) probability of a return to the origin is x, and at the epoch of such a return the (conditional) probability of reaching 1 is again x. Consequently x must satisfy the quadratic equation

$$x = p + qx^2 \tag{1.12}$$

and it is easily seen that we require the *smaller*[4] root. Thus $x = 1$ if $p \geq q$ and $x = p/q$ if $p \leq q$, and $1 - x$ is the defect of the strict ladder variables.

As for the *weak ladder* height $\overline{\mathscr{H}}_1$ it is clear that the probability of a return to the origin without previous entry into $\overline{0, \infty}$ is $\zeta = qx$. Thus $\mathbf{P}\{\overline{\mathscr{H}}_1 = 0\}$ equals q if $p \geq q$ and p if $p \leq q$. The event $\overline{\mathscr{H}}_1 = 1$ occurs iff the first step leads to 1, and so $\mathbf{P}\{\overline{\mathscr{H}}_1 = 1\} = p$ under any circumstances. ▶

2. DUALITY

The amazing properties of the fluctuations in coin tossing were derived in **1**; III by simple combinatorial arguments depending on taking the variables $(\mathbf{X}_1, \ldots, \mathbf{X}_n)$ in reverse order. The same device will now lead to important results of great generality.

For fixed n we introduce n new variables by $\mathbf{X}_1^* = \mathbf{X}_n, \ldots, \mathbf{X}_n^* = \mathbf{X}_1$. Their partial sums are given by $\mathbf{S}_k^* = \mathbf{S}_n - \mathbf{S}_{n-k}$ where $k = 0, \ldots, n$. The joint distributions of $(\mathbf{S}_0, \ldots, \mathbf{S}_n)$ and $(\mathbf{S}_0^*, \ldots, \mathbf{S}_n^*)$ being the same, the correspondence $\mathbf{X}_k \to \mathbf{X}_k^*$ maps any event A defined by $(\mathbf{S}_0, \ldots, \mathbf{S}_n)$ into an event A^* of equal probability. The mapping is easy to visualize because the graphs of $(0, \mathbf{S}_1, \ldots, \mathbf{S}_n)$ and $(0, \mathbf{S}_1^*, \ldots, \mathbf{S}_n^*)$ are rotations of each other through 180 degrees.

Example. (*a*) The dual to the event $\{\mathbf{S}_1 < 0, \ldots, \mathbf{S}_{n-1} < 0, \mathbf{S}_n = 0\}$ is $\{\mathbf{S}_1 > 0, \ldots, \mathbf{S}_{n-1} > 0, \mathbf{S}_n = 0\}$. It follows that a return to the origin without prior visit to $\overline{-\infty, 0}$ has the same probability as a return without prior visit to $\overline{0, \infty}$. In other words, the probability ζ defined in (1.9) remains unchanged if the inequalities are reversed. The dual to the relations (1.10) and (1.11) for descending ladder variables therefore depends on the same number ζ. ▶

[4] If x_k is the probability that $\mathbf{S}_n = 1$ for some $n \leq k$ then $x_1 = p$ and $x_{k+1} \leq p + qx_k^2$. By induction x_k is smaller than the smaller roof of (1.12). This argument is typical in the case of non-uniqueness.

In this section we investigate the consequences of the reversal procedure when applied to the event (1.6) defining a (strict ascending) ladder point. The dual event is defined by $\mathbf{S}_n^* > \mathbf{S}_{n-k}^*$ for $k = 1, \ldots, n$ which is the same as $\mathbf{S}_k > 0$. Thus for every interval $I \subset \overline{0, \infty}$

$$\begin{aligned}(2.1)\qquad \mathbf{P}\{\mathbf{S}_n > \mathbf{S}_j \quad \textit{for} \quad j = 0, \ldots, n-1 \quad \textit{and} \quad \mathbf{S}_n \in I\} = \\ = \mathbf{P}\{\mathbf{S}_j > 0 \quad \textit{for} \quad j = 1, \ldots, n \quad \textit{and} \quad \mathbf{S}_n \in I\}.\end{aligned}$$

The left side is the probability that there exists a ladder point with abscissa n and ordinate in I. The right side is the probability of the event that a visit to I at epoch n takes place without prior visit to the closed half-line $\overline{-\infty, 0}|$. Define a random variable $\mathbf{Y}_n$ to equal 1 or 0 according as this does or does not occur. Then $\mathbf{Y} = \Sigma\mathbf{Y}_n \leq \infty$ is the number of visits to I prior to the first entrance into $\overline{-\infty, 0}|$, but it is by no means obvious that this sum is finite. However, summing (2.1) over all n we get on the right side $\mathbf{E}(\mathbf{Y})$ and the left $\psi\{I\}$ [with ψ the renewal measure defined in (1.7)]. This $\psi\{I\}$ is trivially finite when I is bounded. We have thus the basic

Duality lemma. *The measure* ψ *of* (1.7) *admits of two interpretations. For* $I \subset \overline{0, \infty}$

(*a*) $\psi\{I\}$ *is the expected number of ladder points in* I.

(*b*) $\psi\{I\}$ *is the expected number of visits to* I *prior to the first entry into* $\overline{-\infty, 0}|$.

Example. (*b*) *Simple random walk.* In the random walk of the example in section 1 there exists a ladder point with ordinate k iff the event $\{\mathbf{S}_n = k\}$ occurs for some n, and we saw that the probability for this is 1 or $(p/q)^k$ according as $p \geq q$ or $p \leq q$. By the duality lemma this means that *in a symmetric random walk the expected number of visits to* $k \geq 1$ *prior to the first return to the origin equals* 1 for all k. The fantastic nature of this result appears clearer in the coin-tossing terminology. The assertion is that on the average *Peter's accumulated gain passes once through every value* k, *however large, before reaching the zero level for the first time.* This statement usually arouses incredulity, but it can be verified by direct calculation (problem 1). (Our old result that the waiting time for the first return to 0 has infinite expectation follows now by summation over k.) ▶

The identity (2.1) holds also when the strict inequalities are replaced by weak ones. For $I = |\overline{0, \infty}$ we get

$$(2.2)\qquad \mathbf{P}\{\mathbf{S}_n \geq \mathbf{S}_0, \ldots, \mathbf{S}_n \geq \mathbf{S}_{n-1}\} = \mathbf{P}\{\mathbf{S}_1 \geq 0, \ldots, \mathbf{S}_n \geq 0\}.$$

The left side is simply the probability that $(n, \mathbf{S}_n)$ be a weak ascending ladder point; the right side equals the probability that no first entry to $\overline{-\infty, 0}$ occurs up to epoch n, that is, $1 - \mathbf{P}\{\mathcal{T}_1^- \leq n\}$. If the variable $\mathcal{T}_1^-$ is not defective, the sum of these probabilities equals the expectation $\mathbf{E}(\mathcal{T}_1^-)$, which may be finite or ∞ [see theorem 2 of **1**; XI,1 or V,(6.3)]. The sum of the probabilities on the left in (2.2) equals the expected number of weak ascending ladder points in $\overline{0, \infty}$, that is, $\bar{\psi}(\infty)$. In view of (1.8) and (1.11) we get therefore when $\mathcal{T}_1^-$ is not defective

$$\mathbf{E}(\mathcal{T}_1^-) = \frac{1}{1-\zeta}\,\psi(\infty) = \frac{1}{(1-\zeta)(1-H(\infty))} \tag{2.3}$$

with the obvious interpretation when $H(\infty) = 1$.

This formula permits important conclusions when one remembers that $0 \leq \zeta < 1$ (and $\zeta = 0$ when F is continuous). It follows that $\mathbf{E}(\mathcal{T}_1^-) < \infty$ iff $H(\infty) < 1$, that is, iff the ascending variable $\mathcal{T}_1$ is defective. Thus either one of these variables is defective, or else

$$\mathbf{E}(\mathcal{T}_1) = \infty, \qquad \mathbf{E}(\mathcal{T}_1^-) = \infty. \tag{2.4}$$

If $\mathcal{T}_1^-$ is not defective and $\mathbf{E}(\mathcal{T}_1^-) < \infty$ the ascending renewal process is terminating. With probability one there occurs a last ladder point, and so

$$\mathbf{M} = \max\{\mathbf{S}_0, \mathbf{S}_1, \ldots\}. \tag{2.5}$$

is finite. Given that the nth ladder point occurred, the probability that it is the last equals $1 - H(\infty)$, and so [see XI,(6.3)]

$$\mathbf{P}\{\mathbf{M} \leq x\} = [1 - H(\infty)]\sum_{n=0}^{\infty} H^{n\star}(x) = [1 - H(\infty)]\,\psi(x). \tag{2.6}$$

The argument preceding (2.3) shows that when $\mathcal{T}_1^-$ is defective the probabilities in (2.2) add to infinity and therefore $H(\infty) = 1$. Hence it is impossible that both the ascending and the descending ladder processes terminate. We have thus the important

Theorem 1. *There exist only two types of random walks.*

(i) *The oscillating type. Both the ascending and the descending renewal processes are persistent,* $\mathbf{S}_n$ *oscillates with probability* 1 *between* $-\infty$ *and* ∞, *and* (2.4) *holds.*

(ii) *Drift to* $-\infty$, *(say). The ascending renewal process is terminating, the descending one proper. With probability one* $\mathbf{S}_n$ *drifts to* $-\infty$ *and reaches a finite maximum* $\mathbf{M} \geq 0$. *The relations* (2.3) *and* (2.6) *are true.*

[Walks of type (ii) are obviously transient, but type (i) includes both persistent and transient walks. See end of VI,10.]

Coming to the expectation of the ladder height $\mathscr{H}_1$, we begin by the simple observation that *if* $\mathscr{H}_1$ *is proper and* $\mathbf{E}(\mathscr{H}_1) < \infty$, *then* $\mathbf{X}_1$ *has an expectation* $\mathbf{E}(\mathbf{X}_1) \geq 0$. Indeed, let $\mathbf{X}_n = \mathbf{X}_n^+ - \mathbf{X}_n^-$ be the usual decomposition of $\mathbf{X}_n$ into positive and negative parts. Considering the first step of the random walk one sees that $\mathbf{P}\{\mathscr{H}_1 > x\} \geq \mathbf{P}\{\mathbf{X}_1 > x\}$ and hence $\mathbf{E}(\mathbf{X}_1^+) \leq \mathbf{E}(\mathscr{H}_1) < \infty$ [see V,(6.3)]. The fact that $\mathscr{H}_1$ is proper implies that with probability one infinitely many $\mathbf{S}_n$ will be positive and hence

$$n^{-1}(\mathbf{X}_1^- + \cdots + \mathbf{X}_n^-) < n^{-1}(\mathbf{X}_1^+ + \cdots + \mathbf{X}_n^+)$$

for infinitely many n. By the strong law of large numbers[5] the right side remains bounded with probability one while the left side tends to $\mathbf{E}(\mathbf{X}_1^-)$. This expectation can therefore not exceed $\mathbf{E}(\mathbf{X}_1^+)$, and so $\mathbf{X}_1$ has indeed a finite non-negative expectation.

Proceeding in the opposite direction, assume first that $0 < \mathbf{E}(\mathbf{X}_1) < \infty$. We show that in this case $\mathbf{E}(\mathscr{H}_1) < \infty$ and

$$\mathbf{E}(\mathscr{H}_1) = \mathbf{E}(\mathscr{T}_1)\,\mathbf{E}(\mathbf{X}_1) \tag{2.7}$$

From (2.3) (with the role of positive and negative sides exchanged) it follows in this case that $\mathbf{E}(\mathscr{T}_1) < \infty$. Consider now the subsequence of $\{\mathbf{S}_n/n\}$ obtained by letting n run through the ladder epochs only. The kth term of this subsequence equals

$$\frac{\mathscr{H}_1 + \cdots + \mathscr{H}_k}{\mathscr{T}_1 + \cdots + \mathscr{T}_k}, \tag{2.8}$$

and so as $k \to \infty$ with probability one this ratio approaches $\mathbf{E}(\mathbf{X}_1)$. But dividing numerator and denominator by k it is seen that the ratio approaches $\mathbf{E}(\mathscr{H}_1)/\mathbf{E}(\mathscr{T}_1)$, and hence (2.7) is true whenever $\mathbf{E}(\mathbf{X}_1)$ exists and is positive.

The same argument shows that $\mathbf{E}(\mathbf{X}_1) = 0$ implies $\mathbf{E}(\mathscr{T}_1) = \infty$ (but $\mathscr{H}_1$ may have a finite or infinite expectation; see problem 11). By theorem 1 the random walk is in this case oscillating.[6] We have thus proved

Theorem 2. *If* $\mathbf{E}(\mathbf{X}_1)$ *is finite and positive, then* $\mathscr{H}_1$ *and* $\mathscr{T}_1$ *are proper, have finite expectations, and* (2.7) *is true.*

If $\mathbf{E}(\mathbf{X}_1) = 0$, *then* $\mathscr{H}_1$ *and* $\mathscr{T}_1$ *are proper, and* $\mathbf{E}(\mathscr{T}_1) = \infty$.

Otherwise either the random walk drifts to $-\infty$ (*in which case* $\mathscr{T}_1$ *and* $\mathscr{H}_1$ *are defective*), *or else* $\mathbf{E}(\mathscr{T}_1) = \infty$ *and* $\mathbf{E}(\mathscr{H}_1) = \infty$.

[5] See theorem 2 of VII,7. This section is starred, and the present proof may be omitted since we shall in due course give an analytic proof of the following theorem. Note, incidentally, that for positive variables the strong law of large numbers applies even when the expectation is infinite, as can be seen by the familiar truncation.

[6] Theorem 4 of VI,10 contains the stronger result that the random walk is persistent whenever $\mathbf{E}(\mathbf{X}_1) = 0$.

The truth of (2.7) was first proved by A. Wald in a much more general setting connected with sequential analysis to be discussed in XVIII,2. We shall encounter several analytical proofs[7] for (2.7) (see problems 10–11 and 20 as well as XVIII,2 and 4).

3. DISTRIBUTION OF LADDER HEIGHTS. WIENER-HOPF FACTORIZATION

The calculation of the ladder height distributions H and $\bar{H}$ seems at first to present a formidable problem, and was originally considered in this light. The duality lemma leads to a simple solution, however. The idea is that the first entry into, say, $\overline{-\infty, 0}\rvert$ should be considered together with the section of the random walk prior to this first entry. We are thus led to the study of the modified random walk $\{\mathbf{S}_n\}$ which terminates at the epoch of the first entry into $\overline{-\infty, 0}\rvert$. We denote by ψ_n the defective probability distribution of the position at epoch n in this restricted random walk; that is, for an arbitrary interval I and $n = 1, 2, \ldots$ we put

$$(3.1) \qquad \psi_n\{I\} = \mathbf{P}\{\mathbf{S}_1 > 0, \ldots, \mathbf{S}_n > 0, \mathbf{S}_n \in I\}.$$

(Note that this implies $\psi_n\{\overline{-\infty, 0}\rvert\} = 0$.) As before, ψ_0 is the probability distribution concentrated at the origin. Now it was shown in (2.1) that $\psi_n\{I\}$ equals the probability that $(n, \mathbf{S}_n)$ be a ladder point with $\mathbf{S}_n \in I$. Summing over n we get therefore

$$(3.2) \qquad \psi\{I\} = \sum_{n=0}^{\infty} \psi_n\{I\}$$

where ψ is the renewal function introduced in (1.7). In other words, for an interval in the open positive half-axis $\psi\{I\}$ is the expected number of (strict ascending) ladder points with ordinate in I. For I in the negative half-axis we now define $\psi\{I\} = 0$. It follows that the series in (3.2) converges for every *bounded* interval I (though not necessarily for $I = \overline{0, \infty}$). It is this unexpected result[8] that renders the following theory so incredibly simple.

Studying the first entry into $\overline{-\infty, 0}\rvert$ means studying the weak descending

---

[7] A simple *martingale proof* is as follows. If $\mathbf{E}(\mathbf{X}_1) = \mu > 0$ the variables $\mathbf{S}_n - n\mu$ form a martingale. The martingale property remains preserved under the optional stopping rule that the process terminates as soon as the random walk enters $\overline{0, \infty}$. (See the corollary in VI,12.) The ultimate variable is then $\mathscr{H}_1 - \mathscr{T}_1\mu$ and has zero expectation. From theorem 1 we know that $\mathbf{E}(\mathscr{T}_1) < \infty$, and so (2.7) is true.

[8] In probabilistic terms it states that in *every* random walk and for *every bounded* interval I the expected number of visits to I preceding the first entry into $\overline{-\infty, 0}\rvert$ is finite.

ladder process, and with the notations of section 1 the point of first entry is $\overline{\mathscr{H}}_1^-$, its distribution $\overline{H}^-$. For typographical convenience, however, we replace $\overline{H}^-$ by ρ and denote by $\rho_n\{I\}$ *the probability that the first entry to* $\overline{-\infty, 0}|$ *takes place at epoch* n and within the interval I. Formally for $n = 1, 2, \ldots$

$$(3.3) \qquad \rho_n\{I\} = \mathbf{P}\{\mathbf{S}_1 > 0, \ldots, \mathbf{S}_{n-1} > 0, \mathbf{S}_n \leq 0, \mathbf{S}_n \in I\}.$$

(This implies $\rho_n\{\overline{0, \infty}\} = 0$. The term ρ_0 remains undefined.) This time the series

$$(3.4) \qquad \rho\{I\} = \sum_{n=1}^{\infty} \rho_n\{I\}$$

obviously converges and represents the possibly defective distribution of the point of the first entry (that is, of $\overline{\mathscr{H}}_1^-$).

It is easy to derive recurrence relations for ψ_n and ρ_n. Indeed, given the position y of $\mathbf{S}_n$ the (conditional) probability that $\mathbf{S}_{n+1} \in I$ equals $F\{I - y\}$, where $I - y$ is the translate of I through $-y$. Thus

$$(3.5a) \qquad \rho_{n+1}\{I\} = \int_{0-}^{\infty} \psi_n\{dy\}\, F\{I - y\} \qquad \textit{if } I \subset \overline{-\infty, 0}|$$

$$(3.5b) \qquad \psi_{n+1}\{I\} = \int_{0-}^{\infty} \psi_n\{dy\}\, F\{I - y\} \qquad \textit{if } I \subset \overline{0, \infty}$$

(the origin contributing only when $n = 0$). For bounded intervals I the duality lemma assures the convergence of $\Sigma\psi_n\{I\}$, and $\Sigma\rho_n\{I\}$ always converges to a number ≤ 1. We have thus series representations for ρ and ψ. It is clear that these sums satisfy

$$(3.6a) \qquad \rho\{I\} = \int_{0-}^{\infty} \psi\{dy\}\, F\{I - y\} \qquad \textit{if } I \subset \overline{-\infty, 0}|$$

$$(3.6b) \qquad \psi\{I\} = \int_{0-}^{\infty} \psi\{dy\}\, F\{I - y\} \qquad \textit{if } I \subset \overline{0, \infty}$$

with the proviso that (3.6*b*) is restricted to bounded intervals I. We shall see that in practice the relations (3.6) are more useful than the theoretical series representations for ρ and ψ. It is sometimes convenient to replace the interval function ρ and ψ by the equivalent point functions

$$\rho(x) = \rho\{\overline{-\infty, x}|\} \quad \text{and} \quad \psi(x) = \psi\{\overline{-\infty, x}|\}.$$

Clearly (3.6*a*) is equivalent to

$$(3.7a) \qquad \rho(x) = \int_{0-}^{\infty} \psi\{dy\}\, F(x-y), \qquad x \leq 0.$$

From (3.6*b*) we get for $x > 0$

$$\psi(x) = 1 + \psi\{\overline{0, x}|\} = 1 + \int_{0-}^{\infty} \psi\{dy\}\,[F(x-y) - F(-y)].$$

Taking into account (3.7*a*) we see thus that (3.6*b*) is equivalent to

$$\psi(x) = 1 - \rho(0) + \int_{0-}^{\infty} \psi\{dy\}\, F(x-y), \qquad x \geq 0. \tag{3.7b}$$

To simplify notations we introduce the convolution

$$\psi \star F = \sum_{n=0}^{\infty} \psi_n \star F. \tag{3.8}$$

Since ψ is concentrated on $|\overline{0, \infty}$ the value $\psi \star F\{I\}$ equals the sum of the two integrals in (3.6) and is therefore finite. As ψ has a unit atom at the origin we can combine the two relations (3.6) into the single convolution equation

$$\rho + \psi = \psi_0 + \psi \star F. \tag{3.9}$$

In view of the fact that ρ and $\psi - \psi_0$ are concentrated on $\overline{-\infty, 0}|$ and $\overline{0, \infty}$, respectively, the relation (3.9) is fully equivalent to the pair (3.6).

We shall use (3.9) as an integral equation determining the unknown measures ρ and ψ . A great many conclusions of theoretical importance can be derived directly from (3.9). We list the most remarkable such theorem under the heading of an example in order to indicate that it will not be used in the sequel and that we embark on a digression.

Examples. (*a*) *Wiener-Hopf type factorization.* It follows from the definition (1.7) of ψ that it satisfies the renewal equation

$$\psi = \psi_0 + \psi \star H. \tag{3.10}$$

Take the convolution of (3.9) with $\psi_0 - H$. The term $\psi \star H \star F$ can be simplified using (3.10) with the result

$$F = H + \rho - H \star \rho. \tag{3.11}$$

This identity is equivalent to (3.9), but it is remarkable in that it represents an arbitrary distribution F in terms of two possibly defective probability distributions concentrated on $\overline{-\infty, 0}|$ and $\overline{0, \infty}$ respectively. The equation suffers under the slight asymmetry that H is the distribution of the point of first entry into the open interval $\overline{0, \infty}$, whereas ρ is the analogous distribution for the closed interval $\overline{-\infty, 0}|$. However, we know from example (2.*a*) and (1.10) that $\rho = \zeta\psi_0 + (1-\zeta)H^-$ with ζ as defined in (1.9). Substituting into (3.11) we get after a trite rearrangement

$$\psi_0 - F = (1-\zeta)\,[\psi_0 - H] \star [\psi_0 - H^-]. \tag{3.12}$$

Various versions of this formula have been discovered independently by different methods and have caused much excitement. For a different variant see problem 19, and for the Fourier analytic equivalent see XVIII,3. The connection with the Wiener-Hopf techniques is discussed in section 3*a*.

(*b*) *Wald's identity* (2.7) proved in theorem 2.2 is an easy consequence of (3.11). See problems 10 and 11 as well as XVIII,2. ►

We now turn to the consideration of (3.9) as an integral equation for the unknown measures ρ and ψ. It will be shown that the solution is unique if its meaning in the present context is taken into account. For brevity we agree to say that a pair (ρ, ψ) is *probabilistically possible* if ρ is a possibly defective probability distribution concentrated on $\overline{-\infty, 0}|$, and $\psi - \psi_0$ a measure concentrated on $\overline{0, \infty}$ such that for each bounded interval I the measures $\psi\{I + t\}$ remain bounded. (The last condition follows from the renewal theorems since $\psi = \Sigma H^{n\bigstar}$.)

Theorem 1. *The convolution equation* (3.9) [*or, equivalently, the pair* (3.6)] *admits of exactly one probabilistically possible solution*[9] (ρ, ψ).

Proof. Let $\rho^{\#}$ and $\psi^{\#}$ be two non-negative measures satisfying (3.6), and $\psi^{\#} \geq \psi_0$. From (3.6*b*) we get by induction that $\psi^{\#} \geq \psi_0 + \cdots + \psi_n$ for every n, and hence our solution ψ is *minimal* in the sense that for any other solution $\psi^{\#}$ with a unit atom at the origin $\psi^{\#}\{I\} \geq \psi\{I\}$ for all intervals. In other words, $\delta = \psi^{\#} - \psi$ is a *measure*. From (3.6*a*) it is now seen that the same is true of $\gamma = \rho^{\#} - \rho$. Since both (ρ, ψ) and $(\rho^{\#}, \psi^{\#})$ satisfy (3.9) we have

$$\delta + \gamma = \delta \bigstar F. \tag{3.13}$$

Now two cases are possible. If ρ is a proper distribution its minimal character implies that $\rho^{\#} = \rho$ and hence $\gamma = 0$. Put $z(t) = \delta(I+t)$ where I is a fixed finite interval. Then z is a bounded solution of the convolution equation $z = F \bigstar z$ and hence $z(t) = \text{const}$ by the lemma of XI,2. But z vanishes identically for t near $-\infty$ and hence $z(t) = 0$ for all t. If ρ is defective we can only say that $z \leq F \bigstar z$. By induction in this case

$$z(t) \leq \int_{-\infty}^{+\infty} z(t-y)\, F^{n\bigstar}\{dy\} \tag{3.14}$$

for all n. Since ρ is defective the random walk drifts to ∞ and hence the

---

[9] This implies that ρ is the distribution of the point of first entry into $\overline{-\infty, 0}|$ and $\psi = \Sigma H^{n\bigstar}$ where H is the distribution of the point of first entry into $\overline{0, \infty}$.

mass of $F^{n\star}$ tends to concentrate near $+\infty$. Since $z(t-y) \to 0$ as $y \to \infty$ it follows again that $z(t) = 0$ and this concludes the proof. ▶

3a. THE WIENER-HOPF INTEGRAL EQUATION

To explain the connection between the integral equation (3.9) and the standard Wiener-Hopf equation it is best to begin by a probabilistic problem where the latter occurs.

Example. (*c*) *Distribution of maxima.* For simplicity let us assume that the distribution F has a density f and a negative expectation. The random walk $\{\mathbf{S}_n\}$ drifts to $-\infty$ and a finite-valued random variable

$$\mathbf{M} = \max[0, \mathbf{S}_1, \mathbf{S}_2, \ldots] \tag{3.15}$$

is defined with probability one. We propose to calculate its probability distribution $M(x) = \mathbf{P}\{\mathbf{M} \leq x\}$ which is by definition concentrated on $\overline{0, \infty}$. The event $\{\mathbf{M} \leq x\}$ occurs iff $\mathbf{X}_1 = y \leq x$ and $\max[0, \mathbf{X}_2, \mathbf{X}_2+ +\mathbf{X}_3, \ldots] \leq x-y$. Summing over all possible y we get

$$M(x) = \int_{-\infty}^{x} M(x-y)\, f(y)\, dy, \qquad x > 0 \tag{3.16}$$

which is the same as

$$M(x) = \int_{0}^{\infty} M(s)\, f(x-s)\, ds, \qquad x > 0. \tag{3.17}$$

On the other hand, we know from (2.6) that $M(x) = [1 - H(\infty)]\, \psi(x)$. We saw that ψ satisfies integral equation (3.7*b*) where under the present conditions $\rho(0) = 1$. A simple integration by parts now shows that (3.7*b*) and (3.17) are actually identical. ▶

The standard form of the Wiener-Hopf integral equation is represented by (3.17) and our example illustrates the way in which it can occur in probability theory. General references to the Wiener-Hopf techniques are misleading, however, because the restriction to positive functions and measures changes (and simplifies) the nature of the problem.

The ingenious method[10] used by Wiener and Hopf has attracted wide attention and has been adapted to various probabilistic problems, for example, by Cramér for asymptotic estimates for probabilities of ruin. The ease with which these estimates are obtained from the present approach is almost disquieting, but the deeper reason can be understood. The equation (3.17) represents, at best, only one of the two equations

[10] Dating back to 1931. A huge literature followed the first presentation in book form: E. Hopf, *Mathematical problems of radiative equilibrium*, Cambridge tracts, No. 31, 1934.

(3.7), and when $\rho(0) < 1$ even less. Taken by itself (3.17) is much more difficult to handle than the pair (3.7). For example, the uniqueness theorem *fails* for (3.17) even if only probability distributions are admitted. In fact, the basic idea of the Wiener-Hopf technique consists in introducing an auxiliary function which in the general theory lacks any particular meaning. This *tour de force* in effect replaces the individual equation (3.17) by a pair equivalent to (3.7) but the uniqueness is lost. We proceeded in the opposite direction, starting from the obvious recursion system (3.5) for the probabilities connected with the two inseparable problems: the first entry to $\overline{-\infty, 0}|$ and the random walk restricted to $x > 0$ prior to this first entry. In this way we derived the integral equation (3.9) from the known solution, and the uniqueness of the *probabilistic* solution was easy to establish. The convergence proof, the properties of the solutions, as well as the connection between the distribution M of the maxima and the renewal measure ψ depend on the duality lemma.

The possibility of attacking the Wiener-Hopf equation (3.17) using the duality principle was noticed by F. Spitzer.[11] The usual way of connecting the Wiener-Hopf theory with probabilistic problems starts from formulas related to (9.3) in their Fourier version to which we shall return in chapter XVIII. There exists now a huge literature relating Wiener-Hopf techniques to probabilistic problems and extending the scope of combinatorial methods. Most of this literature uses Fourier techniques.[12]

4. EXAMPLES

Explicit formulas for the first entry distributions are in general difficult to obtain. By a stroke of good fortune there is a remarkable exception to this rule, discussed in example (*a*). At first sight the distribution F of this example appears artificial, but the type turns up frequently in connection with Poisson processes, queuing theory, ruin problems, etc. Considering the extreme simplicity of our general results it is unbelievable how much ingenuity and analytical skill has been spent (often repeatedly) on individual special cases.

Example (*c*) exhibits (in a rather pedestrian fashion) the complete calculations in the case of an arithmetic F with rational generating

[11] *The Wiener-Hopf equation whose kernel is a probability density*, Duke Math. J., vol. 24 (1957) pp. 327–343.

[12] A short survey of the literature is impossible on account of the unsettled state of affairs and because the methodology of many papers suffers under the influence of accidents of historical developments. Much of the literature is quoted in J. H. B. Kemperman (1961). Generalizations beyond probability theory are illustrated by G. Baxter, *An operator identity*, Pacific J. Math., vol. 4 (1958) pp. 649–663.

functions. The calculations are given because the same method is used for rational Laplace or Fourier transforms. Another example is found in problems 3–6. Example (*b*) deals with a general relationship of independent interest.

We adhere to the notations of the preceding section. Thus H and ρ are the distributions of the point of first entry into $\overline{0, \infty}$ and $\overline{-\infty, 0}|$ respectively. (In other words, H and ρ are the distributions of the first strict ascending and the first weak descending ladder heights.) Finally, $\psi = \Sigma H^{n\star}$ is the renewal function corresponding to H. Our main tool is the equation (3.7*a*) stating that for $x < 0$ the distribution of the first entry into $\overline{-\infty, 0}|$ is given by

$$\rho(x) = \int_{0-}^{\infty} \psi\{dy\}\, F(x-y). \tag{4.1}$$

(*a*) *Exponential right tail.*[13] Suppose, by way of introduction, that the *left* tail of F is exponential, that is, $F(x) = qe^{\beta x}$ for $x < 0$. Whatever ψ is, (4.1) shows that $\rho(x) = Ce^{\beta x}$ for $x < 0$ where C is a constant. Having made this discovery we interchange the role of the two half-axes (partly to facilitate reference to our formulas, partly with a view to the most important applications in queuing theory). Assume then that

$$F(x) = 1 - pe^{-\alpha x} \qquad \textit{for} \quad x \geq 0 \tag{4.2}$$

without any conditions imposed for $x < 0$. To avoid unnecessary complications we assume that *F has a finite expectation μ* and that F is continuous. It follows from the preliminary remark that the ladder height distribution H has a density proportional to $e^{-\alpha x}$. We now distinguish two cases.

(i) If $\mu \geq 0$ the distribution H is proper and hence for $x > 0$

$$H(x) = 1 - e^{-\alpha x}, \qquad \psi(x) = 1 + \alpha x. \tag{4.3}$$

[The latter follows trivially from $\psi = \Sigma H^{n\star}$ or the renewal equation in (3.10).] From (4.1) we get

$$\rho(x) = F(x) + \alpha \int_{-\infty}^{x} F(s)\, ds, \qquad x < 0, \tag{4.4}$$

and thus we have explicit expressions for all desired probabilities. An easy calculation shows that

$$\rho(0) = 1 - \alpha\mu. \tag{4.5}$$

[13] In the random walk of example VI,(8.*b*) [and in the corresponding queuing process VI,(9.*e*)] *both* tails are exponential.

This is a special case of (2.7) because $(1 - \rho(0))^{-1} = \mathbf{E}(\mathcal{T}_1)$ by virtue of (2.3).

(ii) If $\mu < 0$, the relations (4.3) and (4.4) still represent a solution of the integral equation (3.9), but because of (4.5) it is probabilistically impossible when $\mu < 0$. For the correct solution we know that H has a density $h(x) = (\alpha - \kappa)e^{-\alpha x}$ where $0 < \kappa < \alpha$ because H is defective. An easy calculation shows that $\psi'(x) = (\alpha - \kappa)e^{-\kappa x}$ for $x > 0$. The unknown constant κ is obtained from the condition that $\rho(0) = 1$. A routine calculation shows that κ must be the unique positive root of the equation (4.6). Given the root of this transcendental equation we have again explicit formulas for H, ρ, and ψ.

The reader will easily verify that the same theory applies when the variables $\mathbf{X}_1, \mathbf{X}_2, \ldots$ of the random walk are integral-valued and the distribution F has a *geometric right tail*, that is, if F attributes to the integer $k > 0$ the weight $q\beta^k$.

(*b*) *Associated random walks.* Suppose that F has an expectation $\mu \neq 0$ and that there exists a number $\kappa \neq 0$ such that

$$\int_{-\infty}^{+\infty} e^{\kappa y}\, F\{dy\} = 1. \tag{4.6}$$

The integral of e^{ty} with respect to F exists in this case for all t between 0 and κ, and is a convex function of t whose derivative at the origin equals μ. It follows that the root κ is unique and that κ and μ have opposite signs. In the following κ stands for this root.

Given an arbitrary measure γ on the line we associate with it a new measure ${}^a\gamma$ defined by

$$ {}^a\gamma\{dy\} = e^{\kappa y}\, \gamma\{dy\}. \tag{4.7}$$

The measure ${}^aF$ associated with F is again a proper probability distribution and we say that the random walks generated by ${}^aF$ and F are *associated with each other.*[14] It is easily seen that the n-fold convolution of ${}^aF$ with itself is associated with $F^{n\bigstar}$ so that the notation ${}^aF^{n\bigstar}$ is unambiguous. Furthermore, the recursion formulas (3.5) show that the transforms ${}^a\rho_n$ and ${}^a\psi_n$ have the same probabilistic meaning in the new random walk as ρ_n and ψ_n in the old one. It follows generally that the transforms ${}^a\rho$, ${}^aH$, ${}^a\psi$, etc., *have the obvious meaning for the random walk associated with* ${}^aF$. [This can be seen also directly from the integral equation (3.9).]

---

[14] This notion was used by Khintchine, Wald, and others but was never fully exploited. The transformation (4.7) was used for renewal theory in XI,6 and (in a form disguised by the use of generating functions) in **1**; XIII,4 and will be used for Laplace transforms in XIII,(1.6). The equation (4.6) serves also in the Wiener-Hopf theory.

We have thus devised a widely applicable method of translating facts about a random walk with $\mu < 0$ into results for a random walk with positive expectation, and vice versa.

If $\mu < 0$ the ladder height distribution is defective, but ${}^aH$ is a proper distribution. This means that

$$\int_0^\infty e^{\kappa y}\, H\{dy\} = 1. \tag{4.8}$$

The power of the method of associated random walks derives largely from this remark. Indeed, we know from XI,6 that excellent asymptotic estimates are available for the ascending ladder process if one knows the root of the equation (4.8). These estimates would be illusory if they required a knowledge of H, but we see now that *the roots of the two equations* (4.6) *and* (4.8) *are identical.*

(*c*) *Bounded arithmetic distributions.* Let a and b be positive integers and let F be an arithmetic distribution with jumps f_k at $k = -b, \ldots, a$. The measures ψ and ρ are also concentrated on integers and we denote their jumps at k by ψ_k and ρ_k, respectively. The first entry into $\overline{-\infty, 0}|$ occurs at an integer $\geq -b$ and so $\rho_k = 0$ for $k < -b$. We introduce the generating functions

$$\Phi(s) = \sum_{k=-b}^{a} f_k s^k, \qquad \Psi(s) = \sum_{k=0}^{\infty} \psi_k s^k, \qquad R(s) = \sum_{k=-b}^{0} \rho_k s^k. \tag{4.9}$$

They differ from those of **1**; XI in that Φ and R involve also negative powers of s, but it is clear that the basic properties and rules remain unchanged. In particular, $\mu = \Phi'(1)$ is the expectation of F. To a convolution of distributions there corresponds the product of the generating functions, and so the basic integral equation (3.9) is equivalent to $\Psi + R = 1 + \Psi\Phi$ or

$$\Psi(s) = \frac{s^b(R(s) - 1)}{s^b(\Phi(s) - 1)}. \tag{4.10}$$

The numerator and denominator are polynomials of degrees b and $a + b$, respectively. The power series on the left is regular for $|s| < 1$, and so all roots of the denominator located within the unit circle must cancel against roots of the numerator. We proceed to show that this requirement uniquely determines R and Ψ.

For concreteness we suppose that $\mu = 0$ (see problem 12), and show that the denominator has exactly $b - 1$ complex roots within the unit circle, $a - 1$ roots outside, and a double root at the point 1. In fact, on the real axis $\Phi'' \geq 0$ and so Φ is a convex function with the minimum $\Phi(1) = 1$.

For complex s such that $|s| \leq 1$ we have $|s^b\,\Phi(s)| \leq 1$, and by Rouché's theorem[15] the unit circle contains exactly as many roots of

$$s^b[\Phi(s) - (1+\epsilon)] = 0$$

as of $s^b(1+\epsilon) = 0$, that is, b. One of these roots is real and tends to 1 as $\epsilon \to 0$, and so the denominator possesses exactly $b - 1$ roots $s_1, \ldots, s_{b-1}$ with $|s_j| < 1$. Let $\sigma_1, \ldots, \sigma_{a-1}$ be the roots with $|\sigma_j| > 1$. Then the denominator is of the form

$$(4.11)\quad s^b(\Phi(s)-1) = C(s-1)^2(s-s_1)\cdots(s-s_{b-1})(s-\sigma_1)\cdots(s-\sigma_{a-1}).$$

The roots $s_1, \ldots, s_{b-1}$ must cancel against those of the numerator, and since the coefficients ψ_n remain bounded the same is true of *one* root $s = 1$. This determines Ψ up to a multiplicative constant. But by definition $\Psi(0) = 1$ and hence we have the *desired explicit formula*

$$(4.12)\qquad \Psi(s) = \frac{1}{(1-s)\left(1 - \dfrac{s}{\sigma_1}\right)\cdots\left(1 - \dfrac{s}{\sigma_{a-1}}\right)}.$$

The standard expansion into partial fractions leads to explicit expressions for ψ_n, the great advantage of this method being that the knowledge of the dominant root leads to reasonable asymptotic estimates (see **1**; XI,4).

For the generating function R of the first entrance probabilities ρ_k we get from (4.10) and (4.12)

$$(4.13)\qquad R(s) = \\ = 1 + C\cdot(-1)^{a-1}\sigma_1\cdots\sigma_{a-1}\left(1 - \frac{1}{s}\right)\left(1 - \frac{s_1}{s}\right)\cdots\left(1 - \frac{s_{b-1}}{s}\right).$$

[The coefficient C is defined in (4.11) and depends only on the given distribution $\{f_k\}$.] Again a partial fraction expansion leads to asymptotic estimates. (Continued in problems 12–15.)

5. APPLICATIONS

It was shown in VI,9 that a basic problem of queuing theory consists in finding the distribution M of

$$(5.1)\qquad \mathbf{M} = \max[0, \mathbf{S}_1, \ldots]$$

in a random walk with variables $\mathbf{X}_k$ such that $\mu = \mathbf{E}(\mathbf{X}_k) < 0$. Examples

[15] See, for example, E. Hille, *Analytic function theory*, vol. I, section 9.2. (Ginn and Co., 1959.)

VI,(9.*a*) to (*c*) show that the same problem turns up in other contexts, for example in connection with ruin problems in compound Poisson processes. In this case, as well as in queuing theory, the underlying distribution is of the form

$$F = A \star B \tag{5.2}$$

where A is concentrated on $\overline{0, \infty}$ and B on $\overline{-\infty, 0}$. We suppose that A and B have finite expectations a and $-b$, so that F has expectation $\mu = a - b$. We suppose also that F is *continuous* so as to avoid the tedious distinction between strict and weak ladder variables.

As in the preceding two sections we denote the ascending and descending ladder height distributions by H and ρ respectively. (For consistency we should write H^- for ρ.) In other words, H and ρ are the distributions of the point of first entry into $\overline{0, \infty}$ and $\overline{-\infty, 0}$ (and also into corresponding closed intervals). It was shown in example (3.*c*) and in (2.6) that *if* $\mu < 0$

$$M(x) = \frac{\psi(x)}{\psi(\infty)} = [1 - H(\infty)] \sum_0^\infty H^{n\star}(x). \tag{5.3}$$

Example (4.*a*) contains an *explicit formula*[16] *for this distribution if one of the tails of F is exponential*, that is,

$$F(x) = 1 - pe^{-\alpha x} \qquad \textit{for} \quad x > 0, \tag{5.4}$$

or else $F(x) = qe^{\alpha x}$ for $x < 0$.

By extreme good luck *the condition* (5.4) *holds if F is of the form* (5.2) with

$$A(x) = 1 - e^{-\alpha x} \qquad \textit{for} \quad x > 0. \tag{5.5}$$

Then

$$p = \int_{-\infty}^{0} e^{\alpha y}\, B\{dy\}. \tag{5.6}$$

Our simple results are therefore applicable in queuing theory whenever *either* the incoming traffic is Poissonian *or* the service time is exponential. Furthermore, the ruin problem in compound Poisson processes is covered by the present conditions. There exists an immense applied literature treating special problems under various assumptions on the distribution B,

[16] Another explicit formula is contained in example (4.*c*) for the case of an arithmetic distribution F with finitely many atoms. This explicit formula is too unwieldy to be practical, but an expansion into partial fractions leads to good *asymptotic estimates if the dominant root of the denominator is known*. The same method applies to Fourier transforms whenever the *characteristic function of F is rational*. This remark covers many special cases treated in the literature.

sometimes, as in ruin problems, in a disguised form. As it turns out, greater generality and much greater simplicity can be achieved by using only the condition (5.4) instead of the combination (5.5) and (5.2). We see here a prime example of the economy of thought inherent in a general theory where one's view is not obscured by accidents of special cases.

Examples. (*a*) *The Khintchine-Pollaczek formula.* Suppose that F is of the form (5.2) with A given by (5.5) and $\mu = \frac{1}{\alpha} - b > 0$. The random walk drifts to ∞ and we have to replace the maximum in (5.1) by the minimum. This means replacing H in (5.3) by the distribution ρ given in (4.4). A simple integration by parts shows that for $x < 0$

$$\rho(x) = \alpha \int_{-\infty}^{x} B(y)\, dy. \tag{5.7}$$

Hence $\rho(0) = \alpha b$ and so for $x < 0$

$$\mathbf{P}\{\min(\mathbf{S}_0, \mathbf{S}_1, \ldots) \leq x\} = (1 - \alpha b) \sum_0^\infty \rho^{n\bigstar}(x). \tag{5.8}$$

This is the celebrated Khintchine-Pollaczek formula, which has been rediscovered time and again in special situations, invariably using Laplace transforms [which method is inapplicable for the more general distributions of the form (5.4)]. We return to it in example XVIII,(3*c*).

(*b*) *The dual case.* Consider the same distributions as in the last example but with $\mu < 0$. As was shown in the second part of example (4.*a*) in this case

$$\mathbf{P}\{\max(\mathbf{S}_0, \mathbf{S}_1, \ldots) \leq x\} = \frac{\kappa}{\alpha}\, \psi(x) = 1 - \left(1 - \frac{\kappa}{\alpha}\right) e^{-\kappa x} \tag{5.9}$$

where κ is the unique positive root of the "characteristic equation" (4.6). (This result can be obtained also by the method of associated random walks recalling the fact that when $\mu \leq 0$ one has $\psi(x) = 1 + \alpha x$ for $x > 0$.) In queuing theory (5.9) implies that *at a server with exponential servicing times the distribution of the waiting times tends to an exponential limit.*

(*c*) *Asymptotic estimates.* The very appearance of formula (5.3) recalls the fact that the maximum of the partial sums $\mathbf{S}_n$ coincides with the maximum ordinate attained by the ladder points. An asymptotic estimate for the distribution of this maximum has been derived in XI,(6.16). It would seem inapplicable in the present situation because it depends on the positive root of the characteristic equation (4.8) for the distribution H, and the latter is in general unknown. However, we saw in example (4.*b*) that this root is the same as the root of (4.6). For the distribution M

of the maximum this means the following: *if F has a negative expectation and a root $\kappa > 0$ of* (4.6) *exists, then* $1 - M(x) \sim Ce^{-\kappa x}$ *as* $x \to \infty$. Only the value of the constant C depends on special properties of the distribution F. The generality of this result is remarkable, in particular since it followed from the simplest renewal theorem by the simple transformation for associated random walks.

(*d*) *Cramér's estimate for probabilities of ruin.* To show how the constant C can be evaluated in practice we return to the general ruin problem of VI,5, which was reformulated as a queuing problem in example VI,(9.*d*). With the present notation we are concerned with a basic distribution F of the form (5.2), where A is the exponential distribution (5.5), and the expectation $\mu = \frac{1}{\alpha} - b > 0$. We seek the distribution of the (negative) minimum of $\mathbf{S}_0, \mathbf{S}_1, \ldots$ given in (5.8). Exactly this problem[17] was studied in example XI,(7.*a*). The characteristic equation for ρ is equivalent to (4.6). If a root $\kappa < 0$ exists, the formulas (7.5)–(7.6) state in the present notation that as $x \to -\infty$

$$\mathbf{P}\{\min(\mathbf{S}_0, \mathbf{S}_1, \ldots) \leq x\} \sim \frac{1 - \alpha b}{|\kappa|\, \beta}\, e^{|\kappa| x}, \tag{5.10}$$

where

$$\beta = \alpha \int_{-\infty}^{0} e^{-|\kappa| y}\, |y|\, B(y)\, dy. \tag{5.11}$$

The estimate (5.10) has been derived repeatedly under special circumstances and by exceedingly laborious methods. It is equivalent to a frequently used estimate in risk theory due to Cramér[18].

6. A COMBINATORIAL LEMMA

The distribution of ladder epochs depends on a simple combinatorial lemma, and the probabilistic part of the argument will appear clearer if we isolate this lemma.

Let $x_1, \ldots, x_n$ be n numbers, and consider their partial sums

$$s_0 = 0, \ldots, s_n = x_1 + \cdots + x_n.$$

We say that $\nu > 0$ *is a ladder index* if $s_\nu > s_0, \ldots, s_\nu > s_{\nu-1}$, that is, if

---

[17] To our defective distribution ρ, which is concentrated on $\overline{-\infty, 0}$, there corresponds in VI,7 the defective distribution L with *density* $\frac{\alpha}{c}(1 - F(x))$ concentrated on $\overline{0, \infty}$.

[18] For a newer derivation by Wiener-Hopf techniques in the complex plane see Cramér's paper cited in VI,5. Our (5.10) is Cramér's (57).

s_ν exceeds all preceding partial sums. There are n ladder indices if all x_ν are positive, whereas there are none if all x_ν are negative.

Consider now the n cyclical reorderings $(x_1, \ldots, x_n)$, $(x_2, \ldots, x_n, x_1), \ldots, (x_n, x_1, \ldots, x_{n-1})$ and number them from 0 to $n - 1$. The partial sums $s_k^{(\nu)}$ in the arrangement number ν are given by

$$(6.1) \qquad s_k^{(\nu)} = \begin{cases} s_{\nu+k} - s_\nu & \text{for} \quad k = 1, \ldots, n-\nu \\ s_n - s_\nu + s_{k-n+\nu} & \text{for} \quad k = n-\nu+1, \ldots, n. \end{cases}$$

Lemma 1. *Suppose $s_n > 0$. Denote by r the number of cyclical rearrangements in which n is a ladder index. Then $r \geq 1$, and in each there are exactly r ladder indices.*

Examples. For $(-1, -1, -1, 0, 1, 10)$ we have $r = 1$: the given order is the only one in which the last partial sum is maximal. For $(-1, 4, 7, 1)$ we have $r = 3$; the permutations number 0, 2, and 3 yield 3 ladder indices each. ▶

Proof. Choose ν so that s_ν is maximal, and if there are several such indices choose ν as small as possible. In other words,

$$(6.2) \qquad s_\nu > s_1, \ldots, s_\nu > s_{\nu-1}, \qquad s_\nu \geq s_{\nu+1}, \ldots, s_\nu \geq s_n.$$

It is then seen from (6.1) that in the νth permutation the last partial sum is strictly maximal and so n is a ladder index. Thus $r \geq 1$. Without loss of generality we now suppose that n is a ladder index in the original arrangement, that is, $s_n > s_j$ for all j. The quantities in the first line in (6.1) are then $< s_n$, and the second line in (6.1) shows that n is a ladder index also in the νth permutation iff $s_\nu > s_1, \ldots, s_\nu > s_{\nu-1}$, that is, iff ν is a ladder index in the original arrangement. Thus the number of permutations in which n is a ladder index equals the number of ladder indices, and the lemma is proved. ▶

Weak ladder indices are defined analogously except that the strict inequality $>$ is replaced by $\geq$. The preceding argument applies to them and leads to

Lemma 2. *If $s_n \geq 0$, lemma 1 applies also to weak ladder indices.*

7. DISTRIBUTION OF LADDER EPOCHS

In the preceding sections we have focused our attention on the ladder height, but now we turn to the ladder epochs. Consider the probability that n is the epoch of the first entry into $\overline{0, \infty}$, that is,

$$(7.1) \qquad \tau_n = \mathbf{P}\{\mathbf{S}_1 \leq 0, \ldots, \mathbf{S}_{n-1} \leq 0, \mathbf{S}_n > 0\}.$$

In other words, $\{\tau_n\}$ is the (possibly defective) distribution of the first ladder epoch $\mathscr{T}_1$. We introduce its generating function

$$\tau(s) = \sum_{n=1}^{\infty} \tau_n s^n, \qquad 0 \le s \le 1. \tag{7.2}$$

The following important theorem was discovered by Sparre-Andersen and has been proved in several ways. [An improved version due to G. Baxter is contained in (9.3).]

Theorem 1:

$$\log \frac{1}{1-\tau(s)} = \sum_{n=1}^{\infty} \frac{s^n}{n} \mathbf{P}\{S_n > 0\}. \tag{7.3}$$

Proof. For fixed n consider together with each sample point $(\mathbf{X}_1, \ldots, \mathbf{X}_n)$ its n cyclical permutations and the corresponding partial sums $\mathbf{S}_0^{(\nu)}, \ldots, \mathbf{S}_n^{(\nu)}$ [defined as in (6.1)]. Fix an integer r and define n random variables $\mathbf{Y}^{(\nu)}$ as follows: $\mathbf{Y}^{(\nu)} = 1$ if n is the rth ladder index for $(\mathbf{S}_1^{(\nu)}, \ldots, \mathbf{S}_n^{(\nu)})$ and $\mathbf{Y}^{(\nu)} = 0$ otherwise. To $\nu = 0$ there corresponds the sequence $\{\mathbf{S}_1, \ldots, \mathbf{S}_n\}$ and so $\mathbf{Y}^{(0)} = 1$ iff n is the rth ladder index in our random walk. But the rth ladder epoch is the sum of r independent random variables distributed as $\mathscr{T}_1$, and so

$$\mathbf{P}\{\mathbf{Y}^{(0)} = 1\} = \tau_n^{(r)} \tag{7.4}$$

where $\tau_n^{(r)}$ is the coefficient of s^n in $\tau^r(s)$. For reasons of symmetry the n variables $\mathbf{Y}^{(\nu)}$ have the same distribution, and therefore

$$\tau_n^{(r)} = \mathbf{E}(\mathbf{Y}^{(0)}) = \frac{1}{n}\mathbf{E}(\mathbf{Y}^{(0)} + \cdots + \mathbf{Y}^{(n)}). \tag{7.5}$$

The last sum vanishes trivially outside the region $\{\mathbf{S}_n > 0\}$. By lemma 6.1 it can assume only the values 0 and r, whence

$$\frac{1}{r}\tau_n^{(r)} = \frac{1}{n}\mathbf{P}\{\mathbf{Y}^{(0)} + \cdots + \mathbf{Y}^{(n)} = r\}. \tag{7.6}$$

Summing over r we get

$$\sum_{r=1}^{\infty} \frac{1}{r}\tau_n^{(r)} = \frac{1}{n}\mathbf{P}\{\mathbf{S}_n > 0\} \tag{7.7}$$

because at each point of $\{\mathbf{S}_n > 0\}$ the sum in (7.6) equals some integer r. Multiply (7.7) by s^n and sum over n to obtain

$$\sum_{r=1}^{\infty} \frac{1}{r}\tau(s) = \sum_{n=1}^{\infty} \frac{s^n}{n}\mathbf{P}\{\mathbf{S}_n > 0\} \tag{7.8}$$

which is the same as the assertion (7.3). ►

The surprising implication of this theorem is that the distribution of ladder epochs is uniquely determined by the sequence of numbers $F^{n\star}(0)$. For example, if F is symmetric and continuous, $\mathbf{P}\{\mathbf{S}_n > 0\} = \frac{1}{2}$ for all n and the right side in (7.3) equals $\log(1/\sqrt{1-s})$. We have thus the

Corollary 1. *If F is continuous and symmetric, then*

$$\tau(s) = 1 - \sqrt{1-s}. \tag{7.9}$$

Obviously *theorem* 1 *remains valid if in* (7.1) *and* (7.3) *the sign* $>$ *is replaced by* $\geq$ *and* $\leq$ *by* $<$, that is, if $\mathcal{T}_1$ is replaced by the weak ladder epoch $\overline{\mathcal{T}}_1$ and $\{\mathbf{S}_n > 0\}$ by $\{\mathbf{S}_n \geq 0\}$.

An important implication of the theorem is contained in

Theorem 2. *The random walk drifts to* $-\infty$ *iff*

$$\sum_{n=1}^{\infty} \frac{1}{n} \mathbf{P}\{\mathbf{S}_n > 0\} < \infty. \tag{7.10}$$

This criterion remains valid[19] *with* $\{\mathbf{S}_n > 0\}$ *replaced by* $\{\mathbf{S}_n \geq 0\}$.

Proof. Drift to $-\infty$ takes place iff the ascending ladder processes are terminating that is, iff the distribution of $\mathcal{T}_1$ is defective. This is the same as $\tau(1) < 1$, and in this case the two sides in (7.3) remain bounded as $s \to 1$. The condition (7.10) is seen to be necessary and sufficient. The same argument applied to weak ladder epochs justifies the concluding assertion. ▶

We know that drift to $-\infty$ takes place if F has an expectation $\mu < 0$, but it is not analytically obvious that $\mu < 0$ implies (7.10). The verification of this fact provides an excellent technical exercise of methodological interest. (See problem 16.)

Theorem 3. *The ladder epoch* $\mathcal{T}_1$ *has a finite expectation (and is proper) iff the random walk drifts to* ∞. *In this case*

$$\log \mathbf{E}(\mathcal{T}_1) = \log \sum k\tau_k = \sum_{n=1}^{\infty} \frac{1}{n} \mathbf{P}\{\mathbf{S}_n \leq 0\}. \tag{7.11}$$

(The series diverges in all other cases).

Proof. For $0 < s < 1$

$$\log \frac{1-\tau(s)}{1-s} = \sum_{n=1}^{\infty} \frac{s^n}{n} [1 - \mathbf{P}\{\mathbf{S}_n > 0\}]. \tag{7.12}$$

Letting $s \to 1$ we get (7.11) if the series converges. In case of divergence

[19] We shall see that $\Sigma\, n^{-1}\mathbf{P}\{\mathbf{S}_n = 0\} < \infty$ under any circumstances [see (9.*c*)].

either $\mathscr{T}_1$ is improper or $\mathbf{E}(\mathscr{T}_1) = \infty$. By theorem 2 convergence takes place iff the random walk drifts to ∞. ▶

In conclusion we turn to an *alternative interpretation* of theorem 1 which leads to the arc sine laws. Put

$$p(s) = \frac{1}{1 - \tau(s)}. \tag{7.13}$$

From the theory of recurrent events it is clear that this is the generating function of the probability p_n that n be a ladder epoch, namely

$$p_n = \mathbf{P}\{\mathbf{S}_n > \mathbf{S}_0, \ldots, \mathbf{S}_n > \mathbf{S}_{n-1}\}. \tag{7.14}$$

Reversing the order of the variables $\mathbf{X}_j$ we get the dual interpretation

$$p_n = \mathbf{P}\{\mathbf{S}_1 > 0, \mathbf{S}_2 > 0, \ldots, \mathbf{S}_n > 0\}. \tag{7.15}$$

For reference we record this in

Theorem 4. *The generating function* (7.13) *of the probabilities* (7.15) *is given by* (7.3).

For reasons of symmetry

$$q_n = \mathbf{P}\{\mathbf{S}_1 \leq 0, \ldots, \mathbf{S}_n \leq 0\} \tag{7.16}$$

has the generating function q given by

$$\log q(s) = \sum_{n=1}^{\infty} \frac{s^n}{n} \mathbf{P}\{\mathbf{S}_n \leq 0\}. \tag{7.17}$$

8. THE ARC SINE LAWS

One of the surprising features of the chance fluctuations in coin tossing finds its expression in the two arc sine laws (**1**; III,5 and 8). One of them implies that the number of positive terms in the sequence $\mathbf{S}_1, \ldots, \mathbf{S}_n$ is more likely to be relatively close to 0 or n than to $n/2$ as one would naïvely expect. The second implies the same for the position of the maximal term. We show now that these laws are valid for arbitrary symmetric and for many other distributions.

In the following formulations we have to cope with the nuisance that the maximum may be assumed repeatedly and that partial sums may vanish. These possibilities can be disregarded if F is continuous, for then the probability is zero that any two partial sums are equal. (Readers are advised to consider only this case.) For the general theory we agree to consider the index of the *first* maximum, that is, the index k such that

$$\mathbf{S}_k > \mathbf{S}_0, \ldots, \mathbf{S}_k > \mathbf{S}_{k-1}, \qquad \mathbf{S}_k \geq \mathbf{S}_{k+1}, \ldots, \mathbf{S}_k \geq \mathbf{S}_n. \tag{8.1}$$

Here n is fixed and k runs through the values $0, 1, \ldots, n$. The event (8.1) must occur for some $k \leq n$, and so we may define the (proper) random variable $\mathbf{K}_n$ *as the index of the first maximum*, that is, the index where (8.1) occurs. Here ($\mathbf{S}_0 = 0$).

The event (8.1) requires the simultaneous realization of the two events $\{\mathbf{S}_k > \mathbf{S}_0, \ldots, \mathbf{S}_k > \mathbf{S}_{k-1}\}$ and $\{\mathbf{S}_{k+1} - \mathbf{S}_k \leq 0, \ldots, \mathbf{S}_n - \mathbf{S}_k \leq 0\}$. The first involves only $\mathbf{X}_1, \ldots, \mathbf{X}_k$, the second only $\mathbf{X}_{k+1}, \ldots, \mathbf{X}_n$, and hence the two events are independent. By the very definition their probabilities are p_k and q_{n-k} [see (7.14) and (7.16)] and so we have

Lemma 1. *For all k, n*

$$\mathbf{P}\{\mathbf{K}_n = k\} = p_k q_{n-k}. \tag{8.2}$$

Suppose now that $\mathbf{P}\{\mathbf{S}_n > 0\} = \mathbf{P}\{\mathbf{S}_n \leq 0\} = \frac{1}{2}$ for all n. The generating functions p and q are then identical and given by (7.17). On the right we recognize the logarithmic expansion and conclude $p(s) = q(s) = 1/\sqrt{1 - s}$. Thus

$$p_k q_{n-k} = \binom{-\frac{1}{2}}{k}\binom{-\frac{1}{2}}{n-k}(-1)^n, \tag{8.3}$$

and this may be rewritten in the more pleasing form

$$p_k q_{n-k} = \binom{2k}{k}\binom{2n-2k}{n-k}\frac{1}{2^{2n}}. \tag{8.4}$$

This formula is identical with the formula **1**; III,(5.1) for the distribution of heads in coin tossing, and we have already discussed its limiting form **1**; III,(5.7). We can can therefore state

Theorem 1. *If F is symmetric and continuous, the probability distribution of $\mathbf{K}_n$ (the index of the first maximum in $\mathbf{S}_0, \mathbf{S}_1, \ldots, \mathbf{S}_n$) is given by* (8.3) *or* (8.4). *For fixed $0 < \alpha < 1$ as $n \to \infty$*

$$\mathbf{P}\{\mathbf{K}_n < n\alpha\} \to 2\frac{1}{\pi}\arc\sin\sqrt{\alpha}. \tag{8.5}$$

The limit distribution has the density $\dfrac{1}{\pi\sqrt{\alpha(1-\alpha)}}$ which is unbounded at the endpoints 0 and 1 and has its minimum at the midpoint $\frac{1}{2}$. This shows that the reduced maximum $\mathbf{K}_n/n$ is much more likely to be close to 0 or 1 than to $\frac{1}{2}$. For a fuller discussion see **1**; III,5 and 8.

One should expect that (8.4) remains valid at least asymptotically if the medians of $\mathbf{S}_n$ tend to 0 sufficiently fast. In fact, by theorem 7.4 we have under any circumstances

$$p(s)\sqrt{1-s} = \exp\sum_{n=1}^{\infty}\frac{s^n}{n}\,[\mathbf{P}\{\mathbf{S}_n > 0\} - \tfrac{1}{2}]. \tag{8.6}$$

One can argue vaguely as follows. If the medians of $\mathbf{S}_n$ are close to 0, the coefficients on the right are small, and therefore the right side is near 1. Hence $p(s)$ is near $1/\sqrt{1-s}$. It is therefore plausible that the coefficients of the two power series should be close to each other. This argument can be made rigorous when the series

$$\sum_{n=1}^{\infty} \frac{1}{n} [\mathbf{P}\{\mathbf{S}_n > 0\} - \tfrac{1}{2}] = c \tag{8.7}$$

converges. As $s \to 1$ the right side in (8.6) tends to e^c and so $p(s) \sim e^c/\sqrt{1-s}$. Because of (7.15) the p_n are monotone, and therefore the last relation implies

$$p_n \sim e^c \binom{-\frac{1}{2}}{n} (-1)^n, \qquad n \to \infty \tag{8.8}$$

by the refined form of the Tauberian theorem 5 in XIII,5. For q_n we get the same relation with c replaced by $-c$ and so if $n \to \infty$ and $n - k \to \infty$

$$\mathbf{P}\{\mathbf{K}_n = k\} \sim \binom{2k}{k} \binom{2n-2k}{n-k} \frac{1}{2^{2n}}. \tag{8.9}$$

We have thus

Theorem 1a.[20] *If the series* (8.7) *converges, then* (8.9) *and* (8.5) *are true.*

It will be shown in XVIII,5 that the series (8.7) converges whenever F has zero expectation and finite variance. The arc sine laws therefore hold for such distributions.

In **1**; III we had to prove the two arc sine laws separately, but the next theorem shows that they are equivalent. Theorem 2 (for continuous distributions) was the point of departure of the investigations by E. Sparre–Andersen introducing the new approach to fluctuation theory. The original proof was exceedingly intricate. Several proofs are now in existence, but the following seems simplest.

Theorem 2. *The number* $\mathbf{\Pi}_n$ *of strictly positive terms among* $\mathbf{S}_1, \ldots, \mathbf{S}_n$ *has the same distribution* (8.2) *as* $\mathbf{K}_n$, *the index of the first maximal term.*

Similarly, the distribution of the non-negative terms is the same as that of the index of the *last* maximum.

We begin with a purely combinatorial lemma in which the word probability occurs merely for convenience of expression. Let $x_1, \ldots, x_n$ arbitrary numbers (not necessarily distinct). Consider the $n!$ permutations $(i_1, \ldots, i_n)$ of the indices and with each the partial sums

$$s_0 = 0, \ldots, s_n = x_{i_1} + \cdots + x_{i_n}. \tag{8.10}$$

We consider the $n!$ permutations as points of a sample space in which each

[20] This theorem was proved by laborious calculations by Sparre–Andersen and also by Spitzer. The remark that the Tauberian theorem removes all trouble is due to Spitzer. For a generalization see 9.*d*.

point has probability $1/n!$. The sums s_j are then random variables and we define four new variables as follows:

$$\mathbf{K} = \text{index of the first maximum in } (s_0, \ldots, s_n)$$
$$\mathbf{K}^* = \text{index of the last maximum in } (s_0, \ldots, s_n)$$
$$\mathbf{\Pi} = \text{number of positive terms in } (s_1, \ldots, s_n)$$
$$\mathbf{\Pi}^* = \text{number of non-negative terms in } (s_1, \ldots, s_n).$$

All four variables range over $0, 1, \ldots, n$.

Example. We list the 12 distinguishable arrangements of the four numbers $1, 1, -1, -2$ and the values of the four variables for each arrangement in the following table.

$(s_0,$	$s_1,$	$s_2,$	$s_3,$	$s_4)$	**K**	**K***	**Π**	**Π***
0	1	2	1	−1	2	2	3	3
0	1	2	0	−1	2	2	2	3
0	1	0	1	−1	1	3	2	3
0	1	0	−2	−1	1	1	1	2
0	1	−1	0	−1	1	1	1	2
0	1	−1	−2	−1	1	1	1	1
0	−1	0	1	−1	3	3	1	2
0	−1	0	−2	−1	0	2	0	1
0	−1	−3	−2	−1	0	0	0	0
0	−2	−1	0	−1	0	3	0	1
0	−2	−1	−2	−1	0	0	0	0
0	−2	−3	−2	−1	0	0	0	0

K and **Π** assume the values 0, 1, 2, 3 with respective probabilities $\frac{5}{12}$, $\frac{4}{12}$, $\frac{2}{12}$, $\frac{1}{12}$ whereas **K*** and **Π*** are uniformly distributed. ▶

We now formulate the basic combinatorial

Lemma 2. *The variables* **K** *and* **Π** *have the same distribution; the same is true of the pair* **K***, **Π***.

Proof. We proceed by induction. If $n = 1$ the lemma is seen to be true by inspection of the three possibilities $x_1 > 0$, $x_1 < 0$, and $x_1 = 0$. Assume then the lemma to be true for $n - 1$ and distinguish three cases.

(*a*) Suppose $x_1 + \cdots + x_n < 0$. Then $s_n < 0$ for all permutations and since $s_0 = 0$ no maximum can occur at the last place. All four variables therefore depend only on the first $n - 1$ coordinates and so the lemma is true by the induction hypothesis.

As a preparation for the next step we require a refinement of this result. As we saw in section 2, reversing the order of $x_{i_1}, \ldots, x_{i_n}$ amounts to rotating the graph of $(s_1, \ldots, s_n)$ through 180 degrees whereby the first maximum becomes the last minimum. The distribution of the index of the last minimum is therefore the same as that of $n - \mathbf{K}$, and this is the number of non-positive partial sums. Thus the place of the last (first) *minimum* has the same distribution as the number of non-positive (negative) terms.

(*b*) Suppose $x_1 + \cdots + x_n > 0$. Then the last statement concerning the minima applies to the arrangement $(-x_1, \ldots, -x_n)$ and this is trivially equivalent to the assertion of the lemma.

(*c*) Suppose $x_1 + \cdots + x_n = 0$. That $\mathbf{K}$ and $\mathbf{\Pi}$ have the same distribution is seen as under (*a*), and for $\mathbf{K}^*$ and $\mathbf{\Pi}^*$ the conclusion follows as under (*b*). This concludes the proof. ▶

Proof *of theorem* 2. We proceed as in the proof of theorem 7.1. For fixed r consider the $n!$ permutations of $(\mathbf{X}_1, \ldots, \mathbf{X}_n)$ and define $n!$ random variables $\mathbf{Y}^{(\nu)}$ by letting $\mathbf{Y}^{(\nu)} = 1$ if there are r positive partial sums in the permutation number ν, and $\mathbf{Y}^{(\nu)} = 0$ otherwise. For reasons of symmetry the $\mathbf{Y}^{(\nu)}$ have a common distribution. If the natural ordering $(1, \ldots, n)$ counts as permutation number zero we have therefore

$$\mathbf{P}\{\mathbf{\Pi}_n = r\} = \mathbf{E}(\mathbf{Y}^{(0)}) = \frac{1}{n!}\mathbf{E}(\sum \mathbf{Y}^{(\nu)}). \tag{8.11}$$

At each sample point $\dfrac{1}{n!}\sum \mathbf{Y}^{(\nu)}$ equals the value of the variable $\mathbf{\Pi}$ in lemma 2 and so the assertion $\mathbf{P}\{\mathbf{\Pi}_n = r\} = \mathbf{P}\{\mathbf{K}_n = r\}$ is an immediate consequence of this lemma. ▶

It should be noticed that the proof does not depend on the independence of the variables $\mathbf{X}_j$ but only the identity of the joint distribution for each of the $n!$ arrangements $(\mathbf{X}_{i_1}, \ldots, \mathbf{X}_{i_n})$. In other words, *theorem* 2 *remains valid for every n-tuple of exchangeable variables* (VII,4) although naturally the common distribution of $\mathbf{K}_n$ and $\mathbf{\Pi}_n$ will depend on the nature of the joint distribution of the $\mathbf{X}_j$. As an interesting example let $\mathbf{X}_1, \mathbf{X}_2, \ldots$ be independent with a common distribution F, and put $\mathbf{Y}_k = \mathbf{X}_k - \mathbf{S}_n/n$ (where $k = 1, \ldots, n$). The variables $\mathbf{Y}_1, \ldots, \mathbf{Y}_n$ are exchangeable and their partial sums are

$$\mathbf{\Sigma}_k = \mathbf{S}_k - \frac{k}{n}\mathbf{S}_n, \qquad k = 1, \ldots, n-1. \tag{8.12}$$

With reference to the graph of $(\mathbf{S}_0, \mathbf{S}_1, \ldots, \mathbf{S}_n)$ we can describe $\mathbf{\Sigma}_k$ as the vertical distance of the vertex $\mathbf{S}_k$ from the chord joining the origin to the endpoint $(n, \mathbf{S}_n)$.

We now suppose that F is continuous (in order to avoid the necessity of distinguishing between the first and the last maximum). With probability 1 there is a unique maximum among the terms $0, \mathbf{\Sigma}_1, \ldots, \mathbf{\Sigma}_{n-1}$. To the cyclical rearrangement $(\mathbf{Y}_2, \ldots, \mathbf{Y}_n, \mathbf{Y}_1)$ there correspond the partial sums $0, \mathbf{\Sigma}_2 - \mathbf{\Sigma}_1, \ldots, \mathbf{\Sigma}_{n-1} - \mathbf{\Sigma}_1, -\mathbf{\Sigma}_1$, and it is clear that the location of the maximum has moved one place ahead in cyclical order. (If the original maximum was at the zero place then $\boldsymbol{\Sigma}_k < 0$ for $k = 1, \ldots, n-1$, and the new maximum is at the place $n - 1$.) In the n cyclical permutations the maximum is therefore assumed exactly once at each place, and its position is uniformly distributed over $0, 1, \ldots, n-1$. We have thus the following theorem due to Sparre-Andersen and related to theorem 3 of **1**; III,2 in coin tossing.

Theorem 3. *In any random walk with continuous F and for any n the number of vertices among* $\mathbf{S}_1, \ldots, \mathbf{S}_{n-1}$ *that lie above the chord from* $(0, 0)$ *to* $(n, \mathbf{S}_n)$ *is uniformly distributed over* $0, 1, \ldots, n-1$.

(The same is true of the index of the vertex with greatest maximal distance.)

9. MISCELLANEOUS COMPLEMENTS

(a) Joint Distributions

The argument leading to theorem 7.1 requires only notational changes to yield the joint distribution of the ladder variables. Adapting the notation of section 1, let I be an interval in $\overline{0, \infty}$ and denote by $H_n^{(r)}\{I\}$ *the probability that n be the* rth *ladder epoch and* $\mathbf{S}_n \in I$. Put

$$H\{I, s\} = \sum_{n=1}^{\infty} s^n H_n\{I\}, \qquad 0 \leq s \leq 1. \tag{9.1}$$

It is seen by induction for fixed s

$$H^{r\bigstar}\{I, s\} = \sum_{n=1}^{\infty} s^n H_n^{(r)}\{I\} \tag{9.2}$$

and the proof of theorem 7.1 yields without difficulty the following result due to G. Baxter.

Theorem. *For* $I \subset \overline{0, \infty}$ *and* $0 \leq s \leq 1$

$$\sum_{r=1}^{\infty} \frac{1}{r} H^{r\bigstar}\{I, s\} = \sum_{n=1}^{\infty} \frac{s^n}{n} \mathbf{P}\{\mathbf{S}_n \in I\}. \tag{9.3}$$

For $I = \overline{0, \infty}$ this reduces to theorem 7.1. A simpler and more tractable form will be derived in XVIII,3.

(b) A Mortality Interpretation for Generating Functions

The following interpretation may help intuition and simplify formal calculations. For fixed s with $0 < s < 1$ consider the *defective* random walk which at each step has probability $1 - s$ to terminate and otherwise subject to the distribution sF. Now $s^n F^{n\bigstar}\{I\}$ is the probability of a position in I at time n, the defect $1 - s^n$ representing the probability of a prior termination. All considerations carry over without change, except that *all* distributions become defective. In particular, *in our random walk with mortality*, (9.1) *is simply the first ladder height* distribution, and (9.2) the analogue to $L^{r\star}$ of sections 2–3. The generating function $\tau(s)$ now equals the probability that a ladder index will occur.

(c) The Recurrent Event

$$\{\mathbf{S}_1 \leq 0, \ldots, \mathbf{S}_{n-1} \leq 0, \mathbf{S}_n = 0\} \tag{9.4}$$

represents a return to the origin without previous visits to the right half-axis. It was considered in section 1 in the definition of weak ladder variables. Denote by ω_n the probability of the *first* occurrence of the event (9.4) at epoch n, that is,

$$\omega_n = \mathbf{P}\{\mathbf{S}_1 < 0, \ldots, \mathbf{S}_{n-1} < 0, \mathbf{S}_n = 0\}. \tag{9.5}$$

If $\omega(s) = \Sigma\, \omega_r s^r$, then ω^r is the generating function for the rth occurrence and so $1/[1 - \omega(s)]$ is the generating function for the probabilities (9.4). A simplified version of the proof of theorem 7.1 leads to the basic identity

$$\log \frac{1}{1 - \omega(s)} = \sum_{n=1}^{\infty} \frac{s^n}{n} \mathbf{P}\{\mathbf{S}_n = 0\}. \tag{9.6}$$

Comparing this with (7.3), (7.11), (7.17), etc., one sees how easy it is to pass from weak to strict ladder variables and vice versa. Formula (9.6) confirms also the remark of section 1 that the probabilities of (9.4) remain unchanged if all inequalities are reversed.

(d) Generalization to Arbitrary Intervals

The theory of section 3 generalizes with trite notational changes to the situation in which $\overline{0, \infty}$ is replaced by an arbitrary interval A, and $\overline{-\infty, 0}$ by the complement A'. In particular, the Wiener-Hopf integral equation remains unchanged. The reader is invited to work out the details; they are fully developed in XVIII,1. (See also problem 15.)

10. PROBLEMS FOR SOLUTION

1. In the binomial random walk [example (2.*b*)] let e_k be the expected number of indices $n \geq 0$ such that $\mathbf{S}_n = k$, $\mathbf{S}_1 \geq 0, \ldots, \mathbf{S}_{n-1} \geq 0$ (visits to k preceding the first negative value). Let $q \geq p$.

(*a*) Considering the case $\mathbf{S}_1 = 1$ and the epoch of the first return to 1 show that $e_k = p[e_{k-1} + e_k]$ if $k \geq 1$ and $e_0 = 1 + pe_0$. Conclude that

$$e_k = (p/q)^k q^{-1} \qquad \text{for } k = 0, 1, \ldots.$$

(*b*) For $k \geq 1$ let ψ_k be the expected number of visits to k prior to the first return to 0. Show that (trivially) $e_k = \psi_k e_0$. This gives a new proof of the surprising result in example (2.*b*).

2. *Continuation.* If $q < p$ the recursion formula becomes $e_k = p\left[e_{k-1} + \frac{q}{p} e_k\right]$ and hence $e_k = p^{-1}$ for $k = 0, 1, 2, \ldots$.

Note. The following problems (3–6) may serve as introduction to the problems of this chapter *and can be solved before studying it.* They present also examples for explicit solutions of the basic integral equations. Furthermore, they illustrate the power and elegance of generating functions [try to solve equation (1) directly!].

3. The variables $\mathbf{X}_k$ of a random walk have a common arithmetic distribution attaching probabilities $f_1, f_2, \ldots$ to the integers $1, 2, \ldots$ and q to -1 (where $q + f_1 + f_2 + \cdots = 1$). Denote by $\lambda_r (r = 1, 2, \ldots)$ the probability that the first positive term of the sequence $\mathbf{S}_1, \mathbf{S}_2, \ldots$ assumes the value r. (In other words, $\{\lambda_r\}$ is the distribution of the first ladder height.) Show that:

(*a*) The λ_r satisfy the recurrence relations

$$\lambda_r = f_r + q(\lambda_{r+1} + \lambda_1\lambda_r). \tag{1}$$

(*b*) The generating functions satisfy

$$\lambda(s) = 1 - \frac{f(s) + qs^{-1} - 1}{\lambda_1 q + qs^{-1} - 1}, \qquad 0 < s < 1. \tag{2}$$

(*c*) If $\mathbf{E}(\mathbf{X}_k) = \mu = f'(1) - q > 0$, there exists a unique root, $0 < \sigma < 1$, of the equation

$$f(s) + \frac{q}{s} = 1. \tag{3}$$

From the fact that λ must be monotone and <1 in $\overline{0, 1}$ conclude that

$$\lambda(s) = s\,\frac{\sigma}{q}\,\frac{f(s) - f(\sigma)}{s - \sigma}. \tag{4}$$

This is equivalent to

$$\lambda_r = \frac{[f_r\sigma + f_{r+1}\sigma^2 + \cdots]}{q}. \tag{5}$$

(*d*) If $\mathbf{E}(\mathbf{X}_k) < 0$ the appropriate solution is obtained letting $\lambda_1 = (1 - q)/q$ in (2). Then (4) and (5) hold with $\sigma = 1$.

4. Adapt the preceding problem to weak ladder heights. In other words, instead of λ_r consider the probability that the first non-negative term of $\mathbf{S}_1, \mathbf{S}_2, \ldots$ assumes the value r $(r = 0, 1, \ldots)$. Show that (1) and (4) are replaced by

$$\gamma_r = f_r + \frac{q}{1 - \gamma_0}\gamma_{r+1} \tag{1a}$$

$$\gamma(s) = 1 - \frac{q}{\sigma} + s\,\frac{f(s) - f(\sigma)}{s - \sigma}. \tag{4a}$$

5. In the random walk of problem 3 (but without considering the problem) let x be the probability that $\mathbf{S}_n < 0$ for some n. Show that x satisfies the equation (3) and hence $x = \sigma$.

6. *Continuation.* Show that the probability that $\mathbf{S}_n \leq 0$ for some $n > 0$ is $q + f(\sigma) = 1 - q(\sigma^{-1} - 1)$. Verify that $\lambda'(1) = \mu\sigma[q(1 - \sigma)]^{-1}$, which is a special case of relation (2.7) (or Wald's equation).

7. Derive (1.11) by straight calculation from (1.10).

8. *Hitting probabilities.* For $t \geq 0$ and $\xi > 0$ denote by $G(t, \xi)$ the probability that the *first* sum $\mathbf{S}_n$ exceeding t will be $\leq t + \xi$. Prove that G satisfies the integral equation

$$G(t, \xi) = F(t+\xi) - F(t) + \int_{-\infty}^{t+} G(t-y, \xi)\, F\{dy\}.$$

In case of non-uniqueness, G is the minimal solution. The ladder height distribution H is uniquely determined by $H(\xi) = G(0, \xi)$.

9. Let $\hbar$ be that term in the sequence $\mathbf{S}_1, \mathbf{S}_2, \ldots$ which follows the first ladder height $\mathscr{H}_1$ and is smaller than it. The distribution of $\hbar$ is given by $H \bigstar H^-$. Consider the renewal process based on $\hbar$ and conclude from the law of large numbers (as in theorem 2.2):

Theorem. *If both $\mathscr{H}_1$ and $\mathscr{H}_1^-$ are proper and have expectations then* $\mathbf{E}(\mathscr{H}_1) + \mathbf{E}(\mathscr{H}_1^-) = \mathbf{E}(\mathbf{X}_1) = 0$.

10. *Analytic proof of Wald's relation* (2.7). From (3.11) conclude

$$1 - F(x) = [1 - \rho(0)][1 - H(x)] + \int_{-\infty}^{0+} \rho\{dy\}[H(x-y) - H(x)]$$

$$F(x) = \int_{-\infty}^{x} \rho\{dy\}[1 - H(x-y)]$$

for $x > 0$ and $x < 0$, respectively. Conclude that F has a positive expectation μ iff H has a finite expectation ν and $\rho(0) < 1$. Conclude by integration over $\overline{-\infty, \infty}$ that $\mu = [1 - \rho(0)]\nu$, which is equivalent to (2.7).

11. From (3.11) conclude: If all three distributions have variances[21] then $\mathbf{E}(\mathbf{X}_1) = 0$ and $\mathrm{Var}(\mathbf{X}_1) = -\mathbf{E}(\mathscr{H}_1)\,\mathbf{E}(\mathscr{H}_1^-)$.

12. *To example* (4.*c*). If $\mu > 0$ the denominator has a positive root $s_0 < 1$, exactly $b - 1$ complex roots in $|s| < s_0$, and $a - 1$ complex roots in $|s| > 1$. The situation for $\mu < 0$ is described by changing s into $1/s$.

13. The generating function of the ascending ladder height distribution in example (4.*c*) is given by

$$\chi(s) = 1 - (1 - s)\left(1 - \frac{s}{\sigma_1}\right) \cdots \left(1 - \frac{s}{\sigma_{a-1}}\right).$$

For descending ladder heights change s/σ_k into s_k/σ.

14. *To example* (4.*c*). Suppose that the $\mathbf{X}_j$ assume the values $-2, -1, 0, 1, 2$ each with probability $\frac{1}{5}$. Show that the *ascending* ladder height distribution is given by

$$\lambda_1 = \frac{1 + \sqrt{5}}{3 + \sqrt{5}}, \qquad \lambda_2 = \frac{2}{3 + \sqrt{5}}.$$

For the *weak* heights $\bar{\lambda}_0 = \frac{1}{10}(7 - \sqrt{5})$, $\bar{\lambda}_1 = \frac{1}{10}(1 - \sqrt{5})$, $\bar{\lambda}_2 = \frac{1}{5}$.

15. In example (4.*c*) denote by $\varphi_k^{(n)}$ the probability that the first n steps do not lead out of the interval $\overline{-B, A}$ and that the nth step leads to the position

[21] For a more precise result see theorem 1 of XVIII,5 where $\mathbf{S}_N$ and $\mathbf{S}_{\tilde{N}}$ stand for $\mathscr{H}_1$ and $\mathscr{H}_1^-$.

k. (Thus $\psi_k^{(n)} = 0$ for $k > A$ and $k < -B$. As usual $\psi_k^{(0)}$ equals 1 when $k = 0$ and 0 otherwise.) Let $\psi_k = \Sigma\, \psi_k^{(n)}$ be the expected number of visits to k prior to leaving $\overline{-B, A}$. Show that

$$\psi_k = \sum_{\nu=-B}^{A} \psi_\nu f_{k-\nu} + \psi_k^{(0)}, \qquad -B \le k \le A,$$

and that for $k > A$ and $k < -B$

$$\rho_k = \sum_{\nu=-B}^{A} \psi_\nu f_{k-\nu}$$

is the probability that the *first exit* from the interval $\overline{-B, A}$ leads to the point k. [This problem is important in sequential *analysis*. It illustrates the situation described in (9.*d*).]

16. Theorem 7.2 implies that if $\mu < 0$ then $\Sigma\, n^{-1}\mathbf{P}\{\mathbf{S}_n > 0\} < \infty$. Fill in the following *direct proof*. It suffices to show (Chebyshev) that

$$\Sigma \int_{|y|>n} F\{dy\} < \infty, \qquad \Sigma \frac{1}{n^2} \int_{-n}^{n} y^2\, F\{dy\} < \infty.$$

The first is obvious. To prove the second relation write the integral as a sum of n integrals over $k-1 < |y| \le k$, $k = 1, \ldots, n$. Reverse the order of summation and conclude that the whole series is $< 2\mathbf{E}(|\mathbf{X}|)$.

17. For the coin-tossing game show that

$$\Sigma \frac{s^n}{n} \mathbf{P}\{\mathbf{S}_n = 0\} = \log \frac{2}{1 + \sqrt{1 - s^2}}\,.$$

Hint: Easy by observing that the left side may be written as the integral of $[(1-x^2)^{-\frac{1}{2}} - 1]x^{-1}$ from 0 to s.

18. Suppose that the random walk is transient, that is $U\{I\} = \sum_0^\infty F^{n\bigstar}\{I\} < \infty$ for every bounded interval. In the notation of section 3 put $\Phi = \sum_0^\infty \rho^{n\bigstar}$. Prove the truth of the renewal equation

$$U = \Phi + U \bigstar H.$$

If ψ^- is the analogue of ψ for the negative half-line then $\psi^- = (1 - \xi)\Phi$ as in (1.11).

19. Conclude that

$$U = \frac{1}{1 - \xi}\, \psi \bigstar \psi^-$$

and show this to be equivalent to the Wiener-Hopf decomposition (3.12).

20. Derive Wald's identity $\mathbf{E}(\mathscr{H}_1) = \mathbf{E}(\mathscr{T}_1)\, \mathbf{E}(\mathbf{X}_1)$ directly from the renewal equation in problem 18.

CHAPTER XIII

Laplace Transforms. Tauberian Theorems. Resolvents

The Laplace transforms are a powerful practical tool, but at the same time their theory is of intrinsic value and opens the door to other theories such as semi-groups. The theorem on completely monotone functions and the basic Tauberian theorem have rightly been considered pearls of hard analysis. (Although the present proofs are simple and elementary, the pioneer work in this direction required originality and power.) Resolvents (sections 9–10) are basic for semi-group theory.

As this chapter must cover diverse needs, a serious effort has been made to keep the various parts as independent of each other as the subject permits, and to make it possible to skip over details. Chapter XIV may serve for collateral reading and to provide examples. The remaining part of this book is entirely independent of the present chapter.

Despite the frequent appearance of regularly varying functions only the quite elementary theorem 1 of VIII,8 is used.

1. DEFINITIONS. THE CONTINUITY THEOREM

Definition 1. *If F is a proper or defective probability distribution concentrated on $\overline{0, \infty}$, the Laplace transform φ of F is the function defined for $\lambda \geq 0$ by*

$$\varphi(\lambda) = \int_0^\infty e^{-\lambda x}\, F\{dx\}. \tag{1.1}$$

Here and in the sequel it is understood that the *interval of integration is closed* (and may be replaced by $\overline{-\infty, \infty}$). Whenever we speak of the Laplace transform of a distribution F it is tacitly understood that F is concentrated on $\overline{0, \infty}$. As usual we stretch the language and speak of "the Laplace transform of the random variable **X**," meaning the transform of its distribution. With the usual notation for expectations we have then

$$(1.2) \qquad \varphi(\lambda) = \mathbf{E}(e^{-\lambda \mathbf{X}}).$$

Example. (*a*) Let $\mathbf{X}$ assume the values $0, 1, \ldots$ with probabilities $p_0, p_1, \ldots$. Then $\varphi(\lambda) = \Sigma\, p_n e^{-n\lambda}$ whereas the generating function is $P(s) = \Sigma\, p_n s^n$. Thus $\varphi(\lambda) = P(e^{-\lambda})$ and the Laplace transform differs from the generating function only by the change of variable $s = e^{-\lambda}$. This explains the close analogy between the properties of Laplace transforms and generating functions. ►

The usefulness of Laplace transforms would be limited if a distribution were not recognizable by its transform. The inversion formulas of section 4 show how to calculate F when its transform is known, but we give here a more restricted preliminary result.

Theorem 1.[1] (*Uniqueness.*) *Distinct probability distributions have distinct Laplace transforms.*

Proof. Put $y = e^{-x}$. As x goes from 0 to ∞ the variable y ranges over $\overline{0, 1}$ and a distribution function G concentrated on $\overline{0, 1}|$ may be defined by letting $G(y) = 1 - F(x)$ at points of continuity. Now $\varphi(\lambda)$ is the limit of Riemann sums $\Sigma\, e^{-\lambda x_k}[F(x_{k+1}) - F(x_k)]$ and these coincide with the Riemann sums $\Sigma\, y_k{}^\lambda[G(y_k) - G(y_{k+1})]$ for the expectation of y^λ with respect to G. Consequently $\varphi(k)$ is the kth moment of G, and so the knowledge of $\varphi(1), \varphi(2), \ldots$ determines G, and hence F. This result is stronger than the assertion of the theorem. (It is further generalized in problem 11.) ►

The following basic result is a simple consequence of theorem 1.

Theorem 2. (*Continuity theorem.*) *For $n = 1, 2, \ldots$ let F_n be a probability distribution with transform φ_n.*

If $F_n \to F$ where F is a possibly defective distribution with transform φ then $\varphi_n(\lambda) \to \varphi(\lambda)$ for $\lambda > 0$.

Conversely, if the sequence $\{\varphi_n(\lambda)\}$ converges for each $\lambda > 0$ to a limit $\varphi(\lambda)$, then φ is the transform of a possibly defective distribution F, and $F_n \to F$.

The limit F is not defective iff $\varphi(\lambda) \to 1$ as $\lambda \to 0$.

Proof. The first part is contained in the basic convergence theorem of VIII,1. For the second part we use the selection theorem 1 of VIII,6. Let $\{F_{n_k}\}$ be a subsequence converging to the possibly defective distribution

[1] This theorem is an immediate consequence of VII,(6.4), which is derived afresh as (4.4) below.

F. If $\varphi_n(\lambda) \to \varphi(\lambda)$ then F is the unique distribution with Laplace transform φ, and so all convergent subsequences converge to the same limit F. This implies the convergence of F_n to F. The last assertion of the theorem is clear by inspection of (1.1). ►

For clarity of exposition we shall as far as possible reserve the letter F for probability distributions, but instead of (1.1) we may consider more general integrals of the form

$$\omega(\lambda) = \int_0^\infty e^{-\lambda x}\, U\{dx\} \tag{1.3}$$

where U is a measure. An important special case are integrals of the form

$$\omega(\lambda) = \int_0^\infty e^{-\lambda x}\, u(x)\, dx \tag{1.4}$$

where $u \geq 0$. This integral converges for all $\lambda \geq 0$ if u is integrable over $\overline{0, \infty}$, but for $\lambda > 0$ it may converge also for non-integrable u.

Examples. (*b*) If $u(x) = x^a$ with $a \geq 0$ then $\omega(\lambda) = \Gamma(a+1)/\lambda^{a+1}$ for all $\lambda > 0$.

(*c*) If $u(x) = e^{ax}$ then $\omega(\lambda) = 1/(\lambda - a)$ for $\lambda > a > 0$, but the integral (1.4) diverges for $\lambda \leq a$.

(*d*) If $u(x) = e^{x^2}$ the integral (1.4) diverges everywhere. ►

We shall be interested principally in measures U derived by simple operations from probability distributions, and the integral in (1.3) will generally converge for all $\lambda > 0$. However, nothing is gained by excluding measures for which convergence takes place only for *some* λ. Now $\omega(a) < \infty$ implies $\omega(\lambda) < \infty$ for all $\lambda > a$, and so the values of λ for which the integral in (1.3) converges fill an interval $\overline{a, \infty}$.

Definition 2. *Let U be a measure concentrated on $\overline{0, \infty}$. If the integral in* (1.3) *converges for $\lambda > a$ then the function ω defined for $\lambda > a$ is called Laplace transform of U.*

If U has a density u, the Laplace transform (1.4) *of U is also called the ordinary Laplace transform of u.*

The last convention is introduced merely for convenience. To be systematic one should consider more general integrals of the form

$$\int_0^\infty e^{-\lambda x}\, v(x)\, U\{dx\} \tag{1.5}$$

and call them "Laplace transform of v with respect to the measure U." Then (1.4) would be the "transform of u with respect to Lebesgue measure" (or ordinary length). This would have the theoretical advantage that one could consider functions u and v of variable signs. For the purposes of this book it is simplest and least confusing to associate Laplace transforms only with measures, and we shall do so.[2]

If U is a measure such that the integral in (1.3) converges for $\lambda = a$, then for all $\lambda > 0$

$$\omega(\lambda+a) = \int_0^\infty e^{-\lambda x} \cdot e^{-ax}\, U\{dx\} \tag{1.6}$$

is the Laplace transform of the bounded measure $U^{\#}\{dx\} = e^{-ax}\, U\{dx\}$, and $\omega(\lambda+a)/\omega(a)$ is the transform of a *probability* distribution. In this way every theorem concerning transforms of probability distributions automatically generalizes to a wider class of measures. Because the new transform $\omega(\lambda+a)$ is obtained by translation from ω we shall refer to this extremely useful method as the *translation principle*. For example, since U is uniquely determined by $U^{\#}$, and $U^{\#}$ by $\omega(\lambda+a)$ for $\lambda > 0$, we can rephrase theorem 1 as follows.

Theorem 1a. *A measure is uniquely determined by the values of its Laplace transform in some interval* $\overline{a, \infty}$.

Theorem 2a. (*Extended continuity theorem.*) *For* $n = 1, 2, \ldots$ *let* U_n *be a measure with Laplace transform* ω_n. *If* $\omega_n(\lambda) \to \omega(\lambda)$ *for* $\lambda > a$, *then* ω *is the Laplace transform of a measure* U *and*[3] $U_n \to U$.

Conversely, if $U_n \to U$ *and the sequence* $\{\omega_n(a)\}$ *is bounded, then* $\omega_n(\lambda) \to \omega(\lambda)$ *for* $\lambda > a$.

Proof. For fixed $\lambda_0 > a$ the function $\omega_n(\lambda+\lambda_0)/\omega_n(\lambda_0)$ is the Laplace transform of the probability distribution $U_n^{\#}\{dx\} = \dfrac{1}{\omega_n(\lambda_0)}\, e^{-\lambda_0 x}\, U_n\{dx\}$. The assertion now follows from theorem 2 applied to the sequence $\{U_n^{\#}\}$. ►

The following example explains the nature of the condition that $\{\omega_n(a)\}$ remain bounded.

Example. (*e*) Let U_n attach weight e^{n^2} to the point n, and zero to the complement. Since $U_n\{\overline{0, n}\} = 0$ we have $U_n \to 0$, but $\omega_n(\lambda) = e^{n(n-\lambda)} \to \infty$ for all $\lambda > 0$. ►

[2] The terminology is not well established, and in the literature the term "Laplace transform of F" may refer either to (1.1) or to (2.7). We would describe (2.7) as the "ordinary Laplace transform of the distribution function F," but texts treating principally such transforms would drop the determinative "ordinary." To avoid ambiguities in such cases the transform (1.1) is then called the *Laplace-Stieltjes* transform.

[3] Recall from VIII,1 that $U_n \to U$ iff $U_n\{I\} \to U\{I\}$ for each *bounded* interval of continuity of U.

One speaks sometimes of the *bilateral transform* of a distribution F with two tails, namely

$$(1.7)\qquad \varphi(\lambda) = \int_{-\infty}^{+\infty} e^{-\lambda x}\, F\{dx\},$$

but this function need not exist for any $\lambda \neq 0$. If it exists, $\varphi(-\lambda)$ is often called the *moment generating function*, but in reality it is the generating function of the sequence $\{\mu_n/n!\}$ where μ_n is the nth moment.

2. ELEMENTARY PROPERTIES

In this section we list the most frequently used properties of the Laplace transforms; the parallel to generating functions is conspicuous.

(i) **Convolutions.** Let F and G be probability distributions and U their convolution, that is,

$$(2.1)\qquad U(x) = \int_0^x G(x-y)\, F\{dy\}.$$

The corresponding Laplace transforms obey the *multiplication rule*

$$(2.2)\qquad \omega = \varphi\gamma.$$

This is equivalent to the assertion that for independent random variables $\mathbf{E}(e^{-\lambda(\mathbf{X}+\mathbf{Y})}) = \mathbf{E}(e^{-\lambda\mathbf{X}})\,\mathbf{E}(e^{-\lambda\mathbf{Y}})$, which is a special case of the multiplication rule for expectations.[4]

More generally, consider two arbitrary measures F and G concentrated on $\overline{0, \infty}$ and such that their Laplace transforms φ and γ exist for $\lambda \geq a$. The convolution (2.1) makes sense and we show that *the multiplication rule* (2.2) *remains valid.* To see this we introduce the *bounded* measure $F^{\#}\{dx\} = e^{-ax}\, F\{dx\}$ with Laplace transform $\varphi(\lambda+a)$ and define $G^{\#}$ and $U^{\#}$ similarly. Multiplying (2.1) by e^{-ax} it is seen that the convolution of $F^{\#}$ and $G^{\#}$ equals $U^{\#}$, and so $\omega(\lambda+a) = \varphi(\lambda+a)\gamma\,(\lambda+a)$, which is the same as (2.2).

In terms of densities (2.1) takes on the form

$$(2.3)\qquad u(x) = \int_0^x g(x-y)\, f(y)\, dy$$

and so the multiplication rule (2.2) holds for ordinary transforms of non-negative functions. (See problem 1.)

Examples. (*a*) *Gamma distributions.* The density $f_\alpha(x) = \dfrac{x^{\alpha-1}}{\Gamma(\alpha)}\, e^{-x}$ has the transform $\varphi_\alpha(\lambda) = (1+\lambda)^{-\alpha}$. The familiar convolution rule $f_\alpha * f_\beta = f_{\alpha+\beta}$ is mirrored in the obvious relation $\varphi_\alpha\varphi_\beta = \varphi_{\alpha+\beta}$.

[4] The converse is false: two variables may be dependent and yet such that the distribution of their sum is given by the convolution formula. [See II,(4.*e*) and problem 1 of III,9.]

(*b*) *Powers.* Put $u_\alpha(x) = x^{\alpha-1}$. The ordinary Laplace transform of u_α is $\omega_\alpha(\lambda) = \lambda^{-\alpha}\,\Gamma(\alpha)$. It follows that the convolution (2.3) of u_α and u_β is given by

$$u(x) = \frac{\Gamma(\alpha)\,\Gamma(\beta)}{\Gamma(\alpha+\beta)}\, x^{\alpha+\beta-1}. \tag{2.4}$$

Note that this result follows from that in example (*a*) by means of the translation principle.

(*c*) *If* $a > 0$ *then* $e^{-a\lambda}\omega(\lambda)$ *is the Laplace transform of the measure with distribution function* $U(x-a)$ assigning the value $U\{I-a\}$ to the interval I. This is obvious from the definition, but may be considered also as a special case of the convolution theorem inasmuch as $e^{-a\lambda}$ is the transform of the distribution concentrated at the point a. ►

(ii) **Derivatives and moments.** If F is a probability distribution and φ its Laplace transform (1.1), then φ *possesses derivatives of all orders given by*

$$(-1)^n\,\varphi^{(n)}(\lambda) = \int_0^\infty e^{-\lambda x} x^n\, F\{dx\} \tag{2.5}$$

(as always, $\lambda > 0$). The differentiation under the integral is permissible since the new integrand is bounded and continuous.

It follows in particular that F *possesses a finite* nth *moment iff a finite limit* $\varphi^{(n)}(0)$ *exists.* For a random variable $\mathbf{X}$ we can therefore write

$$\mathbf{E}(\mathbf{X}) = -\varphi'(0), \qquad \mathbf{E}(\mathbf{X}^2) = \varphi''(0) \tag{2.6}$$

with the obvious conventions in case of divergence. The differentiation rule (2.5) remains valid for arbitrary measures F.

(iii) **Integration by parts** leads from (1.1) to

$$\int_0^\infty e^{-\lambda x}\, F(x)\, dx = \frac{\varphi(\lambda)}{\lambda}, \qquad \lambda > 0. \tag{2.7}$$

For probability distributions it is sometimes preferable to rewrite (2.7) in terms of the tail

$$\int_0^\infty e^{-\lambda x}[1 - F(x)]\, dx = \frac{1-\varphi(\lambda)}{\lambda}. \tag{2.8}$$

This corresponds to formula **1**; XI,(1.6) for generating functions.

(iv) **Change of scale.** From (1.2) we have $\mathbf{E}(e^{-a\lambda\mathbf{X}}) = \varphi(a\lambda)$ for each fixed $a > 0$, and so $\varphi(a\lambda)$ *is the transform of the distribution* $F\{dx/a\}$ [with distribution function $F(x/a)$]. This relation is in constant use.

Example. (*d*) *Law of large numbers.* Let $\mathbf{X}_1, \mathbf{X}_2, \ldots$ be independent random variables with a common Laplace transform φ. Suppose $\mathbf{E}(\mathbf{X}_j) = \mu$.

The Laplace transform of the sum $\mathbf{X}_1 + \cdots + \mathbf{X}_n$ is φ^n, and hence the transform of the average $[\mathbf{X}_1 + \cdots + \mathbf{X}_n]/n$ is given by $\varphi^n(\lambda/n)$. Near the origin $\varphi(\lambda) = 1 - \mu\lambda + o(\lambda)$ [see (2.6)] and so as $n \to \infty$

$$\lim \varphi^n\left(\frac{\lambda}{n}\right) = \lim\left(1 - \frac{\mu\lambda}{n}\right)^n = e^{-\mu\lambda}. \tag{2.9}$$

But $e^{-\mu\lambda}$ is the transform of the distribution concentrated at μ, and so the distribution of $[\mathbf{X}_1 + \cdots + \mathbf{X}_n]/n$ tends to this limit. This is the weak law of large numbers in the Khintchine version, which does not require the existence of a variance. True, the proof is limited to positive variables, but it illustrates the elegance of Laplace transform methods. ▶

3. EXAMPLES

(*a*) *Uniform distribution.* Let F stand for the uniform distribution concentrated on $\overline{0, 1}$. Its Laplace transform is given by $\varphi(\lambda) = (1 - e^{-\lambda})/\lambda$ and hence the n-fold convolution $F^{n\star}$ has the transform

$$\varphi^n(\lambda) = \sum_{k=0}^{n}(-1)^k\binom{n}{k}e^{-\lambda k}\lambda^{-n}. \tag{3.1}$$

As λ^{-n} is the transform corresponding to $U(x) = x^n/n!$ example (2.*c*) shows that $e^{-k\lambda}\lambda^{-n}$ corresponds to $(x-k)_+{}^n/n!$ where x_+ denotes the function that equals 0 for $x \leq 0$ and x for $x \geq 0$. Thus

$$F^{n\star}(x) = \frac{1}{n!}\sum_{k=0}^{n}(-1)^k\binom{n}{k}(x - k)_+{}^n. \tag{3.2}$$

This formula was derived by direct calculation in I,(9.5) and by a passage to the limit in problem 20 of **1**; XI.

(*b*) *Stable distributions with exponent* $\frac{1}{2}$. The distribution function

$$G(x) = 2[1 - \mathfrak{N}(1/\sqrt{x})], \qquad x > 0 \tag{3.3}$$

(where $\mathfrak{N}$ is the standard normal distribution) occurred in the limit theorem 2 of **1**; III,6, and we now use this result to calculate the Laplace transform γ of G. Consider a simple symmetric random walk (coin tossing), and denote by $\mathbf{T}$ the epoch of the first return to the origin. The cited limit theorem states that G is the limit distribution of the normalized sums $\mathbf{S}_n = (\mathbf{T}_1 + \cdots + \mathbf{T}_n)/n^2$, where $\mathbf{T}_1, \mathbf{T}_2, \ldots$ are independent random variables distributed like $\mathbf{T}$. According to **1**; XI,(3.11) the generating function of $\mathbf{T}$ is given by $f(s) = 1 - \sqrt{1-s^2}$, and therefore $\mathbf{S}_n$ has the Laplace transform $\omega_n(\lambda) = f^n(e^{-\lambda/n^2})$. As $s \to 1$ obviously $\log f(s) \sim -\sqrt{2s}$

and hence $\log \omega_n(\lambda) \to -\sqrt{2\lambda}$ as $n \to \infty$. Accordingly, *the Laplace transform of* G *is* $\gamma(\lambda) = e^{-\sqrt{2\lambda}}$. This result can be verified by elementary, but tedious, calculations.

We have mentioned several times that G *is a stable distribution*, but again the direct computational verification is laborious. Now obviously $\gamma^n(\lambda) = \gamma(n^2\lambda)$ which is the same as $G^{n\bigstar}(x) = G(n^{-2}x)$ and proves the stability without effort.

(*c*) *Power series and mixtures.* Let F be a probability distribution with Laplace transform $\varphi(\lambda)$. We have repeatedly encountered distributions of the form

$$G = \sum_{k=0}^{\infty} p_k F^{n\bigstar} \tag{3.4}$$

where $\{p_k\}$ is a probability distribution. If $P(s) = \Sigma\, p_k s^k$ stands for the generating function of $\{p_k\}$ the Laplace transform of G is obviously given by

$$\gamma(\lambda) = P(\varphi(\lambda)). \tag{3.5}$$

This principle can be extended to arbitrary power series with positive coefficients. We turn to specific applications.

(*d*) *Bessel function densities.* In example II,(7.*c*) we saw that for $r = 1, 2, \ldots$ the density[5]

$$v_r(x) = e^{-x} \frac{r}{x} I_r(x) \tag{3.6}$$

corresponds to a distribution of the form (3.4) where F is exponential with $\varphi(\lambda) = 1/(\lambda + 1)$, and $\{p_k\}$ is the distribution of the first-passage epoch through the point $r > 0$ in an ordinary symmetric random walk. The generating function of this distribution is

$$P(s) = \left(\frac{1 - \sqrt{1 - s^2}}{s}\right)^r \tag{3.7}$$

[see **1**; XI,(3.4)]. Substituting $s = (1 + \lambda)^{-1}$ we conclude that *the ordinary Laplace transform of the probability density* (3.6) *is given by*

$$[\lambda + 1 - \sqrt{(\lambda + 1)^2 - 1}\,]^r. \tag{3.8}$$

That v_r *is a probability density and* (3.8) *its transform* has been proved only for $r = 1, 2, \ldots$. However, the statement is true[6] for *all* $r > 0$. It is of probabilistic interest because it implies the convolution formula $v_r * v_s = v_{r+s}$ and thus the *infinite divisibility of* v_r. (See section 7.)

[5] I_r is the Bessel function defined in II,(7.1).

[6] This result is due to H. Weber. An elementary proof is forthcoming in J. Soc. Industr. Appl. Math., vol. 14 (1966).

(*e*) *Another Bessel density.* In (3.4) choose for F the exponential distribution with $\varphi(\lambda) = 1/(\lambda+1)$ and for $\{p_k\}$ the Poisson distribution with $P(s) = e^{-t+ts}$. It is easy to calculate G explicitly, but fortunately this task was already accomplished in example II,(7.*a*). We saw there that the density

$$w_\rho(x) = e^{-t-x}\sqrt{\left(\frac{x}{t}\right)^\rho}\, I_\rho(2\sqrt{tx}) \tag{3.9}$$

defined in II,(7.2) is the convolution of our distribution G with a gamma density $f_{1,\rho+1}$. It follows that the ordinary Laplace transform of w_ρ is the product of our γ with the transform of $f_{1,\rho+1}$, namely $(\lambda+1)^{\rho+1}$. Accordingly, *the probability density* (3.9) *has the Laplace transform*

$$\frac{1}{(\lambda+1)^{\rho+1}}\, e^{-t+t/(\lambda+1)}. \tag{3.10}$$

For $t = 1$ we see using the translation rule (1.6) that $\sqrt{x^\rho}\, I_\rho(2\sqrt{x})$ *has the ordinary transform* $\lambda^{-\rho-1}e^{1/\lambda}$.

4. COMPLETELY MONOTONE FUNCTIONS. INVERSION FORMULAS

As we saw in VII,2 a function f in $\overline{0,1}$ is a generating function of a positive sequence $\{f_n\}$ iff f is absolutely monotone, that is, if f possesses positive derivatives $f^{(n)}$ of all orders. An analogous theorem holds for Laplace transforms, except that now the derivatives alternate in sign.

Definition 1. *A function φ on $\overline{0,\infty}$ is completely monotone if it possesses derivatives $\varphi^{(n)}$ of all orders and*

$$(-1)^n\varphi^{(n)}(\lambda) \geq 0, \qquad \lambda > 0. \tag{4.1}$$

As $\lambda \to 0$ the values $\varphi^{(n)}(\lambda)$ approach finite or infinite limits which we denote by $\varphi^{(n)}(0)$. Typical examples are $1/\lambda$ and $1/(1+\lambda)$.

The following beautiful theorem due to S. Bernstein (1928) was the starting point of much research, and the proof has been simplified by stages.[7]

Theorem 1. *A function φ on $\overline{0,\infty}$ is the Laplace transform of a probability distribution F, iff it is completely monotone, and $\varphi(0) = 1$.*

This theorem may be restated in the fully equivalent form

[7] See also problems 10 and 11 for further results.

Theorem 1a. *The function* φ *on* $\overline{0, \infty}$ *is completely monotone iff it is of the form*

$$\varphi(\lambda) = \int_0^\infty e^{-\lambda x}\, F\{dx\}, \qquad \lambda > 0, \tag{4.2}$$

where F *is not a necessarily finite measure on* $\overline{|0, \infty}$.

(By our initial convention the interval of integration is *closed*: a possible atom of F at the origin has the effect that $\varphi(\infty) > 0$.)

The following proof applies directly to the apparently more general theorem 1*a*, but the reader should verify for himself by an appeal to the translation principle embodied in (1.6) that the second version is really a consequence of the first.

Proof. The necessity of the condition follows by formal differentiation as in (2.5). Assuming φ to be completely monotone consider $\varphi(a-as)$ for fixed $a > 0$ and $0 < s < 1$ as a function of s. Its derivatives are evidently positive and by theorem 3 of VII,2 the Taylor expansion

$$\varphi(a-as) = \sum_{n=0}^{\infty} \frac{(-a)^n \varphi^{(n)}(a)}{n!}\, s^n \tag{4.3}$$

represents the generating function of an arithmetic measure concentrated on the set of points $0, 1, 2, \ldots$. Its Laplace transform is obtained by changing s into $e^{-\lambda}$ and hence $\varphi_a(\lambda) = \varphi(a-ae^{-\lambda/a})$ is the Laplace transform of a measure F_a. Now $\varphi_a(\lambda) \to \varphi(\lambda)$ as $a \to \infty$ and by the extended continuity theorem the limit of Laplace transforms of F_a is again the Laplace transform of a measure F. ►

This concludes the proof, but we have at the same time discovered that $F = \lim F_a$ where F_a is the arithmetic distribution attributing weight $(-a)^n\, \varphi^{(n)}(a)/n!$ to the point n/a. Consequently we have

Theorem 2. (*Inversion formula.*) *If* (4.2) *holds for* $\lambda > 0$, *then at all points of continuity*[8]

$$F(x) = \lim_{a\to\infty} \sum_{n \le ax} \frac{(-a)^n}{n!}\, \varphi^{(n)}(a). \tag{4.4}$$

This formula is of great theoretical interest and permits various conclusions. The following boundedness criterion may serve as an example of particular interest for semi-group theory. [See problem 9.]

[8] The inversion formula (4.4) was derived in VII,(6.4) as a direct consequence of the law of large numbers. In VII,(6.6) we have an analogous *inversion formula for integrals of the form* (4.5) *with continuous* f (not necessarily positive).

Corollary. *For* φ *to be of the form*

$$\varphi(\lambda) = \int_0^\infty e^{-\lambda x} f(x)\, dx \qquad \textit{where} \quad 0 \le f \le C \tag{4.5}$$

it is necessary and sufficient that

$$0 \le \frac{(-a)^n \varphi^{(n)}(a)}{n!} \le \frac{C}{a} \tag{4.6}$$

for all $a > 0$.

Proof. Differentiating (4.5) under the integral we get (4.6) [see (2.5)]. Conversely, (4.6) implies that φ is completely monotone and hence the transform of a measure F. From (4.4) we conclude that

$$F(x_2) - F(x)_1 \le C(x_2 - x_1)$$

for any pair $x_1 < x_2$. This means that F has bounded difference ratios and hence F is the integral of a function $f \le C$ (see V,3). ►

Theorem 1 leads to simple *tests* that a given function is the Laplace transform of a probability distribution. The standard technique is illustrated by the proof of

Criterion 1. *If* φ *and* ψ *are completely monotone so is their product* $\varphi\psi$.

Proof. We show by induction that the derivatives of $\varphi\psi$ alternate in sign. Assume that for *every* pair φ, ψ of completely monotone functions the first n derivatives of $\varphi\psi$ alternate in sign. As $-\varphi'$ and $-\psi'$ are completely monotone the induction hypothesis applies to the products $-\varphi'\psi$ and $-\varphi\psi'$, and we conclude from $-(\varphi\psi)' = -\varphi'\psi - \varphi\psi'$ that in fact the first $n + 1$ derivatives of $\varphi\psi$ alternate in sign. As the hypothesis is trivially true for $n = 1$ the criterion is proved. ►

The same proof yields the useful

Criterion 2. *If* φ *is completely monotone and* ψ *a positive function with a completely monotone derivative then* $\varphi(\psi)$ *is completely monotone.* (*In particular,* $e^{-\psi}$ *is completely monotone.*)

Typical applications are given in section 6 and in the following example, which occurs frequently in the literature with unnecessary complications.

Example. (*a*) *An equation occurring in branching processes.* Let φ be the Laplace transform of a probability distribution F with expectation $0 < \mu \le \infty$, and let $c > 0$. We prove that *the equation*

$$\beta(\lambda) = \varphi(\lambda + c - c\beta(\lambda)) \tag{4.7}$$

has a unique root $\beta(\lambda) \leq 1$ *and* β *is the Laplace transform of a distribution* B *which is proper iff* $\mu c \leq 1$, *defective otherwise.*

Proof. Consider the equation

$$\varphi(\lambda+c-cs) - s = 0 \tag{4.8}$$

for fixed $\lambda > 0$ and $0 \leq s \leq 1$. The left side is a convex function which assumes a negative value at $s = 1$ and a positive value at $s = 0$. It follows that there exists a unique root.

To prove that the root $\beta(\lambda)$ is a Laplace transform put $\beta_0 = 0$ and recursively $\beta_{n+1} = \varphi(\lambda+c-c\beta_n)$. Then $\beta_0 \leq \beta_1 \leq 1$ and since φ is decreasing this implies $\beta_1 \leq \beta_2 \leq 1$, and by induction $\beta_n \leq \beta_{n+1} \leq 1$. The limit of the bounded monotone sequence $\{\beta_n\}$ satisfies (4.7) and hence $\beta = \lim \beta_n$. Now $\beta_1(\lambda) = \varphi(\lambda+c)$ is completely monotone and criterion 2 shows recursively that $\beta_2, \beta_3, \ldots$ are completely monotone. By the continuity theorem the same is true of the limit β, and it remains only to decide whether or not $\beta(0) = 1$. By construction $s = \beta(0)$ is the *smallest* root of (4.8) for $\lambda = 0$. Now $s = 1$ is a root, and the convexity of the graph of $\varphi(c-cs)$ shows that a second root $s < 1$ exists iff the slope at $s = 1$ exceeds unity, that is, iff $-c\varphi'(0) > 1$. Only in this case is β the transform of a defective distribution, and this completes the proof. (See XIV,4 for applications and references.) ▶

5. TAUBERIAN THEOREMS

Let U be a measure concentrated on $\overline{0, \infty}$ and such that its Laplace transform

$$\omega(\lambda) = \int_0^\infty e^{-\lambda x}\, U\{dx\} \tag{5.1}$$

exists for $\lambda > 0$. It will be convenient to describe the measure U in terms of its improper distribution function defined for $x \geq 0$ by $U\{\overline{0, x}|\}$. We shall see that under fairly general conditions the behavior of ω near the origin uniquely determines the asymptotic behavior of $U(x)$ as $x \to \infty$. Any such relation between $\omega(\lambda)$ and $U(x)$ is called a Tauberian theorem. The simplest special case is represented by the trite remark that the measure U is finite iff $\omega(\lambda)$ tends to a finite limit $\omega(0)$ as $\lambda \to 0$; in this case $U(\infty) = \omega(0)$. Even this simple special case permits various conclusions.

Example. (*a*) Let F be a probability distribution with Laplace transform $\varphi(\lambda)$. We know from (2.8) that $\omega(\lambda) = \dfrac{1 - \varphi(\lambda)}{\lambda}$ is the Laplace transform of the measure $U\{dx\} = [1 - F(x)]\, dx$. Here $\omega(0) = -\varphi'(0)$ and so the relation $\omega(0) = U(\infty)$ states that a finite derivative $\varphi'(0)$ exists iff $1 - F$ is integrable over $\overline{0, \infty}$ or, what amounts to the same, iff F has a finite expectation. This result is contained in (2.6) and the point of the present argument is merely to show that the differentiation formulas (2.5) are related to Tauberian theorems. ▶

To avoid unsightly formulas involving reciprocals we introduce two positive variables t and τ related by

$$t\tau = 1. \tag{5.2}$$

Then $\tau \to 0$ when $t \to \infty$.

To understand the background of the Tauberian theorems note that for fixed t the change of variables $x = ty$ in (5.1) shows that $\omega(\tau\lambda)$ is the Laplace transform corresponding to the improper distribution function $U(ty)$. Since ω decreases it is possible to find a sequence $\tau_1, \tau_2, \ldots \to 0$ such that as τ runs through it

$$\frac{\omega(\tau\lambda)}{\omega(\tau)} \to \gamma(\lambda) \tag{5.3}$$

with $\gamma(\lambda)$ finite for all $\lambda > 1$. By the extended continuity theorem the limit γ is the Laplace transform of a measure G and as t runs through the reciprocals $t_k = 1/\tau_k$

$$\frac{U(tx)}{\omega(\tau)} \to G(x) \tag{5.4}$$

at all points of continuity of G. For fixed x it is seen that the asymptotic behavior of $U(t)$ as $t \to \infty$ is intimately connected with the behavior of $\omega(t^{-1})$.

In principle we could formulate this fact as an all-embracing Tauberian theorem, but it would be too clumsy for practical use. To achieve reasonable simplicity we consider only the case where (5.3) is valid for *any* approach $\tau \to 0$, that is, when ω varies regularly at 0. The elementary lemma[9] of VIII,8 states that the limit γ is necessarily of the form $\gamma(\lambda) = \lambda^{-\rho}$ where $\rho \geq 0$ is a constant. Then $G(x) = \dfrac{x^\rho}{\Gamma(\rho+1)}$, and we have shown that

$$\frac{\omega(\tau\lambda)}{\omega(\tau)} \to \frac{1}{\lambda^\rho}, \qquad \tau \to 0 \tag{5.5}$$

[9] This lemma is used *only* to justify the otherwise artificial form of the relations (5.5) and (5.7). The theory of regular variation is *not* used in this section [except for the side remark that (5.17) implies (5.16)].

implies

$$\frac{U(tx)}{\omega(\tau)} \to \frac{x^\rho}{\Gamma(\rho+1)}, \tag{5.6}$$

which in turn obviously implies

$$\frac{U(tx)}{U(t)} \to x^\rho, \qquad t \to \infty. \tag{5.7}$$

Thus U varies regularly at ∞, and the exponents for ω and U are the same in absolute value. Letting $x = 1$ in (5.6) we see that

$$\omega(\tau) \sim U(t)\,\Gamma(\rho+1). \tag{5.8}$$

This is the desired Tauberian theorem. We state it together with its converse.

Theorem 1. *For fixed* $0 \leq \rho < \infty$ *each of the relations* (5.5)–(5.7) *implies the other two.*

Proof. We know already that (5.5) implies (5.6) and (5.6) implies (5.7). To show that (5.7) implies (5.5) we repeat the preceding argument. To $U(tx)$ there corresponds the Laplace transform $\omega(\tau\lambda)$ and so (5.7) leads to

$$\frac{\omega(\tau\lambda)}{U(t)} \to \frac{\Gamma(\rho+1)}{\lambda^\rho} \tag{5.9}$$

provided the extended continuity theorem is applicable, that is, *provided* the left-side remains bounded for some λ. Now (5.9) trivially implies (5.5), and to prove the theorem it suffices to verify that $\omega(\tau)/U(t)$ remains bounded.

On partitioning the domain of integration by the points $t, 2t, 4t, \ldots$ it is clear that

$$\omega(\tau) \leq \sum_0^\infty e^{-2^{n-1}}\, U(2^n t). \tag{5.10}$$

In view of (5.7) there exists a t_0 such that $U(2t) < 2^{\rho+1}\, U(t)$ for $t > t_0$. Repeated application of this inequality yields

$$\frac{\omega(\tau)}{U(t)} \leq \sum_0^\infty 2^{n(\rho+1)} e^{-2^{n-1}} \tag{5.11}$$

and so the left side indeed remains bounded as $t \to \infty$. ►

Example. (*b*) $U(x) \sim \log^2 x$ as $x \to \infty$ iff $\omega(\lambda) \sim \log^2 \lambda$ as $\lambda \to 0$. Similarly $U(x) \sim \sqrt{x}$ iff $\omega(\lambda) \sim \frac{1}{2}\sqrt{\frac{\pi}{\lambda}}$. ►

It is sometimes useful to know to what extent the theorem remains valid in the limit $\rho \to \infty$. We state the result in the form of a

Corollary. *If for some $a > 1$ as $t \to \infty$*

$$\text{(5.12)} \qquad \textit{either} \quad \frac{\omega(\tau a)}{\omega(\tau)} \to 0 \quad \textit{or} \quad \frac{U(ta)}{U(t)} \to \infty$$

then

$$\text{(5.13)} \qquad \frac{U(t)}{\omega(\tau)} \to 0.$$

Proof. If the first relation in (5.12) holds then $\dfrac{\omega(\tau\lambda)}{\omega(\tau)} \to 0$ for $\lambda > a$ and by the extended continuity theorem $\dfrac{U(tx)}{\omega(\tau)} \to 0$ for all $x > 0$. Since $\omega(\tau) \geq e^{-a}\, U(ta)$, the second relation in (5.12) implies (5.13). ►

In applications it is more convenient to express theorem 1 in terms of slow variation. We recall that a positive function L defined on $\overline{0, \infty}$ *varies slowly at* ∞ if for every fixed x

$$\text{(5.14)} \qquad \frac{L(tx)}{L(t)} \to 1, \qquad t \to \infty.$$

L varies slowly at 0 if this relation holds as $t \to 0$, that is, if $L(1/x)$ varies slowly at ∞. Evidently U is of the form (5.7) iff $U(x)/x^\rho$ varies slowly at ∞ and similarly (5.5) holds iff $\lambda^\rho\omega(\lambda)$ varies slowly at 0. Consequently theorem 1 may be rephrased as follows.

Theorem 2. *If L is slowly varying at infinity and $0 \leq \rho < \infty$, then each of the relations*

$$\text{(5.15)} \qquad \omega(\tau) \sim \tau^{-\rho}\, L\!\left(\frac{1}{\tau}\right), \qquad \tau \to 0,$$

and

$$\text{(5.16)} \qquad U(t) \sim \frac{1}{\Gamma(\rho+1)}\, t^\rho\, L(t), \qquad t \to \infty$$

implies the other.

Theorem 2 has a glorious history. The implication (5.16) → (5.15) (from the measure to the transform) is called an Abelian theorem; the converse (5.15) → (5.16) (from transform to measure), a Tauberian theorem. In the usual setup, the two theorems are entirely separated, the Tauberian part causing the trouble. In a famous paper Hardy and Littlewood treated the case $\omega(\lambda) \sim \lambda^{-\rho}$ by difficult calculations. In 1930, J. Karamata created a sensation by a simplified proof for this special case. (This proof is still found in texts on complex variables and Laplace transforms.) Soon afterwards he introduced the class of regularly varying functions and proved theorem 2; the proof was too complicated for textbooks, however. The notion of slow variation was introduced by R. Schmidt about 1925 in the same connection. Our proof simplifies and unifies the theory and leads to the little-known, but useful, corollary.

A great advantage of our proof is that it applies without change when the roles of infinity and zero are interchanged, that is, if $\tau \to \infty$ while $t \to 0$. In this way we get the dual theorem connecting the behavior of ω at infinity with that of U at the origin. [It will not be used in this book except to derive (6.2).]

Theorem 3. *The last two theorems and the corollary remain valid when the roles of the origin and infinity are interchanged, that is, for* $\tau \to \infty$ *and* $t \to 0$.

Theorem 2 represents the main result of this section, but for completeness we derive two useful complements. First of all, when U has a density $U' = u$ it is desirable to obtain estimates for u. Thus, in example (*a*) we are concerned with the tail $u = 1 - F$ and estimates for its integral U are a poor substitute. In the greatest generality trouble arises because a well-behaved function U may have an ill-behaved density u. Fortunately it is easy to amend theorem 2 when the density u is *monotone*, as is the case in typical probabilistic applications.

Lemma. *Suppose that* U *has a monotone density* u. *If* (5.16) *holds with* $0 < \rho < \infty$, *then*

$$u(t) \sim \frac{1}{\Gamma(\rho)} t^{\rho-1} L(t), \qquad t \to \infty. \tag{5.17}$$

[Conversely, (5.17) implies (5.16) even if u is not monotone. This is contained in VIII,(9.5) with $Z = u$ and $p = 0$.]

Proof. For $0 < a < b$

$$\frac{U(tb) - U(ta)}{U(t)} = \int_a^b \frac{u(ty)t}{U(t)}\, dy. \tag{5.18}$$

As $t \to \infty$ the left side tends to $b^\rho - a^\rho$. Because of the monotonicity of u this implies that for fixed $y > 0$ the integrand remains bounded. By the selection theorem of VIII,6 there exists therefore a sequence $t_1, t_2, \ldots \to \infty$ such that as t runs through it

$$\frac{u(ty)t}{U(t)} \to \psi(y) \tag{5.19}$$

at all points of continuity. It follows that the integral of ψ over $\overline{a, b}$ equals $b^\rho - a^\rho$, and so $\psi(y) = \rho y^{\rho-1}$. This limit being independent of the sequence $\{t_k\}$ the relation (5.19) is true for an arbitrary approach $t \to \infty$, and for $y = 1$ it reduces to (5.17). ▶

It is hardly necessary to say that the relations (5.16) and (5.17) remain unchanged if U is modified in some finite interval; accordingly, the lemma remains valid if it is only assumed that u is "ultimately monotone," that is, monotone is some interval $\overline{a, \infty}$. Combining the lemma with theorem 2 we get therefore

Theorem 4.[10] *Let $0 < \rho < \infty$. If U has an ultimately monotone derivative u then as $\lambda \to 0$ and $x \to \infty$, respectively,*

$$\omega(\lambda) \sim \frac{1}{\lambda^\rho} L\left(\frac{1}{\lambda}\right) \quad \text{iff} \quad u(x) \sim \frac{1}{\Gamma(\rho)} x^{\rho-1} L(x). \tag{5.20}$$

The use of this theorem is illustrated in the next section. In conclusion we show how theorem 2 leads to a *Tauberian theorem for power series.* [It is used in XII,(8.8) and in XVII,5.]

Theorem 5. *Let $q_n \geq 0$ and suppose that*

$$Q(s) = \sum_{n=0}^{\infty} q_n s^n \tag{5.21}$$

converges for $0 \leq s < 1$. If L varies slowly at infinity and $0 \leq \rho < \infty$ then each of the two relations

$$Q(s) \sim \frac{1}{(1-s)^\rho} L\left(\frac{1}{1-s}\right), \qquad s \to 1- \tag{5.22}$$

and

$$q_0 + q_1 + \cdots + q_n \sim \frac{1}{\Gamma(\rho+1)} n^\rho L(n), \qquad n \to \infty \tag{5.23}$$

implies the other.

Furthermore, if the sequence $\{q_n\}$ is monotonic and $0 < \rho < \infty$, then (5.22) is equivalent to

$$q_n \sim \frac{1}{\Gamma(\rho)} n^{\rho-1} L(n), \qquad n \to \infty. \tag{5.24}$$

Proof. Let U be the atomic measure attributing weight q_n to the point n, and let ω be its Laplace transform. Then $\omega(\lambda) = Q(e^{-\lambda})$, and so (5.22) is equivalent to $\omega(\lambda) \sim \lambda^{-\rho} L(1/\lambda)$ as $\lambda \to 0$. The equivalence of (5.22) and (5.23) is therefore contained in theorem 2.

To prove (5.24) replace U by the measure V with density $u(x) = q_n$ for $n \leq x < n + 1$. Its Laplace transform is $\omega(\lambda) \dfrac{1 - e^{-\lambda}}{\lambda} \sim \omega(\lambda)$ as $\lambda \to 0$ and clearly $V(x) \sim U(x)$ as $x \to \infty$. Thus (5.24) follows from theorem 4. ►

[10] This includes the famous Tauberian theorem of E. Landau. Our proof serves as a new example of how the selection theorem obviates analytical intricacies.

*6. STABLE DISTRIBUTIONS

To show the usefulness of the Tauberian theorems we now derive the most general stable distributions concentrated on $\overline{0, \infty}$ and give a complete characterization of their domains of attraction. The proofs are straightforward and of remarkable simplicity when compared with the methods required for distributions not concentrated on $\overline{0, \infty}$.

Theorem 1. *For fixed $0 < \alpha < 1$ the function $\gamma_\alpha(\lambda) = e^{-\lambda^\alpha}$ is the Laplace transform of a distribution G_α with the following properties:*

G_α is stable; more precisely, if $\mathbf{X}_1, \ldots, \mathbf{X}_n$ are independent variables with the distribution G_α, then $(\mathbf{X}_1 + \cdots + \mathbf{X}_n)/n^{1/\alpha}$ has again the distribution G_α.

$$x^\alpha[1 - G_\alpha(x)] \to \frac{1}{\Gamma(1-\alpha)}, \qquad x \to \infty, \tag{6.1}$$

$$e^{x^{-\alpha}} G_\alpha(x) \to 0, \qquad x \to 0. \tag{6.2}$$

Proof. The function γ_α is completely monotone by the second criterion of section 4, because $e^{-\lambda}$ is completely monotone and λ^α has a completely monotone derivative. Since $\gamma_\alpha(0) = 1$ the measure G_α with Laplace transform γ_α has total mass 1. The asserted stability property is obvious since $\gamma_\alpha{}^n(\lambda) = \gamma_\alpha(n^{1/\alpha}\lambda)$.

Next recall from (2.8) that $\omega(\lambda) = [1 - \gamma_\alpha(\lambda)]/\lambda$ is the Laplace transform of a measure U with the montone density $u = 1 - G_\alpha$. As $\lambda \to 0$ we have $\omega(\lambda) \sim \lambda^{\alpha-1}$, and so (6.1) is contained in theorem 5.4. Similarly (6.2) is an immediate consequence of the corollary to theorem 5.1. ▶

Theorem 2. *Suppose that F is a probability distribution concentrated on $\overline{0, \infty}$ such that*

$$F^{n\star}(a_n x) \to G(x) \tag{6.3}$$

(at points of continuity) where G is a proper distribution not concentrated at a single point. Then

(a) There exists a function L that varies slowly at infinity[11] and a constant α with $0 < \alpha < 1$ such that

$$1 - F(x) \sim \frac{x^{-\alpha}L(x)}{\Gamma(1-\alpha)} \qquad x \to \infty. \tag{6.4}$$

* Except for (6.2) the results of this section are derived independently in chapters IX and XVII. Stable distributions were introduced in VI,1.

[11] That is, L satisfies (5.14). The norming factor $\Gamma(1-\alpha)$ in (6.4) is a matter of convenience and affects only notations.

(*b*) *Conversely, if F is of the form* (6.4) *it is possible to choose* a_n *such that*

$$\frac{nL(a_n)}{a_n^{\alpha}} \to 1, \tag{6.5}$$

and in this case (6.3) *holds with* $G = G_\alpha$.

This implies that the possible limits G in (6.3) differ only by scale factors from some G_α. It follows, in particular, that *there are no other stable distributions concentrated on* $\overline{0, \infty}$.

Proof. If φ and γ are the Laplace transforms of F and G, then (6.3) is equivalent to

$$-n \log \varphi\left(\frac{\lambda}{a_n}\right) \to -\log \gamma(\lambda). \tag{6.6}$$

By the simple criterion of VIII,8 this implies that $-\log \varphi$ varies regularly at the origin, that is

$$-\log \varphi(\lambda) \sim \lambda^\alpha L\left(\frac{1}{\lambda}\right), \qquad \lambda \to 0, \tag{6.7}$$

with L varying slowly at infinity and $\alpha \geq 0$. Furthermore $-\log \gamma(\lambda) = C\lambda^\alpha$. Since G is not concentrated at a single point we have $0 < \alpha < 1$.

Now (6.7) implies

$$\frac{1 - \varphi(\lambda)}{\lambda} \sim \lambda^{\alpha-1} L\left(\frac{1}{\lambda}\right), \qquad \lambda \to 0. \tag{6.8}$$

Again, the left side is the transform of the measure U with the monotone density $1 - F$, and by virtue of theorem 5,4 the two relations (6.4) and (6.8) imply each other. Finally, if (6.4) holds it is possible to choose a_n so as to satisfy (6.5). From (6.8) it is then evident that as $n \to \infty$ the left side in (6.6) tends to λ^α, and this concludes the proof. ▶

(See problem 20 for the influence of the maximal term.)

*7. INFINITELY DIVISIBLE DISTRIBUTIONS

According to the definition in VI,3 a probability distribution U with Laplace transform ω is infinitely divisible iff for $n = 1, 2, \ldots$ the positive nth root $\omega_n = \omega^{1/n}$ is the Laplace transform of a probability distribution.

Theorem 1. *The function* ω *is the Laplace transform of an infinitely divisible probability distribution iff* $\omega = e^{-\psi}$ *where* ψ *has a completely monotone derivative and* $\psi(0) = 0$.

* Not used in the sequel.

Proof. Using the criterion 2 of section 4, it is seen that when $\psi(0) = 0$ and ψ' is completely monotone then $\omega_n = e^{-\psi/n}$ is the Laplace transform of a probability distribution. The condition is therefore sufficient.

For the converse direction put $\omega = e^{-\psi}$. Noting that $\log z \sim -(1 - z)$ as $z \to 1$, we get for fixed $\lambda > 0$ as $n \to \infty$

$$\psi(\lambda) = -n \log \omega_n(\lambda) \sim \psi_n(\lambda), \tag{7.1}$$

where we put for abbreviation

$$\psi_n(\lambda) = n[1 - \omega_n(\lambda)]. \tag{7.2}$$

It is clear from (7.2) that ψ_n has a completely monotone derivative $\psi_n'(\lambda)$. By the mean value theorem $\psi_n(\lambda) = \lambda\psi_n'(\theta\lambda) \geq \lambda\psi_n'(\lambda)$, and since $\psi_n \to \psi$ this implies that the sequence $\{\psi_n'(\lambda)\}$ is bounded for each fixed $\lambda > 0$. It is therefore possible to find a convergent subsequence, and the limit is automatically completely monotone by the extended continuity theorem (section 1). Thus ψ is the integral of a completely monotone function, and this completes the proof. ▶

An alternative form of this theorem is as follows.

Theorem 2. *The function ω is the Laplace transform of an infinitely divisible distribution iff it is of the form $\omega = e^{-\psi}$ where*

$$\psi(\lambda) = \int_0^\infty \frac{1 - e^{-\lambda x}}{x} P\{dx\} \tag{7.3}$$

and P is a measure such that

$$\int_1^\infty \frac{1}{x} P\{dx\} < \infty. \tag{7.4}$$

Proof. In view of the representation theorem for completely monotone functions the conditions of theorem 1 may be restated to the effect that we must have $\psi(0) = 0$ and

$$\psi'(\lambda) = \int_0^\infty e^{-\lambda x} P\{dx\} \tag{7.5}$$

where P is a measure. Truncating the integral at a changes the equality sign into $\geq$, and this implies that

$$\psi(\lambda) \geq \int_0^a \frac{1 - e^{-\lambda x}}{x} P\{dx\} \tag{7.6}$$

for each $a > 0$ (the integrand being bounded). It follows that (7.3) makes sense and the condition (7.4) is satisfied. Formal differentiation now shows that (7.3) represents the integral of (7.5) vanishing at zero. ▶

(See problems 14–17.)

Examples. (*a*) The compound Poisson distribution

$$U = e^{-c} \sum_{0}^{\infty} \frac{c^n}{n!} F^{n\star} \tag{7.7}$$

has the Laplace transform $e^{-c+c\varphi}$ and (7.3) is true with $P\{dx\} = cx\, F\{dx\}$.

(*b*) *The gamma density* $x^{a-1}\, e^{-x}/\Gamma(a)$ has transform $\omega(\lambda) = 1/(\lambda+1)^a$. Here

$$\psi(\lambda) = a\int_0^\infty \frac{1 - e^{-\lambda x}}{x}\, e^{-x}\, dx \tag{7.8}$$

as can be seen by differentiation.

(*c*) *Stable distributions.* For the transform $\omega(\lambda) = e^{-\lambda^\alpha}$ of section 5 we have $\psi(\lambda) = \lambda^\alpha$ and

$$\lambda^\alpha = \frac{\alpha}{\Gamma(1-\alpha)} \int_0^\infty \frac{1 - e^{-\lambda x}}{x^{\alpha+1}}\, dx \tag{7.9}$$

as is again seen by differentiation.

(*d*) *Bessel functions.* Consider the density v_r of example (3.*d*) with Laplace transform (3.8). It is obvious from the form of the latter that v_r is the n-fold convolution of $v_{r/n}$ with itself, and hence infinitely divisible. Formal differentiation shows that in this case $\psi'(\lambda) = r/\sqrt{(\lambda + 1)^2 - 1}$ and it is easily shown (see problem 5) that this ψ' is of the form (7.5) with

$$P\{dx\} = re^{-x}\, I_0(x)\, dx.$$

(*e*) *Subordination.* It is easily seen from the criteria in section 4 that if ψ_1 and ψ_2 are positive functions with completely monotone derivatives, the composite function $\psi(\lambda) = \psi_1(\psi_2(\lambda))$ has the same property. The corresponding infinitely divisible distribution is of special interest. To find it, denote by $Q_t^{(i)}$ the probability distribution with Laplace transform $e^{-t\psi_i(\lambda)}$ (where $i = 1, 2$), and put

$$U_t(x) = \int_0^\infty Q_s^{(2)}(x)\, Q_t^{(1)}\{ds\}. \tag{7.10}$$

(The distribution U_t is thus obtained by randomization of the parameter s in $Q_s^{(2)}$.) The Laplace transform of U_t is

$$\omega_t(\lambda) = \int_0^\infty e^{-s\psi_2(\lambda)}\, Q_t^{(1)}\{ds\} = e^{-t\psi(\lambda)}. \tag{7.11}$$

Readers of X,7 will recognize in (7.10) the *subordination of processes*: U_t is subordinated to $Q_s^{(2)}$ by the directing process $Q_t^{(1)}$. It is seen with what ease we get the Laplace transforms of the new process although only for the special case that the distributions $Q_t^{(2)}$ are concentrated on $\overline{0, \infty}$.

A special case deserves attention: if $\psi_1(\lambda) = \lambda^\alpha$ and $\psi_2(\lambda) = \lambda^\beta$ then $\psi(\lambda) = \lambda^{\alpha\beta}$. Thus *a stable α-process directed by a stable β-process leads to a stable αβ-process.* Readers should verify that this statement in substance repeats the assertion of problem 13. For a more general proposition see example VI,(2.*g*). ►

*8. HIGHER DIMENSIONS

The generalization to higher dimensions is obvious: not even the definition (1.1) requires a change if x is interpreted as column matrix $(x_1, \ldots, x_n)$ and λ as row matrix $(\lambda_1, \ldots, \lambda_n)$. Then $\lambda x = \lambda_1 x_1 + \cdots + \lambda_n x_n$ is the inner product of λ and x. Within probability theory the use of multidimensional transforms is comparatively restricted.

Examples. (*a*) *Resolvent equation.* Let f be a continuous function in *one* dimension with ordinary Laplace transform $\varphi(\lambda)$. Consider the function $f(s+t)$ of the two variables s, t. Its two-dimensional transform is given by

$$\omega(\lambda, \nu) = \int_0^\infty \int_0^\infty e^{-\lambda s - \nu t} f(s+t)\, ds\, dt. \tag{8.1}$$

After the change of variables $s + t = x$, and $-s + t = y$ the integrand takes on the form $A(x)e^{cy}$ and the integration with respect to y over $-x$, x is trivially performed. The result is that

$$\omega(\lambda, \nu) = -\frac{\varphi(\lambda) - \varphi(\nu)}{\lambda - \nu}. \tag{8.2}$$

We shall encounter this relation in more dignified surroundings as the basic *resolvent equation* for semi-groups [see (10.5)].

(*b*) *Mittag-Leffler functions.* This example illustrates the use of higher dimensions as a technical tool for evaluating simple transforms. We shall prove the following *proposition*:

If F is stable with Laplace transform $e^{-\lambda^\alpha}$ *the distribution*

$$G_t(x) = 1 - F\left(\frac{t}{x^{1/\alpha}}\right), \qquad x > 0, \tag{8.3}$$

(*t fixed*) *has as Laplace transform the Mittag-Leffler function*[12]

$$\sum_{k=0}^\infty \frac{(-\lambda)^k}{\Gamma(1+k\alpha)}\, t^{k\alpha}. \tag{8.4}$$

* Not used in the sequel.

[12] This fact first came up in the theory of recurrent events. The first analytic proof of the completely monotone character of (8.4) was found by H. Pollard.

This result is of considerable interest because the distribution G habitually appears in company with F [see, for example, IX,(5.5)]. A direct calculation seems difficult, but it is easy to proceed as follows. First keep x fixed and take t as variable. The ordinary Laplace transform $\gamma_t(\nu)$ (with ν as variable) of $G_t(x)$ is obviously $(1 - e^{-\nu^\alpha x})/\nu$. Except for the norming factor ν this is a distribution function in x, and *its* Laplace transform is evidently

$$\frac{\nu^{\alpha-1}}{\lambda + \nu^\alpha}. \tag{8.5}$$

This, then, is the bivariate transform of (8.3). In theory it could have been calculated by taking first the transform with respect to x, then t, and so (8.5) is the transform with respect to t of the transform which we seek. But expanding (8.5) into a geometric series one sees that (8.5) is in fact the transform of (8.4) and thus the proposition is proved.

The Mittag-Leffler function (8.4) is a generalization of the exponential to which it reduces when $\alpha = 1$. ►

9. LAPLACE TRANSFORMS FOR SEMI-GROUPS

The notion of Laplace integrals can be generalized to abstract-valued functions and integrals,[13] but we shall consider only Laplace transforms of semi-groups of transformations associated with Markov processes.[14] We return to the basic conventions and notations of X,8.

Let Σ be a space (for example, the line, an interval, or the integers), and $\mathscr{L}$ a Banach space of bounded functions on it with the norm $\|u\| = \sup |u(x)|$. It will be assumed that if $u \in \mathscr{L}$ then also $|u| \in \mathscr{L}$. Let $\{\mathfrak{Q}(t), t > 0\}$ be a continuous semi-group of contractions on $\mathscr{L}$. In other words we assume that for $u \in \mathscr{L}$ there exists a function $\mathfrak{Q}(t)u \in \mathscr{L}$ and that $\mathfrak{Q}(t)$ has the following properties: $0 \leq u \leq 1$ implies $0 \leq \mathfrak{Q}(t)u \leq 1$; furthermore $\mathfrak{Q}(t+s) = \mathfrak{Q}(t)\,\mathfrak{Q}(s)$, and $\mathfrak{Q}(h) \to \mathfrak{Q}(0) = \mathbf{1}$, the identity operator.[15]

We begin by defining integration. Given an arbitrary probability distribution F on $\overline{0, \infty}$ we want to define a contraction operator E from

[13] A fruitful theory covering transforms of the form (9.6) was developed by S. Bochner, *Completely monotone functions in partially ordered spaces*, Duke Math. J., vol. 9 (1942) 519–526. For a generalization permitting an arbitrary family of operators see E. Hille and R. S. Phillips (1957).

[14] The construction of the minimal solution in XIV,7 may serve as a typical example for the present methods.

[15] Recall that strong convergence $T_n \to T$ of endomorphisms means $\|T_n u - Tu\| \to 0$ for all $u \in \mathscr{L}$. Our "continuity" is an abbreviation for "strong continuity for $t \geq 0$."

$\mathscr{L}$ to $\mathscr{L}$, to be denoted by

$$E = \int_0^\infty \mathfrak{Q}(s)\, F\{ds\}, \tag{9.1}$$

such that

$$\mathfrak{Q}(t)E = E\mathfrak{Q}(t) = \int_0^\infty \mathfrak{Q}(t+s)\, F\{ds\}. \tag{9.2}$$

For a semi-group associated with a Markov process with transition probabilities $Q_t(x, \Gamma)$ this operator E will be induced by the stochastic or substochastic kernel

$$\int_0^\infty Q_s(x, \Gamma)\, F\{ds\}. \tag{9.3}$$

A natural (almost trivial) definition of the operator E presents itself if F is atomic and a simple limiting procedure leads to the desired definition as follows.

Let $p_j \geq 0$ and $p_1 + \cdots + p_r = 1$. The linear combination

$$E = p_1\mathfrak{Q}(t_1) + \cdots + p_r\mathfrak{Q}(t_r) \tag{9.4}$$

is again a contraction and may be interpreted as the expectation of $\mathfrak{Q}(t)$ with respect to the probability distribution attaching weight p_j to t_j. This defines (9.1) for the special case of finite discrete distributions, and (9.2) is true. The general expectation (9.1) is defined by a passage to the limit just as a Riemann integral: partition $\overline{0, \infty}$ into intervals $I_1, \ldots, I_n$, choose $t_j \in I_j$, and form the Riemann sum $\Sigma\mathfrak{Q}(t_k)\, F\{I_k\}$ which is a contraction. In view of the uniform continuity property X,(8.7) the familiar convergence proof works without change. This defines (9.1) as a special case of a Bochner integral.

If the semi-group consists of transition operators, that is, if $\mathfrak{Q}(t)1 = 1$ for all t, then $E1 = 1$. The notation (9.1) will be used for E, and for the function Ew we shall use the usual symbol

$$Ew = \int_0^\infty \mathfrak{Q}(s)w \cdot F\{ds\} \tag{9.5}$$

(although it would be logically more consistent to write w outside the integral). The value $Ew(x)$ at a given point x is the ordinary expectation with respect to F of the numerical function $\mathfrak{Q}(s)\, w(x)$.

In the special case $F\{ds\} = e^{-\lambda s}\, ds$ the operator E is called the *Laplace integral of the semi-group*, or *resolvent*. It will be denoted by

$$\mathfrak{R}(\lambda) = \int_0^\infty e^{-\lambda s}\, \mathfrak{Q}(s)\, ds, \qquad \lambda > 0. \tag{9.6}$$

The contraction $\lambda\mathfrak{R}(\lambda)$ is a transition operator iff all $\mathfrak{Q}(s)$ are transition operators.

The Laplace transform (9.6) leads to a simple characterization of the *infinitesimal generator* $\mathfrak{A}$ of the semi-group. By the definition of this operator in X,10 we have

$$\frac{\mathfrak{Q}(h) - \mathbf{1}}{h} u \to \mathfrak{A}u, \qquad h \to 0+, \tag{9.7}$$

iff $\mathfrak{A}u$ exists (that is, if the norm of the difference of the two sides tends to zero).

Theorem 1. *For fixed* $\lambda > 0$

$$u = \mathfrak{R}(\lambda)w \tag{9.8}$$

iff u *is in the domain of* $\mathfrak{A}$ *and*

$$\lambda u - \mathfrak{A}u = w. \tag{9.9}$$

Proof. (i) Define u by (9.8). Referring to the property (9.2) of expectations we have

$$\frac{\mathfrak{Q}(h) - \mathbf{1}}{h} u = \frac{1}{h}\int_0^\infty e^{-\lambda s}\mathfrak{Q}(s+h)w \cdot ds - \frac{1}{h}\int_0^\infty e^{-\lambda s}\mathfrak{Q}(s)w \cdot ds. \tag{9.10}$$

The change of variable $s + h = t$ and the obvious rearrangement reveals the right side to be identical with

$$\frac{e^{\lambda h} - 1}{h}\int_0^\infty e^{-\lambda t}\mathfrak{Q}(t)w \cdot dt - \frac{e^{\lambda h}}{h}\int_0^h e^{-\lambda t}[\mathfrak{Q}(t)w - w]\, dt - \frac{e^{\lambda h} - 1}{\lambda h} w. \tag{9.11}$$

Since $\|\mathfrak{Q}(t)w - w\| \to 0$ as $t \to 0$ the second term tends to 0 as $h \to 0$. The first integral is independent of h and equals $\mathfrak{R}(\lambda)w = u$. Letting $h \to 0$ we see that (9.11) tends to $\lambda u - w$, and so (9.9) is true.

(ii) Conversely, assume that $\mathfrak{A}u$ exists, that is, (9.7) holds. Since $\lambda\mathfrak{R}(\lambda)$ is a contraction commuting with the semi-group, (9.7) implies

$$\frac{\mathfrak{Q}(h) - \mathbf{1}}{h}\mathfrak{R}(\lambda)u \to \mathfrak{R}(\lambda)\mathfrak{A}u. \tag{9.12}$$

But we have just seen that the left side tends to $\lambda\mathfrak{R}(\lambda)u - u$, and the resulting identity exhibits u as the Laplace transform of the function w in (9.9). ►

Corollary 1. *For given* $w \in \mathscr{L}$ *there exists exactly one solution* u *of* (9.9).

Corollary 2. *Two distinct semi-groups cannot have the same generator* $\mathfrak{A}$.

Proof. Given an arbitrary $w \in \mathscr{L}$ the knowledge of $\mathfrak{A}$ uniquely determines the Laplace transform $\mathfrak{R}(\lambda)w$ of $\mathfrak{Q}(t)w$ for all $\lambda > 0$. The value of

$\mathfrak{R}(\lambda)\, w(x)$ at any fixed point x is the ordinary Laplace transform of the numerical function of t defined by $\mathfrak{Q}(t)\, w(x)$. By the uniqueness theorem for Laplace transforms, therefore, $\mathfrak{Q}(t)w$ is uniquely determined. ▶

It is tempting to derive Tauberian theorems analogous to those of section 5, but we shall be satisfied with the rather primitive

Theorem 2. *As* $\lambda \to \infty$

$$\lambda\mathfrak{R}(\lambda) \to \mathbf{1}. \tag{9.13}$$

Proof. For arbitrary $w \in \mathscr{L}$ we have

$$\|\lambda\mathfrak{R}(\lambda)w - w\| \leq \int_0^\infty \|\mathfrak{Q}(t)w - w\| \cdot \lambda e^{-\lambda t}\, dt. \tag{9.14}$$

As $\lambda \to \infty$ the probability distribution with density $\lambda e^{-\lambda t}$ tends to the distribution concentrated at the origin. The integrand is bounded and tends to 0 as $t \to 0$, and so the integral tends to 0 and (9.13) is true. ▶

Corollary 3. *The generator* $\mathfrak{A}$ *has a domain which is dense in* $\mathscr{L}$.

Proof. It follows from (9.13) that every $w \in \mathscr{L}$ is the strong limit of a sequence of elements $\lambda\mathfrak{R}(\lambda)w$, and by theorem 1 these elements are in the domain of $\mathfrak{A}$. ▶

Examples. (*a*) *Infinitely divisible semi-groups.* Let U be the infinitely divisible distribution with Laplace transform $\omega = e^{-\psi}$ described in (7.3). The distribution U_t with transform $e^{-t\psi}$ is again infinitely divisible, and the associated convolution operators $\mathfrak{U}(t)$ form a semi-group. To find its generator[16] choose a bounded continuously differentiable function v. Then clearly

$$\frac{\mathfrak{U}(t) - \mathbf{1}}{t}\, v(x) = \int_0^\infty \frac{v(x-y) - v(x)}{y} \cdot \frac{1}{t}\, y\, U_t\{dy\}. \tag{9.15}$$

The distribution U_t has the Laplace transform $e^{-t\psi(\lambda)}$, and the measure $t^{-1}y\, U_t\{dy\}$ has therefore the transform $-\psi'(\lambda)e^{-t\psi(\lambda)}$ which tends to $-\psi'(\lambda)$ as $t \to 0$. But (7.3) defines $-\psi'$ as the transform of the measure P, and so our measures tend to P. Since the fraction under the last integral is (for fixed x) a bounded continuous function of y, we get

$$\mathfrak{A}v(x) = \int_0^\infty \frac{v(x-y) - v(x)}{y}\, P\{dy\} \tag{9.16}$$

[16] This derivation is given for purposes of illustration. The generator is already known from chapter IX, and can be obtained by a passage to the limit from compound Poisson distributions.

and have thus an interpretation of the measure P in the canonical representation of infinitely divisible distributions.

(*b*) *Subordinated semi-groups.* Let $\{\mathfrak{Q}(t)\}$ stand for an arbitrary Markovian semi-group, and let U_t be the infinitely divisible distribution of the preceding example. As explained in X,7 a new Markovian semi-group $\{\mathfrak{Q}^*(t)\}$ may be obtained by randomization of the parameter t. In the present notation

$$\mathfrak{Q}^*(t) = \int_0^\infty \mathfrak{Q}(s)\, U_t\{ds\}. \tag{9.17}$$

Putting for abbreviation

$$V(s, x) = \frac{\mathfrak{Q}(s) - 1}{s}\, v(x) \tag{9.18}$$

we have

$$\frac{\mathfrak{Q}^*(t) - 1}{t}\, v(x) = \int_0^\infty V(s, x) \cdot \frac{1}{t} s\, U_t\{ds\}. \tag{9.19}$$

For a function v in the domain of $\mathfrak{A}$ and for x fixed the function V depends continuously on s and assumes the value $\mathfrak{A}v(x)$ for $s = 0$. We saw in the last example that $t^{-1}s\, U_t\{ds\} \to P\{ds\}$ if $t \to 0$. Thus the right side in (9.19) tends to a limit and hence $\mathfrak{A}^*v$ exists and is given by

$$\mathfrak{A}^*v(x) = \int_0^\infty V(s, x)\, P\{ds\}. \tag{9.20}$$

The conclusion is that *the domains of* $\mathfrak{A}$ *and* $\mathfrak{A}^*$ *coincide*, and[17]

$$\mathfrak{A}^* = \int_0^\infty \frac{\mathfrak{Q}(s) - \mathbf{1}}{s}\, P\{ds\} \tag{9.21}$$

in the sense that (9.20) holds for v in the domain of $\mathfrak{A}$. ►

10. THE HILLE-YOSIDA THEOREM

The famous and exceedingly useful Hille-Yosida theorem characterizes generators of arbitrary semi-groups of transformations, but we shall specialize it to our contraction semi-groups. The theorem asserts that the properties of generators found in the last section represent not only necessary but also sufficient conditions.

Theorem 1. (*Hille-Yosida.*) *An operator* $\mathfrak{A}$ *with domain* $\mathscr{L}' \subset \mathscr{L}$ *is the generator of continuous semi-group of contractions* $\mathfrak{Q}(t)$ *on* $\mathscr{L}$ (*with* $\mathfrak{Q}(0) = \mathbf{1}$) *iff it has the following properties.*

---

[17] An analogue to (9.20) for more general semi-groups was developed by R. S. Phillips and is used in operational calculus, for example to express fractional powers. The main purpose of the present simple derivation is to elucidate the otherwise obscure probabilistic background.

(i) *The equation*

$$\lambda u - \mathfrak{A}u = w, \qquad \lambda > 0, \tag{10.1}$$

has for each $w \in \mathscr{L}$ *exactly one solution* u;
(ii) *if* $0 \leq w \leq 1$ *then* $0 \leq \lambda u \leq 1$;
(iii) *the domain* $\mathscr{L}'$ *of* $\mathfrak{A}$ *is dense one in* $\mathscr{L}$.

We know already that every generator possesses these properties, and so the conditions are necessary. Furthermore, if the solution u is denoted by $u = \mathfrak{R}(\lambda)w$, we know that $\mathfrak{R}(\lambda)$ coincides with the Laplace transform (9.6). The conditions of the theorem may be restated as follows.
(i′)The operator $\mathfrak{R}(\lambda)$ satisfies the identity

$$\lambda\mathfrak{R}(\lambda) - \mathfrak{A}\mathfrak{R}(\lambda) = \mathbf{1}. \tag{10.2}$$

The domain of $\mathfrak{R}(\lambda)$ is $\mathscr{L}$, the range coincides with the domain $\mathscr{L}'$ of $\mathfrak{A}$.
(ii′) The operator $\lambda\mathfrak{R}(\lambda)$ is a contraction.
(iii′) The range of $\mathfrak{R}(\lambda)$ is dense in $\mathscr{L}$.
From theorem 9.2 we know that $\mathfrak{R}(\lambda)$ must satisfy the further condition

$$\lambda\mathfrak{R}(\lambda) \to \mathbf{1}, \qquad \lambda \to \infty. \tag{10.3}$$

This implies that every u is the limit of its own transforms and hence that the range $\mathscr{L}'$ of $\mathfrak{R}(\lambda)$ is dense. It follows that (10.3) can serve as replacement for (iii′), and thus *the three conditions of the theorem are fully equivalent to the set* (i′), (ii′), (10.3).

We now suppose given a family of operators $\mathfrak{R}(\lambda)$ with these properties and proceed to construct the desired semi-group as the limit of a family of pseudo-Poisson semi-groups. The construction depends on

Lemma 1. *If* w *is in the domain* $\mathscr{L}'$ *of* $\mathfrak{A}$ *then*

$$\mathfrak{A}\mathfrak{R}(\lambda)w = \mathfrak{R}(\lambda)\mathfrak{A}w. \tag{10.4}$$

The operators $\mathfrak{R}(\lambda)$ *and* $\mathfrak{R}(\nu)$ *commute and satisfy the resolvent equation*

$$\mathfrak{R}(\lambda) - \mathfrak{R}(\nu) = (\nu - \lambda)\mathfrak{R}(\lambda)\mathfrak{R}(\nu). \tag{10.5}$$

Proof. Letting $\mathfrak{A}$ operate on (10.1) we see that $\mathfrak{A}u = \mathfrak{R}(\lambda)\mathfrak{A}w$, which is the same as (10.4).

Next, define z as the unique solution of $\nu z - \mathfrak{A}z = w$. Subtracting this from (10.1) we get after a trite rearrangement

$$\lambda(u - z) - \mathfrak{A}(u - z) = (\nu - \lambda)z,$$

which is the same as (10.5). The symmetry of this identity implies that the operators commute. ▶

We are now in a position to proceed with the construction of our semi-group. Put

$$\mathfrak{A}_\lambda = \lambda[\lambda\mathfrak{R}(\lambda) - \mathbf{1}] = \lambda\mathfrak{A}\mathfrak{R}(\lambda). \tag{10.6}$$

Then (10.4) implies that

$$\mathfrak{A}_\lambda u \to \mathfrak{A}u \tag{10.7}$$

for all u in $\mathscr{L}'$, the domain of the given operator $\mathfrak{A}$. The first representation in (10.6) shows that $\mathfrak{A}_\lambda$ is an endomorphism generating the quasi-Poissonian semi-group $\mathfrak{Q}_\lambda(t) = e^{t\mathfrak{A}_\lambda}$ (theorem 1 in X,9). These operators commute with each other.

We can forget about the special definition of $\mathfrak{A}_\lambda$ and consider the remaining assertion of the Hille-Yosida theorem as a special case of a more general limit theorem which is useful in itself. In it λ may be restricted to the sequence of integers.

Approximation lemma 2. *Let $\{\mathfrak{Q}_\lambda(t)\}$ be a family of pseudo-Poissonian semi-groups commuting with each other and generated by the endomorphisms $\mathfrak{A}_\lambda$.*

If (10.7) *holds for a dense set $\mathscr{L}'$, then*

$$\mathfrak{Q}_\lambda(t) \to \mathfrak{Q}(t), \qquad \lambda \to \infty, \tag{10.8}$$

where $\{\mathfrak{Q}(t)\}$ is a semi-group of contractions whose generator agrees with $\mathfrak{A}$ for all $u \in \mathscr{L}'$.

Furthermore, for $u \in \mathscr{L}'$

$$\|\mathfrak{Q}(t)u - \mathfrak{Q}_\lambda(t)u\| \le t\,\|\mathfrak{A}u - \mathfrak{A}_\lambda u\|. \tag{10.9}$$

Proof. For two commuting contractions we have the identity

$$S^n - T^n = (S^{n-1} + \cdots + T^{n-1})(S - T)$$

and hence

$$\|S^n u - T^n u\| \le n\,\|Su - Tu\|. \tag{10.10}$$

Applied to operators $\mathfrak{Q}_\lambda(t/n)$ this inequality yields after a trite rearrangement

$$\|\mathfrak{Q}_\lambda(t)u - \mathfrak{Q}_\nu(t)u\| \le t\left\|\frac{\mathfrak{Q}_\lambda(t/n) - \mathbf{1}}{t/n}u - \frac{\mathfrak{Q}_\nu(t/n) - \mathbf{1}}{t/n}u\right\|. \tag{10.11}$$

Letting $n \to \infty$ we get

$$\|\mathfrak{Q}_\lambda(t)u - \mathfrak{Q}_\nu(t)u\| \le t\,\|\mathfrak{A}_\lambda u - \mathfrak{A}_\nu u\|. \tag{10.12}$$

This shows that for $u \in \mathscr{L}'$ the sequence $\{\mathfrak{Q}_\lambda(t)u\}$ is uniformly convergent as $\lambda \to \infty$. Since $\mathscr{L}'$ is dense in $\mathscr{L}$ this uniform convergence extends to all u, and if we denote the limit by $\mathfrak{Q}(t)u$ we have a contraction $\mathfrak{Q}(t)$

for which (10.8) is true. The semi-group property is obvious. Also, letting $\nu \to \infty$ in (10.12) we get (10.9). Rewriting the left side as in (10.11) we have

$$\left\| \frac{\mathfrak{Q}(t) - \mathbf{1}}{t} u - \frac{\mathfrak{Q}_\lambda(t) - \mathbf{1}}{t} u \right\| \leq \|\mathfrak{A}u - \mathfrak{A}_\lambda u\|. \tag{10.13}$$

Choose λ large enough to render the right side $< \epsilon$. For sufficiently small t the second difference ratio on the left differs in norm from $\mathfrak{A}_\lambda u$ by less than ϵ, and hence from $\mathfrak{A}u$ by less than 3ϵ. Thus for $u \in \mathscr{L}'$

$$\frac{\mathfrak{Q}(t) - \mathbf{1}}{t} u \to \mathfrak{A}u \tag{10.14}$$

and this concludes the proof. ▶

Examples. *Diffusion.* Let $\mathscr{L}$ be the family of continuous functions on the line vanishing at $\pm\infty$. To use familar notations we replace λ by h^{-2} and let $h \to 0$. The difference operator ∇_h is defined by

$$\nabla_h u(x) = \frac{1}{h^2}\left[\frac{u(x+h) + u(x-h)}{2} - u(x)\right]. \tag{10.15}$$

The first part in brackets defines a transition operator, and hence ∇_h generates a semi-group $e^{t\nabla_h}$ of transition operators (a Markovian semi-group). The operators ∇_h commute with each other, and for functions with three bounded derivatives $\nabla_h u \to \frac{1}{2}u''$ uniformly. The lemma implies the existence of a limiting semi-group $\{\mathfrak{Q}(t)\}$ generated by an operator $\mathfrak{A}$ such that $\mathfrak{A}u = \frac{1}{2}u''$ at least when u is sufficiently smooth.

In this particular case we know that $\{\mathfrak{Q}(t)\}$ is the semi-group of convolutions with normal distributions of variance t and we have not obtained new information. The example reveals nevertheless how easy it can be (sometimes) to establish the existence of semi-group with given generators. The argument applies, for example, to more general differential operators and also to boundary conditions. (See problems 18, 19.) ▶

Note *on the resolvent equation and complete monotonicity.* The identity (10.5) may be rewritten in the form

$$\frac{\mathfrak{R}(\lambda) - \mathfrak{R}(\nu)}{\lambda - \nu} = -\mathfrak{R}(\nu)\mathfrak{R}(\lambda) \tag{10.16}$$

which is the so-called *resolvent equation.* We have derived it from the conditions of the Hille-Yosida theorem. The converse is also true: *If a family of contractions* $\lambda\mathfrak{R}(\lambda)$ *satisfies* (10.16) *and the range of* $\mathfrak{R}(\lambda)$ *is dense, then there exists an operator* $\mathfrak{A}$ *such that* (10.2) *is true.*

[First of all, (10.16) implies that the range of $\mathfrak{R}(\lambda)$ is independent of λ for if $u = \mathfrak{R}(\lambda)z$ then also $u = \mathfrak{R}(\nu)z'$ with $z' = z - (\lambda-\nu)u$. If one defines $\mathfrak{A}_\lambda$ by $\mathfrak{A}_\lambda\mathfrak{R}_\lambda = \lambda\mathfrak{R}_\lambda - \mathbf{1}$ then $\mathfrak{A}_\lambda u = \lambda u - z$ and $\mathfrak{A}_\nu u = \nu u - z'$ and (10.16) shows that $\mathfrak{A}_\lambda u = \mathfrak{A}_\nu u$. Thus the operators $\mathfrak{A}_\lambda$ are identical, and this proves the assertion.]

If the semi-group $\mathfrak{Q}(t)$ corresponds to transition probabilities $Q_t(x, \Gamma)$ of a Markov process then [see (9.3)] the operators $\mathfrak{R}(\lambda)$ are induced by the substochastic kernels

$$\int_0^\infty e^{-\lambda t}\, Q_t(x, \Gamma)\, dt \tag{10.17}$$

and for fixed x, Γ the resolvent equation (10.16) reduces to (8.2). It expresses exactly that the composition of Q_s and Q_t leads to the kernel Q_{s+t}, which is the Chapman–Kolmogorov equation.

It is clear from the definition of $\mathfrak{R}(\lambda)$ that formal derivatives can be defined as strong limits of the difference ratios. Just as in the case of ordinary transforms we get

$$(-1)^n\mathfrak{R}^{(n)}(\lambda) = \int_0^\infty e^{-\lambda s} s^n \mathfrak{Q}(s)\, ds. \tag{10.18}$$

As these operators are *positive* the family $\{\mathfrak{R}(\lambda)\}$ represents an abstract analogue to *completely monotone functions.* This casts a new light on the resolvent equation (10.16). In fact, letting $\nu \to \lambda$ we get on the left the derivative $\mathfrak{R}'(\lambda)$, and so $-\mathfrak{R}'(\lambda) = \mathfrak{R}^2(\lambda)$. By induction $(-1)^n\mathfrak{R}^{(n)}(\lambda) = n!\mathfrak{R}^{n+1}(\lambda)$ which is a positive operator. Thus the resolvent equation serves also to guarantee the completely monotone character of $\{\mathfrak{R}(\lambda)\}$.

To emphasize further that the present abstract theory merely paraphrases the theorems concerning ordinary Laplace transforms we prove an *inversion formula.*

Theorem 2. *For fixed $t > 0$ as $\lambda \to \infty$*

$$\frac{(-1)^{n-1}}{(n-1)!}\, \mathfrak{R}^{(n-1)}\left(\frac{n}{t}\right)\left(\frac{n}{t}\right)^n \to \mathfrak{Q}(t). \tag{10.19}$$

Proof. From (10.18) it is seen that the left side is the integral of $\mathfrak{Q}(s)$ with respect to the density $\dfrac{e^{-ns/t}(ns/t)^{n-1}}{t(n-1)!}\, n$ which has expected value t and variance t^2/n. As $n \to \infty$ this measure tends to the distribution concentrated at t, and because of the continuity of $\mathfrak{Q}(s)$, this implies (10.19) just as in the case of functions [formula (10.19) is the same as VII,(1.6)]. ▶

11. PROBLEMS FOR SOLUTION

1. *Generalization of the convolution theorem.* Let u_1 and u_2 be two (say bounded continuous) functions in $\overline{0, \infty}$. Define their "convolution with respect to F" by

$$u(x) = \int_0^x u_1(x-y)\, u_2(y)\, F\{dy\}.$$

Let ω, ω_1, ω_2 be the Laplace transforms of u, u_1, u_2 with respect to F defined as in (1.5). Then $\omega = \omega_1\omega_2$.

2. Let ω be the transform (1.3) of a measure U. Then ω is integrable over $\overline{0, 1}$ and $\overline{1, \infty}$ iff $1/x$ is integrable with respect to U over $\overline{1, \infty}$ and $\overline{0, 1}$, respectively.

3. *Parseval relation.* If $\mathbf{X}$ and $\mathbf{Y}$ are independent random variables with distributions F and G, and transforms φ and γ, the transform of $\mathbf{XY}$ is

$$\int_0^\infty \varphi(\lambda y)\, G\{dy\} = \int_0^\infty \gamma(\lambda y)\, F\{dy\}.$$

4. From example (3.*e*) conclude by integration that $e^{1/\lambda} - 1$ *is the ordinary transform* of $I_1(2\sqrt{x})/\sqrt{x}$.

5. From the definition II,(7.1) show that *the ordinary Laplace transform of* $I_0(x)$ *is* $\omega_0(\lambda) = 1/\sqrt{\lambda^2 - 1}$ for $\lambda > 1$. [Recall the identity **1**; II,(12.5) for $\binom{2n}{n}$.]

6. *Continuation.* Show that $I_0' = I_1$, and hence that I_1 has the ordinary Laplace transform $\omega_1(\lambda) = \omega_0(\lambda)\, R(\lambda)$ where $R(\lambda) = \lambda - \sqrt{\lambda^2 - 1}$.

7. *Continuation.* Show that $2I_n' = I_{n-1} + I_{n+1}$ for $n = 1, 2, \ldots$ and hence by induction that I_n has the ordinary transform $\omega_n(\lambda) = \omega_0(\lambda)\, R^n(\lambda)$.

8. *Rational Laplace transforms.* Let $\varphi(\lambda) = U(\lambda)/V(\lambda)$ where U and V are polynomials without common roots and the degree m of U is lower than the degree of V. Suppose that the equation $V(\lambda) = 0$ has m distinct (real or imaginary) roots $\lambda_1, \ldots, \lambda_m$. Then [**1**; XI,(4.3)]

$$(*)\qquad \varphi(\lambda) = \frac{\delta_1}{\lambda - \lambda_1} + \cdots + \frac{\delta_m}{\lambda - \lambda_m}.$$

Show that this is the ordinary Laplace transform of

$$(\dagger)\qquad f(x) = \delta_1 e^{\lambda_1 x} + \cdots + \delta_m e^{\lambda_m x}.$$

Show that the contribution of two conjugate roots $\alpha \pm i\beta$ is of the form $e^{\alpha x}[a \cos \beta x + b \sin \beta x]$. Discuss the asymptotic behavior of f as $x \to \infty$ in terms of the real parts of the roots.

Note. Many analytic functions belonging to the class of meromorphic functions admit of a partial fraction expansion of the form (*), the finite sum on the right being replaced by a uniformly convergent series. If the real parts α_j of all λ_j are $< a$ then φ is for $\lambda > a$ the ordinary Laplace transform of a function f, and the asymptotic behavior of f at infinity depends only on the largest α_j. The theory generalizes easily to the case of double roots.

9. Show that the corollary to theorem 4.2 remains valid if f and $\varphi^{(n)}$ are replaced by their absolute values.

10. *Interpolation for completely montone functions.* Let $a_0, a_1, \ldots$ be a completely monotone sequence, that is, $(-1)^k \Delta^k a_n \geq 0$ (for the difference notation see VII,1; we use the span 1). Prove that

$$(*)\qquad f(\lambda) = \sum_{k=0}^{\infty} \Delta^k a_r \binom{\lambda - r}{k}, \qquad \lambda > 0$$

($r = 1, 2, \ldots$) does not depend on r, and that f is a completely monotone function such that $f(n) = a_n$ for $n = 1, 2, \ldots$.

Hint: Put

$$f_{r,N}(\lambda) = \sum_{k=0}^{N} \Delta^k a_r \binom{\lambda - r}{k}.$$

For $\lambda < r$ all terms are positive. Evaluate $f_{r+1,N} - f_{r,N}$ and conclude that for fixed N and $\lambda < r$ the sequence $f_{r,N}(\lambda)$ decreases as a function of r. Hence

$f_{r,N}(n) \leq a_n$ for $r \geq n$ and the series (*) converges. Since $f_{r,N}$ is a positive linear combination of polynomials $(r-\lambda)(r+1-\lambda)\cdots(r+k-1-\lambda)$ which are obviously completely monotone for $\lambda < r$ we conclude that f is completely monotone. [The construction generalizes to the case $a_n = \varphi(\lambda_n)$ and $\{\lambda_n\}$ is an increasing sequence of points such that $\Sigma 1/\lambda_n \leq \infty$. (See Duke Math. J., vol. 5 (1939), pp. 661–674.) *This proves that a completely monotone function is uniquely determined by the values* $\varphi(\lambda_n)$ *whenever* $\Sigma 1/\lambda_n = \infty$].

11. *Continuation.* If $\{a_n\}$ is completely monotone the values $a_r, a_{r+1}, \ldots$ uniquely determine the values $a_1, a_2, \ldots$, and also a maximal number a such that $a_0 \geq a$ and the sequence $a, a_1, a_2, \ldots$ is completely monotone.

12. Assuming $e^{-x}I_n(x)$ monotone at infinity, conclude from problem 7 that

$$e^{-x}I_n(x) \sim \frac{1}{\sqrt{2\pi x}} \qquad x \to \infty.$$

13. Let $\mathbf{X}$ and $\mathbf{Y}$ be independent random variables with Laplace transforms φ and $e^{-\lambda^\alpha}$, respectively. Then $\mathbf{Y}\mathbf{X}^{1/\alpha}$ has the Laplace transform $\varphi(\lambda^\alpha)$.

14. Let F be a distribution with transform φ. If $a > 0$ then $\varphi(\lambda+a)/\varphi(a)$ is the transform of the distribution $e^{-ax}\,F\{dx\}/\varphi(a)$. For fixed $t > 0$ conclude that[18] $\exp\left[-t\sqrt{2\lambda + a^2} + at\right]$ is the transform of an infinitely divisible distribution with density $\dfrac{t}{\sqrt{2\pi x^3}} \exp\left[-\dfrac{1}{2}\left(\dfrac{t}{\sqrt{x}} - a\sqrt{x}\right)^2\right]$.

15. Every infinitely divisible distribution is the limit of compound Poisson distributions.

16. If in the canonical representation (7.4) for infinitely divisible distributions $P(x) \sim x^c L(x)$ as $x \to \infty$ with $0 < c < 1$, prove that $1 - F(x) \sim \dfrac{1}{1-c}\, x^{c-1}\, L(x)$. [Continued in example XVII,(3.*j*).]

17. Let P be the generating function of an infinitely divisible integral-valued random variable and φ the Laplace transform of a probability distribution. Prove that $P(\varphi)$ is infinitely divisible.

18. *Diffusion with an absorbing barrier.* In the example of section 10 restrict x to $x > 0$ and when $x - h \leq 0$ put $u(x-h) = 0$ in the definition of ∇_h. Show that the convergence proof goes through if $\mathscr{L}$ is the space of continuous functions with $u(\infty) = 0$, $u(0) = 0$, but not if the last condition is dropped. The resulting semi-group is given in example X,(5.*b*).

19. *Reflecting barriers.* In the example of section 10 restrict x to $x > 0$ and when $x - h < 0$ put $u(x-h) = u(x+h)$ in the definition of ∇_h. Then $\nabla_h u$ converges for every u with three bounded derivatives such that $u'(0) = 0$. The domain $\mathscr{L}'$ of $\mathfrak{A}$ is restricted by this boundary condition. The semi-group is described in example X,(5.*e*).

20. *The influence of the maximal term in the convergence to stable distributions.* Let $\mathbf{X}_1, \mathbf{X}_2, \ldots$ be independent variables with the common distribution F satisfying (6.4), that is, belonging to the domain of attraction of the stable distribution G_α. Put $\mathbf{S}_n = \mathbf{X}_1 + \cdots + \mathbf{X}_n$ and $\mathbf{M}_n = \max[\mathbf{X}_1, \ldots, \mathbf{X}_n]$. Prove that the

[18] This formula occurs in applications and has been derived repeatedly by lengthy calculations.

ratio $\mathbf{S}_n/\mathbf{M}_n$ has a Laplace transform $\omega_n(\lambda)$ converging to[19]

$$(*)\qquad \omega(\lambda) = \frac{e^{-\lambda}}{1 + \alpha\int_0^1 (1 - e^{-\lambda t})t^{-\alpha-1}\, dt}.$$

Hence $\mathbf{E}(\mathbf{S}_n/\mathbf{M}_n) \to 1/(1 - \alpha)$.

Hint: Evaluating the integral over the region $\mathbf{X}_j \leq \mathbf{X}_1$ one gets

$$\omega_n(\lambda) = ne^{-\lambda}\int_0^\infty F\{dx\}\left(\int_0^x e^{-\lambda y/x}\, F\{dy\}\right)^{n-1}.$$

Substitute $y = tx$ and then $x = a_n s$ where a_n satisfies (6.5). The inner integral is easily seen to be

$$1 - \frac{1 - F(a_n s)}{n[1 - F(a_n)]} - \frac{1}{n}\int_0^1 (1 - e^{-\lambda t})\frac{F\{a_n\, dt\}}{1 - F(a_n)} + o\left(\frac{1}{n}\right) = 1 - \frac{s^{-\alpha}\psi(\lambda)}{n} - o\left(\frac{1}{n}\right),$$

where $\psi(\lambda)$ stands for the denominator in (*). Thus

$$\omega_n(\lambda) \to e^{-\lambda}\int_0^\infty e^{-s^{-\alpha}\psi(\lambda)} \cdot \frac{\alpha\, ds}{s^{\alpha+1}} = \omega(\lambda).$$

[19] This result and its analogue for stable distributions with exponent $\alpha > 0$ was derived by D. A. Darling in terms of characteristic functions. See Trans. Amer. Math. Soc., vol. 73 (1952) pp. 95–107.

CHAPTER XIV

Applications of Laplace Transforms

This chapter can serve as collateral reading to chapter XIII. It covers several independent topics ranging from practical problems (sections 1, 2, 4, 5) to the general existence theorem in section 7. The limit theorem of section 3 illustrates the power of the methods developed in connection with regular variation. The last section serves to describe techniques for the analysis of asymptotic properties and first-passage times in Markov processes.

1. THE RENEWAL EQUATION: THEORY

For the probabilistic background the reader is referred to VI,6–7. Although the whole of chapter XI was devoted to renewal theory, we give here an independent and much less sophisticated approach. A comparison of the methods and results is interesting. Given the rudiments of the theory of Laplace transforms, the present approach is simpler and more straightforward, but the precise result of the basic renewal theorem is at present not obtainable by Laplace transforms. On the other hand, Laplace transforms lead more easily to the limit theorems of section 3 and to explicit solutions of the type discussed in section 2.

The object of the present study is the integral equation

$$V(t) = G(t) + \int_0^t V(t-x)\, F\{dx\} \tag{1.1}$$

in which F and G are given monotone right continuous functions vanishing for $t < 0$. We consider them as improper distribution functions of measures and suppose F is not concentrated at the origin and that their Laplace transforms

$$\varphi(\lambda) = \int_0^\infty e^{-\lambda t}\, F\{dt\}, \qquad \gamma(\lambda) = \int_0^\infty e^{-\lambda t}\, G\{dt\} \tag{1.2}$$

exist for $\lambda > 0$. As in the preceding chapter all intervals of integration are taken *closed*. It will be shown that there exists exactly one solution V; it is an improper distribution function whose Laplace transform ψ exists for all $\lambda > 0$. If G has a density g, also a density v of V exists, and satisfies the integral equation

$$v(t) = g(t) + \int_0^t v(t-x)\, F\{dx\} \tag{1.3}$$

obtained by differentiation from (1.1).

Recalling the convolution rule we get for the Laplace transform ψ of the distribution V (or the ordinary transform of its density) $\psi = \gamma + \psi\varphi$ whence formally

$$\psi(\lambda) = \frac{\gamma(\lambda)}{1 - \varphi(\lambda)}\,. \tag{1.4}$$

To show that this formal solution is the Laplace transform of a measure (or density) we distinguish three cases (of which only the first two are probabilistically significant).

Case (a). F is a probability distribution, not concentrated at the origin. Then $\varphi(0) = 1$ and $\varphi(\lambda) < 1$ for $\lambda > 0$. Accordingly

$$\omega = \frac{1}{1 - \varphi} = \sum_0^\infty \varphi^n \tag{1.5}$$

converges for $\lambda > 0$. Obviously ω is completely monotone and therefore the Laplace transform of a measure U (theorem 1 of XIII,4). Now $\psi = \omega\gamma$ is the Laplace transform of the convolution $V = U \star G$, that is

$$V(t) = \int_0^t G(t-x)\, U\{dx\}. \tag{1.6}$$

Finally, if G has a density g then V possesses a density $v = U \star g$. We have thus proved the *existence* and the *uniqueness* of the desired solution of our integral equations. ▶

The asymptotic behavior of V at infinity is described by the Tauberian theorem 2 of XIII,4. Consider the typical case where $G(\infty) < \infty$ and F has a finite expectation μ. Near the origin $\psi(\lambda) \sim \mu^{-1}G(\infty)\lambda^{-1}$ which implies that

$$V(t) \sim \mu^{-1}G(\infty) \cdot t, \qquad t \to \infty. \tag{1.7}$$

The renewal theorems in XI,1 yield the more precise result that

$$V(t+h) - V(t) \to \mu^{-1}G(\infty)h,$$

but this cannot be derived from Tauberian theorems. [These lead to better results when F has no expectation; (section 3).]

Case (*b*). *F is a defective distribution*, $F(\infty) < 1$. Assume for simplicity that also $G(\infty) < \infty$. The preceding argument applies with the notable simplification that $\varphi(0) = F(\infty) < 1$ and so $\omega(0) < \infty$: the measure V *is now bounded.*

Case (*c*). *The last case is* $F(\infty) > 1$. For small values of λ the denominator in (1.4) is negative, and for such values $\omega(\lambda)$ cannot be a Laplace transform. Fortunately this fact causes no trouble. To avoid trivialities assume that F has no atom at the origin so that $\varphi(\lambda) \to 0$ as $\lambda \to \infty$. In this case there exists a unique root $\kappa > 0$ of the equation $\varphi(\kappa) = 1$ and the argument under (*a*) applies without change for $\lambda > \kappa$. In other words, there exists a unique solution V, but its Laplace transform ω converges only for $\lambda > \kappa$. For such values ω is still given by (1.4).[1]

2. RENEWAL-TYPE EQUATIONS: EXAMPLES

(*a*) *Waiting times for gaps in a Poisson process.* Let V be the distribution of the waiting time to the completion of the first gap of length ξ in a Poisson process with parameter c (that is, in a renewal process with exponential interarrival times). This problem was treated analytically in example XI,(7.*b*). Empirical interpretations (delay of a pedestrian or car trying to cross a stream of traffic, locked times in type II Geiger counters, etc.) are given in VI,7. We proceed to set up the renewal equation afresh.

The waiting time commencing at epoch 0 necessarily exceeds ξ. It terminates before $t > \xi$ if no arrival occurs before epoch ξ (probability $e^{-c\xi}$) or else if the first arrival occurs at an epoch $x < \xi$ and the residual waiting time is $\leq t - x$. Because of the inherent lack of memory the probability $V(t)$ of a waiting time $\leq t$ is therefore

$$V(t) = e^{-c\xi} + \int_0^\xi V(t-x) \cdot e^{-cx} c\, dx \tag{2.1}$$

for $t \geq \xi$ and $V(t) = 0$ for $t < \xi$. Despite its strange appearance (2.1) is a renewal equation of the standard type (1.1) in which F has the density $f(x) = ce^{-cx}$ concentrated on $0 < x < \xi$, while G is concentrated at the point ξ. Thus

$$\varphi(\lambda) = \frac{c}{c+\lambda}(1 - e^{-(c+\lambda)\xi}), \qquad \gamma(\lambda) = e^{-(c+\lambda)\xi}, \tag{2.2}$$

[1] The solution V is of the form $V\{dx\} = e^{\kappa x} V^{\#}\{dx\}$ where $V^{\#}$ is the solution [with Laplace transform $\psi^{\#}(\lambda) = \psi(\lambda+\kappa)$] of a standard renewal equation (1.1) with F replaced by the proper probability distribution $F^{\#}\{dx\} = e^{-\kappa x} F\{dx\}$ and G by $G^{\#}\{dx\} = e^{-\kappa x} G\{dx\}$.

and hence the transform ψ of V is given by

$$\psi(\lambda) = \frac{(c+\lambda)e^{-(c+\lambda)\xi}}{\lambda + ce^{-(c+\lambda)\xi}}. \tag{2.3}$$

The expressions XI,(7.9) for the expectation and variance are obtained from this by simple differentiations[2] and the same is true of the higher moments.

It is instructive to derive from (2.3) *an explicit formula* for the solution. For reasons that will become apparent we switch to the *tail* $1 - V(t)$ of the distribution. Its ordinary Laplace transform is $[1 - \psi(\lambda)]/\lambda$ [see XIII,(2.8)] which admits of an expansion into a geometric series

$$\frac{1-\psi(\lambda)}{\lambda} = \xi \sum_{n=1}^{\infty} c^{n-1}\xi^{n-1} \left\{\frac{1-e^{-(c+\lambda)\xi}}{(c+\lambda)\xi}\right\}^n. \tag{2.4}$$

The expression within braces differs from the Laplace transform $(1 - e^{-\lambda})/\lambda$ of the uniform distribution merely by a scale factor ξ and by the change from λ to $\lambda + c$. As was observed repeatedly, this change corresponds to a multiplication of the densities by e^{-ct}. Thus

$$1 - V(t) = e^{-ct} \sum_{n=1}^{\infty} c^{n-1}\xi^{n-1} f^{n*}\left(\frac{t}{\xi}\right) \tag{2.5}$$

where f^{n*} is the density of the n-fold convolution of the uniform distribution with itself. Using I,(9.6) we get finally

$$1 - V(t) = e^{-ct} \sum_{n=1}^{\infty} \frac{(ct)^{n-1}}{(n-1)!} \sum_{k=0}^{n} (-1)^k \binom{n}{k} \left(1 - k\frac{\xi}{t}\right)_+^{n-1}. \tag{2.6}$$

The relation to *covering theorems* is interesting. As was shown in I,(9.9) the inner sum represents (for t, ξ fixed) the probability that $n - 1$ *points chosen at random in* $\overline{0, t}$ *partition this interval into n parts each of which is* $\leq \xi$. Now the waiting time exceeds t iff every subinterval of $\overline{0, t}$ contains at least one arrival and so (2.6) states that if in a Poisson process exactly $n - 1$ arrivals occur in $\overline{0, t}$ *their conditional distribution is uniform*. If one starts from this fact one can take (2.6) as a consequence of the covering theorem; alternatively, (2.6) represents a new proof of the covering theorem *by randomization.*

(*b*) *Ruin problem in compound Poisson processes.* As a second illustrative example we treat the *integro-differential equation*

$$R'(t) = \frac{\alpha}{c} R(t) - \frac{\alpha}{c} \int_0^t R(t-x)\, F\{dx\} \tag{2.7}$$

in which F is a probability distribution with finite expectation μ. This equation was derived in VI,5, where its relevance for collective risk theory, storage problems, etc., is discussed. Its solution and asymptotic properties are derived by different methods in example XI,(7.*a*).

The problem is to find a *probability distribution* R satisfying (2.7).

[2] It saves labor first to clear the denominator to avoid tedious differentiations of fractions.

This equation is related to the renewal equation and can be treated in the same way. Taking ordinary Laplace transforms and noticing that

$$(2.8)\qquad \rho(\lambda) = \int_0^\infty e^{-\lambda x}\, R(x)\, dx = \frac{1}{\lambda}\int_0^\infty e^{-\lambda x} R'(x)\, dx + \frac{1}{\lambda} R(0)$$

we get

$$(2.9)\qquad \rho(\lambda) = \frac{R(0)}{1 - \dfrac{\alpha}{c}\dfrac{1-\varphi(\lambda)}{\lambda}} \cdot \frac{1}{\lambda}$$

where φ is the Laplace transform of F. Recalling that $[1 - \varphi(\lambda)]/\lambda$ is a Laplace transform we note that the first fraction on the right is of the form (1.4) and hence the Laplace-Stieltjes transform of a measure R. The factor $1/\lambda$ indicates an integration, and hence $\rho(\lambda)$ is the *ordinary* Laplace transform of the improper distribution function $R(x)$ [as indicated in (2.8)]. Since $R(x) \to 1$ as $x \to \infty$ it follows from theorem 4 in XIII,5 that $\rho(\lambda) \to 1$ as $\lambda \to 0$. From (2.9) we get therefore for the unknown constant $R(0)$

$$(2.10)\qquad R(0) = 1 - \frac{\alpha}{c}\mu.$$

Accordingly, our problem admits of *a unique solution if $\alpha\mu < c$ and admits of no solution if $\alpha\mu \geq c$.* This result was to be anticipated from the probabilistic setup.

Formula (2.9) appears also in queuing theory under the name Khintchine–Pollaczek formula [see example XII,(5.*a*)]. Many papers derive explicit expressions in special cases. In the case of the *pure Poisson process*, F is concentrated at the point 1, and $\varphi(\lambda) = e^{-\lambda}$. The expression for ρ is now almost the same as in (2.3) and the same method leads easily to the *explicit solution*

$$(2.11)\qquad R(x) = \left(1 - \frac{\alpha}{c}\right)\sum_{k=0}^{\infty}\left(\frac{-\alpha}{c}\right)^k \frac{(x-k)_+^k}{k!}\exp\left(\frac{\alpha}{c}(x-k)_+\right).$$

Although of no practical use, this formula is interesting because of the presence of *positive* exponents which must cancel out in curious ways. It has been known in connection with collective risk[3] theory since 1934 but was repeatedly rediscovered.

3. LIMIT THEOREMS INVOLVING ARC SINE DISTRIBUTIONS

It has become customary to refer to distributions concentrated on $\overline{0,1}$ with density

$$(3.1)\qquad q_\alpha(x) = \frac{\sin \pi\alpha}{\pi}\, x^{-\alpha}(1-x)^{\alpha-1}, \qquad 0 < \alpha < 1$$

[3] An explicit solution for ruin before epoch t is given by R. Pyke, *The supremum and infinum of the Poisson process*, Ann. Math. Statist., vol. 30 (1959) pp. 568–576.

as "*generalized arc sine distributions*" although they are special beta distributions. The special case $\alpha = \frac{1}{2}$ corresponds to the distribution function $2\pi^{-1} \arc\sin \sqrt{x}$ which plays an important role in the fluctuation theory for random walks. An increasing number of investigations are concerned with limit distributions related to q_α, and their intricate calculations make the occurrence of q_α seem rather mysterious. The deeper reason lies in the intimate connection of q_α to distribution functions with regularly varying tails, that is, distributions of the form

$$1 - F(x) = x^{-\alpha} L(x), \qquad 0 < \alpha < 1 \tag{3.2}$$

where $L(tx)/L(t) \to 1$ as $t \to \infty$. For such functions the renewal theorem may be supplemented to the effect that the renewal function $U = \Sigma F^{n\star}$ satisfies

$$U(t) \sim \frac{1}{\Gamma(1-\alpha)\,\Gamma(1+\alpha)} \frac{t^\alpha}{L(t)}, \qquad t \to \infty. \tag{3.3}$$

In other words, if F varies regularly, so does U. It is known (but not obvious) that the constant in (3.3) equals $(\sin \pi\alpha)/\pi\alpha$ and so (3.3) may be rewritten in the form

$$[1 - F(x)]\, U(x) \to \frac{\sin \pi\alpha}{\pi\alpha}, \qquad x \to \infty. \tag{3.4}$$

Lemma. *If F is of the form* (3.2) *then* (3.4) *holds.*

Proof. By the Tauberian theorem 4 of XIII,5

$$1 - \varphi(\lambda) \sim \Gamma(1-\alpha)\lambda^\alpha L(1/\lambda) \qquad \lambda \to 0.$$

The Laplace transform of U is $\Sigma\varphi^n = 1/(1 - \varphi)$ and (3.3) is true by virtue of theorem 2 of XIII,5. ►

Consider now a sequence of positive independent variables $\mathbf{X}_k$ with the common distribution F and their partial sums $\mathbf{S}_n = \mathbf{X}_1 + \cdots + \mathbf{X}_n$. For fixed $t > 0$ denote by $\mathbf{N}_t$ the chance-dependent index for which

$$\mathbf{S}_{\mathbf{N}_t} \leq t \leq \mathbf{S}_{\mathbf{N}_t+1}. \tag{3.5}$$

We are interested in the two subintervals

$$\mathbf{Y}_t = t - \mathbf{S}_{\mathbf{N}_t} \quad \text{and} \quad \mathbf{Z}_t = \mathbf{S}_{\mathbf{N}_t+1} - t.$$

They were introduced in VI,7 as "*spent waiting time*" and "*residual waiting time*" at epoch t. The interest attached to these variables was explained in various connections, and in XI,3 it was proved that as $t \to \infty$ the variables $\mathbf{Y}_t$ and $\mathbf{Z}_t$ have a common proper limit distribution iff F has a finite expectation. Otherwise, however, $\mathbf{P}\{\mathbf{Y}_t \leq x\} \to 0$ for each fixed $x > 0$, and similarly for $\mathbf{Z}_t$. The following interesting theorem emerges as a by-product of our results, but the original proof presented formidable analytical difficulties.[4]

Theorem. *If* (3.2) *is true, then the normed variable* $\mathbf{Y}_t/t$ *has the limit density* q_α *of* (3.1), *and* $\mathbf{Z}_t/t$ *has the limit density given by*[5]

$$p_\alpha(x) = \frac{\sin \pi\alpha}{\pi} \cdot \frac{1}{x^\alpha(1+x)}, \qquad x > 0. \tag{3.6}$$

Proof. The inequality $tx_1 < \mathbf{Y}_t < tx_2$ occurs iff $\mathbf{S}_n = ty$ and $\mathbf{X}_{n+1} > t(1-y)$ for some combination n, y such that $1 - x_2 < y < 1 - x_1$. Summing over all n and possible y we get

$$\mathbf{P}\{tx_1 < \mathbf{Y}_t < tx_2\} = \int_{1-x_2}^{1-x_1} [1 - F(t(1-y))]\, U\{t\, dy\} \tag{3.7}$$

and hence using (3.4)

$$\mathbf{P}\{tx_1 < \mathbf{Y}_t \leq tx_2\} \sim \frac{\sin \pi\alpha}{\pi\alpha} \int_{1-x_2}^{1-x_1} \frac{1 - F(t(1-y))}{1 - F(t)} \cdot \frac{U\{t\, dy\}}{U(t)}. \tag{3.8}$$

Now $\dfrac{U(ty)}{U(t)} \to y^\alpha$ and so the measure $U\{t\, dy\}/U(t)$ tends to the measure with density $\alpha y^{\alpha-1}$ while the first factor approaches $(1 - y)^{-\alpha}$. Because of the monotonicity the approach is uniform, and so

$$\mathbf{P}\{tx_1 < \mathbf{Y}_t < tx_2\} \to \frac{\sin \pi\alpha}{\pi} \int_{1-x_2}^{1-x_1} y^{\alpha-1}(1 - y)^{-\alpha}\, dy, \tag{3.9}$$

which proves the first assertion. For $\mathbf{P}\{\mathbf{Z}_t > ts\}$ we get the same integral between the limits 0 and $1/(1+s)$ and by differentiation one gets (3.6). ►

It is a remarkable fact that the density q_α becomes infinite near the endpoints 0 and 1. The most probable values for $\mathbf{Y}_t/t$ are therefore near 0 and 1.

It is easy to amend our argument to obtain converses to the lemma and the theorem. The condition (3.2) is then seen to be *necessary* for the existence of a limit distribution for $\mathbf{Y}_t/t$. On the other hand, (3.2) characterizes the domain of attraction of stable distributions, and this explains the frequent occurrence of q_α in connection with such distributions.

---

[4] E. B. Dynkin, *Some limit theorems for sums of independent random variables with infinite mathematical expectations.* See Selected Trans. in Math. Statist. and Probability, vol. 1 (1961) IMS-AMS, pp. 171–189.

[5] Since $\mathbf{S}_{\mathbf{N}_t+1} = \mathbf{Z}_t + t$ the distribution of $\mathbf{Z}_t/\mathbf{S}_{\mathbf{N}_t+1}$ is obtained from (3.6) by the change of variable $x = y/(1 - y)$. It is thus seen that *also* $\mathbf{Z}_t/\mathbf{S}_{\mathbf{N}_t+1}$ *has the limit density* q_α.

4. BUSY PERIODS AND RELATED BRANCHING PROCESSES

It was shown in example XIII,(4.*a*) that, if φ is the Laplace transform of a probability distribution F with expectation μ, the equation

$$\beta(\lambda) = \varphi(\lambda + c - c\beta(\lambda)), \qquad \lambda > 0, \tag{4.1}$$

possesses a unique solution β; furthermore *β is the Laplace transform of a distribution B which is proper if $c\mu \leq 1$ and defective otherwise.* This simple and elegant theory is being applied with increasing frequency and it is therefore worthwhile to explain the probabilistic background of (4.1) and its applications.

The derivation of (4.1) and similar equations is simple if one gets used to expressing probabilistic relations directly in terms of Laplace transforms. A typical situation is as follows. Consider a random sum $\mathbf{S_N} = \mathbf{X}_1 + \cdots + \mathbf{X_N}$ where the $\mathbf{X}_j$ are independent with Laplace transform $\gamma(\lambda)$, and $\mathbf{N}$ is an independent variable with generating function $P(s)$. The Laplace transform of $\mathbf{S_N}$ is obviously $P(\gamma(\lambda))$ [see example XIII,(3.*c*)]. For a Poisson variable $\mathbf{N}$ this Laplace transform is of the form $e^{-\alpha[1-\gamma(\lambda)]}$. As we have seen repeatedly, in applications the parameter α is often taken as a random variable subject to a distribution U. Adapting the terminology of distribution functions we can then say that $e^{-a[1-\gamma(\lambda)]}$ is the conditional Laplace transform of $\mathbf{S_N}$ given the value α of the parameter. The absolute Laplace transform is obtained by integration with respect to U. Due to the peculiar form of the integrand the result is obviously $\omega(1-\gamma(\lambda))$ where ω stands for the Laplace transform of U.

Examples. (*a*) *Busy periods.*[6] Customers (or calls) arrive at a server (or trunkline) in accordance with a Poisson process at a rate c. The successive service times are supposed to be independent variables with the common distribution F. Suppose that at epoch 0 a customer arrives and the server is free. His service time commences immediately; the customers arriving during his service time join a queue, and the service times continue without interruption as long as a queue exists. By *busy*

[6] That (4.1) governs the busy periods was pointed out by D. G. Kendall, *Some problems in the theory of queues*, J. Roy. Statist. Soc. (B), vol. 13 (1951) pp. 151–185. The elegant reduction to branching processes was contributed by I. J. Good. Equation (4.1) is equivalent to

$$B(t) = \sum \int_0^t e^{-cx} \frac{(cx)^n}{n!} B^{n\star}(t-x)\, F\{dx\}$$

which is frequently referred to as *Takacs' integral equation.* The intrinsic simplicity of the theory is not always understood.

period is meant the interval from 0 to the first epoch when the server again becomes free. Its duration is a random variable and we denote by B and β its distribution and Laplace transform, respectively.

In the terminology of branching processes the customer initiating the busy period is the "ancestor," the customers arriving during his service time are his direct descendents, and so on. Given that the progenitor departs at epoch x the number $\mathbf{N}$ of his direct descendants is a Poisson variable with expectation cx. Denote by $\mathbf{X}_j$ the total service time of the jth *direct descendant and all of his progeny.* Although these service times are not necessarily consecutive their total duration has clearly the same distribution as the busy period. The total service time required by all (direct and indirect) descendants is therefore $\mathbf{S}_\mathbf{N} = \mathbf{X}_1 + \cdots + \mathbf{X}_\mathbf{N}$ where the $\mathbf{X}_j$ have the Laplace transform β and all the variables are independent. For the busy period we have to add the service time x of the ancestor himself. Accordingly, given the length of the ancestor's service time the busy period $x + \mathbf{S}_\mathbf{N}$ has the (conditional) Laplace transform $e^{-x[\lambda+c-c\beta(\lambda)]}$. The parameter x has the distribution F and integration with respect to x yields (4.1).

If B is defective the defect $1 - B(\infty)$ represents the probability of a never-ending busy period (congestion). The condition $c\mu \leq 1$ expresses that the expected total service time of customers arriving per time unit must not exceed unity. It is easy from (4.1) to calculate the expectation and variance of B.

Special case. If $F(t) = 1 - e^{-\alpha t}$ then (4.1) takes on the form of a quadratic equation for β and B can be represented by a Bessel function; this is shown in example (6.*b*). [This result was used in the queuing example VI,(9.*e*).]

(*b*) *Delays in traffic.*[7] Suppose that cars passing a given point of the road conform to a Poisson process at a rate c. Let the traffic be stopped (by a red light or otherwise) for a duration δ. When traffic is resumed $\mathbf{K}$ cars will wait in line, where $\mathbf{K}$ is a Poisson variable. Because the rth car in the line cannot move before the $r - 1$ cars ahead of it, each car in the line causes a delay for all following cars. It is natural to assume that the several delays are independent random variables with a common distribution F. For the duration of a waiting line newly arriving cars are compelled to join the line, thus contributing to the total delay. The situation is the same as in the preceding example except that we have $\mathbf{K}$ "ancestors." The total delay caused by each car and its direct and indirect descendants has the Laplace transform β satisfying (4.1), and the

[7] This example is inspired by J. D. C. Little's treatment of the number of cars delayed. [Operations Res., vol. 9 (1961) pp. 39–52.]

total "busy period"—the interval from the resumption of traffic to the first epoch where no car stands waiting—has the Laplace transform $e^{-c\delta[1-\beta(\lambda)]}$. It is easy to calculate the expected delay and one can use this result for the discussion of the effect of successive traffic lights, etc. (See problems 5, 6.)

5. DIFFUSION PROCESSES

In the one-dimensional Brownian motion the transition probabilities are normal and the first passage times have a stable distribution with index $\frac{1}{2}$ [see example VI,(2.*e*)]. Being in possession of these explicit formulas we must not expect new information from the use of Laplace transforms. The reason for starting afresh from the diffusion equation is that the method is instructive and applicable to the most general diffusion equation (except that no *explicit* solutions can be expected when the coefficients are arbitrary). To simplify writing we take it for granted that the transition probabilities Q_t have densities q_t (although the method to be outlined would lead to this result without special assumptions).

We begin with the special case of Brownian motion. For a given bounded continuous function f put

$$u(t, x) = \int_{-\infty}^{+\infty} q_t(x, y) f(y)\, dy. \tag{5.1}$$

Our starting point is the fact derived in X,(4.*a*) that (at least for f sufficiently smooth) u will satisfy the diffusion equation

$$\frac{\partial u(t, x)}{\partial t} = \frac{1}{2} \frac{\partial^2 u(t, x)}{\partial x^2} \tag{5.2}$$

with the initial condition $u(t, x) \to f(x)$ as $t \to 0$. In terms of the ordinary Laplace transform

$$\omega_\lambda(x) = \int_0^\infty e^{-\lambda t} u(t, x)\, dt \tag{5.3}$$

we conclude from (5.2) that[8]

$$\lambda\omega_\lambda - \tfrac{1}{2}\omega_\lambda'' = f \tag{5.4}$$

and from (5.1) that

$$\omega_\lambda(x) = \int_{-\infty}^{+\infty} K_\lambda(x, s) f(s)\, ds \tag{5.5}$$

[8] Readers of the sections on semi-groups will notice that we are concerned with a Markovian semi-group generated by the differential operator $A = \frac{1}{2}d^2/dx^2$. The differential equation (5.4) is a special case of the basic equation XIII,(10.1) occurring in the Hille-Yosida theorem.

where $K_\lambda(x, y)$ is the ordinary Laplace transform of $q_t(x, y)$. In the theory of differential equations K_λ is called the Green function of (5.4). In the present case

$$K_\lambda(x, y) = \frac{1}{\sqrt{2\lambda}} e^{-\sqrt{2\lambda}\,|x-y|}. \tag{5.6}$$

In fact, it is easily verified that for bounded continuous f equation (5.4) possesses a unique bounded solution and that it is given by (5.5)–(5.6).

We propose to derive (5.6) by a probabilistic argument applicable to more general equations and leading to explicit expressions for the basic first passage times. We take it as known that the path variables $\mathbf{X}(t)$ depend continuously on t. Let $\mathbf{X}(0) = x$ and denote by $F(t, x, y)$ the probability that the point y will be reached before epoch t. We call F the distribution of the *first-passage epoch* from x to y and denote its Laplace transform by $\varphi_\lambda(x, y)$.

For $x < y < z$ the event $\mathbf{X}(t) = z$ takes place iff a first passage through y occurs at some epoch $\tau < t$ and is followed by a transition from y to z within time $t - \tau$. Thus $q_t(x, z)$ represents the convolution of $F(t, x, y)$ and $q_t(y, z)$, whence

$$K_\lambda(x, z) = \varphi_\lambda(x, y)\, K_\lambda(y, z). \tag{5.7}$$

Now choose for f a function vanishing indentically in $\overline{-\infty, z}$. In this case (5.5) and (5.7) show that

$$\omega_\lambda(x) = \varphi_\lambda(x, y)\, \omega_\lambda(y), \qquad x < y, \tag{5.8}$$

while (5.4) requires that for y fixed $\varphi_\lambda(x, y)$ satisfy the differential equation

$$\lambda\varphi_\lambda - \frac{1}{2}\frac{\partial^2\varphi_\lambda}{\partial x^2} = 0, \qquad x < y. \tag{5.9}$$

A solution which is bounded at $-\infty$ is necessarily of the form $C_\lambda e^{-\sqrt{2\lambda}\,x}$. Since (5.8) shows that $\varphi_\lambda(x, y) \to 1$ as $x \to y$, we have $\varphi_\lambda(x, y) = e^{\sqrt{2\lambda}(x-y)}$ for $x < y$. For reasons of symmetry the *Laplace transform of the first-passage time from x to y is given by*

$$\varphi_\lambda(x, y) = e^{-\sqrt{2\lambda}\,|x-y|}. \tag{5.10}$$

In the present situation K_λ is translation-invariant. Therefore $K_\lambda(y, y)$ must be independent of y and we conclude from (5.7) that

$$K_\lambda(x, y) = C_\lambda e^{-\sqrt{2\lambda}\,|x-y|}.$$

We have thus determined K_λ up to a multiplicative constant C_λ; that $\sqrt{2\lambda}C_\lambda = 1$ follows easily from the fact that to $f = 1$ there corresponds the solution $\omega_\lambda(x) = 1/\lambda$. This proves the truth of (5.6).

The following examples show how to calculate the probability that a point $y_1 > x$ will be reached before another point $y_2 < x$. At the same time they illustrate the treatment of *boundary conditions.*

Examples. (*a*) *One absorbing barrier.* The Brownian motion on $\overline{0, \infty}$ with an absorbing barrier at the origin is obtained by stopping an ordinary Brownian motion with $\mathbf{X}(0) = x > 0$ when it reaches the origin. We denote its transition densities by $q_t^{\text{abs}}(x, y)$ and adapt similarly the other notations.

In the unrestricted Brownian motion the probability density of a passage from $x > 0$ to $y > 0$ with an intermediate passage through 0 is the convolution of the first passage from x to 0 and $q_t(0, y)$. The corresponding Laplace transform is $\varphi_\lambda(x, 0)\, K_\lambda(0, y)$ and hence we must have

$$K_\lambda^{\text{abs}}(x, y) = K_\lambda(x, y) - \varphi_\lambda(x, 0)\, K_\lambda(0, y), \tag{5.11}$$

where $x > 0$, $y > 0$. This is equivalent to

$$K_\lambda^{\text{abs}}(x, y) = \frac{1}{\sqrt{2\lambda}}\, [e^{-\sqrt{2\lambda}\,|x-y|} - e^{-\sqrt{2\lambda}(x+y)}] \tag{5.12}$$

or

$$q_t^{\text{abs}}(x, y) = q_t(x, y) - q_t(x, -y) \tag{5.13}$$

in agreement with the solution X,(5.5) obtained by the *reflection principle.*

The argument leading to (5.7) applies without change to the absorbing barrier process and we conclude from (5.12) that for $0 < x < y$

$$\varphi_\lambda^{\text{abs}}(x, y) = \frac{e^{\sqrt{2\lambda}\,x} - e^{-\sqrt{2\lambda}\,x}}{e^{\sqrt{2\lambda}\,y} - e^{-\sqrt{2\lambda}\,y}}. \tag{5.14}$$

This[9] is the Laplace transform of *the probability that in an unrestricted Brownian motion with* $\mathbf{X}(0) = x$ *the point* $y > x$ *is reached before epoch* t *and before a passage through the origin.* Letting $\lambda \to 0$ we conclude that *the probability that* y *will be reached before the origin equals* x/y, just as in the symmetric Bernoulli random walk (see the ruin problem in **1**; XIV,2).

Finally, note that $\omega_\lambda^{\text{abs}}$ is the unique bounded solution of (5.4) in $\overline{0, \infty}$ satisfying the boundary condition $\omega_\lambda^{\text{abs}}(0) = 0$. [In particular, to $f(x) = 1$ there corresponds the solution $\omega_\lambda^{\text{abs}}(x) = (1 - e^{-\sqrt{2\lambda}\,x})/\lambda$. This is the ordinary transform of the probability $1 - F(t, x, 0)$ that no absorption has taken place before epoch t; an integration by parts shows that the

[9] For y fixed, $\varphi_\lambda^{\text{abs}}$ represents the solution of the differential equation (5.9) which reduces to 0 when $x = 0$ and to 1 when $x = y$. In this form the result applies to arbitrary triples of points $a < x < b$ and $a > x > b$ and to more general differential equations.

Laplace-Stieltjes transform of $F(t, x, 0)$ is $e^{-\sqrt{2\lambda}\,x}$, in agreement with (5.10).]

As an instructive exercise the reader should use the method employed for the unrestricted random walk to derive (5.12) and (5.14) directly from the differential equation (5.4) and the boundary condition $\omega_\lambda^{\text{abs}}(0) = 0$.

(*b*) *Two absorbing barriers.* Consider now a Brownian motion starting at a point x in $\overline{0, 1}$ and terminating when either 0 or 1 is reached. It is easiest to derive this process from the preceding absorbing barrier process by introducing an additional absorbing barrier at 1 so that the reasoning leading to (5.11) applies without change. The transition densities $q_t^{\#}(x, y)$ of the new process have therefore the Laplace transform $K_\lambda^{\#}$ given by

$$K_\lambda^{\#}(x, y) = K_\lambda^{\text{abs}}(x, y) - \varphi_\lambda^{\text{abs}}(x, 1)\, K_\lambda^{\text{abs}}(1, y) \tag{5.15}$$

with x and y restricted to $\overline{0, 1}$. [Note that the boundary conditions $K_\lambda^{\#}(0, y) = K_\lambda^{\#}(1, y)$ are satisfied.] Simple arithmetic shows that

$$K_\lambda^{\#}(x, y) = \frac{e^{-\sqrt{2\lambda}\,|x-y|} - e^{-\sqrt{2\lambda}(2-|x-y|)} - e^{-\sqrt{2\lambda}(x+y)} - e^{-\sqrt{2\lambda}(2-x-y)}}{\sqrt{2\lambda}(1 - e^{-2\sqrt{2\lambda}})} \tag{5.16}$$

Expanding $1/[1 - e^{-2\sqrt{2\lambda}}]$ into a geometric series, one is led to the alternative representation

$$K_\lambda^{\#}(x, y) = \frac{1}{\sqrt{2\lambda}} \sum_{n=-\infty}^{+\infty} [e^{-\sqrt{2\lambda}\,|x-y+2n|} - e^{-\sqrt{2\lambda}\,|x+y+2n|}], \tag{5.17}$$

which is equivalent to the solution X,(5.7) obtained by the *reflection principle.* ▶

The same argument applies to the more *general diffusion equation*

$$\frac{\partial u(t, x)}{\partial t} = \tfrac{1}{2}a(x)\frac{\partial^2 u(t, x)}{\partial x^2} + b(x)\frac{\partial u(t, x)}{\partial x}, \qquad a > 0, \tag{5.18}$$

in a finite or infinite interval. Instead of (5.4) we get

$$\lambda\omega_\lambda - \tfrac{1}{2}a\omega_\lambda'' - b\omega_\lambda' = f \tag{5.19}$$

and the solution is again of the form (5.5) with a Green function K_λ of the form (5.7) where $\varphi_\lambda(x, y)$ is the transform of the *first-passage density* from x to $y > x$. For fixed y, this function must satisfy the differential equation corresponding to (5.9), namely

$$\lambda\varphi_\lambda - \tfrac{1}{2}a\varphi_\lambda'' - b\varphi_\lambda' = 0. \tag{5.20}$$

It must be bounded at the left endpoint and $\varphi_\lambda(y, y) = 1$. These conditions determine φ_λ uniquely except if (5.20) possesses a bounded solution, in which case (as in the above examples) appropriate boundary conditions must be imposed. (See problems 7, 8.)

6. BIRTH-AND-DEATH PROCESSES AND RANDOM WALKS

In this section we explore the connection between the birth-and-death processes of **1**; XVII,5 and the randomized random walk of II,7. The main purpose is to illustrate the techniques involving Laplace transforms and the proper use of boundary conditions.

Consider a simple random walk starting at the origin in which the individual steps equal 1 or -1 with respective probabilities p and q. The times between successive steps are supposed to be independent random variables with an exponential distribution with expectation $1/c$. The probability $P_n(t)$ of the position n at epoch t was found in II,(7.7), but we start afresh from a new angle. To derive an equation for $P_n(t)$ we argue as follows. The position $n \neq 0$ at epoch t is possible only if a jump has occurred before t. Given that the first jump occurred at $x < t$ and led to 1, the (conditional) probability of the position n at epoch t is $P_{n-1}(t-x)$. Thus for $n \neq 0$

$$P_n(t) = \int_0^t ce^{-cx}[pP_{n-1}(t-x) + qP_{n+1}(t-x)]\, dx. \tag{6.1}$$

For $n = 0$ the term e^{-ct} must be added to the right side to account for the possibility of no jumps within $\overline{0, t}$. We have thus an infinite system of *convolution equations* and it will be seen that its solution is easily found. Before proceeding, however, let us remark that our system of equations is equivalent to the infinite system of *differential equations*[10]

$$P_n'(t) = -cP_n(t) + cpP_{n-1}(t) + cqP_{n+1}(t) \tag{6.2}$$

together with the initial conditions $P_0(0) = 1$, $P_n(0) = 0$ for $n \neq 0$. In fact, after the change of variable $y = t - x$ the convolution equations (6.1) are easily differentiated and lead to (6.2).

The two systems (6.1) and (6.2) are equivalent, but the latter has the formal advantage that the special role of $n = 0$ is noticeable only in the initial conditions.

For the use of Laplace transforms it does not matter whether we start

[10] They are a special case of the equations **1**; XVII,(5.2) for general birth-and-death processes and may be derived in like manner.

from (6.1) or (6.2). Multiplying by $e^{-\lambda t}$ and integrating, we obtain

$$(6.3a) \qquad \pi_n(\lambda) = \frac{c}{c+\lambda}\,[p\pi_{n-1}(\lambda) + q\pi_{n+1}(\lambda)], \qquad n \neq 0$$

$$(6.3b) \qquad \pi_0(\lambda) = \frac{1}{c+\lambda} + \frac{c}{c+\lambda}\,[p\pi_{-1}(\lambda) + q\pi_1(\lambda)],$$

where, of course,

$$(6.4) \qquad \pi_n(\lambda) = \int_0^\infty e^{-\lambda t}\, P_n(t)\, dt.$$

The system of linear equations (6.3) is of the type encountered in connection with random walks in **1**; XIV, and we solve it by the same method. The quadratic equation

$$(6.5) \qquad cqs^2 - (c+\lambda)s + cp = 0$$

has the root

$$(6.6) \qquad s_\lambda = \frac{c+\lambda - \sqrt{(c+\lambda)^2 - 4c^2pq}}{2cq}$$

which remains bounded for all $\lambda > 0$, and another root σ_λ which tends with λ to infinity. It is easily verified that with arbitrary constants A_λ, B_λ the linear combinations $\pi_n(\lambda) = A_\lambda s_\lambda{}^n + B_\lambda \sigma_\lambda{}^n$ satisfy (6.3*a*) for $n = 1, 2, \ldots$, and the coefficients can be chosen so as to yield the correct values for $\pi_0(\lambda)$ and $\pi_1(\lambda)$. Given π_0 and π_1 it is possible from (6.3*a*) to calculate recursively $\pi_2, \pi_3, \ldots$, and so for $n \geq 0$ *every* solution is of the form $\pi_n(\lambda) = A_\lambda s_\lambda{}^n + B_\lambda \sigma_\lambda{}^n$. As our solution must remain bounded we must have $B_\lambda = 0$ and hence

$$(6.7) \qquad \pi_n(\lambda) = \pi_0(\lambda) s_\lambda{}^n, \qquad n = 0, 1, 2, \ldots.$$

For $n = -1, -2, \ldots$ we get the analogous expression with the other root, but it is simpler to rely on the remark that *$\pi_{-n}(\lambda)$ is obtained from $\pi_n(\lambda)$ by interchanging p and q. Using this and* (6.3*b*) *we get*

$$(6.8) \qquad \pi_0(\lambda) = \frac{1}{\sqrt{(c+\lambda)^2 - 4c^2pq}}$$

and so all $\pi_n(\lambda)$ are uniquely determined.

Having thus obtained the Laplace transform of the solution we can do three things. First, we may try to extract as much information as possible by the use of Tauberian theorems, calculation of moments, etc. In most practical situations there is no other choice. Second, tables of Laplace transform may contain explicit forms for the unknowns $P_n(t)$. In the present case we have calculated the Laplace transform of the Bessel functions I_n in problem 7 of XIII,11. With the obvious adjustment of the location parameters it is seen that $P_n(t) = a_n(ct)$ with a_n given by

II,(7.7). Finally, in the exceptionally lucky situation where the explicit solution is known in advance we may consider the present setup as a method of calculating the Laplace transform of $P_n(t)$. In this sense we have now given a *new derivation for the Laplace transform of the Bessel functions* I_n.

It is typical for Laplace transforms that immediate conclusions can be drawn from the form of the solution (6.7). Since products of Laplace transforms correspond to convolutions it is clear from (6.7) that P_n is of the form $P_n = F^{n\bigstar} \bigstar P_0$ where F is a (possibly defective) probability distribution with transform s_λ. It is probabilistically obvious that F must be the distribution of the first-passage epoch through the point 1 (and hence $F^{n\bigstar}$ the distribution of the first passage epoch through n). Now it was shown in example XIII,(3.d) that $(\lambda - \sqrt{\lambda^2 - 1})^r$ is (for $\lambda > 1$) the ordinary Laplace transform of $(r/x)I_r(x)$. Changing λ into $\lambda/2c\sqrt{pq}$ merely changes a scale factor, and replacing λ by $\lambda + c$ reflects multiplication of the density by e^{-cx}. It follows that $s_\lambda{}^n$ *(with* $n > 0$) *is the ordinary Laplace transform of*

$$f_n(t) = \sqrt{\left(\frac{p}{q}\right)^n}\, \frac{n}{t}\, I_n(2c\sqrt{pq}\, t)e^{-ct} \tag{6.9}$$

and this is the density of the first-passage time through n. This agrees with II,(7.7), and in the symmetric case $p = q$ also with XIII,(3.6).

As we have seen in **1**; XVII,7 various trunking and servicing problems lead to the same system of differential equations (6.2) except that n is restricted to $n \geq 0$ and that a different equation corresponds to the boundary state $n = 0$. Two examples will show how the present method operates in such cases.

Examples. (a) *Single-server queues.* Example **1**; XVII,(7.b) may be specialized to a queue formed at a single channel. The state of the system equals the number of people in the queue including the person being served. Both the interarrival times and servicing times are exponentially distributed. To conform with the present notations we denote their expectations by $1/(cp)$ and $1/(cq)$, respectively. (In the old notation $cp = \lambda$ and $cq = \mu$.) For $n \geq 1$ the infinitesimal transition probabilities are exactly as in our random walk and so (6.2) holds. For $n = 0$, however, we have

$$P_0'(t) = -cpP_0(t) + cqP_1(t). \tag{6.10}$$

With the initial condition $P_0(0) = 1$ the transformed equation is again given by (6.3a) for $n \geq 1$, but (6.3b) is replaced by

$$(cp+\lambda)\pi_0(\lambda) = 1 + cq\pi_1(\lambda). \tag{6.11}$$

As before we get $\pi_n(\lambda) = \pi_0(\lambda)s_\lambda{}^n$ for $n \geq 1$, but in view of (6.11)

$$\pi_0(\lambda) = \frac{1}{cp + \lambda - cqs_\lambda} = \frac{1 - s_\lambda}{\lambda}. \tag{6.12}$$

(Here the quadratic equation (6.5) for s_λ was used.) Summing a geometric series it follows that $\pi_n(\lambda) + \pi_{n+1}(\lambda) + \cdots = s_\lambda{}^n/\lambda$. Comparing with the last result we conclude finally that for $n > 0$

$$P_n(t) + P_{n+1}(t) + \cdots = F_n(t) \tag{6.13}$$

where F_n *is the distribution with density* (6.9). For $n = 0$ the left side is, of course, unity.

(*b*) *Fluctuations during a busy period.* We consider the same server, but only during a busy period. In other words, it is assumed that at epoch 0 a customer arrives at the empty server, and we let the process *terminate* when the server becomes empty. Analytically this implies that n is now restricted to $n \geq 1$, and the initial condition is $P_1(0) = 1$. Nothing changes in the differential equations (6.2) for $n \geq 2$, but in the absence of a zero state the term $cpP_0(t)$ drops out in equation number one. Thus the Laplace transforms $\pi_n(\lambda)$ satisfy (6.3*a*) for $n \geq 2$ and

$$(\lambda+c)\pi_1(\lambda) = 1 + cq\pi_2(\lambda). \tag{6.14}$$

As before we get $\pi_n(\lambda) = \pi_1(\lambda)s_\lambda^{n-1}$ for $n \geq 2$, but $\pi_1(\lambda)$ is to be determined from (6.14). Taking into account the quadratic equation (6.5) we get easily $\pi_n(\lambda) = s_\lambda{}^n/cp$. We have thus *the final result that* $P_n(t) = f_n(t)/cp$ with f_n given by (6.9).

The sum $P(t) = \Sigma P_n(t)$ equals the probability that *the duration of the busy period exceeds* t. From the differential equations it is obvious that $P'(t) = -cqP_1(t)$, and we see that *the duration of the busy period has the density*

$$-P'(t) = c\sqrt{\frac{q}{p}}\,\frac{1}{t}\,I_1(2c\sqrt{pq}\,t)e^{-ct}. \tag{6.15}$$

This result was derived by a different method at the conclusion of example (4.*a*) and was used in the queuing process VI,(9.*e*). (See problem 11.)

7. THE KOLMOGOROV DIFFERENTIAL EQUATIONS[11]

We return to the Markovian processes restricted to the integers 1, 2, ... The Kolmogorov differential equations were derived in **1**; XVII,9 and

[11] The theorems and the proofs apply equally to the jump processes described in X,3. It is a good exercise to reformulate the proof in terms of the probabilities themselves rather than their Laplace transform. The new version is less elegant, but applies also to the non-stationary case. See footnote 9 in X,3.

For a probabilistic treatment based on the study of sample paths see Chung (1960). For generalizations to *semi-Markov processes* see problem 12.

again in X,3. This section contains an independent treatment by means of Laplace transforms. To render the exposition self-contained we give a new derivation of the basic equations, this time in the form of *convolution* equations.

The basic assumption is that if $\mathbf{X}(\tau) = i$ at some epoch τ, the value $\mathbf{X}(t)$ will remain constant for an interval $\tau \leq t < \tau + \mathbf{T}$ whose duration has the exponential density $c_i e^{-c_i x}$; the probability that $\mathbf{X}(\tau+\mathbf{T}) = j$ is then p_{ij}. Given that $\mathbf{X}(0) = i$ the probability $P_{ik}(t)$ that $\mathbf{X}(t) = k \neq i$ can now be calculated by summing over all possible epochs and results of the *first* jump:

$$P_{ik}(t) = \sum_{j=1}^{\infty} \int_0^t c_i e^{-c_i x} p_{ij} P_{jk}(t-x)\, dx \qquad (k \neq i). \tag{7.1a}$$

For $k = i$ we must add a term accounting for the possibility of no jump:

$$P_{ii}(t) = e^{-c_i t} + \sum_{j=1}^{\infty} \int_0^t c_i e^{-c_i x} p_{ij} P_{ji}(t-x)\, dx. \tag{7.1b}$$

These equations can be unified by introducing the Kronecker symbol δ_{ik} which equals 1 or 0 according as $k = i$ or $k \neq i$.

The backward equations (7.1) *are our point of departure;*[12] given arbitrary $c_i > 0$ and a stochastic matrix $\mathbf{p} = (p_{ik})$ we seek stochastic matrices $P(t) = (P_{ik}(t))$ satisfying (7.1).

Supposing that any finite time interval contains only finitely many jumps we can modify the argument by considering the epoch x of the *last* jump preceding t. The probability of a jump from j to k has density $\Sigma P_{ij}(x) c_j p_{jk}$, while the probability of no jump between x and t equals $e^{-c_j(t-x)}$. Instead of (7.1) we get *the forward equations*

$$P_{ik}(t) = \delta_{ik} e^{-c_i t} + \int_0^t \sum_{j=1}^{\infty} P_{ij}(x) c_j p_{jk} e^{-c_k(t-x)}\, dx. \tag{7.2}$$

As will be seen, however, there exist processes with *infinitely many jumps* satisfying the backward equations, and hence the forward equations are not implied by the basic assumptions underlying the process.

In terms of the Laplace transforms

$$\Pi_{ik}(\lambda) = \int_0^{\infty} e^{-\lambda t} P_{ik}(t)\, dt \tag{7.3}$$

[12] The change of variables $y = t - x$ makes differentiation easy, and it is seen that the convolution equations (7.1) are equivalent to the system of differential equations

$$P'_{ik}(t) = -c_i P_{ik}(t) + c_i \sum_j p_{ij} P_{jk}(t)$$

together with the initial conditions $P_{ii}(0) = 1$ and $P_{ik}(0) = 0$ for $k \neq i$. This system agrees with **1**; XVII,(9.14), except that there the coefficients c_i and p_{ij} depend on time, and hence P_{ik} is a function of two epochs τ and t rather than of the duration $t - \tau$.

the backward equations (7.1) take on the form

$$\Pi_{ik}(\lambda) = \frac{\delta_{ik}}{\lambda + c_i} + \frac{c_i}{\lambda + c_i} \sum_{j=1}^{\infty} p_{ij} \Pi_{jk}(\lambda). \tag{7.4}$$

We now switch to a more convenient matrix notation. (The rules of matrix calculus apply equally to infinite matrices with non-negative elements.) We introduce the matrices $\Pi(\lambda) = (\Pi_{ik}(\lambda))$ and similarly $P(t) = (P_{ik}(t))$, $\mathbf{p} = (p_{ik})$, and the diagonal matrix $\mathbf{c}$ with elements c_i. By $\mathbf{1}$ we denote the column vector all of whose elements equal 1. The row sums of a matrix A are then given by $A\mathbf{1}$. Finally, I is the identity matrix.

It is then clear from (7.4) that the *backward equations* (7.1) are transformed into

$$(\lambda + \mathbf{c})\, \Pi(\lambda) = I + \mathbf{cp}\, \Pi(\lambda), \tag{7.5}$$

and the *forward equations* into

$$\Pi(\lambda)(\lambda + \mathbf{c}) = I + \Pi(\lambda)\mathbf{cp}. \tag{7.6}$$

To construct the *minimal solution* we put recursively

$$(\lambda + \mathbf{c})\, \Pi^{(0)}(\lambda) = I, \qquad (\lambda + \mathbf{c})\, \Pi^{(n+1)}(\lambda) = I + \mathbf{cp}\, \Pi^{(n)}(\lambda). \tag{7.7}$$

For the row sums of $\lambda\Pi^{(n)}(\lambda)$ we introduce the notation

$$\lambda\Pi^{(n)}(\lambda)\mathbf{1} = \mathbf{1} - \xi^{(n)}(\lambda). \tag{7.8}$$

Substituting into (7.7) and remembering that $\mathbf{p1} = \mathbf{1}$ it is seen that

$$(\lambda + \mathbf{c})\xi^{(n+1)}(\lambda) = \mathbf{cp}\xi^{(n)}(\lambda). \tag{7.9}$$

Since $\xi^{(0)} \geq 0$ it follows that $\xi^{(n)}(\lambda) \geq 0$ for all n, and so the matrices $\lambda\Pi^{(n)}(\lambda)$ are substochastic. Their elements are non-decreasing functions of n and therefore there exists a finite limit

$$\Pi^{(\infty)}(\lambda) = \lim_{n \to \infty} \Pi^{(n)}(\lambda) \tag{7.10}$$

and $\lambda\Pi^{(\infty)}(\lambda)$ is substochastic or stochastic.

Obviously $\Pi^{(\infty)}(\lambda)$ satisfies the backward equation (7.5) and for any other non-negative solution $\Pi(\lambda)$ one has trivially $\Pi(\lambda) \geq \Pi^{(0)}(\lambda)$, and by induction $\Pi(\lambda) \geq \Pi^{(n)}(\lambda)$ for all n. Thus

$$\Pi(\lambda) \geq \Pi^{(\infty)}(\lambda). \tag{7.11}$$

Less obvious is that $\Pi^{(\infty)}(\lambda)$ satisfies also the forward equation (7.6).

To show it we prove by induction that

$$\Pi^{(n)}(\lambda)(\lambda+\mathbf{c}) = I + \Pi^{(n-1)}(\lambda)\mathbf{cp}. \tag{7.12}$$

This is true for $n = 1$. Assuming the truth of (7.12), substitution into (7.7) leads to

$$(\lambda + \mathbf{c})\Pi^{(n+1)}(\lambda)(\lambda + \mathbf{c}) = \lambda I + \mathbf{c} + [I + \mathbf{cp}\Pi^{(n-1)}(\lambda)]\mathbf{cp}. \tag{7.13}$$

The expression within brackets equals $(\lambda + \mathbf{c})\Pi^{(n)}(\lambda)$. Premultiplication of (7.13) by $(\lambda + \mathbf{c})^{-1}$ yields (7.12) with n replaced by $n + 1$. This relation is therefore true for all n, and hence $\Pi^{(\infty)}(\lambda)$ satisfies the forward equation. Repeating the above argument it is seen that again any non-negative solution satisfies (7.11). We have thus proved

Theorem 1. *There exists a matrix* $\Pi^{(\infty)}(\lambda) \geq 0$ *with row sums* $\leq \lambda^{-1}$ *satisfying both* (7.5) *and* (7.6) *and such that for every non-negative solution of either* (7.5) *or* (7.6) *the inequality* (7.11) *holds.*

We shall refer to $\Pi^{(\infty)}(\lambda)$ as the *minimal* solution.

Theorem 2. *The minimal solution is the Laplace transform of a family of substochastic or stochastic matrices $P(t)$ satisfying the Chapman-Kolmogorov equation*

$$P(s+t) = P(s)\,P(t) \tag{7.14}$$

and both the backward and forward equations (7.1)–(7.2). *Either all matrices $P(t)$ and $\lambda\Pi^{(\infty)}(\lambda)$ $(t > 0, \lambda > 0)$ are strictly stochastic or none is.*

Proof. We drop the superscript ∞ and write $\Pi(\lambda)$ for $\Pi^{(\infty)}(\lambda)$. From the definition (7.7) it is clear that $\Pi_{ik}^{(n)}(\lambda)$ is the transform of a positive function $P_{ik}^{(n)}$ which is the convolution of finitely many exponential distributions. Because of (7.8) the row sums of $P^{(n)}(t)$ form a monotone sequence bounded by **1** and so it follows that $\Pi(\lambda)$ is the transform of a matrix $P(t)$ which is substochastic or stochastic. From (7.5)–(7.6) it is clear that $P(t)$ satisfies the original forward and backward equations. These imply that $P(t)$ depends continuously on t. It follows that if the ith row sum is < 1 for some t the ith row sum of $\Pi(\lambda)$ is $< \lambda^{-1}$ for all λ and conversely.

To restate the equation (7.14) in terms of Laplace transforms multiply it by $e^{-\lambda t-\nu s}$ and integrate over s and t. The right side leads to the matrix product $\Pi(\lambda)\,\Pi(\nu)$, and the left side is easily evaluated by the substitution $x = t + s$, $y = -t + s$. The result is

$$-\frac{\Pi(\nu) - \Pi(\lambda)}{\nu - \lambda} = \Pi(\lambda)\,\Pi(\nu) \tag{7.15}$$

conversely (7.15) implies (7.14). [This argument is repeated in example XIII,(8.*a*).]

To prove (7.15) consider the matrix equation

$$(7.16) \qquad (\lambda+\mathbf{c})Q = A + \mathbf{cp}Q.$$

If A and Q are non-negative then obviously $Q \geq (\lambda + \mathbf{c})^{-1}A = \Pi^{(0)}(\lambda)A$ and by induction $Q \geq \Pi^{(n)}(\lambda)A$ for all n. Thus $Q \geq \Pi(\lambda)A$. Now $\Pi(\nu)$ satisfies (7.16) with $A = I + (\lambda-\nu)\Pi(\nu)$ and hence for $\lambda > \nu$

$$(7.17) \qquad \Pi(\nu) \geq \Pi(\lambda) + (\lambda-\nu)\Pi(\lambda)\,\Pi(\nu).$$

On the other hand, the right-hand member satisfies the forward equation (7.6) with λ replaced by ν. It follows that it is $\geq \Pi(\nu)$ and thus the equality sign holds in (7.17). This concludes the proof.[13] ►

To see whether the matrix $\lambda\Pi^{(\infty)}(\lambda)$ is strictly stochastic[14] we return to the relations (7.8) and (7.9). Since the elements $\xi_i^{(n)}(\lambda)$ are non-increasing functions of n there exists a limit $\xi(\lambda) = \lim \xi^{(n)}(\lambda)$ such that

$$(7.18) \qquad \lambda\Pi^{(\infty)}(\lambda)\mathbf{1} = \mathbf{1} - \xi(\lambda)$$

and

$$(7.19) \qquad (\lambda+\mathbf{c})\xi(\lambda) = \mathbf{cp}\xi(\lambda), \qquad 0 \leq \xi(\lambda) \leq \mathbf{1}.$$

On the other hand, we have

$$(7.20) \qquad (\lambda + \mathbf{c})\xi^{(0)}(\lambda) = \mathbf{c1} = \mathbf{cp1}$$

and therefore $\xi^{(0)}(\lambda) \geq \xi(\lambda)$ for *any* vector $\xi(\lambda)$ satisfying (7.19). From (7.9) it follows by induction that $\xi^{(n)}(\lambda) \geq \xi(\lambda)$ for all n, and so the vector $\xi(\lambda)$ in (7.18) represents the *maximal* vector satisfying (7.19). We have thus

Theorem 3. *The row defects of the minimal solution are represented by the well-defined maximal vector $\xi(\lambda)$ satisfying* (7.19).

Thus $\lambda\Pi^{(\infty)}(\lambda)$ is strictly stochastic iff (7.19) implies $\xi(\lambda) = 0$.

---

[13] (7.15) is the *resolvent equation* for the family of contractions $\lambda\Pi(\lambda)$ on the Banach space of bounded column vectors. We saw in XIII,10 that it holds iff the range of these transformations is independent of λ, and minimal character guarantees this. (In terms of boundary theory the range is characterized by the vanishing of the vectors at the "active exit boundary.")

[14] *Warning:* A formal multiplication of the forward equations by the column vector **1** would seem to lead to the identity $\lambda\Pi(\lambda)\mathbf{1} = \mathbf{1}$, but the series involved may diverge. The procedure is legitimate if the c_i are bounded (corollary 1).

Corollary 1. *If* $c_i \leq M < \infty$ *for all* i *the minimal solution is strictly stochastic (so that neither the forward nor the backward equations possess other admissible solutions).*

Proof. Since $c/(\lambda+c)$ is an increasing function of c it follows from (7.19) by induction that

$$\xi(\lambda) \leq \left(\frac{M}{\lambda + M}\right)^n \cdot \mathbf{1} \tag{7.21}$$

for all n, and hence $\xi(\lambda) = 0$. ►

If $A(\lambda)$ is a matrix of elements of the form $\xi_i(\lambda)\,\eta_k(\lambda)$ with arbitrary $\eta_k(\lambda)$ then $\Pi(\lambda) + A(\lambda)$ is again a solution of the backward equation (7.5). It is always possible to choose $A(\lambda)$ so as to obtain admissible matrices $P(t)$ satisfying the Chapman-Kolmogorov equation. The procedure is illustrated in the next section. The corresponding processes are characterized by transitions involving infinitely many jumps in a finite time interval. Curiously enough, the forward equations may be satisfied even though their interpretation in terms of a last jump is false.

These are the main results. We conclude with a criterion that is useful in applications and interesting because its proof introduces notions of potential theory; the kernel Γ of (7.25) is a typical *potential.*

We assume $c_i > 0$ and rewrite (7.19) in the form

$$\xi(\lambda) + \lambda\mathbf{c}^{-1}\xi(\lambda) = \mathbf{p}\xi(\lambda). \tag{7.22}$$

Multiplying by $\mathbf{p}^k$ and adding over $k = 0, \ldots, n-1$ we get

$$\xi(\lambda) + \lambda\sum_{k=0}^{n-1}\mathbf{p}^k\mathbf{c}^{-1}\xi(\lambda) = \mathbf{p}^n\xi(\lambda). \tag{7.23}$$

This implies that $\mathbf{p}^n\xi(\lambda)$ depends monotonically on n and so $\mathbf{p}^n\xi(\lambda) \to x$ where x is the minimal column vector satisfying[15]

$$\mathbf{p}x = x, \qquad \xi(\lambda) \leq x \leq 1. \tag{7.24}$$

Now define a matrix (with possibly infinite elements) by

$$\Gamma = \sum_{k=1}^{\infty}\mathbf{p}^k\mathbf{c}^{-1}. \tag{7.25}$$

Letting $n \to \infty$ in (7.23) we get

$$\xi(\lambda) + \lambda\Gamma\xi(\lambda) = x, \tag{7.26}$$

which implies in particular that $\xi_k(\lambda) = 0$ for each k such that $\Gamma_{kk} = \infty$. This is the case if k is a persistent state for the Markov chain with matrix $\mathbf{p}$ and hence we have

---

[15] It is not difficult to see that x is independent of λ and $\lambda\Pi^{(\infty)}(\lambda)x = x - \xi(\lambda)$. (See footnote 14.)

Corollary 2. *The minimal solution is strictly stochastic (and hence unique) whenever the discrete Markov chain with matrix* **p** *has only persistent states.*

8. EXAMPLE: THE PURE BIRTH PROCESS

Instead of pursuing the general theory we consider in detail processes in which only transitions $i \to i+1$ are possible, for they furnish good illustrations for the types of processes arising from non-uniqueness. To avoid trivialities we suppose $c_i > 0$ for all i. By definition $p_{i,i+1} = 1$ whence $p_{ik} = 0$ for all other combinations. The backward and forward equations now reduce to

$$(8.1) \qquad (\lambda+c_i)\Pi_{ik}(\lambda) - c_i\Pi_{i+1,k}(\lambda) = \delta_{ik}$$

and

$$(8.2) \qquad (\lambda+c_k)\Pi_{ik}(\lambda) - c_{k-1}\Pi_{i,k-1}(\lambda) = \delta_{ik},$$

where δ_{ik} equals 1 for $i = k$ and 0 otherwise. We put for abbreviation

$$(8.3) \qquad \rho_i = \frac{c_i}{c_i + \lambda}, \qquad r_i = \frac{1}{c_i + \lambda}.$$

ρ_i is the Laplace transform of the (exponential) sojourn time distribution at i, and r_i is the ordinary Laplace transform of the probability that this sojourn time extends beyond t. The dependence of r_j and ρ_j on λ should be borne in mind.

(*a*) *The minimal solution.* It is easily verified that

$$(8.4) \qquad \Pi_{ik}(\lambda) = \begin{cases} \rho_i\rho_{i+1}\cdots\rho_{k-1}r_k & \text{for } k \geq i \\ 0 & \text{for } k < i \end{cases}$$

is the minimal solution for both (8.1) and (8.2). It reflects the fact that transitions from i to $k < i$ are impossible, and that the epoch of the *arrival* at $k > i$ is the sum of the k independent sojourn times at $i, i+1, \ldots, k-1$.

To see whether the row sums add to unity we note that $\lambda r_k = 1 - \rho_k$, whence

$$(8.5) \qquad \lambda[\Pi_{ii}(\lambda) + \cdots + \Pi_{i,i+n}(\lambda)] = 1 - \rho_i \cdots \rho_{i+n}.$$

Passing to logarithms it is seen that the product on the right tends to 0 iff the series $\Sigma 1/c_n$ diverges. Thus *the transition probabilities of the process defined by* (8.4) *add up to unity iff* $\Sigma 1/c_n = \infty$. (This result was derived in **1**; XVII,4.) In this case there are no surprises: the c_n determine uniquely a birth process satisfying the basic postulates from which we started.

We now assume that

$$\sum 1/c_n < \infty. \tag{8.6}$$

The defect $1 - \Sigma_k P_{ik}(t)$ is the probability that by epoch t the system has passed through *all* states, or has "arrived at the boundary ∞." The epoch of the arrival is the sum of the sojourn times at $i, i+1, \ldots$. The series converges with probability one because by (8.6) the sum of the mean sojourn times converges.

In a process starting at i *the epoch of the arrival at* ∞ *has the Laplace transform*

$$\xi_i = \lim_{n\to\infty} \rho_i\rho_{i+1}\cdots\rho_{i+n} \tag{8.7}$$

and the ξ_i satisfy the equations (7.19), namely,

$$(\lambda+c_i)\xi_i = c_i\xi_{i+1}. \tag{8.8}$$

(*b*) *Return processes.* Starting from the process (8.4) new processes may be defined as follows. Choose numbers q_i such that $q_i \geq 0$, $\Sigma q_i = 1$. We stipulate that on arrival at ∞ *the state of the system passes instantaneously to* i *with probability*[16] q_i. The original process now starts afresh until a second arrival at ∞ takes place. The time elapsed between the two arrivals at ∞ is a random variable with Laplace transform

$$\tau(\lambda) = \sum q_i\xi_i. \tag{8.9}$$

The Markovian character of the process requires that on the second arrival at ∞ the process recommences in the same manner. We now describe the transition probabilities $P_{ik}^{\text{ret}}(t)$ of the new process in terms of its Laplace transforms $\Pi_{ik}^{\text{ret}}(\lambda)$. The probability of a transition from i at epoch 0 to k at epoch t *without* an intervening passage through ∞ has the transform (8.4). The probability to reach k after exactly one passage through ∞ has therefore the Laplace transform $\xi_i\Sigma_j\, q_j\Pi_{jk}(\lambda)$, and the epoch of the *second* arrival at ∞ has transform $\xi_i\tau(\lambda)$. Considering further returns we see in this way that we must have

$$\Pi_{ik}^{\text{ret}}(\lambda) = \Pi_{ik}(\lambda) + \xi_i\frac{1}{1-\tau(\lambda)}\sum_j q_j\Pi_{jk}(\lambda) \tag{8.10}$$

where $[1 - \tau(\lambda)]^{-1} = \Sigma\tau^n(\lambda)$ counts the number of passages through ∞. A trite calculation shows that the row sums in (8.10) equal $1/\lambda$, and so

[16] Variants of the return processes are obtained by letting $\Sigma\, q_i < 1$; on arrival at ∞ the process terminates with probability $1 - \Sigma\, q_i$.

the $\Pi_{ik}^{\text{ret}}(\lambda)$ are the transforms of a strictly stochastic matrix of transition probabilities $P^{\text{ret}}(t)$.

It is easily verified that *the new process satisfies the backward equations* (8.1) *but not the forward equations* (8.2). This is as should be: the postulates leading to the forward equations are violated since no last jump need exist.

(*c*) *The bilateral birth process.* To obtain a process satisfying both the forward and the backward equations we modify the birth process by letting the states of the system run through 0, $\pm 1, \pm 2, \ldots$. Otherwise the conventions remain the same: the constants $c_i > 0$ are defined for all integers, and transitions from i are possible only to $i + 1$. We assume again that $\Sigma 1/c_n < \infty$, the summation now extending from $-\infty$ to ∞.

Nothing changes for the *minimal* solution which is still given by (8.4). The limit

$$\eta_k = \lim_{i \to -\infty} \Pi_{ik}(\lambda) = r_k \rho_{k-1} \rho_{k-2} \rho_{k-3} \cdots \tag{8.11}$$

exists and may be interpreted as the transform of "the probability $P_{-\infty,k}(t)$ of a transition from $-\infty$ at epoch 0 to k at epoch t." With this starting point the process will run through all states from $-\infty$ to ∞ and "arrive at ∞" at an epoch with Laplace transform $\xi_{-\infty} = \lim_{n \to -\infty} \xi_n$. We now define a new process as follows. It starts as the process corresponding to the minimal solution (8.4) but on reaching ∞ it recommences at $-\infty$, and in this way the process continues forever. By the construction used in (*b*) we get for the transition probabilities

$$\Pi_{ik}^{\#}(\lambda) = \Pi_{ik}(\lambda) + \frac{\xi_i \eta_k}{1 - \xi_{-\infty}}. \tag{8.12}$$

It is easily verified that *the* $\Pi_{ik}^{\#}$ *satisfy both the backward and the forward equations* (8.1) *and* (8.2). The process satisfies the hypotheses leading to the backward equations, but *not* those for the forward equations.

9 CALCULATION OF $P(\infty)$ AND OF FIRST-PASSAGE TIMES

As can be expected, the behavior as $t \to \infty$ of the transition probabilities $P_{ij}(t)$ of Markov processes on integers is similar to that of higher transition probabilities in discrete chains with the pleasing simplification, however, that the nuisance of periodic chains disappears. Theorem 1 establishes this fact as a simple consequence of the ergodic theorem of 1;XV. Our main concern will then be to calculate the limits for the processes of section 7 and to show how first passage times can be found. The methods used are of wide applicability.

Theorem 1. *Suppose that for the family of stochastic matrices* $P(t)$

$$P(s+t) = P(s)\,P(t) \tag{9.1}$$

and $P(t) \to I$ *as* $t \to 0$. *If no* P_{ik} *vanishes*[17] *identically then as* $t \to \infty$

$$P_{ik}(t) \to u_k \tag{9.2}$$

where either $u_k = 0$ *for all* k *or else*

$$u_k > 0, \qquad \sum_k u_k = 1, \tag{9.3}$$

and

$$\sum_j u_j\, P_{jk}(t) = u_k. \tag{9.4}$$

The second alternative occurs whenever there exists a probability vector $(u_1, u_2, \ldots)$ *satisfying* (9.4) *for some* $t > 0$. *In this case* (9.4) *holds for all* $t > 0$, *and the probability vector* u *is unique.*

(As explained in **1**;XVII,6 the important feature is that the limits do not depend on i, which indicates that the influence of the initial conditions is asymptotically negligible.)

Proof. For a fixed $\delta > 0$ consider the discrete Markov chain with matrix $P(\delta)$ and higher transition probabilities given by $P^n(\delta) = P(n\delta)$. If all elements $P_{ik}(n\delta)$ are ultimately positive the chain is irreducible and aperiodic, and by the ergodic theorem **1**;XV,6 the assertions are true for t restricted to the sequence $\delta, 2\delta, 3\delta, \ldots$. Since two rationals have infinitely many multiples in common the limit as $n \to \infty$ of $P_{ik}(n\delta)$ is the same for all rational δ. To finish the proof it suffices to show that $P_{ik}(t)$ is a uniformly continuous function of t and positive for large t. Now by (9.1)

$$P_{ii}(s)\,P_{ik}(t) \le P_{ik}(s+t) \le P_{ik}(t) + [1 - P_{ii}(s)] \tag{9.5}$$

[the first inequality is trivial, the second follows from the fact that the terms $P_{ij}(s)$ with $j \neq i$ add up to $1 - P_{ii}(s)$]. For s sufficiently small we have $1 - \epsilon \le P_{ii}(s) \le 1$ and so (9.5) shows the uniform continuity of P_{ik}. It follows from (9.5) also that if $P_{ik}(t) > 0$ then $P_{ik}(t+s) > 0$ in some s-interval of fixed length and hence P_{ik} is either identically zero or ultimately positive. ▶

[17] This condition is introduced only to avoid trivialities that may be circumvented by restrictions to appropriate sets of states. It is not difficult to see that our conditions imply strict positivity of $P_{ik}(t)$ for all t.

We now apply this result to the minimal solution of section 7 assuming that it is strictly stochastic, and hence *unique*. In matrix notation (9.4) reads $uP(t) = u$ and has the ordinary Laplace transform

$$u\lambda\Pi(\lambda) = u. \tag{9.6}$$

If a vector u satisfies (9.6) for some particular value $\lambda > 0$ the resolvent equation (7.15) entails the truth of (9.6) for *all* $\lambda > 0$, and hence the truth of (9.4) for all $t > 0$. Introducing (9.6) into the forward equation (7.6) we get

$$u\mathbf{c}\mathbf{p} = u\mathbf{c}; \tag{9.7}$$

the components $u_k c_k$ are finite though possibly unbounded. On the other hand, if u is a probability vector satisfying (9.7) it follows by induction from (7.12) that $u\lambda\Pi^{(n)}(\lambda) \leq u$ for all n, and hence $u\lambda\Pi(\lambda) \leq u$. But the matrix $\lambda\Pi(\lambda)$ being strictly stochastic the sums of the components on either side must be equal and hence (9.6) is true. We have thus

Theorem 2. *If the minimal solution is strictly stochastic* (*and hence unique*) *the relations* (9.2) *hold with* $u_k > 0$ *iff there exists a probability vector* u *such that* (9.7) *holds.*

This implies in particular that the solution u of (9.7) is unique.

Probabilistic interpretation. To fix ideas consider the simplest case where the discrete chain with transition probabilities p_{ij} is ergodic. In other words, we assume that there exists a strictly positive probability vector $\alpha = (\alpha_1, \alpha_2, \ldots)$ such that $\alpha\mathbf{p} = \alpha$ and $p_{ik}^{(n)} \to \alpha_k$ as $n \to \infty$. It is then clear that *if* $\sigma = \Sigma\alpha_k c_k^{-1} < \infty$, *the probability vector with components* $u_k = \alpha_k c_k^{-1}/\sigma$ *satisfies* (9.7) whereas no solution exists if $\sigma = \infty$.

Now it is intuitively obvious that the *transitions* in our process are the same as in the discrete Markov chain with matrix $\mathbf{p}$, but their timing is different. For an orientation consider a particular state and label it with the index 0. The successive *sojourn times* at 0 alternate with *off times* during which the system is at states $j > 0$. The number of visits to the state j is regulated by $\mathbf{p}$, their duration depends on c_j. In the discrete Markov chain the long-run frequencies of j and 0 are in the ratio $\alpha_j : \alpha_0$ and hence α_j/α_0 should be *the expected number* of visits to j during an off interval. The expected duration of each visit being $1/c_j$ we conclude that in the long run the probabilities of the states j and 0 should stand in the proportion $\alpha_j c_j^{-1} : \alpha_0 c_0^{-1}$ or $u_j : u_0$.

This argument can be made rigorous even in the case where $P_{ij}(t) \to 0$. According to a theorem of Derman mentioned in **1**; XV,11, if $\mathbf{p}$ induces an irreducible and persistent chain there exists a vector α such that $\alpha\mathbf{p} = \alpha$ and α is unique up to a multiplicative constant; here $\alpha_k \geq 0$, but the series $\Sigma\,\alpha_k$ may diverge. Even in this case the *ratios*

$\alpha_j:\alpha_0$ have the relative frequency interpretation given above and the argument holds generally. *If* $\Sigma\, \alpha_k c_k^{-1} < \infty$ *then* (9.2)–(9.4) *are true with* u_k *proportional to* $\alpha_k c_k^{-1}$, *and otherwise* $P(t) \to 0$ *as* $t \to \infty$. The interesting feature is that the limits u_k may be positive even if the discrete chain has only null states.

The existence of the limits $P_{ik}(\infty)$ can be obtained also by a renewal argument intimately connected with the recurrence times. To show how the distribution of recurrence and first passage times may be calculated we number the states $0, 1, 2, \ldots$ and use 0 as pivotal state. Consider a new process which coincides with the original process up to the random epoch of the first visit to 0 but with the state fixed at 0 forever after. In other words, the new process is obtained from the old one by making 0 *an absorbing state.* Denote the transition probabilities of the modified process by ${}^0P_{ik}(t)$. Then ${}^0P_{00}(t) = 1$. In terms of the original process ${}^0P_{i0}(t)$ is the probability of a *first passage from* $i \neq 0$ *to* 0 *before epoch* t, and ${}^0P_{ik}(t)$ gives the probability of a transition from $i \neq 0$ to $k \neq 0$ without intermediate passage through 0. It is probabilistically clear that the matrix ${}^0P(t)$ should satisfy the same backward and forward equations as $P(t)$ except that c_0 is replaced by 0. We now proceed the inverse way: *we modify the backward and forward equations by changing* c_0 *to* 0 *and show that the unique solution of this absorbing-state process has the predicted properties.*

If ξ is the vector represented by the zeroth column of $\Pi(\lambda)$, the backward equations show that the vector

$$(9.8) \qquad (\lambda + \mathbf{c} - \mathbf{cp})\xi = \eta$$

has components $1, 0, 0, \ldots$. Now the backward equations for ${}^0\Pi(\lambda)$ are obtained on replacing c_0 by 0, and so if ξ stands for the zeroth column of ${}^0\Pi(\lambda)$ the vector (9.8) has components $\eta_1 = \eta_2 = \cdots = 0$, but $\eta_0 = \rho \neq 0$. It follows that the vector with components $\xi_k = \Pi_{k0}(\lambda) - \rho{}^0\Pi_{k0}(\lambda)$ satisfies (9.8) with $\eta = 0$, and as $\lambda\Pi(\lambda)$ is strictly stochastic this implies $\xi_k = 0$ for all k (theorem 7.3). Since ${}^0\Pi_{00}(\lambda) = 1/\lambda$ we have therefore for $k \geq 0$

$$(9.9) \qquad \Pi_{k0}(\lambda) = \lambda{}^0\Pi_{k0}(\lambda)\Pi_{00}(\lambda).$$

Referring to the first equation in (9.8) we see also that

$$(9.10) \qquad \Pi_{00}(\lambda) = \frac{1}{\lambda + c_0} + \frac{c_0}{\lambda + c_0} \sum_j p_{0j}\lambda{}^0\Pi_{j0}(\lambda)\Pi_{00}(\lambda).$$

(9.9) and (9.10) are *renewal equations* with obvious probabilistic interpretation. In fact, let the process start at $k > 0$. Then ${}^0\Pi_{k0}$ is the ordinary Laplace transform of the probability ${}^0P_{k0}(t)$ that the first entry to 0 occurs before t, and hence $\lambda{}^0\Pi_{k0}(\lambda)$ is the Laplace transform of the distribution F_k of the *epoch of first entry to* 0. Thus (9.9) states that $P_{k0}(t)$ is the convolution of F_k and P_{00}; the event $\mathbf{X}(t) = 0$ takes place iff the first entry occurs at some epoch $x < t$ and $t - x$ time units later the system is again at 0.

Similarly, $\Sigma p_{0j}\lambda^0\Pi_{j0}$ represents the distribution F_0 of an off time, that is, the interval between two consecutive sojourn times at 0. The factor of $\Pi_{00}(\lambda)$ on the right in (9.10) therefore represents the *waiting time for a first return to* 0 if the system is initially at 0. (This is also the distribution of a complete period = sojourn time plus off time.) The renewal equation (9.10) expresses $P_{00}(t)$ as the sum of the probability that the sojourn time at 0 extends beyond t and the probability of $\mathbf{X}(t) = 0$ after a first return at epoch $x < t$. If 0 is persistent (9.10) implies by the renewal theorem that

$$P_{00}(\infty) = \frac{1}{1 + c_0\mu} \tag{9.11}$$

where μ is the expected duration of an off time and $c_0^{-1} + \mu$ is the expected duration of a complete cycle.

10. PROBLEMS FOR SOLUTION

1. In the renewal equation (1.3) let $F'(t) = g(t) = e^{-t}t^{p-1}/\Gamma(p)$. Then

$$\psi(\lambda) = \frac{(\lambda + 1)^p}{(\lambda + 1)^p - 1}. \tag{10.1}$$

By the method of partial fractions show that for integral[18] p

$$v(t) = \frac{1}{p}\sum_{k=0}^{p-1} a_k e^{-(1-a_k)t} \tag{10.2}$$

where $a_k = e^{-i2\pi k/p}$ and $i^2 = -1$.

2. *Lost calls.* A server has Poisson incoming traffic and a holding time with Laplace transform φ. Given that the server is free at epoch 0, denote by $U(t)$ the probability that up to epoch t all arriving customers find the server free. Show that the ordinary Laplace transform of U is

$$\omega(\lambda) = \frac{1}{\lambda + \alpha} + \frac{\alpha}{\lambda + \alpha} \cdot \frac{1}{\lambda + \alpha - \alpha\varphi(\lambda + \alpha)}.$$

The expected waiting time for the first lost call is $\dfrac{1}{\alpha} + \dfrac{1}{\alpha[1 - \varphi(\alpha)]}$.

3. If F has expectation μ and variance σ^2 and if $c\mu < 1$, the solution of the busy-period equation (4.1) has variance $(\sigma^2 + c\mu^3)/(1 - c\mu)$.

[18] The roots of the denominator are the same for $p = n$ and $p = 1/n$, but the solutions are entirely different. This shows that the popular "expansion according to the roots of the denominator" requires caution when ψ is an irrational function.

4. If F is exponentially distributed the busy-time distribution satisfying (4.1) is a Bessel function.

5. In example (4.*b*) the generating function of the total number of cars delayed is $e^{c\delta[\psi(s)-1]}$ where

$$\psi(s) = s\varphi(c - c\psi(s)). \tag{10.3}$$

6. Show that if φ is the Laplace transform of a proper distribution the solution ψ of (10.3) is the generating function of a possibly defective distribution. The latter is proper iff F has an expectation $\mu \leq 1/c$.

7. Starting from (5.7) show that the Green function of the general diffusion equation (5.19) in any interval is necessarily of the form

$$K_\lambda(x, y) = \begin{cases} \dfrac{\xi_\lambda(x)\,\eta_\lambda(y)}{W(y)} & \text{for } x \leq y \\[2ex] \dfrac{\eta_\lambda(x)\,\xi_\lambda(y)}{W(y)} & \text{for } x \geq y, \end{cases} \tag{10.4}$$

where ξ_λ and η_λ are solutions of the homogeneous equation

$$\lambda\varphi - \tfrac{1}{2}a\varphi'' - b\varphi' = 0 \tag{*}$$

bounded, respectively, at the left and the right boundary. If (*) has no bounded solution then ξ_λ and η_λ are determined up to arbitrary multiplicative constants which can be absorbed in W. (Otherwise appropriate boundary conditions must be imposed.)

Show that ω_λ defined by (10.4) and (5.5) satisfies the differential equation (5.19) iff W is the Wronskian

$$W(y) = \xi_\lambda'(y)\,\eta_\lambda(y) - \xi_\lambda(y)\,\eta_\lambda'(y). \tag{10.5}$$

The solutions ξ_λ and η_λ are necessarily monotonic, and hence $W(y) \neq 0$.

8. *Continuation.* For $x < y$ the first-passage epoch from x to y has the Laplace transform $\xi_\lambda(x)/\xi_\lambda(y)$. For $x > y$ it is given by $\eta_\lambda(x)/\eta_\lambda(y)$.

9. Show that the method described in section 5 for diffusion processes applies equally to a general *birth-and-death process*.

10. Adjust example (6.*a*) to the case of $a > 1$ channels. (*Explicit* calculations of the a constants are messy and not recommended.)

11. In example (6.*b*) show directly from the differential equations that the busy time has expectation $\dfrac{1}{c(q-p)}$ and variance $\dfrac{1}{c^2(q-p)^3}$.

12. *Semi-Markov processes.* A semi-Markov process on 1, 2, . . . differs from a Markov process in that the sojourn times may depend on the terminal state: given that the state i was *entered* at τ the probability that the sojourn time ends before $\tau + t$ by a jump to k is $F_{ik}(t)$. Then $\Sigma_k F_{ik}(t)$ gives the distribution of the sojourn time and $p_{ik} = F_{ik}(\infty)$ is the probability of a jump to k. Denote by $P_{ik}(t)$ the probability of k at epoch $t + \tau$ given that i was *entered* at epoch τ.

Derive an analogue to the Kolmogorov *backward* equations. With self-explanatory notations the transformed version is given by

$$\Pi(\lambda) = \gamma(\lambda) + \Phi(\lambda)\,\Pi(\lambda)$$

where $\gamma(\lambda)$ is the diagonal matrix with elements $[1 - \Sigma_k \varphi_{ik}(\lambda)]/\lambda$. For $F_{ik}(t) = p_{ik}(1 - e^{-c_i t})$ this reduces to the backward equations (7.5). The construction of the minimal solution of section 7 goes through.[19]

[19] For details see Proc. National Acad. of Sciences, vol. 51 (1964) pp. 653–659. Semi-Markov processes were introduced by P. Lévy and W. L. Smith, and were investigated in particular by R. Pyke.

CHAPTER XV

Characteristic Functions

This chapter develops the elements of the theory of characteristic functions and is entirely independent of chapters VI, VII, IX–XIV. A refined Fourier analysis is deferred to chapter XIX.

1. DEFINITION. BASIC PROPERTIES

The generating function of a non-negative integral-valued random variable $\mathbf{X}$ is the function defined for $0 \le s \le 1$ by $\mathbf{E}(s^{\mathbf{X}})$, the expectation of $s^{\mathbf{X}}$. As was shown in chapter XIII, the change of variable $s = e^{-\lambda}$ makes this useful tool available for the study of arbitrary non-negative random variables. The usefulness of these transforms derives largely from the multiplicative property $s^{x+y} = s^x s^y$ and $e^{-\lambda(x+y)} = e^{-\lambda x}e^{-\lambda y}$. Now this property is shared by the exponential function with a purely imaginary argument, that is, by the function defined for real x by

$$e^{i\zeta x} = \cos \zeta x + i \sin \zeta x \tag{1.1}$$

where ζ is a real constant and $i^2 = -1$. This function being bounded, its expectation exists under any circumstances. The use of $\mathbf{E}(e^{i\zeta \mathbf{X}})$ as a substitute for generating functions provides a powerful and universally applicable tool, but it is bought at the price of introducing complex-valued functions and random variables. Note, however, that our independent variables remain restricted to the real line, (or, later on, to $\mathcal{R}^r$).

By a complex-valued function $w = u + iv$ is meant the pair of *real* functions u and v defined for *real* x. The expectation $\mathbf{E}(w)$ is merely an abbreviation for $\mathbf{E}(u) + i\mathbf{E}(v)$. We write, as usual, $\bar{w} = u - iv$ for the conjugate function and $|w|$ for the absolute value (that is, $|w|^2 = w\bar{w} = u^2 + v^2$). The elementary properties of expectation remain valid, and only the *mean value theorem* requires comment: *if* $|w| \le a$ *then* $|\mathbf{E}(w)| \le a$. In fact, by Schwarz' inequality

$$|\mathbf{E}(w)|^2 = (\mathbf{E}(u))^2 + (\mathbf{E}(v))^2 \le \mathbf{E}(u^2) + \mathbf{E}(v^2) = \mathbf{E}(|w|^2) \le a^2. \tag{1.2}$$

Two complex-valued random variables $\mathbf{W}_j = \mathbf{U}_j + i\mathbf{V}_j$ are called *independent* iff the pairs $(\mathbf{U}_1, \mathbf{V}_1)$ and $(\mathbf{U}_2, \mathbf{V}_2)$ are independent. That the multiplicative property $\mathbf{E}(\mathbf{W}_1\mathbf{W}_2) = \mathbf{E}(\mathbf{W}_1)\,\mathbf{E}(\mathbf{W}_2)$ holds as usual is seen by decomposition into real and imaginary parts. (This formula illustrates the advantage of the complex notation.) With these preparations we define an analogue to generating functions as follows.

Definition. *Let* $\mathbf{X}$ *be a random variable with probability distribution* F. *The characteristic function of* F *(or* $\mathbf{X}$*) is the function* φ *defined for real* ζ *by*

$$\varphi(\zeta) = \int_{-\infty}^{+\infty} e^{i\zeta x}\, F\{dx\} = u(\zeta) + iv(\zeta) \tag{1.3}$$

where

$$u(\zeta) = \int_{-\infty}^{+\infty} \cos \zeta x \cdot F\{dx\}, \qquad v(\zeta) = \int_{-\infty}^{+\infty} \sin \zeta x \cdot F\{dx\}. \tag{1.4}$$

For distributions F with a density f, of course,

$$\varphi(\zeta) = \int_{-\infty}^{+\infty} e^{i\zeta x} f(x)\, dx. \tag{1.5}$$

Terminological note. In the accepted terminology of Fourier analysis φ is the *Fourier-Stieltjes transform of* F. Such transforms are defined for all bounded measures and the term "characteristic function" emphasizes that the measure has unit mass. (No other measures have characteristic functions.) On the other hand, integrals of the form (1.5) occur in many connections and we shall say that (1.5) defines the *ordinary Fourier transform of* f. The characteristic function of F is the ordinary Fourier transform of the density f (when the latter exists), but the term Fourier transform applies also to other functions.[1] ▶

For ease of reference we list some basic properties of characteristic functions.

Lemma 1. *Let* $\varphi = u + iv$ *be the characteristic function of a random variable* $\mathbf{X}$ *with distribution* F. *Then*

(*a*) φ *is continuous.*

(*b*) $\varphi(0) = 1$ *and* $|\varphi(\zeta)| \leq 1$ *for all* ζ.

(*c*) $a\mathbf{X} + b$ *has the characteristic function*

$$\mathbf{E}(e^{i\zeta(a\mathbf{X}+b)}) = e^{ib\zeta}\varphi(a\zeta). \tag{1.6}$$

In particular, $\bar{\varphi} = u - iv$ *is the characteristic function of* $-\mathbf{X}$.

---

[1] More generally one may define the "Fourier transform of f with respect to a given measure"; then (1.3) defines the transform of the constant 1 with respect to F.

(d) u is even and v is odd. The characteristic function is real iff F is symmetric.

(e) For all ζ

$$0 \leq 1 - u(2\zeta) \leq 4(1 - u(\zeta)). \tag{1.7}$$

(For variants see problems 1–3.)

Proof. (*a*) Note that

$$|e^{i\zeta(x+h)} - e^{i\zeta x}| \leq |e^{i\zeta h} - 1|. \tag{1.8}$$

The right side is independent of x and is arbitrarily small for h sufficiently close to 0. Thus φ is, in fact, *uniformly* continuous. Property (*b*) is obvious from the mean value theorem, and (*c*) requires no comment. For the proof of (*d*) we anticipate the fact that distinct distributions have distinct characteristic functions. Now φ is real iff $\varphi = \bar{\varphi}$, that is, if $\mathbf{X}$ and $-\mathbf{X}$ have the same characteristic function. But then $\mathbf{X}$ and $-\mathbf{X}$ have the same distribution, and so F is symmetric. Finally, to prove (*e*) consider the elementary trigonometric relation

$$1 - \cos 2\zeta x = 2(1 - \cos^2 \zeta x) \leq 4(1 - \cos \zeta x) \tag{1.9}$$

valid because $0 \leq 1 + \cos \zeta x \leq 2$. Taking expectations we get (1.7). ►

Consider now two random variables $\mathbf{X}_1$, $\mathbf{X}_2$ with distributions F_1, F_2 and characteristic functions φ_1, φ_2. If $\mathbf{X}_1$ and $\mathbf{X}_2$ are independent, the multiplicative property of the exponential entails

$$\mathbf{E}(e^{i\zeta(\mathbf{X}_1+\mathbf{X}_2)}) = \mathbf{E}(e^{i\zeta\mathbf{X}_1})\,\mathbf{E}(e^{i\zeta\mathbf{X}_2}). \tag{1.10}$$

This simple result is used frequently and we record it therefore as

Lemma 2. *The convolution $F_1 \star F_2$ has the characteristic function $\varphi_1\varphi_2$.* In other words: *to the sum $\mathbf{X}_1 + \mathbf{X}_2$ of two independent random variables there corresponds the product $\varphi_1\varphi_2$ of their characteristic functions.*[2]

If $\mathbf{X}_2$ has the same distribution as $-\mathbf{X}_1$, then the sum $\mathbf{X}_1 - \mathbf{X}_2$ represents the symmetrized variable and we have therefore the

Corollary. *$|\varphi|^2$ is the characteristic function of the symmetrized distribution ${}^0F$.*

The following lemma gives a characterization of *arithmetic* distributions.

[2] The converse is false, for it was shown in II,(4.*e*) and again in problem 1 of III,9 that in some exceptional cases the sum of two *dependent* variables may have the distribution $F_1 \star F_2$, and consequently the characteristic function $\varphi_1\varphi_2$.

Lemma 3. *If $\lambda \neq 0$ the following three statements are equivalent:*

(*a*) $\varphi(\lambda) = 1$.

(*b*) *φ has period λ, that is $\varphi(\zeta + n\lambda) = \varphi(\zeta)$ for all ζ and n.*

(*c*) *All points of increase of F are among $0, \pm h, \pm 2h, \ldots$ where $h = 2\pi/\lambda$.*

Proof. Since $1 - \cos \lambda x \geq 0$ for all x the expectation of this function can vanish only if $1 - \cos \lambda x = 0$ at every point of increase of F and hence (*a*) implies (*c*). Conversely, if F attributes weight p_n to the point nh and (*c*) is true, then $\varphi(\zeta) = \Sigma p_n e^{inh\zeta}$. This function obviously has period $\lambda = 2\pi/h$, and so (*b*) and (*a*) are true. Finally, (*b*) trivially implies (*a*). ►

Technically this lemma covers the extreme case of a distribution F concentrated at the origin. Then $\varphi(\zeta) = 1$ for all ζ, and so every number is a period of φ. In general, if λ is a period of φ the same is true of all multiples $\pm\lambda, \pm 2\lambda, \ldots$, but for a non-constant periodic function φ there exists a smallest positive period, and this is called the *true period*. Similarly, for an arithmetic F there exists a *largest* positive h for which property (*c*) holds, and this is called the *span* of F. It follows from lemma 3 that the span h and the period λ are related by $\lambda h = 2\pi$. Thus unless either $\varphi(\zeta) \neq 1$ for all $\zeta \neq 0$, or $\varphi(\zeta) = 1$ identically, there exists a smallest $\lambda > 0$ such that $\varphi(\lambda) = 1$ but $\varphi(\zeta) \neq 1$ for $0 < \zeta < \lambda$.

All this can be restated in a form of more general appearance. Instead of $\varphi(\lambda) = 1$ assume only that $|\varphi(\lambda)| = 1$. There exists then a real b such that $\varphi(\lambda) = e^{ib\lambda}$, and we can apply the preceding result to the variable $\mathbf{X} - b$ with characteristic function $\varphi(\zeta)e^{-ib\zeta}$ which equals 1 at $\zeta = \lambda$. Every period of this characteristic function is automatically a period of $|\varphi|$, and we have thus proved

Lemma 4. *There exist only the following three possibilities:*

(*a*) *$|\varphi(\zeta)| < 1$ for all $\zeta \neq 0$.*

(*b*) *$|\varphi(\lambda)| = 1$ and $|\varphi(\zeta)| < 1$ for $0 < \zeta < \lambda$. In this case $|\varphi|$ has period λ and there exists a real number b such that $F(x+b)$ is arithmetic with span $h = 2\pi/\lambda$.*

(*c*) *$|\varphi(\zeta)| = 1$ for all ζ. In this case $\varphi(\zeta) = e^{ib\zeta}$ and F is concentrated at the point b.*

2. SPECIAL DENSITIES. MIXTURES

For ease of reference we give a table of the characteristic functions of the most common densities and describe the method of deriving them in the following.

Notes. (1) *Normal density*. If one is not afraid of complex integration the result is obvious by the substitution $y = x - i\zeta$. To prove the formula in the real domain use differentiation and integration by parts to obtain $\varphi'(\zeta) = -\zeta\varphi(\zeta)$. Since $\varphi(0) = 1$ it follows that $\log \varphi(\zeta) = -\frac{1}{2}\zeta^2$, as asserted.

(2)–(3) *Uniform densities.* The calculation in (2) and (3) is obvious. The two distributions differ only by location parameters, and the relation between the characteristic functions illustrates the rule (1.6).

(4) *Triangular density.* Direct calculation is easy using integration by parts. Alternatively, observe that our triangular density is the convolution of the uniform density in $-\frac{1}{2}a < x < \frac{1}{2}a$ with itself and in view of (3) its characteristic function is therefore $\left(\frac{2}{a\zeta} \cdot \sin \frac{a\zeta}{2}\right)^2$.

(5) This is obtained by application of the inversion formula (3.5) to the triangular density (4). See also problem 4. This formula is of great importance because many Fourier-analytic proofs depend on the use of a characteristic function vanishing outside a finite interval.

Table 1

No.	Name	Density	Interval	Characteristic Function
1	Normal	$\frac{1}{\sqrt{2\pi}} e^{-\frac{1}{2}x^2}$	$-\infty < x < \infty$	$e^{-\frac{1}{2}\zeta^2}$
2	Uniform	$\frac{1}{a}$	$0 < x < a$	$\frac{e^{ia\zeta} - 1}{ia\zeta}$
3	Uniform	$\frac{1}{2a}$	$\lvert x\rvert < a$	$\frac{\sin a\zeta}{a\zeta}$
4	Triangular	$\frac{1}{a}\left(1 - \frac{\lvert x\rvert}{a}\right)$	$\lvert x\rvert < a$	$2\,\frac{1 - \cos a\zeta}{a^2\zeta^2}$
5	—	$\frac{1}{\pi}\frac{1 - \cos ax}{ax^2}$	$-\infty < x < \infty$	$\begin{cases} 1 - \frac{\lvert\zeta\rvert}{a} & \text{for } \lvert\zeta\rvert \le a \\ 0 & \text{for } \lvert\zeta\rvert > a \end{cases}$
6	Gamma	$\frac{1}{\Gamma(t)} x^{t-1}e^{-x}$	$x > 0,\quad t > 0$	$\frac{1}{(1 - i\zeta)^t}$
7	Bilateral exponential	$\frac{1}{2}e^{-\lvert x\rvert}$	$-\infty < x < \infty$	$\frac{1}{1 + \zeta^2}$
8	Cauchy	$\frac{1}{\pi}\frac{t}{t^2 + x^2}$	$-\infty < x < \infty$, $t > 0$	$e^{-t\lvert\zeta\rvert}$
9	Bessel	$e^{-x}\frac{t}{x} I_t(x)$	$x > 0,\quad t > 0$	$[1 - i\zeta - \sqrt{(1 - i\zeta)^2 - 1}]^t$
10	Hyperbolic cosine[1]	$\frac{1}{\pi \cosh x}$	$-\infty < x < \infty$	$\frac{1}{\cosh (\pi\zeta/2)}$

[1] $\cosh x = \frac{1}{2}(e^x + e^{-x})$.

(6) *Gamma densities.* Use the substitution $y = x(1 - i\zeta)$ or else expand $e^{i\zeta x}$ into a power series and use the identity

$$(-1)^n\binom{-a}{n}n! = \frac{\Gamma(a+n)}{\Gamma(a)}.$$

For the special case $t = 1$ (exponential distribution) the calculation can be performed in the real by repeated integration by parts. The same is true (by recursion) for all integral values of t.

(7) *The bilateral exponential* is obtained by symmetrization from the exponential distribution, and so the characteristic function follows from (6) with $t = 1$. A direct verification is easy using repeated integrations by parts.

(8) *Cauchy distribution.* Again the formula follows from the preceding one by the use of the inversion formula (3.5). The direct verification of this formula is a standard exercise in the calculus of residues.[3]

(9) *Bessel density.* This is the Fourier version of the Laplace transform derived in XIII,(3.*d*).

(10) *Hyperbolic cosine.* The corresponding distribution function is $F(x) = 1 - \frac{2}{\pi}\arctan e^{-x}$. Formula 10 is of no importance, but it has a curiosity value in that it exhibits a "*self-reciprocal pair*": the density and its characteristic function differ only by obvious parameters. (The normal density is the prime example for this phenomenon.) To calculate the characteristic function expand the density into the geometric series

$$\frac{1}{2\pi}\sum(-1)^k e^{-(2k+1)|x|}.$$

Applying number 7 to the individual term one gets the canonical partial fraction expansion for the characteristic function. ▶

Returning to the general theory, we give a method of constructing new characteristic functions out of given ones. The principle is extremely simple, but example (*b*) will show that it can be exploited to avoid lengthy calculations.

Lemma. *Let $F_0, F_1, \ldots$ be probability distributions with characteristic functions $\varphi_0, \varphi_1, \ldots$. If $p_k \geq 0$ and $\Sigma p_k = 1$ the mixture*

$$U = \sum p_k F_k \tag{2.1}$$

is a probability distribution with characteristic function

$$\omega = \sum p_k \varphi_k. \tag{2.2}$$

[3] See, for example, E. Hille, *Analytic function theory*, Boston 1959, vol. 1, p. 247.

Examples. (*a*) *Random sums.* Let $\mathbf{X}_1, \mathbf{X}_2, \ldots$ be independent random variables with a common distribution F and characteristic function φ. Let $\mathbf{N}$ be an integral-valued random variable with generating function $P(s) = \Sigma p_k s^k$ and independent of the $\mathbf{X}_j$. The random sum $\mathbf{X}_1 + \cdots + \mathbf{X}_\mathbf{N}$ has then the distribution (2.1) with $F_k = F^{k\bigstar}$, and the corresponding characteristic function is

$$\omega(\zeta) = P(\varphi(\zeta)). \tag{2.3}$$

The most noteworthy special case is that of the *compound Poisson distribution.* Here $p_k = e^{-t}t^k/k!$ and

$$\omega(\zeta) = e^{-t+t\varphi(\zeta)}. \tag{2.4}$$

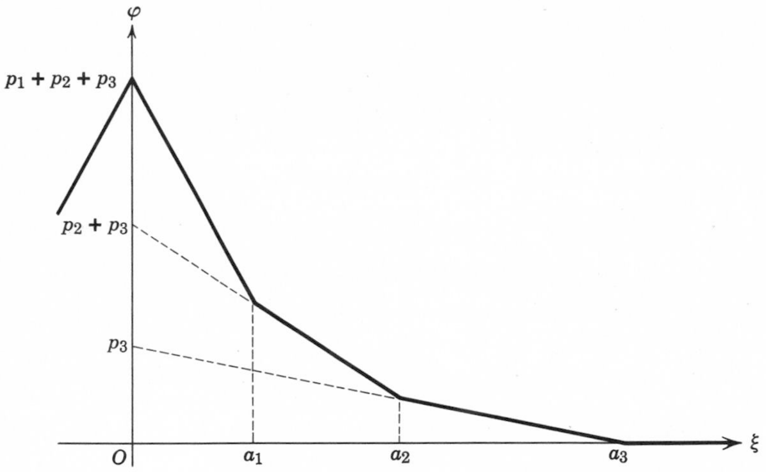

Figure 1.

(*b*) *Concave polygons.* From number 5 in table 1 we know that

$$\varphi(\zeta) = \begin{matrix} 1 - |\zeta| & \text{for} \quad |\zeta| \leq 1 \\ 0 & \text{for} \quad |\zeta| \geq 1 \end{matrix} \tag{2.5}$$

is a characteristic function. If $a_1, \ldots, a_n$ are arbitrary positive numbers, the mixture

$$\omega(\zeta) = p_1\varphi\left(\frac{\zeta}{a_1}\right) + \cdots + p_n\varphi\left(\frac{\zeta}{a_n}\right) \tag{2.6}$$

is an even characteristic function whose graph in $\overline{0, \infty}$ is a concave polygon [fig. 1]. In fact, without loss of generality assume

$$a_1 < a_2 < \cdots < a_n.$$

In the interval $0 < \zeta < a_1$ the graph of ω is a segment of a line with slope

$-\left(\frac{p_1}{a_1}+\cdots+\frac{p_n}{a_n}\right)$. Between a_1 and a_2 the term p_1/a_1 drops out, and so on, until between a_{n-1} and a_n the graph coincides with a segment of slope $-p_n/a_n$. In $\overline{0, \infty}$ the graph is therefore a polygon consisting of n finite segments with decreasing slopes and the segment $\overline{a_n, \infty}$ of the ζ-axis. It is easily seen that every polygon with these properties may be represented in the form (2.6) (the n sides intercepting the ω-axis at the points p_n, $p_n+p_{n-1}, \ldots, p_n+\cdots+p_1 = 1$). We conclude that *every even function $\omega \geq 0$ with $\omega(0) = 1$ whose graph in $\overline{0, \infty}$ is a concave polygon is a characteristic function.*

A simple passage to the limit will lead to the famous Polya criterion [example (3.*b*)] and reveals its natural source. Even the present special criterion leads to surprising and noteworthy results. ▶

Curiosities. (i) *Two distinct characteristic functions can be equal in a finite interval* $\overline{-a, a}$. This obvious corollary to example (*b*) shows that the regularity properties of characteristic functions differ profoundly from those of generating functions and Laplace transforms. We shall return to this point in XIX,5.

(ii) *The relation $F \bigstar F_1 = F \bigstar F_2$ between three probability distributions does not imply*[4] $F_1 = F_2$. Indeed, choose two distinct characteristic functions φ_1 and φ_2 which agree for $|\zeta| < 1$. With φ defined in (2.5) we have then $\varphi\varphi_1 = \varphi\varphi_2$.

(iii) Even more surprising is that *we can exhibit two real characteristic functions φ_1 and φ_2 such that $|\varphi_1| = |\varphi_2|$ identically, and hence $\varphi_1{}^2 = \varphi_2{}^2$.* For φ_1 we take the periodic function with period 2 defined by $\varphi_1(\zeta) = 1 - |\zeta|$ for $|\zeta| \leq 1$. Let $\varphi_2(\zeta) = 2[\varphi_1(\frac{1}{2}\zeta) - \frac{1}{2}]$. The graph of φ_1 is given by the heavy polygonal line above the ζ-axis in figure 2, and the graph of φ_2 is obtained by reflection of every second triangle. We accept it as known that φ_1 is the characteristic function of an arithmetic distribution attributing weight $\frac{1}{2}$ to the origin.[5] Deleting the atom at the origin and

---

[4] Statisticians and astronomers sometimes ask whether a given distribution has a normal component. This problem makes sense because the characteristic function of a normal distribution $\mathfrak{N}_a$ has no zeros and therefore $\mathfrak{N}_a \bigstar F_1 = \mathfrak{N}_a \bigstar F_2$ does imply $\varphi_1 = \varphi_2$ and hence, by the uniqueness theorem, $F_1 = F_2$.

[5] A direct verification requires tedious calculations, but it will be shown in XIX,5 that φ_1 is a characteristic function simply because it is the periodic continuation of a characteristic function (number 5 in the table). Because of symmetry

$$\varphi_1(\zeta) = \sum_{-\infty}^{-\infty} p_k \cos k\pi\zeta;$$

integrating over $-1 < \zeta < 1$ one gets $p_0 = \frac{1}{2}$. The other atoms are at the odd integers, $\pm(2k+1)$ carrying the weight $2/[(2k+1)\pi]^2$. [See XIX,(5.6).]

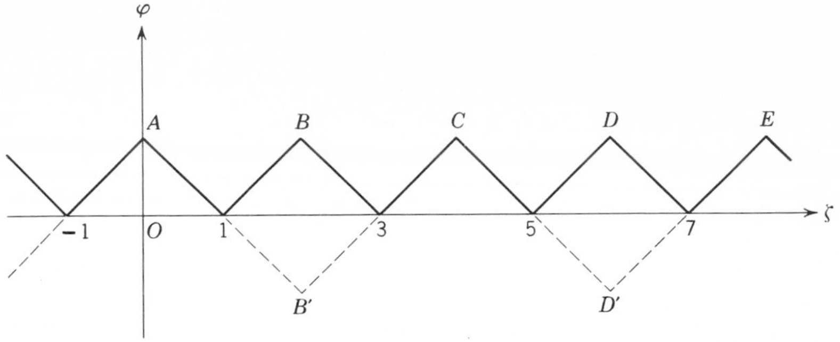

Figure 2.

doubling the weight of the others one gets a new distribution with characteristic function $\varphi = 2[\varphi_1 - \frac{1}{2}]$. Now $\varphi_2(\zeta) = \varphi(\frac{1}{2}\zeta)$ and hence φ_2 is also a characteristic function.

3. UNIQUENESS. INVERSION FORMULAS

Let F and G be two distributions with characteristic functions φ and γ. Then

$$e^{-i\zeta t}\varphi(\zeta) = \int_{-\infty}^{+\infty} e^{i\zeta(x-t)}\, F\{dx\}. \tag{3.1}$$

Integrating with respect to $G\{d\zeta\}$ one gets

$$\int_{-\infty}^{+\infty} e^{-i\zeta t}\varphi(\zeta)\, G\{d\zeta\} = \int_{-\infty}^{+\infty} \gamma(x-t)\, F\{dx\}. \tag{3.2}$$

This identity is known as the *Parseval relation* (which, however, can be written in many equivalent forms; we shall return to it in chapter XIX).

Surprisingly many conclusions can be drawn from the Parseval relation. Here we use it to prove the basic uniqueness theorem which was anticipated in part (*d*) of lemma 1.1.

Theorem 1. *Distinct probability distributions have distinct characteristic functions.*

Proof. Let G stand for the normal distribution $\mathfrak{N}_a$ with density $a\mathfrak{n}(ax)$. Its characteristic function is $\gamma(\zeta) = \sqrt{2\pi}\,\mathfrak{n}(\zeta/a)$, and hence (3.2) takes on the form

$$a\int_{-\infty}^{+\infty} e^{-i\zeta t}\varphi(\zeta)\,\mathfrak{n}(a\zeta)\, d\zeta = \sqrt{2\pi}\int_{-\infty}^{+\infty} \mathfrak{n}\left(\frac{x-t}{a}\right) F\{dx\} \tag{3.3}$$

or

$$(3.4)\qquad \frac{a}{2\pi}\int_{-\infty}^{+\infty} e^{-i\zeta t}\varphi(\zeta)e^{-\frac{1}{2}a^2\zeta^2}\,d\zeta = \int_{-\infty}^{+\infty} \mathfrak{n}\left(\frac{x-t}{a}\right) F\{dx\}.$$

Denote this quantity by $f_a(t)$. The right side shows that f_a is the density of the convolution $F_a = \mathfrak{N}_a \star F$ of F with the normal distribution of variance a^2, and hence $F_a \to F$ as $a \to 0$. The left side in (3.4) expresses F_a in terms of φ, and we see not only that F is uniquely determined by φ, but that we have found a method of calculating F. ▶

Before exploiting the last remark we prove an important consequence of the uniqueness theorem.

Theorem 2. (*Continuity theorem.*) *A sequence $\{F_n\}$ of probability distributions converges to a probability distribution F iff the sequence $\{\varphi_n\}$ of their characteristic functions converges to a continuous limit φ.*

In this case φ is the characteristic function of F, and the convergence $\varphi_n \to \varphi$ is uniform in every finite interval.

Proof. (*a*) *Proper* convergence $F_n \to F$ implies the convergence of the corresponding expectations for every bounded continuous function u. For $u(x) = e^{i\zeta x}$ (and fixed ζ) it follows that $\varphi_n(\zeta) \to \varphi(\zeta)$ where φ is the characteristic function of F. That the convergence is uniform in every finite interval is an immediate consequence of the corollary in VIII,1 [see example VIII,(1.*g*)].

(*b*) Assume $\varphi_n \to \varphi$. By the selection theorem of VIII,6 there exists a sequence $\{n_k\}$ and a possibly defective distribution F such that $F_{n_k} \to F$. Applied to the pair F_{n_k}, φ_{n_k}, formula (3.3) reads

$$(3.3a)\qquad a\int_{-\infty}^{+\infty} e^{-i\zeta t}\varphi_{n_k}(\zeta)\,\mathfrak{n}(a\zeta)\,d\zeta = \sqrt{2\pi}\int_{-\infty}^{+\infty} \mathfrak{n}\left(\frac{x-t}{a}\right) F_{n_k}\{dx\}.$$

Letting $k \to \infty$ we get (3.3) (the left side by bounded convergence, the right side because $\mathfrak{n}$ vanishes at infinity; see VIII,1). Thus (3.3) holds. Since $\sqrt{2\pi}\,\mathfrak{n} \leq 1$ the right side is $\leq F\{\overline{-\infty, \infty}\}$. On the other hand, as $a \to 0$ the normal distribution concentrates near the origin and the left side tends to $\varphi(0) = 1$. It follows that $F\{\overline{-\infty, \infty}\} = 1$, and so the convergence $F_{n_k} \to F$ is proper. By the first part of the theorem, φ is the characteristic function of F, and the uniqueness theorem guarantees that all convergent subsequences $\{F_{n_k}\}$ have the same limit F. Thus $F_n \to F$ and this concludes the proof. ▶

Corollary. *A continuous function which is the pointwise limit of a sequence $\{\varphi_n\}$ of characteristic functions is itself a characteristic function.*

Examples. (*a*) Let G be a continuous distribution with characteristic function γ. Then $|\gamma(\zeta)| < 1$ for $\zeta \neq 0$. The sequence $\{G^{n\bigstar}\}$ does *not* converge properly, and yet $\lim \gamma^n(\zeta)$ exists at all points. Thus the condition that the limit φ be *continuous* is essential both in the theorem and in the corollary. (See problem 9.)

(*b*) *Polya's criterion. Let ω be an even function with $\omega(0) = 1$ and a graph that is concave in $\overline{0, \infty}$. Then ω is a characteristic function.* Indeed, we saw in example (2.*b*) that the assertion is true when the graph is a concave polygon. Now the inscribed polygons to a concave curve are concave, and hence the general assertion is an immediate consequence of the corollary. The criterion (together with a tricky proof) had a surprise value in the early days. Polya used it in 1920 to prove that $e^{-|\zeta|^\alpha}$ for $0 < \alpha \leq 1$ is a characteristic function of a stable distribution. (Cauchy is said to have been aware of this fact, but gave no proof.) Actually $e^{-|\zeta|^\alpha}$ is a characteristic function even for $1 < \alpha \leq 2$, but the criterion breaks down. ►

We defer to chapter XIX a full use of the method developed for the proof of theorem 1. We use it here, however, to derive an important theorem which was used in numbers 5 and 8 of the table in section 2. For abbreviation we write $\varphi \in L$ iff $|\varphi|$ is integrable over $\overline{-\infty, \infty}$.

Theorem 3. (*Fourier inversion.*) *Let φ be the characteristic function of the distribution F and suppose that $\varphi \in L$. Then F has a bounded continuous density f given by*

$$f(x) = \frac{1}{2\pi} \int_{-\infty}^{+\infty} e^{-i\zeta x} \varphi(\zeta)\, d\zeta. \tag{3.5}$$

Proof. We recall that the two sides in (3.4) define the density f_a of a distribution F_a such that $F_a \to F$ as $a \to 0$. From the representation on the left it is clear that $f_a(t) \to f(t)$ boundedly where f is the bounded continuous function defined in (3.5). Thus for every bounded interval I

$$F_a\{I\} = \int_I f_a(t)\, dt \to \int_I f(x)\, dx. \tag{3.6}$$

But if I is an interval of continuity for F the leftmost member tends to $F\{I\}$, and so f is indeed the density of F.

Corollary. *If $\varphi \geq 0$ then $\varphi \in L$ iff the corresponding distribution F has a bounded density.*

Proof. By the last theorem the integrability of φ entails that F has a bounded continuous density. Conversely, if F has a density $f < M$ we get from (3.4) for $t = 0$

$$\text{(3.7)}\qquad \frac{1}{2\pi}\int_{-\infty}^{+\infty}\varphi(\zeta)e^{-\frac{1}{2}a^2\zeta^2}\,d\zeta = \frac{1}{\sqrt{2\pi}\cdot a}\int_{-\infty}^{+\infty}e^{-x^2/(2a^2)}f(x)\,dx < M.$$

The integrand on the left is ≥ 0 and if φ were not integrable the integral would tend to ∞ as $a \to 0$. ►

Examples. (*c*) *Plancherel identity.* Let the distribution F have a density f and characteristic function φ. Then $|\varphi|^2 \in L$ iff $f^2 \in L$ and in this case

$$\text{(3.8)}\qquad \int_{-\infty}^{+\infty} f^2(y)\,dy = \frac{1}{2\pi}\int_{-\infty}^{+\infty}|\varphi(\zeta)|^2\,d\zeta.$$

Indeed, $|\varphi|^2$ is the characteristic function of the symmetrized distribution ${}^0F$. If $|\varphi|^2 \in L$ it follows that the density

$$\text{(3.9)}\qquad {}^0f(x) = \int_{-\infty}^{+\infty} f(y-x)f(y)\,dy$$

of ${}^0F$ is bounded and continuous. Applying (3.5) to ${}^0f$ and letting $x = 0$ we get (3.8). Conversely, if $f^2 \in L$ an application of Schwarz' inequality to (3.9) shows that ${}^0f$ is bounded, and hence $|\varphi|^2 \in L$ by the last corollary. We shall return to the relation (3.8) in XIX,7.

(*d*) *Continuity theorem for densities.* Let φ_n and φ be *integrable* characteristic functions such that

$$\text{(3.10)}\qquad \int_{-\infty}^{+\infty}|\varphi_n(\zeta) - \varphi(\zeta)|\,d\zeta \to 0.$$

By the last corollary the corresponding distributions F_n and F have bounded continuous densities f_n and f, respectively. It is clear from (3.10) and the inversion formula that $f_n \to f$. [The convergence is uniform, the difference $|f_n - f|$ being $< 1/(2\pi)$ times the integral in (3.10).] See problem 13.

(*e*) *Inversion formula for distribution functions.* Let F be a distribution with characteristic function φ, and let $h > 0$ be arbitrary, but fixed. We prove that

$$\text{(3.11)}\qquad \frac{F(x+h) - F(x)}{h} = \frac{1}{2\pi}\int_{-\infty}^{+\infty}\varphi(\zeta)\,\frac{1-e^{-i\zeta h}}{i\zeta h}\,e^{-i\zeta h}\,d\zeta$$

whenever the integrand is integrable (for example, if it is $O(1/\zeta^2)$, that is, if $|\varphi(\zeta)| = O(1/\zeta)$ as $\zeta \to \infty$). Indeed, the left side is the *density* of the convolution of F with the uniform distribution concentrated on $\overline{-h, 0}$; by the product rule the factor of $e^{-i\zeta x}$ under the integral is the characteristic function of this convolution. Thus (3.11) represents but a special case of the general inversion formula (3.5). ►

Note *on so-called inversion formulas.* Formula (3.11) is applicable only when $|\varphi(\zeta)/\zeta|$ is integrable near infinity, but trite variations of this formula are generally applicable. For example, let F_a again denote the convolution of F with the symmetric normal distribution with variance a^2. Then by (3.11)

$$\frac{F_a(x+h) - F_a(x)}{h} = \frac{1}{2\pi}\int_{-\infty}^{+\infty} \varphi(\zeta)e^{-\frac{1}{2}a^2\zeta^2}\,\frac{1-e^{-i\zeta h}}{i\zeta h}\,e^{-i\zeta x}\,d\zeta. \tag{3.12}$$

The statement that if x and $x + h$ are points of continuity of F the right side tends to $[F(x+h) - F(x)]/h$ as $a \to 0$ is a typical "inversion theorem." An infinite variety of equivalent formulas may be written down. The traditional form consists in replacing in (3.12) the normal distribution by the uniform distribution in $\overline{-t, t}$ and letting $t \to \infty$. Such inversion formulas remain a popular topic even though they have lost much of their importance; their derivation from the Dirichlet integral detracts from the logical structure of the theory.

From distributions with integrable characteristic functions we turn to *lattice distributions.* Let F attribute weight p_k to the point $b + kh$, where $p_k \geq 0$ and $\Sigma p_k = 1$. The characteristic function φ is then given by

$$\varphi(\zeta) = \sum_{-\infty}^{+\infty} p_k e^{i(b+kh)\zeta}. \tag{3.13}$$

We suppose $h > 0$.

Theorem 4. *If* φ *is a characteristic function of the form* (3.13) *then*

$$p_r = \frac{h}{2\pi}\int_{-\pi/h}^{\pi/h} \varphi(\zeta)e^{-i(b+rh)\zeta}\,d\zeta. \tag{3.14}$$

Proof. The integrand is a series in which the factor of p_k equals $e^{i(k-r)h\zeta}$. Its integral equals 0 or $2\pi/h$ according as $k \neq r$ or $k = r$, and so (3.14) is true. ►

4. REGULARITY PROPERTIES

The main result of this section may be summarized roughly to the effect that the smaller the tails of a distribution F, the smoother is its characteristic function φ; conversely, the smoother F, the better will φ behave at infinity. (Lemmas 2 and 4.) Most estimates connected with characteristic functions depend on an appraisal of the error committed in approximating e^{it} by finitely many terms of its Taylor expansion. The next lemma states that this error is dominated by the first omitted term.

Lemma 1.[6] *For $n = 1, 2, \ldots$ and $t > 0$*

$$\left| e^{it} - 1 - \frac{it}{1!} - \cdots - \frac{(it)^{n-1}}{(n-1)!} \right| \leq \frac{t^n}{n!}. \tag{4.1}$$

Proof. Denote the expression within the absolute value signs by $\rho_n(t)$. Then

$$\rho_1(t) = i\int_0^t e^{ix}\, dx, \tag{4.2}$$

and for $n > 2$

$$\rho_n(t) = i\int_0^t \rho_{n-1}(x)\, dx. \tag{4.3}$$

By the mean value theorem $|\rho_1(t)| < t$, and the inequality (4.1) now follows by induction. ▶

In the sequel F is an arbitrary distribution function, and φ its characteristic function. For the moments and absolute moments of F (when they exist) we write

$$m_n = \int_{-\infty}^{+\infty} x^n\, F\{dx\}, \qquad M_n = \int_{-\infty}^{+\infty} |x|^n\, F\{dx\}. \tag{4.4}$$

Lemma 2. *If $M_n < \infty$, the* n*th derivative of φ exists and is a continuous function given by*

$$\varphi^{(n)}(\zeta) = i^n \int_{-\infty}^{+\infty} e^{i\zeta x} x^n\, F\{dx\}. \tag{4.5}$$

Proof. The difference ratios of φ are given by

$$\frac{\varphi(\zeta+h) - \varphi(\zeta)}{h} = \int_{-\infty}^{+\infty} e^{i\zeta x}\, \frac{e^{ihx} - 1}{h}\, F\{dx\}. \tag{4.6}$$

According to the last lemma the integrand is dominated by $|x|$ and so for $n = 1$ the assertion (4.5) follows by dominated convergence. The general case follows by induction. ▶

Corollary. *If $m_2 < \infty$ then*

$$\varphi'(0) = im_1, \qquad \varphi''(0) = -m_2. \tag{4.7}$$

The *converse*[7] of the last relation is also true: *If $\varphi''(0)$ exists, then $m_2 < \infty$.*

---

[6] The same proof shows that when the Taylor development for either $\sin t$ or $\cos t$ is stopped after finitely many terms, *the error is of the same sign, and smaller in absolute value, than the first omitted term.* For example, $1 - \cos t \leq t^2/2$.

[7] The argument does not apply to the first derivative. The long outstanding problem of finding conditions for the existence of $\varphi'(0)$ is solved in example XVII,(1.c).

Proof. Denoting the real part of φ by u we have

$$\frac{1-u(h)}{h^2} = \int_{-\infty}^{+\infty} \frac{1-\cos hx}{h^2x^2} \cdot x^2 F\{dx\}. \tag{4.8}$$

Since $u''(0)$ exists the derivative u' exists near the origin and is continuous at the origin. In particular, $u'(0) = 0$ because u is even. By the mean value theorem there exists a θ such that $0 < \theta < 1$ and

$$\left|\frac{u(h)-1}{h^2}\right| = \left|\frac{u'(\theta h)}{h}\right| \leq \left|\frac{u'(\theta h)}{\theta h}\right|. \tag{4.9}$$

As $h \to 0$ the right side tends to $u''(0)$. But the fraction under the integral in (4.8) tends to $\frac{1}{2}$, and so the integral approaches ∞ if $m_2 = \infty$. See problem 11.

Examples. (*a*) A non-constant function ψ such that $\psi''(0) = 0$ cannot be a characteristic function, since the corresponding distribution would have a vanishing second moment. For example, $e^{-|\zeta|^\alpha}$ is not a characteristic function when $\alpha > 2$.

(*b*) *The weak law of large numbers.* Let $\mathbf{X}_1, \mathbf{X}_2, \ldots$ be independent random variables with $\mathbf{E}(\mathbf{X}_j) = 0$ and the common characteristic function φ. Put $\mathbf{S}_n = \mathbf{X}_1 + \cdots + \mathbf{X}_n$. The average $\mathbf{S}_n/n$ has the characteristic function $\varphi^n(\zeta/n)$. Now near the origin $\varphi(h) = 1 + o(h)$, and hence $\varphi(\zeta/n) = 1 + o(1/n)$ as $n \to \infty$. Taking logarithms we see, therefore, that $\varphi^n(\zeta/n) \to 1$. By the continuity theorem 2 of section 3 this implies that *the distribution* of $\mathbf{S}_n/n$ tends to the distribution concentrated at the origin. This is the weak law of large numbers. The simple and straightforward nature of the proof is typical for characteristic functions; a variant will lead to the central limit theorem. ►

Lemma 3. (*Riemann-Lebesgue.*) *If g is integrable and*

$$\gamma(\zeta) = \int_{-\infty}^{+\infty} e^{i\zeta x}\, g(x)\, dx, \tag{4.10}$$

then $\gamma(\zeta) \to 0$ as $\zeta \to \pm\infty$.

Proof. The assertion is easily verified for finite step functions g. For an arbitrary integrable function g and $\epsilon > 0$ there exists by the mean approximation theorem of IV,2 a finite step function g_1 such that

$$\int_{-\infty}^{+\infty} |g(x) - g_1(x)|\, dx < \epsilon. \tag{4.11}$$

The corresponding transforms (4.10) satisfy $|\gamma - \gamma_1| < \epsilon$, and hence there exists a neighborhood of $\pm\infty$ in which $|\gamma(\zeta)| < 2\epsilon$. Since ϵ is arbitrary this implies $\gamma(\zeta) \to 0$. ►

As a simple corollary we get

Lemma 4. *If F has a density f, then $\varphi(\zeta) \to 0$ as $\zeta \to \pm\infty$. If f has an integrable* nth *derivative $f^{(n)}$, then $|\varphi(\zeta)| = o(|\zeta|^{-n})$ as $|\zeta| \to \infty$.*

Proof. The first assertion is contained in lemma 3. If f' is integrable, an integration by parts shows that

$$\varphi(\zeta) = \frac{1}{i\zeta}\int_{-\infty}^{+\infty} e^{i\zeta x} f'(x)\,dx, \tag{4.12}$$

and hence $|\varphi(\zeta)| = o(|\zeta|^{-1})$, and so on. ►

Appendix: The Taylor Development of Characteristic Functions

The inequality (4.1) may be rewritten in the form

$$\left| e^{i\zeta x}\left(e^{itx} - 1 - \frac{itx}{1!} - \cdots - \frac{(itx)^{n-1}}{(n-1)!}\right)\right| \leq \frac{|tx|^n}{n!}. \tag{4.13}$$

From this we get using (4.5)

$$\left|\varphi(\zeta+t) - \varphi(\zeta) - \frac{t}{1!}\varphi'(\zeta) - \cdots - \frac{t^{n-1}}{(n-1)!}\varphi^{(n-1)}(\zeta)\right| < M_n\frac{|t|^n}{n!}. \tag{4.14}$$

If $M_n < \infty$ this inequality is valid for arbitrary ζ and t and provides an upper bound for the difference between φ and the first terms of its Taylor development. In the special case when F is concentrated at the point 1 the inequality (4.14) reduces to (4.1).

Suppose now that all moments exist and that

$$\limsup_{n\to\infty} \frac{1}{n} M_n^{1/n} = \lambda < \infty. \tag{4.15}$$

Stirling's formula for $n!$ then shows trivially that for $|t| < 1/(3\lambda)$ the right side in (4.14) tends to zero as $n \to \infty$, and so the Taylor series for φ converges in some interval about ζ. It follows that φ is analytic in a neighborhood of the real axis, and hence completely determined by its power series about the origin. But $\varphi^{(n)}(0) = (i)^n m_n$, and thus φ is completely determined by the moments m_n of F. Accordingly, *if* (4.15) *holds then F is uniquely determined by its moments*, and φ is analytic in a neighborhood of the real axis. This uniqueness criterion is weaker than Carleman's sufficient condition $\Sigma M_n^{1/n} = \infty$ mentioned in VII,(3.11), but the two criteria are not very far apart. (For an example of a distribution not determined by its moments see VII,3.)

5. THE CENTRAL LIMIT THEOREM FOR EQUAL COMPONENTS

Work connected with the central limit theorem has greatly influenced the development and sharpening of the tools now generally used in probability theory, and a comparison of different proofs is therefore illuminating. Until recently the method of characteristic functions (first used by P. Lévy) was incomparably simpler than the direct approach devised by Lindeberg (not to mention other approaches). The streamlined modern version of the latter (presented in VIII,4) is not more complicated and has, besides, other merits. On the other hand, the method of characteristic functions leads to refinements which are at present not attainable by direct methods. Among these are the local limit theorem in this section as well as the error estimates and asymptotic expansions developed in the next chapter. We separate the case of variables with a common distribution, partly because of its importance, and partly to explain the essence of the method in the simplest situation.

Throughout this section $\mathbf{X}_1, \mathbf{X}_2, \ldots$ are mutually independent variables with the common distribution F and characteristic function φ. We suppose

$$\mathbf{E}(\mathbf{X}_j) = 0, \qquad \mathbf{E}(\mathbf{X}_j^2) = 1 \tag{5.1}$$

and put $\mathbf{S}_n = \mathbf{X}_1 + \cdots + \mathbf{X}_n$.

Theorem[8] **1.** *The distribution of* $\mathbf{S}_n/\sqrt{n}$ *tends to the normal distribution* $\mathfrak{N}$.

By virtue of the continuity theorem 2 in section 3 the assertion is equivalent to the statement that as $n \to \infty$

$$\varphi^n\left(\frac{\zeta}{\sqrt{n}}\right) \to e^{-\frac{1}{2}\zeta^2} \tag{5.2}$$

for all ζ.

Proof. Considering lemma 4.2 and (4.7) it is clear that for fixed ζ

$$\varphi\left(\frac{\zeta}{\sqrt{n}}\right) = 1 - \frac{1}{2n}\zeta^2 + o\left(\frac{1}{n}\right) \qquad n \to \infty. \tag{5.3}$$

From the Taylor series for the logarithm it follows that $\log(1 + z) \sim z$ as $z \to 0$. Thus (5.3) implies

$$n \log \varphi\left(\frac{\zeta}{\sqrt{n}}\right) \to -\tfrac{1}{2}\zeta^2, \tag{5.4}$$

which is the same as (5.2). ▶

It is natural to expect that when F possesses a density f, the *density* of $\mathbf{S}_n/\sqrt{n}$ should tend to the normal density $\mathfrak{n}$. This is not always true, but the exceptions are fortunately rather "pathological." The following theorem covers the cases occurring in common practice.

---

[8] The existence of a variance is not necessary for the asymptotic normality of $\mathbf{S}_n$. For the necessary and sufficient conditions see theorem 1a in XVII,5.

Theorem 2. *If $|\varphi|$ is integrable, then $\mathbf{S}_n/\sqrt{n}$ has a density f_n which tends uniformly to the normal density* $\mathfrak{n}$.

Proof. The Fourier inversion formula (3.5) holds both for f_n and $\mathfrak{n}$, and therefore

$$|f_n(x) - \mathfrak{n}(x)| \leq \frac{1}{2\pi}\int_{-\infty}^{\infty}\left|\varphi^n\left(\frac{\zeta}{\sqrt{n}}\right) - e^{-\frac{1}{2}\zeta^2}\right| d\zeta. \tag{5.5}$$

We have to show that the right side tends to zero as $n \to \infty$.

Choose $\delta > 0$ such that

$$|\varphi(\zeta)| \leq e^{-\frac{1}{4}\zeta^2} \qquad \textit{for} \quad |\zeta| < \delta. \tag{5.6}$$

This is possible because at the origin both sides equal 1, both have a vanishing derivative, but the second derivative of the left side equals -1 and is smaller than the second derivative of the right side (which equals $-\frac{1}{2}$). We now split the integral into three parts and prove that each is $< \epsilon$ for n sufficiently large. (1) As we have seen in the last proof, within a fixed interval $-a \leq \zeta \leq a$ the integrand tends uniformly to zero and so the contribution of $\overline{-a,\ a}$ tends to zero. (2) For $a < |\zeta| < \delta\sqrt{n}$ the integrand is $< 2e^{-\frac{1}{4}\zeta^2}$ and so the contribution of this interval is $< \epsilon$ if a is chosen sufficiently large. (3) We know from lemma 1.4 that $|\varphi(\zeta)| < 1$ for $\zeta \neq 0$, and from lemma 4.3 that $\varphi(\zeta) \to 0$ as $|\zeta| \to \infty$. It follows that the maximum of $|\varphi(\zeta)|$ for $|\zeta| \geq \delta$ equals a number $\eta < 1$. The contribution of the intervals $|\zeta| > \delta\sqrt{n}$ to the integral (5.5) is then less than

$$\eta^{n-1}\int_{-\infty}^{+\infty}\left|\varphi\left(\frac{\zeta}{\sqrt{n}}\right)\right| d\zeta + \int_{|\zeta|>\delta\sqrt{n}} e^{-\frac{1}{2}\zeta^2}\, d\zeta. \tag{5.7}$$

The first integral equals the integral of $\sqrt{n}|\varphi(y)|$, and so the quantity (5.7) tends to zero. ▶

Actually the proof yields[9] the somewhat stronger result that *if $|\varphi|^r \in L$ for some integer r then $f_n \to \mathfrak{n}$ uniformly*. On the other hand, the corollary to theorem 3.3 shows that if no $|\varphi|^r$ is integrable, then every f_n is unbounded. Because of their curiosity value we insert examples showing that such pathologies can in fact occur.

Examples. (*a*) For $x > 0$ and $p \geq 1$ put

$$u_p(x) = \frac{1}{x \log^{2p} x}. \tag{5.8}$$

Let g be a density concentrated on $\overline{0,1}$ such that $g(x) > u_p(x)$ in some interval $\overline{0,h}$. There exists an interval $\overline{0,\delta}$ in which u_p decreases monotonically, and within this interval

$$g^{2*}(x) \geq \int_0^x u_p(x-y)\, u_p(y)\, dy > x\, u_p^2(x) = u_{2p}(x). \tag{5.9}$$

[9] The only change is that in (5.7) the factor η^{n-1} is replaced by η^{n-r}, and φ by φ^r.

By induction it follows that for $n = 2^k$ there exists an interval $\overline{0, h_n}$ in which $g^{n*} \geq u_{np}$, and hence $g^{n*}(x) \to \infty$ as $x \to 0+$. Thus no convolution g^{n*} is bounded.

(*b*) A variant of the preceding example exhibits the same pathology in a more radical form. Let v be the density obtained by symmetrization of g and put

$$f(x) = \tfrac{1}{2}[v(x+1) + v(x-1)]. \tag{5.10}$$

Then f is an even probability density concentrated on $\overline{-2, 2}$, and we may suppose that it has unit variance. The analysis of the last example shows that v is continuous except at the origin, where it is unbounded. The same statement is true of all convolutions v^{n*} Now $f^{2n*}(x)$ is a linear combination of values $v^{2n*}(x+k)$ with $k = 0, \pm 1, \pm 2, \ldots,$ $\pm n$, and therefore unbounded at all these points. The density of the normalized sum $\mathbf{S}_{2n}/\sqrt{2n}$ of variables $\mathbf{X}_j$ with the density f is given by $f_{2n}(x) = \sqrt{2n}\, f^{2n*}(x\sqrt{2n})$. It is continuous except at the $2n + 1$ points of the form $k/\sqrt{2n}$ $(k = 0, \pm 1, \ldots, \pm n)$, where it is unbounded. Since to every rational point t there correspond infinitely many pairs k, n such that $k/\sqrt{2n} = t$ it follows that *the distribution of* $\mathbf{S}_n/\sqrt{n}$ *tends to* $\mathfrak{N}$, *but the densities* f_n *do not converge at any rational point, and the sequence* $\{f_n\}$ *is unbounded in every interval.*

(*c*) *See problem* 17. ▶

To round off the picture we turn to *lattice distributions*, that is, we suppose that the variables $\mathbf{X}_j$ are restricted to values of the form b, $b \pm h$, $b \pm 2h, \ldots$. We assume that h is the *span* of the distribution F, that is, h is the largest positive number with the stated property. Lemma 1.4 states that $|\varphi|$ has period $2\pi/h$, and hence $|\varphi|$ is not integrable. Theorem 2, however, has a perfect analogue for the weights of the atoms of the distribution of $\mathbf{S}_n/\sqrt{n}$. All these atoms are among the points of the form $x = (nb + kh)/\sqrt{n}$, where $k = 0, \pm 1, \pm 2, \ldots$. For such x we put

$$p_n(x) = \mathbf{P}\left\{\frac{\mathbf{S}_n}{\sqrt{n}} = x\right\} \tag{5.11}$$

and we leave $p_n(x)$ undefined for all other x. In (5.12) therefore x is restricted to the smallest lattice containing all atoms of $\mathbf{S}_n/\sqrt{n}$.

Theorem 3. *If F is a lattice distribution with span h, then as $n \to \infty$*

$$\frac{\sqrt{n}}{h}\, p_n(x) - \mathfrak{n}(x) \to 0 \tag{5.12}$$

uniformly in x.

Proof. By (3.14)

$$\frac{\sqrt{n}}{h}\, p_n(x) = \frac{1}{2\pi} \int_{-\sqrt{n}\pi/h}^{\sqrt{n}\pi/h} \varphi^n\left(\frac{\zeta}{\sqrt{n}}\right) e^{-ix\zeta}\, d\zeta. \tag{5.13}$$

Using again the Fourier inversion formula (3.5) for the normal density $\mathfrak{n}$

we see that the left side in (5.12) is dominated by

$$(5.14)\qquad \int_{-\sqrt{n}\pi/h}^{\sqrt{n}\pi/h} \left|\varphi^n\left(\frac{\zeta}{\sqrt{n}}\right) - e^{-\frac{1}{2}\zeta^2}\right| d\zeta + \int_{|\zeta|>\sqrt{n}\pi/h} e^{-\frac{1}{2}\zeta^2}\, d\zeta.$$

Without any change the proof of theorem 2 shows that the first integral tends to zero. The second integral trivially tends to zero and this completes the proof. ▶

6. THE LINDEBERG CONDITIONS

We consider now a sequence of independent variables $\mathbf{X}_k$ such that

$$(6.1)\qquad \mathbf{E}(\mathbf{X}_k) = 0, \qquad \mathbf{E}(\mathbf{X}_k^2) = \sigma_k^2.$$

We denote the distribution of $\mathbf{X}_k$ by F_k, its characteristic function by φ_k, and as usual we put $\mathbf{S}_n = \mathbf{X}_1 + \cdots + \mathbf{X}_n$ and $s_n^2 = \mathrm{Var}(\mathbf{S}_n)$. Thus

$$(6.2)\qquad s_n^2 = \sigma_1^2 + \cdots + \sigma_n^2.$$

We say that the *Lindeberg condition* is satisfied if

$$(6.3)\qquad \frac{1}{s_n^2}\sum_{k=1}^{n}\int_{|x|>ts_n} x^2\, F_k\{dx\} \to 0, \qquad n \to \infty,$$

for each fixed $t > 0$. Roughly speaking, this condition requires that the variance σ_k^2 be due mainly to masses in an interval whose length is small in comparison with s_n. It is clear that σ_k^2/s_n^2 is less than t^2 plus the left side in (6.3) and, t being arbitrary, (6.3) implies that for arbitrary $\epsilon > 0$ and n sufficiently large

$$(6.4)\qquad \frac{\sigma_k}{s_n} \leq \epsilon, \qquad k = 1, \ldots, n.$$

The Lindeberg condition was introduced in VIII,(4.15) and the following theorem coincides with theorem 3 of VIII,4. Each proof has its advantages. The present one permits us to prove that the Lindeberg conditions are, in a certain sense, necessary; it leads also to the asymptotic expansions in chapter XVI, and to convergence theorems for densities (problem 19).

Theorem 1. (*Lindeberg.*) *If* (6.3) *holds the distributions of the normalized sums* $\mathbf{S}_n/s_n$ *tends to the normal distribution* $\mathfrak{N}$.

Proof. Considering the norming (6.1) we have

$$(6.5)\qquad \varphi_k\left(\frac{\zeta}{s_n}\right) - 1 + \frac{1}{2}\frac{\sigma_k^2}{s_n^2}\zeta^2 = \int_{-\infty}^{+\infty}\left(e^{i\zeta x/s_n} - 1 - \frac{i\zeta x}{s_n} + \frac{1}{2}\frac{\zeta^2x^2}{s_n^2}\right) F_k\{dx\}.$$

The basic inequality (4.1) shows

$$(6.6)\qquad \left|\varphi_k\left(\frac{\zeta}{s_n}\right) - 1\right| \leq \tfrac{1}{2}\zeta^2 \cdot \frac{\sigma_k^2}{s_n^2} < \tfrac{1}{2}\epsilon\zeta^2$$

for n sufficiently large. From the Taylor series it is seen that

$$(6.7)\qquad \sum_{k=1}^{n} |\log(1+z_k) - z_k| \leq \sum_{k=1}^{n} |z_k|^2 < \epsilon \sum_{k=1}^{n} |z_k| \qquad |z_k| < \epsilon < \tfrac{1}{2}.$$

With $z_k = \varphi_k(\zeta/s_n) - 1$ this yields for fixed ζ

$$(6.8)\qquad -\sum_{k=1}^{n} \log \varphi_k\left(\frac{\zeta}{s_n}\right) \sim \sum_{k=1}^{n}\left(1 - \varphi_k\left(\frac{\zeta}{s_n}\right)\right)$$

as $n \to \infty$. We have to prove that the right side tends to $-\frac{1}{2}\zeta^2$. For this purpose we estimate the integrand in (6.5) by the basic inequality (4.1). In the interval $|x| \leq ts_n$ we use the upper bound $\dfrac{|\zeta x|^3}{s_n^3} \leq t\dfrac{|\zeta|^3}{s_n^2}x^2$, but for $|x| > ts_n$ the more primitive bound $(\zeta^2 x^2)/s_n^2$. It follows that

(6.9)

$$\sum_{k=1}^{n}\left|\varphi\left(\frac{\zeta}{s_n}\right) - 1 + \frac{1}{2}\frac{\sigma_k^2}{s_n^2}\zeta^2\right| \leq t\,|\zeta|^3 + \zeta^2 \cdot \frac{1}{s_n^2}\sum_{k=1}^{n}\int_{|x|>ts_n} x^2\, F_k\{dx\}.$$

The factor of ζ^2 is the expression occurring in the Lindeberg condition (6.3), and as t can be chosen arbitrarily small, the sum on the left tends to 0. The right side of (6.8) is therefore asymptotically the same as $-\frac{1}{2}\zeta^2 s_n^{-2}\Sigma\sigma_k^2 = -\frac{1}{2}\zeta^2$, which completes the proof. ▶

For examples the reader is referred to VIII,4, to problems 17–20 in VIII,10, and to problem 20 below.

The next theorem asserts that *the Lindeberg condition is also necessary provided that*

$$(6.10)\qquad \frac{\sigma_n}{s_n} \to 0, \qquad s_n \to \infty.$$

Theorem 2. *Assume that the distribution of* $\mathbf{S}_n/s_n$ *tends to* $\mathfrak{N}$ *and that* (6.10) *holds. Then the Lindeberg condition* (6.3) *is satisfied.*

Proof. We begin by showing that (6.4) holds. Suppose $\dfrac{\sigma_k}{s_k} < \epsilon$ for $k > \nu$. The ν quantities $\dfrac{\sigma_1}{s_n}, \ldots, \dfrac{\sigma_\nu}{s_n}$ tend to 0, and for $k > \nu$ one has $\dfrac{\sigma_k}{s_n} \leq \dfrac{\sigma_k}{s_k} < \epsilon$. Now we saw that (6.4) implies (6.8), and so the imaginary part of the right side in (6.8) tends to 0. Thus for fixed $t > 0$ and ζ

$$\tag{6.11} \begin{aligned} \tfrac{1}{2}\zeta^2 - \sum_{k=1}^{n} \int_{|x|\le ts_n} \left(1 - \cos\frac{\zeta x}{s_n}\right) F_k\{dx\} = \\ = \sum_{k=1}^{n} \int_{|x|>ts_n} \left(1 - \cos\frac{\zeta x}{s_n}\right) F_k\{dx\} + o(1) \end{aligned}$$

as $n \to \infty$. The integrand on the right is $\le 2 < \dfrac{2x^2}{t^2 s_n^{\ 2}}$; that on the left, $\le \dfrac{\zeta^2 x^2}{2s_n^{\ 2}}$. Dividing (6.11) by $\frac{1}{2}\zeta^2$ we see therefore that

$$\tag{6.12} 1 - \frac{1}{s_n^{\ 2}} \sum_{k=1}^{n} \int_{|x|\le ts_n} x^2\, F_k\{dx\} \le \frac{4}{t^2\zeta^2} + o(1).$$

The left side is independent of ζ while the right side can be made arbitrarily small by choosing ζ sufficiently large. It follows that the left side tends to zero, and this is evidently the same as (6.3). ►

The ratio σ_n/s_n may be taken as a measure for the contribution of the component $\mathbf{X}_n$ to the weighted sum $\mathbf{S}_n/s_n$ and so (6.10) may be described as stating that asymptotically $\mathbf{S}_n/s_n$ is the sum of "*many individually negligible components.*" In principle the distribution of $\mathbf{S}_n/s_n$ can converge to $\mathfrak{N}$ without (6.10), but this type of convergence differs radically from the phenomenon intuitively associated with the central limit theorem.

Examples. (*a*) Let F_k be a normal distribution with variance $\sigma_k^{\ 2}$. Then $\mathbf{S}_n/s_n$ has the normal distribution $\mathfrak{N}$ irrespective of whether the conditions (6.10) are satisfied.

(*b*) Let G_k be a distribution with zero expectation and unit variance such that $G_k \to \mathfrak{N}$. Put $F_k(x) = G_k(x/k!)$. Then $s_{n-1}^2 = o(s_n^{\ 2})$ and hence the variance of $\mathbf{S}_{n-1}/s_n$ tends to zero. The distribution of $\mathbf{S}_n/s_n$ is therefore asymptotically the same as that of $\mathbf{X}_n/s_n$, which in turn is asymptotically equivalent to the distribution G_n of $\mathbf{X}_n/\sigma_n$. Thus $\mathbf{S}_n$ is asymptotically normally distributed, but only because $\mathbf{X}_n$ is. ►

That the last example describes the general situation of convergence when (6.10) does not hold can be seen from the following theorem (which holds also when n is constrained to a subsequence $n_1, n_2, \ldots$).

Suppose that the distribution of $\mathbf{S}_n/s_n$ *tends to* $\mathfrak{N}$, *and* $\sigma_n/s_n \to p \neq 0$. *Then the distribution of* $\mathbf{X}_n/s_n$ *is asymptotically normal with variance* p^2.

Proof. For simplicity assume first that the distributions F_k are symmetric. By the selection theorem it is possible to find a sequence $n_1, n_2, \ldots$ such that as n runs through it the distributions of $\mathbf{S}_{n=1}/s_n$ and $\mathbf{X}_n/s_n$ tend to (necessarily proper) limits U and V. Then $U \bigstar V = \mathfrak{N}$, and by Cramér's theorem 1 of section 8 this implies that U and V are normal with variances adding up to 1. The variances of $\mathbf{S}_{n-1}/s_n$ and $\mathbf{X}_n/s_n$ tend to

$1-p^2$ and p^2, respectively. Since the variances of V and U cannot exceed these limits it follows that V is the normal distribution with variance p^2.

In the case of unsymmetric distributions we use symmetrization: we know that the symmetrized distributions ${}^0F_n$ are asymptotically normal, and a repeated use of Cramér's theorem shows that the same is true of F_n. ►

The preceding theorems must not be misunderstood: $\mathbf{S}_n/s_n$ *can be asymptotically normally distributed even if* (6.10) *holds and the Lindeberg condition* (6.3) *fails.* In this case, however, the limit distribution is normal with variance $p^2 < 1$.

Example. (*c*) Let $\mathbf{Y}_1, \mathbf{Y}_2, \ldots$ be independent identically distributed variables with $\mathbf{E}(\mathbf{Y}_k) = 0$ and $\text{Var}(\mathbf{Y}_k) = 1$. Let $\mathbf{Z}_1, \mathbf{Z}_2, \ldots$ be independent of each other and of $\{\mathbf{Y}_k\}$ and such that $\mathbf{P}\{\mathbf{Z}_n = \pm n\} = \frac{1}{2}n^{-2}$ and $\mathbf{P}\{\mathbf{Z}_n = 0\} = 1 - n^{-2}$. Then $\mathbf{E}(\mathbf{Z}_n) = 0$ and $\text{Var}(\mathbf{Z}_n) = 1$. By the Borel-Cantelli lemma with probability one only finitely many $\mathbf{Z}_k$ are different from zero. Hence $(\mathbf{Z}_1 + \cdots + \mathbf{Z}_n)/\sqrt{n}$ tends in probability to 0 (see VIII,2) while the distribution of $(\mathbf{Y}_1 + \cdots + \mathbf{Y}_n)/\sqrt{n}$ tends to $\mathfrak{N}$. With this in mind, put $\mathbf{X}_k = \mathbf{Y}_k + \mathbf{Z}_k$. Obviously then the distribution of $\mathbf{S}_n/\sqrt{n}$ tends to $\mathfrak{N}$. But $\text{Var}(\mathbf{S}_n) = 2n$, and the distribution *of the normalized sum* $\mathbf{S}_n/s_n$ *tends to the normal distribution with variance* $\frac{1}{2}$. ►

This example shows that the classical norming of the sums $\mathbf{S}_n$ to zero expectation and unit variance is not *always* natural; to achieve convergence to $\mathfrak{N}$ it is sometimes necessary to use entirely different scale parameters. One may go a step further. The essential feature of the last example is that the series $\Sigma\mathbf{P}\{\mathbf{Z}_k \neq 0\}$ converges. Now this can be true even when the variables $\mathbf{Z}_k$ have no expectations, and hence *it is possible to find variables* $\mathbf{X}_k$ *without expectation such that with appropriate norming constants* a_n *the distribution of* $\mathbf{S}_n/a_n$ *tends to* $\mathfrak{N}$. The preceding theorems can be modified to cover this general situation, but we shall not go into details because the conditions for the convergence are contained in the theorems concerning the triangular arrays $\{\mathbf{X}_k/a_n\}$ derived in chapter XVII. However, the method used for theorems 1 and 2 applies easily when the distributions F_k are symmetric, and the relevant results are instructive. They are covered by problems 21–22, which should not present any great difficulties.

7. CHARACTERISTIC FUNCTIONS IN HIGHER DIMENSIONS

The theory of characteristic functions in higher dimensions is so closely parallel to the theory in $\mathcal{R}^1$ that a systematic exposition appears unnecessary. To describe the basic ideas and notations it suffices to consider the case of two dimensions. Then $\mathbf{X}$ stands for a pair of two real random variables $\mathbf{X}_1$ and $\mathbf{X}_2$ with a given joint probability distribution F. We treat $\mathbf{X}$ *as a column vector* with components $\mathbf{X}_1$ and $\mathbf{X}_2$; similarly, in $F(x)$ the variable x should be interpreted as column vector with components x_1, x_2. On the other hand the variable ζ of the corresponding characteristic function stands for a *row vector* $\zeta = (\zeta_1, \zeta_2)$. This convention has the advantage that ζx now denotes the inner product $\zeta x = \zeta_1 x_1 + \zeta_2 x_2$. *The characteristic function* φ *of* $\mathbf{X}$ *(or of* F*) is defined by*

$$(7.1) \qquad \varphi(\zeta) = \mathbf{E}(e^{i\zeta\mathbf{X}}).$$

This definition is formally the same as in one dimension, but the exponent has a new interpretation and the integration is with respect to a bivariate distribution.

The main properties of bivariate characteristic functions are self-evident. For example, the choice $\zeta_2 = 0$ reduces the inner product ζx to $\zeta_1 x_1$, and hence $\varphi(\zeta_1, 0)$ *represents the characteristic function of the (marginal) distribution of* $\mathbf{X}_1$. For any *fixed choice* of the parameters ζ_1, ζ_2 the linear combination $\zeta_1\mathbf{X}_1 + \zeta_2\mathbf{X}_2$ *is a (one-dimensional) random variable and its characteristic function is given by*

$$(7.2) \qquad \mathbf{E}(e^{i\lambda(\zeta_1\mathbf{X}_1+\zeta_2\mathbf{X}_2)}) = \varphi(\lambda\zeta_1, \lambda\zeta_2);$$

here ζ_1 and ζ_2 are fixed and λ serves as independent variable. In particular, the characteristic function of the sum $\mathbf{X}_1 + \mathbf{X}_2$ is given by $\varphi(\lambda, \lambda)$. In this manner the bivariate characteristic function yields the univariate characteristic function of all linear combinations $\zeta_1\mathbf{X}_1 + \zeta_2\mathbf{X}_2$. Conversely if we know the distributions of all such combinations, we can calculate all expressions $\varphi(\lambda\zeta_1, \lambda\zeta_2)$, and hence the bivariate characteristic function.[10] The next example shows the usefulness and flexibility of this approach. It uses the notations introduced in III,5.

Example. (*a*) *Multivariate normal characteristic functions.* Let $\mathbf{X} = (\mathbf{X}_1, \mathbf{X}_2)$ (thought of as a column vector!) have a non-degenerate normal distribution. For the sake of simplicity we suppose that $\mathbf{E}(\mathbf{X}) = 0$ and denote the *covariance matrix* $\mathbf{E}(\mathbf{X}^T\mathbf{X})$ by C. Its elements are $c_{kk} = \text{Var}(\mathbf{X}_k)$ and $c_{12} = c_{21} = \text{Cov}(\mathbf{X}_1, \mathbf{X}_2)$. For fixed ζ_1 and ζ_2 the linear combination $\zeta\mathbf{X} = \zeta_1\mathbf{X}_1 + \zeta_2\mathbf{X}_2$ has zero expectation and variance

$$(7.3) \qquad \sigma^2 = \zeta C\zeta^T = c_{11}\xi_1^{\,2} + 2c_{12}\zeta_1\zeta_2 + c_{22}\xi_2^{\,2}.$$

---

[10] This proves incidentally that a *probability distribution in* $\mathfrak{R}^2$ *is uniquely determined by the probabilities of all half-planes.* This fact (noted by Cramér and Wold) does not seem to be accessible by elementary methods. For an application to moments see problem 23.

The characteristic function of $\zeta\mathbf{X}$ (with λ as independent variable) is therefore $e^{-\frac{1}{2}\sigma^2\lambda^2}$. Accordingly, the bivariate characteristic function of $\mathbf{X}$ is given by

$$\varphi(\zeta) = e^{-\frac{1}{2}\zeta C\zeta^T}. \tag{7.4}$$

By the same argument *the r-dimensional non-degenerate normal distribution with zero expectation and covariance matrix C has the characteristic function given by* (7.4). Up to the factor $-\frac{1}{2}$ the exponent is the quadratic form in r variables with matrix C. (In the expression for the density the exponent contains the quadratic form with matrix C^{-1}. This is a straightforward generalization of the situation in $\mathcal{R}^1$ where the two exponents reduce to $-\frac{1}{2}\sigma^2\zeta^2$ and $-\frac{1}{2}\sigma^{-2}\zeta^2$, respectively.) ▶

It is occasionally desirable to change both pairs of variables $(\mathbf{X}_1, \mathbf{X}_2)$ and (ζ_1, ζ_2) to *polar coordinates*, that is, to set

$$\mathbf{X}_1 = \mathbf{R}\cos\mathbf{\Phi}, \quad \mathbf{X}_2 = \mathbf{R}\sin\mathbf{\Phi}, \quad \zeta_1 = \rho\cos\theta, \quad \zeta_2 = \rho\sin\theta. \tag{7.5}$$

With this notation we have

$$\varphi(\zeta) = \mathbf{E}(e^{i\rho\mathbf{R}\cos(\theta-\mathbf{\Phi})}). \tag{7.6}$$

It must be borne in mind, however, that this is *not* the characteristic function of the pair of random variables $\mathbf{R}$, $\mathbf{\Phi}$; the latter is given by $\mathbf{E}(e^{i(\zeta_1\mathbf{R}+\zeta_2\mathbf{\Phi})})$.

Examples. (*b*) *Rotational symmetry in* $\mathcal{R}^2$. Suppose that the pair $(\mathbf{X}_1, \mathbf{X}_2)$ represents a "vector issued in a random direction" (see I,10). The joint distribution for $(\mathbf{R}, \mathbf{\Phi})$ factors in the distribution G for $\mathbf{R}$ and the uniform distribution in $\overline{-\pi,\pi}$. Evidently the expectation in (7.6) is independent of θ, and so φ takes on the form

$$\varphi(\zeta_1, \zeta_2) = \int_0^\infty G\{dr\}\int_{-\pi}^{\pi} e^{i\rho r\cos t}\,\frac{dt}{2\pi}. \tag{7.7}$$

The inner integral is easily evaluated on expanding the exponential into a power series. Repeated integration by parts shows that the integral of $\cos^{2k} t$ equals $\binom{2k}{k}2^{-2k}$ while that of $\cos^{2k+1} t$ vanishes. Putting

$$J_0(x) = \sum_{k=0}^{\infty}\frac{(-1)^k}{k!\,k!}\left(\frac{x}{2}\right)^{2k} \tag{7.8}$$

one therefore gets easily

$$\varphi(\zeta_1, \zeta_2) = \int_0^\infty J_0(r\rho)\,G\{dr\}, \tag{7.9}$$

where $\rho^2 = \zeta_1^2 + \zeta_2^2$. The function J_0 is the standard Bessel function of zero order, namely $J_0(x) = I_0(ix)$, where I_0 is the modified Bessel function defined in II,(7.1).

In the special case of *Raleigh's random flights* the distribution G is concentrated at the point 1. Thus *$J_0^n(\sqrt{\zeta_1^2 + \zeta_2^2})$ is the characteristic function of the resultant of n independent unit vectors issued in random directions.* (See I,10.)

(*c*) *Rotational symmetry in* $\mathfrak{R}^3$. The opening argument of the last example is independent of the number of dimensions, but the inner integral in (7.7) takes on various forms. In three dimensions it reduces to

$$\frac{1}{2}\int_0^\pi e^{i\rho r\cos t}\sin t\,dt = \frac{\sin\rho r}{\rho r}. \tag{7.10}$$

In particular, if G is concentrated at the point 1 we get

$$\varphi(\zeta_1, \zeta_2, \zeta_3) = \frac{\sin\rho}{\rho}, \quad \textit{where} \quad \rho^2 = \zeta_1^2 + \zeta_2^2 + \zeta_3^2. \tag{7.11}$$

Letting $\zeta_2 = \zeta_3 = 0$ we get the characteristic function of the $\mathbf{X}_1$-component of a unit vector issued in a random direction. We have thus a new proof that *this component is uniformly distributed in* $\overline{-1, 1}$. (See I,10.) ►

It may be left to the reader to verify that the main theorems concerning characteristic functions in one dimension carry over without essential change. *The Fourier inversion theorem in* $\mathfrak{R}^2$ *states that if* φ *is (absolutely) integrable over the entire plane, then* $\mathbf{X}$ *has a bounded continuous density given by*

$$f(x_1, x_2) = \frac{1}{(2\pi)^2}\iint_{-\infty}^{+\infty} e^{-i(x_1\zeta_1 + x_2\zeta_2)}\varphi(\zeta_1, \zeta_2)\,d\zeta_1\,d\zeta_2. \tag{7.12}$$

Example. (*d*) *Bivariate Cauchy distribution.* We propose to show that the two-dimensional analogue to the Cauchy distribution is represented by the density

$$f(x_1, x_2) = \frac{t}{2\pi\sqrt{(t^2 + x^2 + y^2)^3}}. \tag{7.13}$$

The characteristic function of this density is given by

$$\varphi(\zeta_1, \zeta_2) = e^{-t\sqrt{\zeta_1^2+\zeta_2^2}}, \tag{7.14}$$

which shows that (7.13) shares the main properties of the Cauchy distribution, in particular, that it is *stable*: if $\mathbf{X}^{(1)}, \ldots, \mathbf{X}^{(n)}$ are mutually independent vector variables with the density (7.13). Their average $(\mathbf{X}^{(1)} + \cdots + \mathbf{X}^{(n)})/n$ has the same density.

To verify that (7.14) represents the characteristic function of (7.13) [and, by the way, that (7.13) represents a probability density] it is simplest to show that the pair of functions f, φ satisfies the relation (7.12). With the polar coordinates (7.5) the integral in (7.12) takes on the form[11]

$$(7.15)\qquad -\frac{1}{(2\pi)^2}\frac{d}{dt}\int_{-\pi}^{\pi}d\theta\int_0^{\infty}e^{-\rho[t+ir\cos(\theta-s)]}\,d\rho = \\ = -\frac{1}{(2\pi)^2}\frac{d}{dt}\int_{-\pi}^{\pi}\frac{d\theta}{t+ir\cos(\theta-s)}.$$

The integral being independent of s we can put $s = 0$ to obtain for the real part

$$(7.16)\qquad 2\int_{-\frac{1}{2}\pi}^{\frac{1}{2}\pi}\frac{t}{t^2+r^2\cos^2\theta}\,d\theta = \frac{2\pi}{\sqrt{t^2+r^2}}.$$

(The evaluation depends on the standard substitution $t\tan\theta = y\sqrt{t^2+r^2}$.) Differentiation with respect to t now shows that the quantity (7.15) equals $f(x_1, x_2)$, as asserted. ▶

*8. TWO CHARACTERIZATIONS OF THE NORMAL DISTRIBUTION

We begin by a famous theorem conjectured by P. Lévy and proved in 1936 by H. Cramér. Unfortunately its proof depends on analytic function theory and is therefore not quite in line with our treatment of characteristic functions.

Theorem 1. *Let* $\mathbf{X}_1$ *and* $\mathbf{X}_2$ *be independent random variables whose sum is normally distributed. Then both* $\mathbf{X}_1$ *and* $\mathbf{X}_2$ *have normal distributions.*

In other words, the normal distribution cannot be decomposed except in the trivial manner. The proof will be based on the following lemma of some independent interest.

Lemma. *Let F be a probability distribution such that*

$$(8.1)\qquad f(\eta) = \int_{-\infty}^{+\infty} e^{\eta^2x^2}\,F\{dx\} < \infty$$

for some $\eta > 0$. *The characteristic function* φ *is then an entire function (defined for all complex* ζ*). If* $\varphi(\zeta) \neq 0$ *for all complex* ζ*, then F is normal.*

---

[11] The differentiation with respect to t merely replaces the factor ρ which would otherwise complicate the calculations. This trick is frequently useful.

* This section treats special topics and is not used in the following text.

Proof *of the lemma.* For all complex ζ and real x, η one has $|x\zeta| \leq \eta^2x^2 + \eta^{-2}|\zeta|^2$ and so the integral defining φ converges for all complex ζ and

$$|\varphi(\zeta)| \leq e^{\eta^{-2}|\zeta|^2} \cdot f(\eta). \tag{8.2}$$

This means that φ is an entire function of order ≤ 2, and if such a function has no zeros, then $\log \varphi(\zeta)$ is a quadratic polynomial.[12] Hence $\varphi(\zeta) = e^{-\frac{1}{2}a\zeta^2+ib\zeta}$ where a and b are (possibly complex) numbers. But φ is a characteristic function and hence $-i\varphi'(0)$ equals the expectation, and $-\varphi''(0)$ the second moment of the distribution. It follows that b is real and $a \geq 0$, and so F is indeed normal. ►

Proof *of theorem* 1. Without loss of generality we may assume the variables $\mathbf{X}_1$ and $\mathbf{X}_2$ centered so that the origin is a median for each. Then

$$\mathbf{P}\{|\mathbf{X}_1 + \mathbf{X}_2| > t\} \geq \tfrac{1}{2}\mathbf{P}\{|\mathbf{X}_1| > t\}. \tag{8.3}$$

Now the usual integration by parts [see V,6] shows that

$$f(\eta) \leq \eta^2\int_0^\infty x \cdot e^{\eta^2x^2}[1 - F(x) + F(-x)]\,dx, \tag{8.4}$$

and therefore the functions f_k corresponding to $\mathbf{X}_k$ satisfy the inequalities $f_k(\eta) \leq 2f(\eta)$. As we have seen this implies that the characteristic functions φ_1 and φ_2 are defined for all complex ζ. Since $\varphi_1(\zeta)\,\varphi_2(\zeta) = e^{-\frac{1}{2}a\zeta^2+ib\zeta}$ neither φ_1 nor φ_2 can have a zero, and so $\mathbf{X}_1$ and $\mathbf{X}_2$ are normal. ►

We turn to a proof of the following characterization of the normal distribution enunciated and discussed in III,4.

Theorem 2. *Let* $\mathbf{X}_1$ *and* $\mathbf{X}_2$ *be independent variables and*

$$\mathbf{Y}_1 = a_{11}\mathbf{X}_1 + a_{12}\mathbf{X}_2, \qquad \mathbf{Y}_2 = a_{21}\mathbf{X}_1 + a_{22}\mathbf{X}_2. \tag{8.5}$$

If also $\mathbf{Y}_1$ *and* $\mathbf{Y}_2$ *are independent of each other then either all four variables are normal, or else the transformation* (8.5) *is trivial in the sense that either* $\mathbf{Y}_1 = a\mathbf{X}_1$ *and* $\mathbf{Y}_2 = b\mathbf{X}_2$ *or* $\mathbf{Y}_1 = a\mathbf{X}_2$ *and* $\mathbf{Y}_2 = b\mathbf{X}_1$.

Proof. For the special case of variables $\mathbf{X}_j$ with continuous densities the theorem was proved in III,4. The proof depended on the general solution of the functional equation III,(4.3), and we shall now show that

[12] See, for example, E. Hille, *Analytic function theory*, Boston, 1962, vol. II, p. 199 (Hadamard's factorization theorem). Without use of entire function theory one can argue that $\psi = \log \varphi$ is regular in the whole plane. The inequality (8.2) implies that $|R\psi(\zeta)| \leq C|\zeta|^2$ for large $|\zeta|$, and the conclusion follows from a strengthened version of Liouville's theorem (*ibid.*, p. 193).

an equation of the same type is satisfied by the characteristic functions φ_j of the variables $\mathbf{X}_j$. We show first that it suffices to consider real characteristic functions. This argument illustrates the usefulness of theorem 1.

(*a*) *Reduction to symmetric distributions.* Introduce a pair of variables $\mathbf{X}_1^-$ and $\mathbf{X}_2^-$ that are independent of each other and of the $\mathbf{X}_j$, and distributed as $-\mathbf{X}_1$ and $-\mathbf{X}_2$, respectively. The linear transformation (8.5) changes the symmetrized variables ${}^0\mathbf{X}_j = \mathbf{X}_j + {}^-\mathbf{X}_j$ into a pair $({}^0\mathbf{Y}_1, {}^0\mathbf{Y}_2)$ of *symmetric* independent variables. If the theorem is true for such variables then ${}^0\mathbf{X}_j$ is normal, and by theorem 1 this implies that also $\mathbf{X}_j$ is normal.

(*b*) *The functional equation.* Because of the assumed independence of $\mathbf{Y}_1$ and $\mathbf{Y}_2$ the bivariate characteristic function of $(\mathbf{Y}_1, \mathbf{Y}_2)$ must factor:

$$\mathbf{E}(e^{i(\zeta_1\mathbf{Y}_1+\zeta_2\mathbf{Y}_2)}) = \mathbf{E}(e^{i\zeta_1\mathbf{Y}_1})\,\mathbf{E}(e^{i\zeta_2\mathbf{Y}_2}). \tag{8.6}$$

Substituting from (8.5) we see that this relation implies the following identity for the characteristic functions of $\mathbf{X}_1$ and $\mathbf{X}_2$

$$\begin{aligned}\varphi_1(a_{11}\zeta_1+a_{21}\zeta_2)\,\varphi_2(a_{12}\zeta_1+a_{22}\zeta_2)=&\\ =\varphi_1(a_{11}\zeta_1)\,\varphi_2(a_{12}\zeta_1)\,\varphi_1(a_{21}\zeta_2)\,\varphi_2(a_{22}\zeta_2).&\end{aligned} \tag{8.7}$$

Now (8.7) coincides with III,(4.3) (except that the roles of a_{12} and a_{21} are interchanged). For real and even functions the lemma of III,4 states that in the non-degenerate case $\varphi_j(\zeta) = e^{-a_j\zeta^2}$, and so the $\mathbf{X}_j$ are normal. ►

9. PROBLEMS FOR SOLUTION

1. From the inequality (1.7) conclude (without calculations) that for every characteristic function φ

$$|\varphi(\zeta)|^2 \le 1 - \frac{1 - |\varphi(2\zeta)|}{4} \le e^{-\frac{1}{4}(1-|\varphi(2\zeta)|)}. \tag{9.1}$$

2. If $\varphi = u + iv$ is a characteristic function show that

$$u^2(\zeta) \le \tfrac{1}{2}(1 + u(2\zeta)). \tag{9.2}$$

This in turn implies

$$|\varphi(\zeta)|^2 \le \tfrac{1}{2}(1 + |\varphi(2\zeta)|). \tag{9.3}$$

Hint: For (9.2) use Schwarz' inequality, for (9.3) consider characteristic functions of the form $e^{i\alpha\zeta}\varphi(\zeta)$.

3. With the same notations

$$|\varphi(\zeta_2) - \varphi(\zeta_1)|^2 \le 2[1 - u(\zeta_2 - \zeta_1)].$$

The inequality (1.7) is contained herein when $\zeta_2 = -\zeta_1$.

4. From elementary formulas prove (without explicit integrations) that the characteristic function φ of the density $\frac{1}{\pi}\frac{1-\cos x}{x^2}$ differs only by a constant factor from $2|\zeta| - |\zeta+1| - |\zeta-1|$. Conclude that $\varphi(\zeta) = 1 - |\zeta|$ for $|\xi| \leq 1$.

5. From the characteristic function of the density $ae^{-a|x|}$ derive a new characteristic function by simple differentiation with respect to a. Use the result to show that the convolution of the given distribution with itself has density $\frac{1}{4}ae^{-a|x|}(1 + a|x|)$.

6. Show that $\varphi(\zeta) = e^{t(e^{-|\zeta|}-1)}$ is the characteristic function of a compound Poisson distribution generated by a Cauchy distribution. Find its density for $x > 0$.

7. Using the entry 10 of the table (p. 476) show that $2\pi^2 x \cdot (\sinh x)^{-1}$ is a density with characteristic function $\dfrac{2}{1 + \cosh(\pi\zeta)}$. (*Hint:* Use problem 6 of II,9.)

8.[13] Let $\mathbf{X}$ and $\mathbf{Y}$ be independent random variables with distributions F and G, and characteristic functions φ and γ, respectively. Show that *the product* $\mathbf{XY}$ *has the characteristic function*

$$\int_{-\infty}^{\infty} \gamma\left(\frac{\zeta}{x}\right) F\{dx\} = \int_{-\infty}^{\infty} \varphi\left(\frac{\zeta}{x}\right) G\{dx\}. \tag{9.4}$$

9. In the continuity theorem 3.2 and its corollary it suffices to assume that $\varphi(\zeta) = \lim \varphi_n(\zeta)$ exists for all ζ and that φ is continuous *at the origin*. (It is then automatically continuous everywhere.) An *equivalent* condition is that the convergence be uniform in some interval containing the origin.

10. If $\{\varphi_n\}$ is a sequence of characteristic functions such that $\varphi_n(\zeta) \to 1$ for $-\delta < \zeta < \delta$, then $\varphi_n(\zeta) \to 1$ for all ζ.

11. *Generalization of the converse to* (4.7). Considering the distributions $\dfrac{1}{m_{2k}} x^{2k} F\{dx\}$ (when they exist) prove by induction: the distribution F possesses a finite moment m_{2r} iff the $2r$th derivative of the characteristic function φ exists at the origin.

12. Let f be a probability density with a *positive and integrable* characteristic *function*. Then f has a unique maximum at the origin. If a second derivative f'' exists, then

$$f(0) > f(x) > f(0) - \frac{x^2}{2} f''(0);$$

analogous expansions hold for the first $2r$ terms of the Taylor development. [Note that f is even and hence $f^{(2k+1)}(0) = 0$.]

13. Let g be an even density with a strictly positive characteristic function γ. Then

$$g_a(x) = \frac{g(x)[1 - \cos ax]}{1 - \gamma(a)}$$

[13] Combining (9.4) with the theorem in footnote 1 of V,9 one gets the following criterion due to Khintchine. A function ω *is the characteristic function of a unimodal distribution iff* $\omega(\zeta) = \int_0^1 \varphi(\zeta/x)\,dx$ *where* φ *is a characteristic function.*

is a probability density with characteristic function

$$\gamma_a(\zeta) = \frac{2\gamma(\zeta) - \gamma(\zeta+a) - \gamma(\zeta-a)}{2[1 - \gamma(a)]}. \tag{9.5}$$

As $a \to \infty$ *we have* $\gamma_a \to \gamma$ *but not* $g_a \to g$. This shows that in the continuity theorem for densities the condition (3.10) is essential.

14. If γ is an *arbitrary* positive characteristic function, then γ_a of (9.5) is again a characteristic function.

15. Let φ be a real characteristic function with continuous second derivative φ''. Then [unless $\varphi(\zeta) = 1$ for all ζ]

$$\psi(\zeta) = \frac{1 - \varphi(\zeta)}{\zeta^2} \frac{2}{\varphi''(0)}$$

is a characteristic function belonging to an even density f_2 defined for $x > 0$ by

$$\frac{2}{|\varphi''(0)|} \int_0^\infty [1 - F(t)]\, dt.$$

Generalize to higher moments.

16. Let f be an even density with characteristic function φ. For $x > 0$ put

$$g(x) = \int_x^\infty \frac{f(s)\, ds}{s}, \qquad g(-x) = g(x).$$

Then g is again an even density and its characteristic function is

$$\gamma(\zeta) = \frac{1}{\zeta} \int_0^\zeta \varphi(s)\, ds.$$

17. If u is a density so is

$$f(x) = \sum c_k 2^k\, u(2^k x)$$

if $c_k > 0$, $\Sigma\, c_k = 1$. (If one chooses u concentrated on $\overline{-1, 1}$, only finitely many terms do not vanish and no problems of convergence arise.) If φ is the characteristic function of f show that with an appropriate choice of the c_k

$$\int |\varphi(\zeta)|^n\, d\zeta = \infty, \qquad n = 1, 2, \ldots.$$

Hint: Recall that $(\Sigma c_k p_k)^n \geq \Sigma\, c_k{}^n p_k{}^n$ (if $p_k \geq 0$). The choice $c_k \sim 1/k^2$ will do.

18. Prove the central limit theorem VIII,4.4 for random sums by the method of characteristic functions.

19. From theorem 6.1 derive a central limit theorem for densities analogous to theorem 5.2.

20. Let the $\mathbf{X}_k$ be independent variables such that $\mathbf{X}_k$ assumes the values ± 1 with probabilities $\frac{1}{2}(1 - k^{-1})$, and $\pm\sqrt{k}$ with probabilities $\frac{1}{2}k^{-1}$. Show that there do *not* exist norming constants such that the distribution of $\mathbf{S}_n/a_n$ converges to $\mathfrak{N}$.

21. *Generalized central limit theorem.* Suppose the distributions F_k symmetric

(*a*) By an easy adaptation of the proof of theorem 6.1 show that *the distribution of* $\mathbf{S}_n/a_n$ *tends to* $\mathfrak{N}$ *if for every* $t > 0$

$$\sum_{k=1}^{n} \int_{|x|>ta_n} F_k\{dx\} \to 0, \qquad a_n^{-2}\sum_{k=1}^{n} \int_{|x|\le ta_n} x^2\, F_k\{dx\} \to 1. \tag{9.6}$$

(*b*) Using the proof of theorem 6.2 show that *these conditions are also necessary* provided it is required that $\mathbf{X}_k/a_n \xrightarrow{P} 0$ for $k = 1, \ldots, n$. (If $a_n \to \infty$ monotonically it suffices to require that $\mathbf{X}_n/a_n \xrightarrow{P} 0$.)

22. *Continuation.* In order that there exist norming constants a_n for which the conditions (9.6) are satisfied it is necessary and sufficient that there exists a sequence of numbers $t_n \to \infty$ such that

$$\sum_{k=1}^{n} \int_{|x|>t_n} F_k\{dx\} \to 0, \qquad \frac{1}{t_n^2}\sum_{k=1}^{n} \int_{|x|<t_n} x^2\, F_k\{dx\} \to \infty.$$

In this case one can take

$$a_n^2 = \sum_{k=1}^{n} \int_{|x|<t_n} x^2\, F_k\{dx\}.$$

(This criterion usually can be applied without difficulty.)

23. *Moment problem in* $\mathfrak{R}^2$. Let $\mathbf{X}_1$ and $\mathbf{X}_2$ be two random variables with a joint distribution F. Put $A_k = \mathbf{E}(|\mathbf{X}_1|^k) + \mathbf{E}(|\mathbf{X}_2|^k)$. Show that F is uniquely determined if $\limsup k^{-1} A_k^{1/k} < \infty$.

Hint: Use the uniqueness criterion (4.15) and footnote 10 to section 7. Estimate the kth moment of the linear combinations of $\mathbf{X}_1$ and $\mathbf{X}_2$ in terms of A_k.

24. *Degenerate bivariate distributions.* If φ is a *univariate* characteristic function and a_1, a_2 arbitrary constants, show that $\varphi(a_1\zeta_1 + a_2\zeta_2)$ as a function of ζ_1, ζ_2 represents the *bivariate* characteristic function of a pair $(\mathbf{X}_1, \mathbf{X}_2)$ such that identically

$$a_2\mathbf{X}_1 = a_1\mathbf{X}_2.$$

Formulate the converse. Consider the special case $a_2 = 0$.

25. Let $\mathbf{X}$, $\mathbf{Y}$, $\mathbf{U}$ be mutually independent random variables with characteristic functions φ, γ, ω. Show that the product $\varphi(\zeta_1)\,\gamma(\zeta_2)\,\omega(\zeta_1+\zeta_2)$ represents a bivariate characteristic function, and express the corresponding random vector in terms of $\mathbf{X}$, $\mathbf{Y}$, $\mathbf{U}$.

Hint: Consider a trivariate characteristic function.

Answer: $(\mathbf{U}+\mathbf{X}, \mathbf{U}+\mathbf{Y})$.

CHAPTER XVI*

Expansions Related to the Central Limit Theorem

The topics of this chapter are highly technical and may be divided into two classes. One problem is to obtain estimates for the error in the central limit theorem and to improve on this result by providing asymptotic expansions. A problem of an entirely different nature is to supplement the central limit theorem for large values of the independent variable, where the classical formulation becomes empty.

In order to facilitate access to important theorems, and to explain the basic ideas, we separate the case of identically distributed variables (sections 1–6). The tools used in section 6 for large deviations are independent of the first five sections. The theory developed in these sections depends essentially on two techniques: direct estimation of absolutely convergent Fourier integrals, and smoothing methods. At the cost of some repetitions and some loss of elegance we separate the two main ideas by first treating expansions for densities.

The chapter culminates in the Berry-Esséen theorem of section 5. The smoothing method described in section 3 was first used by A. C. Berry in the proof of this theorem. An endless variety of smoothing procedures are in general use. In fact, the long and glorious history of the subject matter of this chapter has the unfortunate effect that accidents of historical development continue to influence the treatment of individual topics. The resulting diversity of tools and abundance of ad hoc methods has rendered the field proverbial for its messiness. The systematic exploitation of Berry's method and of modern inequalities fortunately permits an amazing unification and simplication of the whole theory.[1]

* This chapter treats special topics and should be omitted at first reading.

[1] The best-known introduction to the asymptotic expansions is H. Cramér (1962). It contains the expansion theorems of sections 2 and 4 for equally distributed variables and a slightly sharper version of theorems 7.2 and 3. Gnedenko and Kolmogorov (1954) treat the material of sections 1–5.

1. NOTATIONS

Except in the last section (which deals with unequal components) we shall denote by F a one-dimensional probability distribution with characteristic function φ. When it exists, the kth moment will be denoted by μ_k:

$$(1.1) \qquad \mu_k = \int_{-\infty}^{+\infty} x^k \, F\{dx\}.$$

We suppose $\mu_1 = 0$ and put, as usual, $\mu_2 = \sigma^2$. For the normalized n-fold convolution we write F_n. Thus

$$(1.2) \qquad F_n(x) = F^{n\bigstar}(x\sigma\sqrt{n}).$$

When a density of F_n exists we shall denote it by f_n.

Except in section 6 (concerned with large deviations) we shall have to deal with functions of the form

$$(1.3) \qquad u(x) = \frac{1}{2\pi}\int_{-\infty}^{+\infty} e^{-i\zeta x} v(\zeta)\, d\zeta,$$

and we will be using the obvious estimate

$$(1.4) \qquad |u(x)| \le \frac{1}{2\pi}\int_{-\infty}^{+\infty} |v(\zeta)|\, d\zeta.$$

Both u and v will be integrable. If u is a probability density, then v is its characteristic function. To simplify expressions we introduce the following

Convention. *The function v in* (1.3) *will be called the Fourier transform of u and the right side in* (1.4) *will be called the Fourier norm of u.*

As always, the normal density is denoted by

$$(1.5) \qquad \mathfrak{n}(x) = \frac{1}{\sqrt{2\pi}}\, e^{-\frac{1}{2}x^2}.$$

Its Fourier transform is the characteristic function $e^{-\frac{1}{2}\zeta^2}$. By repeated differentiation we get therefore the identity

$$(1.6) \qquad \frac{d^k}{dx^k}\,\mathfrak{n}(x) = \frac{1}{2\pi}\int_{-\infty}^{+\infty} e^{-i\zeta x}(-i\zeta)^k e^{-\frac{1}{2}\zeta^2}\, d\zeta$$

valid for $k = 1, 2, \ldots$. Obviously the left side is of the form

$$(1.7) \qquad \frac{d^k}{dx^k}\,\mathfrak{n}(x) = (-1)^k\, H_k(x)\,\mathfrak{n}(x)$$

where H_k is a polynomial of degree k. The H_k are called *Hermite polynomials.*[2] In particular,

$$H_1(x) = x, \qquad H_2(x) = x^2 - 1, \qquad H_3(x) = x^3 - 3x. \tag{1.8}$$

The characteristic property of H_k is, then, that $H_k(x)\, \mathfrak{n}(x)$ *has the Fourier transform* $(i\zeta)^k\, e^{-\frac{1}{2}\zeta^2}$.

2. EXPANSIONS FOR DENSITIES

The central limit theorem XV,5.2 for densities can be strengthened considerably when some higher moments μ_k exist. The important assumption is that[3]

$$\int_{-\infty}^{+\infty} |\varphi(\zeta)|^\nu \, d\zeta < \infty \tag{2.1}$$

for some $\nu \geq 1$. The proof given in XV,5 may be summarized roughly as follows. The difference $u_n = f_n - \mathfrak{n}$ has the Fourier transform

$$v_n(\zeta) = \varphi^n\left(\frac{\zeta}{\sigma\sqrt{n}}\right) - e^{-\frac{1}{2}\zeta^2}. \tag{2.2}$$

The integral of $|v_n|$ tends to zero for two reasons. Given an arbitrarily small, but fixed, $\delta > 0$ the contribution of the intervals $|\zeta| > \delta\sigma\sqrt{n}$ tends to zero because of (2.1). Within $|\zeta| < \delta\sigma\sqrt{n}$ the integrand v_n is small by virtue of the behavior of φ near the origin. The latter conclusion depends only on the fact that $\mu_1 = 0$ and $\mu_2 = \sigma^2$. When higher moments exist we can use more terms in the Taylor development for φ and thus obtain more precise information concerning the speed of convergence $f_n \to \mathfrak{n}$. Unfortunately the problem becomes notationally involved when more than three terms are involved, and we therefore separate the simplest and most important special case.

Theorem 1. *Suppose that μ_3 exists and that $|\varphi|^\nu$ is integrable for some $\nu \geq 1$. Then f_n exists for $n \geq \nu$ and as $n \to \infty$*

$$f_n(x) - \mathfrak{n}(x) - \frac{\mu_3}{6\sigma^3\sqrt{n}}(x^3 - 3x)\, \mathfrak{n}(x) = o\left(\frac{1}{\sqrt{n}}\right) \tag{2.3}$$

uniformly in x.

---

[2] Sometimes Chebyshev–Hermite polynomials. The terminology is not unique. Various norming factors are in use and frequently e^{-x^2} replaces our $e^{-\frac{1}{2}x^2}$.

[3] Concerning this condition see examples XV,(6.*a*, *b*) and problem 17 in XV,9.

Proof. By the Fourier inversion theorem XV,3.3 the left side in (2.3) exists for $n \geq \nu$ and has the Fourier norm

$$(2.4)\qquad N_n = \frac{1}{2\pi}\int_{-\infty}^{+\infty}\left|\varphi^n\left(\frac{\zeta}{\sigma\sqrt{n}}\right) - e^{-\frac{1}{2}\zeta^2} - \frac{\mu_3}{6\sigma^3\sqrt{n}}(i\zeta)^3 e^{-\frac{1}{2}\zeta^2}\right| d\zeta.$$

Choose $\delta > 0$ arbitrary, but fixed. Since φ^n is the characteristic function of a density we have $|\varphi(\zeta)| < 1$ for $|\zeta| \neq 0$ and $\varphi(\zeta) \to 0$ as $|\zeta| \to \infty$ (Lemmas 4 of XV,1 and 3 of XV,4). There exists therefore a number $q_\delta < 1$ such that $|\varphi(\zeta)| < q_\delta$ for $|\zeta| \geq \delta$. The contribution of the intervals $|\zeta| > \delta\sigma\sqrt{n}$ to the integral in (2.4) is then

$$(2.5)\qquad < q_\delta^{n-\nu}\int_{-\infty}^{+\infty}\left|\varphi\left(\frac{\zeta}{\sigma\sqrt{n}}\right)\right|^\nu d\zeta + \int_{|\zeta|>\delta\sigma\sqrt{n}} e^{-\frac{1}{2}\zeta^2}\left(1 + \left|\frac{\mu_3\zeta^3}{\sigma^3}\right|\right) d\zeta$$

and this tends to zero more rapidly than any power of $1/n$.

With the abbreviation

$$(2.6)\qquad \psi(\zeta) = \log\varphi(\zeta) + \tfrac{1}{2}\sigma^2\zeta^2$$

we have therefore

(2.7)

$$N_n = \frac{1}{2\pi}\int_{|\zeta|<\delta\sigma\sqrt{n}} e^{-\frac{1}{2}\zeta^2}\left|\exp\left(n\psi\left(\frac{\zeta}{\sigma\sqrt{n}}\right)\right) - 1 - \frac{\mu_3}{6\sigma^3\sqrt{n}}(i\zeta)^3\right| d\zeta + o\left(\frac{1}{n}\right)$$

The integrand will be estimated using the following general scheme

$$(2.8)\qquad |e^\alpha - 1 - \beta| = |(e^\alpha - e^\beta) + (e^\beta - 1 - \beta)| \leq (|\alpha - \beta| + \tfrac{1}{2}\beta^2)e^\gamma,$$

where $\gamma \geq \max(|\alpha|, |\beta|)$. (That this inequality is valid for arbitrary real or complex α and β becomes evident on replacing e^α and e^β by their power series.)

Given $\epsilon > 0$ it is possible to choose $\delta > 0$ such that for $|\zeta| < \delta$

$$(2.9)\qquad |\psi(\zeta) - \tfrac{1}{6}\mu_3(i\zeta)^3| < \epsilon\sigma^3|\zeta|^3$$

and also

$$(2.10)\qquad |\psi(\zeta)| < \tfrac{1}{4}\sigma^2\zeta^2, \qquad |\tfrac{1}{6}\mu_3(i\zeta)^3| \leq \tfrac{1}{4}\sigma^2\zeta^2.$$

Indeed, owing to the existence of μ_3 there exists a neighborhood of the origin in which ψ is three times continuously differentiable and (2.9) appraises the discrepancy between ψ and its three-term Taylor development.

Using (2.8) it is now obvious that with our choice of δ the integrand in (2.7) is less than

$$(2.11)\qquad e^{-\frac{1}{4}\zeta^2}\left(\frac{\epsilon}{\sqrt{n}}\zeta^2 + \frac{\mu_3^2}{72n}\zeta^6\right),$$

and as ϵ is arbitrary we have $N_n = o(1/\sqrt{n})$ and so (2.3) is true. (See problem 3.) ▶

The same argument leads to higher-order expansions, but their terms cannot be expressed by simple explicit formulas. We therefore postpone the explicit construction of the polynomials involved.

Theorem 2. *Suppose that the moments $\mu_3, \ldots, \mu_r$ exist and that $|\varphi|^\nu$ is integrable for some $\nu \geq 1$. Then f_n exists for $n \geq \nu$ and as $n \to \infty$*

$$(2.12) \qquad f_n(x) - \mathfrak{n}(x) - \mathfrak{n}(x)\sum_{k=3}^{r} n^{-\frac{1}{2}k+1}P_k(x) = o(n^{-\frac{1}{2}r+1})$$

uniformly in x. Here P_k is a real polynomial depending only on $\mu_1, \ldots, \mu_k$ but not on n and r (or otherwise on F).

The first two terms are given by

$$(2.13) \qquad P_3 = \frac{\mu_3}{6\sigma^3}H_3, \qquad P_4 = \frac{\mu_3^{\,2}}{72\sigma^6}H_3 + \frac{\mu_4 - 3\sigma^4}{24\sigma^4}H_4,$$

where H_k stands for the Hermite polynomial defined in (1.7). The expansion (2.12) is called (or used to be called) the Edgeworth expansion for f_n.

Proof. We adhere to the notation (2.6). If p is a polynomial with *real* coefficients $p_1, p_2, \ldots$ then

$$(2.14) \qquad f_n - \mathfrak{n} - n\Sigma p_k H_k$$

has the Fourier norm

$$(2.15) \qquad N_n = \frac{1}{2\pi}\int_{-\infty}^{+\infty} e^{-\frac{1}{2}\zeta^2}\left|\exp\left(n\psi\left(\frac{\zeta}{\sigma\sqrt{n}}\right)\right) - 1 - p(i\zeta)\right| d\zeta.$$

The theorem will be proved by exhibiting appropriate polynomials p. (Their dependence on n is not stressed in order not to encumber the notations.)

We begin by estimating the integrand. The procedure is as in the last proof except that we use the Taylor approximation for ψ up to and including the term of degree r. This approximation will be denoted by $\zeta^2\,\psi_r\,(\zeta)$. Thus ψ_r is a polynomial of degree $r-2$ with $\psi_r(0) = 0$; it is uniquely determined by the property that

$$\psi(\zeta) - \zeta^2\psi_r(\zeta) = o(|\zeta|^r) \qquad \zeta \to 0.$$

We now put

$$(2.16) \qquad p(\zeta) = \sum_{k=1}^{r-2}\frac{1}{k!}\left[\zeta^2\psi_r\left(\frac{\zeta}{\sqrt{n}}\right)\right]^k.$$

Then $p(i\zeta)$ is a polynomial with *real* coefficients depending on n. For fixed ζ, on the other hand, p is a polynomial in $1/\sqrt{n}$ whose coefficients can be calculated explicitly as polynomials in $\zeta, \mu_2, \ldots, \mu_r$. As in the last proof it is obvious that for fixed $\delta > 0$ the contribution of $|\zeta| > \delta\sigma\sqrt{n}$ to the integral in (2.15) tends to zero more rapidly than any power of $1/n$, and thus we are concerned only with the integrand for $|\zeta| < \delta\sigma\sqrt{n}$. To estimate it we use [instead of (2.8)] the inequality

$$(2.17)\qquad \begin{aligned} |e^\alpha - 1 - \sum_1^{r-2} \beta^k| &\le |e^\alpha - e^\beta| + |e^\beta - 1 - \sum_1^{r-2} \beta^k| \\ &\le e^\gamma\left(|\alpha - \beta| + \frac{1}{(r-1)!}|\beta|^{r-1}\right) \end{aligned}$$

valid when $|\alpha| < \gamma$ and $|\beta| < \gamma$.

By analogy to (2.9) we now determine δ such that for $|\zeta| < \delta$

$$(2.18)\qquad |\psi(\zeta) - \zeta^2\psi_r(\zeta)| \le \epsilon\sigma^r|\zeta|^r.$$

The coefficient of ζ in ψ_r being $i^3\mu_3/6$, we can suppose that for $|\zeta| < \delta$ also

$$(2.19)\qquad |\psi_r(\zeta)| < a|\zeta| < \tfrac{1}{4}\sigma^2$$

provided $a > 1 + |\mu_3|$. Finally we require that for $|\zeta| < \delta$

$$(2.20)\qquad |\psi(\zeta)| < \tfrac{1}{4}\sigma^2\zeta^2.$$

For $|\zeta| < \delta\sigma\sqrt{n}$ the integrand in (2.15) is then less than

$$(2.21)\qquad e^{-\frac{1}{4}\zeta^2}\left(\frac{\epsilon\,|\zeta|^r}{n^{\frac{1}{2}r-1}} + \frac{a^{r-1}}{(r-1)!}\,\frac{|\zeta|^{3(r-1)}}{n^{\frac{1}{2}r-\frac{1}{2}}}\right).$$

As ϵ is arbitrary we have $N_n = o(n^{-\frac{1}{2}r+1})$.

We have now found real coefficients p_k depending on n such that the left side in (2.14) is $o(n^{-\frac{1}{2}r+1})$ uniformly in x. For fixed ζ the left side is a polynomial in $1/\sqrt{n}$. Rearranging it according to ascending powers of $1/\sqrt{n}$ we get an expression of the form postulated in the theorem except that the summation extends beyond r. But the terms involving powers $1/n^k$ with $k > \frac{1}{2}r - 1$ can be dropped, and we get then the desired expansion (2.12).

The explicit definition of the polynomials P_k is thus as follows. A polynomial ψ_r of degree $r - 2$ is uniquely determined by the Taylor formula

$$(2.22)\qquad \log\varphi(\zeta) = \zeta^2[-\tfrac{1}{2} + \psi_r(\zeta)] + o(|\zeta|^r)$$

valid near the origin. Rearrange (2.16) according to powers of $1/\sqrt{n}$. Denote the coefficient of $n^{-\frac{1}{2}k+1}$ by $q_k(i\zeta)$. Then P_k is the polynomial such that $\mathfrak{n}(x)\,P_k(x)$ has the inverse Fourier transform $e^{-\frac{1}{2}\zeta^2}q_k(i\zeta)$.

3. SMOOTHING

When the condition (2.1) holds an integration of the expansions for the densities f_n yields analogous expansions for the distributions F_n. To cope with more general situations, however, we shall have to proceed indirectly. To estimate the discrepancy $F_n - \mathfrak{N}$ or a similar function Δ we shall use the Fourier methods of the last section to estimate an approximation ${}^T\Delta$ to Δ, and then appraise the error ${}^T\Delta - \Delta$ by direct methods. In this section we develop the basic tools for this procedure.

Let V_T be the probability distribution with density

$$v_T(x) = \frac{1}{\pi}\frac{1 - \cos Tx}{Tx^2}, \tag{3.1}$$

and characteristic function ω_T. For $|\zeta| \le T$ we have

$$\omega_T(\zeta) = 1 - \frac{|\zeta|}{T}, \tag{3.2}$$

but this explicit form is of no importance. What matters is that $\omega_T(\zeta)$ *vanishes for* $|\zeta| \ge T$, for this circumstance will eliminate all questions of convergence.

We shall be interested in upper bounds for $F_n - \mathfrak{N}$ and, more generally, for functions of the form $\Delta_n = F_n - G_n$. Such functions will be approximated by their convolutions with V_T and we put generically ${}^T\Delta = V_T \star \Delta$. In other words, given a function Δ we define

$${}^T\Delta(t) = \int_{-\infty}^{+\infty} \Delta(t-x)\, v_T(x)\, dx. \tag{3.3}$$

If Δ is bounded and continuous, then ${}^T\Delta \to \Delta$ as $T \to \infty$. Our main problem is to estimate the maximum of $|\Delta|$ in terms of the maximum of $|{}^T\Delta|$.

Lemma 1. *Let F be a probability distribution and G a function such that* $G(-\infty) = 0$, $G(\infty) = 1$, *and* $|G'(x)| \le m < \infty$.

Put

$$\Delta(x) = F(x) - G(x) \tag{3.4}$$

and

$$\eta = \sup_x |\Delta(x)|, \qquad \eta_T = \sup_x |{}^T\Delta(x)|. \tag{3.5}$$

Then

$$\eta_T \ge \frac{\eta}{2} - \frac{12m}{\pi T}. \tag{3.6}$$

Proof. The function Δ vanishes at infinity and the one-sided limits $\Delta(x+)$ and $\Delta(x-)$ exist everywhere, and so it is clear that at some point x_0 either $|\Delta(x_0+)| = \eta$ or $|\Delta(x_0-)| = \eta$. We may assume $\Delta(x_0) = \eta$. As F does not decrease and G grows at a rate $\leq m$ this implies

$$\Delta(x_0+s) \geq \eta - ms \qquad \textit{for} \quad s > 0. \tag{3.7}$$

Putting

$$h = \frac{\eta}{2m}, \qquad t = x_0 + h, \qquad x = h - s, \tag{3.8}$$

we have then

$$\Delta(t-x) \geq \frac{\eta}{2} + mx \qquad \textit{for} \quad |x| \leq h. \tag{3.9}$$

We now estimate the convolution integral in (3.3) using (3.9) and the bound $\Delta(t-x) \geq -\eta$ for $|x| > h$. The contribution of the linear term vanishes for reasons of symmetry; since the density v_T attributes to $|x| > h$ a mass $\leq 4/(\pi Th)$ we get

$$^T\Delta(x_0) \geq \frac{\eta}{2}\left[1 - \frac{4}{\pi Th}\right] - \eta \cdot \frac{4}{\pi Th} = \frac{\eta}{2} - \frac{6\eta}{\pi Th}. \tag{3.10}$$

With h defined by (3.8) this reduces to the assertion (3.6), and the proof is complete. ►

In our applications G will have a derivative g coinciding either with the normal density $\mathfrak{n}$ or with one of the finite expansions described in the last section. In every case g will have a Fourier transform γ with two continuous derivatives such that $\gamma(0) = 1$ and $\gamma'(0) = 0$. Obviously then the convolution $^Tg = V_T \bigstar g$ has the Fourier transform $\gamma\omega_T$. Similarly, by the Fourier inversion theorem 3 of XV,3 the product $\varphi\omega_T$ is the Fourier transform of the density ^Tf of $V_T \bigstar F$. In other words,

$$^Tf(x) - {^Tg(x)} = \frac{1}{2\pi}\int_{-T}^{T} e^{-i\zeta x}[\varphi(\zeta) - \gamma(\zeta)]\, \omega_T(\zeta)\, d\zeta. \tag{3.11}$$

We now show that this is equivalent to

$$^T\Delta(x) = \frac{1}{2\pi}\int_{-T}^{T} e^{-i\zeta x}\, \frac{\varphi(\zeta) - \gamma(\zeta)}{-i\zeta x}\, \omega_T(\zeta)\, d\zeta. \tag{3.12}$$

First of all, since $\varphi(0) = \gamma(0) = 1$ and $\varphi'(0) = \gamma'(0) = 0$ the fraction is a continuous function vanishing at the origin, and so no problem of convergence arises. By the Riemann-Lebesgue lemma 4 of XV,4 the right side tends to 0 as $|x| \to \infty$. Formal differentiation of (3.12) leads to (3.11), and so the two sides in (3.12) can differ only by a constant. As both vanish at infinity they must be identical.

In (3.12) we have an upper bound for η_T which, combined with (3.6), yields an upper bound for η, namely

$$|F(x) - G(x)| \le \frac{1}{\pi}\int_{-T}^{T}\left|\frac{\varphi(\zeta)-\gamma(\zeta)}{\zeta}\right| d\zeta + \frac{24m}{\pi T}. \tag{3.13}$$

As this inequality will be the basis for all estimates in the next two sections we recapitulate the conditions of its validity.

Lemma 2. *Let F be a probability distribution with vanishing expectation and characteristic function φ. Suppose that $F - G$ vanishes at $\pm\infty$ and that G has a derivative g such that $|g| \le m$. Finally, suppose that g has a continuously differentiable Fourier transform γ such that $\gamma(0) = 1$ and $\gamma'(0) = 0$. Then* (3.13) *holds for all x and $T > 0$.*

We shall give two *independent* applications of this inequality: In the next section we derive integrated versions of the expansion theorems of section 2. In section 5 we derive the famous Berry-Esséen bound for the discrepancy $F_n - \mathfrak{N}$.

4. EXPANSIONS FOR DISTRIBUTIONS

The formal analogue to theorem 2.1 obtained by integrating (2.3) would state that

$$F_n(x) - \mathfrak{N}(x) - \frac{\mu_3}{6\sigma^3\sqrt{n}}(1 - x^2)\,\mathfrak{n}(x) = o\left(\frac{1}{\sqrt{n}}\right). \tag{4.1}$$

Now if F is a lattice distribution the jumps of F_n are of the order of magnitude $1/\sqrt{n}$ [see XV,(5.12)], and so (4.1) cannot be true of lattice distributions. We shall show, however, that (4.1) is true for *all* other distributions and that even lattice distributions require only a minor amendment. For convenience we separate the two cases.

Theorem 1. *If F is not a lattice distribution and if μ_3 exists, then* (4.1) *holds uniformly in x.*

Proof. Put

$$G(x) = \mathfrak{N}(x) - \frac{\mu_3}{6\sigma^3\sqrt{n}}(x^2 - 1)\mathfrak{n}(x). \tag{4.2}$$

Then G satisfies the conditions of the last lemma with

$$\gamma(\zeta) = e^{-\frac{1}{2}\zeta^2}\left[1 + \frac{\mu_3}{6\sigma^3\sqrt{n}}(i\zeta)^3\right]. \tag{4.3}$$

We shall use the inequality (3.13) with $T = a\sqrt{n}$ where the constant a is chosen so large that $24|G'(x)| < \epsilon a$ for all x. Then

$$(4.4) \qquad |F_n(x) - G(x)| \le \int_{-a\sqrt{n}}^{a\sqrt{n}} \left| \frac{\varphi^n\left(\frac{\zeta}{\sigma\sqrt{n}}\right) - \gamma(\zeta)}{\zeta} \right| d\zeta + \frac{\epsilon}{\sqrt{n}}.$$

The numerator coincides with the integrand in (2.4), and we can repeat the proof of theorem 2.1 without change. Since F is not a lattice distribution the maximum of $|\varphi(\zeta)|$ for $\delta \le |\zeta| \le a\sigma$ is strictly less than 1 owing to lemma 4 of XV,1. As in section 2 it follows that the contribution of $|\zeta| > \delta\sigma\sqrt{n}$ tends to zero faster than any power of $1/n$, and for $|\zeta| < \delta\sigma\sqrt{n}$ we have the estimate (2.11) for the numerator in (4.4). Thus the right side in (4.4) is $< 1000 \dfrac{\epsilon}{\sqrt{n}} + o\left(\dfrac{1}{n}\right)$ and, ϵ being arbitrary, the theorem is proved. ►

This argument breaks down for lattice distributions because their characteristic functions are periodic (and so the contribution of $|\zeta| > \delta\sigma\sqrt{n}$ does not tend to zero at all). The theorem can nevertheless be saved by a natural reformulation which takes into account the lattice character. The distribution function F is a stepfunction, but we shall approximate it by a continuous distribution function $F^{\#}$ with polygonal graph.

Let F be concentrated on the lattice of points b, $b \pm h$, $b \pm 2h$, ... but on no sublattice. (In other words, h is *the span* of F.) The convolution of F with the uniform distribution on $-\frac{1}{2}h < x < \frac{1}{2}h$ is defined by

$$(4.5) \qquad F^{\#}(x) = \frac{1}{h} \int_{-h/2}^{h/2} F(x-y)\, dy.$$

The graph of $F^{\#}$ is a polygonal line with vertices at the points of the form $b + (n + \frac{1}{2})h$. At such points $F^{\#}(x) = F(x)$, whereas at the points of the lattice

$$(4.6) \qquad F^{\#}(x) = \tfrac{1}{2}(F(x) + F(x-)).$$

We shall call $F^{\#}$ *the polygonal approximant to F.*

Theorem 2.[4] *For lattice distributions the expansion* (4.1) *remains true when applied to the polygonal approximant $F_n^{\#}$ of F_n rather than to F itself.*

---

[4] Despite the difference in appearance this theorem is equivalent to a theorem of Esséen in which a periodic function is added to (4.1). The proof of the latter depends on Fourier series and very intricate calculations. (See, for example, Gnedenko and Kolmogorov [1954].) Formal elegance would require the combination of theorems 1 and 2 and their proofs by permitting any smoothing with a uniform distribution.

This means, in particular, that *at lattice points* the approximation (4.1) holds when F_n is replaced by the arithmetic mean $\frac{1}{2}[F_n(x) + F_n(x-)]$.

Proof. The polygonal approximant $F_n^{\#}$ to F_n is the convolution of F_n with the uniform distribution in $-\dfrac{h}{2\sigma\sqrt{n}} < x < \dfrac{h}{2\sigma\sqrt{n}}$. Denote by $G^{\#}$ the convolution of G with the same uniform distribution. In (4.5) the integral of the linear term of the Taylor expansion vanishes, and it is seen that if $|F''(x)| < m$ then $|F^{\#}(x) - F(x)| < mh^2$. For the same reason the difference $G^{\#} - G$ is uniformly $O(1/n)$ and hence it suffices to prove that $F_n^{\#} - G^{\#} = o(1/\sqrt{n})$. But for this difference the inequality (4.4) takes on the form

(4.7)
$$|F_n^{\#}(x) - G^{\#}(x)| \le \int_{-a\sqrt{n}}^{a\sqrt{n}} \left| \frac{\varphi^n\left(\dfrac{\zeta}{\sigma\sqrt{n}}\right) - \gamma(\zeta)}{\zeta} \right| \cdot \left| \frac{\sin \dfrac{h\zeta}{2\sigma\sqrt{n}}}{\dfrac{h\zeta}{2\sigma\sqrt{n}}} \right| d\zeta + \frac{\epsilon}{\sqrt{n}},$$

the new factor being the characteristic function of our uniform distribution. The integrand is dominated by that in (4.4) and it remains only to prove that for fixed δ the contribution of $|\zeta| > \delta\sigma\sqrt{n}$ to the integral in (4.7) is $o(1/\sqrt{n})$. Actually it is $O(1/n)$. To see this it suffices to verify that

$$\int_{\delta}^{a/\sigma} \left| \varphi^n(y) \sin \frac{hy}{2} \right| dy = O\left(\frac{1}{n}\right). \tag{4.8}$$

By lemma 4 of XV,1 the integrand is an even function with period $2\pi/h$ and hence (4.8) will be true if

$$\int_0^{\pi/h} |\varphi^n(y)|\, y\, dy = O\left(\frac{1}{n}\right).$$

This relation holds because in a neighborhood of the origin $|\varphi(y)| < e^{-\frac{1}{4}\sigma^2 y^2}$ while outside this neighborhood the integrand decreases faster than any power of n. ▶

We turn to higher-order expansions. The proof of (4.1) differs from the proof of theorem 2.1 only by the smoothing, which accounts for the finite limits in the integral (4.4). The same smoothing can be applied to the higher expansions of theorem 2.2, but it is obvious that to achieve an error term of the order of magnitude $n^{-\frac{1}{2}r+1}$ we shall have to take $T \sim an^{\frac{1}{2}r-1}$. Here one difficulty arises. The proof of (4.1) depended on the fact that the maximum of $|\varphi(\zeta/(\sigma\sqrt{n}))|$ in $\delta\sigma\sqrt{n} < |\zeta| < T$ is less than one. For non-lattice distributions this is always true when $T = a\sqrt{n}$, but not necessarily when T increases as some higher power of n. For higher-order expansions we are therefore compelled to introduce the assumption that

$$\limsup_{|\zeta|\to\infty} |\varphi(\zeta)| < 1 \tag{4.9}$$

which for non-lattice distributions implies that the maximum q_δ of $|\varphi(\zeta)|$ for $|\zeta| > \delta$ is less than 1. With this additional assumption the method of proof given in detail for (4.1) applies *without change* to the expansions of theorem 2.2 and leads to

Theorem 3. *If* (4.9) *holds and the moments* $\mu_3, \ldots, \mu_r$ *exist, then as* $n \to \infty$,

$$F_n(x) - \mathfrak{N}(x) - \mathfrak{n}(x)\sum_{k=3}^{r} n^{-\frac{1}{2}k+1}R_k(x) = o(n^{-\frac{1}{2}r+1}) \tag{4.10}$$

uniformly in x. *Here* R_k *is a polynomial depending only on* $\mu_1, \ldots, \mu_r$ *but not on* n *and* r (*or otherwise on* F).

The expansion (4.10) is simply the integrated version of (2.12) and the polynomials R_k are related to those in (2.12) by

$$\mathfrak{n}(x)\,P_k(x) = \frac{d}{dx}\,\mathfrak{n}(x)\,R_k(x). \tag{4.11}$$

There is therefore no need to repeat their construction. The condition (4.9) is satisfied by every non-singular F.

(4.10) is called the *Edgeworth expansion* of F. If F has moments of all orders, one is tempted to let $r \to \infty$, but the resulting infinite series need not converge for any n. (Cramér showed that it converges for all n iff $e^{\frac{1}{4}x^2}$ is integrable with respect to F.) The formal Edgeworth series should not be confused with the Hermite polynomial expansion

$$F(x) - \mathfrak{N}(x) = \sum_{k=1}^{\infty} c_k\, H_k(x)e^{-\frac{1}{2}x^2} \tag{4.12}$$

which is convergent whenever F has a finite expectation, but is without deeper probabilistic meaning. For example even if it is possible to expand each F_n into a series of the form (4.12) the coefficients are not indicative of the speed of convergence $F_n \to \mathfrak{N}$.

5. THE BERRY-ESSÉEN THEOREM

The following important theorem was discovered (with different proofs) by A. C. Berry (1941) and G. Esséen (1942).

Theorem 1. *If* F *has zero expectation and*

$$\rho = \int_{-\infty}^{+\infty} |x|^3\, F\{dx\} < \infty, \tag{5.1}$$

then for all x *and* n

$$|F_n(x) - \mathfrak{N}(x)| < \frac{33}{4}\cdot\frac{\rho}{\sigma^3\sqrt{n}}. \tag{5.2}$$

The striking feature is that the upper bound is independent of the individual distribution. Theorem 4.1 provides a better asymptotic estimate, but the speed of convergence depends on the given distribution F. The two theorems emphasize different aspects of the same situation and the proofs here presented differ only in the details of the estimate. In view of the importance of the theorem we repeat the argument and rely entirely on the tools developed in section 3. The factor $\frac{33}{4}$ in (5.2) can be lowered, but we shall not attempt to get good estimates (or the true bound C.)[5]

Proof.[6] When $G = \mathfrak{N}$ the basic inequality (3.13) takes on the form

$$(5.3)\quad |F_n(x) - \mathfrak{N}(x)| \leq \frac{1}{\pi}\int_{-T}^{T} \left|\varphi^n\left(\frac{\zeta}{\sigma\sqrt{n}}\right) - e^{-\frac{1}{2}\zeta^2}\right| \frac{1}{|\zeta|}\, d\zeta + \frac{24}{T\pi\sqrt{2\pi}}\cdot$$

In an interval around the origin free of zeros of φ we have

$$(5.4)\quad -\log\varphi(\zeta) - \tfrac{1}{2}\sigma^2\zeta^2 = (1 - \varphi(\zeta) - \tfrac{1}{2}\sigma^2\zeta^2) + \sum_{k=2}^{\infty} \frac{1}{k}(1 - \varphi(\zeta))^k.$$

Owing to the moment inequality $\sigma^6 < \rho^2$, and therefore

$$(5.5)\quad |1 - \varphi(\zeta)| \leq \tfrac{1}{2}\sigma^2\zeta^2 < \tfrac{1}{2} \qquad \text{for}\quad |\zeta| < \frac{\sigma^2}{\rho}\cdot$$

The first term on the right in (5.4) is dominated by $\frac{1}{6}\rho|\zeta|^3$ [see XV,(4.1)]. Comparing the series to a geometric series with ratio $\frac{1}{2}$ we get therefore for $|\zeta| < \sigma^2/\rho$

$$(5.6)\quad |\log\varphi(\zeta) + \tfrac{1}{2}\sigma^2\zeta^2| \leq \tfrac{1}{6}\rho|\zeta|^3 + \tfrac{1}{4}\sigma^4\zeta^4 \leq \tfrac{5}{12}\,\rho|\zeta|^3.$$

Let $T = (\sigma^3/\rho)\sqrt{n}$. Using (5.6) and remembering that $|e^t - 1| \leq |t|e^{|t|}$ we see that the integrand in (5.3) is dominated by

$$(5.7)\quad \begin{aligned} e^{-\frac{1}{2}\zeta^2}\,\frac{\exp\left(\frac{5}{12}\frac{\rho}{\sigma^3}\frac{|\zeta|^3}{\sqrt{n}}\right) - 1}{\zeta} &\leq \frac{5}{12}\frac{\rho}{\sigma^3\sqrt{n}}\zeta^2\exp\left(-\frac{1}{2}\zeta^2 + \frac{5}{12}\frac{\rho}{\sigma^3}\frac{|\zeta|^3}{\sqrt{n}}\right)\\ &\leq \frac{5}{12}\frac{\rho}{\sigma^3\sqrt{n}}\zeta^2 e^{-\frac{1}{12}\zeta^2}. \end{aligned}$$

[5] Berry calculated $C \leq 1.88$ and Esséen $C \leq 7.59$, but the former calculation was found in error. Unpublished calculations mention $C \leq 2.9$ (Esséen, 1956) and $C \leq 2.05$ (D. L. Wallace, 1958). See problem 6.

[6] A simpler and better proof is outlined in problem 5. The advantage of the present proof is that it applies *without change* to the case of variable distributions (theorem 7.1).

The integral of $\zeta^2 e^{-\frac{1}{12}\zeta^2}$ being $6\sqrt{12\pi}$ we get finally from (5.3)

$$(5.8)\qquad \frac{\sigma^3\sqrt{n}}{\rho}\,|F_n(x) - \mathfrak{N}(x)| \leq \frac{1}{\sqrt{2\pi}}\left(5\sqrt{6} + \frac{24}{\pi}\right) < \frac{12.5 + 8}{\sqrt{2\pi}} < 8.2,$$

which proves (5.2). ►

6. LARGE DEVIATIONS

For very large x both $F_n(x)$ and $\mathfrak{N}(x)$ are close to unity, and our expansions and approximations become redundant: One needs an estimate of the *relative* error in approximating $1 - F_n$ by $1 - \mathfrak{N}$. Many times we would like to use the relation

$$(6.1)\qquad \frac{1 - F_n(x)}{1 - \mathfrak{N}(x)} \to 1$$

in situations where both x and n tend to infinity. This relation cannot be true generally since for the symmetric binomial distribution the numerator vanishes for all $x > \sqrt{n}$. We shall show, however that (6.1) is true if x varies with n in such a way that $xn^{-1/6} \to 0$ provided that the integral

$$(6.2)\qquad f(\zeta) = \int_{-\infty}^{+\infty} e^{\zeta x}\, F\{dx\}$$

exists for all ζ in some interval $|\zeta| < \zeta_0$. [This amounts to saying that the characteristic function $\varphi(\zeta) = f(i\zeta)$ is analytic in a neighborhood of the origin, but it is preferable to deal with the real function f.]

Theorem 1.[7] *If the integral* (6.2) *converges for* $|\zeta| < \zeta_0$ *and* x *varies with* n *in such a way that* $x = o(n^{1/6})$, *then* (6.1) *is true.*

Changing x into $-x$ we obtain the dual theorem for the left tail. The theorem is presumably general enough to cover "all situations of practical interest," but the method of proof will lead to much stronger results.

For the proof we switch from f to its logarithm. In a neighborhood of the origin

$$(6.3)\qquad \psi(\zeta) = \log f(\zeta) = \sum \frac{\psi_k}{k!}\zeta^k$$

defines an analytic function. The coefficient ψ_k depends only on $\mu_1, \ldots, \mu_k$ and is called the *semi-invariant of order* k of F. In general $\psi_1 = \mu_1$, $\psi_2 = \sigma^2, \ldots$. In the present case $\mu_1 = 0$ and therefore $\psi_1 = 0$, $\psi_2 = \sigma^2$, $\psi_3 = \mu_3, \ldots$.

---

[7] See theorem 7.4 for a generalization to unequal components.

The proof is based on the technique of associated distributions.[8] With the distribution F we associate the new probability distribution V such that

$$V\{dx\} = e^{-\psi(s)}e^{sx}\, F\{dx\}, \tag{6.4}$$

where the parameter s is chosen within the interval of convergence of ψ. The function

$$v(\zeta) = \frac{f(\zeta+s)}{f(s)} \tag{6.5}$$

plays for V the same role as does f for the original distribution F. In particular, it follows by differentiation of (6.5) that V has expectation $\psi'(s)$ and variance $\psi''(s)$.

The idea of the proof can now be explained roughly as follows: It is readily seen from either (6.4) or (6.5) that the distributions $F^{n\bigstar}$ and $V^{n\bigstar}$ again stand in the relationship (6.4) except that the norming constant $e^{-\psi(s)}$ is replaced by $e^{-n\psi(s)}$. Now $V^{n\bigstar}$ has expectation $n\psi'(s)$ and the central limit theorem therefore provides a good approximation to $F^{n\bigstar}(n\psi'(s)) = F_n(\sqrt{n}\,\psi'(s)/\sigma)$. Choosing s such that

$$\frac{1}{\sigma}\,\psi'(s) = \frac{x}{\sqrt{n}}, \tag{6.6}$$

we shall get (6.1) and other relations of similar nature. The idea is simple, but the calculations are messy.

Proof *of theorem* 1. From the definition

$$1 - F^{n\bigstar}(n\psi'(s)) = e^{n\psi(s)}\int_{n\psi'(s)}^{\infty} e^{-sy}\, V^{n\bigstar}\{dy\}. \tag{6.7}$$

We now proceed in two steps:

(*a*) We begin by calculating the quantity A_s obtained on replacing $V^{n\bigstar}$ by the normal distribution having the same expectation $n\psi'(s)$ and the same variance $n\psi''(s)$. The standard substitution $y = n\psi'(s) + t\sqrt{n\psi''(s)}$ yields

$$A_s = e^{n[\psi(s)-s\psi'(s)]}\cdot\frac{1}{\sqrt{2\pi}}\int_0^{\infty} e^{-ts\sqrt{n\psi''(s)}-\frac{1}{2}t^2}\,dt. \tag{6.8}$$

Completing the square in the exponent we get

$$A_s = e^{n[\psi(s)-s\psi'(s)]}\rho(s\sqrt{n\,\psi''(s)}) \tag{6.9}$$

[8] It was employed in renewal theory (XI,6) and for random walks (XII,4).

where we put for abbreviation

$$\rho(t) = e^{\frac{1}{2}t^2}\,[1 - \mathfrak{N}(t)]. \tag{6.10}$$

From **1**; VII,(1.8) we know that for $t > 0$

$$\frac{1}{t} - \frac{1}{t^3} < \sqrt{2\pi}\,\rho(t) < \frac{1}{t}. \tag{6.11}$$

By differentiation of (6.10) it follows therefore that

$$0 \leq -\sqrt{2\pi}\,\rho'(t) < \frac{1}{t^2}. \tag{6.12}$$

We turn to the choice of the parameter s. For sufficiently small values of the right side the equation (6.6) determines uniquely a root s *which is an analytic function of* $x/\sqrt{n}$ *such that*

$$s \sim \frac{x}{\sigma\sqrt{n}} \qquad\qquad \frac{x}{\sqrt{n}} \to 0. \tag{6.13}$$

Consider A_s as an analytic function of x. Near the origin we have

$$n[\psi(x) - s\psi'(s)] = -\tfrac{1}{2}n\sigma^2 s^2 + \cdots$$

and hence

$$A_s = e^{-\frac{1}{2}x^2}\rho(\bar{x})\left[1 + O\left(\frac{x^3}{\sqrt{n}}\right)\right] \tag{6.14}$$

where we put for abbreviation

$$\bar{x} = s\sqrt{n\,\psi''(s)}. \tag{6.15}$$

A trite calculation shows that the expansion of $\bar{x} - x$ in powers of s begins with the cubic term, and hence by (6.12) and (6.11)

$$|\rho(\bar{x}) - \rho(x)| = O\left(\frac{x^3}{n}\,|\rho'(x)|\right) = O\left(\frac{x}{n}\right) = O\left(\frac{x^3}{n}\,\rho(x)\right). \tag{6.16}$$

Substituting into (6.14) we get finally

$$A_s = [1 - \mathfrak{N}(x)]\cdot\left[1 + O\left(\frac{x^3}{\sqrt{n}}\right)\right]. \tag{6.17}$$

(*b*) When s is the analytic function of x defined in (6.6) the value of $1 - F_n(x)$ is given by (6.7). We have calculated the approximation A_s to this value obtained on replacing $V^{n\star}$ by the approximating normal distribution, say G_s. For s in a neighborhood of the origin the first three moments of V are close to those of F and so the Berry-Esséen theorem guarantees the existence of a constant C such that $|V^{n\star}(y) - G_s(y)| < C/\sqrt{n}$

for all $|s| < s_0$. An integration by parts in (6.7) now shows that the substitution of G_s for $V^{n\bigstar}$ causes an error less than

$$2C\frac{1}{\sqrt{n}}\cdot e^{n[\psi(s)-s\psi'(s)]} = O\left(\frac{x}{\sqrt{n}}A_s\right). \tag{6.18}$$

We have thus not only proved the theorem, but have shown that *if $x \to \infty$ and $n \to \infty$ the left side in* (6.1) *is* $O(x^3/\sqrt{n})$. ▶

The proof carries through without difficulty if the condition $x = o(n^{\frac{1}{6}})$ is replaced by $x = o(\sqrt{n})$. In fact, the last part of the argument shows that the *relative* error committed by introducing the normal approximation for $V^{n\bigstar}$ is always $O(x/\sqrt{n})$, and the normal approximation leads to an expression of the form (6.9). The estimate (6.16) remains valid. We get therefore the general approximation formula

$$1 - F_n(x) = e^{n[\psi(s)-s\psi'(s)+\frac{1}{2}\psi'^2(s)]}[1 - \mathfrak{N}(x)]\cdot[1 + O(x/\sqrt{n})]. \tag{6.19}$$

The exponent is a power series in s commencing with the term of third order. As in (6.6) we now define an analytic function s of the variable z by $\psi'(s) = \sigma z$. With this function we define a *power series λ such that*

$$z^2\,\lambda(z) = \lambda_1 z^3 + \lambda_2 z^4 + \cdots = \psi(x) - s\psi'(s) + \tfrac{1}{2}\psi'^2(s). \tag{6.20}$$

In terms of this series we have

Theorem 2.[9] *If in theorem* 1 *the condition* $x = o(n^{\frac{1}{6}})$ *is replaced by* $1 < x = o(\sqrt{n})$, *then*

$$\frac{1 - F_n(x)}{1 - \mathfrak{N}(x)} = e^{x^2\lambda(x/\sqrt{n})}\left[1 + O\left(\frac{x}{\sqrt{n}}\right)\right]. \tag{6.21}$$

In particular, if x increases faster than $n^{\frac{1}{6}}$ but $x = o(n^{\frac{1}{4}})$, only the first term in the power series matters, and we get

$$\frac{1 - F_n(x)}{1 - \mathfrak{N}(x)} \sim e^{\lambda_1 x^3/\sqrt{n}}, \qquad \lambda_1 = \frac{\mu_3}{6\sigma^3}. \tag{6.22}$$

For an increase such that $x = o(n^{\frac{3}{10}})$ we get

$$\frac{1 - F_n(x)}{1 - \mathfrak{N}(x)} \sim \exp\left(\lambda_1\frac{x^3}{\sqrt{n}} + \lambda_2\frac{x^2}{n}\right), \qquad \lambda_2 = \frac{\sigma^2\psi_4 - 3\psi_3{}^2}{24\sigma^6}, \tag{6.23}$$

and so on. The theorem as such is conceptually interesting in that it reveals the role of the normal distribution as a mere first approximation. [The form of the limit in (6.21) helps also to explain puzzling phenomena connected with cases where the law of the iterated logarithm breaks down.]

---

[9] The use of the transformation (6.4) in connection with the central limit theorem seems due to F. Esscher (1932). The present theorem is due to H. Cramér (1938), and was generalized to variable components by Feller (1943). For newer results in this case see V. V. Petrov, Uspekhi Matem. Nauk, vol. 9 (1954) (in Russian), and W. Richter, *Local limit theorems for large deviations*, Theory of Probability and Its Applications (transl.), vol. 2 (1957) pp. 206–220. The latter author treats densities rather than distributions. See also theorem 4 in section 7.

7. UNEQUAL COMPONENTS

The theory developed in the preceding sections is easily generalized to sequences of variables with distinct distributions, at least if one does not aim at optimal conditions. In fact, all our notations and arguments were conducted so as to prepare for this task, and were therefore not always the simplest.

From now on *we drop the notational conventions of section 1.* Instead, we consider a sequence of mutually independent random variables $\mathbf{X}_k$ with distributions U_k. We suppose that

$$\mathbf{E}(\mathbf{X}_k) = 0, \qquad \mathbf{E}(\mathbf{X}_k^2) = \sigma_k^2 \tag{7.1}$$

$$s_n^2 = \sigma_1^2 + \cdots + \sigma_n^2, \qquad s_n \to \infty. \tag{7.2}$$

To facilitate comparisons we again let F_n *stand for the distribution of the reduced sum* $(\mathbf{X}_1 + \cdots + \mathbf{X}_n)/s_n$. Thus F_n has the same conceptual meaning as before, but analytically it is now defined by

$$F_n(x) = U_1 \star \cdots \star U_n(s_n x). \tag{7.3}$$

We denote by ω_k and φ_n the characteristic functions of U_k and F_n, respectively. Then

$$\varphi_n(\zeta) = \omega_1\left(\frac{\zeta}{s_n}\right) \cdots \omega_n\left(\frac{\zeta}{s_n}\right) \tag{7.4}$$

and this function takes over the role of $\varphi^n(\zeta/(\sigma\sqrt{n}))$. The Fourier-theoretic part of all our proofs carries over without change, but in calculations involving logarithms of the characteristic functions ω_k we must make sure that these do exist in a common interval. The simplest way is to impose sufficient uniformity conditions. Typical for this procedure is

Theorem 1. (*Berry.*) *If for* $k = 1, 2, \ldots$

$$\frac{1}{\sigma_k^2}\mathbf{E}(|\mathbf{X}_k|^3) < \lambda, \tag{7.5}$$

then for all n *and* x

$$|F_n(x) - \mathfrak{N}(x)| \le \frac{33}{4} \cdot \frac{\lambda}{s_n}. \tag{7.6}$$

(See problem 8 for an improvement.)

Proof. We use the inequality (5.3) with $T = s_n/\lambda$ [and, of course, $\varphi^n(\zeta/(\sigma\sqrt{n}))$ replaced by $\varphi_n(\zeta)$]. The inequality (7.5) assures that throughout the interval of integration each individual component $\omega_k(\zeta/s_n)$

satisfies the inequalities (5.5) previously imposed on $\varphi(\zeta/(\sigma\sqrt{n}))$, and so absolutely no new calculations are necessary. ►

Consider next the one-term expansion (4.1). The factor $\mu_3/(\sigma^3\sqrt{n})$ corresponds to the coefficient of the cubic term in the Taylor expansion of $n \log \varphi(\zeta/(\sigma\sqrt{n}))$. This quantity is now replaced by a sum of logarithms and we should expect an expansion of the form

$$F_n(x) - \mathfrak{N}(x) - \frac{\mu_3^{(n)}}{6s_n^3}(1 - x^2)\,\mathfrak{n}(x) = o\left(\frac{n}{s_n^3}\right) \tag{7.7}$$

where

$$\mu_3^{(n)} = \sum_{k=1}^{n} \mathbf{E}(\mathbf{X}_k^3). \tag{7.8}$$

The validity of this expansion will now be proved under conditions designed to avoid new arguments. They can be easily relaxed; in particular (7.10) is extravagantly luxurious. (See problems 10–13.)

Theorem 2. *Suppose that there exist constants C and $q_\delta < 1$ such that for all k*

$$\mathbf{E}(|\mathbf{X}|^4) < C, \tag{7.9}$$

$$\max_{\zeta > \delta} |\omega_k(\zeta)| < q_\delta. \tag{7.10}$$

Then (7.7) *holds uniformly in x.*

Proof. The proof of theorem 4.1 started from (4.4), which is a special case of the general inequality (3.13). The same procedure is applicable, but to get the error term $o(n/s_n^3)$ we must take $T = as_n^3/n$ (instead of $T = a\sqrt{n}$). Thus our starting point is the inequality

$$|F_n(x) - G(x)| \le \frac{1}{\pi}\int_{-as_n^3/n}^{as_n^3/n} \left|\frac{\varphi_n(\zeta) - \gamma(\zeta)}{\zeta}\right| d\zeta + \frac{\epsilon n}{s_n^3}, \tag{7.11}$$

satisfied by the left side in (7.7). (Here ϵ is given and a is a constant depending on ϵ.)

Owing to the moment inequality the condition (7.9) guarantees also the uniform boundedness of $\mathbf{E}(\mathbf{X}_k^2)$ and $\mathbf{E}(|\mathbf{X}_k|^3)$. It follows that there exists an interval $\overline{-\eta, \eta}$ *independent of* n in which $u_n(\zeta) = \log \varphi_n(\zeta)$ is a continuous function with four derivatives that have an upper bound independent of n. The estimates used in the proof of theorem 4.1 now apply trivially and without change.[10] ►

[10] The old proof used only three derivatives of $u = \log \varphi$ but depended on the choice of a fixed interval in which $|u'''(\zeta) - u'''(0)| < \epsilon$. The condition (7.9) serves to make this possible for our u_n and can be relaxed in many ways. (See problem 9.)

In consequence of (7.9) the expression n/s_n^3 is at least of the order of magnitude $1/s_n$, but could be considerably greater. An exhaustive discussion of the higher-order expansions is complicated by the fact that the error term is due to several components whose relative order of magnitude depends on the conditions imposed on the variables $\mathbf{X}_k$.[11] We shall suppose that there exist two positive constants c and C such that for all j

$$c < \mathbf{E}(|\mathbf{X}_j|^k) < C \qquad k = 1, \ldots, r+1. \tag{7.12}$$

This is an unnecessarily strong uniformity condition, but it has the great advantage of implying $c^2 s_n^2 < n < C^2 s_n^2$. Thus n and s_n^2 are comparable and we can use asymptotic expansions in ascending powers of $1/\sqrt{n}$. In fact, condition (7.12) enables us to use the old expansion (4.10) without change. Indeed, as in the last proof it is seen that in some neighborhood of the origin we may define a function $\psi_n^{\#}$ by

$$\psi_n^{\#}(\zeta) = \frac{1}{n}\sum_{k=1}^{n} \log \omega_k\left(\frac{\zeta\sqrt{n}}{s_n}\right). \tag{7.13}$$

Then

$$\log \varphi_n(\zeta) = n\psi_n^{\#}\left(\frac{\zeta}{\sqrt{n}}\right) \tag{7.14}$$

which is exactly of the form used in case of equal components. It follows that we can use the calculations that led to (4.10) without further change by substituting $\psi_n^{\#}$ for $\log \varphi(\zeta)$ (and letting $\sigma = 1$). Of course, the coefficients of the polynomials R_k will now depend not only on the moments but also on n. Similarly, the new error term involves an upper bound of the rth derivative of $\varphi_n^{\#}$ in a neighborhood of the origin, but due to the uniformity condition (7.12) there exists such an upper bound independent of n. In this way we arrive at

Theorem 3.[12] *Suppose that the conditions* (7.10) *and* (7.12) *are satisfied. Then the asymptotic expansion* (4.10) *holds uniformly in* x.

The polynomials R_k depend on the moments occurring in (7.12) and on n, but as functions of n they are bounded. The condition (7.10) can be easily weakened (problem 12). Needless to say, the *expansion theorems for densities* carry over in like manner.

---

[11] For example, under mild conditions the error of the expansion (7.7) is $O(n^2 s_n^{-6}) + O(n s_n^{-4})$ and each of the two terms can preponderate. In Cramér's form of the expansion they are lumped together in the form $O\left(\sqrt{n}\, s_n^{-6}\sqrt{\left(\sum_1^n \mathbf{E}(\mathbf{X}_k^4)\right)^3}\right)$ which may be worse than either.

[12] This is essentially Cramér's theorem, but Cramér uses a somewhat milder uniformity condition.

The limit theorem 6.1 for large deviations applies to sequences with variable distributions in the following form.

Theorem 4. *Suppose that there exists an interval* $\overline{-a, a}$ *in which all the characteristic functions* ω_k *are analytic, and that*

$$\mathbf{E}(|\mathbf{X}_n|^3) \leq M\sigma_n^2, \tag{7.15}$$

where M *is independent of* n.

If x *and* n *vary so that* $s_n \to \infty$ *and* $x = o(\sqrt{s_n})$, *then*

$$\frac{1 - F_n(x)}{1 - \mathfrak{N}(x)} \to 1 \tag{7.16}$$

[*with an error* $O(x^3/s_n)$ *uniformly in* $x > 1$].

Proof. The proof follows step for step the proof in section 7, and we shall be satisfied to indicate in detail the one point that requires a new argument. Within $\overline{-a, a}$ we introduce the real-valued analytic function

$$\psi_n(s) = \frac{1}{n}\sum_{k=1}^{n} \log \omega_k(-is). \tag{7.17}$$

In the formal calculations now ψ_n replaces ψ, and xs_n replaces $x\sigma\sqrt{n}$. The basic equation (6.6) takes on the form

$$\psi_n'(s) = \frac{xs_n}{n}. \tag{7.18}$$

We take x as an independent variable varying together with n as stated in the theorem. From the three-term Taylor formula for ψ_n it is then seen that (7.18) has a unique continuous root such that $s = \dfrac{nx}{s_n} + O(s^2)$, and with it the calculations proceed as in section 6. ▶

8. PROBLEMS FOR SOLUTION

1. Show that the Hermite polynomials satisfy the orthogonality relation

$$\frac{1}{\sqrt{2\pi}}\int_{-\infty}^{+\infty} e^{-\frac{1}{2}x^2}\, H_m(x)\, H_n(x)\, dx = \begin{cases} 0 & \text{for } m \neq n \\ n! & \text{for } m = n. \end{cases} \tag{8.1}$$

Conversely, if H_n is a real polynomial of degree n with positive leading coefficient, and (8.1) holds, then the H_n are the Hermite polynomials defined by (1.7).

2. If f is a symmetric density with variance σ^2 and integrable characteristic function φ, then $\sqrt{n}f^{n*}(x) \to 1/\sqrt{2\pi}\sigma$, even in the absence of a third moment. Deduce this from theorem 2.1 and prove it independently by the same method.

3. When $\mu_4 < \infty$ show that the proof of theorem 2.1 leads to an error term $O(1/n)$ and that the same applies to theorem 4.1.

4. Lemma 3.1 may be improved when F has a density bounded by m. Discuss the details.

5. The Berry-Esséen theorem may be proved with less calculations by using in (5.3) the trivial inequality $|a^n - b^n| \leq n\,|a - b|\,c^n$ valid when $|a| \leq c$, $|b| \leq c$. Apply this method with $T = 2\sqrt{n}\,\sigma^3/\rho$ thus improving the constant $\frac{33}{4}$ to $\frac{22}{5}$.

6. *Continuation.* Show that the estimate of the Berry-Esséen theorem may be replaced by $\dfrac{5}{2}\,\dfrac{\rho}{\sigma^3\sqrt{n}} + \dfrac{C_\rho}{n}$, where C_ρ is a constant depending only on ρ.

7. Formula (6.7) implies that[13]

$$1 - F^{n\bigstar}(n\psi'(s)) \leq e^{n[\psi(s) - \psi'(s)]}.$$

8. Replace the condition (7.5) in Berry's theorem of section 7 by the Lindeberg conditions. (Use truncation.)

9. The condition (7.9) in theorem 7.2 may be replaced by the weaker one that there exist constants a and M such that

$$\int_{|x|>a} |x|^3\, U_k\{dx\} < M$$

for all k. An analogous improvement is possible for theorem 7.3. (See the footnote to theorem 7.2.)

10. Condition (7.10) is equivalent to the following. There exist positive numbers a and $\eta < 1$ such that $|\omega_k(\zeta)| < \eta$ for all k and $\zeta > a$.
[Use the inequality XV,(9.1). No calculations necessary.]

11. The condition of the last problem is satisfied if the distributions U_k have densities with derivatives such that $|u_k'| < M$.

12. The condition (7.10) in theorem 7.2 may be replaced by the condition that for arbitrary δ

$$(*) \qquad |\omega_1(\zeta)\cdots\omega_n(\zeta)| = o\left(\frac{1}{n}\right)$$

uniformly in $\zeta \geq \delta > 0$.

13. *Continuation.* The condition (*) is amply satisfied if

$$\frac{1}{\log n}\sum_1^n |1 - \omega_k(\zeta)| \to \infty$$

uniformly in some interval $\zeta > a$.

[13] Related inequalities were derived by H. Chernoff, Ann. Math. Statist., vol. 23 (1952) pp. 493–502.

CHAPTER XVII

Infinitely Divisible Distributions

This chapter presents the core of the now classical limit theorems of probability theory—the reservoir to which innumerably many individual streams have contributed. The spade work is done in section 1, and all further results are comparatively simple corollaries of its main theorem. The logical path leads from here directly to the triangular arrays in section 7, but once more we separate the simplest special situation in order to facilitate access to important topics.

The main results of this chapter were derived by other methods in chapter IX. The present treatment is independent and provides more detailed information.

For the notions of infinite divisibility, stability, etc., the reader is referred to chapter VI.

1. A CONVERGENCE THEOREM

Let $\{F_n\}$ stand for a sequence of probability distributions with characteristic functions φ_n. Much of the theory of this chapter revolves about sequences of functions of the form

$$(1.1) \qquad \psi_n(\zeta) = c_n[\varphi_n(\zeta) - 1 - i\beta_n\zeta]$$

where $c_n > 0$ and β_n is a real constant. Note that $e^{c_n(\varphi_n - 1)}$ is the characteristic function of a compound Poisson distribution [XV,(2.4)], and e^{ψ_n} is the characteristic function of the same distribution with a different centering. Functions of the form (1.1) will be called *quasi-characteristic*.

In this section we prove an important convergence theorem analogous to the continuity theorem 2 of XV,3 for characteristic functions. The novel feature is that in general $c_n \to \infty$, which necessitates introducing unbounded measures. No difficulties arise, however, because we shall be concerned only with measures M such that $M\{I\} < \infty$ for every finite interval I and the integrals

$$(1.2)\qquad M^+(x) = \int_{x-}^{\infty} \frac{1}{y^2}\, M\{dy\}, \qquad M^-(-x) = \int_{-\infty}^{-x+} \frac{1}{y^2}\, M\{dy\}$$

converge for all $x > 0$. Typical examples are the Lebesgue measure and—more to the point—the measure $x^2\, F\{dx\}$ associated with a probability distribution. The function M^+ is monotone on $\overline{0, \infty}$ and in general unbounded at the origin. It remains undefined on $\overline{-\infty, 0}|$. Similarly M^- exists only on $\overline{-\infty, 0}$.

We recall (definition 1 of VIII,1) that a sequence of measures M_n converges to M iff $M_n\{I\} \to M\{I\}$ for every *bounded* interval of continuity for M. The gist of the next theorem is that the convergence of (1.1) is tied to the existence of a measure M such that

$$(1.3)\qquad c_n x^2\, F_n\{dx\} \to M\{dx\}.$$

Outside a neighborhood of the origin this can be rewritten in the form

$$(1.4)\qquad c_n\, F_n\{dx\} \to \frac{1}{x^2}\, M\{dx\}.$$

Just as in the case of proper convergence of probability distributions we shall require that "no masses are lost at infinity." Analytically this amounts to requiring that (1.4) be applicable also to unbounded intervals, that is,

$$(1.5)\qquad c_n[1 - F_n(x)] \to M^+(x), \qquad c_n F_n(-x) \to M^-(-x) \qquad x > 0$$

at all points of continuity. Since $M^+(\infty) = M^-(-\infty) = 0$ the relation (1.5) will hold iff the left sides are uniformly small for large x, that is, iff for given $\epsilon > 0$ there exists a $\tau > 0$ such that

$$(1.6)\qquad c_n[1 - F_n(x) + F_n(-x)] < \epsilon$$

for $x > \tau$ and all n.

Definition. *A measure M is canonical if the integrals* (1.2) *converge.*

We say that the measures $c_n x^2\, F_n\{dx\}$ converge properly to M iff (1.3) *and* (1.5) *hold.* [*The condition* (1.5) *is equivalent to* (1.6).]

Examples. (*a*) Let F_n attribute weight $\frac{1}{2}$ to each of the two points $\pm 1/\sqrt{n}$. Then $nx^2\, F_n\{dx\} = F_n\{dx\}$, and this converges to the probability measure concentrated at the origin. For $\beta_n = 0$ we have $\psi_n(\zeta) \to -\frac{1}{2}\zeta^2$. Note that the limit function is unbounded.

(*b*) Let F_n stand for the Cauchy distribution with density $\dfrac{1}{\pi}\dfrac{n}{1 + n^2x^2}$.

The density of $\pi n x^2 F_n\{dx\}$ tends to 1 and $\pi n x^2 F_n\{dx\}$ tends properly to the Lebesgue measure. For $\beta_n = 0$ we have

$$\psi_n(\zeta) = \pi n[e^{-|\zeta|n^{-1}} - 1] \to -\pi |\zeta|.$$ ►

We now consider an arbitrary sequence of probability distributions F_n with characteristic functions φ_n and ask under what conditions

$$\psi_n(\zeta) \equiv c_n[\varphi_n(\zeta) - 1 - i\beta_n\zeta] \to \rho(\zeta) \tag{1.7}$$

for *all* ζ. Only continuous limits will be considered, and we put for abbreviation

$$b_n = \int_{-\infty}^{+\infty} \sin x \cdot F_n\{dx\}. \tag{1.8}$$

Theorem. *A continuous limit* ρ *in* (1.7) *exists iff there exists a canonical measure* M *and a number* b *such that*

$$c_n x^2 F_n\{dx\} \to M\{dx\} \tag{1.9}$$

properly and

$$c_n(b_n - \beta_n) \to b. \tag{1.10}$$

In this case

$$\rho(\zeta) = \psi(\zeta) + ib\zeta \tag{1.11}$$

where[1]

$$\psi(\zeta) = \int_{-\infty}^{+\infty} \frac{e^{i\zeta x} - 1 - i\zeta \sin x}{x^2} \cdot M\{dx\}. \tag{1.12}$$

The measure M *is uniquely determined by* (1.12).

For given φ_n and c_n it follows that *if there exists any choice of* β_n *which produces convergence of* $\{\psi_n\}$, *the choice* $\beta_n = b_n$ *will do.* This is not surprising since this choice amounts to a norming of ψ_n in such a way that $\text{Im}\, \psi_n(1) = 0$. More about the constants β_n will be said at the end of this section.

Example. (*c*) *Derivatives of characteristic functions.* Let F be a probability distribution with characteristic function φ. If F has an expectation μ then φ has a derivative φ' and $\varphi'(0) = i\mu$. (See XV,4.) The converse is not true, but the preceding theorem implies that[2] $\varphi'(0) = i\mu$ *exists iff* $t \to \infty$

$$t[1 - F(t) + F(-t)] \to 0 \tag{1.13}$$

[1] For fixed ζ the integrand is to be interpreted as the continuous function taking on the value $-\frac{1}{2}\zeta^2$ at the origin.

[2] This result was proved by A. Zygmund in 1947 assuming smoothness properties of φ, and in full generality by E. J. G. Pitman in 1956. Their methods are different.

and

$$\int_{-t}^{t} x\, F\{dx\} \to \mu. \tag{1.14}$$

Note that $\varphi'(0) = i\mu$ iff

$$\lim_{\epsilon\to 0} \frac{\varphi(\epsilon\zeta) - 1 - i\mu\epsilon\zeta}{\epsilon} \to 0. \tag{1.15}$$

Proof. When ϵ runs through a sequence $\epsilon_1, \epsilon_2, \ldots \to 0$ the relation (1.15) may be taken as a special case of (1.7) with $c_n = \epsilon_n^{-1}$ and

$$F_n\{dx\} = F\{\epsilon_n^{-1}\, dx\}.$$

Accordingly, (1.15) holds iff $\epsilon_n^{-1}x^2\, F\{\epsilon_n^{-1}\, dx\} \to 0$ properly and

$$\epsilon_n^{-1}\int_{-\infty}^{+\infty} \sin x \cdot F\{\epsilon_n^{-1}\, dx\} = \epsilon_n^{-1}\int_{-\infty}^{+\infty} \sin \epsilon_n y \cdot F\{dy\} \to \mu \tag{1.16}$$

for any approach $\epsilon_n \to 0$. In view of (1.6) the proper convergence takes place iff (1.13) is true, and in this case (1.16) is clearly equivalent to (1.14). ▶

The *proof of the theorem* will be broken up into lemmas of which the first merely restates the definition of proper convergence in terms of expectations. Throughout we use the notation (1.7) so that

$$\psi_n(\zeta) = \int_{-\infty}^{+\infty} [e^{i\zeta x} - 1 - i\zeta \sin x] c_n\, F_n\{dx\} + ic_n(b_n - \beta_n)\zeta. \tag{1.17}$$

Lemma 1. *If $c_n x^2\, F_n\{dx\} \to M\{dx\}$ properly, then*

$$c_n\int_{-\infty}^{+\infty} z(x)\, F_n\{dx\} \to \int_{-\infty}^{+\infty} x^{-2}\, z(x)\, M\{dx\} \tag{1.18}$$

for every bounded continuous function z such that $x^{-2}z(x)$ is continuous at the origin.

Proof. If $|x| < t < \infty$ is an interval of continuity of M the contribution of this interval to the left side obviously converges to the contribution of the same interval on the right. Because of (1.6) it is possible to choose t so large that the contribution of $|x| \geq t$ to either side in (1.18) is $<\epsilon$ (independently of n), and so (1.18) is true. ▶

Lemma 2. *If $\psi_n(\zeta) \to \rho(\zeta)$ uniformly in $|\zeta| \leq \zeta_0$, then for $0 < h \leq \zeta_0$*

$$c_n\int_{-\infty}^{+\infty}\left(1 - \frac{\sin xh}{xh}\right)F_n\{dx\} \to -\frac{1}{2h}\int_{-h}^{h} \rho(\zeta)d\zeta. \tag{1.19}$$

Note that nothing is assumed concerning $\psi_n(\zeta)$ for $|\zeta| > \zeta_0$.

Proof. Multiply (1.17) by $1/(2h)$ and integrate over $-h \leq \zeta \leq h$ to obtain (1.19). ▶

Lemma 3. *Under the conditions of the last lemma there exists a canonical measure M and a sequence* $n_1, n_2, \ldots \to \infty$ *such that* $c_{n_k} x^2 F_{n_k}\{dx\} \to M\{dx\}$ *properly.*

Proof. For each n put $M_n\{dx\} = c_n x^2 F_n\{dx\}$. The integrand on the left in (1.19) behaves near the origin like $\frac{1}{6}x^2h^2$ and off the origin it is strictly positive. It follows that for each finite interval I the measures $M_n\{I\}$ remain bounded. By the selection theorem 2 of VIII,6 there exists therefore a sequence $\{n_k\}$ such that M_{n_k} tends to a limit measure. It remains to show that the condition (1.6) is satisfied. Now $\rho(0) = 0$, and hence we can choose h so small that the right side in (1.19) is $<\frac{1}{2}\epsilon$. In the intervals $|xh| > 2$ the integrand on the left is $>\frac{1}{2}$, and elsewhere it is ≥ 0. The left side is therefore at least $\frac{1}{2}c_n[1 - F_n(2/h) + F_n(-2/h)]$, and so (1.6) holds as soon as $t > 2/h$. ▶

Lemma 4. *For any canonical measure M the integral in* (1.12) *defines a continuous function* ψ, *and to distinct canonical measures there correspond distinct functions.*

Proof. Since the integrand is continuous and the numerator bounded, the integral converges owing to the condition (1.2) on canonical measures. Obviously ψ is continuous, and for arbitrary $h > 0$

$$(1.20)\qquad \psi(\zeta) - \frac{\psi(\zeta+h) + \psi(\zeta-h)}{2} = \int_{-\infty}^{+\infty} e^{i\zeta x} \frac{1 - \cos xh}{x^2} M\{dx\}.$$

On the right we recognize the Fourier-Stieltjes transform of the *bounded* measure $A_h\{dx\} = \dfrac{1 - \cos xh}{x^2} M\{dx\}$. By the uniqueness theorem for characteristic functions the measure A_h is uniquely determined by the left side in (1.20), and in its turn the measure A_h determines the measure M except for possible atoms at the points where $1 - \cos xh = 0$. But the knowledge of two measures A_{h_1} and A_{h_2} with incommensurable h_j uniquely determines M, and so M is uniquely determined by ψ. (See problems 1–2.) ▶

Proof *of the theorem.* Assume $\psi_n(\zeta) \to \rho(\zeta)$ for all ζ, with ρ continuous. Since e^{ψ_n} is a characteristic function the convergence is uniform in finite intervals (theorem 2 of XV,3), and so lemmas 2 and 3 apply. As n runs through the sequence $n_1, n_2, \ldots$ of lemma 3 the integral in (1.17) converges to $\psi(\zeta)$ by virtue of lemma 1. It follows that the limit ρ is indeed of the form (1.11). Now $\psi(1)$ is real, and hence $b = \operatorname{Im} \rho(1)$. Thus ψ and b are uniquely determined and independent of the sequence $\{n_k\}$, which shows that the convergence of ψ_n to a continuous limit ρ is indeed equivalent with the conditions (1.9) and (1.10) of the theorem. ▶

Note *on alternative centerings.* The choice of the function $\sin x$ in (1.8) and (1.12) is by no means unique. In fact, lemmas 1–3 are entirely independent of this choice and lemma 4 applies to any function of the form

$$\psi(\zeta) = \int_{-\infty}^{+\infty} \frac{e^{i\zeta x} - 1 - i\zeta\tau(x)}{x^2}\, M\{dx\} \tag{1.21}$$

if the integrand is continuous and the numerator bounded.[3] With any admissible choice of $\tau(x)$ the proof of the theorem applies without change provided that $\sin x$ is replaced by $\tau(x)$ also in the definition (1.8) of b_n [and consequently in the expression (1.17) for $\psi_n(\zeta)$].

A choice of $\tau(x)$ clearly preferable to $\sin x$ exists under special circumstances. Thus, if the F_n have expectations m_n it is desirable to replace the centering constants b_n by m_n, that is to replace $\sin x$ by x. This choice renders the numerator in (1.21) unbounded, and to carry through the proof of the theorem we must strengthen the condition (1.6) on proper convergence by requiring that for t sufficiently large

$$c_n \int_{|x|>t} |x|\, F_n\{dx\} < \epsilon. \tag{1.22}$$

Under this condition the integral of $|x|^{-1} M\{dx\}$ will exist for every interval excluding a neighbourhood of the origin and in (1.18) it suffices to require that $|z(x)| = O(|x|)$ as $x \to \pm\infty$. It follows that *if* (1.22) *is true the theorem remains valid with* $\sin x$ *replaced by* x *in* (1.12) *and* (1.8). For the same reason, *if for* t *sufficiently small*

$$c_n \int_{|x|<t} |x|\, F_n\{dx\} < \epsilon \tag{1.23}$$

$\sin x$ *may be replaced by* 0. The integrand in (1.21) is no longer bounded at the origin, but the measure M is now such that the integral of $x^{-1}M\{dx\}$ is meaningful over every finite interval.

2. INFINITELY DIVISIBLE DISTRIBUTIONS

We continue the practice of using descriptive terms interchangeably for distributions and their characteristic functions. With this understanding the definition given in VI,3 may be rephrased as follows.

[3] For an example see (7.2). The centering by $\sin x$ has the distinguishing feature that the canonical form for ψ can be characterized by an intrinsic property, namely that $\psi(1)$ is real.

Definition. *A characteristic function ω is infinitely divisible iff for each n there exists a characteristic function ω_n such that*

$$\omega_n{}^n = \omega. \tag{2.1}$$

It will be shown that nothing changes if the identity (2.1) is replaced by the formally weaker condition

$$\varphi_n{}^n(\zeta) \to \omega(\zeta). \tag{2.2}$$

Relations of this sort are covered by the theory of the last section because (2.2) turns out to be equivalent to

$$n[\varphi_n(\zeta) - 1] \to \rho(\zeta). \tag{2.3}$$

Lemma. *Let $\{\varphi_n\}$ be a sequence of characteristic functions. If the limit on the right is continuous, then each of the relations* (2.2) *and* (2.3) *implies the other and $\omega(\zeta) = e^{\rho(\zeta)}$.*

It follows, in particular, that ω can have no zero.

Proof. We begin by recalling the definition of the logarithm in the complex domain. If $a = re^{i\theta}$ is the polar representation of the complex number $a \neq 0$ then $\log a = \log r + i\theta$ where $\log r$ is the familiar real logarithm of the positive number r. The argument θ is determined only up to multiples of 2π and, in principle, this indeterminacy is inherited by the logarithm. Nevertheless, in any interval $|\zeta| < \zeta_0$ in which $\varphi(\zeta) \neq 0$ the characteristic function φ admits of a *unique* polar representation $\varphi(\zeta) = r(\zeta)e^{i\theta(\zeta)}$ such that θ is *continuous* and $\theta(0) = 0$. In such an interval we can write without ambiguity $\log \varphi = \log r + i\theta$, and this is the *only* determination which makes $\log \varphi$ a continuous function vanishing at the origin. We use the symbol $\log \varphi$ only in this sense. In any interval $|\zeta| < \zeta_0$ free of zeros of φ the continuous function $\log \varphi$ is well defined, but the definition breaks down as soon as $\varphi(\zeta_0) = 0$. A similar remark applies to the roots.[4]

Now to the proof. Assume (2.3). Then $\varphi_n(\zeta) \to 1$ for each fixed ζ and the convergence is uniform in each finite interval $|\zeta| < \zeta_0$ (theorem 2 of XV,3). For n sufficiently large $\log \varphi_n(\zeta)$ is therefore well defined. Since for $|z - 1| < 1$

$$\log z = z - 1 - \frac{(z-1)^2}{2} + \cdots \tag{2.4}$$

[4] In XV,2 we gave an example of two real characteristic functions such that $\varphi_1{}^2 = \varphi_2{}^2$ which shows that in the presence of zeros the square root of a characteristic function is not uniquely defined.

(*b*) *The case* $1 < \alpha < 2$. The use of the formal substitution

$$\zeta = t^{\alpha-1} \exp\left(-i\frac{\pi\gamma}{2\alpha}\right)$$

can be justified as in the case $\alpha < 1$. The new integrand is of the form $e^{-t-ct^{\alpha^{-1}}} t^{\alpha^{-1}-1}$. Expanding $e^{-ct^{\alpha^{-1}}}$ into an exponential series we get

$$p(-x;\alpha,\gamma) =$$

$$(6.6)\qquad = \frac{1}{\alpha\pi} \operatorname{Re} \exp\left(-i\frac{\pi\gamma}{2\alpha}\right) \sum_{n=0}^{\infty} \frac{\Gamma\left(\frac{n+1}{\alpha}\right)}{n!} \left(-ix \exp\left[-i\frac{\pi\gamma}{2\alpha}\right]\right)^n.$$

Changing the summation index n to $k - 1$ and using the familiar recursion formula $\Gamma(s+1) = s\,\Gamma(s)$ leads to

$$(6.7)\quad p(-x;\alpha,\gamma) = \frac{1}{\pi x} \operatorname{Re}\, i \sum_{k=1}^{\infty} \frac{\Gamma(k\alpha^{-1}+1)}{k!} \left(-x \exp\left[-i\frac{\pi}{2\alpha}(\gamma-\alpha)\right]\right)^k.$$

We have thus proved

Lemma 1. *For* $x > 0$ *and* $0 < \alpha < 1$

$$(6.8)\qquad p(x;\alpha,\gamma) = \frac{1}{\pi x} \sum_{k=1}^{\infty} \frac{\Gamma(k\alpha+1)}{k!} (-x^{-\alpha})^k \sin\frac{k\pi}{2}(\gamma-\alpha).$$

For $x > 0$ *and* $1 < \alpha < 2$

$$(6.9)\qquad p(x;\alpha,\gamma) = \frac{1}{\pi x} \sum_{k=1}^{\infty} \frac{\Gamma(k\alpha^{-1}+1)}{k!} (-x)^k \sin\frac{k\pi}{2\alpha}(\gamma-\alpha).$$

The values for $x < 0$ *are given by* (6.4).

Note that (6.8) provides asymptotic estimates for $x \to \infty$. A curious by-product of these formulas is as follows:

Lemma 2. *If* $\alpha < 1$ *and* $x > 0$ *then*

$$(6.10)\qquad \frac{1}{x^{\alpha+1}}\, p\left(\frac{1}{x^\alpha}; \frac{1}{\alpha}, \gamma\right) = p(x;\alpha,\gamma^*)$$

where $\gamma^* = \alpha(\gamma+1) - 1$.

A trite check shows that γ^* falls within the range prescribed by (6.2). The identity (6.10) was first noticed (with a different proof) by V. M. Zolotarev.

7. TRIANGULAR ARRAYS

The notion of a triangular array was explained in VI,3 as follows. For each n we are given finitely many, say r_n, independent random variables $\mathbf{X}_{k,n}$ $(k = 1, 2, \ldots, r_n)$ with distributions $F_{k,n}$ and characteristic functions $\varphi_{k,n}$. We form the row sum $\mathbf{S}_n = \mathbf{X}_{1,n} + \cdots + \mathbf{X}_{r_n,n}$, and denote its distribution and its characteristic function by U_n and ω_n, respectively. For reasons explained in VI,3 we are interested primarily in arrays where the influence of individual components is asymptotically negligible. To ensure this we imposed the condition VI,(3.3) that the variables $\mathbf{X}_{k,n}$ tend in probability to zero uniformly in $k = 1, \ldots, r_n$. In terms of characteristic functions this means that given $\epsilon > 0$ and $\zeta_0 > 0$ one has for all n sufficiently large

$$(7.1) \qquad |1 - \varphi_{k,n}(\zeta)| < \epsilon \qquad \textit{for} \quad |\zeta| < \zeta_0, \quad k = 1, \ldots, r_n.$$

Such an array is called a *null array*.

In effect sections 1 and 2 are concerned with triangular arrays in which the distributions $F_{k,n}$ do not depend on k, and such arrays are automatically null arrays. The condition (7.1) makes it possible to apply the same arguments with practically no change.

Theorem 1. *Let* $\{\mathbf{X}_{k,n}\}$ *be a null array, and* $\{\beta_n\}$ *a sequence of real constants. If the distributions of* $\mathbf{S}_n + \beta_n$ *tend to a probability distribution* U, *then* U *is infinitely divisible.*

We shall combine the proof of this theorem with the derivation of necessary and sufficient conditions for the convergence. A new centering will be used, partly for a change, and partly because it simplifies the general criterion.

Centering to zero expectation is, of course, best whenever practicable. For the general case we introduce *truncated expectations*. Put

$$(7.2) \qquad \tau(x) = \begin{cases} -1 & \textit{for} \quad x \leq -1 \\ x & \textit{for} \quad -1 \leq x \leq 1 \\ 1 & \textit{for} \quad x \geq 1 \end{cases}$$

and use $\mathbf{E}(\tau(\mathbf{X}))$ as a substitute for the expectation of $\mathbf{X}$. Since τ is continuous and monotone $\mathbf{E}(\tau(\mathbf{X}+t))$ is a continuous monotone function of t and hence there exists a value t such that $\mathbf{E}(\tau(\mathbf{X}+t)) = 0$. For our triangular array this means that there exist constants $t_{k,n}$ such that $\mathbf{E}(\tau(\mathbf{X}_{k,n}+t_{k,n})) = 0$ for all k, n. Obviously $\{\mathbf{X}_{k,n}+t_{k,n}\}$ is again a null array and it suffices to prove the theorem for this array. Thus, if we put

$$(7.3) \qquad b_{k,n} = \mathbf{E}(\tau(\mathbf{X}_{k,n}))$$

there is no loss of generality in supposing that $b_{k,n} = 0$ for all k and n. Then

$$A_n = \sum_{k=1}^{r_n} \mathbf{E}(\tau^2(\mathbf{X}_{k,n})) \tag{7.4}$$

will serve as a substitute for the variance of the row sum $\mathbf{S}_n$.

Proof *of theorem* 1. Assuming that $b_{k,n} = 0$ we have

$$\varphi_{k,n}(\zeta) - 1 = \int_{-\infty}^{+\infty} [e^{i\zeta x} - 1 - i\zeta\,\tau(x)]\, F_{k,n}\{dx\}. \tag{7.5}$$

For $|x| \le 1$ the integrand is dominated by $\frac{1}{2}\zeta^2 x^2$, and for $|x| \ge 1$ by $2 + |\zeta|$. It follows that for all ζ

$$\sum_{k=1}^{r_n} |\varphi_{k,n}(\zeta) - 1| \le (2 + \zeta + \zeta^2) A_n. \tag{7.6}$$

In view of (7.1) we can, at least for n sufficiently large, pass to logarithms[14] and see that for fixed ζ as $n \to \infty$

$$\sum_{k=1}^{r_n} \log \varphi_{k,n}(\zeta) = \sum_{k=1}^{r_n} [\varphi_{k,n}(\zeta) - 1] + o(A_n). \tag{7.7}$$

Denote the characteristic function of the limit distribution U by ω. The left side in (7.7) is the logarithm of the characteristic function of $\mathbf{S}_n$, and hence

$$\sum_{k=1}^{r_n} \log \varphi_{k,n}(\zeta) + i\beta_n\zeta \to \log \omega(\zeta) \tag{7.8}$$

uniformly in any interval $|\zeta| < \zeta_0$ in which ω has no zeros. Multiply (7.8) by $1/(2h)$ and integrate over $|\zeta| < h < \zeta_0$. The integral of $i\beta_n\zeta$ vanishes and from (7.7) we get

$$\sum_{k=1}^{r_n} \int_{-\infty}^{+\infty} \left(1 - \frac{\sin xh}{xh}\right) F_{k,n}\{dx\} + o(A_n) \to -\frac{1}{2h}\int_{-h}^{h} \log \omega(\zeta)\, d\zeta. \tag{7.9}$$

The integrand on the left is $> \frac{1}{10}h^2x^2$ when $|hx| \le 1$ and $> \frac{1}{10}$ otherwise. In every case it is $> \frac{1}{10}h^2\tau^2(x)$, and the sum on the left is therefore greater than $\frac{1}{10}h^2 A_n$ and so (7.9) implies that A_n remains bounded. But then by (7.7)

$$\sum_{k=1}^{r_n} [\varphi_{k,n}(\zeta) - 1] + i\beta_n\zeta \to \log \omega(\zeta). \tag{7.10}$$

---

[14] Concerning logarithms of characteristic functions see the initial remark in the first proof of section 2.

The left side is a quasi-characteristic function of the form (1.1) with

$$F_n = \frac{1}{r_n}\sum_{k=1}^{r_n} F_{k,n}, \qquad c_n = r_n. \tag{7.11}$$

Thus ω is infinitely divisible by the theorem of section 1. ▶

We have not only proved the theorem, but we know that (7.10) implies

$$\sum_{k=1}^{r_n} x^2\, F_{k,n}\{dx\} \to M\{dx\} \tag{7.12}$$

where M is a canonical measure and the convergence is proper. Conversely if this is true it becomes obvious from (7.5) that (7.10) holds with $\beta_n = 0$ and

$$\log \omega(\zeta) = \int_{-\infty}^{+\infty} \frac{e^{i\zeta x} - 1 - i\zeta\tau(x)}{x^2}\, M\{dx\} \tag{7.13}$$

(this being a special case of lemma 1.1). We have thus the

Criterion. *Let $\{\mathbf{X}_{k,n}\}$ be a triangular null array centered so that $b_{k,n} = 0$ for all k and n.*

If proper convergence (7.12) *takes place, the distributions of the row sums $\mathbf{S}_n$ tend to the infinitely divisible distribution with characteristic function given by* (7.13). *In the contrary case the distributions of $\mathbf{S}_n + \beta_n$ do not converge properly, no matter how the constants β_n are chosen.*

In applications the centering causes trouble and we therefore restate the criterion in a form applicable to arbitrary null arrays. The functions M^+ and M^- are defined in (1.2).

Theorem 2. *Let $\{\mathbf{X}_{k,n}\}$ be an arbitrary null array. If there exists a canonical measure M such that at points of continuity $x > 0$*

$$\sum_{k=1}^{r_n} [1 - F_{k,n}(x)] \to M^+(x), \qquad \sum_{k=1}^{r_n} F_{k,n}(-x) \to M^-(-x) \tag{7.14}$$

and

$$\sum_{k=1}^{r_n} \mathrm{Var}(\tau(\mathbf{X}_{k,n})) \to M\{\overline{-1, 1}\} + M^+(1) + M^-(-1), \tag{7.15}$$

then the distributions of the row sums of $\{\mathbf{X}_{k,n} - b_{k,n}\}$ tend to the distribution with characteristic function (7.13).

In the contrary case there exist no constants β_n such that the distributions of $\{\mathbf{S}_n + \beta_n\}$ converge to a probability distribution.

Proof. When $b_{k,n} = 0$ the conditions (7.14)–(7.15) are equivalent to proper convergence in (7.12). For arrays centered so that $\mathbf{E}(\tau(\mathbf{X}_{k,n})) = 0$ the theorem therefore merely restates our criterion.

Consider now an *arbitrary* null array $\{\mathbf{X}_{k,n}\}$ and put $\mathbf{Y}_{k,n} = \mathbf{X}_{k,n} - \theta_{k,n}$, where the constants $\theta_{k,n}$ are chosen so that $\mathbf{E}(\tau(\mathbf{Y}_{k,n})) = 0$. Then $\theta_{k,n} \to 0$ uniformly in $k = 1, \ldots, r_n$ and so $\{\mathbf{Y}_{k,n}\}$ is a null array to which the theorem applies. We have to show that the conditions of the theorem are fully equivalent to the corresponding conditions for the array $\{\mathbf{Y}_{k,n}\}$. The distribution function of $\mathbf{Y}_{k,n}$ is given by $F_{k,n}(x+\theta_{k,n})$, and (7.14) obviously remains valid if on the left sides x is replaced by $x + \theta_{k,n}$. Thus (7.14) and the corresponding relations for the array $\{\mathbf{Y}_{k,n}\}$ imply each other, and hence the condition (7.14) is necessary. To complete the proof it suffices therefore to show that it entails

(7.16)
$$\sum_{k=1}^{r_n} \mathrm{Var}(\tau(\mathbf{Y}_{k,n})) \sim \sum_{k=1}^{r_n} \mathrm{Var}(\tau(\mathbf{X}_{k,n}))$$

and

(7.17)
$$\sum_{k=1}^{r_n} (b_{k,n} - \theta_{k,n}) \to 0.$$

Put

(7.18)
$$\tau(\mathbf{Y}_{k,n}) - \tau(\mathbf{X}_{k,n}) + \theta_{k,n} = \mathbf{Z}_{k,n}.$$

The function $\tau(x-\theta) - \tau(x) + \theta$ vanishes except when $|x|$ lies between $1 - \theta$ and $1 + \theta$, and even for such values it is dominated by $|\theta|$. This implies that

$$\sum \mathbf{E}(|\mathbf{Z}_{k,n}|) \to 0 \qquad \text{as } n \to \infty.$$

This relation is obviously stronger than (7.17), and it is easily seen that (7.16) is a consequence of it.

Example. *The role of centering.* Let $\mathbf{X}_{k,n}$ $(k = 1, \ldots, n)$ be normally distributed with expectation $n^{-1/4}$ and variance n^{-1}. Then $\mathbf{S}_n - n^{3/4}$ is normally distributed and a limiting distribution exists. Nevertheless $\Sigma\mathbf{E}(\mathbf{X}_{k,n}^2) = 1 + \sqrt{n} \to \infty$. This shows that theorem 1 depends essentially on the centering, and that in general the highest-order terms in the expansion of the logarithms are not negligible. (See also problems 16 and 17.) ►

*8. THE CLASS L

As an illustration of the power of theorem 7.1 we give a simple proof of a theorem discovered by P. Lévy. We are once more concerned with partial sums $\mathbf{S}_n = \mathbf{X}_1 + \cdots + \mathbf{X}_n$ of a sequence of mutually independent random variables but, in contrast to section 5, the distribution F_n of $\mathbf{X}_n$ is permitted to depend on n. We put $\mathbf{S}_n^* = (\mathbf{S}_n - b_n)/a_n$ and wish to

* This section treats a special topic.

characterize the possible limit distributions of $\{\mathbf{S}_n^*\}$, under the assumption that

$$a_n \to \infty, \qquad \frac{a_{n+1}}{a_n} \to 1. \tag{8.1}$$

The first condition eliminates convergent series $\Sigma\mathbf{X}_k$ which are treated in section 10. Situations avoided by the second condition are best illustrated by the

Example. Let $\mathbf{X}_n$ have an exponential distribution with expectation $n!$. Put $a_n = n!$ and $b_n = 0$. Obviously the distribution of $\mathbf{S}_n^*$ tends to the exponential distribution with expectation 1, but the convergence is due entirely to the preponderance of the term $\mathbf{X}_n$. ▶

Following Khintchine it is usual to say that *a distribution belongs to the class L if it is the limit distribution of a sequence* $\{\mathbf{S}_n^*\}$ *satisfying the conditions* (8.1).

In this formulation it is not clear that all distributions of the class L are infinitely divisible, but we shall prove this as a consequence of the following

Lemma. *A characteristic function* ω *belongs to the class L iff for each* $0 < s < 1$ *the ratio* $\omega(\zeta)/\omega(s\zeta)$ *is a characteristic function.*

[This implies that $\omega(\zeta) \neq 0$ for all ζ.]

Proof. (*a*) *Necessity.* Denote the characteristic function of $\mathbf{S}_n^*$ by ω_n and let $n > m$. The variable $\mathbf{S}_n^*$ is the sum of $(a_m/a_n)\mathbf{S}_m^*$ and a variable depending only on $\mathbf{X}_{m+1}, \ldots, \mathbf{X}_n$, and on the norming constants. Therefore

$$\omega_n(\zeta) = \omega_m\left(\frac{a_m}{a_n}\zeta\right) \cdot \varphi_{m,n}(\zeta) \tag{8.2}$$

where $\varphi_{m,n}$ is a characteristic function. Now let $n \to \infty$ and $m \to \infty$ in such a way that $a_m/a_n \to s < 1$. [This is possible on account of (8.1).] The left side tends to $\omega(\zeta)$ and the first factor on the right tends to $\omega(s\zeta)$ because the convergence of characteristic functions is uniform in finite intervals. [Theorem 2 of XV,3.] We conclude first that ω has no zeros. In fact, since $\varphi_{m,n}$ remains bounded $\omega(\zeta_0) = 0$ would imply $\omega(s\zeta_0) = 0$, and hence $\omega(s^k\zeta_0)$ for all $k > 0$, whereas actually $\omega(s^k\zeta_0) \to 1$. Accordingly, the ratio $\omega(\zeta)/\omega(s\zeta)$ appears as the continuous limit of the characteristic functions $\varphi_{m,n}$, and is therefore a characteristic function.

(*b*) *Sufficiency.* We start from the identity

$$\omega(n\zeta) = \omega(\zeta) \cdot \frac{\omega(2\zeta)}{\omega(\zeta)} \cdots \frac{\omega(n\zeta)}{\omega((n-1)\zeta)}. \tag{8.3}$$

Under the conditions of the lemma the factor $\dfrac{\omega(k\zeta)}{\omega((k-1)\zeta)}$ is the characteristic function of a random variable $\mathbf{X}_k$ and hence $\omega(\zeta)$ is the characteristic function of $(\mathbf{X}_1 + \cdots + \mathbf{X}_n)/n$. ►

We have not only proved the theorem but have found that ω is the characteristic function of the nth row sum in a triangular array. The condition (7.1) for null arrays is trivially satisfied, and hence ω is infinitely divisible. To find the canonical measure M determining ω we note that also the ratio $\omega(\zeta)/\omega(s\zeta)$ is infinitely divisible as can be seen from the factorization (8.3). The canonical measure N determining $\omega(\zeta)/\omega(s\zeta)$ is related to M by the identity

$$N\{dx\} = M\{dx\} - s^2M\{s^{-1}\,dx\}. \tag{8.4}$$

In terms of the functions M^+ and M^- introduced in (1.2) this relation reads

$$N^+(x) = M^+(x) - M^+(x/s), \qquad N^-(-x) = M^-(-x) - M^-(-x/s). \tag{8.5}$$

We have shown that if the canonical measure M determines a characteristic function ω of class L, then the functions N^+ and N^- defined in (8.5) must be monotone for each $0 < s < 1$. Conversely, if this is true then (8.4) defines a canonical measure determining $\omega(\zeta)/\omega(s\zeta)$. We have thus proved the

Theorem. *A characteristic function ω belongs to the class L iff it is infinitely divisible and its determining canonical measure M is such that the two functions in* (8.5) *are monotone for every fixed* $0 < s < 1$.

Note. It is easily verified that the functions are monotone iff $M^+(e^x)$ and $M^-(-e^x)$ are *convex* functions.

*9. PARTIAL ATTRACTION. "UNIVERSAL LAWS"

As we have seen, a distribution F need not belong to any domain of attraction, and the question arises whether there exist general patterns in the asymptotic behavior of the sequence $\{F^{n\star}\}$ of its successive convolutions. The sad answer is that practically every imaginable behavior occurs and no general regularity properties are discernible. We describe a few of the possibilities principally for their curiosity value.

The characteristic function φ *is said to belong to the domain of partial attraction of* γ *iff there exist norming constants* a_r, b_r *and a sequence of*

* This section treats special topics.

integers $n_r \to \infty$ *such that*

$$\left[\varphi\left(\frac{\zeta}{a_r}\right)e^{-ib_r\zeta}\right]^{n_r} \to \gamma(\zeta). \tag{9.1}$$

Here it is understood that $|\gamma|$ is not identically 1, that is, the corresponding distribution is not concentrated at one point. Thus (9.1) generalizes the notion of domains of attraction by considering limits of subsequences.

The limit γ *is necessarily infinitely divisible* by virtue of theorem 2.1. The following examples will show that both extremes are possible: *there exist distributions that belong to no domain of partial attraction and others that belong to the domain of partial attraction of every infinitely divisible distribution.*

Examples. (*a*) Example (3.*f*) exhibits a characteristic function φ which is not stable but belongs to its own domain of partial attraction.

(*b*) *A symmetric distribution with slowly varying tails belongs to no domain of partial attraction.* Suppose that $L(x) = 1 - F(x) + F(-x)$ varies slowly at infinity [that is, (5.5) holds]. By theorem 2 of VIII,9 in this case

$$U(x) = \int_{-x}^{x} y^2\, F\{dy\} = o(x^2L(x)), \qquad x \to \infty. \tag{9.2}$$

By the criterion of section 7, for F to belong to some domain of partial attraction it is necessary that as n runs through an appropriate sequence $n[1 - F(a_nx) + F(-a_nx)]$ and $na_n^{-2}\, U(a_nx)$ converge at all points of continuity. The first condition requires that $n\, L(a_n) \sim 1$, the second that $n\, L(a_n) \to \infty$.

(*c*) *An infinitely divisible* γ *need not belong to its own domain of partial attraction.* Indeed, it follows from the proof of theorem 2.1 that if φ belongs to the domain of attraction of γ so does the characteristic function $e^{\varphi-1}$, which is infinitely divisible. The last example shows that $e^{\varphi-1}$ need not belong to any domain of partial attraction.

(*d*) As a preparation to the oddities in the subsequent examples we prove the following proposition. Consider an arbitrary sequence of infinitely divisible characteristic functions $\omega_r = e^{\psi_r}$ with bounded exponents. Put

$$\lambda(\zeta) = \sum_{k=1}^{\infty} \frac{1}{n_k}\, \psi_k(a_k\zeta). \tag{9.3}$$

It is possible to choose the constants $a_k > 0$ and integers n_k such that as $r \to \infty$

$$n_r\lambda\left(\frac{\zeta}{a_r}\right) - \psi_r(\zeta) \to 0 \tag{9.4}$$

for all ζ.

Proof. Choose for $\{n_k\}$ a monotone sequence of integers increasing so rapidly that $n_k/n_{k-1} > 2^k \max |\psi_k|$. The left side in (9.4) is then dominated by

$$n_r \sum_{k=1}^{r-1} \left| \psi_k\left(\frac{a_k}{a_r}\zeta\right) \right| + \sum_{k=r+1}^{\infty} \frac{1}{2^k}. \tag{9.5}$$

We choose the coefficients a_r recursively as follows. Put $a_1 = 1$. Given $a_1, \ldots, a_{r-1}$ choose a_r so large that the quantity (9.5) is $<1/r$ for all $|\zeta| < r$. This is possible because the first sum depends continuously on ζ and vanishes for $\zeta = 0$.

(*e*) *Every infinitely divisible characteristic function* $\omega = e^{\psi}$ *possesses a domain of partial attraction.* Indeed, we know that ω is the limit of a sequence of characteristic functions $\omega_k = e^{\psi_k}$ of the compound Poisson type. Define λ by (9.3) and put $\varphi = e^{\lambda}$. Then φ is a characteristic function and (9.4) states that

$$\lim \varphi^{n_r}\left(\frac{\zeta}{a_r}\right) = \lim e^{\psi_r(\zeta)} = \omega(\zeta). \tag{9.6}$$

(*f*) *Variants.* Consider two infinitely divisible characteristic functions e^{α} and e^{β}. Choose the even-numbered ψ_k so that $\psi_{2k} \to \alpha$, and the odd-numbered so that $\psi_{2k+1} \to \beta$. Then $\varphi = e^{\lambda}$ *belongs to the domain of partial attraction of the distributions of the type determined by* $e^{p\alpha+q\beta-1}$ *where* $p + q = 1$ *and of no others.* This example generalizes easily. In the terminology of convex sets it shows that a distribution F may belong to the domains of partial attraction of the distributions in the *convex hull of n prescribed infinitely divisible distributions.*

(*g*) *Given a sequence of infinitely divisible characteristic functions* e^{α_1}, $e^{\alpha_2}, \ldots$ *there exists a* $\varphi = e^{\lambda}$ *belonging to the domain of partial attraction of each of them.* Partition the integers into infinitely many subsequences. (For example, let the nth subsequence contain all those integers that are divisible by 2^{n-1} but not by 2^n.) We can then choose the ψ_r in example (*d*) such that $\psi_r \to \alpha_n$ when r runs through the nth subsequence. With this choice (9.4) shows that $\varphi = e^{\lambda}$ has the desired property.

(*h*) *Doblin's "universal laws." It is possible that* φ *belongs to the domain of partial attraction of every infinitely divisible* ω. Indeed, it is obvious from the definition (9.1) that if φ belongs to the domain of partial attraction of $\omega_1, \omega_2, \ldots$ and $\omega_n \to \omega$, then φ belongs also to the domain of partial attraction of ω. Now there exist only countably many infinitely divisible characteristic functions with the property that the determining canonical measure is concentrated at finitely many rational points and attributes to each of them a rational weight. We can therefore order all these functions in a simple sequence $e^{\alpha_1}, e^{\alpha_2}, \ldots$. Then *every* infinitely divisible ω is the limit of a subsequence of $\{e^{\alpha_k}\}$. The characteristic function φ of the last example belongs to the domain of partial attraction of each α_k, and therefore also of ω.

[**Note.** The last result was obtained by Doblin in a masterly study in 1940, following previous work by Khintchine in 1937. The technical difficulties presented by the problem at that time were formidable. The phenomenon of example (*b*) was discovered in special cases by Gnedenko, Khintchine, and Lévy. It is interesting to observe the complications encountered in a special example when the underlying phenomenon of regular variation is not properly understood.]

*10. INFINITE CONVOLUTIONS

Let $\mathbf{X}_1, \mathbf{X}_2, \ldots$ be independent random variables with characteristic functions $\varphi_1, \varphi_2, \ldots$. As in (7.2) we denote by τ the continuous truncation function defined by $\tau(x) = x$ for $|x| \leq 1$ and $\tau(x) = \pm 1$ for $|x| \geq 1$. The basic theorem on infinite convolutions states that *the distributions of the partial sums* $\mathbf{X}_1 + \cdots + \mathbf{X}_n$ *converge to a probability distribution U iff*

$$\sum_{k=1}^{\infty} \text{Var}(\tau(\mathbf{X}_k)) < \infty, \qquad \sum_{k=1}^{\infty} \mathbf{P}\{|\mathbf{X}_k| > 1\} < \infty \tag{10.1}$$

and

$$\sum_{k=1}^{n} \mathbf{E}(\tau(\mathbf{X}_k)) \to b \tag{10.2}$$

where b is a number.

The special case of finite variance was treated in VIII,5 together with examples and applications. In full generality the theorem appears in IX,9 where the result is also extended by proving the convergence of the series $\Sigma \mathbf{X}_n$ (the "three-series theorem"). The theorem was shown to be a simple corollary to the basic theorems concerning triangular arrays, and it is not necessary to repeat the argument.[15] We shall therefore be satisfied with examples illustrating the use of characteristic functions.

Examples. (*a*) *Factorization of the uniform distribution.* Let $\mathbf{X}_k = \pm 2^{-k}$ with probability $\frac{1}{2}$. It was shown in example I(11.*c*) informally that $\Sigma \mathbf{X}_k$ may be interpreted as "a number chosen at random between 1 and -1." This amounts to the assertion that the characteristic function

---

* This section treats a special topic.

[15] It is a good exercise to verify *directly* that the conditions (10.1)–(10.2) assure that the products $\varphi_1 \cdots \varphi_n$ converge uniformly in every finite interval. (The necessary estimates are given at the beginning of section 7.) The *necessity* of the conditions is less obvious, but follows easily on observing that the triangular array whose nth row is $\mathbf{X}_n, \mathbf{X}_{n+1}, \ldots, \mathbf{X}_{n+r_n}$ must satisfy the conditions of theorem 7.2 with $M = 0$.

$(\sin \zeta)/\zeta$ of the uniform distribution is the infinite product of the characteristic functions $\cos(\zeta/2^k)$. For an analytic proof we start from the identity

$$(10.3)\qquad \frac{\sin \zeta}{\zeta} = \cos\frac{\zeta}{2}\cdot\cos\frac{\zeta}{4}\cdots\cos\frac{\zeta}{2^n}\cdot\frac{\sin(\zeta/2^n)}{\zeta/2^n} \qquad ▶$$

which is proved by induction using the formula $\sin 2\alpha = 2\sin\alpha\cos\alpha$. As $n \to \infty$ the last factor tends to 1 uniformly in every finite interval.

Note that the product of the even-numbered terms again corresponds to a sum of independent random variables. We know from example I,(11.*d*) that this sum has a *singular distribution* of the Cantor type.[16]

[See problems 5, 7, and 18.]

(*b*) Let $\mathbf{Y}_k$ have density $\frac{1}{2}e^{-|x|}$ with characteristic function $1/(1+\zeta^2)$. Then $\Sigma\mathbf{Y}_k/k$ converges. For the characteristic function we get the canonical product representation for $\dfrac{\pi\zeta}{\sinh \pi\zeta}$ where sinh denotes the hyperbolic sine. Using problem 7 in XV,9 we find that *the density of* $\Sigma\mathbf{Y}_k/k$ *is given by*

$$\frac{1}{2+e^x+e^{-x}} = \frac{1}{4(\cosh(x/2))^2}. \qquad ▶$$

11. HIGHER DIMENSIONS

The theory developed in this chapter carries over without essential changes to higher dimensions, and we shall not give all the details. In the canonical form for infinitely divisible distributions it is best to separate the normal component and consider only canonical measures without atom at the origin. The formulas then require no change provided ζx is interpreted as an inner product in the manner described in XV,7. For definiteness we spell out the formula in two dimensions.

A measure M is canonical if $1/(1+x_1^2+x_2^2)$ is integrable with respect to it, and if it has no atom at the origin. Choose an appropriate centering function in *one* dimension, say $\tau(x) = \sin x$ or the one defined in (7.2). Put

$$(11.1)\qquad \psi(\zeta_1, \zeta_2) = \int \frac{e^{i(\zeta_1x_1+\zeta_2x_2)} - 1 - i\zeta_1\tau(x_1) - i\zeta_2\tau(x_2)}{x_1^2+x_2^2}\, M\{dx\},$$

the integral extending over the whole plane. Then $\omega = e^\psi$ is an infinitely divisible bivariate characteristic function. The most general infinitely divisible characteristic function is obtained by multiplication by a normal characteristic function.

---

[16] Choquet gave a charming geometric proof applicable to more general infinite convolutions. It is given in A. Tortrat, J. Math. Pures. Appl., vol. 39 (1960) pp. 231–273.

A reformulation in polar coordinates may render the situation more intuitive. Put

$$\zeta_1 = \rho \cos \varphi, \quad \zeta_2 = \rho \sin \varphi, \quad x = r \cos \theta, \quad y = r \sin \theta. \tag{11.2}$$

Define the canonical measure in polar coordinates as follows. For each θ with $-\pi < \theta \leq \pi$ choose a one-dimensional canonical measure Λ_θ concentrated on $\overline{0, \infty}$; furthermore, choose a finite measure W on $-\pi < \theta \leq \pi$ (the circle). Then M may be defined by randomization of the parameter θ, and (with a trite change in centering) (11.1) may be recast in the form

$$\psi(\zeta_1, \zeta_2) = \\ = \int_{-\pi}^{\pi} W\{d\theta\} \int_{0+}^{\infty} \frac{e^{i\rho r \cos(\varphi-\theta)} - 1 - i\rho\tau(r)\cos(\varphi-\theta)}{r^2} \Lambda_\theta\{dr\}. \tag{11.3}$$

(This form permits one to absorb the normal component by adding an atom at the origin to Λ_θ.)

Example. *Stable distributions.* By analogy with one dimension we put $\Lambda_\theta\{dr\} = r^{-\alpha+1}\,dr$. One could add an arbitrary factor C_θ, but this would merely change the measure W. As we have seen in section 4, with this measure (11.3) takes on the form

$$\psi(\zeta_1, \zeta_2) = -C\rho^\alpha \int_{-\lambda}^{\pi} |\cos(\varphi-\theta)|^\alpha \left(1 \mp \tan\frac{\pi}{2^\alpha}\right) W\{d\theta\}, \tag{11.4}$$

where the upper or lower sign prevails according as $\varphi - \theta > 0$ or $\varphi - \theta < 0$. It is clear from (11.4) that e^ψ is a strictly stable characteristic function, and as in section 4 one sees that there are no others. There are, however, stable distributions in $\mathfrak{R}^2$ corresponding to the characteristic functions $e^{\psi_{1,\delta}}$ with the logarithmic term in the exponent.

When $\alpha = 1$ and W is the uniform distribution we get the characteristic function $e^{-a\rho}$ of *the symmetric Cauchy distribution in* $\mathfrak{R}^2$ [see example XV,(7.*d*) and problems 20–22]. ▶

12. PROBLEMS FOR SOLUTION

1. In the proof of lemma 1.4 it was shown that if ψ is given by the canonical form (1.12) then

$$\psi(\zeta) - \frac{\psi(\zeta+h) + \psi(\zeta-h)}{2} = \chi(\zeta) \tag{12.1}$$

is proportional to a characteristic function. Prove the converse: If ψ is continuous and if $\chi(\zeta)/\chi(0)$ is a characteristic function for all choices of h, then ψ differs from (1.12) only by a linear function. (*Hint:* Prove that the solutions of the homogeneous equation are linear.)

2. A function ψ is the logarithm of an infinitely divisible characteristic function if, and only if, for each $\delta > 0$

$$\psi(\zeta) - \frac{1}{2\delta}\int_{-\delta}^{\delta} \psi(\zeta - s)\, ds = \chi(\zeta) \tag{12.2}$$

is a multiple of a characteristic function and $\psi(0) = 0$, $\psi(-\zeta) = \overline{\psi(\zeta)}$.

[*Hint:* This differs from the last problem and lemma 1.4 in that the uniform distribution replaces the distribution concentrated at $\pm h$. See the next problem.]

3. Let R be an arbitrary even probability distribution with finite variance. If ω is an infinitely divisible characteristic function and $\psi = \log \omega$, then

$$\chi = \psi - R \star \psi$$

is a multiple of a characteristic function. The converse is also true (see problems 1 and 2).

4. If ω is an infinitely divisible characteristic function then there exist constants a and b such that $|\log \omega(\zeta)| < a + b\zeta^2$ for all ζ.

5. *Shot noise in vacuum tubes.* In example VI,(3.*h*) we considered a triangular array in which $\mathbf{X}_{k,n}$ had the characteristic function

$$\varphi_{k,n}(\zeta) = 1 + \alpha h[e^{i\zeta I(kh)} - 1],$$

where $h = 1/\sqrt{n}$. Show that the characteristic functions of the sums $\mathbf{S}_n = \mathbf{X}_{1,n} + \cdots + \mathbf{X}_{n,n}$ tend to the limit e^{ψ} where

$$\psi(\zeta) = \alpha \int_0^{\infty} [e^{i\zeta I(x)} - 1]\, dx;$$

e^{ψ} is the characteristic function of the random variable $\mathbf{X}(t)$, and by differentiation one gets *Campbell's theorem* VI,(3.5).

6. Let $U = \Sigma\, \mathbf{X}_n/n$ where the variables $\mathbf{X}_k$ are independent and have the common density $\frac{1}{2}e^{-|x|}$. Show that[17] U is infinitely divisible with the canonical measure $M\{dx\} = |x|\dfrac{e^{-|x|}}{1 - e^{-|x|}}\, dx$. [No calculations beyond summing a geometric series are required.]

7. Let $P(s) = \Sigma p_k s^k$ where $p_k \geq 0$ and $\Sigma p_k = 1$. Assume $P(0) > 0$ and that $\log \dfrac{P(s)}{P(0)}$ is a power series with positive coefficients. If φ is the characteristic function of an arbitrary distribution F show that $P(\varphi)$ is an infinitely divisible characteristic function. Find its canonical measure M in terms of $F^{n\star}$.

Special case of interest: if $0 \leq a < b < 1$ then $\dfrac{1-b}{1-a} \cdot \dfrac{1 - a\varphi}{1 - b\varphi}$ is an infinitely divisible characteristic function.

7*a*. Interpret $P(\varphi)$ in terms of randomization and subordinated processes using the fact that P is the generating function of an infinitely divisible integral-valued random variable.

---

[17] The characteristic function ω is defined by an infinite product which happens to be the well-known canonical product of $\dfrac{\pi|\zeta|}{e^{\pi|\zeta|} - e^{-\pi|\zeta|}}$.

8. Let $\mathbf{Y}$ be a *positive* stable variable with exponent $\alpha < 1$, and $\mathbf{X}$ a stable variable with exponent β. Verify that $\mathbf{X}\mathbf{Y}^{1/\alpha}$ *is stable with exponent* $\alpha\beta$. [See example VI,(2.*g*). For characteristic functions of products see XV,(9.4).]

9. Let ω be a characteristic function such that $\omega^2(\zeta) = \omega(a\zeta)$ and $\omega^3(\zeta) = \omega(b\zeta)$. Then ω is stable.

[Example (3.*f*) shows that the first relation does not suffice. The exponents 2, 3 may be replaced by any two relatively prime integers.]

10. Show that the simple lemma 2 of VIII,8 applies (not only to monotone functions but also) to logarithms of characteristic functions. Conclude that if $\omega_n(\zeta) = \omega(a_n\zeta)$ for all n then $\log \omega(\zeta) = A\zeta^\alpha$ for $\zeta > 0$, where A is a complex constant.

11. *Continuation.* Using the result of problem 23 in VIII,10 show (without use of the theory of stable distributions) that if ω is a stable characteristic function then for $\zeta > 0$ either $\log \omega(\zeta) = A\zeta^\alpha + ib\zeta$ or else $\log \omega(\zeta) = A\zeta + ib\zeta \log \zeta$ with b real.

12. Let F be carried by $\overline{0, \infty}$ and $1 - F(x) = x^{-\alpha}L(x)$ with $0 \leq \alpha < 1$ and L slowly varying at infinity. Prove that $1 - \varphi(\zeta) \sim A\zeta^\alpha L(1/\zeta)$ as $\zeta \to 0+$.

13. *Continuation.* From the results of section 5 prove the *converse*, and also that $A = -\Gamma(1-\alpha)e^{i\pi\alpha/2}$.

14. *Continuation.* By induction on k prove: in order that $1 - F(x) \sim ax^{-\alpha}L(x)$ as $x \to \infty$ with L slowly varying and $k < \alpha < k + 1$ it is necessary and sufficient that as $\zeta \to 0+$

$$(*) \qquad \varphi(\zeta) - 1 - \frac{\mu_1(i\zeta)}{1!} - \cdots - \frac{\mu_k(i\zeta)^k}{k!} \sim A\zeta^\alpha L\left(\frac{1}{\zeta^{-1}}\right).$$

Then automatically $A = -a\Gamma(k-\alpha)e^{-i\frac{1}{2}\pi\alpha}$ where $\Gamma(k-\alpha)$ is defined by induction from $\Gamma(2-\alpha) = (1-\alpha)\,\Gamma(1-\alpha)$.

15. Formulate the weak law for triangular arrays as a special case of the general theorem of section 7.

16. Let $\{\mathbf{X}_{k,n}\}$ be a null array whose row sums have a limit distribution determined by the canonical measure M. Show that for $x > 0$

$$\mathbf{P}\{\max[\mathbf{X}_{1,n}, \ldots, \mathbf{X}_{r_n,n}] \leq x\} \to e^{-M^+(x)}.$$

Formulate a converse.

17. Let $\{\mathbf{X}_{k,n}\}$ be a null array of symmetric variables whose row sums have a limit distribution determined by the canonical measure M with an atom of weight σ^2 at the origin. Show that the distribution of $\mathbf{S}_n^* = \Sigma\mathbf{X}_{k,n}^2 - \sigma^2$ converges to a distribution determined by a measure M_* without atom at the origin and such that $M_*^+(x) = 2M^+(\sqrt{x})$ for $x > 0$.

18. Let $0 < r_j < 1$ and $\Sigma r_j < \infty$. For arbitrary real a_j the infinite product

$$\frac{1 - r_1}{1 - r_1e^{ia_1\zeta}} \cdot \frac{1 - r_2}{1 - r_2e^{ia_2\zeta}} \cdots$$

converges and represents an infinitely divisible characteristic function. (*Hint:* Each factor is infinitely divisible by problem 7.)

19. Use the method of example (9.*d*) to construct a distribution F such that $\limsup F^{n\star}(x) = 1$ and $\liminf F^{n\star}(x) = 0$ at all points.

20. In (11.4) let W stand for the uniform distribution. Then

$$\psi(\zeta_1,\zeta_2) = -c[\zeta_1^2 + \zeta_2]^{\frac{1}{2}\alpha},$$

and e^{ψ} is a symmetric stable distribution.

21. In (11.4) let W attribute weight $\frac{1}{4}$ to each of the four points 0, π, $\frac{1}{2}\pi$, $-\frac{1}{2}\pi$. Then (11.4) represents the bivariate characteristic function of two *independent* one-dimensional stable variables.

22. In (11.4) let W be concentrated on the two points σ and $\sigma + \pi$. Then (11.4) represents a *degenerate* characteristic function of a pair such that

$$\mathbf{X}_1 \sin \sigma - \mathbf{X}_2 \cos \sigma = 0.$$

More generally, any discrete W leads to a convolution of degenerate distributions. Explain (11.4) by a limiting process.

CHAPTER XVIII

Applications of Fourier Methods to Random Walks

To a large extent this chapter treats topics already covered in chapter XII (for which reason applications are kept to a minimum). A serious attempt has been made to make it self-contained and accessible with a minimum of previous knowledge (except the Fourier analysis of chapter XV). The theory is entirely independent of the last two chapters.

1. THE BASIC IDENTITY

Throughout this chapter $\mathbf{X}_1, \mathbf{X}_2, \ldots$ are mutually independent random variables with a common distribution F and characteristic function φ. As usual we put $\mathbf{S}_0 = 0$ and $\mathbf{S}_n = \mathbf{X}_1 + \cdots + \mathbf{X}_n$; the sequence $\{\mathbf{S}_n\}$ constitutes the random walk generated by F.

Let A be an arbitrary set on the line and A' its complement. (In most applications A' will be a finite or infinite interval.) If I is a subset (interval) of A' and if

$$\mathbf{S}_1 \in A, \ldots, \mathbf{S}_{n-1} \in A, \mathbf{S}_n \in I \qquad (I \subset A') \tag{1.1}$$

we say that the set A' *is entered at epoch n and at a point of I*. Since A' need not be entered at all the *epoch* $\mathbf{N}$ *of the entry* is a possibly defective random variable, and the same is true of *the point* $\mathbf{S_N}$ *of first entry*. For the joint distribution of the pair $(\mathbf{N}, \mathbf{S_N})$ we write

$$\mathbf{P}\{\mathbf{N} = n, \mathbf{S_N} \in I\} = H_n\{I\}, \qquad n = 1, 2, \ldots. \tag{1.2}$$

Thus $H_n\{I\}$ is the probability of the event (1.1), but the distribution (1.2) is defined for all sets I on the line by the convention that $H_n\{I\} = 0$ if $I \subset A$. The probabilities (1.2) will be called *hitting probabilities*. Their study is intimately connected with the study of the random walk prior to the first entry to A', that is, *the random walk restricted to A*. For $I \subset A$ and $n = 1, 2, \ldots$ put

$$G_n\{I\} = \mathbf{P}\{\mathbf{S}_1 \in A, \ldots, \mathbf{S}_{n-1} \in A, \mathbf{S}_n \in I\}; \tag{1.3}$$

in words, this is the probability that at epoch n the set $I \subset A$ is visited and up to epoch n no entry to A' took place. We extend this definition to all sets on the line by letting $G_n\{I\} = 0$ if $I \subset A'$.

Note that by definition

$$G_n\{A\} = 1 - \mathbf{P}\{\mathbf{N} \leq n\}. \tag{1.4}$$

The variable $\mathbf{N}$ is not defective iff this quantity tends to 0 as $n \to \infty$.

Considering the position $\mathbf{S}_n$ of the random walk at epochs $n = 1, 2, \ldots$ it is obvious that for $I \subset A'$

$$H_{n+1}\{I\} = \int_A G_n\{dy\}\, F\{I-y\} \tag{1.5a}$$

whereas for $I \subset A$

$$G_{n+1}\{I\} = \int_A G_n\{dy\}\, F\{I-y\}. \tag{1.5b}$$

We now agree to let G_0 *stand for the probability distribution concentrated at the origin*. Then the relations (1.5) hold for $n = 0, 1, 2, \ldots$ and determine recursively all the probabilities H_n and G_n. The two relations can be combined in one. Given an arbitrary set I on the line we split it into the components IA' and IA and apply (1.5) to these components. Recalling that H_n and G_n are concentrated, respectively, on A' and A we get

$$H_{n+1}\{I\} + G_{n+1}\{I\} = \int_A G_n\{dy\}\, F\{I-y\} \tag{1.6}$$

for $n = 0, 1, \ldots$ and arbitrary I. The integral on the right represents the familiar convolution $G_n \star F$.

The special case $A = \overline{0, \infty}$ was treated in XII,3, the relation XII,(3.5) being the same as the present (1.5). We could retrace our steps and derive an integral equation of the Wiener-Hopf type analogous to XII,(3.9) and again possessing only one probabilistically possible solution (though the uniqueness is not absolute). It is preferable, however, to rely this time on the powerful method of Fourier analysis.

We are concerned with the distribution of the pair $(\mathbf{N}, \mathbf{S}_\mathbf{N})$. Since $\mathbf{N}$ is integral-valued we use the notation of generating functions for $\mathbf{N}$ and characteristic functions for $\mathbf{S}_\mathbf{N}$. Accordingly we put

$$\chi(s, \zeta) = \sum_{n=1}^{\infty} s^n \int_{A'} e^{i\zeta x} H_n\{dx\}, \qquad \gamma(s, \zeta) = \sum_{n=0}^{\infty} s^n \int_A e^{i\zeta x} G_n\{dx\}. \tag{1.7}$$

(The effective domains of integration are inserted for clarity, but the limits of integration could be denoted also by $-\infty$ and ∞. In the second series the zero term equals 1.)

The total masses of G_n and H_n being ≤ 1 the two series in (1.7) converge at least for $|s| < 1$. For such s we get from (1.6) *the basic identity*

$$\chi + \gamma = 1 + s\gamma\varphi \tag{1.8}$$

or

$$1 - \chi = \gamma[1 - s\varphi]. \tag{1.9}$$

(For an alternative proof see problem 10.)

In principle χ and γ can be calculated recursively from (1.5), and the identity (1.9) appears at first glance redundant. In reality direct calculations are rarely feasible, but much valuable information can be extracted directly from (1.9).

Example. Let F stand for the bilateral exponential distribution with characteristic function $\varphi(\zeta) = 1/(1 + \zeta^2)$, and let $A = \overline{-a, a}$. In view of the properties of the exponential distribution discussed in the first chapter it is plausible that the distributions H_n should be exponential and identical. If so we should have for reasons of symmetry

$$\chi(s, \zeta) = P(s)\frac{e^{i\zeta a}}{1 - i\zeta} + P(s)\frac{e^{-i\zeta a}}{1 + i\zeta} \tag{1.10}$$

where $2P(s)$ is the generating function of the epoch $\mathbf{N}$ of first entry into $|x| \geq a$. Now the right side in (1.9) vanishes for $\zeta = \pm i\sqrt{1 - s}$, and so for this value (1.10) must reduce to 1. Thus

$$P(s) = \left[\frac{e^{-a\sqrt{1-s}}}{1 + \sqrt{1 - s}} + \frac{e^{a\sqrt{1-s}}}{1 - \sqrt{1 - s}}\right]^{-1}. \tag{1.11}$$

The starting assumption is easily verified from (1.5*a*) without any explicit calculations: if F has an exponential density the same is true of H_{n+1} whatever the form of G_n. The final result embodied in (1.10) and (1.11) is therefore rigorously justified. A direct calculation would be messy. (For further examples see problems 3–6.) ►

*2. FINITE INTERVALS. WALD'S APPROXIMATION

Theorem. *Let* $A = \overline{-a, b}$ *be a finite interval containing the origin and let* $(\mathbf{N}, \mathbf{S_N})$ *be the hitting point for the complement* A'.

* Not used in the sequel.

The variables **N** *and* $\mathbf{S_N}$ *are proper. The generating function*

$$\sum_{n=0}^{\infty} s^n \mathbf{P}\{\mathbf{N} > n\} = \sum_{n=0}^{\infty} s^n G_n\{A\} \tag{2.1}$$

converges for some[1] $s > 1$ *and hence* **N** *has moments of all orders. The hitting point* $\mathbf{S_N}$ *has an expectation iff the random-walk distribution* F *has an expectation* μ, *in which case*

$$\mathbf{E}(\mathbf{S_N}) = \mu \cdot \mathbf{E}(\mathbf{N}). \tag{2.2}$$

Proof. Let r be fixed. For $\nu r < n \leq (\nu + 1)r$ we have trivially

$$G_n\{A\} \leq \mathbf{P}\{-a < \mathbf{S}_{kr} < b \text{ for } k = 1, \ldots, \nu\}. \tag{2.3}$$

The event on the right cannot occur unless $|\mathbf{S}_{kr} - \mathbf{S}_{(k-1)r}| < a + b$. These ν events are mutually independent and have the common probability $\eta = \mathbf{P}\{|\mathbf{S}_r| < a + b\}$. Thus $G_n\{A\} \leq \eta^\nu \leq \eta^{n/r-1}$. The series on the right in (2.1) converges therefore at least for $0 < s < \eta^{-1/r}$, which can be made > 1 by choosing r sufficiently large. It follows, in particular, that $G_n\{A\} \to 0$. In view of (1.4) this implies that **N** is proper.

Next, for $t > 0$

$$\mathbf{P}\{|\mathbf{S_N}| > t+a+b\} \leq \sum_{n=1}^{\infty} \mathbf{P}\{\mathbf{N} = n\}\mathbf{P}\{|\mathbf{X}_n| > t\} = \mathbf{P}\{|\mathbf{X}_1| > t\}. \tag{2.4}$$

$\mu = \mathbf{E}(\mathbf{X}_1)$ exists iff the right side is integrable over $\overline{0, \infty}$, and then the same is true of the left side, and so $\mathbf{E}(\mathbf{S_N})$ exists. On the other hand, $|\mathbf{X}_1| > t + a + b$ implies $|\mathbf{S_N}| > t$ and so the existence of $\mathbf{E}(\mathbf{S_N})$ implies that $\mu = \mathbf{E}(\mathbf{X}_1)$ exists. We know that (1.9) holds for all s for which the series (2.1) converges. When expectations exist it follows that

$$\mathbf{E}(\mathbf{S_N}) = \frac{\partial \chi(1, 0)}{\partial \zeta} = \varphi'(0) \cdot \gamma(1, 0) = \mu \cdot \mathbf{E}(\mathbf{N}). \tag{2.5}$$ ►

The identity (2.2) was found (under slight restrictions) by A. Wald. For the case of a semi-infinite interval it agrees with XII,(2.7) and the martingale proof given there applies without change when A is finite. This proof can be adopted also to yield the identity (2.7).

To avoid the use of an imaginary argument in the characteristic function we introduce the notation

$$f(\lambda) = \int_{-\infty}^{+\infty} e^{-\lambda x}\, F\{dx\}. \tag{2.6}$$

[1] This is known to statisticians as C. Stein's lemma. For an alternative proof see problem 7.

Wald's identity.[2] *If* $f(\lambda) < \infty$ *for* $\lambda_0 < \lambda < \lambda_1$ *then in this interval*

$$\mathbf{E}(f^{-\mathbf{N}}(\lambda) \cdot e^{-\lambda \mathbf{S_N}}) = \chi(f^{-1}(\lambda), i\lambda) = 1. \tag{2.7}$$

Proof. It is evident from its derivation that the identity (1.9) holds for imaginary arguments of ζ for which γ and χ are analytic. Now (2.7) is obtained formally from (1.9) by setting $s = f^{-1}(\lambda)$ and $\zeta = i\lambda$. To justify this it suffices to show that the series (2.1) converges for $s = f^{-1}(\lambda)$. Now if $f(\eta) < \infty$

$$\begin{aligned} G_n\{A\} \leq \mathbf{P}\{-a < \mathbf{S}_n < b\} &\leq e^{(a+b)|\eta|} \cdot \int_{-a}^{b} e^{-\eta x} \, F^{n\bigstar}\{dx\} \\ &\leq e^{(a+b)|\eta|} \cdot f^n(\eta). \end{aligned} \tag{2.8}$$

The series (2.1) therefore converges at $s = f^{-1}(\lambda)$ if $f(\lambda) > f(\eta)$. As we are free to choose η this proves (2.7) for all λ excepting values where f assumes its minimum. But being convex f has at most one minimum, and at it (2.7) follows by continuity. ▶

To illustrate the use of (2.7) to *estimates of the distribution of* **N** we put

$$p_k = \mathbf{P}\{\mathbf{N}{=}k, \ \mathbf{S_N}{\geq}b\}, \qquad q_k = \mathbf{P}\{\mathbf{N}{=}k, \ \mathbf{S_N}{\leq}-a\} \tag{2.9}$$

and write for the corresponding generating functions $P(s)$ and $Q(s)$. (Then $P + Q$ is the generating function for **N**.) Suppose now that a and b are large in comparison with the expectation and variance of F. The hitting point $\mathbf{S_N}$ is then likely to be relatively close to either b or $-a$. If these were the only possible values of $\mathbf{S_N}$ the identity (2.7) would take on the form

$$P\left(\frac{1}{f(\lambda)}\right)e^{-\lambda b} + Q\left(\frac{1}{f(\lambda)}\right)e^{\lambda a} = 1, \tag{2.10}$$

and one expects naturally that under the stated assumptions (2.10) will be satisfied at least approximately. The function f is convex and it is usually possible to find an interval $s_0 < s < s_1$ such that in it the equation

$$s\,f(\lambda) = 1 \tag{2.11}$$

admits of two roots $\lambda_1(s)$ and $\lambda_2(s)$ depending continuously on s. Substituting into (2.10) we get *two linear equations for the generating functions* P and Q, and thus we get (at least approximately) the distribution of **N** and the probabilities for an exodus to the right and left.

---

[2] Wald used (2.7) in connection with sequential analysis. This was before 1945 and before the general random walks were systematically explored. It is therefore natural that his conditions were severe and his methods difficult, but they still influence the statistical literature. The argument of the text utilizes an idea of H. D. Miller (1961).

Examples. (*a*) *Binomial random walk.* Let F have atoms of weight p and q at $+1$ and -1, respectively, $(p+q=1)$. Then $-a$ and b are indeed the only possible values for $\mathbf{S_N}$ and hence the method becomes exact. The equation (2.11) has the two roots such that $\tau_j = e^{-\lambda_j}$ is given by

$$(2.12)\qquad \tau_1(s) = \frac{1+\sqrt{1-4pqs^2}}{2ps}, \qquad \tau_2(s) = \frac{1-\sqrt{1-4pqs^2}}{2ps},$$

and the described method leads to

$$(2.13)\qquad P(s) = \frac{\tau_2^{\ a} - \tau_1^{\ a}}{\tau_2^{a+b} - \tau_1^{a+b}}, \qquad Q(s) = \left(\frac{q}{p}\right)^a \frac{\tau_2^{\ b} - \tau_1^{\ b}}{\tau_2^{a+b} - \tau_1^{a+b}}.$$

It is easily seen that this differs only notationally from the expression **1**; XIV,(4.11) for the ruin probabilities[3] and that the linear equations derived from (2.10) are equivalent to the boundary conditions used in **1**; XIV,4.

(*b*) *Arithmetic distributions* with finitely many atoms lead to an algebraic equation (2.11) for $e^{-\lambda}$. It was described in **1**; XIV,8 how the *exact* solutions P and Q can be obtained using all the roots of this equation. Furthermore, it was described how a simple modification of our simple approximation leads to *strict inequalities* for the probabilities p_k and q_k. This method is readily adaptable to arbitrary distributions concentrated on a finite interval.

3. WIENER-HOPF FACTORIZATION

We adhere to the notations of section 1 and choose $A = \overline{-\infty, 0}|$. Then $(\mathbf{N}, \mathbf{S_N})$ is the point of first entry into the open interval $A' = \overline{0, \infty}$ and

$$(3.1)\qquad \chi(s, \zeta) = \mathbf{E}(s^{\mathbf{N}} e^{i\zeta \mathbf{S_N}}).$$

The following lemma is not exciting in itself, but it serves as a key to all subsequent results. [It is a restatement of XII,(9.3).]

Lemma 1.[4] For $|s| < 1$

$$(3.2)\qquad \log \frac{1}{1-\chi(s,\zeta)} = \sum_{n=1}^{\infty} \frac{s^n}{n} \int_{0+}^{\infty} e^{i\zeta x}\, F^{n\star}\{dx\}.$$

[3] To identify U_z with Q change z and a to a and $a+b$, respectively.

[4] Discovered by G. Baxter. A simplified (but still rather technical) proof was given by F. Spitzer, Trans. Amer. Math. Soc., vol. 94 (1960) pp. 150–169.

Proof. Taking logarithms[5] in (1.9) we get

$$\sum_1^\infty \frac{s^n}{n} \varphi^n(\zeta) = \log \frac{1}{1-\chi(s,\zeta)} + \log \gamma(s,\zeta). \tag{3.3}$$

For sufficiently small s expand the logarithms in powers of χ and $(\gamma - 1)$, respectively. The first expansion has positive coefficients and so the first logarithm is the Fourier-Stieltjes transform of a measure concentrated on $\overline{0, \infty}$. On the other hand, $\gamma - 1$ is the difference of the transforms of two measures concentrated on $\overline{-\infty, 0}|$, and the same is therefore true of $\log \gamma$. The left side in (3.3) is the transform of the measure $\Sigma n^{-1}s^n F^{n\bigstar}$, and equating the components in $\overline{0, \infty}$ one gets (3.2). Because of the analytic character of the two sides this relation remains valid for all $|s| < 1$. ▶

As a simple corollary we get

Lemma 2. *Let* $(\tilde{\mathbf{N}}, \mathbf{S}_{\tilde{\mathbf{N}}})$ *be the point for first entry into* $\overline{-\infty, 0}|$ *and define* $\tilde{\chi}$ *by analogy with* (3.1). *Then for* $|s| < 1$

$$\log \gamma(s,\zeta) = \log \frac{1}{1-\tilde{\chi}(s,\zeta)} = \sum_{n=1}^\infty \frac{s^n}{n} \int_{-\infty}^{0+} e^{i\zeta x} F^{n\bigstar}\{dx\}. \tag{3.4}$$

Proof. The equality between the extreme members is seen on subtracting (3.2) from (3.3). The other identity is obtained by interchanging the roles of $\overline{0, \infty}$ and $\overline{-\infty, 0}|$ in lemma 1. ▶

Substituting from (3.4) into (1.9) we get for $|s| < 1$

$$1 - s\,\varphi(\zeta) = [1 - \chi(s,\zeta)] \cdot [1 - \tilde{\chi}(s,\zeta)]. \tag{3.5}$$

For reasons of continuity this identity remains valid also for $s = 1$. Put for abbreviation $\alpha(\zeta) = \chi(1, \zeta)$ and $\tilde{\alpha}(\zeta) = \tilde{\chi}(1, \zeta)$. Then α and $\tilde{\alpha}$ are the Fourier-Stieltjes transforms of the (possibly defective) variables $\mathbf{S}_\mathbf{N}$ and $\mathbf{S}_{\tilde{\mathbf{N}}}$ and we have

$$1 - \varphi = (1 - \alpha)(1 - \tilde{\alpha}). \tag{3.6}$$

The positive and negative half-axes enter this formula in a slightly unsymmetric way, but this can be easily remedied. The argument is postponed to section 6 in order to avoid sidelines; we record here the theorem in its simplest form.

[5] The logarithm of a characteristic function is uniquely defined by continuity as long as the function has no zeros (see the first proof in XVII,2). For $|s| < 1$ no term in (3.3) can vanish.

Factorization theorem. *For an arbitrary characteristic function* φ *the identities* (3.5) *and* (3.6) *hold for* $|s| \leq 1$.

The salient feature of this factorization is that it involves two (possibly defective) distributions concentrated on two disjoint intervals.

The argument leading to the theorem shows also that the factorization is unique and so determines the distributions of the ladder variables. Before embarking on a discussion of the theorem and its connection with the results of chapter XII we give a few examples.

Examples. (*a*) *Binomial random walk.* For the classical random walk with $p \geq q$ the factorization (3.5) takes on the form

$$1 - pe^{i\zeta} - qe^{-i\zeta} = (1 - e^{i\zeta})(1 - q - qe^{-i\zeta}). \tag{3.7}$$

This shows that an entry into $\overline{-\infty, 0}|$ has probability $2q$, whence

$$\gamma(1, \zeta) = \frac{1}{p - qe^{-i\zeta}} = \frac{1}{p}\sum_{0}^{\infty}\left(\frac{q}{p}\right)^{k} e^{-ik\zeta}. \tag{3.8}$$

By the definition of γ this may be interpreted as follows: *the expected number of visits to* $k \leq 0$ *preceding the first entry into* $\overline{0, \infty}$ *equals* $\dfrac{1}{p}\left(\dfrac{q}{p}\right)^{k}$. In particular, when $p = q = \frac{1}{2}$ we have the amazing result that before the occurrence of the first positive term $\mathbf{S}_n$ on the average every point $k \leq 0$ is visited twice. [See example XII,(2.*b*) and problems 1, 2 in XII,10.]

(*b*) *Bilateral exponential.* If F has the density $\frac{1}{2}e^{-|x|}$ then (3.6) takes on the form

$$1 - \frac{1}{1 + \zeta^2} = \left(1 - \frac{1}{1 - i\zeta}\right)\left(1 - \frac{1}{1 + i\zeta}\right). \tag{3.9}$$

On the right one recognizes the characteristic functions of one-sided exponential distributions.

(*c*) *Khintchine-Pollaczek formula.* Let F be the convolution of an exponential with expectation $1/a$ concentrated on $\overline{0, \infty}$ and a distribution B concentrated on $\overline{-\infty, 0}$. Denote the characteristic function of B by β, its expectation by $-b < 0$. We suppose that the expectation $a^{-1} - b$ of F is positive. Then (3.6) takes on the form

$$1 - \frac{a}{a - i\zeta}\beta(\zeta) = \left(1 - \frac{a}{a - i\zeta}\right)\left(1 - a\frac{1 - \beta(\zeta)}{i\zeta}\right). \tag{3.10}$$

The last factor corresponds to the defective distribution with *density* $aB(x)$ and total mass ab. The same result was derived by direct methods in XII,4. (See problem 8.)

(*d*) *Bounded arithmetic distributions.* With the present terminology we can say that example XII,(4.*c*) contains the explicit calculations leading to the factorization (3.5) when F is concentrated on finitely many integers.

(*e*) *Ladder variable distribution in exponential random walk.* In the random walk associated with the important queuing process of VI,(9.*e*) the distribution F was the convolution of two exponential distributions and hence

$$\varphi(\zeta) = \frac{a}{a+i\zeta}\cdot\frac{b}{b-i\zeta}. \tag{3.11}$$

By good fortune it is possible in this case to perform the factorization (3.5) explicitly for all $s < 1$. In fact, it is easily verified that

$$1 - s\varphi(\zeta) = \left(1 - \frac{p(s)}{a+i\zeta}\right)\left(1 - \frac{q(s)}{b-i\zeta}\right) \tag{3.12}$$

where

$$2p(s) = a + b - \sqrt{(a+b)^2 - 4abs}. \tag{3.13}$$

For $\zeta = 0$ it follows that the *ascending and descending ladder epochs* have generating functions $b^{-1}p(s)$ and $a^{-1}p(s)$, respectively.

One is led to (3.12) heuristically because the inherent lack of memory of the exponential distribution requires that for each n the first-entry probabilities H_n have a density of the form $b_n \cdot e^{-bx}$. In this case χ must be of the form $B(s)/(b - i\zeta)$. For the same reason we should expect that $\chi(s, \zeta) = A(s)/(a + i\zeta)$. Substituting these expressions into (3.5) it is seen that $A(s) = B(s) = p(s)$. ▶

4. DISCUSSION AND APPLICATIONS

It will be noticed that the results of the last section differ only notationally from results derived by combinatorial methods in chapter XII. [The factorization (3.6) is equivalent to XII,(3.11) while (3.3) is the same as XII,(9.3).] The following remarks should clarify the relation between the two approaches.

Transposed to the positive half-line, the identity (3.4) reads

$$\frac{1}{1-\chi(s,\zeta)} = \tilde{\gamma}(s,\zeta), \tag{4.1}$$

where $\tilde{\gamma}$ is the combination of generating function and Fourier-Stieltjes transform of

$$\tilde{G}_n\{I\} = \mathbf{P}\{\mathbf{S}_1 \geq 0, \ldots, \mathbf{S}_n \geq 0, \mathbf{S}_n \in I\}. \tag{4.2}$$

We now show that the left side in (4.1) is the analogous transform for

$$L_n\{I\} = \mathbf{P}\{0 < \mathbf{S}_n, \mathbf{S}_1 < \mathbf{S}_n, \ldots, \mathbf{S}_{n-1} < \mathbf{S}_n \in I\}. \tag{4.3}$$

Indeed, (4.3) merely states that $(n, \mathbf{S}_n)$ is a ladder point as defined in VI,8, where it was also shown that the ladder points form a renewal process. Now χ is the transform of the first ladder point, and therefore χ^k is the transform of the kth ladder point, and so $\Sigma\chi^k$ corresponds to the probabilities $L_n\{I\}$ of finding some ladder point in I.

Having identical transforms, the distributions (4.2) and (4.3) are identical. This was proved in XII,2 by combinatorial methods, and so we have now an alternative combinatorial proof of lemma 2.[6] The intuitive and elementary nature of the duality principle accounts for its great appeal, but it is also true that combinatorial methods can sometimes be used in situations that are not tractable by analytical methods. (Exchangeable variables are an example.) On the other hand, the use of Fourier transforms simplifies formulas greatly, and more delicate arguments involving Tauberian theorems would be impossible without Fourier transforms.

By way of applications we begin by an alternative interpretation of $\chi(s, \zeta)$ which plays an important role in queuing theory. [See VI,(9.5).]

Theorem.[7] *The characteristic function of*

$$\mathbf{U}_n = \max[0, \mathbf{S}_1, \ldots, \mathbf{S}_n] \tag{4.4}$$

is given by the coefficient of s^n *in*

$$\frac{\gamma(s, 0)}{1 - \chi(s, \zeta)} = \frac{1}{1-s} \exp \sum_{n=1}^{\infty} \frac{s^n}{n} \int_0^{\infty} [e^{i\zeta x} - 1] F^{n\star}\{dx\}. \tag{4.5}$$

Proof. There exists a uniquely determined *first* subscript $0 \leq \nu \leq n$ such that $\mathbf{S}_\nu = \mathbf{U}_n$. It is characterized by the following conditions. First $\mathbf{S}_\nu > \mathbf{S}_j$ for $j < \nu$, and second, for $k > \nu$ the difference $\mathbf{S}_k - \mathbf{S}_\nu$ is non-positive. The first condition involves only the variables $\mathbf{X}_1, \ldots, \mathbf{X}_\nu$, the second the variables $\mathbf{X}_{\nu+1}, \ldots, \mathbf{X}_n$. Accordingly

$$\mathbf{P}\{\mathbf{U}_n \in I\} = \sum_{\nu=0}^{n} L_\nu\{I\} G_{n-\nu}\{A\}, \tag{4.6}$$

where L_0 stands for the probability distribution concentrated at the origin. From the multiplicative property of generating functions it now

---

[6] For historical reasons the analytic proof usually uses deeper complex-variable methods, and this sets the two approaches further apart than necessary or natural.

[7] (4.5) is essentially the same as XII,(2.6). For improvements see theorem 5.2 and problem 9.

follows that $\Sigma s^n \mathbf{P}\{\mathbf{U}_n \in I\}$ has the Fourier-Stieltjes transform given by the left side in (4.5). That (4.5) is true follows from (3.2) and (3.4). ►

It was shown in XII,8 how the relation (4.6) may be exploited to derive the probability distribution of the *position* of the maximum U_n and the arc sine distribution as its limiting form.

We turn to the study of the expectations of the several random variables. In that connection we recall from XII,3 that there exist two essentially different types of random walks.

(*a*) *Drift to* $+\infty$ occurs if the hitting point $\mathbf{S}_{\tilde{\mathbf{N}}}$ for $\overline{-\infty, 0}|$ has a defective distribution, that is, when $\tilde{\chi}(1, 0) < 1$. For the hitting epoch $\mathbf{N}$ for $\overline{0, \infty}$ we have then from the very definition

$$(4.7) \qquad \mathbf{E}(\mathbf{N}) = \sum_{n=0}^{\infty} \mathbf{P}\{\mathbf{N} > n\} = \sum_{0}^{\infty} G_n\{\overline{-\infty, 0}|\} = \gamma(1, 0).$$

Putting for abbreviation

$$(4.8) \qquad a_n = \mathbf{P}\{\mathbf{S}_n > 0\}$$

we get therefore from (3.4) for $s = 1$ and $\zeta = 0$

$$(4.9) \qquad \mathbf{E}(\mathbf{N}) = \exp \sum_{n=1}^{\infty} \frac{1 - a_n}{n} < \infty.$$

If all expectations exist, differentiation of (1.9) leads to

$$-\chi'(1, 0) = -\gamma(1, 0) \cdot \varphi'(0);$$

that is,

$$(4.10) \qquad \mathbf{E}(\mathbf{S}_\mathbf{N}) = \mathbf{E}(\mathbf{N}) \cdot \mathbf{E}(\mathbf{X}_1).$$

This relation was derived in XII,2, where it was also shown that $\mathbf{E}(\mathbf{S}_\mathbf{N})$ exists iff $\mathbf{E}(\mathbf{X}_1)$ exists and is positive.

(*b*) *Oscillating random walks*. If $\alpha(0) = \tilde{\alpha}(0) = 1$ both half-lines are entered with probability one at least once (and hence infinitely often). From (4.7) one concludes that $\mathbf{E}(\mathbf{N}) = \infty$; persistent oscillation requires that the hitting epochs have infinite expectation (just as in coin tossing).

Under what circumstances do the hitting points $\mathbf{S}_\mathbf{N}$ and $\mathbf{S}_{\tilde{\mathbf{N}}}$ have finite expectations? If $\mathbf{E}(\mathbf{S}_\mathbf{N}) < \infty$ the characteristic function α is differentiable. From (3.6) it is clear that the existence of derivatives α' and $\tilde{\alpha}'$ implies that φ is differentiable and $\varphi'(0) = 0$. Now divide (3.6) by ζ^2 and let $\zeta \to 0$. The right side tends to $\alpha'(0)\ \tilde{\alpha}'(0) = -\mathbf{E}(\mathbf{S}_\mathbf{N})\ \mathbf{E}(\mathbf{S}_{\tilde{\mathbf{N}}})$. As was shown in XV,(4.8), the fact that the left side remains bounded implies that F possesses a second moment. Thus $\mathbf{E}(\mathbf{X}_j) = \varphi'(0) = 0$ and $\mathbf{X}_j$ *has a finite variance* σ^2 *such that*

$$\tag{4.11} \tfrac{1}{2}\sigma^2 = \mathbf{E}(\mathbf{S}_{\mathbf{N}})\,\mathbf{E}(\mathbf{S}_{\tilde{\mathbf{N}}}).$$

*5. REFINEMENTS

The main purpose of this section is to illustrate appropriate methods for explicit calculations and for the use of Tauberian theorems. We begin by a refinement of the last result.

Theorem 1.[8] *If* $\mathbf{E}(\mathbf{X}_1) = 0$ *and* $\mathbf{E}(\mathbf{X}_1{}^2) = \sigma^2 < \infty$, *then*

$$\tag{5.1} \mathbf{E}(\mathbf{S}_{\mathbf{N}}) = \frac{\sigma}{\sqrt{2}}\,e^{-c}, \qquad \mathbf{E}(\mathbf{S}_{\tilde{\mathbf{N}}}) = \frac{\sigma}{\sqrt{2}}\,e^{c}$$

where

$$\tag{5.2} c = \sum_{n=1}^{\infty} \frac{1}{n}\,(a_n - \tfrac{1}{2}),$$

the series being at least conditionally convergent.

Proof. Differentiating (3.2) with respect to ζ and setting $\zeta = 0$ leads to

$$\tag{5.3} -i\chi'(s, 0)\cdot\frac{\sqrt{1-s}}{1-\chi(s, 0)} = \sqrt{1-s}\sum_{n=1}^{\infty}\frac{s^n}{n}\int_0^{\infty} x\,F^{n\bigstar}\{dx\}.$$

By the central limit theorem the distribution function $F^{n\bigstar}(\sigma\sqrt{n}\,x)$ tends to the normal in such a way that all absolute moments of order ≤ 2 converge. From this it follows easily that the coefficient of s^n in the last series is $\sim \sigma/\sqrt{2\pi n}$, and by the Tauberian theorem 5 of XIII,5 this implies that

$$\tag{5.4} -i\chi'(s, 0)\,\frac{\sqrt{1-s}}{1-\chi(s, 0)} \to \frac{\sigma}{\sqrt{2}}.$$

Now $-i\chi'(s, 0) \to \mathbf{E}(\mathbf{S}_{\mathbf{N}})$ as $s \to 1$. The limit is finite or infinite, but certainly not zero. It follows that the fraction on the left tends to a finite limit. Now the reciprocal of this fraction occurs in the dual relation for $\tilde{\chi}$, and hence the limit is not zero. But from (3.2)

$$\tag{5.5} \log\frac{\sqrt{1-s}}{1-\chi(s, 0)} = \sum_{n=1}^{\infty}\frac{s^n}{n}\,(a_n - \tfrac{1}{2}).$$

* Not used in the sequel.

[8] First proved (by deeper methods) by F. Spitzer (see footnote in section 3). The convergence of (5.2) played a role in connection with the refined arc sine law in XII,(8.7).

We have proved that the right side tends to a finite limit c, and this implies (5.2) by the elementary Tauberian theorem for power series.[9] This completes the proof. ▶

Theorem 2. *If* $\mathbf{E}(\mathbf{X}_1) = \mu < 0$ *the maxima* $\mathbf{U}_n$ *have a limit distribution whose Laplace transform* ω *is given by*

$$\omega(\lambda) = \exp \sum_1^{\infty} \frac{1}{n} \int_0^{\infty} [e^{-\lambda x} - 1] F^{n\star}\{dx\}. \tag{5.6}$$

Proof. Formula (4.5) remains meaningful for $\zeta = i\lambda$ if $\lambda \geq 0$. The Laplace transform of $\mathbf{U}_n$ is given by the coefficient of s^n in

$$\frac{1}{1-s} \exp \sum_{n=1}^{\infty} \frac{s^n}{n} \int_0^{\infty} [e^{-\lambda x} - 1] F^{n\star}\{dx\}. \tag{5.7}$$

It is easily seen that the condition $\mu < 0$ implies the convergence[10] of the last series for $s = 1$, and so the quantity (5.7) is $\sim \omega(\lambda)(1-s)^{-1}$ as $s \to 1$, with ω defined in (5.6). Now the maxima $\mathbf{U}_n$ cannot decrease, and a trite integration by parts shows that this implies that the corresponding Laplace transforms form a monotone sequence. The Tauberian theorem 5 of XIII,5 therefore guarantees that the coefficient of s^n in (5.7) indeed tends to $\omega(\lambda)$. ▶

6. RETURNS TO THE ORIGIN

A slight unsymmetry was introduced in the preceding calculations by the fact that the negative half-axis was taken closed. This is not noticeable when the underlying distribution F is continuous and can be remedied in general. Put

$$r_n = \mathbf{P}\{\mathbf{S}_0 \leq 0, \ldots, \mathbf{S}_{n-1} \leq 0, \mathbf{S}_n = 0\}, \qquad n \geq 0, \tag{6.1}$$

$$f_n = \mathbf{P}\{\mathbf{S}_1 < 0, \ldots, \mathbf{S}_{n-1} < 0, \mathbf{S}_n = 0\}, \qquad n \geq 1, \tag{6.2}$$

The event in (6.1) signifies a return to the origin prior to the first entry into $\overline{0, \infty}$, and when such a return occurs the starting situation is re-established. In other words, (6.1) defines a recurrent event, and (6.2) gives the distribution of its recurrence times. Since $\Sigma f_n \leq \mathbf{P}\{\mathbf{X}_1 \leq 0\}$ the event is *transient* (except in the trivial case where F is concentrated at the origin).

---

[9] See, for example, p. 11 in E. C. Titchmarsh, *Theory of functions*, Oxford, 1939.

[10] Indeed, using the particular values $\zeta = 0$ and $s = 1$ it is seen from (3.2) that $\Sigma\, n^{-1}\mathbf{P}\{\mathbf{S}_n > 0\} < \infty$ whenever the random walk drifts to $-\infty$. For alternative proofs see theorem XII,7.2 and problem 16 in XII,9.

If $r(s)$ and $f(s)$ stand for the generating functions of $\{r_n\}$ and $\{f_n\}$, the basic relation for recurrent events states that

$$(6.3) \qquad r(s) = \frac{1}{1 - f(s)}.$$

Now r_n is the mass attributed to the origin by the measure G_n and hence $\gamma(s, \zeta) = r(s) + \gamma_1(s, \zeta)$ where γ_1 is the Fourier-Stieltjes transform of a measure concentrated on the *open* interval $\overline{-\infty, 0}$. Factoring out $r(s)$ reduces (3.5) to the symmetric form

$$(6.4) \qquad 1 - s\varphi(\zeta) = [1 - f(s)] \cdot [1 - \chi(s, \zeta)] \cdot [1 - \chi^-(s, \zeta)]$$

where χ^- is now the transform of the hitting point for the open interval $\overline{-\infty, 0}$. For $s = 1$ we get

$$(6.5) \qquad 1 - \varphi(\zeta) = [1 - f(1)] \cdot [1 - \alpha(\zeta)] \cdot [1 - \alpha^-(\zeta)]$$

where α and α^- are the transforms of the hitting points of the open half-lines. This is the *symmetric form of the Wiener-Hopf factorization.*

If one wishes to take the right half-line closed one has merely to combine the first two factors in (6.5) to obtain the mixture

$$(6.6) \qquad f(1) + [1 - f(1)]\, \alpha(\zeta)$$

for the transform of the hitting point for $\overline{0, \infty}$. This formula has the obvious probabilistic interpretation: with probability $f(1)$ the first entry takes place at the origin, and with probability $1 - f(1)$ the first entries into $\overline{|0, \infty}$ and $\overline{0, \infty}$ are the same. [This fact was exploited in XII,(1.10).] For reasons of symmetry our formulas imply that the probabilities f_n and r_n remain unchanged when all the inequalities in (6.1) and (6.2) are reversed. (This fact was established in XII,2 by reversing the order of the random variables.) In conclusion let it be remarked that the argument leading to (3.2) applies equally to the mass carried by the origin. It follows that

$$(6.7) \qquad \log \frac{1}{1 - f(s)} = \sum_{n=1}^{\infty} \frac{s^n}{n} \mathbf{P}\{\mathbf{S}_n = 0\}.$$

[This is the same as XII,(9.6).]

7. CRITERIA FOR PERSISTENCY

The material of this section is independent of the preceding theory. It is devoted to the method developed by K. L. Chung and W. H. J. Fuchs (1950) to decide whether a random walk is persistent or transient.

Despite the criteria and methods developed in chapter XII the Fourier-analytic method preserves its methodological and historical[11] interest and is at present the only method applicable in higher dimensions. In the following F stands for a one-dimensional distribution with characteristic function $\varphi = u + iv$. For the pertinent definitions the reader is referred to VI,10.

Criterion. *The distribution F is transient iff for some $\alpha > 0$*

$$\int_0^\alpha \frac{1 - su}{(1-su)^2 + s^2v^2}\,d\zeta \tag{7.1}$$

remains bounded as $s \to 1$.

(It will be seen that in the contrary case the integral tends to ∞.)

Proof. For $0 < s < 1$ we introduce the finite measure

$$U_s = \sum_{n=0}^{\infty} s^n F^{n\bigstar}. \tag{7.2}$$

The distribution F is transient iff $U_s\{I\}$ remains bounded for some open interval about the origin (in which case $U_s\{I\}$ remains bounded for every finite interval I). The Parseval relation XV,(3.2) applied to $F^{n\bigstar}$ and a triangular density (number 4 in XV,2) reads

$$2\int_{-\infty}^{+\infty} \frac{1 - \cos ax}{a^2x^2}\, F^{n\bigstar}\{dx\} = \frac{1}{a}\int_{-a}^{a}\left(1 - \frac{|\zeta|}{a}\right)\varphi^n(\zeta)\,d\zeta. \tag{7.3}$$

Hence

$$\begin{aligned} 2\int_{-\infty}^{+\infty} \frac{1 - \cos ax}{a^2x^2}\, U_s\{dx\} &= \frac{1}{a}\int_{-a}^{a}\left(1 - \frac{|\zeta|}{a}\right)\frac{d\zeta}{1 - s\varphi(\zeta)} \\ &= \frac{2}{a}\int_0^a\left(1 - \frac{\zeta}{a}\right)\cdot\frac{1 - su}{(1 - su)^2 + s^2v^2}\,d\zeta \end{aligned} \tag{7.4}$$

(because the real part is even). Let I stand for the interval $|x| < 2/a$. In I the left integrand in (7.3) is $> \frac{1}{3}$ and so $U_s\{I\}$ remains bounded. The condition of the theorem is therefore *sufficient*. That is it necessary follows in like manner by using Parseval's relation with the characteristic

[11] The fact that $\mathbf{E}(\mathbf{X}_j) = 0$ implies persistency was first established by Chung and Fuchs. It is interesting to reflect that in 1950 this presented a serious problem and many attempts to solve it had ended in failures. Attention on this problem was focused by the surprise discovery of the unfavorable "fair" random walk in which $\mathbf{P}\left\{\mathbf{S}_n > \frac{n}{\log n}\right\} \to 1$. (See **1**; X,3 and problem 15 in **1**; X,8.)

function $1 - \dfrac{|\zeta|}{a}$ (number 5 in XV,2). This replaces (7.4) by

$$(7.5)\qquad \int_{-a}^{a}\left(1-\frac{|x|}{a}\right)U_s\{dx\} = \frac{2}{\pi}\int_0^{\infty}\frac{1-\cos a\zeta}{a\zeta^2}\cdot\frac{1-su}{(1-su)^2+s^2v^2}\,d\zeta.$$

For a transient F the left side remains bounded, and so the integral (7.1) with $\alpha = \frac{1}{2}a$ remains bounded. ▶

Applications. (*a*) *Let the derivative*[12] $\varphi'(0) = i\mu$ *exist. Then F is transient if* $\mu \neq 0$, *persistent if* $\mu = 0$. In particular, if F has an expectation μ then $\mu = 0$ is necessary and sufficient for persistency.

For the proof we note that for fixed $\alpha > 0$ and $\eta > 0$

$$(7.6)\qquad \int_0^{\alpha}\frac{1-s}{(1-s)^2+\eta^2\zeta^2}\,d\zeta = \frac{1}{\eta}\arctan\frac{\eta\alpha}{1-s} \to \frac{\pi}{2}\cdot\frac{1}{\eta}$$

as $s \to 1$. Since u is even we have $u'(0) = 0$ and $v'(0) = \mu$. If $\mu \neq 0$ we take $\eta = 2|\mu|$ and choose α so small that for $|s| > \frac{1}{2}$ the integrand in (7.1) is dominated by a fixed multiple of the integrand in (7.6). As this integral remains bounded, F is transient. If, on the contrary, $\mu = 0$ we can choose η arbitrarily small and find $\alpha > 0$ such that the integrand in (7.1) dominates a multiple of the integrand in (7.1). The limit being arbitrarily large, F is persistent. (For a stronger version see problem 11.)

(*b*) It is clear from the criterion that F is persistent if

$$(7.7)\qquad \int_0^{\alpha}\frac{1-u}{(1-u)^2+v^2}\,d\zeta = \infty$$

for every $\alpha > 0$, and transient if

$$(7.8)\qquad \int_0^{\alpha}\frac{d\zeta}{1-u} < \infty$$

for some $\alpha > 0$. For applications see problems 11–14.

(*c*) *A truly two-dimensional distribution with zero expectations and finite variances is persistent.* For a proof note that the criterion applies without change to bivariate characteristic functions. Putting $r^2 = \zeta_1^2 + \zeta_2^2$ it is clear from the Taylor formula for u that in a neighborhood of the origin $1 - u$ lies between two positive multiples of r^2 and hence that the integrand in (7.7) exceeds a multiple of $1/r^2$.

(*d*) *Every three-dimensional distribution is transient.* Indeed, from the

[12] Concerning the existence of $\varphi'(0)$ see example XVII,(1.*c*).

Taylor expansion of the cosine it is clear that for any characteristic function $(1-u)/r^2$ is bounded away from zero. The three-dimensional analogue to (7.8) is therefore dominated by an integral of r^2 which is convergent in three dimensions.

8. PROBLEMS FOR SOLUTION

1. Do the example of section 1 for the case of an unsymmetric interval $\overline{-a, b}$. (Derive two linear equations for two generating functions corresponding to the two boundaries. Explicit solutions are messy.)

2. In the example of section 1 prove that $\mathbf{E}(\mathbf{N}) = 2P'(1) = 1 - \frac{a}{2} + \frac{a^2}{4}$. *Hint:* Use implicit differentiation in (1.10).

Problems 3–6 *refer to a symmetric binomial random walk*, that is, $\varphi(\zeta) = \cos\zeta$. The notations are those of section 1.

3. Let A consist of the two points 0, 1. Show by elementary considerations that $\chi(s, \zeta) = \frac{1}{1-\frac{1}{4}s^2}\left(\frac{s}{2}e^{-i\zeta} + \frac{s^2}{4}e^{2i\zeta}\right)$ and $\gamma(s, \zeta) = \frac{1}{1-\frac{1}{4}s^2}\left(1 + \frac{s}{2}e^{i\zeta}\right)$. Verify (1.9).

4. If in the preceding problem the roles of A and A' are interchanged one gets

$$\chi(s, \zeta) = \frac{s}{2}e^{i\zeta} + \tfrac{1}{2}(1 - \sqrt{1-s^2}), \qquad \gamma(s,\zeta) = \left[1 - \frac{1-\sqrt{1-s^2}}{s}e^{-i\zeta}\right]^{-1}.$$

Interpret probabilistically.

5. If A consists of the origin alone χ depends only on s and γ must be the sum of two power series in $e^{i\zeta}$ and $e^{-i\zeta}$, respectively. Using this information derive χ and γ directly from (1.9).

6. If A' consists of the origin alone one has $\chi = s\varphi$ and $\gamma = 1$.

7. Prove the convergence of (2.1) by showing that a truncation of F at the points $\pm(a+b)$ has no influence on the problem, and so inequalities of the form (2.8) are applicable.

8. In example (3.*c*) (Khintchine-Pollaczek formula) let $ab > 1$. Show that there exists a unique positive number κ between 0 and a such that

$$a\beta(-i\kappa) = a - \kappa.$$

Prove that $\tilde{\chi}(\zeta) = \dfrac{a - \kappa - a\beta(\zeta - i\kappa)}{i\zeta}$. [Compare examples XIII,5 *a–b*.]

9. Let $\mathbf{U}_n = \max[0, \mathbf{S}_1, \ldots, \mathbf{S}_n]$ and $\mathbf{V}_n = \mathbf{S}_n - \mathbf{U}_n$. By a very slight change of the argument used for (4.5) show that the bivariate characteristic function of the pair $(\mathbf{U}_n, \mathbf{V}_n)$ is the coefficient of s^n in[13]

$$\exp \sum_{n=1}^{\infty} \frac{s^n}{n}\left[\int_0^{\infty}(e^{i\zeta_1 x} - 1)F^{n\star}\{dx\} + \int_{-\infty}^{0}(e^{i\zeta_2 x} - 1)F^{n\star}\{dx\}\right].$$

[13] First derived analytically by F. Spitzer, Trans. Amer. Math. Soc., vol. 82 (1956) pp. 323–339.

10. *Alternative proof of the identity* (1.9). With the notations of section 1 show that

$$(*)\qquad F^{n\bigstar}\{I\} = \sum_{k=1}^{n} \int_{A'} H_k\{dy\}\, F^{(n-k)\bigstar}\{I-y\} + G_n\{I\}$$

(*a*) by a direct probabilistic argument, and
(*b*) by induction. Put $U_s = \Sigma_0^\infty s^n F^{n\bigstar}$. Show that (*) is equivalent to (1.9).

11. Suppose that in a neighborhood of the origin $|1 - \varphi(\zeta)| < A \cdot |\zeta|$. Then F is persistent unless it has an expectation $\mu \neq 0$.

Hint: The integral in (7.7) exceeds $\int_0^\alpha d\zeta \int_{-1/\zeta}^{1/\zeta} x^2\, F\{dx\}$. Substitute $\zeta = 1/t$ and interchange the order of integration to see that this integral diverges unless μ exists.

12. Using the criterion (7.8) show that if $t^{-1-\rho}\int_{-t}^{t} x^2\, F\{dx\} \to \infty$ for some $\rho > 0$ as $t \to \infty$ the distribution F is transient.[14]

13. The distribution with characteristic function $\varphi(\zeta) = e^{-1}\sum \frac{1}{n!} \cos(n!\,\zeta)$ is transient.

Hint: Use (7.8) and the change of variable $\zeta = \frac{1}{n!}\, t$.

14. The unsymmetric stable distributions with characteristic exponent $\alpha = 1$ are transient, but the Cauchy distribution is persistent.

---

[14] This shows that under slight regularity conditions F is transient whenever an absolute moment of order $\rho < 1$ diverges. The intricacies of the problem without any regularity conditions are shown in L. A. Shepp, Bull. Amer. Math. Soc., vol. 70 (1964) pp. 540–542.

CHAPTER XIX

Harmonic Analysis

This chapter supplements the theory of characteristic functions presented in chapter XV and gives applications to stochastic processes and integrals. The discussion of Poisson's summation formula in section 5 is practically independent of the remainder. The whole theory is independent of chapters XVI–XVIII.

1. THE PARSEVAL RELATION

Let U be a probability distribution with characteristic function

$$\omega(\zeta) = \int_{-\infty}^{+\infty} e^{i\zeta x}\, U\{dx\}. \tag{1.1}$$

Integrating this relation with respect to some other probability distribution F we get

$$\int_{-\infty}^{+\infty} \omega(\zeta)\, F\{d\zeta\} = \int_{-\infty}^{+\infty} \varphi(x)\, U\{dx\}, \tag{1.2}$$

where φ is the characteristic function of F. This is one form of the *Parseval relation* from which the basic results of XV, 3 were derived. Surprisingly enough, a wealth of new information can be obtained by rewriting Parseval's formula in equivalent forms and considering special cases. A simple example of independent interest may illustrate this method, which will be used repeatedly.

Example. The formula

$$\int_{-\infty}^{+\infty} e^{-ia\zeta}\omega(\zeta)\, F\{d\zeta\} = \int_{-\infty}^{+\infty} \varphi(x)\, U\{a + dx\} \tag{1.3}$$

differs from (1.2) only notationally. We apply the special case where F is the uniform distribution in $\overline{-t,\, t}$ and $\varphi(x) = \dfrac{\sin tx}{tx}$. This function does not exceed 1 in absolute value and as $t \to \infty$ it tends to 0 at all points $x \neq 0$. By bounded convergence we get therefore

$$(1.4) \qquad U(a) - U(a-) = \lim_{t\to\infty} \frac{1}{2t} \int_{-t}^{t} e^{-ia\zeta}\omega(\zeta)\, d\zeta.$$

This formula makes it possible to decide whether a is a point of continuity and to find the weight of the atom at a, if any. The most interesting result is obtained by applying (1.4) to the symmetrized distribution ${}^0U$ with characteristic function $|\omega|^2$. If $p_1, p_2, \ldots$ are the weights of the atoms of U then ${}^0U$ has an atom of weight Σp_k^2 at the origin (problem 8 in V, 11) and so

$$(1.5) \qquad \frac{1}{2t} \int_{-t}^{t} |\omega(\zeta)|^2\, d\zeta \to \sum p_k^2.$$

This formula shows, in particular, that the characteristic functions of continuous distributions are, on the average, small. ►

A versatile and useful variant of the Parseval formula (1.2) is as follows. *If A and B are arbitrary probability distributions with characteristic functions α and β, respectively, then*

$$(1.6) \qquad \iint_{-\infty}^{+\infty} \omega(s-t)\, A\{ds\}\, B\{dt\} = \int_{-\infty}^{+\infty} \alpha(x)\, \overline{\beta(x)}\, U\{dx\}$$

where $\bar\beta$ is the conjugate of β. For a direct verification it suffices to integrate

$$(1.7) \qquad \omega(s-t) = \int_{-\infty}^{+\infty} e^{i(s-t)x}\, U\{dx\}$$

with respect to A and B. This argument produces the erroneous impression that (1.6) is more general than (1.2), whereas the relation (1.6) *is in reality the special case of the Parseval relation* (1.2) *corresponding to* $F = A \bigstar {}^-B$ where ${}^-B$ is the distribution with characteristic function $\bar\beta$ (that is, ${}^-B(x) = 1 - B(-x)$ at all points of continuity). Indeed, F has the characteristic function $\varphi = \alpha\bar\beta$, and so the right sides in (1.2) and (1.6) are identical. That the left sides differ only notationally is best seen using two independent random variables **X** and **Y** with distributions A and B, respectively. The left side in (1.6) represents the direct definition of the expectation $\mathbf{E}(\omega(\mathbf{X}-\mathbf{Y}))$, whereas the left side in (1.2) expresses this expectation in terms of the distribution F of $\mathbf{X} - \mathbf{Y}$.

(We return to Parseval's formula in section 7.)

2. POSITIVE DEFINITE FUNCTIONS

An important theorem due to S. Bochner (1932) makes it possible to describe the class of characteristic functions by intrinsic properties. The following simple criterion will point the way.

Lemma 1. *Let* ω *be a bounded continuous (complex-valued) function that is integrable*[1] *over* $\overline{-\infty, \infty}$. *Define* u *by*

$$u(x) = \frac{1}{2\pi}\int_{-\infty}^{+\infty} e^{-i\zeta x}\,\omega(\zeta)\,d\zeta. \tag{2.1}$$

In order that ω *be a characteristic function it is necessary and sufficient that* $\omega(0) = 1$ *and that* $u(x) \geq 0$ *for all* x. *In this case* u *is the probability density corresponding to* ω.

Proof. The Fourier inversion theorem XV,3.3 shows that the conditions are necessary. Now choose an arbitrary even density f with integrable characteristic function $\varphi \geq 0$. Multiply (2.1) by $\varphi(tx)e^{iax}$ and integrate with respect to x. Since the inversion formula XV,(3.5) applies to the pair f, φ the result is

$$\int_{-\infty}^{+\infty} u(x)\,\varphi(tx)e^{iax}\,dx = \int_{-\infty}^{+\infty}\omega(\zeta)f\left(\frac{\zeta - a}{t}\right)\frac{d\zeta}{t}. \tag{2.2}$$

The right side is the expectation of ω with respect to a probability distribution, and hence it is bounded by the maximum of $|\omega|$. For the particular value $a = 0$ the integrand on the left is non-negative and tends to $u(x)$ as $t \to 0$. The boundedness of the integral therefore implies that u is *integrable*. Letting $t \to 0$ in (2.2) we get therefore

$$\int_{-\infty}^{+\infty} u(x)e^{iax}\,dx = \omega(a) \tag{2.3}$$

(the left side by bounded convergence, the right side because the probability distribution involved tends to the distribution concentrated at the point a). For $a = 0$ we see that u is a probability density, and ω is indeed its characteristic function. ►

The integrability condition of the lemma looks more restrictive than it is. In fact, by the continuity theorem a continuous function ω is characteristic iff $\omega(\zeta)e^{-\epsilon\zeta^2}$ is a characteristic function for every fixed $\epsilon > 0$. It follows that a bounded continuous function with $\omega(0) = 1$ is characteristic iff for all x and $\epsilon > 0$

$$\int_{-\infty}^{+\infty} e^{-i\zeta x}\omega(\zeta)e^{-\epsilon\zeta^2}\,d\zeta \geq 0. \tag{2.4}$$

[1] As elsewhere this means *absolute* integrability.

This criterion is perfectly general, but it is not easy to apply in individual situations; moreover, the arbitrary choice of the convergence factor $e^{-\epsilon\zeta^2}$ is a drawback. For this reason we restate the criterion in a form in which the condition is sharpened.

Lemma 2. *A bounded continuous function* ω *is characteristic iff* $\omega(0) = 1$ *and if for every probability distribution* A *and all* x

$$\int_{-\infty}^{+\infty} e^{-i\zeta x}\omega(\zeta)\ \ {}^0A\{d\zeta\} \geq 0 \tag{2.5}$$

where ${}^0A = A \bigstar {}^-A$ *is the distribution obtained by symmetrization.*

Proof. (*a*) *Necessity.* If α is the characteristic function of A then ${}^0A$ has the characteristic function $|\alpha|^2$ and the necessity of (2.5) is implicit in the Parseval relation (1.3).

(*b*) *Sufficiency.* It was shown in (2.4) that the condition is sufficient if A is restricted to normal distributions with arbitrary variances. ▶

We have seen that (2.5) may be rewritten in the form (1.6) with $B = A$. In particular, if A is concentrated at finitely many points $t_1, t_2, \ldots, t_n$ with corresponding weights $p_1, p_2, \ldots, p_n$, then (2.5) takes on the form

$$\sum_{j,k} \omega(t_j - t_k)e^{-ix(t_j-t_k)}p_jp_k \geq 0. \tag{2.6}$$

If this inequality is valid for all choices of t_j and p_j then (2.5) is satisfied for all discrete distributions A with finitely many atoms. As every distribution may be taken as limit of such discrete distributions the condition (2.6) is necessary and sufficient. With the change of notation $z_j = p_je^{-ixt_j}$ it takes on the form

$$\sum_{j,k} \omega(t_j - t_k)z_j\bar{z}_k \geq 0. \tag{2.7}$$

For the final formulation of our criterion we introduce a frequently used term.

Definition. *A complex-valued function*[2] *of the real variable* t *is called positive definite iff* (2.7) *holds for every choice of finitely many real numbers* $t_1, \ldots, t_n$ *and complex numbers* $z_1, \ldots, z_n$.

Theorem. (*Bochner.*) *A continuous function* ω *is the characteristic function probability distribution iff it is positive definite and* $\omega(0) = 1$.

Proof. We have shown that the condition is necessary, and also that it is sufficient when ω is bounded. The proof is completed by the next lemma which shows that all positive definite functions are bounded. ▶

[2] For "generalized" positive definite functions (= distributions in the sense of L. Schwartz) in arbitrary spaces, see Gelfand and Wilenkin (1964).

Lemma 3. *If ω is positive definite then*

$$\omega(0) \geq 0, \qquad |\omega(t)| \leq \omega(0). \tag{2.8}$$

Proof. Let $t_2 = 0$ and $z_2 = 1$. For $n = 2$ we get from (2.7)

$$\omega(0)[1 + |z_1|^2] + \omega(t_1)z_1 + \omega(-t_1)\overline{z_1} \geq 0. \tag{2.9}$$

Letting $z_1 = 0$ one sees that $\omega(0) \geq 0$. Furthermore (2.9) implies that $\omega(-t_1)$ is the conjugate of $\omega(t_1)$. With $z_1 = \lambda \cdot \overline{\omega(t_1)}$ the left side in (2.9) reduces to a quadratic polynomial in λ which assumes no negative value. It follows that its discriminant is non-positive, and this implies the boundedness relation in (2.8). ▶

3. STATIONARY PROCESSES

The last theorem has important consequences for stochastic processes with stationary covariances. By this is meant a family of random variables $\{\mathbf{X}_t\}$ defined for $-\infty < t < \infty$ on some space and having covariances such that

$$\mathrm{Cov}(\mathbf{X}_{s+t}, \mathbf{X}_s) = \rho(t) \tag{3.1}$$

is independent of s. So far we have considered only real random variables, but now the notations will become simpler and more symmetric if we admit *complex-valued* random variables. A complex random variable is, of course, merely a pair of real variables written in the form $\mathbf{X} = \mathbf{U} + i\mathbf{V}$ and nothing need be assumed concerning the joint distribution of $\mathbf{U}$ and $\mathbf{V}$. The variable $\overline{\mathbf{X}} = \mathbf{U} - i\mathbf{V}$ is called the conjugate of $\mathbf{X}$ and the product $\mathbf{X}\overline{\mathbf{X}}$ takes over the role of $\mathbf{X}^2$ in the real theory. This necessitates a slight unsymmetry in the definition of variances and covariances: *if*

$$\mathbf{E}(\mathbf{X}) = \mathbf{E}(\mathbf{Y}) = 0$$

we define

$$\mathrm{Cov}(\mathbf{X}, \mathbf{Y}) = \mathbf{E}(\mathbf{X}\overline{\mathbf{Y}}). \tag{3.2}$$

Then $\mathrm{Var}(\mathbf{X}) = \mathbf{E}(|\mathbf{X}|^2) \geq 0$.

Theorem. *Let $\{\mathbf{X}_t\}$ be a family of random variables such that*

$$\rho(t) = \mathbf{E}(\mathbf{X}_{t+s}\overline{\mathbf{X}}_s) \tag{3.3}$$

is a continuous function[3] *independent of s. Then ρ is positive definite, that is,*

$$\rho(t) = \int_{-\infty}^{+\infty} e^{i\lambda t}\, R\{d\lambda\} \tag{3.4}$$

where R is a measure on the real line with total mass $\rho(0)$.

---

[3] Continuity is important: for mutually independent variables $\mathbf{X}_t$ one has $\rho(t) = 0$ except when $t = 0$, and this covariance function is not of the form (3.4). See problem 2.

If the variables $\mathbf{X}_t$ *are real the measure* R *is symmetric and*

$$\rho(t) = \int_{-\infty}^{+\infty} \cos \lambda t \, R\{d\lambda\}. \tag{3.5}$$

Proof. Choose arbitrary real points $t_1, \ldots, t_n$ and complex constants $z_1, \ldots, z_n$. Then

$$\begin{aligned} \sum \rho(t_j - t_k) z_j \bar{z}_k &= \sum \mathbf{E}(\mathbf{X}_{t_j} \bar{\mathbf{X}}_{t_k}) z_j \bar{z}_k = \\ &= \mathbf{E}(\sum \mathbf{X}_{t_j} z_j \bar{\mathbf{X}}_{t_k} \bar{z}_k) = \mathbf{E}(|\sum \mathbf{X}_{t_j} z_j|^2) \geq 0 \end{aligned} \tag{3.6}$$

and so (3.4) is true by the criterion of the last section. When ρ is real the relation (3.4) holds also for the mirrored measure obtained by changing x to $-x$, and because of the uniqueness R is symmetric. ►

The measure R is called the *spectral measure*[4] of the process; the set formed by its points of increase is called the *spectrum* of $\{\mathbf{X}_t\}$. In most applications the variables are centered so that $\mathbf{E}(\mathbf{X}_t) = 0$, in which case $\rho(t) = \mathrm{Cov}(\mathbf{X}_{t+s}, \mathbf{X}_s)$. For this reason ρ is usually referred to as *the covariance function* of the process. Actually the centering of $\mathbf{X}_t$ has no influence on the properties of the process with which we shall be concerned.

Examples. (*a*) Let $\mathbf{Z}_1, \ldots, \mathbf{Z}_n$ be mutually uncorrelated random variables with zero expectation and variances $\sigma_1^2, \ldots, \sigma_n^2$. Put

$$\mathbf{X}_t = \mathbf{Z}_1 e^{i\lambda_1 t} + \cdots + \mathbf{Z}_n e^{i\lambda_n t} \tag{3.7}$$

with $\lambda_1, \ldots, \lambda_n$ real. Then

$$\rho(t) = \sigma_1^2 e^{i\lambda_1 t} + \cdots + \sigma_n^2 e^{i\lambda_n t} \tag{3.8}$$

and so R is concentrated at the n points $\lambda_1, \ldots, \lambda_n$. We shall see that the most general process may be treated as a limiting case of this example.

If the process (3.7) is real it can be put into the form

$$\begin{aligned} \mathbf{X}_t = \mathbf{U}_1 \cos \nu_1 t + \cdots + \mathbf{U}_r \cos \nu_r t &+ \\ + \mathbf{V}_1 \sin \nu_1 t + \cdots &+ \mathbf{V}_r \sin \nu_r t \end{aligned} \tag{3.9}$$

where the $\mathbf{U}_j$ and $\mathbf{V}_j$ are real uncorrelated random variables and

$$\mathbf{E}(\mathbf{U}_j^2) = \mathbf{E}(\mathbf{V}_j^2) = \sigma_j^2.$$

A typical example occurs in III,(7.22). The corresponding covariances are $\rho_t = \sigma_1^2 \cos \nu_1 t + \cdots + \sigma_r^2 \cos \nu_r t$. A similar remark applies to the other examples.

(*b*) *Markovian processes.* If the variables $\mathbf{X}_t$ are normal and the process

[4] In communication engineering, also called the "power spectrum."

is Markovian, then $\rho(t) = e^{-a|t|}$ [see III,(8.14)]. The spectral measure is proportional to a Cauchy density.

(*c*) Let $\mathbf{X}_t = \mathbf{Z}e^{it\mathbf{Y}}$ where $\mathbf{Y}$ and $\mathbf{Z}$ are independent *real* random variables, $\mathbf{E}(\mathbf{Z}) = 0$. For this process R is proportional to the probability distribution of $\mathbf{Y}$. ▶

Theoretically it matters little whether a process is described in terms of its covariance function ρ or, equivalently, in terms of the corresponding spectral measure R, but in practice the description in terms of the spectral measure R is usually simpler and preferable. In applications to communication engineering the spectral analysis has technical advantages in instrumentation and measurement, but we shall not dwell on this point. Of greater importance from our point of view is that linear operations (often called "filters") on the variables $\mathbf{X}_t$ are more readily described in terms of R than of ρ.

Example. (*d*) *Linear operations.* As the simplest example consider the family of random variables $\mathbf{Y}_t$ defined by

$$\mathbf{Y}_t = \sum c_k \mathbf{X}_{t-\tau_k} \tag{3.10}$$

where the c_k and τ_k are constants (τ_k real) and the sum is finite. The covariance function of $\mathbf{Y}_t$ is given by the double sum

$$\rho_{\mathbf{Y}}(t) = \sum c_j \bar{c}_k\, \rho(t-\tau_j + \tau_k), \tag{3.11}$$

and the corresponding spectral measure $R_{\mathbf{Y}}$ is determined by

$$R_{\mathbf{Y}}\{d\lambda\} = |\sum c_j e^{-i\tau_j\lambda}|^2\, R\{d\lambda\}. \tag{3.12}$$

In contrast to (3.11) this relationship admits of an intuitive interpretation: the "frequency" λ is affected by a "frequency response factor" $f(\lambda)$ which depends on the given transformation (3.10).

This example is of much wider applicability than appears at first sight because integrals and derivatives are limits of sums of the form (3.10) and therefore a similar remark applies to them. For example, if $\mathbf{X}_t$ serves as input to a standard electric circuit, the output $\mathbf{Y}_t$ can be represented by integrals involving $\mathbf{X}_t$; the spectral measure $R_{\mathbf{Y}}$ is again expressible by R and a frequency response. The latter depends on the characteristics of the network, and our result can be used in two directions; namely, to describe the output process and also to construct networks which will yield an output with certain prescribed properties. ▶

We turn to the converse of our theorem and show that *given an arbitrary measure R on the line there exists a stationary process $\{\mathbf{X}_t\}$ with spectral measure R.* Since the mapping $\mathbf{X}_t \to a\mathbf{X}_t$ changes R into a^2R there is no loss of generality in assuming that R is a probability measure. We take the λ-axis equipped with the probability measure R as sample space and denote by $\mathbf{X}_t$ the random variable defined by $\mathbf{X}_t(\lambda) = e^{it\lambda}$. Then

$$\mathbf{E}(\mathbf{X}_{t+s}\overline{\mathbf{X}}_s) = \rho(t) \tag{3.13}$$

and we have thus constructed *an explicit model of a stationary process with the prescribed spectral measure.* That such a model is possible with the *real line as sample space* is surprising and gratifying. We shall return to it in section 8.

It is easy to modify the model so as to obtain variables with zero expectation. Let $\mathbf{Y}$ be a random variable that is independent of all the $\mathbf{X}_t$ and assumes the values ± 1 each with probability $\frac{1}{2}$. Put $\mathbf{X}_t' = \mathbf{Y}\mathbf{X}_t$. Then $\mathbf{E}(\mathbf{X}_t') = 0$ and $\mathbf{E}(\mathbf{X}'_{t+s}\overline{\mathbf{X}}'_s) = \mathbf{E}(\mathbf{Y}^2)\,\mathbf{E}(\mathbf{X}_{t+s}\overline{\mathbf{X}}_s)$. Thus $\{\mathbf{X}_t'\}$ *is a stationary process and* ρ *is its true covariance function.*

4. FOURIER SERIES

An arithmetic distribution attributing probability φ_n to the point n has the characteristic function

$$\varphi(\zeta) = \sum_{-\infty}^{+\infty} \varphi_n e^{in\zeta} \tag{4.1}$$

with period 2π. The probabilities φ_n can be expressed by the inversion formula

$$\varphi_k = \frac{1}{2\pi}\int_{-\pi}^{\pi} e^{-ik\zeta}\,\varphi(\zeta)\,d\zeta \tag{4.2}$$

which is easily verified from (4.1) [see XV,(3.14)].

We now start from an arbitrary function φ with period 2π and define φ_k by (4.2). Our problem is to decide whether φ is a characteristic function, that is, whether $\{\varphi_n\}$ is a probability distribution. The method depends on investigating the behavior of the family of functions f_r defined for $0 < r < 1$ by

$$f_r(\zeta) = \sum_{-\infty}^{+\infty} \varphi_n r^{|n|} e^{in\zeta}. \tag{4.3}$$

Despite its simplicity the same argument will yield important results concerning Fourier series and characteristic functions of distributions concentrated on finite intervals.

In what follows it is best to interpret the basic interval $\overline{-\pi, \pi}$ as a *circle* (that is, to identify the points π and $-\pi$). For an integrable φ the number φ_k *will be called the* kth *Fourier coefficient of* φ. The series occurring in (4.1) is the corresponding "formal Fourier series." It need not converge, but the sequence $\{\varphi_n\}$ being bounded the series (4.3) converges to a continuous (even differentiable) function f_r. When $r \to 1$ it is possible for f_r to tend to a limit ψ even when the series in (4.1) diverges. In this case one says that the series is "Abel summable" to ψ.

Examples. (*a*) Let $\varphi_n = 1$ for $n = 0, 1, 2, \ldots$, but $\varphi_n = 0$ for $n < 0$. The terms in (4.1) do not tend to zero and so the series diverges for all ζ. On the other hand, the right side in (4.3) reduces to a geometric series, and hence

$$f_r(\zeta) = \frac{1}{1 - re^{i\zeta}}. \tag{4.4}$$

As $r \to 1$ a limit exists at all points except $\zeta = 0$.

(*b*) An important special case of (4.3) is represented by the functions

$$p_r(t) = \frac{1}{2\pi} \sum_{-\infty}^{+\infty} r^{|n|} e^{int} \tag{4.5}$$

obtained when $\varphi_n = 1/(2\pi)$ for all n. The contribution of the terms $n \geq 0$ was evaluated in (4.4). For reasons of symmetry we get

$$2\pi p_r(t) = \frac{1}{1 - re^{it}} + \frac{1}{1 - re^{-it}} - 1 \tag{4.6}$$

or

$$p_r(t) = \frac{1}{2\pi} \cdot \frac{1 - r^2}{1 + r^2 - 2r \cos t}. \tag{4.7}$$

This function is of constant use in the theory of harmonic functions [where $p_r(t-\zeta)$ is called the "*Poisson kernel*"]. For reference we state its main property in the next lemma. ▶

Lemma. *For fixed* $0 < r < 1$ *the function* p_r *is the density of a probability distribution* P_r *on the circle. As* $r \to 1$ *the latter tends to the probability distribution concentrated at the origin.*

Proof. Obviously $p_r \geq 0$. That the integral of p_r over $\overline{-\pi, \pi}$ equals one is evident from (4.5) because for $n \neq 0$ the integral of e^{int} vanishes. In every open interval excluding the origin $p_r(t) \to 0$ boundedly as $r \to 1$, and so P_r has a limit distribution concentrated at the origin. ▶

Theorem 1. *A continuous function* φ *with period* 2π *is a characteristic function iff its Fourier coefficients* (4.2) *satisfy* $\varphi_k \geq 0$ *and* $\varphi(0) = 1$. *In this case* φ *is represented by the Fourier series* (4.1).

(In other words, a formal Fourier series with non-negative coefficients φ_k converges to a continuous function iff $\Sigma\varphi_k < \infty$. In this case (4.1) holds.)

Proof. In view of (4.2) and (4.5) the function f_r of (4.3) may be put into the form

$$f_r(\zeta) = \int_{-\pi}^{\pi} \varphi(t) \cdot p_r(\zeta - t)\, dt. \tag{4.8}$$

On the right we recognize the convolution of φ and the probability distribution P_r, and we conclude

$$f_r(\zeta) \to \varphi(\zeta), \qquad r \to 1. \tag{4.9}$$

Furthermore, if m is an upper bound for $|\varphi|$ then

$$f_r(0) = \sum_{-\infty}^{+\infty} \varphi_n r^{|n|} \leq m. \tag{4.10}$$

The terms of the series being non-negative it follows for $r \to 1$ that $\Sigma\varphi_n \leq m$. Therefore $\Sigma\varphi_n e^{in\zeta}$ converges and it is evident from (4.3) that $f_r(\zeta)$ tends to this value. Thus (4.1) is true, and this concludes the proof. ►

Note that (4.9) is a direct consequence of the convergence properties of convolutions and hence independent of the positivity of the coefficients φ_n. As a by-product we thus have

Theorem 2.[5] *If φ is continuous with period 2π, then* (4.9) *holds uniformly in ζ.*

(For generalizations to functions with jumps see problems 5, 6.)

Corollary 1. (*Féjer.*) *A continuous periodic function φ is the uniform limit of a sequence of trigonometric polynomials.*

In other words, given $\epsilon > 0$ there exist numbers $a_{-N}, \ldots, a_N$ such that

$$\left| \varphi(\zeta) - \sum_{n=-N}^{N} a_n e^{in\zeta} \right| < \epsilon \tag{4.11}$$

for all ζ.

Proof. Choose r such that $|f_r - \varphi| < \frac{1}{2}\epsilon$. The series in (4.3) being dominated by a geometric series it is possible to choose N so large that the terms with $n > N$ add up to less than $\frac{1}{2}\epsilon$. ►

The following result is mentioned for completeness only.

Corollary 2. *Two integrable periodic functions with identical Fourier coefficients differ at most on a set of measure zero* (*that is, their integrals are the same*).

Proof. For an integrable periodic φ with Fourier coefficients φ_n put

$$\Phi(x) = \int_{-\pi}^{x} [\varphi(t) - \varphi_0]\, dt. \tag{4.12}$$

---

[5] The theorem may be restated as follows: *The Fourier series of a continuous periodic function φ is Abel summable to φ.* The theorem (and the method of proof) apply equally to other methods of summability.

The phenomenon was first discovered by L. Féjer using Cesaro summability (see problem 8) at a time when divergent series still seemed mysterious. The discovery therefore came as a sensation, and for historical reasons texts still use Cesaro summability although the Abel method is more convenient and unifies proofs.

Then Φ is continuous and periodic and an integration by parts shows that its Fourier coefficients Φ_n are given by $\Phi_n = -i\varphi_n/n$. By the last theorem Φ is uniquely determined by the coefficients φ_n. ►

*5. THE POISSON SUMMATION FORMULA

Let f be a probability density with an integrable characteristic function[6] φ. Under slight regularity conditions (for example, if a second moment exists) the condition

$$\sum_{-\infty}^{+\infty} f(n\,\pi/\lambda) < \infty \tag{5.1}$$

will be satisfied for all $\lambda > 0$, and we can consider the arithmetic measure attributing weight $f(n\pi/\lambda)$ to the point $n\pi/\lambda$. Its Fourier-Stieltjes transform is a Fourier series with period 2λ. The next theorem shows that the same series can be expressed also in terms of the characteristic function φ. At first sight the result may appear as a mere curiosity, but it turns out that special cases of it are important and useful.

Theorem 1. *Let the probability density f have an integrable characteristic function φ. Then for each fixed λ*

$$\sum_{-\infty}^{+\infty} \varphi(\zeta+2k\lambda) = \frac{\pi}{\lambda}\sum_{-\infty}^{+\infty} f(n\,\pi/\lambda)e^{in(\pi/\lambda)\zeta} \tag{5.2}$$

whenever one of the two sides represents a continuous function. Then also (5.1) *holds.*

Proof.[7] The left side represents a function with period 2λ. We formally calculate its Fourier coefficients showing at the same time that the function is integrable. Adjusting the definition (4.2) to the interval $\overline{-\lambda, \lambda}$, we get for the nth Fourier coefficient of the left side

$$\frac{1}{2\lambda}\sum_{k=-\infty}^{+\infty}\int_{-\lambda}^{\lambda} \varphi(\zeta+2k\lambda)e^{-in(\pi/\lambda)\zeta}\,d\zeta = \frac{1}{2\lambda}\sum_{k=-\infty}^{+\infty}\int_{(2k-1)\lambda}^{(2k+1)\lambda} \varphi(s)e^{-in(\pi/\lambda)s}\,ds \tag{5.3}$$

The intervals $(2k-1)\lambda \le s < (2k+1)\lambda$ cover the real axis without overlap and hence the right side equals

$$\frac{1}{2\lambda}\int_{-\infty}^{+\infty} \varphi(s)e^{-in(\pi/\lambda)s}\,ds = \frac{\pi}{\lambda} f(n\,\pi/\lambda) \tag{5.4}$$

---

* This section treats important special topics. It is not used in the sequel and is practically independent of the preceding sections.

[6] The Fourier inversion formula XV,(3.5) shows that the integrability of φ implies the existence of a continuous density. Throughout this section it is therefore understood that f is continuous.

[7] For an alternative proof see problems 12–13. Problem 13 shows that the continuity condition is not redundant.

by the Fourier inversion theorem of XV,3. Now it was shown in theorem 1 of the last section that a function with non-negative Fourier coefficients is continuous iff the series of these coefficients converges. Furthermore, a continuous function is uniquely determined by its Fourier coefficients, and so (5.1) and (5.2) are true. ►

For an interesting special case consider a characteristic function φ vanishing identically outside an interval $\overline{-a, a}$ where $a \leq \lambda$. For $-\lambda < \zeta < \lambda$ the left side in (5.2) reduces to $\varphi(\zeta)$ since all terms with $k \neq 0$ vanish identically. Thus the left side simply represents a periodic continuation of φ and is therefore continuous. For $\zeta = 0$ we get

$$\sum_{-\infty}^{+\infty} \frac{\pi}{\lambda} f\left(n \frac{\pi}{\lambda}\right) = 1, \tag{5.5}$$

which shows that (5.2) represents a characteristic function. In other words: *if a characteristic function φ vanishes for $|\zeta| > a$ then all its periodic continuations with periods $\lambda \geq a$ again represent characteristic functions.* We have here a systematic method of constructing infinitely many *characteristic functions which agree within a finite interval.*

This result is used in communication engineering where it is known as "*the sampling theorem*" and variously ascribed to Nyquist or Shannon. We state it formally as

Theorem 2. *Let the probability density f have a characteristic function vanishing outside $\overline{-a, a}$. Then f is uniquely determined by the values $\frac{\pi}{\lambda} f\left(n \frac{\pi}{\lambda}\right)$ for any fixed $\lambda \geq a$, and these values induce an arithmetic probability distribution.*[8]

A sort of dual theorem to this will be proved in the next section.

---

[8] An *explicit formula for $f(x)$* may be obtained as follows. Within the interval $-\lambda \leq \zeta \leq \lambda$ the characteristic function φ agrees with the characteristic function of the arithmetic distribution $\{(\pi/\lambda)f(n\pi/\lambda)\}$, but outside this interval φ vanishes identically. By the Fourier inversion formula therefore

$$f(x) = \frac{1}{2\pi} \frac{\pi}{\lambda} \sum_{-\infty}^{+\infty} \int_{-\lambda}^{\lambda} f\left(n \frac{\pi}{\lambda}\right) e^{in(\pi/\lambda)\zeta - i\zeta x} \, d\zeta$$
$$= \frac{\sin \lambda x}{\lambda} \sum_{-\infty}^{+\infty} f\left(n \frac{\pi}{\lambda}\right) \frac{(-1)^n}{x - n\pi/\lambda}.$$

This formula has a wider applicability than is suggested by theorem 2. [See theorem 16 in J. M. Whittaker, *Interpolatory function theory*, Cambridge Tracts No. 33, 1935. For an analogue in higher dimensions see D. P. Petersen and D. Middleton, Information and Control vol. 5 (1962) pp. 279–323.]

Examples. (*a*) Consider the density $f(x) = (1 - \cos x)/(\pi x^2)$ with the characteristic function $\varphi(\zeta) = 1 - |\zeta|$ vanishing for $|\zeta| > 1$. For $\lambda = 1$ we get from (5.5) the well-known relation

$$\frac{1}{2} + \frac{4}{\pi^2}\sum_{\nu=0}^{\infty}\frac{1}{(2\nu+1)^2} = 1. \tag{5.6}$$

The periodic continuation of φ with period $2\lambda = 2$ is graphed in figure 2 of XV,2. A variety of other characteristic functions can be constructed by choosing larger periods. For example, to $\lambda = 2$ there corresponds a characteristic function represented in figure 2 by the polygonal line with vertices $\ldots, -3, -1, A, 1, 3, C, 5, 7, E, 9, \ldots$ For each choice of λ we get an identity analogous to (5.6).

[The fact that our periodic continuations are characteristic functions was exploited in XV,2(iii) to construct two real characteristic functions such that $\varphi_1{}^2 = \varphi_2{}^2$.]

(*b*) For a simple example for (5.2) see problem 11. ►

As usual in similar situations, formula (5.2) may be rewritten in a form that *looks* more general. Indeed, applying (5.2) to the density $f(x+s)$ we get *the alternative form of the Poisson summation formula*

$$\sum_{-\infty}^{+\infty}\varphi(\zeta + 2k\lambda)e^{-is(\zeta+2k\lambda)} = \frac{\pi}{\lambda}\sum_{-\infty}^{+\infty} f\left(n\frac{\pi}{\lambda} + s\right)e^{in(\pi/\lambda)\zeta}. \tag{5.7}$$

Examples. (*c*) Applying (5.7) to the normal density and using only the special value $\zeta = \lambda$ one gets

$$\sum_{-\infty}^{+\infty} e^{-\frac{1}{2}(2k+1)^2\lambda^2}\cos(2k+1)\lambda s = \frac{\pi}{\lambda}\sum_{-\infty}^{+\infty}(-1)^k\mathfrak{n}\left(\frac{(2k+1)\pi}{\lambda} + s\right). \tag{5.8}$$

This is a famous formula from the theory of theta functions to which reference was made in X,5. [On taking derivatives with respect to x it is seen that the equivalence of X,(5.8) and X,(5.9) is an integrated version of (5.8) with $\lambda = (\pi/a)\sqrt{t}$ and $s = x/\sqrt{t}$. The proof given in X,5 is more elementary.]

(*d*) For the density $f(x) = \pi^{-1}(1 + x^2)^{-1}$ with characteristic function $\varphi(\zeta) = e^{-|\zeta|}$ we get from (5.2) for $\zeta = 0$

$$\frac{e^{\lambda} + e^{-\lambda}}{e^{\lambda} - e^{-\lambda}} = \sum_{n=-\infty}^{+\infty}\frac{\lambda}{\lambda^2 + n^2\pi^2}. \tag{5.9}$$

This is the *partial fraction decomposition for the hyperbolic cotangent.*

(*e*) *Densities on the circle* of length 2π may be obtained by wrapping the real axis around the circle as described in II,8. To a given density f on the line there corresponds on the circle the density given by the series on the right in (5.7) with $\lambda = \frac{1}{2}$ and $\zeta = 0$. The identity (5.7) yields a new representation of this density in terms of the original characteristic function.

For the special case of the normal density with zero expectation and variance t we get

$$(5.10) \qquad \frac{1}{\sqrt{2\pi t}} \sum_{-\infty}^{+\infty} \exp\left(-\frac{1}{2t}(s+2n\pi)^2\right) = \frac{1}{2\pi} \sum_{-\infty}^{+\infty} e^{-\frac{1}{2}n^2 t} \cos ns.$$

The left side represents the original definition of the density, but the right side provides a more useful form. It exhibits the semi-group property of normal densities. ►

6. POSITIVE DEFINITE SEQUENCES

Let F be a probability distribution on the open interval $\overline{-\pi, \pi}$, and φ its characteristic function. As in section 4 we identify the points $-\pi$ and π and interpret F as a distribution on a *circle*. By analogy with (4.2) we define *the Fourier coefficients* φ_k of F by

$$(6.1) \qquad \varphi_k = \frac{1}{2\pi} \int_{-\pi}^{\pi} e^{-ikt}\, F\{dt\}, \qquad k = 0, \pm 1, \ldots,$$

so that $2\pi\varphi_k = \varphi(-k)$. It will now be shown that the coefficients φ_k uniquely determine the distribution. Allowing for a trivial change of scale the assertion is equivalent to the following: *A distribution concentrated on* $\overline{-\lambda, \lambda}$ *is uniquely determined by the knowledge of the values* $\varphi(n\pi/\lambda)$ assumed by its characteristic function at the multiples of π/λ. This explains the formal difference between the spectral theories for stationary sequences $\{\mathbf{X}_n\}$ and processes $\{\mathbf{X}_t\}$ depending on a continuous time parameter. The assertion represents the dual to theorem 2 of the preceding section (the "sampling theorem") according to which a characteristic function vanishing outside $\overline{-\lambda, \lambda}$ is uniquely determined by the values $f(n\pi/\lambda)$ of the density.

Theorem 1. *A distribution F on the circle is uniquely determined by its Fourier coefficients φ_k.*

Proof. As in (4.3) we put for $0 < r < 1$

$$(6.2) \qquad f_r(\zeta) = \sum_{-\infty}^{+\infty} \varphi_n \cdot r^{|n|} \cdot e^{in\zeta}.$$

The trite calculation that led to (4.8) shows that now

$$(6.3) \qquad f_r(\zeta) = \int_{-\pi}^{\pi} p_r(\zeta - t)\, F\{dt\},$$

where p_r is the density of the probability distribution P_r (see the lemma of section 4). Thus f_r is the density of the convolution $P_r \star F$ which tends to F as $r \to 1$, and so F is actually calculable in terms of f_r. (See also problem 10.) ▶

Lemma 1. *Let* $\{\varphi_n\}$ *be an arbitrary bounded sequence of complex numbers. In order that there exists a measure* F *with Fourier coefficients* φ_n *it is necessary and sufficient that for each* $r < 1$ *the function* f_r *defined in* (6.2) *satisfies*

$$f_r(\zeta) > 0. \tag{6.4}$$

Proof. The necessity is obvious from (6.3) and the strict positivity of p_r. Multiply (6.2) by $e^{-ik\zeta}$ and integrate to obtain

$$\varphi_k \cdot r^{|k|} = \frac{1}{2\pi} \int_{-\pi}^{\pi} f_r(\zeta) e^{-ik\zeta}\, d\zeta. \tag{6.5}$$

For the particular value $k = 0$ it is seen that $\varphi_0 > 0$ and without loss of generality we may assume that $\varphi_0 = 1/(2\pi)$. Then (6.5) states that f_r is the density of a probability distribution F_r on the circle, and $\varphi_k r^{|k|}$ is the kth Fourier coefficient of F_r. By the selection theorem it is possible to let $r \to 1$ in such a manner that F_r converges to a probability distribution F. From (6.5) it is obvious that φ_k satisfies (6.1), and this completes the proof. ▶

We proceed as in section 2 and derive a counterpart to Bochner's theorem; it is due to G. Herglotz.

Definition. *A sequence* $\{\varphi_k\}$ *is called positive definite if for every choice of finitely many numbers* $z_1, \ldots, z_n$

$$\sum_{j,k} \varphi_{j-k}\, z_j \bar{z}_k \geq 0. \tag{6.6}$$

Lemma 2. *If* $\{\varphi_n\}$ *is positive definite then* $\varphi_0 \geq 0$ *and* $|\varphi_n| \leq \varphi_0$.

Proof. The proof of lemma 2.3 applies. (See also problem 14.)

Theorem 2. *A sequence* $\{\varphi_n\}$ *represents the Fourier coefficients of a measure* F *on the circle iff it is positive definite.*

Proof. (*a*) A trite calculation shows that if the φ_k are given by (6.1) the left side in (6.6) equals the integral of $\frac{1}{2\pi} |\Sigma e^{-ijt} z_j|^2$ with respect to F. The condition is therefore necessary.

(*b*) To show its sufficiency choose $z_k = r^k e^{ikt}$ for $k \geq 0$ and $z_k = 0$ for $k < 0$. It is true that sequence $\{z_k\}$ so defined is infinite but a simple passage to the limit shows that the inequality (6.6) is still satisfied. The left side equals

$$(6.7) \qquad \sum_{j=0}^{\infty}\sum_{k=0}^{\infty}\varphi_{j-k}r^{j+k}e^{i(j-k)t} = \sum_{n=-\infty}^{+\infty}\varphi_n e^{int}\sum_{k=0}^{\infty}r^{|n|+2k}.$$

The last series is geometric with sum $r^{|n|}/(1-r^2)$, and so the quantity (6.7) equals $f_r(t)/(1-r^2)$. By lemma 1 therefore the φ_k are indeed Fourier coefficients of a measure. ▶

Theorem 2 leads immediately to the following analogue to the theorem of section 3.

Theorem 3. *Let $\{\mathbf{X}_n\}$ be a sequence of random variables defined on some probability space such that*

$$(6.8) \qquad \rho_n = \mathbf{E}(\mathbf{X}_{n+\nu}\bar{\mathbf{X}}_\nu)$$

is independent of ν. Then there exists a unique measure R on the circle $\overline{-\pi, \pi}$ such that ρ_n is its nth *Fourier coefficient.*

Proof. Clearly

$$(6.9) \qquad \Sigma\rho_{j-k}z_j\bar{z}_k = \Sigma\mathbf{E}(\mathbf{X}_jz_j\bar{\mathbf{X}}_k\bar{z}_k) = \mathbf{E}(|\Sigma\mathbf{X}_jz_j|^2)$$

which shows that the sequence $\{\rho_n\}$ is positive definite. ▶

As in section 3 one proves the converse to theorem 3 by exhibiting a concrete model of random variables with the prescribed covariances. We shall return to this in section 8.

Examples. (*a*) A sequence of mutually independent variables has the uniform distribution for its spectral measure.

(*b*) *Markov processes.* From the construction in section 4 it is clear that the density defined for fixed $r < 1$ and real θ by $p_r(t-\theta)$ has Fourier coefficients

$$(6.10) \qquad \rho_n = r^{|n|}e^{in\theta}.$$

It was shown in III,8 that stationary Markov sequences of real normal variables have covariances of the form $\rho_n = r^{|n|}$ with $0 \le r \le 1$. A similar argument shows that the covariances of arbitrary stationary Markov sequences are of the form (6.10). When $r < 1$ the spectral measure has density $p_r(t-\theta)$; when $r = 1$ it is concentrated at the point θ. ▶

7. L^2 THEORY

For purposes of probability theory it was necessary to introduce characteristic functions as transforms of measures, but other approaches to harmonic analysis are equally natural. In particular, it is possible to define Fourier transforms of functions (rather than measures) and the Fourier inversion formula makes it plausible that greater symmetry can be achieved in this way. It turns out that the greatest simplicity and elegance is attained when only square integrable functions are admitted. This theory will now be developed for its intrinsic interest and because it is extensively used in the harmonic analysis of stochastic processes.

For a complex-valued function u of the real variable x we define the *norm* $\|u\| \geq 0$ by

$$\|u\|^2 = \int_{-\infty}^{+\infty} |u(x)|^2\, dx. \tag{7.1}$$

Two functions differing only on a set of measure zero will be considered identical. (In other words, we are actually dealing with equivalence classes of functions, but indulge in a usual harmless abuse of language.) With this convention $\|u\| = 0$ iff $u = 0$. The class of all functions with finite norm will be denoted by L^2. The *distance* of two functions u, v in L^2 is defined by $\|u - v\|$. With this definition L^2 is a metric space and a sequence of functions u_n in L^2 converges in this metric to u iff[9] $\|u_n - u\| \to 0$. This convergence[10] will be indicated by $u = \text{l.i.m.}\, u_n$ or $u_n \xrightarrow{\text{i.m.}} u$. We mention without proof that the metric space L^2 is complete in the sense that every Cauchy sequence[11] $\{u_n\}$ possesses a unique limit $u \in L^2$.

The *inner product* (u, v) of two functions is defined by

$$(u, v) = \int_{-\infty}^{+\infty} u(x)\, \overline{v(x)}\, dx. \tag{7.2}$$

It exists for every pair of functions in L^2 since by Schwarz' inequality

$$(u, v)^2 \leq \|u\| \cdot \|v\|. \tag{7.3}$$

In particular, $(u, u) = \|u\|^2$. With this definition of the inner product L^2 becomes a *Hilbert space*. The analogy of the inner product (7.2) with the covariance of two random variables with zero expectations is manifest and will be exploited later on.

[9] This type of convergence is also called "convergence in the mean square".

[10] Pointwise convergence of u_n to a limit v does not imply that $u_n \xrightarrow{\text{i.m.}} v$ [see example IV,(2.*d*)]. However, if it is known that $u = \text{l.i.m.}\, u_n$ exists, then $u = v$. In fact, by Fatou's lemma

$$\int_{-\infty}^{+\infty} |u(x) - v(x)|^2\, dx \leq \lim \int_{-\infty}^{+\infty} |u(x) - u_n(x)|^2\, dx = 0.$$

[11] $\{u_n\}$ is called a Cauchy sequence iff $\|u_n - u_m\| \to 0$ as $n, m \to \infty$.

After these preparations we turn to our main object, namely to define transforms of the form

$$\hat{u}(\zeta) = \frac{1}{\sqrt{2\pi}} \int_{-\infty}^{+\infty} u(x) e^{i\zeta x}\, dx. \tag{7.4}$$

When u is a probability density, $\hat{u}$ differs by the factor $\sqrt{2\pi}$ from the characteristic function and to avoid confusion $\hat{u}$ will be called *the Plancherel transform of u*. The definition (7.4) applies only to integrable functions u, but we shall extend the domain of definition of $\hat{u}$ to all L^2. For abbreviation let us say that a function u belonging to L^2 is "good" if both u and $\hat{u}$ are integrable. Since $\hat{u}$ is bounded it too belongs to L^2.

First we show that for good functions the *inversion formula*

$$u(t) = \frac{1}{\sqrt{2\pi}} \int_{-\infty}^{+\infty} \hat{u}(\zeta) e^{-i\zeta t}\, d\zeta \tag{7.5}$$

holds. (This follows easily from our previous results, but the proof is simple enough to bear repetition.) Multiply (7.4) by $\dfrac{1}{\sqrt{2\pi}} e^{-i\zeta t - \frac{1}{2}\epsilon^2\zeta^2}$ and integrate to obtain

$$\frac{1}{\sqrt{2\pi}} \int_{-\infty}^{+\infty} \hat{u}(\zeta) e^{-i\zeta t - \frac{1}{2}\epsilon^2\zeta^2}\, d\zeta = \int_{-\infty}^{+\infty} u(x)\, \mathfrak{n}\left(\frac{t-x}{\epsilon}\right) \frac{dx}{\epsilon} \tag{7.6}$$

where $\mathfrak{n}$ denotes the standard normal density. As $\epsilon \to 0$ the integral on the left tends to the integral in (7.5) while the convolution on the right tends to $u(t)$. Thus (7.5) holds for good functions.

Now let v be another good function. Multiply (7.5) by the conjugate $\bar{v}$ and integrate. The result is the identity

$$(\hat{u}, \hat{v}) = (u, v) \tag{7.7}$$

which will be referred to as the *Parseval relation*. For $v = u$ it reduces to

$$\|\hat{u}\| = \|u\| \tag{7.8}$$

which shows that among good functions the Plancherel transform is an *isometry*.

We are now ready for the final step, namely to extend the definition of the Plancherel transform to the whole of L^2. Suppose that for some $u \in L^2$ there exists a sequence of good functions $u^{(n)}$ tending to u in our metric. In view of (7.8) the transforms $\hat{u}^{(n)}$ form a Cauchy sequence and $\hat{u}^{(n)} \to \hat{u}$ whenever u is good. When u is not good we wish to *define* $\hat{u}$ as the unique limit of $\hat{u}^{(n)}$. In other words, we wish to define a Plancherel transform by the convention that

$$\textit{if}\quad u^{(n)} \to u \quad \textit{we put}\quad \hat{u} = \text{l.i.m}\, \hat{u}^{(n)}. \tag{7.9}$$

Since two Cauchy sequences may be combined into one the limit is independent of the choice of the sequence $\{u^{(n)}\}$. To justify the convention (7.9) it remains to show that it is consistent with the original definition (7.4) whenever u is integrable. For such functions put $u_\epsilon(x) = u(x)\, e^{-\epsilon^2 x^2/2}$ and denote the Plancherel transform of u_ϵ by $\hat{u}_\epsilon$. Taking in (7.4) convolutions with the normal density it is seen that (7.6) remains valid when u and $\hat{u}$ are interchanged. The left side then equals $\hat{u}_\epsilon(t)$, and so $\hat{u}_\epsilon$ is the convolution of the bounded continuous function u with a normal density. It follows that $\hat{u}_\epsilon$ is integrable and that $\hat{u}_\epsilon(t) \to \hat{u}(t)$ as $\epsilon \to 0$. The functions u_ϵ are therefore good. Now $u_\epsilon \xrightarrow{\text{i.m.}} u$, and hence $\hat{u}_\epsilon \xrightarrow{\text{i.m.}} \hat{u}$ (see footnote[10]). This shows that the convention (7.9) is compatible with (7.4), and we now adopt it generally.

Since integrable functions are dense in L^2 we have shown at the same time that every function u in L^2 is the limit of a sequence of good functions. Accordingly, *every function* $u \in L^2$ *possesses a Plancherel transform* $\hat{u}$ *defined by* (7.9). The relations (7.8) and (7.9) are satisfied. Furthermore, $u(-t)$ is the Plancherel transform of $\hat{u}$, and so every function in L^2 appears as transform of some other function. In other words, *the mapping* $u \to \hat{u}$ *is an isometric mapping of* L^2 *onto itself.*

Examples. (*a*) The function $u(x) = (\sin x)/x$ is not integrable but is in L^2. Since u is the characteristic function of the uniform density in $\overline{-1, 1}$ one should expect that

$$\hat{u}(\zeta) = \begin{matrix} \sqrt{2\pi} & \textit{for} & |\zeta| < 1 \\ 0 & \textit{for} & |\zeta| > 1. \end{matrix} \tag{7.10}$$

For a formal verification consider the sequence of characteristic functions $u^{(n)}(x) = u(x)e^{-x^2/n}$ which tend to u. The transforms $\hat{u}^{(n)}$ are the convolutions of (7.10) with a normal density and tend to (7.10).

(*b*) A square integrable function u is automatically integrable over every *finite* interval. If the functions $u^{(n)}$ are defined by $u^{(n)}(x) = u(x)$ for $|x| < n$ and $u^{(n)}(x) = 0$ for $|x| > n$ then $u^{(n)}$ is integrable and $u^{(n)} \to u$ in our metric. Now

$$\hat{u}^{(n)}(\zeta) = \frac{1}{\sqrt{2\pi}} \int_{-n}^{n} u(x) e^{i\zeta x}\, dx \tag{7.11}$$

and so $\hat{u}$ is the limit of the transforms (7.11) in the sense that

$$\|\hat{u} - \hat{u}^{(n)}\| \to 0.$$

The particular form of the truncation is of no importance and one could as well use the approximations $u(x)e^{-x^2/n}$ occurring in the last example. ▶

To recapitulate, *a Plancherel transform* $\hat{u}$ *is defined for every* $u \in L^2$ *and the Parseval relation* (7.7) *holds generally.* The transform is skew symmetric in the sense that *the transform of* $\hat{u}$ *equals* $\bar{u}$.

As we have seen in other contexts, the Parseval relation (7.7) may be rewritten in various forms that *look* more general. One possibility is to replace $\hat{v}(x)$ by $\hat{v}(x)e^{-i\lambda x}$, which is the transform of $v(x+\lambda)$. The special case $v = u$ yields

$$\int_{-\infty}^{+\infty} |\hat{u}(x)|^2 e^{i\lambda x}\, dx = \int_{-\infty}^{+\infty} u(x)\, \overline{u(x+\lambda)}\, dx. \tag{7.12}$$

This remarkable identity is widely used in prediction theory. Given an arbitrary integrable function $f \geq 0$ it is possible to choose $\hat{u}$ such that $|\hat{u}|^2 = f$ and thus (7.12) implies that a function φ *is the characteristic function of a probability density iff*[12]

$$\varphi(\lambda) = \int_{-\infty}^{+\infty} u(x)\, \overline{u(x+\lambda)}\, dx \tag{7.13}$$

where $\|u\| = 1$. The choice of u is not unique. (One problem of prediction theory concerns the possibility of choosing u vanishing on a half-line.)

The preceding L^2 theory for Fourier integrals carries over without essential change to *Fourier series*. The norms $\|u\|$ and the inner product are defined as in (7.1) and (7.2) except that integration extends only over the basic interval $\overline{-\pi, \pi}$. The role of "good functions" is played by finite trigonometric polynomials of the form

$$u(x) = \sum u_n e^{inx}, \tag{7.14}$$

and it is obvious that their Fourier coefficients u_n are given by

$$u_k = \frac{1}{2\pi} \int_{-\pi}^{\pi} u(x) e^{-inx}\, dx. \tag{7.15}$$

To a good function there corresponds the finite sequence $\{u_n\}$ of its coefficients, and, conversely, to every finite sequence of complex numbers there corresponds a good function. The relations (7.14) and (7.15) define the Fourier transform $\hat{u} = \{u_n\}$ and its inverse. Formal multiplication and integration shows that for two good functions

$$\int_{-\pi}^{\pi} u(x)\, \overline{v(x)}\, dx = 2\pi \sum u_k \bar{v}_k. \tag{7.16}$$

---

[12] This special case of Parseval's relation occurs in Wiener's classical work but is frequently referred to as *Khintchine's criterion*, and it is treated as if it required a special proof.

We now consider the Hilbert space $\mathfrak{H}$ of infinite sequences $\hat{u} = \{u_n\}$, $\hat{v} = \{v_n\}$, etc., with norm and inner product defined by

$$(7.17) \qquad \|\hat{u}\| = \sum |u_n|^2, \qquad (\hat{u}, \hat{v}) = \sum u_n \overline{v_n}.$$

This space enjoys properties analogous to L^2; in particular, finite sequences are dense in the whole space. It follows that there exists a one-to-one correspondence between the sequences $\hat{u} = \{u_n\}$ in $\mathfrak{H}$ and the functions u in $L^2(\overline{-\pi, \pi})$. *To each sequence* $\{u_n\}$ *such that* $\Sigma\, |u_n|^2 < \infty$ *there corresponds a square integrable function* u *with Fourier coefficients* u_n *and conversely*. The mapping $u \leftrightarrow \{u_n\}$ is again an *isometry*, and the *Parseval relation* $(u, v) = (\hat{u}, \hat{v})$ holds. The Fourier series (7.14) need not converge but the partial sums $\sum_{-n}^{n} u_k e^{ikx}$ form a sequence of continuous functions that converges to u in the L^2 metric. The same statement is true of other continuous approximations. Thus $\Sigma u_k r^{|k|} e^{ikx}$ tends to u as $r \to 1$.

As above, we consider the special case of the Parseval relation represented by

$$(7.18) \qquad \frac{1}{2\pi}\int_{-\pi}^{\pi} u(x)\, \bar{v}(x) e^{-inx}\, dx = \sum_k u_{k+n} \overline{v_k}.$$

Choosing $v = u$ one sees again that *a sequence* $\{\varphi_n\}$ *represents the Fourier coefficients of a probability density on* $\overline{-\pi, \pi}$ *iff it is of the form*

$$(7.19) \qquad \varphi_n = \sum u_{k+n} \overline{u_k} \quad \textit{where} \quad \sum |u_k|^2 = 1.$$

A covariance of this form occurs in III,(7.4). (See also problem 17.)

8. STOCHASTIC PROCESSES AND INTEGRALS

For notational simplicity we refer in this section to *sequences* $\{\mathbf{X}_n\}$ of random variables, but it will be evident that the exposition applies to families depending on a continuous time parameter with the sole change that the spectral measure is not confined to a finite interval and that series are replaced by integrals.

Let, then, $\{\mathbf{X}_n\}$ stand for a doubly infinite sequence of random variables defined on some probability space $\mathfrak{S}$ and having finite second moments. The sequence is assumed stationary in the restricted sense that

$$\mathbf{E}(\mathbf{X}_{n+\nu}\bar{\mathbf{X}}_\nu) = \rho_n$$

is independent of ν. According to theorem 6.3 there exists a unique measure R on the circle $\overline{-\pi, \pi}$ such that

$$(8.1) \qquad \rho_n = \frac{1}{2\pi}\int_{-\pi}^{\pi} e^{-inx}\, R\{dx\}, \qquad n = 0, \pm 1, \ldots.$$

We shall now elaborate on the idea mentioned in section 3 that the circle equipped with the spectral measure R may be used to construct *a concrete representation for the stochastic process* $\{\mathbf{X}_n\}$ (at least for all properties depending only on second moments). The description uses Hilbert space terminology, and we shall consider two Hilbert spaces.

(*a*) *The space* L^2_R. We construct a space of functions on the circle by literal repetition of the definition of L^2 in section 7, except that the line is replaced by the circle $\overline{-\pi, \pi}$ and Lebesgue measure by the measure R. The norm and the inner product of (complex-valued) functions on the circle are defined by

$$(8.2)\quad \|u\|^2 = \frac{1}{2\pi}\int_{-\pi}^{\pi} |u(x)|^2\, R\{dx\}, \qquad (u, v) = \frac{1}{2\pi}\int_{-\pi}^{\pi} u(x)\, \overline{v(x)}\, R\{dx\},$$

respectively. The basic convention now is that *two functions are considered identical if they differ only on a set of R-measure zero.* The impact of this convention is serious. If R is concentrated on the two points 0 and 1 then a "function" (in our sense) is completely determined by its values at these two points. For example, $\sin n\pi x$ is the zero function. Even in such radical cases no harm is done in using the customary formulas for continuous functions and in referring to their graphs. Thus reference to a "step function" is always meaningful and it simplifies the language.

The Hilbert space L^2_R *consists of all functions on the circle with finite norm.* If $\|u_n - u\| \to 0$ the sequence $\{u_n\}$ is said to converge to u in our metric (or in mean square with respect to the weight distribution R). The Hilbert space L^2_R is a complete metric space in which the continuous functions are dense. (For definitions see section 7.)

(*b*) *The Hilbert space* $\mathfrak{H}$ *spanned by* $\{\mathbf{X}_n\}$. Denote by $\mathfrak{H}_0$ the family of random variables with finite second moments defined in the arbitrary, but fixed, sample space $\mathfrak{S}$. By Schwarz' inequality $\mathbf{E}(\mathbf{U}\overline{\mathbf{V}})$ exists for any pair of such variables, and it is natural to generalize (8.2) from the circle to the sample space $\mathfrak{S}$ using the underlying probability measure instead of R. We accordingly agree again to identify two random variables if they differ only on a set of probability zero and define inner products by $\mathbf{E}(\mathbf{U}\overline{\mathbf{V}})$; the norm of $\mathbf{U}$ is the positive root of $\mathbf{E}(\mathbf{U}\overline{\mathbf{U}})$. With these conventions $\mathfrak{H}_0$ again becomes a Hilbert space; it is a complete metric space in which a sequence of random variables $\mathbf{U}_n$ is said to converge to $\mathbf{U}$ if $\mathbf{E}(|\mathbf{U}_n - \mathbf{U}|^2) \to 0$.

In dealing with a sequence $\{\mathbf{X}_n\}$ one is usually interested only in random variables that are functions of the $\mathbf{X}_k$ and in many connections one considers only linear functions. This restricts the consideration to finite linear combinations $\Sigma a_k \mathbf{X}_{n_k}$ and limits of sequences of such finite linear combinations. Random variables of this kind form a subspace $\mathfrak{H}$ of $\mathfrak{H}_0$, called the *Hilbert space spanned by the* $\mathbf{X}_k$. In it inner products, norms, and convergence are defined as just described and $\mathfrak{H}$ is a complete metric space.

In the present context the expectations $\mathbf{E}(\mathbf{X}_n)$ play no role whatever, but as "covariance" sounds better than "inner product" we introduce the usual convention that $\mathbf{E}(\mathbf{X}_n) = 0$. The sole purpose of this is to establish ρ_n as a covariance, and no centering is necessary if one agrees to call $\mathbf{E}(\mathbf{X}\bar{\mathbf{Y}})$ the covariance of $\mathbf{X}$ and $\mathbf{Y}$. We come now to the crucial point, namely that for our purposes the intuitively simple space $L^2{}_R$ *may serve as concrete model for* $\mathfrak{H}$. Indeed, by definition the covariance $\rho_{j-k} = \text{Cov}(\mathbf{X}_j, \mathbf{X}_k)$ of any pair equals the inner product of the functions e^{ijx} and e^{ikx} in $L^2{}_R$. It follows that the covariance of two finite linear combinations $\mathbf{U} = \Sigma a_j \mathbf{X}_{n_j}$ and $\mathbf{V} = \Sigma b_k \mathbf{X}_{n_k}$ equals the inner product of the corresponding linear combinations $u = \Sigma a_j e^{in_jx}$ and $v = \Sigma b_k e^{in_kx}$. By the very definition of convergence in the two spaces this mapping now extends to all random variables. We have thus the important result that the mapping $\mathbf{X}_k \leftrightarrow e^{ikx}$ *induces a one-to-one correspondence between the random variables in* $\mathfrak{H}$ *and the functions in* $L^2{}_R$, *and this correspondence preserves inner products and norms* (and hence limits). In technical language the two spaces are isometric.[13] We are in a position to study $\mathfrak{H}$ and $\{\mathbf{X}_n\}$ referring explicitly only to the concrete space $L^2{}_R$. This procedure has theoretical advantages in addition to being an aid to intuition. Since functions on the circle are a familiar object it is relatively easy to discover sequences $\{u^{(n)}\}$ with desirable structural properties. To $u^{(n)}$ there corresponds a random variable $\mathbf{Z}_n$ on the original sample space $\mathfrak{S}$; if the Fourier coefficients of $u^{(n)}$ are known it is possible to represent $\mathbf{Z}_n$ explicitly as a limit of finite linear combinations of the variables $\mathbf{X}_k$. If the joint distributions of the $\mathbf{X}_k$ are normal the same is true for those of the $\mathbf{Z}_n$.

In practice this procedure is usually reversed. Given a complicated process $\{\mathbf{X}_k\}$ our aim is to express it in terms of the variables $\mathbf{Z}_n$ of a

[13] Readers acquainted with Hilbert space theory should note the connection with the standard *spectral theorem for unitary operators*. The linear operator which maps $\mathfrak{H}$ into itself in such a way that $\mathbf{X}_n \to \mathbf{X}_{n+1}$ is called a *shift operator*, and $L_R{}^2$ serves as a model for the action of this shift operator. Conversely, given an arbitrary unitary operator T on a Hilbert space $\mathfrak{H}_0$ and an arbitrary element $\mathbf{X}_0 \in \mathfrak{H}_0$, the sequence of elements $\mathbf{X}_n = T^n\mathbf{X}_0$ may be treated as a stationary sequence and T as the shift operator on the subspace $\mathfrak{H}$ spanned by this sequence. *If* $\mathbf{X}_0$ can be chosen such that $\mathfrak{H} = \mathfrak{H}_0$ we have obtained the standard spectral theorem for T except that we have a concrete representation of the "resolution of the identity" based on the choice of $\mathbf{X}_0$. If $\mathfrak{H} \subset \mathfrak{H}_0$, then $\mathfrak{H}_0$ is the direct sum of two invariant subspaces, and the presentation applies to each of them. By a simple change of notations one derives the general spectral representation, including the theory of multiplicity for the spectrum.

simpler stochastic process. Some simple examples will illustrate the point better than a theoretical discourse.

Examples. (*a*) *Representation of* $\{\mathbf{X}_n\}$ *by independent random variables.* We consider the situation when the spectral measure R has an ordinary density r. For simplicity[14] r will be assumed strictly positive and continuous. Choose a function γ such that

$$|\gamma(x)|^2 = r(x). \tag{8.3}$$

The Fourier series of γ converges in the L^2 norm as explained in section 7. Denoting the Fourier coefficients of γ by γ_k we have $\Sigma\ |\gamma_k|^2 < \infty$ and by the Parseval relation (7.19)

$$\rho_n = \sum_{k=-\infty}^{+\infty} \gamma_{k+n}\overline{\gamma_k}. \tag{8.4}$$

Consider now the doubly infinite sequence of functions $u^{(n)}$ defined by

$$u^{(n)}(x) = \frac{e^{inx}}{\gamma(x)}. \tag{8.5}$$

Substituting into (8.2) it is seen that

$$\|u^{(n)}\| = 1, \qquad (u^{(n)}, u^{(m)}) = 0 \tag{8.6}$$

for $m \neq n$. For the random variables $\mathbf{Z}_n$ corresponding to the functions $u^{(n)}$ this implies that they are uncorrelated and of unit variance. In particular, *if the* $\mathbf{X}_k$ *are normal the* $\mathbf{Z}_k$ *are mutually independent.*

It is interesting that the space spanned by the variables $\mathbf{X}_k$ contains a stationary sequence $\{\mathbf{Z}_n\}$ of uncorrelated variables. An explicit expression of $\mathbf{Z}_n$ in terms of the $\mathbf{X}_k$ can be obtained from the Fourier expansion of the function $u^{(n)}$, but it is more profitable to proceed in the opposite direction: the structure of $\{\mathbf{Z}_n\}$ being simpler than that of $\{\mathbf{X}_k\}$ it is preferable to express the $\mathbf{X}_k$ in terms of the $\mathbf{Z}_n$. Now

$$\sum_{n=-N}^{N} \gamma_n\, u^{(n+k)}(x) = \frac{e^{ikx}}{\gamma(x)} \sum_{n=-N}^{N} \gamma_n e^{inx}. \tag{8.7}$$

The sum on the right is a section of the Fourier series for γ and tends in the Hilbert space metric to γ. It follows that the quantity (8.7) tends to e^{ikx}. In our mapping $u^{(n+k)}$ corresponds to $\mathbf{Z}_{n+k}$ and so the series $\Sigma\gamma_n\mathbf{Z}_{n+k}$ converges, and we can write

$$\mathbf{X}_k = \sum_{n=-\infty}^{+\infty} \gamma_n \mathbf{Z}_{n+k}. \tag{8.8}$$

[14] The restriction is not used except to avoid trite explanations of what is meant by $r(x)/\gamma(x)$ when $r(x) = \gamma(x) = 0$ and of how series converge.

We have thus obtained *an explicit representation of* $\mathbf{X}_k$ *as a "moving average" in a stationary sequence of uncorrelated variables* $\mathbf{Z}_k$.

The representation (8.8) is evidently not unique. The natural question arises whether it is possible to express $\mathbf{X}_k$ solely by the variables $\mathbf{Z}_k$, $\mathbf{Z}_{k-1}, \mathbf{Z}_{k-2}, \ldots$ (representing the "past"), that is, whether the function γ in (8.3) can be chosen such that $\gamma_n = 0$ for $n \geq 1$. This problem is fundamental in prediction theory, but lies outside the scope of the present volume. For typical examples see III,(7.5), and problem 18.

(*b*) *The associated process with uncorrelated increments.* For each t with $-\pi < t \leq \pi$ define y_t by

$$(8.9) \qquad y_t(x) = \begin{cases} 1 & \text{for } x \leq t \\ 0 & \text{for } x > t \end{cases}$$

and denote by $\mathbf{Y}_t$ the corresponding random variable in $\mathfrak{H}$. The increments $\mathbf{Y}_t - \mathbf{Y}_s$ for non-overlapping intervals have obviously covariance 0; furthermore $\operatorname{Var}(\mathbf{Y}_t) = R\{\overline{-\pi, t}\}$. Thus $\{\mathbf{Y}_t\}$ is a process *with uncorrelated increments and variances given by R.* If the $\mathbf{X}_t$ are normal, the increments of the $\mathbf{Y}_t$ process are actually independent.

With every stationary sequence $\{\mathbf{X}_k\}$ there is in this way associated a process with uncorrelated increments. An explicit expression of $\mathbf{Y}_t$ in terms of the $\mathbf{X}_k$ is obtainable in the standard way be expanding the function y_t in (8.9) into a Fourier series. Once more it is preferable to proceed in the opposite direction. This will be done in the next example.

(*c*) *Stochastic integrals.* The representation of a random variable $\mathbf{U}$ in terms of the $\mathbf{X}_k$ depends (as we have seen) on the Fourier expansion of the function corresponding to $\mathbf{U}$. By contrast, the representation in terms of the variables $\mathbf{Y}_t$ is almost too simple for comfort. It refers to the graph of the function, and for simplicity we assume the latter continuous.

Consider first a step function w, that is, a function of the form

$$(8.10) \qquad w = a_1 y_{t_1} + a_2(y_{t_2} - y_{t_1}) + \cdots + a_n(y_\pi - y_{t_{n-1}})$$

where the a_j are constants and $-\pi < t_1 < t_2 < \cdots < t_{n-1} < \pi$. The associated random variable $\mathbf{W}$ is obtained on replacing in this expression each y_{t_j} by $\mathbf{Y}_{t_j}$. Now an arbitrary continuous function w can be approximated uniformly by step functions $w^{(n)}$ of the form (8.10). Uniform convergence of $w^{(n)}$ to w implies the convergence in the norm of L_R^2 and hence also the convergence of the corresponding random variables $\mathbf{W}^{(n)}$ to $\mathbf{W}$. This gives us a prescription for finding the image $\mathbf{W}$ of an arbitrary continuous function w by a simple limiting procedure: approximate w

by step functions of the form (8.10) and replace y_{t_j} by $\mathbf{Y}_{t_j}$. Remember that (8.10) is a function, and not a number, just as the limit w of $w^{(n)}$ is a function rather than a number. But (8.10) *looks* like a Riemann sum and our procedure is formally reminiscent of the definition of the Riemann integral. It has therefore become standard practice to use the notation

$$\mathbf{W} = \int_{-\pi}^{\pi} w(t)\, d\mathbf{Y}_t \tag{8.11}$$

to indicate the described limiting process. The random variable (8.11) is called *the stochastic integral* of the continuous function w. The name is arbitrary and the notation mere shorthand for the limiting procedure which we have rigorously defined. By definition the function e^{int} corresponds to the random variable $\mathbf{X}_n$ and hence we can write

$$\mathbf{X}_n = \int_{-\pi}^{\pi} e^{int}\, d\mathbf{Y}_t. \tag{8.12}$$

This is the basic *spectral representation of the arbitrary stationary sequence* $\{\mathbf{X}_n\}$ *in terms of the associated process with uncorrelated increments.*

The notation for stochastic integrals is, perhaps, more suggestive than logical but we are not concerned with this usage. Our aim was to show that this useful concept and the important representation (8.12) are easily established by means of Fourier analysis. This illustrates the power of the canonical mapping used in this section and first introduced by Cramér. ►

The theory depends only on the second moments of $\{\mathbf{X}_n\}$ and is in practice applicable only when these moments are truly significant. Such is the case when the process is normal, because normal distributions are completely determined by their covariances. In other applications one may trust that the process is "not too far off a normal process" just as the oldest regression analysis trusted in a universal applicability of methods developed for normal variables. Unfortunately the mere existence of a beautiful theory in no way justifies this trust. In example (3.*c*) the sample functions of the process are strictly periodic. The future of an individual path is completely determined by the data for a full period, but the prediction theory based on the L^2 theory takes no account of this fact and identifies all processes with the same spectral measure. One who observes the sequence $1, -1, 1, -1, \ldots$ going on since time immemorial can safely predict the next observation, but L_2 methods will lead him to predict the miraculous occurrence of 0. These methods are not universally applicable, but they are the ideal tool for treating normal processes.

9. PROBLEMS FOR SOLUTION

1. *Curious characteristic functions.* Let $\tau_h(x) = 1 - \dfrac{|x|}{h}$ for $|x| \le h$ and $\tau_h(x) = 0$ for $|x| \ge h$. Put

$$\alpha(x) = \sum_{n=-\infty}^{+\infty} a_n\, \tau_h(x-n). \tag{9.1}$$

When the a_n are real and $h = 1$ *the graph of* α *is the polygonal line with vertices* (n, a_n). When $h < \frac{1}{2}$ the graph of α consists of segments of the x-axis and the sloping sides of isosceles triangles with vertices (n, a_n). When the a_n are complex the situation is essentially the same.

If $\Sigma\, |a_n| < \infty$ show (without calculations) that

$$\frac{1}{2\pi}\int_{-\infty}^{+\infty} \alpha(x)e^{-i\zeta x}\, dx = \frac{h}{\pi}\,\frac{1-\cos\zeta}{\zeta^2}\sum_{-\infty}^{+\infty} a_n e^{-in\zeta}. \tag{9.2}$$

Conclude that α *is a characteristic function iff* $a_0 = 1$ *and the last series is* ≥ 0 for all ζ. Find examples. Generalize the other choices of τ_h. (See problems 15–16.)

2. The covariance function ρ defined in (3.1) is continuous everywhere iff it is continuous at the origin. This is the case iff $\mathbf{E}((\mathbf{X}_t - \mathbf{X}_0)^2) \to 0$ as $t \to 0$.

3. Let $\{\mathbf{X}_t\}$ be a stationary process with spectral measure R. For $h > 0$ put $\mathbf{X}_t^{(h)} = \dfrac{1}{h}[\mathbf{X}_{t+h} - \mathbf{X}_t]$.

(*a*) Find the spectral measure for this process and show that as $h \to 0$ a limit exists iff R has a second moment (that is, iff $x^2\, R\{dx\}$ defines a finite measure).

(*b*) For fixed t in this case $\mathrm{Var}(\mathbf{X}_t^{(h)} - \mathbf{X}_t^{(\epsilon)}) \to 0$ as $h \to 0$, $\epsilon \to 0$. (In the Hilbert space terminology of section 8, this states that $\{\mathbf{X}_t^{(h)}\}$ is Cauchy as $h \to 0$ and hence a limit $\mathbf{X}_t'$ exists.)

4. If φ is the characteristic function of F then

$$f_\lambda(x) = \frac{1}{2\pi}\int_{-\infty}^{+\infty} e^{-\lambda|\zeta|}\varphi(\zeta)e^{-i\zeta x}\, d\zeta$$

is the density of a probability distribution F_λ such that $F_\lambda \to F$. [This is the analogue to (4.3).]

5. *To theorem 4.2.* If φ is continuous except for a jump at the origin then (4.9) holds at all $\zeta \ne 0$ and $f_r(0) \to \frac{1}{2}[\varphi(0+) - \varphi(0-)]$.

6. *Continuation.* If φ is the difference between two monotone functions then $f_r(\zeta) \to \frac{1}{2}[\varphi(\zeta+) - \varphi(\zeta-)]$ at all points.

7. A bounded periodic function φ with non-negative Fourier coefficients φ_n is necessarily continuous and $\Sigma\, \varphi_n < \infty$. The example $\varphi_n = 1/n$ shows that this is false if φ is only supposed to be integrable.

8. *Cesaro summability.* Replace (4.3) by

$$f_r(\zeta) = \sum \varphi_n a_n e^{in\zeta}$$

where $a_n = 1 - \dfrac{|n|}{2N+1}$ for $|n| \le 2N$ and $a_n = 0$ for $|n| > 2N$. Show that the theory of section 4 goes through with $p_r(t)$ replaced by

$$q_N(t) = \frac{1}{2N+1}\frac{\sin^2(N+\frac{1}{2})t}{\sin^2\frac{1}{2}t},$$

which is again a probability density.

9. *Continuation.* Show, more generally, that the theory goes through if the a_n are the Fourier coefficients of a symmetrized probability density on the circle.

10. Show that corollary 4.2 is an immediate consequence of theorem 6.1 and, conversely, the latter theorem can be proved by the method used in (4.12).

11. Use the Poisson summation formula (5.2) to show that

$$\sum_{-\infty}^{+\infty}\left\{\mathfrak{n}\left(\frac{y-x+2k\lambda}{\sqrt{t}}\right)+\mathfrak{n}\left(\frac{y+x+2k\lambda}{\sqrt{t}}\right)\right\} = \frac{1}{a}\sum_{-\infty}^{+\infty}\exp\left(-\tfrac{1}{2}tn^2\frac{\pi^2}{\lambda^2}\right)\cos\frac{n\pi}{\lambda}x\cdot\cos\frac{n\pi}{\lambda}y,$$

where $\mathfrak{n}$ stands for the standard normal density. [This is the solution of the reflecting barrier problem in example X,(5.*e*).]

12. *Alternative derivation of the Poisson summation formula.* Let φ be the characteristic function of F. Using the example of section 4 (but no further calculations) show that for $0 < r < 1$

$$\frac{1}{2\pi}\sum_{n=-\infty}^{+\infty}\varphi(\zeta+n)r^{|n|}e^{in\lambda} = \int_{-\infty}^{+\infty}e^{i\zeta x}\,p_r(x+\lambda)\,F\{dx\}. \tag{9.3}$$

Hence the left side is a characteristic function. Letting $r\to 1$ conclude that if F has a density f then

$$\frac{1}{2\pi}\sum_{n=-\infty}^{+\infty}\varphi(\zeta+n)e^{in\lambda} = \sum_{k=-\infty}^{+\infty}e^{i\zeta(-\lambda+2k\pi)}f(-\lambda+2k\pi) \tag{9.4}$$

whenever $\Sigma f(-\lambda+2k\pi) < \infty$. Show that (9.4) is equivalent with (5.7).

12*a*. *Continuation.* For $\zeta = \lambda = 0$ conclude from (9.4) that $\frac{1}{2\pi}\Sigma\,\varphi(n)$ is Abel summable to $\Sigma f(2k\pi)$ whenever the last series converges.

13. *To theorem 5.1.* Let $g(x) = \frac{1}{2}e^{-|x|}$ and

$$f(x) = \frac{6}{\pi^2}\sum_{n=1}^{\infty}\frac{1}{n}g(n(x-n)).$$

Show that f is a probability density with characteristic function

$$\varphi(\xi) = \frac{6}{\pi^2}\sum\frac{1}{n^2+\xi^2}e^{in\zeta}.$$

From (5.2) conclude (without calculations) that $\varphi(\xi)\geq 0$ for all ξ, and hence that φ is integrable (see the corollary to theorem 3 of XV,3). We have thus an example of a *continuous density f with integrable characteristic function φ and such that* $\Sigma f(n) = \infty$. (This argument is due to B. Weiss.)

14. The sequence $\{\varphi_n\}$ is positive definite iff $\{\varphi_n r^{|n|}\}$ is positive definite for every $0 < r < 1$. Necessary and sufficient is that $\Sigma\,\varphi_n r^{|n|}e^{in\lambda}\geq 0$ for all λ.

15. From problems 1 and 14 derive (without calculations) the following theorem (observed by L. Shepp): *Let $\{\varphi_n\}$ be positive definite and denote by* α

the piecewise linear function with vertices at (n, φ_n). Then α *is positive definite.*

16. *Let* φ *be a characteristic function and denote by* α *the piecewise linear function with vertices* $(n, \varphi(n))$. *Then* α *is a characteristic function.* (This merely paraphrases problem 15 and is a special case of problem 1 for $h = 1$.) Use the other cases of problem 1 to describe other curious characteristic functions obtainable from φ.

17. If $r < 1$ the covariances (6.9) of Markov sequences satisfy (7.19) with $u_k = \sqrt{1 - r^2}\, r^k e^{ik\theta}$ for $k \geq 0$ and $u_k = 0$ for $k < 0$. Find alternative representations.

18. *Continuation.* Let $\{\mathbf{X}_n\}$ be Markovian with covariances $\rho_n = r^{|n|}e^{in\theta}$. If $r < 1$ one has $\mathbf{X}_n = \sqrt{1 - r^2} \sum_{k=0}^{\infty} r^k e^{ik\theta}\mathbf{Z}_{n-k}$ where the $\mathbf{Z}_k$ are uncorrelated. If $r = 1$ one has $\mathbf{X}_n = e^{in\theta}\mathbf{Z}_0$.

Answers to Problems

CHAPTER I

1. (i) $\frac{\alpha}{3}\frac{1}{\sqrt[3]{x^2}}e^{-\alpha x^{\frac{1}{3}}}$ (ii) $\frac{\alpha}{2}e^{-\alpha(x-3)/2}$ for $x > 3$

(iii) $\frac{\alpha}{2}e^{-\alpha|x|}$, all x (iv) $\alpha e^{-\alpha x}$, $x > 0$

(v) $\alpha\left(1 + \frac{1}{3}\frac{1}{\sqrt[3]{x^2}}\right)e^{-\alpha x - \alpha x^{\frac{1}{3}}}$

(vi) $\alpha e^{-\alpha x} + \frac{\alpha}{3}\frac{1}{\sqrt[3]{x^2}}e^{-\alpha x^{\frac{1}{3}}} - \alpha\left(1 + \frac{1}{3}\frac{1}{\sqrt[3]{x^2}}\right)e^{-\alpha x - \alpha x^{\frac{1}{3}}}$.

2. (i) $\frac{1}{6}\frac{1}{\sqrt[3]{x^2}}$ for $|x| < 1$ (ii) $\frac{1}{4}$ for $1 < t < 5$

(iii) $\frac{1}{2}\left(1 - \frac{|x|}{2}\right)$ for $|x| < 2$ (iv) $1 - \frac{x}{2}$ for $0 < x < 2$

(v) $\frac{1}{4} - \frac{1}{3}x^{\frac{1}{3}} + \frac{1}{12}x^{-\frac{2}{3}}$ for $|x| < 1$ (vi) $\frac{1}{4} + \frac{1}{3}x^{\frac{1}{3}} + \frac{1}{12}x^{-\frac{2}{3}}$ for $|x| < 1$.

3. (i) $h^{-1}(1 - e^{-\alpha x})$ for $0 < x < h$, and $h^{-1}(e^{\alpha h} - 1)e^{-\alpha x}$ for $x > h$

(ii) $h^{-1}(1 - e^{-\alpha(x+h)})$ for $-h < x < 0$, and $h^{-1}(1 - e^{-\alpha h})e^{-\alpha x}$ for $x > 0$.

4. (i) $1 - \frac{1}{3}h$ if $h < 1$ but $\frac{2}{3}\frac{1}{\sqrt{h}}$ if $h > 1$

(ii) $\sqrt{\alpha\pi}\, e^{\frac{1}{4}\alpha}(1 - \mathfrak{N}(\sqrt{\alpha r}))$.

5. (i) $1 - x^{-1}$ for $x > 1$; (ii) $x^2(x + 1)^{-2}$.

8. $\mathbf{P}\{\mathbf{Z} \leq x\} = 1 - e^{-\alpha x}$ for $x < t$ and $=1$ for $x > t$.

15. $p = \sum_{0}^{m-1}\binom{m + k - 1}{k}2^{-n-k}$. For $m = 1$, $n = 2$ one gets $p = \frac{1}{4}$.

17. $nt^{n-1} - (n - 1)t^n$.

18. (i) $2\int_0^1 dx \int_x^1 (1 - z)\, dz = \frac{1}{3}$

(ii) The *density* is $2t - t^2$ for $0 < t \leq 1$ and $(2 - t)^2$ for $1 \leq t < 2$

(iii) The density is $2t^2$ for $0 < t < 1$ and again $(2 - t)^2$ for $1 \leq t < 2$.

19. $2\int_0^1 x(1-x)\,dx = \frac{1}{3}$. Two out of six permutations produce an intersection.

20. X_{11}: $4\log\frac{1}{4x}$ for $x < \frac{1}{4}$; X_{12} and X_{21}: $4\log 2$ for $x < \frac{1}{4}$; $4\log\frac{1}{2x}$ for $\frac{1}{4} < x < \frac{1}{2}$; X_{22}: $4\log 4x$ for $\frac{1}{4} < x < \frac{1}{2}$; $4\log\frac{1}{x}$ for $\frac{1}{2} < x < 1$
The expectations are $\frac{1}{16}, \frac{3}{16}, \frac{9}{16}$.

22. $q_n(t) = nt^{-n}\int_0^{t-h}(t-x-h)^{n-1}\,p_{n-1}(t-x-h)\,dx = t^{-n}(t-(n-1)h)_+{}^n$.

25. Distributions $\frac{2}{\pi}\arcsin\frac{1}{2}x$ and $\frac{1}{4}x^2$; densities $\frac{2}{\pi}\frac{1}{\sqrt{4-x^2}}$ and $\frac{1}{2}x$ for $0 < x < 2$.

26. $2\pi^{-1}\arcsin\frac{1}{2}x$.

28. (a) $\log\frac{1}{x}$, (b) $\frac{2}{\pi}\log\frac{1+\sqrt{1-x^2}}{x}$ where $0 < x < 1$.

29. $\frac{4}{\pi}\int_{0<\cos\theta<x}\sin^2\theta\,d\theta = \frac{4}{\pi}\int_0^x\sqrt{1-y^2}\,dy = 2\pi[\arcsin x + x\sqrt{1-x^2}\,]$
where $0 < x < 1$.

30. $F(t) = \frac{2}{\pi}\int_0^{\pi/2} V\left(\frac{t}{\cos\theta}\right)(1-\cos 2\theta)\,d\theta.$

CHAPTER II

4. $g * g(x) = \frac{1}{4}e^{-|x|}(1+|x|)$
$g^{3*}(x) = \frac{1}{16}e^{-|x|}(3+3|x|+x^2)$
$g^{4*}(x) = \frac{1}{32}e^{-|x|}(5+5|x|+2x^2+\frac{1}{3}|x|^3)$.

10. $\lambda e^{-\lambda t} - \mu e^{-\mu t} + (\mu-\lambda)e^{-(\mu+\lambda t)}$.

12. For a person arriving at random the density is $1-\frac{1}{2}t^2$ for $0 < t < 1$ and $\frac{1}{2}(2-t)^2$ for all $1 < t < 2$. The expectation equals $\frac{7}{12}$.

CHAPTER III

6. (a) e^{-x} and $1 - e^{-x} - e^{-y} + e^{-x-y-axy}$ for $x > 0$, $y > 0$.
(b) $\mathbf{E}(\mathbf{Y} \mid \mathbf{X}) = \frac{1+a+ax}{(1+ax)^2}$,
$$\text{Var}(\mathbf{Y} \mid \mathbf{X}) = \frac{1}{(1+ax)^2} + \frac{2a}{(1+ax)^3} - \frac{a^2}{(1+ax)^4}.$$

7. If f has expectation μ and variance σ^2 then $\mathbf{E}(\mathbf{X}) = \mathbf{E}(\mathbf{Y}) = \frac{1}{2}\mu$, $\text{Var}(\mathbf{X}) = \text{Var}(\mathbf{Y}) = \frac{1}{3}\sigma^2 + \frac{1}{12}\mu^2$, $\text{Cov}(\mathbf{X}, \mathbf{Y}) = \frac{1}{3}\sigma^2 - \frac{1}{12}\mu^2$.

8. Density $2x_2$ in unit square. In n variables $(n-1)\mathbf{X}_2\mathbf{X}_3{}^2\cdots\mathbf{X}_n^{n-1}$.

9. $\frac{1}{3}e^{-(x+y)}$ for $y > x > 0$ and $\frac{1}{3}e^{-y+2x}$ for $y > x$, $x < 0$. Interchange x and y when $y < x$.

10. (*a*) $8\int f(s)\, f\left(\frac{x}{s}\right) f\left(\frac{y}{1-s}\right)\frac{ds}{s(1-s)}$

where $0 < x < \frac{1}{4} < y < 1$ and the domain of integration satisfies the conditions that $2x < s < \frac{1}{2}$ and also $1 - 2y < s < 1 - y$.

(*b*) $4\int_{2x}^{\frac{1}{2}} f(s)\, f\left(\frac{x}{s}\right)\frac{ds}{x}, \qquad 0 < x < \frac{1}{4}.$

11. Bivariate normal with variances m, n and covariance $\sqrt{m/n}$. Conditional density has expectation $\frac{m}{n}t$ and variance $m\cdot\frac{n-m}{n}$ as is clear intuitively.

12. $\mathbf{X}_1^2 + \cdots + \mathbf{X}_n^2$ has the gamma density $f_{\frac{1}{2},\frac{n}{2}}$ [see II,(2.2)]. From (3.1) therefore

$$u_t = \frac{\Gamma\left(\frac{n}{2}\right)}{\Gamma\left(\frac{m}{2}\right)\Gamma\left(\frac{n-m}{2}\right)}\left(\frac{x}{t}\right)^{\frac{1}{2}m-1}\left(1-\frac{x}{t}\right)^{\frac{1}{2}(n-m)-1}\frac{1}{t}.$$

For $m = 2$, $n = 4$ we get example (3.*a*).

14. (*a*) $4xy$ when $x + y < 1$, $x > 0$, $y > 0$
$4xy - 4(x + y - 1)^2$ when $x + y > 1$, $0 < x, y < 1$
$4x(2 - x - y)$ when $y > 1$, $x + y < 2$, $x > 0$
$4y(2 - x - y)$ when $x > 1$, $x + y < 2$, $y > 0$.

(*b*) $2(1 - x - y)^2$ for $0 < x, y < 1$, $x + y < 1$
$2(1 - x)^2$ for $x > 0$, $y < 0$, $x + y > 0$
$2(1 + y)^2$ for $x > 0$, $y < 0$, $x + y < 0$.
For $x < 0$ by symmetry.

15. $2\frac{1}{\pi^2}\left(\arccos\frac{r}{2} - \frac{r}{2}\sqrt{1-\frac{r^2}{4}}\right).$

16. $\int_0^\infty f(\rho)\rho\, d\rho\int_0^{2\pi} g(\sqrt{r^2+\rho^2-2r\rho\cos\theta})\, d\theta.$

17. (*a*) $\mathbf{X}_n = \mathbf{U}\cos\frac{1}{2}\pi n + \mathbf{V}\sin\frac{1}{2}\pi n$
(*b*) $\mathbf{U} + \mathbf{V}(-1)^n$
(*c*) $\mathbf{U}\cos\frac{1}{2}\pi n + \mathbf{V}\sin\frac{1}{2}\pi n + \mathbf{W}$.

18. (*a*) $\mathrm{Var}(\mathbf{Y}_{n+1}) - \mathrm{Var}(\mathbf{Y}_n) = \mathrm{Var}(\mathbf{C}_n) - 2\,\mathrm{Cov}(\mathbf{Y}_n, \mathbf{C}_n) + 1$ whence
(*b*) $\alpha^2 - 2\alpha\sigma\rho + 1 = 0$

(*c*) $\sigma = \frac{1}{2}\left(\alpha + \frac{1}{\alpha}\right), \quad \mathbf{Y}_{n+1} = a\frac{1}{ap} + \delta + \sum_{k=0}^{n-1}(1-p)^k\,\mathbf{X}_{n-k} + p^n\mathbf{Y}_0.$

19. $\sigma^2 \geq \frac{1}{4}\left(\alpha + \frac{1}{\alpha}\right)^2 + N.$

CHAPTER VI

7. Not necessarily. It is necessary that $n[1 - F(\epsilon n)] \to 0$.
8. For $x > 0$ the densities are given by 1 and $\frac{1}{2}(1-e^{-2x})$.
9. $qU(x) = 1 - qe^{-pct}$. The number of renewal epochs is *always* geometrically distributed.
14. $Z = z + F \star Z$ where $z(t) = 1 - e^{-ct}$ for $t \leq \xi$ and $z(t) = z(\xi)$ for $t \geq \xi$ and $F(t) = e^{-c\xi} - c^{-ct}$ for $t > \xi$.
15. V is the convolution of Z and an exponential distribution.
16. $V = A + B \star V$ where $A\{dx\} = [1 - G(x)]\, F\{dx\}$ and $B\{dx\} = G(x)\, F\{dx\}$.
19. The arc sine density $g(y) = \dfrac{1}{\pi} \dfrac{1}{\sqrt{y(1-y)}}$.

CHAPTER VII

6. (*a*) $\binom{n}{k} p^k(1-p)^{n-k}$ with F concentrated at p.

   (*b*) $\dfrac{1}{n+1}$, density $f(x) = 1$.

   (*c*) $\dfrac{2(k+1)}{(n+1)(n+2)}$, density $2x$.

Some Books on Cognate Subjects

Some books in the following list appeared, or will appear, after completion of the present volume.

A. INTRODUCTORY TEXTS

Hennequin, P. L. and A. Tortrat [1965], *Théorie des Probabilités et Quelques Applications*. Masson, Paris, 457 pp.

Krickeberg, K. [1963], *Wahrscheinlichkeitstheorie*. Teubner, Stuttgart. 200 pp. (An English translation is promised.)

Loève, M. [1963], *Probability Theory*. 3rd ed. Van Nostrand, Princeton. 685 pp.

Neveu, J. [1964], *Bases Mathématiques du Calcul des Probabilités*. Masson, Paris. 203 pp.

B. SPECIFIC SUBJECTS

Bochner, S. [1955], *Harmonic Analysis and the Theory of Probability*. Univ. of California Press. 176 pp.

Gelfand, I. M. and N. J. Wilenkin [1961], *Verallgemeinerte Funktionen* (*Distributionen*), vol. IV. (Translated from the Russian; an English translation is promised.) Deutscher Verlag der Wissenschaften, Berlin. 359 pp.

Grenander, U. [1963], *Probabilities on Algebraic Structures*. John Wiley, New York. 218 pp.

Lukacs, E. [1960], *Characteristic Functions*. Griffin, London. 216 pp.

Lukacs, E. and R. G. Laha [1954], *Applications of Characteristic Functions*. Griffin, London. 202 pp.

C. STOCHASTIC PROCESSES WITH EMPHASIS ON THEORY

Chung, K. L. [1960], *Markov Chains with Stationary Transition Probabilities*. Springer, Berlin. 278 pp.

Dynkin, E. B. [1961], *Markov Processes*. Two vols. (Translation from the Russian.) Springer, Berlin. 174 pp.

Ito, K. and H. P. McKean Jr. [1965], *Diffusion Processes and Their Sample Paths*. Springer, Berlin. 321 pp.

Kemperman, J. H. B. [1961], *The Passage Problem for a Stationary Markov Chain*. University of Chicago Press. 127 pp.

Lévy, Paul [1965], *Processus Stochastiques et Mouvement Brownien*. 2nd ed. Gauthier-Villars, Paris. 438 pp.

Spitzer, Frank [1964], *Principles of Random Walk*. Van Nostrand, Princeton. 406 pp.

Skorokhod, A. V. [1965], *Studies in the Theory of Random Processes*. (Translation from the Russian.) Addison-Wesley, Reading. 199 pp.

Yaglom, A. M. [1962], *Stationary Random Functions.* (Translation from the Russian.) Prentice-Hall, Englewood Cliffs. 235 pp.

D. STOCHASTIC PROCESSES WITH EMPHASIS ON APPLICATIONS OR EXAMPLES

Barucha-Reid, A. T. [1960], *Elements of the Theory of Stochastic Processes and Their Applications.* McGraw-Hill, New York. 468 pp.

Beneš, V. E. [1963], *General Stochastic Processes in the Theory of Queues.* Addison-Wesley, Reading. 88 pp.

Grenander, U. and M. Rosenblatt [1957], *Statistical Analysis of Stationary Time Series.* John Wiley, New York. 300 pp.

Khintchine, A. Y. [1960], *Mathematical Methods in the Theory of Queueing.* (Translation from the Russian.) Griffin, London. 120 pp.

Prabhu, N. U. [1965], *Stochastic Processes.* Macmillan, New York. 233 pp.

——— [1965], *Queues and Inventories*, John Wiley, New York. 275 pp.

Riordan, J. [1962], *Stochastic Service Systems.* John Wiley, New York. 139 pp.

Wax, N. (editor) [1954], *Selected Papers on Noise and Stochastic Processes.* Dover, New York. 337 pp.

Methuen's Monographs on Applied Probability and Statistics present short self-contained introductions as follows:

- Bartlett, M. S. [1960], *Stochastic Population Models in Ecology and Epidemology.* 90 pp.
- Cox, D. R. and W. L. Smith [1961], *Queues.* 180 pp.
- Hannan, E. J. [1960], *Time Series Analysis.* 152 pp.
- Moran, P. A. P. [1959], *The Theory of Storage.* 111 pp.
- Takacs, L. [1960], *Stochastic Processes.* 137 pp.

E. BOOKS OF HISTORICAL INTEREST

Cramér, H. [1962], *Random Variables and Probability Distributions.* 2nd ed. (The first appeared in 1937.) Cambridge Tracts. 179 pp.

Doob, J. L. [1953], *Stochastic Processes.* John Wiley, New York. 654 pp.

Gnedenko, B. V. and A. N. Kolmogorov [1954], *Limit Distributions for Sums of Independent Random Variables.* (Translated from the Russian.) Addison-Wesley, Reading. 264 pp.

Kolmogorov, A. N. [1950], *Foundations of the Theory of Probability.* Chelsea Press, New York. 70 pp. (The German original appeared in 1933.)

Lévy, P. [1925], *Calcul des Probabilités.* Gauthier-Villars, Paris. 350 pp.

Lévy, P. [1937 and 1954], *Théorie de l'Addition des Variables Aléatoires.* Gauthier-Villars, Paris. 384 pp.

F. SEMI-GROUPS AND GENERAL ANALYSIS

Hille, E. and R. S. Phillips [1957], *Functional Analysis and Semi-groups.* (Revised edition.) Amer. Math. Soc.. 808 pp.

Karlin, S. and W. Studden [1966], *Tchebycheffian Systems and Applications to Analysis.* Interscience, New York.

Yosida, A. M. [1962], *Functional Analysis.* Springer, Berlin. 458 pp.

Index